MAHOMMEDAN LAW

COMPILED FROM
AUTHORITIES IN THE ORIGINAL ARABIC

CONTAINING THE LAW RELATING TO
GIFTS, WAKFS, WILLS, PRE-EMPTION AND BAILMENT
(With an Appendix on the Law of Wakf)

BY
SYED AMEER ALI, P.C., C.I.E., M.A., LL.D
BARRISTER-AT-LAW
MEMBER OF THE JUDICIAL COMMITTEE OF HIS MAJESTY'S PRIVY COUNCIL

FIFTH EDITION
BY
RAJA SAID AKBAR KHAN,
SENIOR ADVOCATE SUPREME

Vol. I

KITAB BHAVAN
NEW DELHI-110002

First Published in India 1986
Reprinted ---- 2008

Published by
Nusrat Ali Nasri for Kitab Bhavan
1214, Kalan Mahal, Darya Ganj, New Delhi-110002.

Printed at : Lahooti Fine Art Press 1711, Sui Walan
New Delhi-110002 Tel.: 23286349

PREFACE TO THE FIFTH EDITION

In February 1965 I had the proud privilege of presenting to the legal world the fifth edition of 2nd Volume (relating to family laws and inheritance) of the late Syed Amir Ali's classical work by removing the dust that had gathered over it during the long course of years since the publication of the 4th edition by Syed Sahib himself in July 1928.

Paradoxically enough the late Syed Amir Ali had himself bifurcated the publication of the two volumes in so far as in 1928 he published the fifth edition of the 2nd Volume, while the Ist Volume of the Book relating to gifts and Wakfs stood as it was in 1912 when the 4th edition was published.

Unfortunately in 1965 also the Ist Volume could not be placed before the Legal fraternity for various reasons.

Volume I of Amir Ali's Muslim law has a peculiarity of its own as distinguished from the treatises on the subject including the classical works like Fatawa-i-Alamgiri, Fatwa-i-Qazi Khan, Hedaya and other standard works on the Anglo-Mohammadan Law, compiled during the British regime. The law of Wakfs and gifts was developed to the highest pitch by Syed Amir Ali who took up cudgles on its behalf against the non-Muslim Judges of the superior Courts in the realm including the Privy Council.

Syed Amir Ali who was an astute scholar of Arabic and Persian, well-versed in Qur'an and the Sunna possessed forensic capacity of high order and an analytic mind of superb quality was a qualified Barrister with deep knowledge of Islamic law. He had ransaked all the classical and standard works on Islamic Sharia and was therefore fully competent to deduce new principles as corollaries to the text of the Holy revelation of the Qur'an and the Sunna in the light of the present day development of knowledge of social sciences and experience gained over centuries. Naturally he could not agree with the view that the Courts of the country in administering Muslim law, should not. as a rule, attempt to put their own construction on the Qur'an in opposition to the express ruling of the Muslim commentators of great antiquity and high authority (*Agha Mohammad Jaffar* v. *Kulsoom Bibi* I L R 25 Cal. 9 (18) =L R 24 I A 196 (204). Similarly he could not agree with the deduction that neither the ancient texts nor the precepts of the Prophet should be taken literally so as to deduce from them new rules of law, especially, when such rules do not conduce to substantial justice (of the British pattern) *Baqar Ali* v. *Anjuman* (1902) I L R 25 All. 236 (254)=L R 30 I A 94.

The first parting of the ways came to notice in Wakf case of *Bikani Mia* v. *Sukh Lal* (1893) 20 Cal. 116 in which the question referred to the Full Bench was whether a gift by a Muslim to his own children and their descendants from generation to generation was a gift to charity so as not to be hit by the Muslim law principle that 'a gift in perpetuity is not valid unless it is gift to charity'.

The question was answered in the negative by the majority of Judges. It was answered in the affirmative by Syed Amir Ali in a dissenting Judgment. The learned Judge, quoted Chapter and Verse of classical works on Hadis and Fiqah, and observed (page 139): "The institution of Wakfs, in which the endower's family and descendants are the immediate recipients of the benefaction, owes its origin to the direct ordinances of the Prophet. Not only did he declare that a provision for one's family was the best of alms giving but he encouraged the members of his household and his companions to create such wakfs and himself set the example by consecrating certain lands at Khaibar. In dealing with the Mussalman law, the meanings attached by Mussalmans to "charitable purposes" has been unfortunately often been lost sight of charity has been construed to mean "charity to the poor, irrespective of the endower and his descendants ; "piety" and "religion" to mean sucn acts, as would, in practical Europe, be regarded, as pious or religious. This is not the Mussalman law."

At page 140, after quoting copiously from authentic Books of Hadis, the learned Judge observed : "The Prophet of God declared that a pious offering to one's family (to provide against their getting into Want) is more pious than giving alms to beggars. The most excellent of Sadakah is that which a man bestows on his family". In *Abul Fatta Mohammad Ishaque* v. *Rasamayya Dhur Chowdery* I. L. R. 22 Cal. 619=L R 22 I. A. 76, Lord Hobhouse, while delivering the Judgment of the Privy Conncil, approved the majority view in *Bhikani Mia's case* and disagreed with the opinion of Mr. Justice Amir Ali. At page 631 of the report, their Lordships were pleased to observe : "The opinion of that learned Muhammadan lawyer (Amir Ali) is founded, as their Lordships understand upon texts of an abstract character and upon precedents very unperfectly stated. For instance he quotes a precedent of the Prophet Mohammad (p. b. u. h.) himself to the effect that "A pious offering to one's family to provide against their getting into want, is more pious than giving alms to beggars. The most excellent Sadakah is, that which a man bestows on his family". Dilating on the subject their Lordships observed : "As regards precepts, which are held up as the fundamental principles of Mohammadan law, their Lordships are not forgetting how far law and religion are mixed up together in the Mohammadan communities ; general law of Islam, at least as known in India (Indo-Pak. subcontinent), simple gifts by a private person to remote unborn, generation of descendants, successions, that is, of inalienable life interests, are forbidden, and whether it is to be taken that the very same dispositions, which are illegal when made by ordinary words of gift, become legal if only the settler says that they are made as Wakf, in the name of God or for the sake of the poor ? At page 632, their Lordships further observed : "Their Lordships have endeavoured to the best of their ability to ascertain and apply the Mohammadan law as known and administered in India (Indo-Pak subcontinent), but they cannot find that it is in accordance with the absolute, and as it seems to them extravagent, application of abstract precepts taken from the mouth of the Prophet. These precepts may be excellent in their proper application. They may, for aught their Lordships know, have had the effect in moulding the law and practice of Wakf, as the learned Judge says they have. But it would be doing wrong to the great law-giver to suppose that he is thereby commending gifts for which the donor exercises no self-denial, in which he takes back with one hand what he appears to put away with the other ; which are to form the centre of attraction for accumulation of income and further accessions of family property ; which carefully protect so-called managers from being called to account ; which give to the donors and their family the enjoyment of property free from all liability to creditors, and which do not seek the benefit of others beyond the use of empty words. At page 634 their Lordships observed : "A gift may be illusory whether from its small amount or from its uncertainty and remoteness. If a man were to settle a crore of Rupees, and provide ten for the poor, that would be at once recognized as illusory. It is equally illusory to make a provision for the poor till after the total extinction of a family; possibly not for hundreds of years, possibly not until the property had vanished away, under the Wasting agency of litigation or malfeasance or misfortune; certainly not as long as exists on the earth one of those objects whom the donor really cared to maintain in a high position. Their Lordships agree that the poor have been put into this settlement merely to give it a colour of piety and so to legalise arrangements meant to serve for the aggrandisement of a family".

The decision of the highest judicial tribunal in the realm in *Abul Fatta's case* created a stir amongst the Muslim community not only of the Indo-Pak subcontinent, that is British India, as it then was but in fact shook the entire Muslim world. Their Lordships were not, far wrong in their estimation, as they were looking at the problem through the coloured glasses of the English law of trust with its own notions of dedication to charity, while Syed Amir Ali, as the exponent of the Islamic law of Wakf, was quite sure of his ground, that notions of charity in English law where charity means catering to the needs of beggars and the destitute ; were wholly different from the view of charity in Islamic law which included the making provisions for the endowers own descendants from generation to generation, so as to keep them free from want, poverty and penury, irrespective of the fact whether they are at the time of donations, rich or poor.

The dissatisfaction caused by the Privy Council judgment made Muslim legal minds to get together to undo the harm done by the judgment which became a law declared for the realm and which would nullify hundreds of *wakaf-alo-al-aulad* institutions which had been created by the Muslim sovereigns and nobles during the heyday of their powers, for the benefit of their less fortunate descendants and lethargic future generations. A deputation waited on the then Viceroy and consequently "the Mussalman Wakf Validating Act of 1913, which was moved as a private Bill, by a young member of the Central Assembly, M. A. Jinnah, a man of destiny, the future Quaid-i-Azam of the Muslims of India and the founder of Pakistan, was placed on the statute Book. This Act is given verbatim in the Appendix.

The world has moved very fastly during the 63 odd years since the enactment of the Act, 1913. A new state, established, in the name of Islam. founded on the bed-rock of the Qur'an and the Sunna, was ushered into existence on 14th of August 1947, by the noble efforts of the self same sponsor of the Mussalman Wakf Validating Act of 1913, Quaid-i-Azam Muhammad Ali Jinnah (may his soul rest in peace).

Now the Holy Qur'an and the Sunna, is the fundamental and basic law of the country, the strict interpretation of which is the duty of our courts. Whatever fell from the lips of the Prophet, if reported by authentic sources, is a law laid down which, is binding on the Courts of the realm.

Islam has been declared to be the official religion of the State, which has undertaken to provide opportunities for the Muslims to order their lives according to the Qur'an and the Sunna. The State is duty bound to bring all the laws of the country in accordance with the principles of the Qur'an, and precedents of the Prophet.

Muslims are in fact one people, for they believe in, One God, one Prophet and one Qur'an which is word for word the same as the Prophet left it without the difference of a comma or a full-stop, a distinction which is not only rare but unique, for no other book in the world possesses this quality.

I am not oblivious of the fact, of the accute differences between the Shias and the Sunnis. That is really unfortunate but those differences are purely political in nature on the question of succession to the Prophet as the head of the State, and it is a fortunate part of our history, that no sectarian difference, stood in the way of Pakistan, for one hundred millions of the Muslim people of the sub-continent stood firmly like a rock behind one man, and succeeded in placing on the map of the world the largest Muslim State and the 5th most populous State of the world.

The interpretation of the old orthodox Sunni or Shia Schools which came into existence in the 2nd century of the Muslim era, had marked in differences on the petty matters, continued till the sack of Baghdad.

The massacre of Baghdad in 1258 A. D. second only to the Tragedy of Karbla, shook the Islamic Caliphate from its very foundation, pulled down the prontifical throne of the Caliph, and dragged its honour and prestige in a quagmire. The progress of dynamic thought in the realm of law and religion came suddenly to a stand-still. The *ulema*, the doctors of law, and the learned scholars of Islam lost their position of Vantage and prestige. The door of Ijtehad or progressive thinking in the field of Islamic Sharia was permanently hanged and whatever had been given by the standard Jurists of the 2nd century became the final word on the subject and the *ummat* clung, to it, tenaciously, fearing lest the slightest departure from the path pursued by one or other of the orthodox Imams whom they chose to follow might lead them to unforseeable disaster.

It is an undeniable episode of history that Changez Khan, and his progeny Halaku Khan, Batu Khan, Mango Khan and Kublai Khan destroyed the wordly power of Islam and uprooted its culture and all that was brought by it in the development of human civilisation but within a few decades the self same Tartars, and their wild hordes became the vanguard of Islamic forces, and replanted the tree of Islamic culture more firmly and more vigorously than ever before. But the sad memory of the deback remained ever fresh throughout, and the dynamic, and fragrant laws of Islam became rigid, terse and unbendable and to move an inch from the lines chalked out by the Jurists of the second century became so abhorrent, that alongwith the finality of prophethood the schools of legal thought also development to an awe-inspiring extent. "This was indeed a great blow" says Allama Iqbal, and all contemporary historians of the invasions of Tartars describe the havoc of Baghdad with a self-suppressed pessimism about the future of Islam. For fear of further disintegration, which is only natural in such a period of political decay, the conservative thinkers of Islam focussed all their efforts on the one point, of preserving a uniform social life for the people by a Jealous exclusion of all innovations in law of the Shariat as expounded by the early doctors of Islam. Their leading idea was social order, and there is no doubt that they were partly right, because organization does to a certain extent counteract the forces of decay." But the tendency to over organization by false reverence of the past as manifested in the legists of Islam in the thirtieth century and later, was contrary to the inner impluse of Islam and consequently invoked the powerful reaction of Ibn-i-Taimiyya one of the most indefatiguible writers and preachers of Islam, who was born in 1263 A. D. five years after the destruction of Baghdad.

But the decadence that had set in, made the law of Islam static, immobile and stagnant for years together, and as a result of that lethargy and stupor the Muslim empire of Indo-Pak. subcontinent fell in the lap of the British, the Turkish Empire was torn to smitheron on and its parts distributed in small bits into un-Islamic, territorial, and subnational states. This most tragic deback brought in a renaissance and reorientation of the law of Islam by men of the eminence of Syed Ahmad Khan and his colleagues followed among others by Syed Mahmud, Syed Amir Ali and Iqbal.

Syed Amir Ali outshone his compears not only as a Judge, and a Jurist of great eminence but he was in fact a pioneer of the movement of reconstruction of Islamic legal thought in the light of the multifarious problems which are a creation of the modern civilization, for which no precedents are available in the life of the Prophet or his righteous companions. Here, on the basis of Qias (anological deductions) or doctrine of Istehsan fresh corollaries are to be drawn from the fundamental principles of the Qur'an and the Sunna.

In Pakistan, a state carved out of the Indian subcontinent, a territory for the practical experimentation of the basic law of Islam, and the practice of its ever fresh culture and civilization, it is the duty of the State, to base its fabric of law on the principles of democracy, freedom, quality, tolerance, and social justice, as enunciated by Islam. Herein the Muslims shall be enabled to order their lives, in the individual and collective spheres, in accordance with the teachings and requirements of Islam, as set out in the Holy Qur'an and the Sunna. Islam shall be the State religion of Pakistan, according to the Constitution of 1973. Accordingly therefore our Courts and Legislatures are no longer to be the blind followers of what the Jurists in the days of limited sources of knowledge of arts and science and non-existence of the modern complicated problems of today decided. They are now called upon to reinterpret the basic principles of the Qur'an, and the Sunna in the light of the present day, knowledge of modern social sciences etc. Of course the invaluable works of the old Jurists of the Sunni and Shia schools which are our most precious treasure must always serve as the leading lights and the most shining stars in guiding us to the ideal goal of the revival and rejuvenation of the Islamic Sharia. For this laudable task the Book of Syed Amir Ali will provide the basic ground work over which the beautiful edifice of the Islamic laws and learning can in the light of the modern developments be superstructed.

I have a reverential regard for every word that came from the immortal pen of the great Muslim lawyer of undying fame and I consider it an unpardonable sacrilege to remove even a comma or a full-stop from the original text of the Book which is preserved in its pristine purity. I have, however, added in the addenda the case-law on the subject that has come during the course of almost three quarters of a century that have elapsed since the publication of the 4th edition in 1912.

20th October 1976. RAJA SAID AKBAR KHAN

PREFACE TO THE FOURTH EDITION

The last edition of this work appeared in 1904. Since then various decisions of the Indian High Courts have necessitated a further examination of the rules of law applicable to the subjects under codsideration. Consequently, in this edition a great deal of new matter has been added, and many of the chapters have been re-arranged. Those relating to gifts and *wakf* have been either re-written or considerably amplified, and the work has generally been brought up-to-date.

The prosperity and well-being of the Mussalmans of India, a matter of importance not only to the community but also to the State, depend largely, if not entirely, on the system of family benefaction or *wakf* by which the law endeavours to neutralise the effects of distribution of property under the rules of inheritance. For this reason I have given in the Appendix copious translations from recognised works of authority, bearing on that branch of the Mussalman Law.

Like other legal systems, the Mahommedan Law requires a certain amount of critical and analytical study. Unfortunately, such study has fallen greatly into disuse ; even its professed expounders scarcely attempt to deal with or discuss the subject in a manner satisfactory to the critical lawyer. When passages are cited in the Courts of Justice from works on Mahommedan Law, no reference is made to their character or relative authority, or to the evolution of the principle involved in the discussion. Nor do the Courts endeavour to divert the arguments into that channel.

I have tried in these pages to meet the difficulty to which I have referred, and to assist, in some degree, the practical lawyer as well as the Judge administering the law, by indicating the position of the authorities and the development of the system.

AMEER ALI.

Reform Club,
Pall Mall, S. W.
1912.

PREFACE TO THE SECOND EDITION

THE law relating to Gifts, *Wakfs* and Wills formed the subject of my Tagore Law Lectures for 1884, and, to some extent, the present work may be regarded as a reprint of those lectures, but it possesses several features of its own, which, I venture to think, entitle it to a higher position than that of a mere second edition. The Introduction has been altered and considerably enlarged; the Shiah Law relating to life-grants and limited estates in general is fully discussed; the Chapters dealing with the Hanafi Law relating to *Wakfs* have been almost completely re-written with quotations from the most important authorities; those dealing with the Shiah Law of *Wakf* have been amplified; and the subject of Pre-emption and Bailment has been added. The Chapters in the old Lectures on the Hanafi Law of *Wakf* were founded chiefly on the *Radd-ul-Muhtar* and the *Fatawa-i-Alamgiri*. For the present work I have consulted nearly thirty recognised standard authorities and have embodied their statements in my compilation. Additional extracts are given in the Appendix.

The law relating to *Wakfs* is, to the Mahommedans of India from every point of view, the most important branch of their legal system. Not only does it form an essential part of their religion, but the existence of their principal families is dependant upon it. I have, therefore, endeavoured in these pages, to the best of my ability, to state clearly and precisely what the Mussalman Law is.

In some places I have rendered the term "*wakf*" as trust, in others, as dedication or consecration. Ryan, C. J., in the case of *Doe dem Jaun Beebee* v. *Abdollah Barber*, used the latter expression, and M. Tornouw, in his *Droits Mussalman*, has done the same. Properly analysed, it will be found that the word *wakf* combines all the ideas conveyed by these different expressions. The Mussalman Law holds that there can be no *milk* (property). without a *malik* (proprietor), that all property owned by human beings is God's free gift to them; and that when a man creates a *wakf*, he transfers the *milk* (the ownership in "the substance of the thing") to the Almighty, on the condition that the *usufruct* should be applied to the benefit of His creatures, whoever they may be. It will thus be seen that the word combines the elements of trust, dedication and consecration. From one point of view, God is the owner of the *substance* (*asl*), the recipients of the benefaction being His creatures; in another sense, He is the trustee on their behalf. The *mutwalli* is a mere manager; he has no power of mortgage, sale or lease over the *wakf* property, even for a necessity, save and except so far as is provided in the *wakf-namah*. His position is more analogous to that of a manager of a minor's estate than to that of a trustee in the technical sense. I mention this here in order to prevent any misapprehension.

AMEER ALI.

CALCUTTA—1892.

ADDENDA

Since the original text of the book was not desired to be tampered with in deference to the illustrious memory of the author, the case-law which has developed after the publication of the last edition is being given as an Addenda.

Page 33

Foot Note (1) See also I L R 9 Cal. 138 ; I L R 23 Mad. 70 ; P L D 1955 Lah. 191 ; P L D 1975 Kar. 979 ; P L D 1967 S C 200.

Page 34

Foot Note (3) See also P L D 1958 Lah. 198 (201) ; P L D 1975 S C 377, A I R 1925 Oudh 568 ; P L D 1975 Lah. 1484 ; P L D 1972 Pesh. 37.

Page 39

Foot Note (la) P L D 1958 Lah. 198 (201); P L D 1975 Lah. 1484 P L D 1975 Lah. 1095.

Page 41

Foot Note (1) See also A I R 1922 P C 281 (288)=L R 49 P C 195= I L R 44 All. 301.

Foot Note (5) See also A I R 1936 All. 600.

Page 60

Foot Note (1) See also 23 M L J 734 ; 32 P R 1895 (page 241) ; 141 P L R 1901 (page 545).

Foot Note (4) See I L R 31 Cal. 319 affirmed by the Privy Council in 35 Cal. 271=L R 35 I A 67.

Page 61

Foot Note (1) See also 35 Cal. 271=35 I A 67, albuminuria for more than a year 35 Cal. 1 (22)=34 I A 167 (177) sudden bursting of a blood-vessel in the stomach 3 C W N 57 ; A I R 1934 Pesh. 91. Asthma, A I R 1937 Cal. 500 lingering consumption are not cases of marzul maut ; I L R 3 All. 731. Lingering illness, I L R 50 Bom. 537 paralysis, not marzul maut I L R 31 Bom. 264 rapid consumption,

I L R 40 All. 238 ; A I R 1933 All. 341 cases of galloping consumption, A I R 1957 All. 395 ; Pneumonia are marzul maut.

Page 62

Foot Note (2) See also 52 P. R. 1895, L R 35 I A 67 = I L R 35 Cal. 271; A I R 1932 Lah. 229 = I L R 12 Lah. 683; I L R 35 Cal. 1 = L R 34 I A 167 ; A I R 1941 Lah. 58 ; P L D 1964 S C 143 ; P L D 1976 B J 119 ; P L D 1964 S C 173 ; P L D 1967 Lah. 613 ; P L D 1974 S C 22.

Page 63

Foot Note (1) See Note 1 page 61.

Foot Note (2) See A I R 1922 Cal. 429 (436) ; P L D 1964 S C 143 ; P L D 1964 S C 173.

Foot Note (3) See also 1931 A L J 851 (952), I L R 42 Cal. 361 (363-364).

Foot Note (4) See author Mohammadan Law, Vol. II, page 453.

Page 64

Foot Note (1) See also A I R 1929 P C 149, A I R 1948 P C 134 = 75 I A 62.

Page 66

Foot Note (1) See also I L R 10 All. 1112 (1125).

Foot Note (2) See also P L D 1964 S C 143, P L D 1964 S C 173.

Foot Note (3) See also P L D 1971 Azad J & K 55.

Foot Note (4) See also I L R 44 All 465.

Foot Note (5) A I R 1939 All. 744 (Gift of insurance policy valid).

Page 70

Foot Note (1) See P L D 1957 Kar. 258.

Page 73

Foot Note (1) See also 38 Cal. 518 ; A I R 1930 Oudh 71 ; A I R 1937 Cal. 500, A I R 1960 Mad. 447 ; P L D 1971 Kar. 108.

Page 83

Foot Note (1) See also A I R 1929 Lah. 45 ; I L R 1940 Kar. 319, P L D 1964 S C 143.

Page 89

Foot Note (1) See also I L R 38 Cal. 518 ; (1935) 62 C L J 424 ; P L D 1963 B J 1 ; P L D 1971 Pesh. 150 ; P L D 1971 Kar. 708.

Page 93

Foot Note (1) See also I L R 38 Cal. 518 (521) ; I L R 18 All. 1 ; I L R 30 All. 250 ; 9 Bom. P J 22 (32); 17 C L J 85 (86); 141 P L R 1901 (page 545) ; 138 I C 851 (852).

Foot Note (6) See also A I R 1930 Oudh 71 ; A I R 1937 Cal. 500 ; A I R 1960 Mad. 477 ; 65 C L J 34 ; 1968 S C M R 311 ; 1972 S C M R 295.

Page 94

Foot Note (1) See also A I R 1929 Lah. 309 = I L R 10 Lah. 760 ; A I R 1935 Cal. 739.

Page 95

Foot Note (1) See also I L R 34 All. 478 (481); 5 All. 285 (288) ; L R 49 I A 195 = I L R 34 All. 301 (P. C.) at page 314 ; L R 49 I A 153 = I L R 49 Cal. 820 (P. C.) at page 837 ; 102 P R 1882 (355) ; A I R 1944 Mad. 181 (190) ; P L D 1971 Kar. 708, Per contra 1972 S C M R 629 (631).

Page 97

Foot Note (1) See also I L R 38 Cal. 518 (521) ; I L R 18 All. 1 ; I L R 30 All. 250 (251) ; 9 Bom. P J 22 (32); 17 C L J 85 (86) ; 141 P L R 1901 (page 545) ; 138 I C 851 (852).

Foot Note (2) See also 15 C W N 328 ; I L R 1944 Ker. 319 (322) ; 22 Bom. L R 846 (848).

Page 108

Foot Note (1) See also A I R 1949 Lah. 238 ; P L D 1971 Kar. 708 ; P L D 1971 Pesh. 150 ; P L D 1958 Lah. 218 ; A I R 1958 Pat. 193 ; A I R 1946 Nag. 351 ; 1972 S C M R 295 ; 1968 S C M R 311 (2).

Page 113

Foot Note (1) See also I L R 23 Bom. 682 (684).

Foot Note (3) See also P L D 1965 S C 665 ; P L D 1975 Lah. 1170 ; P L D 1975 Kar. 491.

Page 114

Foot Note (1) See also L R (1916) 43 I A 221 (222) = I L R 38 All. 627 (645-46) ; (1922) L R 49 I A 195 (255) = A I R 1922 P C 281 ; P L D 1956 Lah. 760 (763).

Foot note (3) See also I L R 29 Bom. 468 (477) ; I L R 28 All. 147 (152) ; 17 C L J 85 (87); 92 P R 1917 (366); 4 P L J 397 (400) ; P L D 1964 S C 143.

Foot Note (4) See also 16 I A 205 (217); L R 59 I A 1 (13)=A I R 1932 P C 13 ; A I R 1931 Oudh 177 ; P L D 1956 S C 309 ; P L D 1958 Dacca 19.

Page 119

Foot Note (1) See also L R (1927) 54 I A 23 = A I R 1927 P C 22 ; L R (1932) 59 I A 1 (6) = A I R 1932 P C 13.

Foot Note (2) See also P L D 1957 Kar. 258.

Foot Note (3) See also 59 I A 1 = I L R 6 Luck. 556 (570) ; 92 P R 1917 ; I L R 28 All. 147 (152) ; I L R 29 Bom. 468 (471); 4 P L T 297 (300) ; A I R 1932 P C 13.

Foot Note (4) See also A I R 1927 P C 22.

Page 120

Foot Note (2) See also A I R 1933 Mad. 86 ; (1936) A L J 590=164 I C 720.

Page 121

Foot Note (1) Per contra See also A I R 1935 Lah. 795 = I L R 16 Lah. 629, A I R 1960 Madh. Pra. 60 ; A I R 1956 Tra.-Co. 292 = P L D 1964 S C 143.

Foot Note (2) See also A I R 1937 All. 547=I L R 1937 All. 609; A I R 1939 Pat. 316=183 I C 71 ; A I R 1939 Pat. 321=184 I C 508 ; A I R 1949 Lah. 238.

Page 122

Foot Note (1) Amina Bibi v. Khatija Bibi (1864) 1 Bom. H. C. 157 ; Azim-un-Nissa v. Dale (1868) 6 Mad. H. C. 455. See also A I R 1927 P C 22 ; A I R 1932 P C 13 ; 13 Bom 352 (354).

Foot Note (3) See also I L R 39 Bom. 267 (274-276) ; I L R 34 Bom. 604 ; I L R 36 Bom. 216 ; I L R 42 Cal. 933 (938) ; A I R 1928 Rang. 323 ; A I R 1935 Bom. 34.

Page 123

Foot Note (1) P L D 1965 S C 665 ; Father ; or mother when *de facto* guardian or any person maintaining the child whose father is dead makes a gift to the infant the gift is complete without any formal delivery of possession.

Page 131

Foot Note (2) See also P L D 1965 S C 665 (at p. 668) ; P L D 1975 Kar. 491 ; P L D 1975 S C 328.

Page 132

Foot Note (2) See also A I R 1948 P C 134=L R 75 I A 134 ; P L D 1975 S C 377.

Page 133

Foot Note (1) See also 7 Bom. L R 306 (307) ; (1940) 2 Cal. 189 (196) ; I L R 13 Rang. 679=156 I C 1038.

Page 134

Foot Note (1) See also (1913) I L R 37 Bom. 447 (458) ; A I R 1935 Rang. 318 ; P L D 1975 S C 377 (381).

Page 141

Foot Note (3) See also A I R 1932 P C 13 ; P L D 1964 S C 143 (162) ; P L D 1972 S C M R 50.

Page 143

Foot Note (1) See also A I R 1948 P C 134.

Page 167

Foot Note (5) See also I L R 31 Bom. 271 (277) ; I L R 34 Cal. 999 (1008, 1111) ; 30 M L J 415.

Page 170

Foot Note (1) See also I L R 1945 Nag. 820, I L R 47 Cal. 537.

Page 173

Foot Note (1) See also 100 I C 62 (Mad.) ; 108 I C 435.

Page 179

Foot Note (4) See also (1937) Bom. 18 (26, 35) ; I L R 2 Luck. 216 (22) ; P L D 1958 Lah. 198 (201) ; P L D 1975 Lah. 1484 ; P L D 1972 Pesh. 37.

Page 182

Foot Note (2) See A I R 1948 P C 134 ; L R 75 I A 62 ; I L R 2 Luck 187 (197).

Page 183

Foot Note (1) See also A I R 1933 Mad. 96 ; A I R 1935 Lah. 795 ; 1936 A L J 590=164 I C 720 ; A I R 1949 Lah. 238 ;

P L D 1954 Lah. 545 ;1972 S C M R 632 ; P L D 1976 Kar. 316.

Foot Note (2) See also I L R 29 Bom. 468 (477) ; 2 Cal. 184 (P. C.) = 3 I A 291 (308) ; A I R 1929 Lah. 45 ; I L R 1940 Ker. 319 ; P L D 1964 S C 143.

Foot Note (3) See also 141 P L R 1901.

Page 255

Foot Note (2) See A I R 1930 Bom. 101 ; L R (1937) 64 I A 138 ; A I R 1904 Mad. 504.

Foot Note (3) See also A I R 1942 Sind 137 ; P L D 1958 Lah. 824 (Wakf of cash is valid provided the fund is not intended to be consumed. Per Contra See A I R 1947 All. 127, where it has been held that a wakf of a decree is not valid as the decretal amount may not be realized.

Page 399

Foot Note (1) See also I L R 35 Cal. 294 ; I L R 1 Lah. 317 ; A I R 1933 Lah. 759 ; A I R 1934 All. 732.

Page 479

Foot Note (5) I L R 43 Cal. 1085 (P. C.) [Qazi has the complete discretion of the matter of the Public Wakif like a mosque and can go even against the wishes of the Wakif]. I L R 43 Cal. 467 (478) [The Deputy Qazi has no power of setting aside the Wakf].

Page 480

Foot Note (2) See also I L R 46 Cal. 492 (495), A I R 1924 Cal. 327 [District Judge equivalent to Qazi, his order not appealable] A I R 1924 Cal. 473 [Powers akin to powers of a District Judge under Trust Act ; Section 29 of the Guardians and Wards Act and section 21, Lunacy Act].

Page 554

Foot Note (1) See also I L R 20 Cal. 810 (815, 816), I L R 32 All. 631 (634, 635) ; I L R 35 All. 197 (199) ; 94 P R 1895 (207);

38 P W R 1919 ; I L R 18 All. 227 (232); I L R 24 Bom. 170 (175, 176, 180) ; 87 P R 1892 (302) ; I L R 8 Luck. 882 ; I L R 2 Pat. 391 (397) ; 13 Burm. L T 183 (187).

Page 555

Foot Note (1) See also I L R 20 Cal. 810 (816) ; I L R 32 All. 284 (286) ; I L R 30 All. 630 (634); 94 P R 1885 (207).

Page 563

Foot Note (1) See also 73 P R 1884 (205).

Foot Note (2) See also (1938) 2 M L J 663.

Page 737

Foot Note (2) See also I L R 30 All. 372 (374), I L R 36 All. 488 (491), I L R 32 Cal. 982 (986).

CONTENTS

INTRODUCTION.

PAGE.

CHAPTER I.

THE LAW RELATING TO GIFTS.

CHAPTER XIII.

PAGE.

THE INCOME OF THE *wakf* ESTATE HOW TO BE APPLIED.

CHAPTER XIV.

GENERAL PRINCIPLES.

The powers of the wâkif.

CHAPTER XV.

THE GOVERNANCE OF THE *Wakf*.

CHAPTER XVI.

THE SHIAH LAW OF *Wakf*.

CHAPTER XXI.

PAGE.

THE CONSTITUTION OF A *Wasiat*.

CHAPTER XXII.

CHAPTER XXIII.

WHAT MAY BE DEVISED.

CHAPTER XXIV.

GENERAL PRINCIPLES.

CHAPTER XXV.

EXECUTORS.

TABLE OF CASES CITED.

A

INDEX

TO

TECHNICAL WORDS AND PHRASES EXPLAINED IN THE TEXT.

NOTE I.

The following passage from Mr. Justice Arnold's judgment in the great Khoja case may, I think, prove of some interest to the students of the history of Mahommedanism :—

" The general expectation of Islâm had been that Ali, the first disciple, the beloved companion of the Apostle of God, the husband of his only surviving child Fâtima, would be the first Caliph. It was not so to be. The influence of Ayesha, the young and favourite wife of Mahomet, a rancorous enemy of Fâtima and of Ali, procured the election of her own father Abubekr ; to Abubekr succeeded Omar, and to him Osman ; upon whose death, in the year 665 of our era, Ali was at last raised to the Caliphate. He was not even then unopposed ; aided by Ayesha, Moawiyah, of the family of the Ommeiades, contested the Caliphate with him, and while the strife was still doubtful in the year A.D. 660, Ali was slain by a Kharegite, or Mussulman fanatic, in the mosque of Cufa, at that time the principal Mahommedan city on the right or west bank of the Euphrates, itself long since a ruin, at no great distance from the ruins of Babylon."

" This assassination of Ali caused a profound sensation in the Mahommedan world. He was, and deserved to be, deeply beloved, being clearly and beyond comparison the most heroic of that time fertile in heroes—a man brave and wise, and magnanimous and just, and self-denying in a degree hardly exceeded by any character in history. He was, besides, the husband of the only and beloved child of the Apostle of God and their two sons, Hassan and Hussain, had been the darlings of their grandfather, who had publicly given them the title of 'the foremost among the youth of paradise.' "

" Of these sons, Hassan, the elder, a saint and a recluse, on the death of his father sold his birthright of empire to Moawiyah for a large annual revenue which during the remainder of his life he expended in works of charity and religion at Medina. In the year A.D. 669, this devout and blameless grandson of the Apostle of God was poisoned by one of his wives, who had been bribed to that wickedness by Yezid, the son of Moawiyah and the second of the Ommeiade Caliphs of Damascus."

" There thus remained, as head of the direct lineage of the Apostle of God, Hussain, the younger son of Fâtima and Ali, a brave and noble man in whom dwelt much of the spirit of his father."

" Eleven years after his elder brother's murder in the year 680 of our era, yielding to the repeated entreaties of the chief Moslem people of Irak Arabi (or Mesopotamia), who promised to meet him with a host of armed supporters, Hussain set forth from Medina to Cufa to assert his right to the Caliphate against the hated Ommeiades. He crossed the desert with only a feeble train,—his wife, his sister Fâtima, two of his sons, and a few armed horsemen, when on reaching Kerbela, then a desert station about a day's journey from the west bank of the Euphrates and in the near neighbourhood of Cufa, he found drawn up to meet him a host, not of retainers, but of foes. The narrative of what follows is among the most pathetic in all history. The noble son of Ali and Fâtima, the favourite grandson of the Apostle of God, after deeds of valour romantic even in an Arab of that age, fell pierced through and through with the arrows and javelins of the cowardly assailants who did not dare to come within the sweep of his arm. One of his sons and nephew had already been slain in his sight. His other son, his wife, and his sister were carried away captive to Damascus. They smote off the head of the son of Ali, and paraded it in triumph through the streets of Cufa. As it passed along, the brutal Obeidullah, the governor of the city, struck the mouth of the dead man with his staff. 'Ah,' cried an aged Mussulman whom horror and just wrath made bold, 'what a foul deed is that ?—on those lips I have seen the lips of the Apostle of God. This tragic event stirred the heart of Islâm to its very depth.''

NOTE II.

D'Ohsson following Ibrahim Halebi, the author of the *Multaka*, classifies the Sunni jurists into seven ranks. In the first rank he places the four principal Imâms ; with reference to the others the classification is as follows.

Seconde Classe.

Elle comp rend un trés grand nombre de docteurs, dont les plus estimès son *l'Imam Ebn Youssouph, l'Imam Mahammed, l'Imam Zufer, l'Imam Mezny et l'Imam Buweyly.* Ils sont presque tous disciples de *l'Imam Azam,* dont ils suivirent l'ésprit dans l'explication des differénts points de morale et de pratique ; à la réserve de quelques-uns, sur lesquels ils debitérent des opinions opposées, une partie de ces variantes fut même adoptée par les juristes postérieurs, dans leurs codes de jurisprudence, ainsi qu'il sera expliqué plus bas.

Troisieme Classe.

Les docteurs les plus notables de cette classe sont les *Imams Khassaf, Tahhawy, Hassan-Kerkhy, Schems'-ul-Eymet' ul-hœulvany, Es-Serakh'sy Fakhr' ul Islam pezd-wy, Fakhr'ud-dinn* et *Cazi-Khaun.* Ils sont tous partisans et observateurs fidelés de ce qui a eté généralement établi et statué par les *Imams* de la premiére classe, et expliqué par ceux de la seconde.

Ils n'ont fait qn'eclaircir et résoudre plusieurs questions omises jusqu, alors en les developpant d'apres l'esprit et les décisions des quatre premiers *Imams.* Ainsi cette classe de docteurs, n'ayant rien donné de son propre fond, est, par cela mêrvie, désignée sous le nom de *tabaka-sufla,* qui signifie classe inferieure.

Quatrieme Classe.

On distingue, entre autres, *Kerkky, Razy el Asshab'y.* Ils portent la dénomination particuliére *Asshab-takhridj,* pour désigner que ces juristes se sont bornés d'un côté, à donner de l'extension aux points déja expliqués et éclaircis per les *Imams* des trois premiéres classes, et de l'autre, à en tirer des conséquences absolument dans le même esprit.

Cinquieme Classe.

Les *Imams* les plus distingués de cette classe, sont *Eby-Hassan-Coudoury,* et *Sahhib-Hidaye.* On les appelle *Asshab'y-Terdjihh,* parce que leur principal mérite est d'avoir compulsé les ouvrages des précedens *Imams,* distuté leurs variantes, et fixé, par leur choix, celles qui devoient avoir la préférence

Sixieme Classe.

Sahhib-Kenz, *Sahhib ul-Mukhtar*, *Sahhib-ul-Medjhma* et *Sahhib-Wikaye* sont les plus estimés de ces docteurs. Tout leur travail se réduit à exposer leur opinion particuliére sur la mérite des œuvres et des decisions canoniques des *Imams* de la quatriéme et cinquiéme classe.

Septieme Classe.

Elle contient tous les *Imams* postérieurs qui ont écrit sur le culte comme sur la jurisprudence, d'aprés l'esprit et l'opinion de ceux des six autres classes. Tels sont les fameux ouvrages de *Tatar-Khaniye*, de *Hindiye*, de *Eb'ul Leyss*, de *Medjhma-ul-Bahh-reynn*, d' *Ebul-Cassim*, de *Kirahiyeth'ul-Fetawa*, &c., &c. On donne généralement à tous ces écrites le nom de *Mutawlath*, parce qu'ils sont trés-volumineux, et qu'ils traitent fort au long de toutes les matieres rélatives à ceslois canoniques.

Cette derniere classée est censée comprende aussi tous les docteurs et tous les jurisconsultes qui étudient la science du droit, comme sont, dit le méme auteur les *Oulemas* de nos jours, décorés, l'egal dés anciens *Imams* dés titres de *Meschaykh* de *Foukahha*, et d'*Oulema* c'est-a-dire anciens juristes, docteurs ; mais jamais de celui de *Mudjhtehhid* ou interprétes sacrés.

INTRODUCTION.

SECTION I.

THE APPLICABILITY OF THE MUSSULMAN LAW.

IN India, the Legislature has preserved intact the laws of the Mussulmans in all matters relating to inheritance and dispositions of property. Excepting the special Statutes which are of general application and which are properly speaking municipal laws, there is no *lex loci* in this country. In India, the law is, in the main, personal. This not only adds to the difficulty of legislation, but considerably enhances the risk of failure in the administration of justice. In the case of the Mahommedan Law especially, clothed as it is for the most part in the garb of an unfamiliar language, it is often extremely difficult to ascertain and apply its principles. And it is apparently on this account that often a certain reluctance is evinced to give effect to the rules of the Mussulman Law; and English Law and sometimes even Hindu Law are invoked either to cut down or to explain away the meaning of the Mahommedan Law.(1) These indirect endeavours to repeal the laws of the Mussulmans seem to be in direct conflict with the spirit of British legislation.

The British Government at the commencement of its ascendancy in this country assured to the inhabitants of India by a solemn Act of Parliament the full enjoyment of their laws and customs. One of the objects of that Act,(2) as stated in the preamble, was "that the inhabitants should be maintained and protected in the enjoyment of all their ancient laws, usages, rights and privileges." Had the question been *res integra*, it would have been fairly open to contention, whether it was ever the intention of the Legislature to make any change in the personal laws of the inhabitants of this country, of whatever race or creed. Regard, however, being had to the decision in the case of *Musleah* v. *Musleah*(3) and other cases

(1) See the case of *Moosabhai* v. *Yacoobbhai*, [1904] I. L., 29 Bom., 267, 276.
(2) 21 Geo. III, cap. 71.
(3) Fulton's Rep., p. 420.

it would appear that the tendency of the Courts has been to restrict the operation of the personal laws, in the main, to Hindus and Mahommedans. The provisions of 21 Geo. III, cap. 71, s. 17, have been re-enunciated in later Statutes and are now substantially embodied in Act XII of 1887, and "constitute one of the most important guarantees given to the people of India by the British rule."(1) The attempt to restrict the operative effect of section 17 to "succession and inheritance," is as distinctly opposed to the wording of the section itself as to the entire course of decisions and the intention of the Legislature. The word "dealing," in fact, would include dispositions. Besides, the Legislature has declared in express terms, that when there is no special enactment governing any particular question, the Courts of Justice should be guided by rules of equity and good conscience, and two well-known Judges of the High Court of Calcutta, STEER and LEVINGE, JJ., have held that it is in conformity with equity and good conscience, that, as between Mahommedans, all questions relating to dispositions of property should be governed by the Mahommedan Law. In *Zohorooddeen Sirdar* v. *Baharoollah Sirdar*,(2) those learned Judges expressed themselves in the following terms :—

"It is contended by the pleaders for the plaintiff, special respondent, that the Mahommedan Law is not applicable to contract of the nature before the Court; that according to section 15, Regulation IV of 1793, it is only on questions of inheritance, marriage, and caste that the Court is called upon to decide in conformity to the Mahommedan Law, and that the present matter before the Court, not being of the nature above expressed, is to be decided by the ordinary rules of equity and good conscience. In answer to this it may be remarked that the Courts of this country have invariably applied in practice, the Mahommedan Law to a variety of cases other than those coming under the denomination of inheritance, marriage, caste, and even if immemorial and recognized practice did not legalize the action of the Courts, it cannot be said that when this Court administers to Mahommedans their own law, they do otherwise than administer justice according to equity and good conscience."

(1) Mr. Justice Mahmood in *Muzhar Ali* v. *Budh Sing*, [1884] **I. L., 7 All.,** 302.

(2) 1864, Gap Number W. R., 187.

A similar contention was raised in the case of *Yusuf Ali* v. *the Collector of Tippera*,(1) but the learned Judges (GARTH, C. J., and MACDONELL, J.) decided the question before them on the basis of the Mahommedan Law.

It has been emphatically recognized by the Bombay High Court that the Mahommedan Law should be applied in the construction of deeds dealing with property executed by Mahommedans, whatever may be the language in which the disposition is made.(2) And in the case of *H. H. Azimunnissa Begum* v. *Clement Dale*,(3) Mr. Justice Bittleston dealing with the question whether 13 Eliz., cap. VI and 27 Eliz., cap. IV, were applicable to Hindus and Mahommedans, expressed himself thus: "In Morton's Col. Rep., 358, there is a *semble* that the Statute (which is *in pari materia*), 13 Eliz., cap. V, appears to be considered as extending in India; and in a case arising entirely between British subjects other than Hindus or Muhammadans, I am disposed to think that in accordance with the reasoning in *Freeman* v. *Fairlie* (1 Moo., I. A., p. 305) and the *Mayor of Lyons* v. *The E. I. C.*, id., p. 175, the Statute 27 Eliz. ought also to be so considered. But the gift in this case was by a Muhammadan to a Muhammadan, and any question as to its validity must, I think, be decided by Muhammadan Law. It is true that the defendant is not a Muhammadan but an European British subject, and the persons from whom he claims, *i.e.*, the Nawab's creditors, were also in one case; *viz.*, as respects Turnbull's Gardens, not Muhammadans, but East Indians, who would be governed by English Law; but this cannot affect the plaintiff's title. The provisions of the charter of the Supreme Court is that 'in the cases of Muhammadans, their inheritance and succession to lands, rents and goods, and all matters of contract and dealing between party and party, shall be determined by the laws and usages of the Muhammadans; and when one of the parties shall be a Muhammadan by the laws and usages of the defendant.' But that does not mean that whenever the defendant in a suit is an European British subject, no law but the law of England

(1) [1882] I. L., 9 Cal., 138.

(2) *Gangabai* v. *Thavar Mulla*, [1863] 1 Bom. H. C. R., 71, *per* SAUSSE, C. J. See also *Fatima Bibee* v. *The Advocate General*, [1881] I. L., 6 Bom., 42, *per* WEST, J.; and *Gosain* v. *Gosain*, [1854] 6 Moo. I. A., 81.

(3) [1868] 6 Mad. H. C. R., 455.

shall be applied to ascertain the validity of any past transactions which may be brought under consideration in the suit. Its only effect, as I apprehend, is this, when a dealing takes place between two parties of whom one only is Muhammadan, and a suit is brought in respect of that transaction, the dispute between these parties is to be decided according to the law of the defendant. The transaction on which the plaintiff's title depends, was, however, between Muhammadans only, and though the donor afterwards dealt with persons not Muhammadans, and not subject to Muhammadan Law, the plaintiff was no party to any such dealing, and she cannot by the Nawab's acts be rendered subject (as regards her property) to any other than the Muhammadan Law."

In *Moonshee Buzloor Ruheem* v. *Shumsoon-nissa Begum*,(1) the Judicial Committee of the Privy Council dealing with certain remarks of the Judges of the Sudder Court of Calcutta, refusing to follow the Mahommedan Law in that case, made the following observations:—

"Their Lordships most emphatically dissent from that conclusion. It is, in their opinion, opposed to the whole policy of the law in British India, and particularly to the enactment already referred to (Reg. IV of 1793, Sec. 15), which directs, that in suits regarding marriage and caste, and all religious usages and institutions, the Mahommedan Laws with respect to Mahommedans, and the Hindu Laws with regard to Hindus are to be considered as the general rules by which Judges are to form their decisions; and they can conceive nothing more likely to give just alarm to the Mahommedan community than to learn by a judicial decision that their law, the application of which has been justly secured to them, is to be over-ridden upon a question which so materially concerns their domestic relations."

Section II.

The Growth of Mussulman Jurisprudence.

Of all systems of law, the Islâmic system furnishes, from an historical point of view, the most interesting phenomenon of growth. The small beginnings from which it grew up, and the comparatively

(1) [1867] 11 Moo. I. A., 551.

short space of time within which it attained its wonderful development, mark its position as one of the most important juridical systems in the civilised world.

The grand superstructure of Islâmic jurisprudence is founded on the Koranic laws and the traditional sayings of the Prophet, but much of the coping stone was supplied at Bagdad, in Bokhâra, in Syria, in Andalusia and Persia. I have, in another place,(1) referred to the resemblance that exists between the family laws of Islâm and the Rabbinical Law. Similarly, many of the conceptions of the Saracenic jurists, who flourished in the full tide of Moslem development and ascendancy, bear a strong and startling analogy to the rules of the Roman Civil Law on cognate subjects. Often the analogy is so startling as to make the careful and critical student ask himself whether it arises from mere accidental coincidence, or is the result of mutual action and reaction? Considering the close proximity of the two nations and their frequent contact in schools and colleges, as in the field and in the hall, it is impossible to suppose that Byzantine ideas exercised no influence on the legal conceptions of the Arabian jurists.

Shiah and Sunni schools of Law.

The unhappy schism, which at this moment divides the Islâmic world into the two great sects of Shiahs and Sunnis, owed its origin to secular causes which led ultimately to a wide divergence in their juridical conceptions. It originated with dynastic questions and grew into a separation on doctrinal and legal points. The great Sunni sect is divided in its own bosom into four schools; and the doctrinal and legal differences among them are as great as between the Shiahs and any one of the Sunni schools, and yet they are not regarded by each other with the same bitterness as collectively they regard the Shiahs. The reason is plain, and is to be found in the reception which the two sects accorded to the doctrine of the *Imâmate*.

The Imâmate.

The question of the *Imàmate*, that is, "the spiritual headship of the Mussulman Commonwealth," forms the distinctive feature of difference between the Sunnis and the Shiahs, and gives a characteristic complexion to the juridical doctrines of the two schools. The Shiahs repudiate entirely the authority of the *Jamâ'at* (or the universality of the people) to elect a spiritual chief, who should supersede the rightful claims of the persons indicated by

(1) Mahommedan Law, Vol. II, p. 2.

the Founder of the Faith, whilst the Sunnis regard the decisions of the assemblies, however obtained, as of œcumenical importance. The question came up for discussion and settlement immediately on the decease of Mohammed when it became necessary to elect a Caliph or successor to the Prophet to assume the leadership of Islâm. The Hâshimites, the kinsmen of Mohammed, maintained that the office belonged by right to Ali as one who had been pointed out by the Prophet as his successor. The other Koreishites, who were traditionally hostile to the Banû Hâshim, insisted upon proceeding by election. Whilst the Banû Hâshim were engaged in the obsequies of Mohammed, Abû Bakr, who by virtue of his age and position at Mecca, held a high place in the estimation of the Arabs, was elected to the office of Caliph by the votes of the Koreish.

The first Caliph of Islâm.

Abû Bakr died in the third year of his Caliphate(1) and was succeeded by Omar (*Ibn-ul-Khattâb*). Under this Caliph the conquest of Syria, Egypt and Persia was achieved by the Moslems. Upon his decease the Caliphate was offered to Ali on condition that he should govern in accordance with the precedents established by the two former Caliphs. Ali declined to accept the office on those terms, declaring that in all cases respecting which he found no positive law or decision of the Prophet, he would rely upon his own judgment. This notable declaration forms another point of difference between the Shiahs and the Sunnis. The Caliphate was then offered to Osmân who consented to the terms imposed by the electoral body.

The legal divergence.

The legal divergence between the Sunni and the Shiah schools dates virtually from this epoch. The willingness of Osmân to follow implicitly the precedents established by Abû Bakr and Omar, without any question as to their applicability to the ever-varying exigencies of human life, impressed a distinctive character upon the Sunni doctrines. Both Abû Bakr and Omar had during their Caliphates deferred to Ali's exposition of the law; and judgments were invariably given according to his interpretation of the traditions. Osmân seems to have set a different example. This well-intentioned but weak chief, governed entirely by his secretary and kinsman Merwân, afterwards a Caliph himself,

(1) August 634, A. C.

was killed, after a short and troubled reign, by the revolted Egyptian soldiery led by Mohammed, the son of Abû Bakr. Upon his death Ali was elected to the Caliphate. His accession was the signal for two fierce revolts on the part of the opposite faction. The one which was headed by Ayesha, the daughter of Abû Bakr, was suppressed without much difficulty; the other was more successful. Osmân had, during his lifetime, appointed one of his kinsmen M'uâwiyah, the son of Abû Sufiân, to the Governorship of Syria. This ambitious chief perceived in the murder of Osmân an opportunity for his own aggrandisement; and the insurrection raised by him proved, indirectly, the cause of the many disasters which have befallen Islâm. Defeated in several consecutive battles, he appealed to arbitration which was agreed to by Ali with the object of avoiding further bloodshed. Abû Mûsa al-Ash'aâry was appointed arbitrator on behalf of the House of Mohammed, and 'Amr ibn-ul-'Aâs on behalf of M'uâwiyah. 'Amr persuaded Abû Mûsa that, with the view of healing the wounds which the differences betwen Ali and M'uâwiyah had inflicted on the Moslem world, it was necessary to set aside both chiefs and elect another Caliph. Abû Mûsa agreed to the suggestion, and on the people assembling to hear the verdict of the arbitrators, he pronounced the deposition of both M'uâwiyah and Ali. He was followed by 'Amr ibn-ul-'Aâs, who declared that he agreed with Abû Mûsa in deposing Aii, but that he confirmed M'uâwiyah in his office. The boldness of the artifice, and the shamelessness with which it was carried into execution struck with dismay all those who had seen in the arbitration a means for preventing further bloodshed in Islàm. This proceeding of 'Amr ibn-ul-'Aâs exasperated the Fâtimides, and both parties separated vowing undying hatred towards each other. Ali was shortly after assassinated whilst engaged in prayers in a mosque at Kufa.(1) His assassination enabled M'uâwiyah to consolidate his power both in Syria and Hijâz.

M'uâwiyah;

Until the accession of this chief to the office of the Caliphate, which the stern virtues of the early Caliphs had sanctified and adorned, no distinctive appellation was assigned to or assumed by either party. The partisans of Ali were known simply as the Banû-Hâshim. Under M'uâwiyah, the followers of the House of Mohammed

(1) Mr. Justice Arnold calls Ali, "the most heroic of that time, most fruitful in heroes;" 12 Bom. H. C. R., 323.

began to be called "Shiahs" or "adherents;"(1) whilst the partisans of M'uâwiyah were called *Amawis*.(2) When the Abbasides acquired the dominion, the party which advocated the principle of election in preference to hereditary succession adopted the name of *Ahl-us-Sunnat wa'l Jamâ'at* ("People of the Traditions and Assembly").(3) The Fâtimides adopted green, the colour of the Prophet, as the symbol of their cause; the Banû Ommeyya, on the other hand, assumed white for their standard. Up to this time the divergence between the two factions was chiefly political and dynastic. Their doctrinal and legal differences began now to assume the type and proportions they retain at the present moment. The Shiahs reject not only the decisions of the Œcumenical Councils, but also all traditions not handed down by Ali or his immediate descendants—those who had seen the Prophet and held familiar intercourse with him.

The Koran.

Though the Mahommedan Law purports to be founded essentially on the Koran, most of the rules and principles which now regulate the lives of Moslems are not to be found there. It undoubtedly contains the germs of the fundamental principles, which regulate the various relations of life; the religious, civil and criminal laws which provide for the constitution and continuance of the body politic; and even of political rules and social economy. The absence of a systematic arrangement, which has frequently been considered as its greatest defect, is explained by the circumstance that it was gradually built up during the lifetime of the Prophet. The moral principles and the legal rules, which make up the work, were enunciated, not simultaneously as a completed Code of Law, but in accordance with the exigencies of the moment and the passing requirements of each special case arising in the midst of a simple and primitive society.

Shiah doctrine.

According to the Shiah doctrine, the oral precepts of the Prophet are in their nature supplementary to the Koranic ordinances and their binding effect depends on the degree of harmony existing between them and the laws of the Koran. Thus, those traditions which seem to be in conflict with the positive directions in the

(1) In the *Jawâhir-ul-Kalâm*, the term "Shiah" is explained as meaning "a propagator of the true doctrine."

(2) From Ommey'a an ancestor of M'uâwiyah; in other words, the Ommeyades.

(3) See *The Spirit of Islâm*, p. 528, (pop. Ed. p. 286) where I have fully explained the subject.

text are considered to be apocryphal. The process of elimination is conducted upon certain recognised principles founded upon logical rules and definite data. These rules have acquired a distinctive type among the M'utazalas, who have eliminated from the *Hadîs Kudsî* (the holy traditions) such alleged sayings of the Prophet as appeared incompatible and out of harmony with his developed teachings, as explained and illustrated by the philosophers and jurists of his race.

The Sunnis, on the other hand, base their doctrines on the entirety of the traditions. They regard the concordant decisions of the successive Caliphs and of the general body of *ulema* (*Ijmâ'a-ul-Ummat*) as supplementing the Koranic rules and regulations, and as almost equal in authority to them.

The sources of the Mussulman Law.

According to the Sunni doctrines, the sources of the Mahommedan Law are invariable in their order and limited in their number. With reference to these fundamental bases of jurisprudence, as they are called, there is little or no divergence among the several branches of the Sunni school, though they differ much in their mode of interpretation and exposition of the laws. (1) The Koran; (2) The *Hadis* or *Sunnat* (traditions handed down from the Prophet); (3) the *Ijmâ'a-ul-Ummat* (concordance among the followers); and (4) the *Kiyâs*, (analogical reasoning), constitute the bases upon which Sunni jurisprudence is essentially founded. The *Hadîs* (pl. *Ahâdîs*) embraces (*a*) all the words, counsels, and oral laws of the Prophet (*Kawl*); (*b*) his actions, his works, and daily practices (*Fyl*); (*c*) and his silence (*Takrîr*) implying a tacit approbation on his part of any individual act committed by his disciples. The rules deduced from these subsidiary sources vary considerably in respect of the degree of authority which is attached to them. If the rules, or traditional precepts, are of public and universal notoriety (*Ahâdîs-i-mutwâttireh,*) they are regarded as absolutely authentic and decisive. If the traditions, though known publicly by a great majority of people, do not possess the character of universal notoriety, they are designated as *Ahâdîs-i-mashhûra*; whilst the *Akhbâr-i-wâhid,* which depend for their authenticity upon the authority of isolated individuals, have little or no value attached to them. Thus, every tradition purporting to be handed down by the contemporaries and companions of the Prophet, regardless of their actual relationship to him, is considered to be authentic and genuine, provided certain arbitrary conditions, framed with the view of testing the value of personal testimony, are complied with.

(3) *Ijmâ'a-ul-Ummat* implies general concordance. Under this collective name are included all the apostolic laws, the explanations, glosses, and decisions of the leading disciples of the Prophet, their successors and the principal jurists on theological, civil and criminal matters.

(4) *Kiyâs*, the exercise of analogical reasoning, forms the principal point of difference among the four sub-divisions of the Sunni school of jurisprudence.

Sources of the Mussulman Law: Shiah doctrine.

The Shiahs do not admit the genuineness of any tradition not received from the *Ahl-ul-Bait*, ("the People of the House,") consisting of Ali and Fâtima and their descendants, and repudiate entirely the validity of all decisions not passed by their own spiritual leaders and Imâms. In the application of private or analogical reasoning, and in drawing conclusions from the ancient precedents they also differ widely from the Sunnis.

Until the Seffavian sovereigns made the Shiah creed the State religion of Persia, it was the religion of a persecuted and hated sect. The persecutions to which the Shiahs have been, from time to time, subjected,—have created a marked impression upon their legal conceptions regarding the connection between the secular and the spiritual power,—the Church and the State.(1) Partly in consequence of the mysterious disappearance of their last Imâm, and the existing belief that he is still alive and will re-appear to overthrow the enemies of Islâm, and partly owing to the frequent repression from which they have suffered, the Shiahs have dissociated the secular from the spiritual power. Nevertheless the *Mujtahids* (the expounders of the law) exercise in Shiah countries an amount of authority which is not possessed even by the Sheikh-ul-Islâm in Turkey.

Doctrine of escheat.

The effect of this separation of the spiritual from the temporal power is most clearly marked in the doctrine of escheats. According to the Shiahs there is no escheat to the *Bait-ul-Mâl* (the Public Treasury).(2) The idea of *Bait-ul-Mâl* is "abhorrent" to the Shiah creed. All escheats, which occur only in cases where the deceased leaves no possible heir, go to the spiritual Imâm, and in his absence

(1) I. D'Ohsson, *Tableau Generale de l'Empire Ottoman*, p. 76.

(2) See *The Spirit of Islâm*, 2nd Ed., p. 316.

(*ghîbat*) to his representative the Mujtahid, who distributes the proceeds among the poor of the intestate's native city.

Shiah sub-sections.

The Shiahs are divided into several sub-sections; for example, the *Asnâ 'Aasharias* or *Imâmias*, (the followers of the twelve Imâms), the *Ismailias*, the followers of Ismail, one of the sons of Imâm Jaafar as-Sâdik (the sixth Imâm),(1) the *Zaidias*, the *Batinias* (the allegorists), &c. They differ from each other not so much on the interpretation of the law as on doctrinal points. The school of the M'utazalas, an offshoot from the Shiah branch, bears the closest analogy to the early Medinite School of the Fâtimide Imâms. The rise of M'utazalaism forms one of the most interesting features in the history of Islâm.(2) It originated in the secession of Wâsil bin-'Aatâ, a contemporary of Abû Hanîfa, from the doctrines taught by Imâm Hassan al-Basrî (of Bussorah).

Hassan was educated in the school of the early Fâtimide philosophers, and the liberality of his views contrasted remarkably with that of his age. Wâsil had imbibed his knowledge at the same source, but he separated from Hassan on the question of free-will and predestination, and founded a school of his own. His disciples have, from the fact of his secession, assumed the designation of *M'utazalas* or *Ahl-ul-'Itizâl* (Dissenters or Protestants). Proceeding upon the lines of the Fâtimide philosophers and appropriating the principles which they had laid down, Wâsil formulated the doctrines which constituted the basis of his difference from patristicism generally. His impulsiveness often led him to overstep the bounds of moderation in his antagonism to intellectual tyranny, yet the general rationalism of his school rallied round his standard the most advanced and cultured minds. Imâm Zamakhshari, (the author of the *Kashshâf*,) Abu'l Hassan Ali al-Mas'ûdi,(3) "Imam, historian and doctor," Mirkhond and Khondemir, authors of the *Rouzat-us-Safa* and *Habib-us-Siyar*, were all M'utazalas. There can be no doubt, that the moderate M'utazalas represented the views of Ali and the most liberal and learned of his early descendants, for the doctrines of the Fâtimides bear the

(1) The *Jamaa-ush-Shittât*.

(2) See *The Spirit of Islam*, 2nd Ed., p. 385.

(3) The "far-famed" author of the *Murûj-uz-zahab*, "the Meadows of Gold." This great writer who has been styled the Herodotus of the East, was not only a philosopher, a historian and a geographer, but a voluminous writer on Shiah traditions.

closest analogy to those of the school founded by Wâsil and reformed by Zamakshari.(1) It is a well-known fact that the chief doctors of the M'utazalas were either Fâtimides themselves or were educated under the Fâtimides.

The M'utazala doctrines.

The M'utazalas maintain that justice is the animating principle of human actions, justice being the embodiment in action of the dictates of reason. They maintain further that there is no eternal, immutable law as regards the actions of man, and that the divine ordinances which regulate his conduct are the result of individual and collective development; that, in fact, the commands and the prohibitions, "the promises and the threats," which have been promulgated among, or held out, to mankind, have invariably been in consonance with the progress of humanity, and that the Law has always grown with the growth of the human mind. The doctrines of the *Ahl-ul-'Itizâl* were adopted by Abdullah al-Mâmûn. He and his two immediate successors strived to introduce the Mutazalite philosophy and theology throughout the Moslem world. Unfortunately, for Islâm, Patristicism proved too powerful even for those sovereign pontiffs, and the triumph of a factitious orthodoxy, opposed to all improvement and progress, under the bigot Mutawakkil, led eventually to the downfall of the Caliphate.

The Imâmias.

The Indian Shiahs are chiefly *Asnâ 'Aasharias* or *Imâmias*. The *Asnâ 'Aasharias* are divided into two sub-sections, the *Akhbâri* and the *Usûli*, namely, (*i*) those who adhere to certain principles of interpretations laid down by the *Mujtahids* (the jurists of their school), and (*ii*) those who absolutely deny the influence of authority in matters of opinion unless such authority should be in harmony with the dictates of reason and judgment.(2) The *Usûlis* allow the exercise of *Kiyâs* (private judgment) on every legal question, and, as will be seen hereafter, coincide in this respect with the principal Sunni school. In their acceptance of the doctrine of evolution they approach most closely the Mutazalas.

The Khojahs.

The Khojahs, who are to be found in the Bombay Presidency, belong like many of the Borahs, to the *Ismailia* sect. Although

(1) The great author of the *Kashshâf*, a most important, learned, and well-reasoned commentary on the Koran "a production the like of which," says Ibn-Khalikân, "had never before appeared on the interpretation of the Koran." Imâm Zamakhshari was born in 1075, A. C. and died in 1144, A. C.

(2) See *The Spirit of Islâm*, 2nd Ed., pp. 318 et seq.

on questions of succession they have been held to be governed by Hindu customs, it does not appear that the same rule is applicable to their dispositions. It is to be presumed that in those cases they would be subject to the law of the sect to which they belong. And as the Ismailias have no separate legal system, that would be the general Shiah law.

A majority of the Borahs are Ismailias. They do not, however, follow the Imâm of the Khojahs. Their spiritual preceptor is said to be in Yemen. Their dispositions appear to be governed by the general Mussulman law. The Borah.

The Sunni Borahs of certain parts of Gujarat, who were originally Rajput converts, are quite apart from the *Ismailia* Borahs.(1)

In A. H. 905 (A. C. 1499) Shah Ismâil Saffavi, the great founder of the Seffavian dynasty, adopted the Shiah doctrines as the national religion and law of the Persians, which have continued so from that period until the present time, notwithstanding the violent efforts of the Afghan usurper Ashraf and the cruel Nadir Shah to substitute the Sunni creed. Until the return of Humâyûn from Persia in the year 1555, the Shiahs were confined chiefly to the kingdoms of Bijapur and Golconda. The Bahmani and Aâdil-shâhi sovereigns were Shiahs, and with the doctrines of the Persians they had also borrowed Persian culture. When Humâyûn returned to India after the death of Shèr Shah Suri, he is alleged to have come back pledged to introduce the Shiah doctrines in return for the Persian support. Whatever truth there may be in this report, there can be no doubt that many learned men accompanied Humâyûn to India and established themselves there. Shiahism began to spread among the people, though the State-religion continued to be Sunni. Shah Shujah, Shah Jehan's second son, was a Shiah. In 1847, King Amjad Ali Shah made the Shiah religion the State-religion in Oudh. Thus the bulk of the Mussulman population in that province is Shiah. Similarly, in the District of Moorshedabad Shiahs constitute a preponderant majority. Shîahism.

SECTION III.

THE SUNNI SCHOOLS OF LAW.

THE four principal schools of law among the Sunnis, named after their founders, originated with certain great jurists to whom

(1) See Vol. II, p. 14.

has been assigned the distinguished position of *Mujtahid Imâms* namely, Expounders of Law *par excellence*. By virtue of their learning and their eminence, they were entitled not to be bound in the interpretation of the law by any precedent, but to interpret it according to their own judgment and analogy (*kyâs*). Though the doctrines of these schools are essentially the same as regards fundamental dogmas (*usûl*), they differ from each other in the respective weight allowed to *kyâs*, and the application of private judgment in the interpretation and exposition of the law.

Imâm Abû Hanîfa.

The founder of the first distinctive juridical school among the Sunnis was Abû Hanifa. He was born in the year 80 of the Hijra (Hegira), during the reign of Abdul Malik ibn Merwân, was educated in the Shiah school of law and received his first instructions in jurisprudence from the Imâm J'aafar as-Sâdik (the sixth Imâm of the House of Mohammed). He received his knowledge of the traditions from Abû 'Abdullah ibn al-Mubârak and Hâmid ibn-Suleiman. This great jurist often quotes the Fâtimide Imâm as his authority. On his return to his native city of Kûfa, though he continued to remain a zealous and consistent partisan of the House of Ali, he seceded from the Shiah school of law and founded a system of his own diverging completely on many important points from the doctrines of the Shiahs ; and yet so close is the resemblance between his exposition of the law and their views, that there is no reason to doubt the source from which he derived his original inspiration. The latitude, which he allowed to private judgment in the interpretation of the law, seems to be unquestionably a reflex of the opinions of the Fâtimide doctors. Abû Hânifa died in the year A. H. 150.(1) The school, which he founded, goes by the name Hanafî, and is in force among the major portion of the Indian Mussulmans, among the Afghans, Turkomans, almost all Central Asian Mahommedans, the Turks and Egyptians. In fact, his school owns by far the largest number of followers. Abû Hanîfa's teachings were amplified, illustrated, and explained by his two great disciples, Abû Yusuf and Mohammed.

Imâm Abû Yusuf.

Abû Yusuf [Y'aakub ibn Ibrâhim al-Kûfi] was born in A. H. 113 (A. C. 731), and died at Baghdad in A. H. 182 (A. C. 798). He was a pupil of Abû Hanifa and was first appointed to the office of Kâzi of Baghdad by the Caliph al-Hâdi ; subsequently he was raised to

(1) A. C. 699-769.

the dignity of Kâzi-ul-Kuzzât or Chief Justiciary of the Empire by the Caliph Hârûn ar-Rashîd, being the first who held that high office.

A collection of the decisions of Abû Yusuf was published under the auspices of the Vizier of Hârûn, J'aafar ibn Yayha Barmaki, (the Barmecide), and hence called the *Fatâwai Barâmika.* It is frequently referred to by the text-writers.

[Abû 'Abdullah] Mohammed [ibn Hussain ash-Shaibani] was born at Wâsit in Mesopotamia in A. H. 132 (A. C. 749) and died at Rai in A. H. 187 (A. C. 802). The Imâm Mohammed, as he is most generally called, was a fellow-pupil of Abû Yusuf under Abû Hanîfa, and on the death of the latter pursued his studies under Abû Yusuf. He has left a number of works upon which commentaries have been written by some of the foremost jurists of the Hanafî school. Imâm Mohammed.

After Abû Hanîfa and his two above-named disciples, the next in authority among the Hanafî Sunnis are the Imâm Zuffar [ibn-ul Hâzil], Chief Judge at Bussorah (Basra), where he died in A. H. 158 (A. C. 774), and Hassan bin-Ziyâd. These lawyers were contemporaries, friends and pupils of Abû Hanîfa.(1)

With reference to the respective authority of these masters of the Hanafî system, opinion seems to have become more crystalised in later times than was the case at the beginning. Sir William Jones says " that although Abû Hanîfa be the acknowledged head of the prevailing sect, and has given his name to it, yet so great is the veneration paid to Abû Yusuf and the lawyer Mohammed, that, when they both dissent from their master, the Mussulman Judge is at liberty to adopt either of the two decisions which seems to him the more consonant and founded on the better authority."(2) The respective authority of 'the masters.'

This statement, however, needs amplification and some degree of qualification.

In the *Durr-ul-Mukhtâr*(3) the rule is stated in the following terms :—The Kâzi (Judge) like the Mufti (jurisconsult) has to adopt (*lit.* take) the opinion (قول) of Abû Hanîfa absolutely

(1) D'Ohsson I, p. 18. For matters in which Imâm Zuffar's veiws are adopted for decrees, see Mahommedan Law Vol. II, p. 602. They are not, however, exhaustive.

(2) Sir William Jones' works, Vol. III, p. 510 ; 1 Harrington's *Analysis*, p. 228.

(3) Hooghly Ed., p. 523.

(علی الاطلاق) [*viz.*, whether the disciples agree with him or not]; and after him that of Abû Yusuf; and after him that of Mohammed, and after him that of Zuffar and Hassan bin Ziyâd.'' But this broad statement is applicable only when the Kâzi does not possess the capacity of drawing conclusions (ادراک).

The respective authority of 'the masters'—contd.

In the *Hamâdia* also it is similarly stated that "the *Fatwas* (decisions) are given primarily according to the doctrine of Abû Hanîfa, next according to Abû Yusuf, next according to Imâm Mohammed, next according to Zuffar, and then according to Hassan ibn Ziyad. It is said that if Abû Hanîfa be of one opinion and his two Disciples of another, the Mufti is at liberty to choose either, but the preceding rule must be observed when the Mufti is not a scientific jurist [and therefore not competent to judge of the opposite opinions]. This view is expressed in the *Kinia*. Imâm Sarakhsi has declared it safe to rely upon Abû Yusuf in judicial matters, and the learned have followed him in such cases, though if there be a difference between the two Disciples whoever agrees with Abû Hanîfa should be preferred. The joint opinion of the Disciples may also be adopted, though different from that of Abû Hanîfa, if the difference appear to proceed from a change of human affairs [lit. a change of men and alteration of times]; and modern lawyers are agreed that the doctrine of the Disciples should be adopted for adjudication in matters of civil justice.''

In the *Jâm'aa-ul-Fusalain* the same rule is expressed in the following words:—And if on any doctrine 'our masters' differ, in that case if either of the Disciples should agree with Abû Hanîfa, that opinion should be taken because that would appear to be the correct view. And if both the Disciples differ from Abû Hanîfa, then it must be considered whether their divergence arises from change of circumstances and the requirements of justice, in that case the doctrine (قول) of the Disciples should be adopted on account of the alteration in the conditions of mankind. In matters of business (مزارعات) and transactions (معاملات) their opinions should be accepted as on this there is a concurrence of the moderns Besides this, jurists have laid down that the Kâzi should come to a decision by drawing conclusions upon analogical reasoning.''

Dealing with the duties of the *Mufti*, Kâzi Khân speaks thus: "if it is a question on which our masters are disagreed, then it must be seen whether any of the disciples is in agreement with Abû Hanîfa. In that case, the opinion of Abû Hanîfa and of that disciple who agrees with him should be adopted, because the arguments are strong on their side.....If both disagree with Abû Hanîfa, then it must be considered whether their disagreement arises from change in the times, and decision should be pronounced in accordance with [the requirements of] justice, and the doctrine should be adopted which keeps in view the changed conditions of people, (احوال الناس). *In matters pertaining to contracts and civil transactions*, and *such like, their* [the disciples,] *views should be adopted.*"(1)

Respective authority of 'the masters'—contd.

But, although the respective authority of the "masters" is sometimes enunciated in rather wide terms, a careful study of the law shows that considerable latitude is left to the Judge to follow the rule which is most consistent with justice, the changed conditions of society, the requirements of particular localities and the needs of the inhabitants. And, accordingly, although in doctrinal matters and in what may be called ecclesiastical discipline, the opinion of Abû Hanîfa is supreme, there is no hard and fast rule regarding secular questions. On some his pronouncement is accepted as furnishing the governing principle,(2) in others that of the Disciples if they agree in differing from him.(3) Where the Disciples differ among themselves and there is no express statement of Abû Hanîfa on the point to incline the balance, it is open to the Judge to accept and give effect to the exposition most consistent with the requirements of justice. In some cases where even Abû Hanîfa agrees with one, the individual opinion of the other is accepted and enforced.

Again, in certain matters the doctrine of one is regarded by consensus as of greater authority than that of the other. And when there is no general agreement with regard to a particular exposition, in some localities the views of Abû Yusuf are accepted, in others those of Mohammed.(4)

---

(1) *Fatâwaî Kâzi Khân*, Vol. I, p. 1.

(2) For example, on the question whether the wife is entitled to refuse cohabitation for non-payment of dower by the husband, see Vol. II, pp. 494—9.

(3) For example, on the subject whether a man is liable to punishment if he contracts a marriage with a woman knowing that she was prohibited to him; see Mahommedan Law Vol. II, p. 375.

(4) They are fully stated in the following pages.

Reason for conformity to principles.

Again, it must be observed that the statements regarding the respective authority of the Hanafî "masters" occur chiefly in the chapters which deal with "the duties of the Kâzi," and are directed in the main to secure uniformity and adherence to principles and to prevent a capricious exercise of discretion on the part of the Judge. It is for this reason that a Kâzi who is not endowed with the capacity of analogical reasoning or deducing conclusions, is directed to adopt the principle laid down by one "master" or the other.

Limitation for claims.

Although the Mussulman Law proper does not recognise a period of limitation for claims, it became common in later times for the sovereigns (Sultans) to lay down rules regarding the length of time after which in respect of certain matters no action could be brought. For example, it is stated that "in Rûm (the Turkish Empire) the Sultans had ordered no claims should be heard after 15 years, except in the matter of inheritance and wakf,"(1) the object, according to Tahtâwi, being to avoid "deceit and tricks."

The legal works which have for the last eight centuries been regarded as binding authorities among the Hanafîs are generally divided into two groups, *viz.*, (*a*) Text-books, and (*b*) Digests of Decisions which pass under the name of *Fatâwa*.

Hanafî text-writers

Among the Hanafî jurists and text-writers the following are the most noted :—

Abû Bakr Ahmed ibn Omar al-Khassâf, who was the author of the most celebrated of several treatises known by the name of *Adâb-ul-Kazi* (*the Duties of the Kâzi*). He died in A. H. 261 (A. C. 874). The most esteemed commentary on Khassâf's *Adâb-ul-Kâzi* is that of Omar ibn Abdul Aziz bin Mâja commonly called Hussâm Shahîd, who was killed in A. H. 536 (A. C. 1141). Al-Khassâf will be frequently referred to in the following pages.

Abû J'aafar Ahmed ibn Mohammed at-Tahâwi is one of the numerous commentators on the *Jâm'aa-as-Saghîr* of Imâm Mohammed. He also compiled a synopsis of the Hanafî doctrines called the *Mukhtasar-ut-Tahâwi*. Both works are quoted as authorities, but they are not easily available in India. At-Tahâwi died in A. H. 321 (A. C. 933).

(1) *Durr-ul-Mukhtâr*, Hooghly. Ed., p. 533.

Al-Kudûri (Abû Hussain ibn Ahmed Mohammed) is another eminent jurist. His *Mukhtasar*(1) is a work of great weight and authority in India. "Indeed it is in such general repute that Hâji Khalîfa, when speaking of those several works which are emphatically designated by autonomasia, 'Al-Kitab' or 'the Book,' says that, if in matters connected with jurisprudence such expression be used, it signifies the *Mukhtasar al-Kuduri.*"(2) It is a general treatise on law and contains upwards of twelve thousand cases. It is only natural that a work of such celebrity should have been commented upon by numerous writers: several of the commentaries upon it are quoted in the *Fatâwai Alamgiri.* Al-Kudûri died in A. H. 428 (A. C. 1036).

There is a well-known commentary on the *Mukhtasar al-Kuduri*, entitled *al-Jouharat-un-Nayyirèh*, sometimes called *al-Jouharat-ul-Munîrah*. Barthe says that this work, though of later date than the *Hedâya*, is more valuable in some respects. I have made use of the *Jouharat-un-Nayyirèh* as well as of the other commentary on the *Mukhtasar* called *Sirâj-ul-Wahâj.*

Shams-ul-Aïmmah Abû Bakr Mohammed as-Sarakhsi, the author of several commentaries upon the *Jâmaa-al-Kabîr* and the *Jâm'aa-as-Saghîr* of the Imâm Mohammed and other works, whilst in prison at Uzjand, compiled a law-book of great merit entitled the *Mabsût*. He was also the author of the most generally quoted of his many works entitled *al-Muhît*, compiled from the *Mabsût*, the *Ziyâdât* and the *Nawâdir* of the Imâm Mohammed. The *Muhît* of Sarakhsi is regarded with great veneration in India, and is frequently referred to in the *Fatâwai Alamgiri.*

Burhân-ud-din Mohammed ibn Ahmed also wrote a *Muhît* which though known in India is not so highly esteemed as the *Muhît-us-Sarakhsi*. The work of Burhân-ud-din Mohammed is commonly known as the *Muhît-ul-Burhâni* and is taken principally from the *Mabsût*, the *Jâm'aas*, the *Siyar* and the *Ziyâdât* of the Imâm Mohammed. The author also utilised the *Nawâdir* of the same doctor in composing his work.

The Shaikh 'Aalâ-ud-din Mohammed as-Samarkandi composed a compendium of Al-Kudûri's *Mukhtasar* which he entitled the *Tuhfa-ul-Fukahâ*. The work of Aalâ-ud-din was commented upon

(1) Frequently referred to in the *Fatâwai Alamgiri.*

(2) Morley's *Digest*, I, Introd., p. cclxv.

by his pupil Abû Bakr ibn Masûd al-Kashâni who died in A. H. 587 (A. C. 1191). This comment is entitled *Badâia as-Sanâia*. Both the text and its comment are frequently referred to as authorities.

Hanafî Text-writers.

The *Hedâya* is one of the most celebrated treatises on Hanafî Law. It is a commentary on the *Badâia-al-Mubtada ;* and both the text and comment are from the pen of Burhân-ud-din Ali ibn Abû Bakr al-Marghinâni (of Marghinân in Ferghâna), who is said to have spent thirteen years in compiling the *Hedâya*. He died in A. H. 593 (A. C. 1196).

The *Hedâya* has been illustrated by a large number of commentaries, the first of which was written by Hamîd-ud-din Ali al-Bokhâri, who died in A. H. 667 (A. C. 1268) and is a short tract entitled the *Fawâid*. The glosses of the *Hedâya*, which are most reputed in India, are the *Nihâya*, the *Inâya*, the *Ghâit-ul-Bayân*, the *Kifâya*, and the *Fath-ul-Kâdir*.

The first of these, the *Nihâya*, was composed by Hisâm-ud-din Hussain ibn Ali, who is said to have been a pupil of Burhân-ud-din Ali. It is important as supplying the omission of the Law of Inheritance in the *Hedâya*, although the chapter on this subject is supposed not to be equal in authority to the *Farâiz-us-Sirâjia*.

There are two commentaries on the *Hedâya* entitled the *Inâya*, but the one more commonly known by that name was written by the Shaikh Akmal-ud-dîn Mohammed ibn Mahmûd, who died in A. H. 786 (A. C. 1374). The *Ghâit-ul-Bayân* and the *Kifâya* are by the same author, Imâm-ud-din Ameer Kâtib bin Ameer Omar. Both works are extremely valuable and give not only the author's own comments and observations, but also the substance of other commentaries. The *Kifâya* was finished according to Haji Khalîfa in A. H. 747 (A. C. 1347). Both these works have proved of great assistance to me in the compilation of the following pages.

By far the most important of these commentaries is the *Fath-ul-Kadir*. It is a commentary merely in name, for it contains the opinions, dicta and decisions of the highest Judges and *Muftis* explaining, illustrating and elucidating the principles of the Hanafî Law as stated by Burhân-ud-din Ali. It also shows the development in the legal conceptions of Jurists and Judges in the course of two centuries. Morley speaks of this work in these terms :— "The *Fath ul-Kadîr l'il-'aajûz ul-Fakîr* by Kamâl-ud-dîn al-Siwâsi, commonly called Ibn Hammâm who died in A. H. 861 (A. C. 1456) is the most comprehensive of all the comments on the *Hedâya*, and includes a collection of decisions which render it extremely useful."

I have largely utilised this work and refer to it frequently in my compilation. The *Hedâya* was translated into Persian by a number of Moulvis under the auspices of Warren Hastings and was subsequently rendered into English from the Persian translation by Mr. Hamilton.

Another work which I have made use of for the purposes of my compilation, and which is regarded as a work of considerable authority in India, is the *Ramz-ul-Hakâik*, a commentary on the *Kanz-ud-Dakâik*, a book of great reputation among the Hanafîs of India, by Allâmah al-Aini Badr-ud-dîn Mahmûd. Another commentary on the *Kanz-ud-Dakâik* highly thought of in Sunni countries is the *Bâhr-ur-Râik* by Allâmah al-Zain ul-Aâbidîn ibn Nujaim al-Misri who died in A. H. 970 = A. C. 1562.

Another work of authority is the *Tas-hîl*, a commentary on the *Latâif-ul-Ishârât* by Imâm Badr-ud-din Mahmûd. I have also made use of this book.

The most celebrated of the law-works published in Turkey is the *Multaka-ul-Abhar* by the Sheikh Ibrahim ibn Mohammed al-Halabi(1) (of Aleppo), who flourished under Solyman the Magnificent, and died in A. H. 956 (A. C. 1549). This work, which is an universal code of the Hanafî Law, contains the opinions of the four chief Mujtahid Imâms and illustrates them by those of the principal jurisconsults of that school. Throughout Turkey, it is more frequently referred to as an authority than any other treatise on jurisprudence. I have frequently referred to this work also.

The *Multaka-ul-Abhar* was published in the original Arabic at Constantinople in A. H. 1251 (A. C. 1835), and a commentary on it entitled the *Majmaa-ul-Anhar* by Abdur-Rahman ibn Shaikh Mohammed, commonly known by the name of Shaikh Zadèh, was published at the same metropolis in A. H. 1240 (A. C. 1824). This commentary is extremely valuable and interesting as it represents the views in vogue among the *Ulemas* of modern Turkey. The *Majmaa-ul-Anhar* has been of great use to me in the compilation of the present work.

---

(1) D'Ohsson compiled his own magnificent Digest from this work.

Mulla Khusru,(1) who is one of the most renowned of the Turkish jurisconsults, completed his great work called the *Durrur-ul-Akhâm* in A. H. 883 (A. C. 1478). As an authority it is second only to the *Multaka-ul-Abhar*, and is frequently referred to in the later works.

The Digest.

The other class of law-works, *viz.*, the *Fatâwas* (collections of decisions) which I have made use of are the *Fatâwai Kâzi Khân*, the *Fusûl-i-Imâdia*, the *Kiniat-ul-Munia*, the *Fatâwai-Zainia*, the *Fatâwai Durr-ul-Mukhtâr*, the *Fatâwai Alamgiri* and the *Fatâwai Ankirawia* and the *Radd-ul-Muhtâr.*

The first is thus spoken of by Morley :—"The *Fatâwai Kâzi Khân*, or collection of decisions of the Imâm Fakhr-ud-din Hassan Mansûr al-Uzjandi al-Farghâni, commonly called Kâzi Khân, who died in A. H. 692 (A. C. 1195), is a work held in the highest estimation in India and indeed is received in the Courts as of equal authority with the *Hedâya* of Burhan-ud-din Ali with whom Kâzi Khân was a contemporary : it is replete with cases of common occurrence, and is therefore of great practical utility, the more especially as many of the decisions are illustrated by the proofs and reasoning on which they are founded." As Kâzi Khân was himself a judge as well as a jurist, his decisions are of great value.(2)

The *Fusûl-ul-Imâdia* consists of two portions :—The first composed by Abu'l Fath Mohammed bin Abû Bakr al-Marghinâni who died at the end of the 7th century of the Hegira ; the other by Imâm Jamâl-ud-din bin Imâd-ud-din.

The *Kiniat-ul-Munia* is a collection of decisions of considerable authority by Mukhtâr bin Mahmûd bin Mohammed az-Zâhidi Abû ar-Rija al-Ghaznunî surnamed Najm ud-din who died in A. H. 658=A. C. 1259.

The *Fatâwai Zainia* contains decisions by Zain al-Aâbidin Ibrâhîm bin Nujaim al-Misri (the Egyptian), the celebrated author of the *Bâhr-ur-Râik* and the *Ashbâh wan-Nazâir*. They were collected by his son Ahmed about A. H. 970=A. C. 1662.

The *Durr-ul-Mukhtâr* is a commentary on the *Tanwîr-ul-Absâr* of Shaikh Shams ud-din Mohammed bin Abdullah al-Ghâzzi A. H. 995=A. C. 1586), itself a work of great authority and merit.

---

(1) Died in A. H. 885 (A. C. 1480).

(2) D'Ohsson places Kâzi Khân on a higher footing than the author of the *Hedâya*.

The *Durr-ul-Mukhtâr* was written in A. H. 1071 = A. C. 1660 by Mohammed Aalâ ud-dîn bin Shaikh Ali al-Hiskafi and is full of important decisions.

The *Fatâwai Alamgiri* is a digest of cases compiled under the orders of the Emperor Aurangzeb Alamgir (hence the name). It is a work of a comprehensive nature and of great authority in India, and is referred to in Western works as *the Hindièh.* In the original, the names of the authorities from which the decisions are collected are invariably given with many of the reasons and often with comments by the compilers, the learned Muftis of the Court. Mr. Neill Baillie, who has paraphrased portions of the *Fatâwai Alamgiri,* has omitted altogether the authorities and often a large amount of important matter with the comments and reasons, with the result that the reader, unable to get at the original, finds a certain amount of incoherency and sometimes divergences which do not appear in the Arabic.

The *Fatâwai Ankirawia* is a collection of the decisions of Imâm al-Ankirawi by the Shaikh-ul-Islâm Mohammed bin al-Hussain who died in A. H. 1098 = A. C. 1686

By far, however, the most practical and well-reasoned work of this class is the *Radd-ul-Muhtâr*,(1) a commentary on the *Durr-ul-Mukhtâr*, by Mohammed Amin (the Syrian) who flourished under Amurath IV. The *Radd-ul-Muhtâr* is certainly esteemed now-a-days as the best authority on Hanafî Law. It contains a critical *résumé* of previous decisions, the opinions of the most important earlier legists, with a full account of the recognised and accepted principles in modern times. I have greatly utilised this work in the following pages. Another commentary on the *Durr-ul-Mukhtâr*, which I have also quoted in this book, is the *Tuhfat-ul-Akhiâr.*

Imâm Mâlik—second Sunni school.

The founder of the second school of law among the Sunnis was [Abû Abdullah] Mâlik ibn Ans, whose tenets are in force in Northern Africa, especially in Morocco and Algeria. He died in the year A. H. 179 during the reign of Hârûn ar-Rashîd. The best known writer on the tenets of this school was Sîdi Khalîl, whose encyclopædic work has been translated into French by M. Perron under the patronage of the French Government.

(1) Called among the Indian Mahommedans, the *Shâmi* or *Syrian*, on ccount of the author being a native of Damascus.

Imâm Shâfeï—third Sunni School.

Shâfeï was the founder of the third school. He was born at Ghizah in Syria in the same year in which Abû Hanîfa died. He died in Egypt in the year A. H. 204 (A. C. 819) during the Caliphate of Al-Mâmun. He was a contemporary of the Shiah Imâm Ali ibn Mûsa ar-Razâ. Shâfeï's doctrines are generally followed in Northern Africa, partially in Egypt, in Southern Arabia, in Java and the Malayan peninsula generally, and among the Mussulmans of Ceylon and the Malabar coast. His followers are also to be found among the Borahs of the Bombay Presidency. Among the Shâfeï works of repute are the following :—

(1) The *Mukhtasar* of Abû Khoja ;

(2) The *Takrîb* of Shams-ud-din Abû Abdullah ibn Kâsim al-Ghazzi.

(3) The *Muharrar* of Abu'l Kâsim Abd-ul-Karîm ibn Mohammed ar-Râfi ; and

(4) The *Minhâj-ut-Tâlibin* of Mohi-ud-din Abû Zakaria Yahya ibn Sharaf an-Nawâwi (who died in A. H. 676). This work has recently been published with a learned translation into French by M. Van Den Berg, under the authority of the Dutch Government.

It is a noticeable fact that Shâfeïsm is spreading among the Indian Mussulmans.

Imâm Ahmed bin Hanbal—fourth Sunni School.

The fourth school was originated by Ibn Hanbal. He flourished during the reigns of al-Mâmûn and his successor M'utasim b'illah. These two Caliphs were M'utazalas. Ibn Hanbal's extreme fanaticism, and the persistency with which he tried to inflame the bigotry of the masses against the sovereigns, brought him into trouble with the rulers. He died in the odour of great sanctity in the year A. H. 241. Ibn Hanbal and his patristicism are responsible for the ill-success of Mâmûn in introducing the M'utazala doctrines throughout the empire, and for the frequent outbursts of persecution which deluged the Mahommedan world with the blood of Moslems.

Abû Hanîfa, Mâlik, Shâfeï and Ibn Hanbal are the founders of the four orthodox schools among the Sunnis (the *Mazâhib-i-arbaa*). Their doctrines, as already stated, are essentially the same as regards the fundamental dogmas (*usûl*), though they differ from each other in the application of private judgment and in the interpretation and exposition of the Koran.

Mâlik and Ibn Hanbal, almost entirely, exclude the exercise of private judgment in the exposition of legal principles. They are wholly governed by the force of precedents; they do not admit the validity of recourse to analogical deductions, or of such an interpretation of the law whereby its spirit is adapted to the special circumstances of any particular case. Shâfeï less speculative than Abû Hanifa is more enlightened than Mâlik and Ibn Hanbal. His followers are however designated equally with the Mâlikis and Hanbalîs, *Ahl-ul-hadîs* (traditionists *par excellence*).(1)

The *Gair-mukallid.*

Within recent years a new sect has sprung up among the Sunnis of India, the members of which call themselves *Ghair-mukallidîn* or *non-conformists.* Their opponents sometimes designate them *Wahâbis,* which is neither correct nor just. The *Ghair-mukallid,* as his name implies, does not conform to any particular sect, but approaches most closely the Shâfeïs in doctrinal matters. Like them he pronounces, during prayers, the word *âmîn* in a loud voice (which is technically called *âmîn b'il-jahr*), and makes the ceremonial gesture of raising the hands *above* the ears at a particular point of the service, which is called *raf'aa-eddain.* These have been held to be "merely minor matters of difference not affecting the essentials of the service."(2) Apart from doctrinal differences a *Ghair-mukallid* is generally subject to the Hanafî school of law.

A Sunni Mahommedan belonging to any of these sects may validly perform his devotions under the leadership of a member of another sect.(3)

The exercise of private judgment, consecrated by the Prophet and adhered to strictly by his immediate descendants, had induced the development of a liberal spirit among the Fâtimides, and this had its legitimate influence on the mind of Abû Hanîfa. The value which he and his early disciples attached to the exercise of *Kiyâs* is proved by a series of passages given in the *Fatâwai-Alamgiri.* The followers of Abû Hanîfa are styled *Ahl-ur-rai wa'l kiyâs* (people of judgment and reason).

Ibn Khaldûn, one of the greatest critical scholars and jurists among the Mussulmans, speaks thus of the latitude given to reason

(1) See *The Spirit of Islâm,* p. 518.

(2) *Fazl Karim* v. *Haji Mowla Bukhsh.* [1891] L. R., 18 I. A., 59; s. c., I. L., 18 Cal., 448.

(3) *Ibid.*

or analytical judgment by the followers of the several Sunni schools. "The science of jurisprudence forms two systems, that of the followers of private judgment and analogy (*Ahl-ur-rai wa'l kiyâs*), who were natives of Irâk, and that of the followers of tradition, who were natives of Hijâz. As the people of Irâk possessed but few traditions, they had recourse to analogical deductions and attained great proficiency therein, for which reason they are called the followers of private judgment; the Imâm Abû Hanîfa, who was their chief, had acquired a perfect knowldge of this system and taught it to his disciples. The people of Hijâz had for Imâm, Mâlik ibn Ans and then ash-Shâfeï. Some time after, a portion of the learned men disapproved of analogical deductions, and rejected that mode of proceeding; these were the *Zâhiris* or *literalists* (followers of Abû Daûd Sulaiman), and they laid it down as a principle that all points of law should be taken from the *Nusûs* (text of the Koran and traditions) and the *Ijmâa* (universal concordance of the ancient Imâms)."

The exercise of private judgment.

The early Hanafî jurists declared in explicit terms the necessity for the exercise of private judgment in the exposition of the law and the administration of justice. And in this they approached closely the doctrines of the Usûli Shiahs.

Râzi-ud-Din Nishâpuri has declared in his *Muhît*, "If the concurrent opinion of the Companions be not found in any case which their contemporaries may have agreed upon, the Kâzi must be guided by the latter. Should there be a difference of opinion between the contemporaries, let the Kâzi compare their arguments and adopt the judgment he deems preferable. If, however, none of the authorities referred to be forthcoming and the Kâzi be a person capable of analogical deduction (*Ijtihâd*), *he may consider in his own mind what is consonant with the principles of right and justice and applying the result with a pure intention to the facts and circumstances of the case, let him pass judgment accordingly.*" Abû Bakr ibn Masûd al-Kâshâni has stated in the *Badâia*, "Where there is neither express statement of the law nor concurrence of opinions for the guidance of the Kâzi, if he be capable of legal disquisition and have formed a decisive judgment in the case, he should carry such judgment into effect by his sentence although other scientific lawyers may differ in opinion from him, for that which upon deliberate investigation appears to be right and just is accepted as such in the sight of God." And again, a third passage may be quoted to the same effect from the last mentioned work: "If in any case the Kâzi be perplexed by opposite proofs, let him reflect upon the case and determine as he shall judge right, or for greater certainty let him consult other able lawyers; and if they differ, after weighing the arguments, *let him decide as appears just.*"(1) These dicta furnish the amplest reply to the absurd attacks which have often been levelled against Islâm, that it does not contain within it any elasticity or the germs of development, for its laws are stereotyped and cramped.

Unfortunately, the conception which has obtained a hold on the Sunni world, that *Ijtihâd*(2) or authoritative exposition of law by analogical deductions or the exercise of judgment, ceased in the third century of the Hegira, has exercised a most pernicious effect on the progress and advancement of the Mahommedan communities governed by the Sunni doctrines. The modern Sunnis recognise three degrees of *Ijtihâd*.(3) The jurists of the first order are supposed to have possessed a total independence in the exposition of the law. They constituted, as it were, a connecting link between the law and their own disciples, who had no right to question their exposition of the Koran, the *Sunnat* and the *Ijmâa*, even when apparently at variance with those elements or sources of jurisprudence. The *Mujtahids* of this high degree flourished in the first three centuries of the Hegira, and as they fixed the law upon certain defined lines the exercise of private judgment soon ceased to be acknowledged.(4) Some later doctors, az-Zâhiri and as-Suyûti, for instance, claimed the right, but public opinion having commenced to run in a channel made for it by authority rejected the claim advanced by them. Henceforth there is a complete subjugation of private judgment to blind precedent.

Those *Mujtahids*, who had arrived at the second degree of *Ijtihâd*, possessed the authority of solving questions not provided for by the authors of the chief sects, and were the immediate dis-

(1) *Fatâwai Alamgiri*, III, p. 583.

(2) The word *Ijtihâd* signifies in its most common acceptation, the striving to accomplish a thing, the making a great effort; but in speaking of a jurist it denotes the bringing into operation the whole capacity of forming a private judgment relative to a legal proposition.

(3) D'Ohsson, I, p. 7.

(4) *Fatâwai Kâzi Khân*, I, p. 13.

ciples of the acknowledged *Mujtahids* of the first class, who, in some instances, allowed their pupils to follow and teach opinions contrary to their own doctrines and occasionally even adopted their views.

Those who had attained the third degree of *Ijtihâd* were empowered to pronounce decisions upon their own proper authority, in all cases not provided for by the founders of the sects or their disciples. Their decisions were, however, to be founded upon a comparison of the Koran, the *Sunnat*, and the *Ijmâa*, taken conjointly with the opinions of the *Mujtahids* of the first and second classes, and they were not authorised to controvert their published doctrines either respecting the elements of the law or the principle derived therefrom. The *Mujtahids* of the third class were required to possess a perfect knowledge of all the branches of jurisprudence according to the doctrines of all the schools, and this class comprises a large number of doctors of greater or less celebrity, some of whom were raised to the rank during their lifetime, but the greater portion after their decease.(1)

As a title the term *Mujtahid* has long since fallen into disuse amongst the Sunnis.

The present stationary condition of the Mahommedan nations as compared with their rapid progress in the early centuries of Islâm, is due principally to this conception regarding *Ijtihâd*, and the general view that a person, who has not attained to that factitious eminence or empirical stage of juridical knowledge possessed by the *Mujtahids* of the first three centuries, can only construe principles with the help of precedents without the power of striking out new paths.(2)

Progress in legal conceptions. In spite of these obstacles and limitations, the legal conceptions have steadily advanced, and old constructions have been abandoned in favour of views more in accord with the progress of social conditions. This statement is clearly supported by the frequent preference of the doctrines of the "moderns" (متاخرين), as also the liberty which is accorded to the Mussulman Judge to draw from the dicta of the Imâms and jurists his own conclusion most consistent with the requirements of justice, the changed cir-

(1) See Note II at the end of the Introduction.

(2) On this point see *The Spirit of Islâm*, pp. 284—289.

cumstances of the times or the conditions of society, or follow the doctrine most in accord with the above considerations.

Procedure.

Many of the rules included under the head of "the Duties of the Kâzi," relate to procedure. For example whilst under the Shâfeï and Hanbali systems the Kâzi is empowered to make an order against an absent person, under the Hanafi law "no decree can be passed against or in favour of the *ghâib*, and [if made] it would be inoperative, and on this is the *fatwa*, unless it is in the presence of his *nâib* (deputy), that is, the representative in fact of the absent, such as his *wakîl* (attorney) or *wasi* (executor) or the *mutwalli* of the *wakf*." According to Tahtâwi, "if evidence be taken in the presence of the *wakîl* and then he disappears and the principal appears or *vice versâ*; or if the evidence be taken in the presence of the *muris* [*i.e.*, the *propositus*] and he then disappears and the heir appears, or if one heir appears for another heir, in all such cases the decree is validly made against the absent person." The *Durr-ul-Mukhtâr* goes on to add that "where such a decree is passed against the absent or the deceased and not against the *wakîl* or the executor, the Kâzi should enter in his records (*sijil*) that he had made the decree against the absent defendant in the presence of his *wakîl* or against the deceased in the presence of his executor." "So one of the heirs can stand as a litigant for the rest, or a partner in debt (liability)(1) for the other partner; so can a stranger in whose hands is the property of an orphan stand as a litigant for the latter; so can one of the beneficiaries of a *wakf* stand for the rest if the *wakf* be established." "And it is lawful to pass a decree in the presence of a *wakîl* appointed by the Kâzi to represent the absent defendant....which may be done in five cases," among them being "when the defendant (*al-khasam*) conceals himself or is missing." "In all such circumstances the moderns have held the Kâzi has the power to appoint a *wakîl* and this is the opinion of the second (Abû Yusuf)."(2) "In the *Wahbânièh* it is stated all are agreed on this point. And the Kâzi can seal up the house of the absent as long as he thinks fit and then appoint a *wakîl*."

"And the power of selling the inheritance of an insolvent person (*mustaghrak b'id-dain*) belongs to the Judge and not to his heirs." But according to Tahtâwi "if the heirs offer to discharge

(1) *Sharîk-ud-dain*. (2) *Durr-ul-Mukhtâr*, p. 532.

the debt, the creditors should be compelled to accept the same."

Section IV.

The Shiah Jurists.

Shiah communities.

Among the Shiah communities also, the same blight has fallen over the ideas of men by the introduction among the common folk of the *Akhbârî*, in preference to, or supersession of, the *Usûli* doctrines. The freedom of judgment allowed by the latter school gave ample scope to social progress and moral development.

The *Akhbârî* submits himself implicitly to the law as enunciated by its constituted expounder called in Shiah countries the *Mujtahid*, and rejects all liberty of thought.

This suppression of the human mind has naturally given birth to that movement in Islâm, symptoms of which are perceptible on all sides and which are so full of the most hopeful auguries for the future of the Moslem world. Shâfeïsm seems to have shaken off its ancient fetters, and now stands forth in the presence of the Sunnis as the embodiment of those aspirations for moral regeneration and legal reform which are agitating so many minds in Islâm.

The Shiah jurists.

Among the Shiah jurists the following are the most eminent :—(1) Shaikh Mohammed ibn Mohammed ibn an-N'umân Abû Abdallah, who was surnamed al-Mufîd, because of his numerous pupils, born in A. H. 333 or 338, died in 413 ; (2) Shaikh Mohammed al-Hassan ibn Ali Abû J'aafar at-Tûsi, surnamed "the Shaikh of the Imamite faith" or shortly "The Shaikh" (A. H. 385—460). He was the most distinguished disciple of Shaikh Mufîd, and has left numerous works, which are regarded as authoritative and binding wherever the Shiah doctrines are followed; among others the *Istibsâr*, the *Khilâf wa'l wifâk* ("Divergences and Concordances"), the *Nihâya fi-bahr ul fikh wa'l ferâyè*, and lastly the *Mabsût*, the most important and most erudite of all, and on which there exist no less than eighty commentaries and glosses. He was an enlightened and liberal-minded lawyer, and his views are far in advance of many of his successors. (3) Shaikh Syed Murtaza Abu'l Kâsim Ali ibn Abi Ahmed al-Hussaini, a descendant of the Prophet surnamed "al-Huda" ("the guide to the way of salvation"). He was also a pupil of Shaikh Mufîd and was one of the most prominent lawyers of his times. His views, which are decidedly more in conformity with modern thought and the requirements of an advancing civilisation, are chiefly in force among the Usûlis. One of his works which I have utilised in the compilation of the following pages is the *Kitâb ul-Intisâr*.

Unfortunately, the narrow conceptions of Shaikh Najm-ud-din-Abu'l Kâsim Jaafar Abû Ali Yahyâ, surnamed "*al-Mohakkik*" "the learned," have gained ground among the Akhbârî Shiahs and stopped all growth. This doctor was born at Hilleh on the Euphrates in the year 602 of the Hegira. Al-Mohakkik exercised his magisterial and professorial functions until 676, at which time he died of a fall from the terrace of his house. He was buried at Najaf, near the tomb of the Caliph Ali. He is the author of the *An-Nâfè*, of several commentaries on the *Nihâya* of the Shaikh Tûsi, and of the well-known work called the *Sharâya-ul-Islâm fi-masâil ul-halâl wa'l harâm* ("the Mussulman Law regarding what is lawful and what is unlawful"), which has been paraphrased by Baillie and translated into French by Querry.

The author of the *Sharâya-ul Islâm*.

This work is divided into four parts: the first treats of religious duties; the second of contracts and synallagmatic obligations; the third, of unilateral acts, and the fourth comprises the prescripts relating to hunting, food, etc., and treats of the penalty applicable to crimes and delinquencies, from the point of view of canonical as well as civil law. It is hardly possible to exaggerate the baleful influence of this legist among the Shiah communities who have adopted his views. His literal views, which have paralysed all movement of the intellect, are chiefly in force among the Akhbârîs.

The *Sharâya-ul-Islâm*.

There are several commentaries on the *Sharâya* in existence. Among these the *Masâlik-ul-Afhâm* by Zain-ud-din Ali as-Sâili commonly called the Shahîd-i-Sâni (second martyr), and the *Jawâhir-ul-Kalâm* by Shaikh Mohammed Hassan an-Najafi are by far the most copious and erudite. This latter work, though called a commentary on the *Sharâya* of al-Mohakkik, discusses legal questions from an independent basis, gives the dicta of other jurists and displays a great amount of critical spirit. It also gives references to the opinions of the Caliph Ali and his immediate descendants.

Among other legal works of note are the *Sarâir* of Abi'l Makârim Mohammed ibn Idris al-Hilli, the *Ghunia* of ibn Zuhrâ, the *Makn'aa* and *Hedâya* of Abû Jafaar as-Sadûk, the *Nâsiria* of Shaikh

Syed Murtaza, the *Talkhîs-ul-Marâm*, the *Ghâyat-ul-Ahkâm* and the *Tahrîr-ul-Ahkâm* by Shaikh Allâmah Jamâl-ud-din Hassan ibn Yusuf ibn al-Murtaza al-Hilli. His *Irshâd-ul-Azhân* is also a work of great merit and learning and is quoted as an authority under the name of the *Irshâd-i-Allâmah.*

The *Jâmaa-i-Abbâsi* is a concise and comprehensive treatise on Shiah Law, in twenty books or chapters. It is generally considered to be the work of Bahâ-ud-din Mohammed Aâmili, who died in A. H. 1031 (A. C. 1621).

The *Mafâtîh* by Mohammed ibn Murtaza surnamed Muhsan, and the commentary on it by his nephew who was of the same name, but surnamed Hâdi, are modern works deserving of notice

The *Rouzat-ul-Ahkâm,* written by a Mujtahid of Oude, consists of four chapters. The first chapter deals with the law of inheritance, most fully and perspicuously. All these works belong to the Akbâri school.

Another work of great merit is the *Jâm'aa-ush-Shittât,* which is a grand collection of decisions and dicta published within the last century in Persia by the leading Mujtahids of Teheran.

In the compilation of the following pages I have made use of chiefly, the *Mabsût*, the *Nihâya* and the *Istibsâr* of Imâm Jaafar Tûsi; the *Intisâr* of Shaikh Syed Murtaza and the *Hedâyq* of as-Sadûk, the *Sarâir*, the *Ghunia*, the *Sharâya*, the *Jawâhir-ul-Kalâm,* the *Jâm'aa-ush-Shittât* and the *Sîrat-un-Nijât* of Shaikh Abu'l Hassan, chief Mujtahid of Teheran.(1)

In dealing with questions arising under the Mahommedan Law, it must always be borne in mind that in the Islâmic system the different schools and sub-schools are so intimately connected with the different persuasions, sects or communions to which they appertain, that when a person belonging to one communion or sect or sub-sect goes over to another, his status and the dispositions made by him, as well as the succession to his inheritance, are thenceforward governed by the rules of the school to which he now belongs. For example, a Shiah on adopting the Sunni persuasion would subject himself to the Sunni Law. So a Hanafî becoming a Shâfeïte or an Akhbâri becoming an Usûli would be governed by the Shâfeï or Usûli principles as the case may be.

(1) Besides the works Sunni and Shiah to which I have referred in the Introduction, I have utilised a number of others which are mentioned in the Appendix.

CHAPTER I.

THE LAW RELATING TO GIFTS.

SECTION I.

GENERAL OBSERVATIONS.

UNDER the Mahommedan Law, there is no distinction between ancestral and self-acquired property. The owner for the time being has absolute dominion over all property in his possession, whether he has acquired it himself or whether it has devolved upon him by inheritance. He can sell or dispose of it in any way he likes, provided operation is given to the transaction in his lifetime. It is only with regard to dispositions intended to take effect after the owner's death or made when he is suffering from a malady which creates in his mind the fear of death that his power of disposition is limited by the right of his heirs and restricted to a third.

This restriction on the disposing powers of a Mahommedan is referred to in the following terms by the Privy Council in the case of *Rani Khujoor-unnissa* v. *Mussamut Roushan Jehan*.(1)

Rani Khujoor-unnissa v. Mussamut Roushan Jehan.

"The policy of the Mahommedan Law appears to be to prevent a testator interfering by will with the course of the devolution of property according to law among his heirs, although he may give a specified portion, as much as a third, to a stranger. But it also appears that a holder of property may, to a certain extent, defeat the policy of the law by giving in his lifetime the whole or any part of his property to one of his sons, provided he complies with certain forms."

This restriction, which is not without analogy in certain European systems,(2) is surrounded with conditions which require great attention in the study of the Mussulman Law.

Dispositions of property divide themselves under two heads, *viz.* :—

(1) Dispositions *inter vivos*.

(1) [1871] L. R., 3 Ind. App., 291; s. c. I. L., 2 Cal., 184.
(2) See Peterson's English and Scotch Law (1860), pp. 223-224.

(2) Dispositions which are in their nature testamentary, and which are not intended to operate until after the death of the person disposing.

A disposition, however, made at a time when the disposer was suffering from a disease, which is technically called "death-illness" (*marz-ul-mout,*) is treated as a testamentary disposition. But we shall discuss this in detail in due course.

Dispositions of property.

The dispositions *inter vivos* with which we have principally to concern ourselves are *Hiba* and *Wakf*.

(1) HIBA.—A *hiba* is a grant, and is, generally speaking, divisible under three heads :

(*a*) A *hiba*, pure and simple.

(*b*) A *hiba b'il ewaz* (a grant or gift for a consideration) which is more in the nature of an exchange than a gift.

(*c*) A *hiba ba-shart-ul-ewaz*, or a grant made on the condition that the donee or transferee should pay to the donor at some future time or periodically some determinate thing in return for the grant.

(2) WAKF.—A *wakf* is the settlement in perpetuity of the usufruct of any property for the benefit of individuals or for a religious or charitable purpose.

A *hiba*, pure and simple, is the voluntary transfer, without consideration, of some specific property (whether existing in substance or as a *chose in action*). This definition will be more fully explained later.(1)

In the Sunni Law, the grant of the usufruct for a limited time, without consideration and resumable at will, is called an *'aâriat* (*commodatum*).(2) The distinction between *hiba* and *'aâriat*, between the gift of the *corpus* or substance of a thing, and of the mere income for a limited time, was discussed at considerable length by the learned Subordinate Judge of Aligarh in the case of *Muhammad Faiz Ahmad Khan* v. *Ghulam Ahmad Khan*,(3) whose judg-

Muhammad Faiz Ahmad Khan v. *Ghulam Ahmad Khan*.

(1) In the Transfer of Property Act, a gift is defined thus :—" Gift is the transfer of certain existing moveable or immovable property made voluntarily and without consideration, by one person called the donor, to another called the donee, and accepted by or on behalf of the donee. Such acceptance must be made during the lifetime of the donor and while he is still capable of giving. If the donee dies before acceptance, the gift is void."

(2) For the Shiah rule, see *post*.

(3) [1881] I. L.. 3 All., 490.

ment was subsequently affirmed and adopted by both the High Court and the Privy Council. The judgment is so exhaustive and thorough, that I cannot do better than transcribe a portion to illustrate my meaning :—

"To make a person the owner of the substance of a thing without consideration is a *hiba* (gift), while to make him the owner of the profits only without consideration is an *'aâriat* or *commodatum*; *'Aariat.* (vide *Durr-ul-Mukhtâr*, *Kitâb-ul-hiba*). In a gift it is essential that the donor should be sane, owner and of age, that the thing given be not undivided (*mushâa*), and be in possession of the donor, and that there be proposal and acceptance. A gift is not void for invalid conditions; on the contrary, the conditions are void.

"For example, if a slave be made a gift of, with the condition that the donee should set him free, the condition is void but the gift is valid (*Durr-ul-Mukhtâr*, *Kitâb-ul-hiba*). In an *'aâriat*, it is not necessary that the donor should be of age, nor that the thing given should be divided, nor is acceptance after proposal a condition (*Alamgiri*). In the *Imâdia*, it is explained that the *'aâriat* of a joint property is valid, and so are its deposit and sale (*Durr-ul-Mukhtâr*, *Kitâb-ul-'aâriat*). The words by which an *'aâriat* is constituted have a special chapter assigned to them in the *Alamgiri*, and I shall copy it in this place to show what words are used in giving a thing in *'aâriat*, and of what signification :—(Second Chapter, *Kitâb-ul-'aâriat*, *Alamgiri*.) If he said, 'I have made thee owner of the profits of this house for a month,' or, without saying 'a month,' 'without a consideration,' it will be an *'aâriat*. This is in the *Fatâwa* of Kazi Khan. And it is valid by the words :—'I lent thee this robe, thou mayest wear it for a day,' or 'I lent thee this house, thou mayest live therein for a year' (*Tatarkhania*). If he said, 'I make this house of mine thy residence for one month' or, if he said, 'thy residence for my lifetime,' this will be an *'aâriat*; (this is in the *Zahiria*). .... And if he said, 'my house is for thee a gift by way of residence,' or 'a residence by way of gift,' it is an *'aâriat*; this is so in the *Hedâya*. And if he said, 'my house is for thee given by way of a residence,' or 'a residence by way of *sadkah* (alms),' or 'a *sadkah* by way of *'aâriat*,' or 'a loan (*'aâriat*) by way of gift,' all this is '*aâriat*; this is so in the *Kâfi*. And if he said, 'my house is for thee, if thou survivest me, and for me if I survive thee,' or 'for thee a *wakf*,' it is an *'aâriat* according to Abû Hanîfa and Mohammed, but a gift according to Abû Yusuf, and the words '*rakba*' and '*habas*' are void; this is so in the *Badâia*. If he said, 'my house is for thee, if thou outlivest me, and for me, if I outlive thee,' or 'a *wakf* for thee,' it will be an *'aâriat* according to all; this is so in *Yanabia*. 'I made over this ass to thee, so that thou mayest use it and feed him with grass at thy own cost,' this will be an *'aâriat*. This is so in *Kunia*. If he said, 'I have given thee this tree for eating the fruit thereof, it is an '*aâriat*, unless he intends a gift by it. This is so in *Tamar Tashi*."

Muhammad Faiz Ahmad Khan v. *Ghulam Ahmad Khan*—(contd.)

"These are the words from which an *'aâriat* is construed, and it will also appear from looking at all of them that the word '*wahabto*' (I made a gift) is not found anywhere among them. The words '*hibatan suknah*' or '*suknah hibatan*,' which are used above, do not mean a gift of the substance of the thing. They are only an elucidation of '*dari laka*,' so that the meaning is that the house which is given is for residence. I shall now give those words which constitute a gift, and they are of three kinds:—*First*, those which are specially made (adapted) for a gift; *secondly*, those which denote a gift, metaphorically or by implication; and, *thirdly*, those which import *hiba* or *'aâriat* equally. I copy the following from the *Alamgiri*, *Kitâb-ul-hiba*, Chapter I. "The words by which gift is made are of three kinds:—*First*, those which are specially adapted or made for *hiba*; *secondly*, those which denote *hiba* by implication or metaphorically; and *thirdly*, those which may import *hiba* or *'aâriat* equally. Of the first kind there are such as these:—'I made a gift of this thing to thee,' or 'I made thee owner of it,' or 'I made it for thee,' or 'this is for thee,' or 'I bestowed upon thee or gave thee this.' All this is *hiba*. Of the second description are such as these:—'I clothed thee in this garment,' or 'I gave thee this house for thy lifetime.' This is a gift. In the same way, if he said 'this house is for thee for my age,' or 'for thy age' or 'for my lifetime' or 'for thy lifetime, so that when thou art dead it will revert to me,' then the gift will be valid and the condition void. But the third kind are such as these:—Should he say 'this house is for thee,' or 'for me if I survive thee,' or 'a *wakf* for thee,' and make it over to him, it is an *'aâriat*, according to the two, Abû Hanifa and Mohammed, and a *hiba* (gift) according to Abû Yusûf. The above question shows that the word '*wahab-to*,' the meaning of which is 'I made a gift of,' is a word specially adapted for gift (*hiba*), and is not used to denote a loan. And this is the word which has been used in the document entitled *hibanâ-mah* (deed of gift). None of the doubtful words have been used in this document, and the words used after it are by way of advice (*mashwara*). There is an example in the law-books eminently applicable to the present case, which makes it clear that the transaction in dispute was one of *hiba* and not of *'aâriat*. This example is to be found in all the books, in the *Hedâya*, in the *Durr-ul-Mukhtâr*, and in the *Alamgiri* :—'*dari laka hibatan taskunahu*,'—'My house is for thee by way of gift that thou mayest live in it.' It is a rule in Arabic that a verb sentence is never used as explicative (*tafsir*) of a noun sentence; '*dari laka hibatan*' is a noun sentence and '*taskunahu*' a verb sentence; '*taskunahu*' cannot therefore be explicative of the preceding sentence. On the contrary, the donor, by way of advice, counsels the donee to live in it; and the latter is free to adopt the counsel or not. Among the sentences by which a valid gift may be made the following appears in the law-books :— *Durr-ul-Mukhtâr*, 'my house is for thee that thou mayest live in it.' Because the words 'that thou mayest live' (*taskunahu*) are an advice and not an explanation, for a verb is not adapted to be explicative of a noun. So then he counsels him in the mode of his proprietorship by telling him to live in it. So if he likes, he can accept the advice, or he may not accept it. But if it be said, '*dari laka hibatan suknah*' or '*suknah hibatan*' as mentioned in the words used to describe an *'aâriat*, there '*hibatan suknah*' is a *tafsir* or explanation of ownership, contrary to '*dari laka hibatan taskunahu*' where it is not a *tafsir*. *Hedâya* :—If he said 'by way of gift, that thou mayest live in it,' then it is a gift, for his saying '*taskunahu*' 'that thou mayest live in it,' is an advice, and not an explanation and it is an index of the object, unlike his saying '*hibatan suknah*,' for it is *tafsir* to it. In the deed of gift, the words, 'made a gift of' and 'put her in possession,' are followed by the direction that the sister-in-law may manage the villages and apply their income to meet her necessary expenses and to pay the Government revenue; this is all by way of advice and the transaction of gift concluded with the preceding words. The words *hiba kiya* '(made a gift of),' de-

Distinction between *'aâriat* and *hiba*.

Distinction between *'aâriat* and *hiba*—(contd.)

note their real meaning and are made use of with reference to the two villages. It is a rule in every language that a word is always understood to be used in its literal meaning, though of course when the literal meaning is not applicable the metaphorical one may be understood. It is not necessary to refer to Arabic books alone for further corroboration of this fact. The word 'gift' is perfectly applicable in its literal sense in the document, where these words are used. The donor was not a minor, nor the subject of gift *mushâa* (undivided). There is no reason why the word *hiba* should be held to mean an *'aâriat* (loan), and why, when it is clearly stated that the mouzas of Sahauli and Kamalabad are made a gift of, the context should be construed to mean that the profits of the mouzas, Kamalabad and Sahauli were given as *'aâriat.* On a perusal of the whole document, it clearly appears that Faiz Ahmad Khan never even thought of effecting an *'aâriat.* He has used sufficient words by which nothing but a gift could be intended. The whole manner is that of a gift, and there is not even the trace of an *'aâriat.* The value of the property was fixed, the full stamp-duty was paid, and lest the property should be suspected to be *mushâa*, or undivided, and the gift vitiated on that account, he stated that 'both villages are owned by me without the partnership of any one else.' Then using the word '*hiba*,' he declared that he had made a gift and confirmed it, so far as to write that neither he nor his heirs shall have any claim. At the conclusion, he expressed the nature of the document by saying that he had written it by way of a deed of gift. He also stated in the document that he had made over the possession to the Mussamât, which is the completion of the gift (but which is not necessary in an *'aâriat* or loan). He made the Mussamât execute a document in the way of *kabuliat* (acceptance) which was necessary for the validity of the gift (not necessary in an *'aâriat*). After the conclusion of the words of the document and writing '*fakat*' (end), the words headed 'P. S. I promise,' used by the defendant, further elucidated the nature of the gift and show that it was a *hiba-bil-ewaz* (gift for consideration). There is no reason why all the words should not be understood in their literal sense, and why the transaction should be considered as *'aâriat* (*commodatum*), about which there is no word at all in the whole document. The transaction cannot be considered to be an *'aâriat*, unless all the words be construed in a sense othe than literal: but for this there must be a very strong reason, which the Court thinks does not exist."(1)

The result of the ruling of the Privy Council in this case appears to me to be this, that "where there is an absolute gift words describing its objects do not limit or cut down its operation." The distinction between *hiba* and *'aâriat* may be stated in a very few words. In one case the transferee acquires a right to the property; in the other, he only obtains its use or beneficial enjoyment for a limited time; the property does not pass to him.

SECTION II.

'HIBA' OR GIFT SIMPLE.

HIBA OR GIFT SIMPLE.—Among Mahommedans, the law relating to the subject of *hiba* possesses special importance. The principle of exclusion which prevails in all the schools and the absence of the right of representation, cause much hardship. For example, if a man has three sons, one of whom dies in the lifetime of his father leaving children, these children are excluded from the inheritance of their grandfather by their uncles. Females under the Mahommedan Law take smaller shares than sons. Under the Sunni Law especially, owing to the principle of agnacy (*t'asîb*), considerable injustice is frequently occasioned which it is often the endeavour of owners of property to avert in their lifetime. The children of a daughter are excluded from inheritance in favour of brother's sons. To remedy these evils, it has become frequent among Mussulman families in India, as elsewhere, to have recourse to *hibas*, whereby it is not only endeavoured to correct any such injustice as I have indicated, but oftentimes to give a larger share to one heir than the other. The lawfulness of giving a larger share to one heir by a disposition *inter vivos* is specially recognised. Principle.

The *Durr-ul-Mukhtâr*, quoting the *Fatâwai Kâzi Khan* under its usual designation of *Khâniêh*, says—"There is no objection to being more fond of one child than another for it is an act of the heart; similarly in the matter of gifts so long as there is no intention of injury to the others; and if there is an intention to de-

---

(1) I have given this judgment *in extenso* to throw into strong relief, the distinction between *hiba* and *'aâriat* so clearly pointed out by the Subordinate Judge in this case.

tract (*i.e.*, to reduce their shares) then he should make their shares equal, that is, give to a daughter, the same as to a son. This is according to the second [Abû Yusuf] and on this is the *Fatwa*. And if a man were to give in health all his property to one child it would be operative, but he would be incurring a sin."(1)

The same rule is given in the *Fatâwai Alamgiri* :—

"If a man in health makes a gift to his children and desires to prefer some to others, there is no tradition with reference to this in the *Asl* from our masters. But it is stated from Abû Hanîfa that he may give more to the child, who is superior to the others in religion, but when it is not so it is reprehensible. And it is stated in *al-M'ualla* from Abû Yusûf, that an unequal distribution may lawfully be made when there is no intention of injuring [any of the children] and as much should be given to a daughter as to a son. And on this is the *fatwâ*, so in the *Fatâwai Kâzi Khan* and it is the approved doctrine according to the *Zahîria*."

" A man in health gives the whole of his property to one child, it is *lawful judicially*, though he is sinful for so doing according to the *Fatâwai Kâzi Khan*."(2)

The same rule is given in the *Durr-ul-Mukhtâr*

The frequency with which *hibas* are made in India makes it necessary that we should examine carefully the provisions of the law on this subject.

DEFINITION OF HIBA.—In the *Durr-ul-Mukhtâr*, a *hiba* is defined as the transfer of the right of property in the substance (***tamlîk-ul-'ain***) by one person to another without consideration (***'ewaz***) but the absence of consideration is not a condition in it. In other words a *hiba* is a voluntary gift without consideration of property or the substance of a thing by one person to another

(1) *Durr-ul-Mukhtâr*, p. 636.

(2) *Fatâwai Alamgiri*, IV, p. 545. In the case of *Chaudri Mehdi Hasan* v. *Muhamad Hasan*, [1905] L. R., 33 I. A., 68, the Judicial Committee stated somewhat broadly the principles of the Mahommedan Law relating to gifts. " By Mahommedan Law the holder of property may alien by deed of gift accompanied by delivery of the thing given so far as it is capable of delivery ; or by deed of gift coupled with consideration in which case although delivery of possession is unnecessary yet actual payment of the consideration must be proved and also a *bonâ fide* intention on the part of the donor to divest himself *in præsenti* of the property and to confer it on the donee." This statement of the law, however, is subject to qualifications as will be shown later on.

so as to constitute the donee, the proprietor of the subject-matter of the gift. It requires for its validity three conditions: (*a*) a manifestation of the wish to give on the part of the donor; (*b*) the acceptance of the donee, either impliedly or expressly; and (*c*) the taking possession of the subject-matter of the gift by the donee either actually or constructively.(1)

The Hanafî lawyers define *hiba* as an act of bounty (تبرع) by which a right of property is conferred in something specific without an exchange. In order to distinguish a *hiba* or gift, from a *wasiat* or bequest, Ibni Kamâl (the author of the *Fath-ul-Kadîr*) defines it as an *immediate* (*fi'l hâl*) conferment of the right of property.(2) Similarly Sîdi Khalîl (the Mâliki lawyer) defines it as an act of liberality by which the proprietor bestows a thing without the intention of receiving anything in exchange.(3)

The Shiah lawyers, on the other hand, declare it to be an obligation (*akd*) by which the property in a specific object is transferred immediately and unconditionally without any exchange and free from any pious or religious purpose on the part of the donor.(4)

A verbal gift

Kamar-un-nissa Bibi v. *Hussaini Bibi.*

A gift may be made verbally or by writing. The Transfer of Property Act (IV of 1882) leaves this provision of the Mahommedan Law untouched. And the Privy Council in the case of *Kamar-un-nissa Bibi* v. *Hussaini Bibi*(5) upheld a verbal gift when it appeared to be supported by all the circumstances.

Sadakah or pious gift.

There is another species of donation in vogue among the Mussulmans, which is pious in its character and made in view of the future life. This is called *Sadakah*.(6) It takes its origin from the directions contained in the Koran, notably in Sura II, verse 211, "the goods that you give shall be known to God." This species of gift is irrevocable according to all the schools, but we shall deal with it in the order in which it occurs

Technically the donor or grantor is called *Wâhib*, the donee *Mouhoob-lèh* and the subject-matter of the gift *Mouhoob*.

---

(1) *Nunda Singh* v. *Meer Jaffer Shah*, 2 Sel. Rep., 5.

(2) If an exchange is obtained, the character of the gift is changed.

(3) *Jâmaa-ur-Ramûz.*

(4) *Mabsût*; *Irshâd-ul-Azhân*; *Sharâya-ul-Islâm*, p. 241.

(5) [1880] I. L., 3 All., 266.

(6) Pious offerings made with the object of obtaining divine approbation.

Section III.

Capacity for making a gift.

Capacity to make a hiba or gift.—The qualities necessary for making a valid *hiba*, in other words, *the capacity for making a donation*, or what might be called a voluntary settlement, are the same as those required for the validity of any other contract. Every act which, in the Mahommedan Law, would be treated under the head of *tasurrufât-i-shariyêh* (legal transactions) presupposes a certain amount of free volition. "Consent," as has been well remarked, "is an act of reason accompanied with deliberation, the mind weighing as in a balance the good and evil on both sides." Every legal act under the Mahommedan Law is regarded as an *akd* or obligation (*aakd*), and the validity of every obligation depends on the faculty or capacity of the person doing the act to consider freely and rationally the consequences resulting therefrom. If the person is, by virtue of an inherent or super-imposed and accidental disqualification, incapable of exercising his volition in a rational manner and with perfect reasoning, any obligation entered into by him is null and void.

The conditions, therefore, necessary for the validity of any disposition are the following :—

(1) Majority.

(2) Understanding.

(3) Freedom.

(4) Ownership of the subject-matter of the disposition.

These conditions are not restricted to gifts alone ; they apply to all dispositions of property.

Minority.—Persons under the age of puberty are deemed infants (*saghîr*), and are treated as having no capacity to bind themselves for want of sufficient discernment and understanding. Ordinarily minority ceases on the completion of the 15th year, when it is presumed, in the case of the youth of both sexes, that discretion is attained.(1) And, therefore, before the passing of Act IX of 1875, a Mahommedan, who had attained the 15th year, was qualified to make a valid disposition of his property. Since Act IX has come into force, there are three ages of majority recognised

(1) The subject is fully discussed in Vol. II, pp. 581-5.

by law. Section 3 of Act IX of 1875 saves the Mahommedan Law of majority in questions relating to marriage, dower and divorce. " In respect of all other acts, the age of majority of persons who are wards of Courts or for whom a guardian has been appointed by a Court of Justice, is 21, for others, it is 18. " In the first case, a person would not be able to make a gift under the Mahommedan Law unless he has completed his 21st year, and, in the latter case, his 18th year. Owing to this peculiarity in the Majority Act, serious difficulties might arise concerning the capacity of one and the same individual in respect of different acts. For example, though a person on the completion of his 15th year, may enter into a contract of marriage for any dower, would he have the power of commuting the dower by a *bai-mukâsa* (*i.e.*, the sale of a property for the dower)? Similarly, would a woman over 15, but under the age of majority fixed by the Act, have the power of making a gift of her dower or remitting it to her husband.

NON COMPOTES MENTIS.—Obligations entered into by idiots, lunatics and other persons *non compotes mentis* are null and void; but when a person, afflicted by lunacy, has lucid intervals, any act committed during such interval would be valid, subject to certain restrictions.

Causes of inhibition.

" The causes of inhibition,"(1) says the *Hedáya*, " are three, *viz.*, infancy, slavery and *junûn* (insanity)."(2) Though the law-books use the term *junûn*, as the only cause of " inhibition," it may safely be taken from the examples cited, that the classes of persons around whom the law throws its safeguards, are not confined simply to the persons who are afflicted with lunacy or insanity, in some form or other, but also to those who, from accidental circumstances, lose for the time being their power of understanding. Story has adopted the enumeration of Lord Coke of the different classes of persons who are deemed in law to be *non compotes mentis*, and this enumeration may be taken as a safe guide to the principle upon which the Mahommedan Law proceeds in holding the acts of persons not *'aâkil* as invalid in law.

---

(1) "Inhibition" (*hijr*) is a proceeding under the Mussulman Law by which a person is judicially declared by the Court (the Kâzi) to be incompetent to deal with his property or to contract any obligation. A person against whom such a declaration is made is called a *mahjûr*.

(2) *Hed.*, III (English translation), p. 468.

Non compotes mentis.

"Lord Coke has enumerated four different classes of persons who are deemed in law to be *non compotes mentis*. The first is an idiot or fool natural; the second is he who was of good and sound memory, and by the visitation of God has lost it; the third is a lunatic, *lunaticus qui gaudet lucidis intervallis* and sometimes is of a good and sound memory and sometimes *non compos mentis*; and the fourth is a *non compos mentis* by his own act, as a drunkard. In respect to the last class of persons, although it is regularly true that drunkenness doth not extenuate any act or offence committed by any person against the laws but it rather aggravates it, and he shall gain no privilege thereby, and although in strictness of law the drunkard has less ground to avoid his own acts and contracts than any other *non compos mentis*, yet Courts of Equity will relieve against acts done and contracts made by him, while under this temporary insanity, where they are procured by the fraud or imposition of the other party. For whatever may be the demerit of the drunkard himself, the other party has not the slightest ground to claim the protection of Courts of Equity against his own grossly immoral and fraudulent conduct."

Drunkenness.

"But to set aside any act or contract on account of drunkenness, it is not sufficient that the party is under undue excitement from liquor. It must rise to that degree which may be called excessive drunkenness, where the party is utterly deprived of the use of his reason and understanding; for in such a case, there can, in no just sense, be said to be a serious and deliberate consent on his part, and without this no contract or other act can or ought to be binding by the law of nature. If there be not that degree of excessive drunkenness, then Courts of Equity will not interfere at all, unless there has been some contrivance or management to draw the party into drink or some unfair advantage taken of his intoxication to obtain an unreasonable bargain or benefit from him. For in general, Courts of Equity, as a matter of public policy, do not incline on the one hand to lend their assistance to a person who has obtained an agreement or deed from another in a state of intoxication, and, on the other hand, they are equally unwilling to assist the intoxicated party to get rid of his agreement or deed merely on the ground of his intoxication at the time. They will leave the parties to their ordinary remedies at law unless there is some fraudulent contrivance or some imposition practised." * * *

"In regard to drunkenness, the writers upon natural and public law adopt it, as a general principle, that contracts made by persons in liquor, even though their drunkenness be voluntary, are utterly void, because they are incapable of any deliberate consent, in like manner, as persons who are insane or *non compotes mentis*. The rule is so laid down by Heineccius and Pufendorf. It is adopted by Pothier, one of the purest of jurists, as an axiom which requires no illustration. Heineccius in discussing the subject has made some sensible observations. Either, says he, the drunkenness of the party entering into a contract is excessive, or moderate. If moderate, and it did not quite so much obscure his understanding as that he was ignorant with whom or for what he had contracted, the contract ought to bind him. But if his drunkenness was excessive, that could not fail to be perceived, and therefore the party dealing with him must have been engaged in a manifest fraud, or that at least he ought to impute it to his own fault, that he had dealt with a person in such a situation. The Scottish Law seems to have adopted this distinction, for by that law persons in a state of absolute drunkenness, and consequently deprived of reason, cannot bind themselves by any contract. But a lesser degree of drunkenness which only darkens reason has not the effect of annulling contracts."

Imbecility

"Closely allied to the foregoing are cases where a person although not positively *non compos*, or insane, is yet of such great weakness of mind as to be unable to guard himself against imposition or to resist importunity or undue influence. And it is quite immaterial from what cause such weakness arises, whether from temporary illness, general mental imbecility, the natural incapacity of early infancy, the infirmity of extreme old age, or those accidental depressions which result from sudden fear or constitutional despondency or overwhelming calamities. For it has been well remarked, that, although there is no direct proof that a man is *non compos* or delirious, yet if he is a man of weak understanding and is harassed and uneasy at the time, or if the deed is executed by him *in extremis*, or when he is a paralytic, it cannot be supposed that he had a mind adequate to the business which he was about, and he might be very easily imposed upon."(1)

---

(1) Story's *Equity Jurisprudence*, I, §§ 230—234.

Mere imbecility or *safâhat* is no ground of "inhibition."(1) The acts therefore of a person who, without being positively *non compos* or insane, is yet of a weak mind are valid, unless they are stamped with the indicia of fraud. In the consideration of cases falling under this head, it will be as well to bear in mind the words of Mr. Justice Story, as explaining the principles upon which the Courts of Chancery in England would avoid the acts of persons, who are suffering from such extreme weakness of mind as to be unable to guard themselves against imposition, or to resist importunity or undue influence.

HURRIYET.—*Hurriyèt* or freedom is another necessary condition for the validity of a contract. A bondsman labours equally under the inhibition which applies to the acts of infants and *non compotes mentis*. But there is this difference between the case of a bondsman and those suffering from insanity, that whereas the act of a bondsman may be ratified by his master as the act of an infant may in some cases be ratified by his guardian, the acts of a lunatic are absolutely null and void.(2) The reason of the inhibition upon the acts of the bondsman is given at great length in the *Hedâya*.

Since slavery, however, does not exist in British India, even in the mild form in which it is recognised under the Mahommedan Law, the question has little more than a mere antiquarian interest as throwing light upon a state of manners rapidly passing away, in the full light of modern civilisation and owing to a more correct reading of the laws of the Arabian Prophet.

The doctrine of *Ikráh* or compulsion.

COMPULSION.—The incapacity resulting from bondage is attached to the status of the bondsman, who stands, in the eye of the law, in the position of a minor, and is not treated as *sui juris*. But temporary loss of liberty, or rather freedom of volition, by the exercise of constraint, duress or undue influence, as it does not affect the status, is not a ground of "inhibition," and consequently contracts entered into under undue influence or coercion are valid, if ratified by the person contracting after the constraint or undue influence

(1) In the case of *Kamar-un-nissa Bibi* v. *Hussaini Bibi*, [1880] I. L., 3 All., 266, the Judicial Committee of the Privy Council had to deal with a similar question, and they held on a review of all the circumstances that the donor was able to comprehend the transaction though apparently a person of weak intellect, and that the gift could not be impugned on that ground.

(2) *Hedâya*, III, p. 473.

has ceased. In the Mahommedan law-books a special chapter under the head of *Ikrâh* is devoted to the doctrines applicable to questions referred to in this place, but though some of the principles seem at first sight to fall short of the rules recognised by the English Courts of Equity with reference to cases of undue influence, in general the principles are analogous.(1) The doctrine, that in order to avoid a contract entered into by a free, sane and adult person, on the ground of *ikrâh* or compulsion, it must be shown that the "compeller" was in a position to carry out any threat held out by him, and that the threat itself was such as would influence the conduct of a reasonable person, only represents in another form the rule of equity, that the undue influence was such as would give rise to the presumption, that it might *bonâ fide* stop the exercise of free volition on the part of the person affected thereby. Any circumstance which so entirely overcomes the free agency of the party and exposes him to a fraudulent advantage or imposition would justify the Kâzi to set aside the contract. "*Ikrâh* or compulsion," says the *Hedâya*,(2) "applies to a case where the compeller has it in his power to execute what he threatens whether he (the compeller) be the Sultan or any other person, as a thief (for instance). The reason of this is that compulsion implies an act, which men exercise upon others, and in consequence of which the will of the other is set at naught at the same time that his power of action still remains. Now this characteristic does not exist unless the other (namely, the person compelled) be put in fear, and apprehend that if he do not perform what the compeller desires, the threatened evil will fall upon him, and this fear and apprehension cannot take place unless the compeller be possessed of powers to carry his menace into execution; but provided this power does exist, it is of no importance whether it exist in the Sultan or in any other person. With respect to what is recorded from Abû Hanîfa, that compulsion cannot proceed from any except the Sultan, the learned remark that this difference originates merely in the difference of times and not in any difference of argument, for in his time none possessed power except the Sultan, but afterwards changes took place with respect to the customs of mankind. It is to be observed

Ikrâh or compulsion.

(1) Compare *De Montmorency* v. *Devereux*, 7 Cl. & Fin., p. 118; and the provisions of the Indian Contract Act (IX of 1872), ss. 14, 15 & 16.

(2) *Hedâya*, III, p. 452.

that in the same manner as it is essential to the establishment of compulsion, that the compeller be able to carry his menace into execution, so likewise it is requisite that the person compelled be in fear that the thing threatened will actually take place, and this fear is not supposed, except it appears most probable to the person compelled, that the compeller will execute what he has threatened, so as to force and constrain him to the performance of the act which the compeller requires of him."

Ikrâh or compulsion —(contd.)

"A person forced into a contract may afterwards dissolve it. If a person exercise compulsion upon another by cutting, beating, or imprisonment, with a view to make him sell his property, or to purchase merchandise, or acknowledge a debt of one thousand dirhems to a particular person, or let his house on hire, and this other accordingly sell his property, purchase merchandise or so forth, he has it afterwards at his option either to adhere to the contract into which he has been so compelled, or to dissolve it and take back or restore the article purchased or sold, because one essential to the validity of any of these contracts is, that it has the consent of both parties which is not the case here as the compulsion by blows or other means rather occasions a dissent, and the contract is therefore invalid, unless the means of compulsion be trifling. (This rule, however, does not hold where the compulsion consists only of a single blow or of imprisonment for a single day, since fear is not usually excited by this degree of beating or confinement.) Compulsion therefore is not established by a single blow or a single day's imprisonment, unless the compelled be a person of rank,(1) to whom such a degree of beating or confinement would appear detrimental or disgraceful; for with respect to such a person compulsion is established by this degree of violence, as by it his volition is destroyed."

Fraud and undue influence.

These principles are stated in almost identical terms in the *Durr-ul-Mukhtâr*, where it is stated that there are four conditions which constitute complete *ikrâh*, *viz.*: (*a*) that the person compelling—whether sovereign or any other like a robber has the power to carry out his threat; (*b*) that the person compelled (*mukrah*) is under the fear that the threat will be carried out; (*c*) that the

---

(1) A *Zi-jâh*; *Durr-ul-Mukhtâr*.

threat is of such a nature as would really over-power free volition and (*d*) that the compelled would not have committed the act in question except for the compulsion or threat.(1)

Ikrâh or compulsion—(contd.)

Any act done under such circumstances, such as buying or selling or acknowledging or leasing is liable to be set aside by the compelled on the compulsion being withdrawn. And this right does not cease with the death of the compeller or compelled, or [if the sale is to a third person] of the vendee or by the fact that a separable accretion has taken place to the property sold.(2) And it will be restored even if it has passed through several hands. But the *compelled* has a right to ratify the contract, and such ratification may be by word (that is expressly) or by conduct, such as by accepting the price.(3)

As in the English Law, compulsion is not confined to actual duress or restraint or even threats. It extends to all class of cases where the person has no free will, but stands in *vinculo juris* in consequence of extreme terror or apprehension for himself or any other individual. Extreme necessity or distress, gross misapprehension as to the nature of the relationship between the contracting parties, circumvention or the influence of one mind over another, all come within the doctrine of compulsion. The Mahommedan Law contains no specific rules relating to the obligations imposed on persons standing in a fiduciary relationship to the donor, but generally the doctrines recognised by the English Courts of Equity are applicable to such cases. The Bombay High Court has gone so far as to hold a gift invalid which contravened the principles recognised by English Courts of Equity with regard to persons standing in a fiduciary relationship to the donor, though the donor, who was a Mahommedan lady, apparently possessed the capacity requisite under the Mahommedan Law to make a valid *hiba*.(4) And the same principle was enunciated and enforced by the Judicial Committee of the Privy Council in the case of *Tacoordeen Tewary* v. *Nawab Syed Ali Hussain Khan*.(5)

Tacoordeen Tewary v. *Nawab Syed Ali Hussain Khan.*

(1) Threats of this nature are technically called *Ikrâh-ul-mulji*.

(2) The commentator adds the right is *à fortiori* not lost if the accretion is inseparable.

(3) *Durr-ul-Mukhtâr*, p. 677.

(4) *Rujabai* v. *Ismail Ahmed* [1870], 7 Bom. H. C. R., O. C., 27.

(5) (1874) L. R., 1 Ind. App., p. 192.

SUBJECT-MATTER MUST BE THE PROPERTY OF THE DONOR.—It is also a condition to the validity of a gift that the subject-matter should be the property of the donor, otherwise the gift is *ipso facto* void.(1)

The *Fatâwai Alamgiri* goes on to add that "another (4th) condition is that the subject of the gift must be property, for what is merely *mubâh* (common property) can not be given, and it is impossible to constitute another person the owner of what is not property," in other words over which no right of property can be acquired, such as the wind, *feræ naturæ*, the water in the ocean. "And a further condition is that it should be the property of the donor, for the donor can not make another the owner of something which belongs to a third person without his consent, so in the *Badâia*."(1)

And a gift takes effect in two ways, (*lit* ' is of two sorts"), either by transfer of a right of property (*tamlik*),(2) or by cancellation or discharge (*iskât*). The gift of a debt to the debtor comes under the latter category. In the *Durr-ul-Mukhtâr* the same principles are given but more concisely.

"The conditions for the validity of a gift on the part of the donor are discretion and puberty (majority) and that he should possess the right of property; accordingly the gift of a minor or a bondsman even though a *mukâtib*(3) is not valid." * * * "And the subject of the gift (*mouhoob*) should be capable of being possessed without confusion [with the donor's property] and distinct [from the same] and not contained [in anything belonging to him].(4) Its pillars are declaration and acceptance, and its legal effect is that it vests the right of property in the donee [but] not absolutely."(5) In other words, subject to certain exceptions, the donor may revoke the gift.

Voluntary settlement by a person in insolvent circumstances.

INSOLVENT DONOR.—Whether a person in insolvent circumstances, or extremely involved in debt, can make a voluntary settlement, is a question answered in two different ways by the Mâlikis and Hanafis, though in the result the two schools seem to coincide.

(1) See *Hedâya* III, Eng. (translation), p. 484.

(2) From *milk*, property.

(3) A bondsman conditionally enfranchised.

(4) مقدض غير مشاع مميزا غير مشغول

(5) P. 633.

Among the Mâlikis a person in insolvent circumstances or extremely involved (مستغرق) is under an "inhibition" (حجر) regarding any dealing of a gratuitous character with his property. A gift by a person so situated is, according to the Mâliki doctrines, inoperative. According to the Hanafîs there is no such incapacity, but the Kâzi may avoid the act at the instance of the creditors if the gift was intended to defraud them. This principle is analogous to the rule of English Law according to which voluntary settlements in fraud of creditors are held to be voidable. The English cases under 13 Eliz., cap. VI, s. 6, which is reproduced in s. 53 of the Indian Transfer of Property Act (IV of 1882), serve to illustrate the principle of the Hanafî Law.

Fraudulent intent.

Mere indebtedness or the fact that the donor was in embarrassed circumstances is not a sufficient ground for invalidating a voluntary settlement or for inferring a fraudulent intent, the real basis on which such gratuitous transfers can be avoided.(1) But it must be shown that there were unpaid debts *existing at the time when the gift was made*, and the settlor was, if not necessarily insolvent, so largely indebted as to impel the Court to believe that the intention was to defraud persons who, at the time of the transfer, were creditors of the donor.(2)

---

(1) *Azimmunessa Begum* v. *Dale*, [1868] 6 Mad. H. C. Rep., p. 468; *Ramtonoo Mookerjea* v. *Bibi Jeenut*, Fulton's Reports, p. 154. In the former case Mr. Justice Bittleston says as follows:—"First was the gift to the plaintiff altogether void as being in fraud of creditors. I will assume that according to Mahommedan Law it might be impeached on that ground, though the mere existence of debts due by the donor at the time of the gift would not be sufficient to establish such fraud" [see p. 441 of App. to Mr. Sloan's Edn. of Macnaughten, citing a case from Morris' Cases, S. D. A., Bom., Vol. II, p. 103]. At page 154 of Fulton's Reports, Sir L. Peel, in the case already referred to says, "There is no evidence before us that the donor (who was a trader) was in debt at the time of making this gift, nor is there any evidence to show that he executed it in contemplation of insolvency, or with a view to defraud creditors, but it is not to be inferred from these words that if he had been shown to be in debt, the gift would, on that account., have been held invalid."

(2) See the remarks of V. C. Wood in *Holmes* v. *Penny*, 3 K. & J., p. 90; also *Thompson* v. *Webster*, 4 Drew., p. 628; *Lush* v. *Wilkinson*, 5 Ves., p. 384; *Martyn* v. *Macnamara*, 4 D. & W., p. 427.

Story, I, § 367; *Dundas* v. *Dutens*, 1 Ves. Jr., p. 196.

Ramtonoo Mookerjea v. *Bibi Jeenut*, Fulton's Reports, p. 154; *Chunder Madhub Dass* v. *Ameer Ali* and others, 25 W. R., p. 119. In *Skarf* v. *Soulby* (1 M. & G., p. 344), the bill alleged "that at the time of executing a voluntary settlement, the settlor was in insolvent or in embarrassed circumstances, or indebted to divers persons." It was held that "in the absence of any proof of actual insolvency, the mere fact of the settlor then owing some debts was not sufficient

Extent of indebtedness fatal to a voluntary conveyance.

The extent of the indebtedness fatal to a voluntary conveyance as against *existing* creditors may shortly be stated as that from which it *must* be presumed that the intention of the donor was not to provide honestly for the donees, and to put the property out of his own reach, but to do so at the expense of the just claims against him. But the existence of property at the time of the settlement not included in it, ample for the payment of debts then due, would negative the fraudulent intention.(1)

---

to invalidate the settlement." The judgment in *Bibi Jeenut's* case is too important not to be given *in extenso* :—

PEEL, C. J.—" The passage cited from Macnaughten, p. 222, for the lessor of the plaintiff is not applicable, as that relates to a gift of money for money, and there possession is necessary. In this case, the lessor of the plaintiff claims under Jumeat Khan, and as such, is estopped by the recitals in this deed of gift, which is of a prior date. This is not a case in which the assignee is disputing the validity of the deed for the benefit of creditors. There is no doubt the deed is genuine, and as to the time of execution, no evidence having been given to the contrary, we must presume that it was executed at the time it purports to be dated. The deed has been proved in the usual manner by calling one of the attesting witnesses, and it was not necessary to go further. The Kâzi, however, before whose predecessor it was registered, in confirmation of this presumption, states that, in his opinion and from the practice of his office, the seal of the Kâzi, who registered the deed, was affixed about the time at which it is alleged to have been affixed. This, however, is merely in confirmation and strengthens the presumption. This deed then being of a prior date, the subsequent purchaser must impeach it for fraud. All those grounds on which a deed is generally impeached are, however, wanting in this case. There is no evidence before us that the donor was in debt at the time of making this gift, nor is there any evidence to show that he executed it in contemplation of insolvency or with a view to defraud creditors. This, moreover, is not the case of a simple and voluntary gift, but of a gift for a consideration. The lessor of the plaintiff is in no better position than the donor. The prior conveyance or marriage settlement and recital of possession rendered are evidence against the donor, and so against the lessor of the plaintiff who comes in under him. The evidence thus clearly shows that possession was given, but none of the authorities even in cases of gift show that possession must be continuous, indeed it would be absurd to suppose the necessity of the husband's never occupying those premises which he has given to his wife. Now, though the validity of a gift depends upon the seisin, the validity of a sale is derived not from the seisin but from the contract, and the passage cited from Macnaughten, p. 221, clearly shows that this deed must be construed according to the rules affecting the laws of sale. Under this gift, the wife may have a good title when the other donees would not from failure of consideration. As the defendant has taken defence to the whole of the premises, and has only proved the title to a portion, the verdict must be for the lessor of the plaintiff, but execution will be limited to that portion of the premises not given to the wife in this deed of gift. We will, however, reserve the liberty to Mr. Leith to move to enter a verdict for the lessor of the plaintiff for the whole, should he upon consideration think that by the principles of Mahommedan Law he is entitled to such a verdict."

(1) *Skarf* v. *Soulby*, 1 Mac. & G., p. 344 ; *Holloway* v. *Millard*, 1 Mad., p. 414 ; *Kent* v. *Reilly*, L. R., 14 Eq., p. 190 ; *White* v. *Witt*, 24 W. R., p. 727.

Under the Mahommedan Law future creditors have no right to question a voluntary conveyance by a person *not* indebted at the time.

Family settlements—*Tamlîknamahs.*

Settlements which are honest family arrangements are regarded with favour by Courts of Equity in England and are not within the Statute of Elizabeth, although not founded on actual valuable consideration, unless the rights of existing creditors are thereby directly interfered with.(1) Among the Mahommedans of India, it is not infrequently the case for owners of property, with the object of preventing future disputes, to make, during their lifetime, a division or distribution of their property. Such dispositions are in the nature of family arrangements, and the deeds by which the dispositions are made are called *Tamlîknâmahs* or *Taksîmnâmahs*. Sometimes the donor reserves a small interest in the properties disposed of for his support and maintenance. Often the transferees, if likely to be the heirs of the donor, take smaller shares than they would in case of his dying intestate. Such dispositions, it is submitted, will be treated as settlements in the nature of family arrangements.

Under the Mahommedan Law, when there is consideration, however small, the character of the gift changes. It is not merely a *hiba* or donation pure and simple, requiring some evidence of parting of title on the part of the donor; it is a transfer for a consideration, in which no delivery of possession is requisite. How far such transfers can be impeached by creditors on the ground of fraud we shall consider later.

A *bonâ fide* voluntary conveyance in which possession has been transferred is effective against a subsequent purchaser for value. 27 Eliz. cap. IV had no application in this country (beyond the Presidency Towns) before the Transfer of Property Act. Section 53 of this Act, however, embodies the principle contained in 27 Eliz. cap. IV, but clause (*d*) of Section 2 expressly declares that, "nothing in the second chapter of this Act shall be deemed to affect any rule of Mahommedan Law."

Dispositions by a married woman.

A married woman is not debarred by the status of marriage from making any disposition during the subsistence of marriage. She can deal with her property as if she were a *femme sole*. Nor

(1) *Penhall* v. *Elwin*, 1 Sm. & G., p. 258.

is the widow's right to deal with any property she has inherited from her deceased husband limited by the rights of his heirs, as under the Hindu Law. She can give away her property to whomsoever she pleases, so long as this is done in "health."(1)

SECTION IV.

GIFTS BY PERSONS SUFFERING FROM MARZ-UL-MOUT.

Marz-ul-Mout.

ACTS of bounty by persons suffering from a mortal sickness are treated differently by the several schools. According to the Mâliki doctrines a disposition made under such circumstances is inoperative.

According to the *Jâmaa-ush-Shittât*, which is a work of authority among the Shiahs, a gift made by a person suffering from a mortal illness which ends fatally, is valid with reference to the entire disposition, provided delivery takes place before the death of the donor, and provided the donor is in perfect possession of his senses.

The proposition is stated thus :—

"A man makes a gift during the 'illness of death' (*marz-ul-mout*) of all his property to another whilst in possession of his senses; is this gift valid with reference to the whole property or only to one-third ? Is possession of the donee necessary for the validity of this gift ? Is possession of only a portion effectual with reference to the whole ? If the donee takes possession of the subject-matter of the gift, locks it up in a case and leaves it with the donor, or in the case of a gift of a house, if the donor being sick sleeps in it, whilst the donee is in possession thereof, is his possession sufficient in law ?" These involved questions are answered in this way :— "Yes, the gift is valid with reference to the entire property and is not restricted to a third."

"Possession of the whole is necessary; without possession it is not valid."

"If the donor dies before possession, the gift is void, unless the donee is an infant and the donor is his guardian, for the possession of the guardian is tantamount to the possession of the minor and separate possession is not necessary. Possession of a portion is not effectual with reference to the whole;

---

(1) See *Lutufunnissa* v. *Rajaoor Rahman*, [1869] 8 W. R., 84.

"If possession is actually taken of a moveable thing it is sufficient, though it may be left in the house of the donor. As regards a house, if it is sufficiently clear possession has been taken by the donee, the mere fact of the donor dwelling in it according to custom or owing to illness will not affect the validity of the gift."(1) ***Marz-ul-mout.***

سوال

چه میفرمایند در این مسئله که هرگاه شخصی در مرض الموت
هبه و بخشش نماید کل مال خود را بشخصی در حال صحت عقل ایا
این هبه معتبر و صحیح است از اصل مال یا از ثلث و ایا در لزوم
این موهبه شرط است تصرف متهب در مال یا نه بر فرض اشتراط ایا
تصرف در بعض در حکم تصرف در کل است یا نه و هرگاه واهب
موهوب را بتصرف متهب بدهد و متهب اورا در اطاق واهب در دولابه
گذاشته و کلیدان دولابه را خود متهب بر دارد ایا این را تصرف
معتبر در شرع میگویند یا نه و هر گاه واهب یورتے را بمتهب هبه
نموده باشد و رفع موانع از تصرف متهب نموده باین معنی که متهب
دران یورت آمد و شد کند و واهب مانع او نشود و لیکن واهب
بجهته ناخوشي و بیماري دران یورت خوابیده باشد ایا این را
تصرف متهب میگیرند یا نه *

جواب

بلے هبه صحیح است و اظهر است این که در تمام مال صحیح
است و منحصر در ثلث نیست و تصرف و قبض در مطلق هبه شرط
است و بدون ان لزومي ندارد و اگر قبل از اقباض بمیرد هبه باطل
میشود مگر آنکه متهب صغیر باشد و واهب ولي باشد که قبض
ولی قبض صغیر است و ضرور بقبض علیحده نیست و قبض بعض

---

(1) *Jâmaa-ush-Shittât*, Chapter on *Hiba*.

در لزوم کل کافي نیست و در منقولات همان اخذ باید بخصوص
باین نحو که درجای مظبوط کند کفیست هرچند در خانه واهب
باشد و هم چنین در اقباض یورت تخلیه باو رفع مانع از تصرفات
کافیست هرگاه بقصد اقباض بوده و خوابیدن خود را درانجا مانع
از تخلیه نمیدانیست و ظاهر اینست که هرگاه بگوید خانه از تو
و تصرف کن و بیا و برو لیکن من هم چند روزے در اینجا هستم چون
بیمارم یا انکه در عرف و عادت مضایقه از بودن ان دران مکان نمیشده
رمیگفته اند که بتصرف او داده کافیست و شاید که این از باب
اقباض صندوق باشد باوجو آنکه متاع واهب دران باشد *

Shiah doctrines—the *Sharâya-ul-Islâm.*

In the *Sharâya*, the principle is laid down thus—"When a person has made a gift being dangerously ill at the time, but afterwards recovers, the gift is valid. If, however, he should die of the disease, and the heirs refuse their assent to the gift, it is valid only to the extent of a third of his estate, according to the best traditional authority." This evidently assumes that possession was delivered to the donee before the donor's death, for in another place, it is stated that if the donor dies after the *'akd* (*i.e.*, the contract of gift) but before delivery of possession, the property falls into the inheritance.

Hanafî doctrines.

Under the Hanafî Law, any disposition by a person suffering from an illness which, in the ordinary course, is fatal and from which he eventually dies, takes effect only partially, if at the time he was under the apprehension of death, or if the circumstances and condition of his illness were such as were likely to create in him the apprehension of death. As the author of the *Radd-ul-Muhtâr* observes, it is not merely the fact that the disease is ordinarily fatal that requires consideration, but the effect it is likely to have on the mind of the sufferer which is the chief determining element. A malady of such a nature is called *marz-ul-mout* or the "illness of death." But when a person has suffered from an illness for a long time so that it has become, as it were, "a part of his constitution," or where the progress of the disease is so imperceptible as to cause no apprehension to him, it does not come within the definition of *marz-ul-mout*.

The policy of the law with respect to the dispositions of a person stricken by a mortal malady proceeds on the assumption that dealings with property, especially "acts of bounty," in such circumstances might not improbably spring from a wish to deprive the lawful heirs of their legal rights, and that such dealings should, therefore, be restricted by those rights—and not be allowed to take effect beyond the limit of testamentary dispositions. Accordingly a gift made when the person is suffering from an "illness of death" (*marz-ul-mout*) takes effect when made in favour of a non-heir, in respect of a third of his estate unless assented to by the heirs; when made to an heir, it is altogether inoperative unless it is assented to by the other heirs.(1)

Gifts made in *marz-ul-mout.*

As the operativeness of dispositions made by a person suffering from a mortal illness depends on the sufferer's state of mind, the Mussulman lawyers have indicated certain tests, more or less of an empirical character, for the purpose of determining whether at the time of the dealings in question he was labouring under the fear (خوف) of death. This was the only course possible, as a learned Indian Judge observes,(2) before the science of diagnosis had attained the perfection of modern times. Symptoms and conditions were indicated from which one might infer whether the malady was such as would be likely to create or, in fact, created that fear in the sufferer's mind. But those tests were in no sense to be regarded as conclusive either with respect to the disease or to the mental condition. "The gift of a person suffering from paralysis, palsy and phthisis," says the *Durr-ul-Mukhtâr*, "is valid as to the whole when the disease has lasted over a year(3) and there is no fear of death from it but if it has not extended for a year and there is fear of death [on his part] the gift will take effect in respect of a third."(4) The reason of this principle is thus stated in the *Durrar ;* when a person suffers from a malady which is ordinarily mortal for over a year, it ceases to have any apprehensive

(1) Comp. *Wazir Jan* v. *Saiyyad Altaf Ali*, [1887] I. L., 9 All., 357 ; see also *Ashrufunnissa* v. *Azeemun*, [1864] 1 W. R., 17 ; *Kurreeman* v. *Mallick Enaet Hossein*, [1864] W. R., 1865 ; on appeal [1865], 3 W. R., 40.

(2) In *Sarabai* v. *Rabiabai*, post.

(3) The dictum was not, it is submitted, correctly apprehended in *Lubbi Beebee* v. *Bibbun Beebee*, [1874] 6 N.-W. P. H. C. R., 159 ; see also *Mahammad Gulshere Khan* v. *Mariam Begum*, [1881] I. L., 3 All., 931.

(4) *Durr-ul-Mukhtâr*, Hooghly Ed., p. 821.

influence on his mind as it has become part of his nature. "Some have said that *marz-ul-mout* is an illness that disables a person from attending [lit. going out] for his personal necessities (حوائج نفسه)..[But] the approved doctrine is that *marz-ul-mout* is a malady in which there is a preponderant fear of death, although the sufferer may not have taken to his bed; this is as stated by Kahastâni."(1)

"When an illness does not go on increasing from day to day, it becomes a part of the sufferer's nature as in the case of a cripple or a blind man there is no apprehension of death....for a *marz-ul-mout* is a disease from which there is a probability of death, and that happens when it gets worse from day to day until death ensues." But when it is stationary and death is not apprehended from it, "as in the case of a blind man," and treatment is therefore not resorted to, it does not come within the category of "the illness of death."

The statement that if an illness has lasted over a year it ceases to be regarded as a *marz-ul-mout* does not lay down a rule of law; it only gives expression to the general doctrine that a long continued illness unattended with any circumstances of aggravation as is likely to cause an apprehension of death, is not to be treated in its effects as a "fatal malady." Where, however, the disease is long-standing but becomes suddenly aggravated and the patient becomes confined to his bed, "it would be like a new illness," that is, it would be taken as likely to create a fear of death in the mind of the sufferer, and his acts in that state would, therefore, in case of death from the illness, take effect with respect to a third.(2)

Divorce by a person suffering from a mortal malady.

The *Fatâwai Kâzi Khân* dealing with the right of the wife divorced by a man suffering from a mortal malady says, "if a man has become so debilitated from an illness that he is bed-ridden and rendered incapable of managing his outside affairs, and the illness is increasing day by day, then the right of the second party [the wife] attaches to his property, because the probability from his condition is death; and if the man in such a condition divorces his wife he is declared to be a *farr* (or evader)." "But a person who, though ill, is able to attend to his daily avocations, although

(1) *Durr-ul-Mukhtâr*, Hooghly Edn., p. 821; Comp. the *Fatâwai Alamgiri*, Vol. IV, p. 561; see *post*.

(2) *Radd-ul-Muhtâr*, Vol. V, p. 648.

the illness may eventually cause his death, is not regarded as one suffering from a mortal illness (*marz-ul-mout*)." Similarly one struck with paralysis, phthisis or palsy is accounted "sick" whilst the disease is on the increase; but when the illness has lasted a long time and is not becoming worse, the sufferer "is as one in health." "Some lawyers have laid down that if a disease, however mortal, lasts for or over a year, it should not be regarded as such, because the man becomes so accustomed to it as to lose all apprehension as to his own condition."

Marz-ul mout.

The same test is given in the *Durr-ul-Mukhtâr.* It says on the authority of the *Bazâzia* "when a person is in imminent fear of death whether from disease or any other cause, so that in the case of an illness the man is so broken [or weakened] by it as to be incapacitated from conducting his ordinary avocations outside his house; for example, a *fakîh* (a jurist) from going to the mosque, a tradesman to his shop, a woman from attending to her indoor occupations," it is a *marz-ul-mout.* And it adds from the *Mujtaba* that "when the illness has become so severe as to make it permissible for the sufferer to offer his prayers without standing up [lit. n a sitting posture] it must be regarded as an illness of death."

"The author of the *Manzûma* was asked," says the *Radd-ul-Muhtâr*, "as to the definition of (the term) *marz-ul-mout* and he nswered there were many." The Hanafî doctors generally have roceeded on the doctrine laid down by Fazli, *viz.*, that "when a an is incapacitated from leaving his house (*dâr*)(1) for his rsonal needs, or a woman from attending to her avocation sowing difficulty in getting up and down, that is an indication of *marz--mout.*"(2)

The rule of *marz-ul-mout* is applicable not only to dispositions property but also to divorce (*talâk*). For example, if a man suffer- from an "illness of death" were to pronounce a definitive divorce inst his wife, she would not lose her right to inherit from him the period of her *iddat* (probation).(3)

In the chapter in the *Fatâwai Alamgiri*(4) dealing with "the gift he sick" the principles are set forth at some length. In the first e it is stated from the *Âsal* that neither a gift nor a *sadakah*(4)

Dispositions in marz-ul-mout.

(1) It may also mean room.
(2) *Radd-ul-Muhtâr*, Vol. V, p. 649.
(3) Mahommedan Law, Vol. II. p. 542.
(4) *Fatâwai Alamgiri*. Vol. IV. p. 559, Bk. on Gifts, Chap. X.

by a *mariz*—a person suffering from *marz-ul-mout* of which the definition is given later on—is effective without possession : and if possession is taken, it is valid in respect of a third.(1) If the donor were to die before delivery (*taslîm*) the whole disposition would be invalid.(2) " It is, therefore, necessary to understand that a gift by a *marîz* is a contract and not a *wasiat*, and the right of disposition is restricted to a third on account of the right of the heirs which attaches to the property of the *marîz*. And as it is an act of bounty it is effective so far only as the law allows and that is a third. And being a contractual disposition it is subject to the conditions relating to gifts, among them the taking of possession by the donee before the death of the donor ; so in the *Muhît*. If a person [suffering from *marz-ul-mout*] were to die after making a gift of a house and delivering possession thereof to the donee, and it were found that there was no other property belonging to him, the gift would be valid in respect of a third of the house, and the remaining two-thirds would be returned to the heirs. And this principle applies to all subjects whether they be partible or not ; so in the *Mabsut*."

" If a *mariz* makes a gift of a property which cannot come out of a third, the donee must return the excess over a third in respect of which the donor has no power."(3)

" A sick woman (مريضة) makes a gift of her dower (*sadâk*) to her husband, if she recovers from her illness, it is valid ; and even if she dies from that illness the answer would be the same, if it was not *marz-ul-mout* ; but if it was an illness of death the gift would not be valid except with the assent of the heirs. And it has been said with regard to the definition of *marz-ul-mout* (في حد مرض الموت), and this is accepted for passing decisions, that when the probability is preponderant that death will ensue from that disease it is *marz-ul-mout*, although she may or may not be confined to her bed ; so in the *Muzmirât*. Abû Lais has said that it is so [*i.e.*, it is an illness of death] if a man cannot pray standing, and we adopt this ; so in the *Jouharat-un-Nayyirèh*."(4)

---

(1) Comp. *Sharifa Bibi* v. *Gulam Mahomed*, [1892] I. L., 16 Mad., 43.

(2) *Valayet Hossein* v. *Maniran*, [1879] 5 C. L. R., 91 ; in this case possession as manager during the lifetime of the donor was not considered sufficient.

(3) *Fatawai Alâmgiri*, Vol. IV, p. 561.

(4) *Ibid*, pp. 561—62.

"A *marîzeh* (sick woman) dies after making a gift of her dower (*mahr*) to her husband, the Jurist Abû Jaafar has stated that if at the time of the *hiba* she was able to stand up for her personal needs (حاجتها) and raise herself without help, she should be regarded as in the position of one in health and the gift would be valid; so in the *Fatâwai Kâzi Khân*. And a cripple or a person struck with paralysis or suffering from consumption or palsy if the disease is long continued and there is no (immediate) apprehension of death therefrom, may make a gift of the whole of the property; so in the *Tabiïn* in 'The Book on Wills. Dispositions in *mazr-ul-mout*—(contd.)

"The dispositions of a (pregnant) woman in labour is valid in respect of a third of her property; but they become operative as to the whole on her recovery; so in the *Jouharat-un-Nayyirèh*. And if a (pregnant) woman makes a gift of her dower to her husband whilst suffering from the pains of labour, and dies during the *nifâs*(1) the gift is not valid; so in the *Sirâjia*. A woman suffering from *marz-ul-mout* gives her dower to her husband who dies before her, she has no claim, for the gift is valid until her decease, and if she were to die of that illness, her heirs can claim her dower; so in the *Kinia*.... the gift of a dower to a dead husband is valid by *istehsân* (*i.e.* according to a liberal interpretation of the law); so in the *Sirajia*.(2) An act of bounty (تبرع) by a pregnant woman in labour takes effect in respect of a third of her estate. Similarly when two bodies of men (*at-tâifatân*) meet in deadly fight and they are equally balanced(3) or one body is over-powered by the other, in such circumstances the rule of *marz-ul-mout* applies." In other words the act of any member of those two bodies will take effect like a bequest in respect of a third. But so long as they do not engage in actual combat it would not be so.

"And a person travelling on the ocean (*râkib-ul-bahrain*) when it is quiet has no apprehension; but when he is overtaken by storm and waves there is fear of death. A person who is imprisoned for a crime punishable with death also suffers from the same *khauf* (fear)."(4)

---

(1) The prescribed period for purification after child-birth, usually forty days.
(2) *Ibid*, p. 563.
(3) Lit. when they are all equal to one another.
(4) *Radd-ul-Muhtâr*, Vol. V. p. 649.

Marz-ul-mout.

These principles are better set forth in the chapter dealing with the *talâk* of people suffering from *marz-ul-mout.* It is not merely disease which may induce apprehension of death in a person. If a man advances to engage in actual fight with an enemy or is being led out to execution and in either situation divorces his wife, she would not lose her right of inheritance. Similarly, "if he is on board a ship which is wrecked and if he finds himself on a plank in imminent risk of drowning, a *talâk* pronounced by him does not destroy the wife's right. But when a divorce is given [or a disposition made] before he has advanced from the ranks of a fighting force, or when in prison though condemned to death, or before the ship is actually wrecked, the *talâk* [or the gift] is effective—for in these situations there is still a hope of escape.(1).

Although in the earlier cases the law on the subject of *marz-ul-mout* or the "illness of death" had to a certain extent been misapprehended, recent decisions in the Calcutta and Bombay High Courts have placed the doctrines on their proper basis.

In *Hassarat Bibi* v. *Golam Jaffar*,(2) where the validity of a gift was impugned on the ground that it was made in death-illness, the High Court of Calcutta indicated the questions which require to be considered in determining whether the disease comes within the category of a *marz-ul-mout* illness; *viz.*, (*i*) was the donor suffering at the time of the gift from a disease which was the immediate cause of his death; (*ii*) was the disease of such a nature or character as to induce in the person suffering the belief that death would be caused thereby, or to engender in him the apprehension of death; (*iii*) was the illness such as to incapacitate him from the pursuit of his ordinary avocations or standing up for prayers, a circumstance which might create in the mind of the sufferer an apprehension of death; (*iv*) had the illness continued for such a length of time as to remove or lessen the apprehension of immediate fatality or to accustom the sufferer to the malady? And it was added that, "the limit of one year mentioned in the law-books does not, in our opinion, lay down any hard and fast rule regarding the character of the illness; it only indicates that a continuance

---

(1) *Fatâwai Kâzi Khân*, Chapter on the Divorce by the Sick; *Durr-ul-Mukhtâr*, p. 246; *Radd-ul-Muhtâr* Vol. III, p. 855.

(2) [1898] 3 Cal. W. N., 57.

of the malady for that length of time may be regarded as taking it out of the category of a mortal illness."

Fatima Bibee v. *Ahmad Bakhsh.*

The view expressed in this case was followed in *Fatima Bibee* v. *Ahmad Baksh,*(1) where it was held further that "whilst the lawyers have suggested that certain physical incapacities indicated a dangerous illness, they did not lay down positively that these incapacities are conclusive." In the case of *Sarabai* v. *Rabiabai*, the learned Judge pointed out that in order to establish *marz-ul-mout* there must be at least the following conditions :—" (*a*) proximate danger of death so that there is, as it is paraphrased, a preponderance (*ghaliba*) of *khauf* or apprehension, that is, at the given time death must be more probable than life ; (*b*) there must be some degree of subjective apprehension in the mind of the sick person ; (*c*) there must be some external indicia, chief among which I would place the inability to attend to ordinary avocations."

Sarabai v. *Rabiabai.*

It must be noted, however, that the last element which seems to have been regarded as a condition is merely a test.(2)

Ghulam Mustafa v. *Hurmut.*

In the case of *Ghulam Mustafa* v. *Hurmut,*(3) the Allahabad High Court held that the provisions of the Mahommedan Law applicable to gifts, made by persons labouring under a fatal disease, do not apply to a so-called gift made in lieu of a dower-debt, which is really in the nature of a sale.

But this view seems to be in conflict with the Mahommedan Law which declares that even a sale by a person labouring under a fatal illness is valid only to the extent of one-third of his estate.(4)

SECTION V.

THE MOUHUB-LEH OR DONEE.

The *Mouhūb-lèh* or Donee—Hanafi Law.

ANY person may receive a gift, without distinction of sex or age or creed, but under the Hanafî Law the donee must be legally

(1) [1903] I. L., 31 Cal., 319 ; affirmed by the Judicial Committee, [1908] L. R., 35 I. A., 67.

(2) [1906] I. L., 30 Bom., 519 ; in this case the question for determination was whether a *talâk* pronounced by a deceased Hanafî Mahommedan deprived or not the divorced wife of her share in his inheritance ; this case was followed in *Rashid* v. *Sherbanoo*, [1907] I. L., 31 Bom., 264.

(3) [1850] I. L., 2 All., p. 854, *per* Pearson and Oldfield, JJ.

(4) With regard to the Shiah Law on the subject of a divorce in *marz-ul-mout*, see Mahomedan Law, Vol. II, p. 541.

in existence at the time of the gift. A gift, therefore, to an unborn person, one not *in esse*, either actually or presumably, is invalid.

Child *en ventre sa mère.*

A gift, however, to a child *en ventre sa mère* is valid, if the child is born within six months from the date of the gift, because in that case it is presumed that the child was actually existing as a distinct entity in the womb of its mother.

Shiah doctrines.

It is different, however, under the Shiah Law, where an estate may be devised to an unborn person if the commencement is made with a person *in esse*.

If a gift is made to *A* for life—under the Hanafî Law, the condition limiting the estate to the donee's life would be invalid and the gift would take effect as an absolute gift. Under the Shiah Law, *A* would take a life-estate, and upon *A's* death the property would revert to the donor or his heirs. If the gift is to *A* for life and then to *B* for life, under the Shiah Law, both the life-estates would take effect, and upon the death of *B*, the property would revert to the donor or his heirs. A gift to *A* for life and then to *B* and his descendants would give a life-estate to *A* and an estate in fee to *B*.(1)

Under both the systems, a gift to *A* and his children or descendants generally, or to his descendants "line after line," or any gift coupled with such terms as necessarily imply that the property is bestowed without any limitation, would take effect as an absolute gift to *A*.

SECTION VI.

THE MOUHOOB.—THE SUBJECT-MATTER OF THE GIFT.

The *Mouhoob.*

ANYTHING over which dominion or the right of property may be exercised, or anything which can be reduced into possession or which exists as a specific entity or as an enforceable right, or anything, in fact, which comes within the meaning of the word *mâl*, may form the subject of gift. *Choses in action* and incorporeal rights may form the subject of gift equally with corporeal property. "A debt" says the *Kifâya*, "considered with reference to the prospect of payment is *mâl* or corporeal property (so much so that *zâkat*(2) is obligatory on it); and it is susceptible of *tamlîk*. Considered with

(1) *Jawâhir-ul-Kalâm*; see *post*.

(2) Religious tithes.

reference to its present state, it is a *wasf* or a *quality*, [*i.e.*, indebtedness] and is susceptible of *iskât* or extinction. Hence, a gift of it to the debtor, which is an extinction, is valid both by analogy and on a liberal interpretation [of the law], but a gift of it to another which is *tamlîk* (transfer of property) is valid on the latter ground."(1) Similarly, it is stated in the *Radd-ul-Muhtâr* that a gift of a debt to a person other than a debtor is valid because although it is not *'ain* in the present, it is capable of becoming property in the future.(2)

Mullick Abdul Guffoor* v. *Musst. Maleka.

The argument, therefore, which was endeavoured to be raised in the case of *Mullick Abdul Guffoor* v. *Musst. Maleka*(3) has no foundation whatsoever. On the contrary, the Hanafî Law, as given in the *Kifâya*, expressly recognises the legality of gifts of incorporeal rights and *choses in action*. And custom (*'urf*), to which Mahommedan lawyers have always attached considerable force in deciding questions on the ground of *istehsân* (" favourable construction " or " liberal interpretation"), to make the law harmonise with social progress, has accepted the rule and carried it into practice in different directions. Hence the gift of Government securities, which

(1) *Kifâya* (published with the *Hedâya*, Cal. Ed., Vol. III, p. 698. Comp. *Durr-ul-Mukhtâr*, p. 641 and *Fatâwai Alamgiri*, Vol. V, p. 234.

Under the Transfer of Property Act (IV of 1882) actionable claims are transferable, but under s. 135 the debtor is entitled to a discharge upon paying the transferee the price actually paid by him with incidental. expenses and interest. This provision does not apply to gifts, but whether it would apply to a *hiba-bi'l-ewaz* is a question not unattended with difficulty. A *hiba-bi'l-ewaz*, where not in reality a *hiba simple* is, in its legal incidents, equivalent to a sale, and yet is subject in most of its aspects to the rules governing *hiba simple*. Would s. 135 then apply to the case of a *hiba-bi'l-ewaz*, where some consideration is proved, bearing in mind the provisions of s. 129? The Calcutta High Court has held that s. 135 applies also to a mortgage (I. L., 21 Cal., 568). The correctness of this view is open to question.

In case I, Macnaughten's Mahommedan Law, Precedents of Wills, it is declared, that " the term *tamlîk* is one of general import, and may be applied to a gift, whether unconditional or conditional, to a sale or to a will. But the term *hiba* (gift) signifies the immediate transfer of property to another without consideration. Thus the difference between an assignment of proprietary right and gift is, that the one is general and the other particular."

Again, there is this passage in the *Ashbâh-wan-Nazâir* :—"The circumstances which constitute *tamlîk* are interchange of property ; dower, compensation by a wife to her husband for divorce from him, inheritance, gift, charity, bequest, endowment or appropriation, plunder, or conquest over lawful things and animals, finding of waifs, and amends to a person killed and subsequently inherited by his heir are all *tamlîk*."

(2) *Radd-ul-Muhtâr*, Vol. IV, p. 776.

(3) [1884] I. L., 10 Cal., 1112.

only carry the right of drawing the interest on them,(1) the grant of *malikana* rights, which confers on the donee the right of obtaining from Government the proprietor's share in the income of an estate, and the like, form frequent subjects of gift. Similarly, under the Mahommedan sovereigns, assignments of revenue, which were called *Suyurghûl* grants, were often transferred by the grantees.

Thus a gift of property in the occupation of tenants is lawful for this implies the grant of the right to receive the rent from the occupying tenant or lessee.(2) So is a gift of property in the hands of a mortgagee,(3) or under attachment,(4) of an undistributed share inherited by the donor of which he has not obtained possession,(5) of the *malikana* interest or the right to receive from Government the proprietor's share of the assets of landed property which has been settled with another *zemindar* or *malguzar*.(6)

Gift of property in the occupation of tenants.

When property is held by another under a lease or *ijara*, it cannot be given so as to convey the actual possessory right to the donee, or to enable him to obtain direct, or what is called in the legal language of Upper India, *khas* possession of the subject-matter of the gift, as it would be inconsistent with, and in contravention of, the contract between the donor and his lessee. But there is no rule to prevent the assignment or gift of the right to receive the rent reserved under the lease. A gift, therefore, of property in the occupation of tenants is lawful, for this implies the grant of the right to receive the rents from the occupying tenants or lessees.

The passage in the *Fatâwai-Alamgiri*,(7) "but if it be in the hands of an usurper or of a pledgee, or of a *mustâjir* (hirer or

(1) *Nawab Amjad Ally Khan* v. *Mahomdi Begum* [1867], 11 M. I. A., 517; s. c., 10 W. R., 25, P. C.; *Dorab Ally Khan* v. *Suliman Kadr*, I. L., 8 Cal., 1.

(2) *Ibrahim* v. *Suleman* [1884], I. L., 9 Bom., 146.

(3) *Rahim Buksh* v. *Muhammad Hassan* [1888], I. L., 11 All., 1. In *Mohinudin* v. *Manchershah* [1882], I. L., 6 Bom., 650, and *Ismal* v. *Ramje* [1899], I. L., 23 Bom., 682, the Bombay High Court has, it is respectfully submitted, misconceived the Mahommedan Law.

(4) *Anwari Begam* v. *Nizam-ud-din* [1898], I. L., 21 All., 165.

(5) *Mahomed Buksh* v. *Hossaini Bibi* [1888], L. R., 15 I. A., 81; s. c., I. L., 15 Cal., 684.

(6) *Mullick Abdul Guffoor* v. *Mussummat Maleka*, supra.

(7) Vol. III, p. 521.

lessee),(1) the gift is not lawful for want of possession," has been wholly misunderstood. It occurs in the chapter dealing with the subject of gifts to minors or infants (*saghîr*), (2) who cannot themselves take possession of the subject of a gift, and in whose case the requisite of seisin, which will be discussed later on, is fulfilled by the possession of the father or the person standing for the time being *in loco parentis*. And it is therefore declared that "a gift by a father to his infant child is completed by the [mere] *'akd* (declaration or contract)(3) whether the property be in his own hands or in the hands of his depositary;" in other words whether his possession is real or constructive—for the depositary's possession is his own possession.

But this is not the case when the property is in the hands of somebody else who is claiming to hold *direct* possession of it by some title either derived from or independently of the donor. For example, a *mustâjir* (a lessee) and a mortgagee in possession claim the right to hold the property under an act of the donor himself; an usurper has it in his hands under an adverse title. In neither of such cases the possession is with the donor that he can transfer the possessory right or vest it by a mere declaration, as is the case when the property is in his own hands or in the hands of his depositary, for he can at any time resume possession. For the completion of a gift of property in the hands of a pledgee or a person holding possession under an invalid sale or an adverse title, something more is needed than a "mere declaration," *viz.*, an *authority* to receive the income or to take possession on the expiration of the lease or mortgage, or to sue for recovery. That the gift itself is not *inoperative* is clear from the following statement of the law:—
"And Saijâni has stated that a gift by a father of property in the hands of a pledgee, or a usurper, or a vendee under an invalid sale, will take effect when the pledge or lease expires or the sale is set

---

(1) The term "*ijara*" or lease, from which *mustâjir* is derived, under the Mahommedan law, is not restricted to a lease of lands or immovable property. It comprehends various classes of contracts which come under the head of Bailment, with the exception of pledge and deposits, which are treated separately under the head of *Rahn* and *Wadia't* respectively; *Majm'aa-ul-Anhar* (Constantinople Ed.), p. 343, Chapter on Gifts.

(2) *Fatâwai Alamgiri*, Vol. IV, p. 544.

(3) The father's declaration that he has given such a thing to his infant child forms the contract, for no assent is required from the donee.

aside or the thing usurped has been recovered."(1) Although the word *mustâjir* has, apparently by analogy, been introduced in the *Fatâwai-Alamgiri* it does not occur in the *Hedâya*.

The passage in the *Hedâya* (Arabic) runs thus :—

ما اذا كان في يده او في يد مودعه لان يده كيده بخلاف ما اذا
كان مرهونا او مغصوبا او مبيعا بيعا فاسدا لانه في يد غيره او في ملك
غيره و الصدقة في هذا مثل الهبة *

The gift is valid—"when it [the subject of the gift] is in his [the donor's] hands or in the hands of his depositary for being in the latter's hands is like being in his own, which is contrary to its being pledged, or usurped or sold under an invalid sale, for it is in such cases in the hands of another or in his property; and a *sadakah* under such circumstances is like a *hiba*."

The gloss of the *Kifâya* on the above is the following :—

بخلاف ما اذا كان مرهونا او مغصوبا الى اخره يعني اذا كان مال
الاب مغصوبا او كذا و كذا لم يتم الهبة بالعقد لانه في يد غيره في
الرهن و الغصب او في ملك غيره في البيع الفاسد فان قيل ينبغي
ان لا يتم الهبة اذا كان في يد مودعه لاشتراط الكمال في القبض
و كون هذا القبض حكما وهو نقص من القبض حقيقة قلنا القبض
حكما كاف لاتمام الهبة *

"'Contrary to its being pledged or usurped, etc.' that is when the property of the father has been usurped or the like [pledged or sold under an invalid sale] the gift is not completed by the *contract*, for it is in the hands of another when pledged or usurped, and in the property of another when sold under an invalid sale. Then if it is objected that complete seisin being conditioned, a gift of property in the hands of a depositary cannot take effect, and seisin in such a case is merely constructive falling short of real seisin, then I say [with reference to this objection] that constructive seisin is sufficient for the completion of the gift."

Nor does the word *mustâjir* occur in the *Majm'âa-ul-Anhar*, the restriction apparently as in the *Hedâya* being confined to pro-

(1) *Radd-ul-Muhtâr*, Vol. IV, p. 785.

perties in the hands of a pledgee or a *ghâsib* (usurper) and properties transferred under an invalid sale (*ba'i-fâsid*).

Hypothecation.

To understand the restriction it is necessary to bear in mind that under the Hanafî Law there is no hypothecation without seisin.(1) Consequently, when a property is in the hands of a mortgagee or a bailee, the interest of the mortgagor or bailor, *viz.*, the reversionary right, can only be conveyed by gift to the donee, and not the actual possessory right, which by the fact of bailment or mortgage has been transferred to the mortgagee in possession, or the bailee. So where immovable property is in the occupation of a lessee or a tenant, the right of receipt to the rents alone can be granted by the donor. The Bombay High Court, in the case of *Mohinudin* v. *Manchershah*,(2) has decided that lands in the possession of a mortgagee cannot form the subject of *hiba* under the Mahommedan Law. This view, it is respectfully submitted, is founded upon an erroneous apprehension of the Hanafî Law under which seisin is requisite for hypothecation. Under the Mâliki Law, seisin is not necessary. But, according to the correct view of the Hanafî doctrine on the subject, there is nothing in it to preclude the mortgagor from granting his equity of redemption to another. On the contrary, under the law relating to *hawâlât*,(3) the debtor may transfer his liability to another. And, as the property forms the security for the debt, the transferee obtains the right to redeem the property subject to the payment of the debt. But, when the property is not in the hands of the mortgagee, as is usually the custom in India and is only burdened with certain debts, which are secured upon it, the mortgagor is unquestionably entitled to make a disposition thereof.

Mohinudin v. *Manchershah*, erroneously decided.

Property in the hands of a usurper.

The gift of a property in the hands of a usurper probably stands on a different footing. The right of the donor to such property is a mere inchoate right, *viz.*, to sue for recovery of possession, and it is possible that, in early times, the gift of a mere speculative right of suit without express authority to take action was regarded with disfavour. But there seems to be no sufficient ground for holding that where a property, to which a person is rightfully

(1) *Hedâya*, III, p. 189.
(2) [1881], I. L., 6 Bom., 650.
(3) *Hedâya*, II, p. 606.

entitled, happens to be in the hands of another claiming adversely to him, the rightful owner may not make a gift of the same to a third person. In the case of *Mohammed Bukhsh Khan* v. *Hossaini Bibi*,(1) the Privy Council laid down the principle, that where a gift is public and authorises the donee to take possession which is in fact taken subsequently, the gift is not invalid on the ground that the donor was not, at the time, in possession of the subject of the gift. This view is in conformity with the rule of the Mahommedan Law.

In the case of *Mohinudin* v. *Manchershah*,(2) the Bombay High Court has held that the sale of property of which the vendor is out of possession is valid. Consequently, a *hiba-bi'l-ewaz* thereof, which is equivalent to a sale in its legal incidents, would without question be valid.

Mullick Abdul Guffoor v. *Musst. Maleka.*

Regarding the validity of a gift of lands and tenements in the occupation of tenants, the judgment in the case of *Mullick Abdul Guffoor* v. *Musst. Maleka*(3) has settled the question beyond any room for doubt. The Chief Justice dealing with the arguments urged against the validity of the gift said :—

"The question, therefore, in this Court, so far as this deed is concerned, has been, whether having regard to the subject-matter of the gift, and the fact of there having been no actual partition made of it, at the time when the deed was executed, as between the two donees, the transaction is valid in law as against the plaintiffs."

"This question has been argued before us at some length, and we are much indebted to the learned Counsel on both sides for the pains which they have taken to refer us to all the authorities upon the subject. But having heard the matter fully argued, we are satisfied that the gift is valid, and that the conclusion at which the Lower Court arrived is just."

"The property, which is the subject of the gift, consists of several zemindaries, and shares in zemindaries, let out to tenants and ryots, as such estates usually are; a good many lakheraj properties also let out to tenants; several *malikana* rights of some

---

(1) [1888], L. R., 15 I. A., 81.
(2) [1882], I. L., 6 Bom., 650.
(3) [1884], I. L., 10 Cal., 1112.

value, and a variety of house-property in Patna, and elsewhere, consisting of houses, sheds, roads, gardens, &c." *Mullick Abdul Guffoor* v. *Musst. Maleka.* —contd.

"There is no satisfactory evidence as to how this latter property was occupied or utilized at the time when the gift was made."

"The arguments on the part of the plaintiff resolve themselves into three main points :—"

"1*st*, That by Mahommedan Law, a gift cannot be made of lands which are not in the possession of the donor, nor of incorporeal properties, such as rents, *malikana* rights and the like; 2*nd*, that an undivided share of a house or a zemindari cannot be made the subject of a gift; and 3*rd*, that a gift to two persons without previous division and separation is invalid."

"In dealing with these points, we must not forget that the Mahommedan Law, to which our attention has been directed in works of very ancient authority, was promulgated many centuries ago in Baghdad, and other Mahommedan countries, under a very different state of laws and society from that which now prevails in India; and that, although, we do our best here in suits between Mahommedans to follow the rules of Mahommedan Law, it is often difficult to discover what those rules really were, and still more difficult to reconcile the differences which so constantly arose between the great expounders of the Mahommedan Law ordinarily current in India, namely, Abû Hanîfa and his two disciples."

"We must endeavour, so far as we can, to ascertain the true principles upon which that law was founded, and to administer it with a due regard to the rules of equity and good conscience, as well as to the laws, and the state of society and circumstances which now prevail in this country."

"Having premised thus far, we think that the first of the above point, although it has occupied some time in argument, may be very readily disposed of. In fact it appears to us to have been already settled."

"We have been referred to several authorities, and, amongst others, to the *Durr-ul-Mukhtâr*, *Book on Gifts*, p. 635, which lays down that no gift can be valid unless the subject of it is in the possession of the donor at the time when the gift is made. Thus, when land is in the possession of a *usurper* (*or wrong-doer*), *or of a lessee or mortgagee, it cannot be given away;* because in these

Mullick Abdul Guffoor v. *Musst. Maleka*—contd.

cases the donor has not possession of the thing which he purports to give."(1)

"But we think that this rule, which is undoubtedly laid down in several works of more or less authority, must, so far as it relates to land, have relation to cases where the donor professes to give away *the possessory interest* in the land itself, and not merely a reversionary right in it; of course an actual seisin or possession cannot be transferred, except by him who has it for the time being."

"It is possible, too, that these texts may be explained by what we are informed was the law in Baghdad in early times with reference to land let on lease; we are told that an *ijara* lease, which in this country means generally a farming lease of ryoti holdings, meant, according to the law of Baghdad, a lease of the land itself or its usufruct; and that the owner of the land having made such a lease, could not by law transfer his reversionary interest, so as to give the transferee a right to receive the rent from the *ijaradar* (see *Fatâwa-i-Alamgiri*, Vol. III, *Book on Gifts*, p. 521)."

"Whether this is the real meaning of the authorities may be doubtful; but it is certain that such a state of the law in this country would render the transfer by gift of a zemindari and other landlords' interest simply impossible: lands here are almost always let out on leases of some kind, and there are often four or five different grades of tenants between the zemindar and the occupying ryot. What is usually called *possession* in this country is *not actual or khas possession*, but the receipt of the rents and profits; and, if lands let on lease could not be made the subject of a gift, many thousands of gifts, which have been made over and over again, of zemindari properties would be invalidated. If we were disposed to agree with this novel view of Mahommedan Law (which we are not), we think we should be doing a great wrong to the Mahommedan community, by placing them under disabilities with regard to the transfer of property, which they have never hitherto experienced in this country. Such a view of the law is quite inconsistent with several cases decided by the Sudder Dewany Adalut (under the advice of the *Kâzis*), and also by this Court (see 1 Select Reports, 5, 12, and 115 note; 1 Bombay High Court Reports, 157; 16 W. R., 88; and 12 W. R., 498); and it is

(1) The learned Chief Justice's attention was not called to the fact that the passage in question occurs in the chapter dealing with gifts to infants.

directly opposed to the case of *Amirunnissa* v. *Abedunnissa*(1) decided by their Lordships of the Privy Council."

Mullick Abdul Guffoor v. *Musst. Maleka*—concld.

"In that case a gift of large zemindaries was held to be valid, although it is clear that they consisted, as such estates generally do, of tenures and interests of all kinds; no objection was then taken to the gift upon the ground that has been urged before us here, and indeed, so far as it appears, that point has now been taken for the first time."

"Similarly, as regards the *malikana* rights, we are not aware of any reason, why rights of this description should not be made the subject of a gift, in the same way as rents or other incorporeal property of that nature. We have already decided that reversionary interests, carrying with them the right to receive rents, may be thus transferred; and it is clear that debts and Government notes and other *choses in action*, which give the parties entitled to them the right to receive money from the Government or third persons, may be made the subject of a gift."

"A *malikana* right is the right to receive from the Government a sum of money, which represents the *malik's* share of the profits of the revenue-paying estate, when from his declining to pay the revenue assessed by the Government, or from any other cause, his estate is taken into *khas* possession of Government, or transferred to some other person, who is willing to pay the rate assessed. There is nothing in principle, so far as we can see, to distinguish a *malikana* right from a right to receive rents, or the dividend payable upon Government paper."

Gift of a debt under the Shiah Law

Regarding the assignment of a *chose in action*, there are two divergent opinions in force among the Shiahs. The Mohakkik states in the *Sharâya-ul-Islâm*, "that the donation of a debt, or what rests on the obligation of another, is not valid to any other than the debtor or the person by whom it is due, according to the generally received doctrine, by reason of the condition already mentioned that it requires possession to complete it, whereas if made to the debtor himself, it is quite valid and operates as a release of the debt,"(2) whilst the great author of the *Mabsût* and other eminent Shiah jurists agree with the Hanafi lawyers in holding that, according to a liberal interpretation, the transfer or

(1) [1875], L. R., 2 I. A., 87; s. c., 15 B. L. R., 67; 23 W. R., 208.
(2) *Sharâya-ul-Islâm*, p. 242.

assignment of a debt to a third person by the creditor is lawful. And even the *Jâm'aa-ush-Shittât*, which often adopts the opinion of the Mohakkik, says that the gift of a debt to a third person is valid according to *'urf* (custom). The doctrine laid down in the *Mabsût* has been so generally approved by *'urf* or custom, which is the embodiment in practice of the general consensus of a progressive community, that the rule mentioned by the author of the *Sharâya* may be regarded as entirely exploded.

Doctrine of the *Mabsût* recognised in practice.

Hanafî Law.

Under the Hanafî Law the release of a debt to the debtor is valid without his consent, but becomes inoperative, if the debtor refuses to accept the release.

Shiah Law.

Here, again, there is a conflict of opinion among the Shiah jurists. The author of the *Mabsût* declares the release of a debt (*ibrâ*) to a debtor is not valid or operative without the debtor's express or implied consent. According to the author of the *Sharâya* such a release is valid without acceptance,(1) and though he does not say what the result would be, if the debtor rejects it, his meaning probably is that it would be effective. In the *Zakhîra-i-M'aâd*, Shaikh Zain-ul-'aâbidîn, late Mujtahid of Teheran adopts the opinion of the *Mabsût*, and in the *Jâm'aa-ush-Shittat*, a case is given from which it would appear that under the Shiah Law, as under the Sunni Law, when a creditor discharges the debtor, he cannot again enforce the liability, but the debtor may insist upon his performing any obligation which rests on the creditor, or even force him to accept the debt.

"Release of a debt."

A gift of property which is not in existence at the time of the donation and whose existence at some future time is problematical, is invalid.

A gift of non-existent objects.

With regard to the invalidity of the gift of things absolutely non-existent, the *Durrar-ul-Akkâm* gives the following explanation :— "The secret (reason) of the invalidity of such objects as flour in the wheat, &c., consists in the fact that they change completely their character in the process of making, and a new thing altogether comes into being after the *istehâla* (استحاله)."(2)

In the *Durr-ul-Mukhtâr* the principle is stated thus :— "The gift of flour in the wheat, of oil in the sesame, or the butter which is in the milk is altogether invalid as it is non-existent (*m'aadûm*),

(1) *Sharâya-ul-Islâm*. p. 242.

(2) *Istehâla* means practically transmutation.

so that right of property cannot be acquired in any of those things, without a new *'akd* (declaration or contract)," (1) in contradistinction to the case of a gift of "milk in the udder, or of fleece on the sheep, or of palm-trees in the ground, or of fruit on the trees, which although invalid on the ground of *mushâ'a* or confusion(2) becomes operative if the subject of the gift is separated and made over to the donee." And then the question is formulated—"Is the separation by the donee with the permission of the donor sufficient to constitute a valid gift ?(3) According to the approved doctrine (*zâhir-ur-rawâyet*) it is."

Speaking of the subject-matter of gifts, *viz.*, what may or may not form the subject of *hiba*, the *Fatâwai-Alamgiri* has the following :—

What may or may not form the subject of *hiba.*

"Among the conditions which are required in the case of the subject of the gift there are several, one of these being that it must be in existence at the time of the gift; thus a gift of something which is not in existence at the time of the *'akd* (contract) will not be valid. For example, if one were to give the fruit that may be produced by his tree in the course of the year,....or what is in the womb of this sheep, or in its udder, the gift is unlawful though power be given to take possession at the time of production, as of birth, or of milking ; so is invalid the gift of the butter in milk, the oil in sesame, or the flour in wheat, though the donee be empowered to take possession on production, for they are non-existent at present and are therefore not fitting subjects for the *'akd* (contract) to take effect : and this is correct, so in the *Jawâhir-ul-Akhlâti.*"

Where, however, a person has a subsisting recurring right in something which is neither variable nor uncertain, there is no reason in principle why its gift should not be valid. Thus an assignment of the ascertained rents and issues of any particular property movable or immovable may validly be effected. The Bombay High Court in the case of *Amtul Nissa Begam* v. *Mir Nurudin Hussein Khan*(4) seems to have missed, it is submitted, the real principle under which a gift of something not in existence at the time is invalid, *viz.*, the uncertainty

(1) *Durr-ul-Mukhtâr*, p. 635.
(2) See *post*.
(3) *Durr-ul-Mukhtâr*, p. 636.
(4) [1896], I. L., 22 Bom., 489.

relating to the subject-matter of the gift, not merely the inability to give possession.

The subject of gift must have legal value.

"Another condition is that the subject of the gift must have legal value, so that anything in which there can be no right of property, such as carrion, pork, or in which the right of property has been abandoned as an emancipated slave, or what has no value at all as wine, cannot be the subject of gift."

"The third condition is that possession must be taken of it to establish in it the right of the donee, and if it is in its nature divisible, it must be divided and distinguished from, and not joined to, or occupied with anything else that is not given. Hence the gift of land without the crop then standing on it, which belongs to the donor, or of a palm-tree in bearing without its fruit, and *vice versâ*, is invalid. So also of a house or vessel in which there is something belonging to the donor without its contents, thus in the *Nihâya*."(1)

Mushâ'a. Divergence between the schools.

The Hanafî doctrine.

As regards the latter principle, there is considerable difference between the Hanafîs on one side and the Shâfeïs and the Shiahs on the other. Under the Hanafî Law, if the subject is in its nature divisible, or forms part of a thing which is capable of physical partition or division, the gift is not valid until it is divided off, or separated from the other property of the donor which is not given. But where it forms part of an indivisible thing, or of a thing which cannot be divided without considerable damage to the entire property, the gift is valid though there is no partition.

The Shiah and Shâfeï doctrines.

The Shiahs and Shâfeïs differ *in toto* from the Hanafîs regarding this principle. They maintain that the gift is valid in either case, because a gift is a *tamlîk* and valid as such in respect of all things, whether they form portions of a divisible or indivisible thing. The Shiahs, however, insist that there must not be a complete ignorance as to the substance of the gift, *i.e.*, that the subject should be sufficiently indicated in order to leave no room for doubt as to what is given. Indefiniteness or ignorance as to the very subject-matter of the gift would avoid the grant, but not mere ambiguity which can be explained by other circumstances. According to the Shâfeïs, mere indefiniteness does not render a gift void, for an undefined but known share may be as much the subject of proprietary right as a definite specific share.

Shiah doctrine.

Shâfeï doctrine.

(1) *Fatâwai Alamgiri*, Vol. IV. p. 521.

Impartible *mushâ'a.* The rule of Hanafî Law.

The *Fatâwai Alamgiri* devotes a special chapter to what may and what may not validly form the subject of gift.(1)

"The *hiba* of a thing of which possession can be taken(2) and which has been separated from the property of the donor and his rights is valid. So is the gift of a *mushâ'a* that is incapable of partition, or is of such a nature that some kind of benefit or advantage that can be derived from it while whole or undivided cannot be derived from it after partition, as for instance, a small house (*bait-us-saghîr*) or a small bath. But the gift of a *mushâ'a* in a thing that admits of partition, preserving the benefit which was derivable from it before partition, is not valid. So it is stated in the *Kâfi*. *What is required is that the thing given be partitioned and capable of being taken possession of at the seisin, not at the time of the 'akd* (contract)."

"An illustration of this is furnished by a case where a man makes a gift of an undivided half of a house to one person but does not deliver possession until he has made a gift of the other half to another; if he were then to give seisin of both at one and the same time, it would be valid according to the *Zahîria.* But if he were to make a gift of a moiety to one and deliver possession and a gift of the other moiety to a third person and similarly deliver possession, it would not be valid and both gifts would be *fâsid* (invalid) according to the *Nihâya.*"

* * * * * *

Possession of *mushâ'a* establishes right of property.

"The gift of a *mushâ'a* which does not admit of partition is valid to a partner or to a stranger, according to the *Fusûl-i-'Imâdia.* The gift of a *mushâ'a* in what does admit of partition is not valid whether it be to a partner or one who is not a partner, and if possession is taken of it, Hisâm-ud-din has stated in the *Kitâb-ul-Wâk'iât* that it would not avail to establish property in the donee, but he has said in another place that it would avail to establish it *invalidly, and decisions are passed accordingly; so in the Sirâjia.*"(3)

The subject of *mushâ'a* has furnished a fruitful source of discussion in the Indian law-courts and the difficulties with which

(1) P. 524.

(2) Mr. Baillie has translated *Muhawwaz* as separated. I think *Muffaragh* conveys the idea of separation.

(3) *Fatâwai Alamgiri*, Vol. IV, p. 526.

it is surrounded render it necessary, that the meaning of the doctrine, its *raison d'être* and the legal principles which govern it, should be considered with some degree of care.

Mushâ'a— its *raison d'être.*

Mushâ'a has been defined by Freytag as meaning "pluribus communis." Every joint undivided property subject to the right of more than one individual is a *mushâ'a*. The word *mushâ'a* is derived from *shuyû'u* which means confusion. Where several persons own a particular property joint and undivided, no one of them can predicate that his interest is attached to any specific portion. The gift by one of the co-sharers of his share in such a property is likely to create confusion in its enjoyment by all the co-sharers. It will be seen, therefore, that the doctrine of *mushâ'a*, which implies a prohibition against the *hîba* of joint undivided properties that are partible in their nature, owes its origin among the Hanafîs to a rather nervous dread on the part of some of their principal lawyers, notably Abû Hanîfa, that unless divisible things were divided off, it would give rise to disputes and complications in the enjoyment of such subjects.

Mushâ'a.

Abû Hanîfa carries his objection to "indefiniteness," in other words, to the gift of a share in joint undivided property which is capable of partition, to the utmost limit. But there is a marked difference between him and his disciples on the point in question. Generally speaking, their views are more in accord with the requirements of a progressive community and less casuistical than those of Abû Hanîfa. The following passage from the *Fatâwai Alamgiri* will bring into prominent relief, not only the views entertained by the early writers on the subject, but also the nature of the divergence between the master and disciples, though the principles laid down there must be taken subject to the enunciations of later authorities.

"With regard to the validity of the gift of a *mushâ'a* (undivided part of a property) which does not admit of partition, it is a condition that its quantity should be known, as if a person were to give to another a share in a bondsman, and the share is not known [not specified], the gift would not be valid, for the want of specification [*lit.* ignorance of the share] would cause disputes; so in the *Bahr-ur-Râik*. When the share of the donor is known to the donee in such a case the gift, according to Abû Hanîfa, ought to be valid, but not so according to the other two [Abû Yusuf and Mohammed]; so in the *Muhît-as-Sarakshi.*" (1)

"The gift of a *mushâ'a,* that admits of partition, to two men or to a group, is valid according to the two disciples, and invalid according to Abû Hanîfa. But it is not *bâtil* (void), so that it avails to establish [the right of] property by possession. This is according to the *Jawâhir-ul-Akhlâti.* Sadr-ush-Shahîd(2) has stated that when a person has given what admits of partition to two men, so that the gift is invalid according to him [Abû Hanîfa], and possession is afterwards taken of it, *the right of property is established in them invalidly and* that the *fatwa* (decree) is passed according to this doctrine; so in the *Fatâwai 'Itâbia.*" Possession.

"And the right of property is not established in the donee until he takes possession [of the subject-matter of the gift], and this is the approved doctrine; so in the *Fusûl 'Imâdia.*"

As Mr. Baillie(3) points out, a gift of *mushâ'a* may be made in three different ways. *First,* a person being the owner of the whole may give an undivided and unspecified share to another. In this case there is *shuyû'u* or confusion on both sides, and the gift is invalid by *consensus. Second,* a person being the owner of the entire subject of the gift gives the whole to two or more persons "undividedly," *i.e.,* without partition or apportionment. Here there is confusion on the side of the donees only; and the gift would be valid according to Abû Yusuf and Mohammed though not according to Abû Hanîfa. The third case is where two or more persons own a property jointly in undivided shares and they combine in making a gift of the whole to one single person. In such a case the confusion is on the side of the donors and the gift is valid *bi'l ijmâ'a* (by consensus).

These principles are formulated thus in the *Fatâwai Alamgiri.* "Confusion on both sides in property capable of partition prevents the validity of gift *bi'l ijmâ'a* (by consensus), but when the confusion is only on the side of the donee, it prevents the validity of the gift, according to Abû Hanîfa, in opposition to the other two [Abû Yusuf and Mohammed] so in the *Zakhîra.* And if one should make a gift to two persons who are poor, it would be

(1) *Fatâwai Alamgiri,* Vol. IV, p. 526.

(2) A great jurist of Khorasan who flourished in the 13th century.

(3) Baillie's Dig., 2nd Ed., p. 525.

lawful by consensus, as a *sadakah* (a pious offering). But if they are rich, and the gift is made to each of them in halves, or if it is made vaguely, by saying, 'I have given to you both,' or with an excess in favour of one, as by saying, 'to this one a third of it, and to this one two-thirds of it,' it is invalid in the three cases according to Abû Hanîfa; while, according to Mohammed, it is valid in them all; and according to Abû Yusuf, it is lawful in the two cases where the gift is made to both indefinitely, or in halves, but it is not lawful with any excess in favour of one of them. And Karkhi reports from Ibn Samâ'a that Abû Yusuf has declared, when a man says to two men 'I have made a gift of this mansion to you two, and the half is for one and the other half for the other,' it would be valid, for he has made a gift of the whole and explained its effect."

The extreme technicality of the doctrine is, however, apparent from the following statement:—"If he (the donor) were to say 'I give a half of this mansion to you and the other half to him,' the gift would not be valid for the contract (*'akd*) itself is affected with *shuyû'u.*" "If a person were to say 'I have made a gift of this mansion to you two, two-thirds for one and one-third for the other,' the gift would not be valid according to Abû Hanîfa and Abû Yusuf, but would be valid according to Mohammed." Abû Hanîfa and Abû Yusuf differ, however, in their reasons for holding the gift to be invalid; whilst Abû Hanîfa thinks the contract (*'akd*) is vitiated by confusion, Abû Yusuf considers that as the shares are different, the gift is separable into two contracts, and as possession is a necessary condition to the validity of a gift, it is hardly possible under the circumstances.(1) "When two [persons] make a gift of a house to another, it is valid by consensus, so in the *Muzmirât.*"

"Original confusion," *viz.*, such as was existing at the time of the gift, "alone vitiates the contract, but not one which came into existence subsequently (*shuyû'u at-târi*). For example, if one were to give to another the whole of something, and afterwards were to rescind the gift in respect of an undivided part, or if an adverse right was established in respect of a similar part, that circumstance would not invalidate the gift, which is different from the case of a

(1) *Fatâwai Alamgiri*, Vol. IV, pp. 526-7.

pledge which is invalidated by a supervenient confusion ; so in the *Sharh-ul-Vikâyah*."

"If a person were to make a gift of an undivided part of some thing which admits of division, and were afterwards to divide it and deliver the share to the donee, it would be valid as is stated in the *Sirâj-ul-Wahâj*."

"If he were to make a gift of a moiety and deliver the whole, it would not be valid,(1) but if he were to give the whole and deliver possession in part, it would be valid ; so it is stated in the *Tâtâr-Khâniêh*."

"It has been said that if a person were to make a gift of an undivided moiety of a house to one person and deliver it to him, and were afterwards to give the other moiety to another, neither of the two would be valid ; but if he had not delivered possession to the first donee and then made the second gift and thereafter delivered possession to both, in that case the gift would be valid in favour of them both, according to Abû Yusuf and Mohammed, for such a gift is tantamount to a gift of the *whole* house to the two donees ; so in the *Mabsût*." * * * *

This authority, although occasionally cited by the compilers of the *Fatâwai Alamgiri*, is not nowadays extant in India. Anyhow the view expressed in the *Wajîz-l'il-kurdi* is in direct conflict with the statement of the law given in the *Durr-ul-Mukhtâr* as the one "on which decrees are passed." After stating the opinion held by some writers that when a person makes a gift of an undivided part of a thing and delivers to the donee possession of the same, the latter does not acquire a right of property over it so as to entitle him to deal with it, and if he does so he incurs a liability (for compensation), whilst the donor retains his power of disposition, the author proceeds to add —" but in the *Durrar* [*ul-Ahkâm*] it is stated from the *Fusûl* that an invalid gift (*hibat-ul-fâsid*) avails to establish the right of property by possession, and on this doctrine is the *fatwa* (*wa-bihi-iftâ*). And similarly it is laid down in the *Bazâziah*. This is contrary to what the '*Imâdia* states as correct. But the word *fatwa* is stronger (اكد) than the word *sahîh* as the author has stated in detail when dealing with the remaining rules relating to *mushâ'a*. And whether

(1) There is no reason given for this doctrine.

an invalid gift to a kinsman(1) can be revoked—in the *Durrar*, it is stated, it can. But this is objected to by Sharnibilâlièh, who has laid down that such a revocation is against the approved doctrine based on the rule on which decrees are made that in an invalid gift possession avails in vesting right of property, so this must be remembered.''(2)

The same principle is given by Shibli from Itqâni "that a gift of *mushâ'a* is only invalid or *incompletely* valid (*sahîh ghair tâm*) "which is borne out by the statements in the *Bahr-ur-Râik*."

The *Kifâyah* states the principle still more clearly—"and the gift of a *mushâ'a* which is capable of division is not valid either to a partner or stranger, but 'Usam (may the peace, etc.) has declared that if possession is taken it will avail to establish the right of property.''(3)

" The sale of a *mushâ'a*, whether it admits of partition or not, is valid ; so its lease to the partner, though not to a stranger, and on this is the *fatwa*. But a lease of an undivided share to a stranger is only invalid....A loan of an undivided part (*mushâ'a*) is valid to the partner, but to a stranger only if the share is delivered *dividedly*. The mortgage (*rahn*) of *mushâ'a* is invalid whether it admits of partition or not, and whether it is made to a partner or stranger.''(4)

The following passages in the *Fatâwa-i-Alamgiri* show still more clearly how technical the doctrine of *mushâ'a* is.

" If a person were to make a gift of a share of a partition wall or a way or a bath and were to specify the same and were to empower the donee to take possession, it would be valid as is the case of a house given to another with all its rights and boundaries which is taken possession of by the donee separately and dividedly, but the right of egress and ingress thereto is common between them; such a gift is valid according to the *Jawâhir-ul-Akhlâti*.* * *

"It is reported in the *Asl*(5) that if half a mansion is given undividedly to a person, and delivered to him, and he were to sell it, the sale would not be valid, and it is expressly stated in some *Fatâwa* that this is approved ; so in the *Wajiz l'il Kurdi*."

---

(1) See *post*, Chapter on Revocation.

(2) *Durr-ul-Mukhtâr*, p. 634.

(3) *Kifâyah*, Vol. III, p. 680.

(4) Tahtâwi. For the *wakf* of *mushâ'a*, see *post*.

(5) Another name for the *Mabsût* of Imâm Mohammed.

"If a man were to make a gift of a mansion in which there are some effects belonging to him, and should deliver the mansion to the donee, or deliver it with the effects, the gift would not be valid. But there is a device (حيلة) [by which a valid gift can be made]; it is first to make a deposit of the effects with the donee, and then to vacate them for him, and then make delivery of the mansion. In the opposite case, if he should make a gift of the effects without the mansion, and vacate them for the donee, and then make delivery of the mansion, or if he should make a gift of the mansion and effects together, and vacate them both for the donee, the gift would be valid in all these cases according to the *Jouharat-un-Nayyirèh.*"(1)

"If a separation is made in the delivery, as by giving one of the two and delivering it, and then by giving the other and delivering it, and a beginning is made with the mansion, the gift of the mansion is not valid, but that of the effects is valid, while, if a beginning were made with the effects, the gift of both would be valid, so in the *Jouharat-un-Nayyirèh.*"

"And if one should give land without the growing crop, or the crop without the land or trees without their fruit, or fruit without the trees, and vacate them for the donee, the gift would not be valid in either case; for they are so connected as to form parts of one another, and the gift is like that of a *mushâ'a* in a thing susceptible of partition. But if he should give each of them separately, as, for instance, the crop and then the land, or the land and then the crop, and deliver them together, the gift would be lawful as to both; while, if he separate them in delivery, it is valid as to neither whichever he may begin with; so in the *Siraj-ul-Wahâj.*"

"If a person were to make a gift of a mansion and not deliver it till he gives the effects also, and then delivers them together, the gift is lawful; in the same manner as when one gives a bag and corn-sacks, and does not deliver them until he makes a gift of the corn contained in them, and then delivers both, the gift is lawful as to the whole; so in the *Muhît.* If at the time of gift the house is empty, but at the time of delivery it is occupied, it is not valid; nor would his saying, 'Take possession,' or 'I have delivered,' be

---

(1) Comp. *Bibi Khaver Sultan* v. *Bibi Rukhia Sultan* [1905], I. L., 29 Bom., *post.*

valid when the donor, or his people, or goods are in the mansion; so in the *Tâtâr-Khânièh.*"(1)

Gift of things occupying and occupied.

"The gift of a thing which occupies another (*shâghil*) is lawful, but the gift of the thing occupied (*mashgûl*), is invalid. The principle in this class (*jins*) of cases is that the thing given being contained in [or mixed with] the property of the donor prevents the completion of the gift, because seisin is necessary, but when the thing given holds the property of the donor it does not prevent the completion (effectuation) of the *hiba.* .... *If a man were to make a gift of the crop on his land, or the fruit on his tree, or the scabbard on his sword, or the structure of a building or a measure of corn from a heap, and direct the donee to reap or to gather it, or to draw it or to remove it or to measure it, and he should do so, the gift would be lawful on a favourable construction* (*istehsân*); but if he is not permitted to take possession and does so, he is responsible; so in the *Kâfi.*"

"A gift by a wife to her husband of her house when they are both residing in it, is valid, as stated in the *Wajiz-l'il Kurdi.*"(2)

A gift rendered void by a right being established in part of it.

"If a man holds a house on lease and the lessor were to make him a gift of the building, it would be valid according to the *Tâtâr-Khânièh.* If a person were to make a gift of a house with its furniture and deliver them both and a right is subsequently established in respect of the furniture, the gift of the house is valid according to the *Kâfi.*"

With regard to the question "whether the fact that the thing given is contained in the property of a person other than the donor prevents the completion of the gift, the author of the *Muhît* has stated in the first chapter of his treatise on the gift of increments that it does not. For, he has said if a person were to lend another a house, and the bailee (*must'aîr*) were to misappropriate some property and put it in the house, and after that the bailor was to make a gift of the house to the bailee, it would be valid: similarly if the goods were stolen by the bailor himself and deposited in the house ......If a person were to entrust another with a house and furniture, and afterwards to make a gift of the house to the depositary, the gift would be valid; and if the furniture becomes destroyed whilst in the hands of the donee, the person entitled to it

---

(1) *Fatáwái Alamgiri,* Vol. IV, p. 529.

(2) Comp. *Amina Bibi* v. *Khatija Bibi* (1864), 1 Bom. H. C. R., 157.

will have recourse to the donee for compensation. Ibni Rustam has stated this to be Mohammed's doctrine, although Abû Yusuf thinks that in case of a person entitled to either coming forward the gift of the house would be invalid; so in the *Tâtâr-Khândiêh.*"

"If one should give sacks with goods in them, or a bag with food in it, and deliver them to the donee, and a right is subsequently established to the contents, in either case the gift remains complete as to the sacks and the bag; so in the *Muhît.* And if a man were to make a gift of a bag with its contents, and a claim is established as to the bag, the gift would be established in respect of the contents; so in the *Fatâwai Kâzi Khân.*"

"If a person were to make a gift of a house which has furniture in it, and were to deliver possession of both; and subsequently another were to establish his right to the furniture, the gift of the house will not be invalidated. And if the furniture is destroyed before the person rightfully entitled has appeared, whether the furniture was made over [expressly] or not to the donee, the rightful owner can recover compensation from the donor or the donee. Some have said this is the doctrine of Mohammed, but all our masters are agreed that until the thing is removed, there is no liability for compensation; others have said this is the doctrine of all our masters and it is *correct*, as is stated in the *Muhît-i-Sarakshi.*"

"If one should give a mansion, of which possession is taken, and a right is then established in a part of it, the gift is void according to the *Yenâbiah.* And if one should give land with the crop upon it, or a date-tree with the fruit on it, and make delivery of both, and a right should then be established in the crop or the fruit, the gift in the land or trees is void; so it is stated in the *Muhît.* A person makes a gift of his land with the crop on it, and cuts and delivers the crop, after which a right is established in one of them, the gift is void as to the other; so in the *Muhît-i-Sarakhshi.*"

"If a man is the owner of a house and part owner of another and were to say to a person 'I give thee these two houses' it would not be valid as to either, but if he were to say 'I give thee this one and my share in the other' it would be valid (in respect of both) as is stated in the *Khazânat-ul-Muftiïn.* It is stated in the *Fatâwai-ul-'Itâbiah* that if a man were to make a gift of his house in favour of his wife and of what is in her womb (*i.e.*, unborn child), or were to bestow it on them in charity, it would not be valid; but if he were to make a gift in favour of a living person and another who is dead or a non-living thing like a wall, the whole gift would be valid in favour of the living; so in the *Tâtâr Khânièh*."

"A man loses a pearl and then makes a gift of it to another and empowers him to demand it and take possession when recovered. Abû Yusuf declares such a gift to be invalid as it is a mere contingency; this is according to the *Zahîria*."

"When a man makes a gift to his partner (*muzârib*) of the property of the business, part being due from people and part being in the partner's hands, the gift is valid as to what is in his hands, but with regard to what is due from others, if he says 'realise same,' then it is valid; but with regard to any part which is unaccrued profit (*rabah*), it would not be valid; so in the *Muhût*."

Gift by one partner to another of a share in the profits not unlawful.

"When one of two partners says to the other 'I have given thee my share of the profit,' it has been said that if the property itself be in existence, the gift is not valid, by reason of its being *mushâ'a* in what admits of partition; but if the partner has lost the property, the gift is valid by reason of its being an *iskât*, or extinction of right, so in the *Zahîria*."

Doctrine of *Mushâ'a*.

These doctrines are more simply stated in the *Durr-ul-Mukhtâr*. "The rule is that if the thing given contains something belonging to the donor (which is not given) it prevents the completion of the gift, but not if it is contained in something belonging to the donor not given, (thus) when a man gives to another a bag which contains the food of the donor, or his house which contains his furniture or the animal on which is his saddle, and delivers them, the gift is not valid; but in the reverse case the gift is valid, for example, if he were to give the food, the furniture or the saddle, it would take effect..."(1) "The fact that the thing given contains the property of somebody other than the donor does not prevent the completion of the gift." This is explained thus by Tahtâwi; for example, a man makes a gift of a house with the furniture in it, and delivers possession of the same to the donee; subsequent thereto it is established that the furniture was the property of a third person, the gift is operative in respect of the house alone; for at the time of the gift, the house and furniture were both in fact in the possession of the donor and the delivery thereof was valid; the subse-

(1) *Durr-ul-Mukhtâr*, p. 634.

quent establishment of the right of another to the furniture will not invalidate the gift of the house...." According to the *Ashbâh* the gift of a containing thing is valid when the gift is by a father to his minor child."

"And the gift by a wife to her husband *containing things* is valid according to the approved doctrine for the wife and her property are in the hands of the husband, and consequently the delivery of the same to him is operative. So when a wife makes a gift to her husband of a house in which they both live and she has her effects in it, the gift is valid, and this is the correct doctrine." "In the *Jouhara*(1) a device is given for validating the gift of a thing containing [the donor's property], *viz.*, first to place the latter in the donee's hands by way of deposit and then deliver to him the subject of the gift, that is, the thing *containing* such as a house, in such a case the gift would be valid, for the furniture or effects of the donor being already in the hands of the donee as depositary, it would not interfere with the completion of the gift."(2)

The objection of *mushâ'a* does not apply to things "which do not retain their usefulness after division, such as a small house (*bait*) or a small bath." It is only with regard to objects that are capable of partition without losing their usefulness or deteriorating in their purpose that a division is required to complete the gift. According to the *Bahr-ur-Râik*, "the rule as to what is partible and what is not depends on the fact whether the Kâzi can legally compel one partner who refuses whilst the other seeks partition, to divide the property."

The objection of *Mushâ'a* how far applicable.

The objection on the ground of *mushâ'a* (confusion) applies whether the donee is a partner or a stranger, "but others have said that such a gift is valid in the case of the partner and this is the approved doctrine."(3)

"And it is stated in the *Durrar*(4) if the donor divides the property given and delivers possession the gift is valid, for the objection is removed. But if he delivers possession whilst it is mixed [with his other property], the donee does not acquire an absolute right over it, nor can he deal with it without liability attaching to

In invalid gifts possession avails to establish right of property.

(1) *Jouharat-un-Nayyirèh.*
(2) *Durr-ul-Mukhtâr*, p. 634.
(3) وقيل يجوز لشريكه وهو المختار
(4) *Durrar-ul-Ahkâm.*

him, and the donor's right of disposition remains intact. But it adds from the *Fusûl* that *an invalid gift* (*hibat-ul-fâsida*) avails to establish the right of property by possession and on this is the *fatwa*, and similarly it is stated in the *Bazâzia* contrary to what is mentioned as correct in the *'Imâdia*, that the word *al-fatwa* is stronger than *as-sahîh* (correct) as the author has discussed in detail in dealing with the rest of the rules relating to *mushâ'a*."

"The *shuyû'u* (confusion) which stands in the way of the completion of a gift is one existing at the time (*makârin*) and not one which supervenes afterwards (*târi*)."(1)

The extreme technicality of the doctrine of *mushâ'a* is illustrated by the difference of opinion regarding the validity of the gift of a piece of land with crops standing thereon. "Some lawyers have held that if a right is established by a third person in the crops, it amounts to an original confusion (*shuyû'u makârin*), and therefore vitiates the gift of the land; whilst others, among them the Sadr-ush-shariyèh and Ibn-i-Kamâl(2) have declared that it is only supervenient *shuyû'u* and does not affect the validity of the gift of the land."(3)

The accepted doctrine.

According to the *Moontika*, Abû Yusuf seems to have thought that neither of the married parties can make a valid gift to the other of the house in which they are both residing. But the recognised doctrine is opposed to his view, and it is now settled by judicial decision that such a gift is valid in either case.(4)

"According to Abû Hanîfa, if a person makes a gift of his house to two people it is not valid and (this is his view) regarding all objects which are capable of division, but according to the two disciples the gift is valid."(5) Nor is it valid according to Abû Hanîfa, if the donor defines the shares. But the accepted rule is directly contrary to his view. "If a man make a gift of a moiety of his house in favour of one person and of the other half in favour of another person, and deliver the same to both simultaneously (معاً) it is a valid gift. But if the delivery to one is before the

(1) An example of *supervenient shuyû'u* is furnished by the gift of a *whole* house in which the donor subsequently revokes a part.

(2) The author of the *Fath-ul-Kadîr*.

(3) *Durr-ul-Mukhtâr*, 635; *Radd-ul-Muhtâr*, Vol. IV., p. 781.

(4) *Amina Bibi* v. *Khatija Bibi*, supra.

(5) *Fatâwai Kâzi Khân* (Cal. Ed. II), p. 282.

other, it would not be valid, althougn Abû Hanîfa says it is not valid in either case.''

A *hiba-bi'l-mushâ'a* or a gift of an undivided joint property is not void but only invalid, and possession remedies the defect.(1)

Possession perfects an invalid gift.

The *Majm'aa-ul-Anhar*(2) says "and Y'aakûb Pasha has held, that if a person make a gift to two persons of a thing which is capable of division. that is an invalid *hiba*, but it is not void (*bâtil*) according to Imâm Abû Hanîfa, so if the donees take possession, it establishes property in them according to his saying and the *fatwa* is according to it.'' This view is in exact accordance with what Sadr-ush-Shahîd holds. That a right of property in a share of a joint undivided property comes into existence upon possession being taken of it, is clear from the following passage in the *Majm'aa-ul-Anhar* :—"In the *Jâm'aa-ul-Fusûlain* and *Bazâziah* it is stated that a *hibat-ul-fasid* is perfected by possession, and the *fatwa* is according to this, though some have said the other is correct, *but the word 'fatwa' is stronger than 'correct'*.'' Regarding the words of the author that *mushâ'a* prevents the completeness of a gift, the commentator says, "the reason is that seisin is necessary, so it is mentioned in the *Fusûlain*, but Zailye has held that the gift of such a thing in which the right of the donor is attached is invalid, and in the *'Imâdia* it is stated that the gift is only incomplete; and Hamawi has stated in his commentary on the *Ashbâh* that this doctrine is subject to two sayings, owing to which difference has arisen regarding such *mushâ'a*, which is capable of division, that is, whether such *hiba* is void or only incomplete, *but it is more correct that it is incomplete as is stated in the Bazâziah.* And in the *Durrar-ul-Ahkâm* it is stated that an invalid *hiba* (gift) confers the right of property by possession and the *fatwa* is upon this, so in the *Fusûlain*."

Fatwa.

The *Durr-ul-Mukhtâr* also quotes the passage in the *Durrar*, "in the *Durrar* it is stated from the *Fusûlain* that possession under an invalid gift avails to establish the right of property and the *fatwa* is in accordance with this. And so also it is stated in the *Bazâziah*, which is contrary to what is mentioned as correct

---

(1) Comp. *Mohibullah* v. *Abdul Khalik* [1908], I. L., 30 Cal., 256 *post*.
(2) *Majm'aa-ul-Anhar*, p. 345.

in the *'Imâdia*, but the word *fatwa* is stronger than the word *correct*, &c."(1)

SECTION VII.

THE DOCTRINE OF SEISIN.

BEARING in mind the principle, that *possession validates an imperfect or incomplete gift*, the author of the *Majm'aa-ul-Anhar*(2) defines thus the term *kabz-ul-kâmil* (complete possession.)—" And the meaning of *kabz-ul-kâmil* (complete seisin) with reference to movables depends upon their nature, and with reference to immovable property as is suitable to its nature, as the taking of the key of a house, which is equivalent to its seisin."

Authority to take possession sufficient.

Actual possession, however, does not seem to be necessary to complete the *hiba*. According to the *Durr-ul-Mukhtâr* " to be in a position to take possession is tantamount to taking possession," in other words, to place the donee in a position to take possession is equivalent to delivery of possession. Similarly investing with authority for that purpose is equally sufficient.

" In the *Himâdia* it is stated from the *Jâm'aa-ul-Fatâwa* that if a person make a gift of the crop which is standing on the land, or of the dates which are hanging on the trees, or of the scabbard which is on the scimitar, or of a building, or of *dinârs* which are owing from another person, or of anything which may be measured, and authorise (the donee) to reap it, or to take it down, or to take it off, or to take possession thereof, or to measure it, *and (the donee) has done it*, it is valid by a liberal interpretation."(3) And again, " If the donor himself or his deputy makes a division, or if the donor authorises the donee to make the division with his partner, this makes the gift complete (*kâmil*)."(4) And this opinion is still further enforced by reference to the *Fatâwai Kâzi Khân*. " If a

---

(1) لكن فيها (اى في الدرر) عن الفصولين الهبة الفاسدة تفيد الملك بالقبض و به يفتى و مثله في البزازية على خلاف ما صححه في العمادية لكن لفظ الفتوى آكد من لفظ يصح * p. 634.

(2) P. 342.

(3) *Radd-ul-Muhtâr*, Vol. IV, p. 782.

gift be made to a man, and he appoint two persons to take possession on his behalf, and they both take possession, that is lawful as is stated in the *Fatâwai Kâzi Khân.*"(1)

Doctrine of *Mushâ'a* not applicable to zemindaris.

From the examples given in the Arabian law-works, it can easily be inferred that the doctrine of *mushâ'a* was applicable only to small plots of lands and houses; it does not seem to have been contemplated by the Arabian jurists, that the doctrine should be applicable to specific shares in large estates or what are called in India, zemindaris. At the time when this doctrine was first enunciated among the Hanafîs, there does not appear, from contemporaneous records, to have existed large estates such as are known to us in India. The Arab conquest had broken up the landed proprietary of ancient Persia, and the *Dehkân*, who was a zemindar under the Sassanides, became a mere yeoman or farmer. Under the Arab rule, the land of the country was distributed either among the Arab colonists, or allowed to remain in the hands of the old proprietors on a scale which would prevent their forming combinations to destroy the new government; such seems to have been the economic condition of society about the beginning of the Hanafî Law, and the time when the early jurists of that school flourished. The wealth of the people was chiefly derived from common trade, immense flocks of sheep and goats, large groves and plantations. Apparently, therefore, the doctrine of *mushâ'a* was not intended to apply to large landed estates such as came into existence in later times.

Abedoonnissa v. *Ameeroonnissa.*

The Judicial Committee of the Privy Council, in the case of *Abedoonnissa* v. *Ameeroonnissa*,(2) discussed the question whether the objection of invalidity to a gift on the ground of *mushâ'a* was applicable to shares in a zemindary which themselves paid revenue separately.

"A legal objection to the validity of these gifts was made in the High Court on the ground that the gift of *mushâ'a*, or an undivided part in property capable of partition, was, by Mahommedan Law, invalid. This point appears to have been taken for

---

(1) فان قسمه الواهب بنفسه او نائبه او امر الموهوب له بان يقسم مع شريكه كل ذلک تتم به الهبة * Delivery of possession (*taslîm*) is presumed.
و كل، الموهوب له رجلين بقبض الدار فقبضهما جاز—خانيه *

(2) Supra.

the first time in the High Court, and was argued at this Bar. That a rule of this kind does exist in Mahommedan Law with regard to some subjects of gift is plain. The *Hedâya* gives the two reasons on which it is founded : *First*, that complete seisin being a necessary condition in cases of gift, and this being impracticable with respect to an indefinite part of a divisible thing, the condition cannot be performed ; and, *secondly*, because it would throw a burden on the donor, he had not engaged for, *viz.*, to make a division. (See Book XXX, c. i, 3 vol., 293). Instances are given by the writers of undivided things which cannot be given, such as fruit unplucked from the tree, and crops unsevered from the land. It is obvious that with regard to things of this nature separate possession cannot be given in their undivided state, and confusion might thus be created between donor and donee which the law will not allow."

"In the present case the subjects of the gifts are definite shares in certain zemindaris, the nature of the right in them being defined and regulated by the public Acts of the British Government."

"The High Court, after stating that the shares were, for revenue purposes, distinct estates, each having a separate number in the Collector's books, and each being liable to the Government only for its own separately assessed revenue, and further that the proprietor collected a definite share of the rents from the ryots, and had a right to this definite share and no more, held that the rule of the Mahommedan Law did not apply to property of that description."

"In their Lordship's opinion this view of the High Court is correct. The principle of the rule and the reasons on which it is founded do not in their judgment apply to property of the peculiar description of these definite shares in zemindaris, which are in their nature separate estates with separate and defined rents. It was insisted by Mr. Leith that the land itself being undivided, and the owners of the shares entitled to require partition of it, the property remained *mushâ a.* But although this right may exist, the shares in zemindaris appear to their Lordships to be, from the special legislation relating to them, in themselves and before any partition of the land, definite estates, capable of distinct enjoyment by perception of the separate and defined rents belonging to them, and therefore not falling within the principle and reason of the law relating to *mushâ'a.*" And the same principle was enunciated in the case of *Shaikh Mohammad Mumtaz Ahmad* v. *Zubaïda Jan.*(1)

When a gift *bi'l-mushâ'a* is made of property that does not admit of partition, it is a condition of the gift that the quantity be known or specified,(2) for if one were to give his share, the share being unknown, the gift would not be lawful as ignorance of the share might lead to disputes.(3) In the case of *Jaffar Khan* v. *Hubshee Bibi*,(4) it was held by the Sudder Court, that a gift of land forming a part of joint property, to be valid, must be distinct, and the boundaries and extent of the property given be known. The older rulings of the Sudder Court, however, it must be admitted, gave effect to the objection based on the ground of *mushâ'a* to an extent perhaps not warranted by the recognised rules of the Mahommedan Law.(5) But the more recent decisions of the High Courts of Calcutta and Allahabad have taken a broader view of the question, and more in accordance with the principles enunciated in modern works like the *Durr-ul-Mukhtâr*, the *Majm'aa-ul-Anhar* and the *Radd-ul-Muhtâr*. In the case of *Jewan Buksh* v. *Imtiaz Begum*,(6) the daughter of a deceased Mahommedan sued to set aside a gift of her father's estate made by him during his lifetime to the defendant his eldest son, and for possession of her share. It appeared that the gift to the defendant by the father comprised, amongst other properties, one-third share in certain joint and undivided zemindary villages. As the holder of these shares, the defendant's father was entitled to a one-third share of the profits of the villages after payment of the Government revenue, village expenses and costs of collection. The plaintiff contended that the gift of these shares was invalid on the ground of *mushâ'a*. The High Court held, that the gift of a defined share of landed estates was not open to the objection of *mushâ'a*, a defined share in a landed estate being separate property.

Jaffar Khan v. *Hubshee Bibi.*

Jewan Buksh v. *Imtiaz Begum.*

(1) [1887], L. R., 16 I. A., p. 205; s. c., I. L., 11 All., 460.

(2) *Sahiba Begum* v. *Atchamaun and others*, 4 Mad. Reports, 115.

(3) *Fátáwai-Alamgiri*, IV, p. 523.

(4) 1 Sel. Reports, 12.

(5) *Meer Abdul Kureem* v. *Musst. Fuckrunnissa Begum*, 3 Sel. Reports, 44 note; *Syud Shah Basit Ally* v. *Syed Shah Imam-ud-din*, 3 Sel. Reports, 176, *Musst. Khanum Jaun* v. *Musst. Jaun Bibee*, 4 Sel. Reports, 210.

(6) [1882] I. L., 2 All., 93.

Kasim Hussain and another v. Sharif-unnissa.

In *Kasim Hussain and another* v. *Sharif-un-nissa,*(1) in which the gift was by one person to two donees, the *hiba-nâma* was in the following terms :—

"I, Bechi, do hereby declare that one-twelfth *muafi* share, and a dwelling-house containing a room facing north and east, and five yards of land in front thereof, two halls (*dalan*) facing the east, a door, a privy, a court-yard and a staircase constitute my ancestral property, and are held by me under a partition deed. I have made *Kasim Hussain* and *Nazim Hussain* (defendants) absolute owners of the above property together with all its boundaries, '*asli*' and '*dakhili*' rights, whether large or small, and appertaining to it. The property is free from the right of any one else and unincumbered by hypothecation, charge, gift, sale or mortgage. There is nothing to prevent the validity of the transfer, and the property is in my exclusive possession up to this day, and I have placed them in proprietary possession thereof. Neither I nor my heirs have any right or interest left in it. I have substituted (*Kasim Hussain* and *Nazim Hussain*) on the following terms :—During my lifetime the income of the property shall remain under my control; after my death they shall become absolute proprietors thereof in equal shares, and apply its income to meet their necessary expenses; they shall not have power at any time to transfer or create a charge upon the property; should they directly or indirectly transfer the property, such transfer shall be invalid in Court in face of this instrument."

Upon a suit by one of her heirs, two grounds were taken to set aside the deed : *first*, that it was a will, and therefore invalid as regards two-thirds, being without the consent of heirs ; *second*, that the gift was bad on account of *mushâ'a.* With reference to the *first* objection, the learned Judges held as follows :—

"The deed purports to transfer the title in the donor's share in the *muafi* estate to the defendants and constitutes them proprietors but reserves to the donor the income for life. A gift of specific shares is not open to the objection under Mahommedan Law, and the gift is not otherwise void by reason of the condition for reserving to the donor the profits either for want of the seisin required by Mahommedan Law of the property given, or in consequence of the

(1) [1883] I. L., 5 All., 285.

condition vitiating the gift. It was held by the Privy Council in *Nawab Umjad Ally Khan* v. *Mohumdee Begum*,(1) that though the transfer of a legal title will satisfy that provision of the Mahommedan Law which relates to the point of seisin in its legal and technical sense, yet that alone will not suffice when no intention exists to transfer the beneficial ownership, either present or future, but when there is real transfer of property by a donor in his lifetime under the Mahommedan Law, reserving not the dominion over the *corpus* of the property, nor any share of dominion over the *corpus*, but simply stipulating for, and obtaining a right to the recurring produce during his lifetime, there will be a complete gift by Mahommedan Law. Their Lordships observe :—

'The text of the *Hedâya* seems to include the very proposition and to negative it. The thing to be returned is not identical but something different. See *Hedâya*, Chap. Gifts, Vol. III, Book XXX, p. 294, where the objection being raised that a participation of property in the thing given invalidates the gift, the answer is, the donor is subjected to a participation in a thing which is not the subject of his grant, namely, the use of the whole indivisible article, for his gift related to the substance of the article not to the use of it.'

"In that case the subject of the gift was Government Promissory Notes, the interest of which had been reserved by the donor, and their Lordships go on to say :—'Again, if the agreement for the reservation of the interest to the father for his life be treated as a repugnant condition, repugnant to the whole enjoyment by the donee—here the Mahommedan Law defeats not the grant but the condition, *Hedâya*, Chap. Gifts, Vol. III, Book XXX, p. 307.' The mere reservation of the income of the estate will not therefore vitiate the gift, and the Subordinate Judge's finding in this respect is erroneous. The deed contained a condition against alienation, but that will not vitiate the gift."

With reference to the second ground of objection the learned Judge said as follows :—

"The appellant's objection as to the finding in respect of the stair-case, door and privy is also valid. This portion of the gift has been disallowed, because the above things are undivided."

(1) [1867] 11 M. I. A., 517.

"On this subject, the *Hedâya* on 'Gifts,' Book XXX, Ch. I is as follows :—'A gift of part of a thing which is capable of division is not valid, unless the said part be divided off, and separated from the property of the donor, but the gift of part of an indivisible thing is valid.' The things referred to appear to be common to the occupants of the premises which in other respects were divided, and are incapable of division, and the donor gave all her interest in them to the donees, the gift is not, in consequence, invalid. It is obviously absurd to give effect to the gift in respect of a house, and disallow all means of ingress and egress."

Doctrine of *Mushâ'a*—confusion.

In the case of *Mullick Abdul Guffoor* v. *Musst. Maleka*,(1) the Chief Justice, dealing with the argument urged on behalf of the appellant that the gift was bad on the ground of *mushâ'a*, held as follows :—"It is urged : (*a*) that a gift of an undivided share in any property is invalid because of *mushâ'a*, or confusion, on the part of the *donor ;* and (*b*) that a gift of property to two donees without first separating and dividing their shares is bad, because of confusion on the part of the *donees*."

"But it must be borne in mind that this rule applies only to those subjects of gift, which are capable of partition. See the *Hedâya*, Vol. III, *Book on Gifts*, p. 293, where the rule laid down is to the effect that—'A gift is not valid of *what admits of division* unless separated and divided.' See also *Baillie's Mahommedan Law*, 2nd Ed., p. 520 ; *Fatâwa-i-Alamgiri, Book on Gifts*, p. 521; *Macnaughten's Mahommedan Law*, p. 201."

"The rule, therefore, applies only to gifts of such property as is capable of division ; whereas, reversionary interests or *malikana* or other *choses in action*, are not capable of division."

"It is said that one main reason for this rule, which applies only to gifts, and not to sales, is to protect a man's heirs against gifts made in defeasance of their rights. We were referred to certain texts which apparently favoured that view ; and it is also probable that another reason for the rule was to protect creditors against fraudulent gifts made by debtors, it being a well-known test of the *bonâ fides* of a gift, whether possession of the thing given has passed to the donee."

"It has been urged upon us, very strongly, that, according to this rule of *mushâ'a*, the gift, which was made to the defendants in

(1) Supra.

his case. is wholly void, because, the gift being of lands, no partition of such lands was made; and even supposing the gift to be valid, as regards the zemindari properties which were let out on lease, it would still be invalid as regards the house-property, gardens, sheds, &c., which are not shown to have been let out on lease, and which were capable therefore of actual partition."

"We think, however, that this objection is not well-founded as regards any part of the property in question."

"As regards the zemindaris, the estate of the donor, as we have seen, was an interest in reversion, and the property which was transferred by the gift of these zemindaries was merely that sort of estate which entitled the donees to receive the rents and profits. We find from the evidence of the defendants (which was so clear upon this point that the Judge in the Court below desired to hear no more than that of the first two witnesses), that during Kaniz Fatima's lifetime, she and Muleka were in separate collection of the rents, and that immediately upon the gift being made the possession was transferred, in the only way in which it could be transferred, to the two donees."

Declaration that possession had been given binding on heirs

A formal and solemn declaration by the donor that he had complied with all the requirements of the law in perfecting the gift would be binding evidence of delivery of possession.

This principle was accepted in the case of *Shaikh Muhammad Mumtaz Ahmad* v. *Zubaida Jan*(1) where their Lordships of the Privy Council held that a declaration by the donor in the deed of gift that possession had been given bound his heirs.

When two persons own a property jointly, either sharer may, under the Hanafî Law, give his share to the other, without the formality of a delivery of possession or any objection founded on the ground of *mushâ'a*. In the case of *Mahomed Bukhsh Khan* v. *Hosseini Bibi*(2), the Judicial Committee of the Privy Council held that where a property is held by several co-sharers any one of them may give his share to any one of the other co-

(1) [1887] L. R., 16 I. A., 205, supra. See also *Mohib-ullah* v. *Abdul Khalik* [1908] I. L., 30 All., 250, where it was held that the gift of *mushâ'a* or joint undivided property is valid if the donee obtains possession.

(2) [1887] L. R., 15 I. A., 81.

sharers, and that such a gift would not be open to the objection of *mushâ'a*.

To the same fear that confusion in the enjoyment of undivided property may lead to disputes among joint owners, is due the formulation by the ancient jurists of the doctrine that "if a father were to make a gift of a house to two of his sons, one of whom is a minor in his charge, it would be an invalid *hiba* although if they were both adults, and he delivered possession to both of them it would be valid, for there would be no confusion either at the time of the contract or at the time of possession, for when one is a minor the father himself becomes entitled to the possession of the share given to the infant, consequently there will arise *shuyû'u* at the time of possession."(1)

Gift to two persons conjointly.

In the section on the "*hiba* of *mushâ'a*" in the *Fatâwai Kâzi Khan* the principle relating to gifts by one person to two or more donees is thus stated :—"If a man were to give to another who is not a partner his share in something which is partible, such as a house, land or which is capable of being measured or weighed, in such a case the gift is not valid according to all [the Imâms] but when he makes the gift to his partner it is not valid according to us, but is valid according to Abû Laila (may the peace, &c.). And if he were to make a gift of his house to two people, it is not valid according to Abû Hanîfa (may the peace, &c.), and so with reference to all things partible, *but it is valid according to his disciples* (may the peace, &c.); and if he mortgages a house with two men it is valid according to all; and similarly if he leases it to two people. And if he gives half of his house to one person and half to another and delivers the same to both *together* (معا) the gift is valid; but if he were to deliver to one first and then to the other it would not be valid—although Abû Hanîfa says it would not be valid in either case (2) .... Tahâwi and 'Ussâm (may the peace, &c.) have laid down that possession establishes the right of property in invalid gifts, and this doctrine has been adopted by several of our doctors (may the peace, &c.)"(3)

---

(1) *Fatâwai Kâzi Khan* (Cal. Ed., 1835). Vol. IV, p. 177.
(2) *Ibid*, p. 172.
(3) *Ibid*, p. 174.

"Mere *emptying*(1) is not sufficient possession in an invalid gift, as it is in an invalid sale, although in a valid gift it is according to Mohammed."

"When the thing given is not present, the authority to take possession is sufficient."

This doctrine is stated more widely in the *Durr-ul-Mukhtâr* :— "I [*i.e.*, the author](2) have limited [the validity of the gift by one person to two] to two adults because if the donor were to make a gift to an adult person and to a minor who is in the charge of this adult person or to his (the donor's) minor and adult sons the gift would not be valid by consensus."

In the *Bahr-ur-Râik* and the *Manah-ul-Ghuffâr* the passage bearing on the subject runs thus :—"When a person makes a gift to an adult and an infant (*saghîr*) and the *saghîr* is in his charge,"(3) "and in both the works," says Tahtâwi, "the reason of the doctrine, as stated in the *Muhît*, is mentioned to be that at the time of the gift the donor takes seisin of the minor's share, thus the other part becomes confused with it; this proves that the pronoun 'his' applies to the donor, contrary to what the commentator [the author of the *Durr-ul-Mukhtâr*] has stated"

The author of the *Radd-ul-Muhtâr* takes the same view regarding the applicability of the pronoun "his." "And the correct principle is that the minor is in the charge of the donor as is proved by the statements in the *Bahr*, etc."(4)

After referring to the statement in the *Durr-ul-Mukhtâr* he goes on to add, "and the approved doctrine is, if the donees are both minors in the charge of the donor, the gift is valid according to the Disciples [Abû Yusuf and Mohammed], and what is stated in the *Bazâzia* establishes it. And I say that it would have been preferable not to impose this limitation,(5) for according to

(1) *Takhlieh, retirement* or *emptying* means, in this connection, merely removing the obstruction to taking possession, *e.g.*, a man makes a gift of a house and vacates it, that amounts to *takhlieh*; but if he does not place the donee in actual possession it is not regarded as sufficient *complete* possession in the case of an invalid gift.

(2) In the commentaries he himself is called the commentator, for he was commenting on the *Tanwîr-ul-Absâr*.

(3) والصغير في عياله

(4) *Radd-ul-Muhtâr*, Vol. IV, p. 785.

(5) Limiting the validity of a gift to two adults.

Abû Hanîfa there is no difference between two adults, or two minors or an adult and a minor; and he holds that the objection(1) is applicable to all. It follows, therefore, that there is no difference in the donees being both adults or both minors, or an adult and a minor. And the Disciples have differed from him regarding the first two (cases) as is stated in Ramli.''(2)

Gift to an adult and a minor conjointly.

Then, after quoting the passage already given from the *Fatâwai Kâzi Khan*, the author of the *Radd-ul-Muhtâr* resumes his comment on the *Durr-ul-Mukhtâr*, "His saying, 'that it would not be valid'—the device (*al-hîla*) to cure this is to make over the house to the adult, and then make a gift to both, and this is what is stated in the *Bazâziah*....and a gift to two minors would be valid as there is no reason for preference whether one obtains possession before the other, for the guardian of both is one, so that at the time of possession there is no *shuyû'u*. And the statement in the *Khâniëh* (*Fatâwai Kâzi Khan*) supports this view, and it is 'if a person were to say this house of mine is for my infant children it would be invalid for he does not mention the children.' The inference from this is that if he had indicated the children the gift would have been valid. And I have seen in the *Ankarawiëh*(3) stated from the *Bazâziah* that in the case of a gift to an adult and a minor jointly the device [to make it valid] is to entrust the house to the adult and then to make a gift of the whole to both.''(4)

It is clear, therefore, that according to the doctrines actually in force the original strictness of the technical rule relating to *mushâ'a* has been considerably cut down.

E.G.: (*a*) Although a gift of property capable of division or partition to two or more persons is not valid, yet if they take possession under the authority of the donor it vests in them the right of property.

(*b*) Authority to take possession or placing the donees in a position to take possession is equivalent to delivery of possession.

(*c*) Partition by the donees themselves after possession is sufficient to validate the gift.

(*d*) A gift to two persons one of whom is a minor in charge of the donor is valid.

---

(1) *Shuyû'u.*

(2) *Radd-ul-Muhtâr*, Vol. IV, p. 785.

(3) *Fatâwai-Ankarawiëh.*

(4) *Radd-ul-Muhtâr*, Vol. IV, p. 786.

The Allahabad High Court appears to have misapprehended the principle relating to a joint gift to an adult and a minor in the case of *Nizam-ud-din* v. *Zabida Bibi*.(1)

Nizam-ud-din v. Zabida Bibi.

In this case it appeared that one Sheikh Kadir Buksh devised certain property amounting to a one-fourth share of his estate to his eldest son Zahir-ud-din, subject, however, to the reservation, that a portion of the property situate on the north side of the River Ravi, and consisting of "lakheraj lands should pass on the testator's death to Zahir-ud-din, but that the remainder situate on the south of the river should be held and possessed by the testator's youngest son Aman-ullah for the purpose of collecting and paying the revenue due on both portions without any rendition of accounts, until such time as a competent son should be born to Zahir-ud-din," the reason assigned being that Zahir-ud-din wa, unfit to look after the lands paying revenue to Government. On the death of their father, Zahir-ud-din and Aman-ullah held and possessed the property above-mentioned in accordance with the will of the testator. On the 1st of September 1864, Zahir-ud-din executed a deed of gift of the one-fifth share devised to him in favour of two of his sons, Nizam-ud-din and Sadr-ud-din, a minor. No mention was made in the deed as to the respective shares of the brothers, or as to the manner in which the property was to be held or divided. The deed was duly registered, and mutation of names was effected in respect of the lands on the north of the River Ravi, in the same year. Zahir-ud-din died in 1869, leaving several daughters and a minor son, born after the execution of the deed of gift in favour of Nizam-ud-din and Sadr-ud-din, never having held possession of the property on the south side of the Ravi, which had remained in the possession of Aman-ullah and his son, who rendered no accounts of profits to Zahir-ud-din, and it was not till the year 1871 that the donees obtained possession. With regard to the property on the north bank of the Ravi, it appeared that the donees had been put into immediate possession. Upon a suit instituted by Zabida Bibi, one of Zahir-ud-din's daughters, to recover the share of the property left by her father to which she was entitled under the Mahommedan Law, by the cancelment of the deed of gift, the First Court held that the deed was valid, the property given being therein

---

(1) 6 N.-W. P., H. C. Reports, p. 538.

Nizam-ud-din v. Zabida Bibi—(contd.)

defined and specified. The Lower Appellate Court reversed the decree and remanded the case for the determination of the amount of the mesne profits due to the plaintiff, holding that the deed was, under Mahommedan Law, invalid, as the gift had been made without division or specification of the respective shares of the donees and as the donees had not obtained possession of a portion of the property, *viz.*, that situate on the south of the River Ravi, till after the decease of the donor. The Court, however, did not distinctly determine whether the deed had operated immediately in respect of the portion lying on the north of the river. It found that there were no good reasons for thinking the donor insane, or even a simpleton, although his father had refused to allow him to manage lands paying revenue. In special appeal, the principal grounds were to the effect that the deed of gift was *not* invalid under the Mahommedan Law, as the donees had received such possession as the donor could grant of the lands on the south of the Ravi and had received actual possession of those on the north, and, *although a gift of undivided property was contrary to that law, yet, as the donees had obtained possession, the gift was not invalid.*

The High Court held as follows :—

"In this case the claim of the plaintiff to a daughter's share in the estate left by her father, Zahir-ud-din, is resisted on the ground of a deed of gift executed by him, a somewhat weak person, in favcur of the appellants, his sons, in 1864. Another son was born to him after that date, so that the effect of the deed is to exclude from inheritance, for no sufficient apparent cause, the younger son as well as several daughters. The Court of First Instance, holding the deed to be valid, dismissed the claim. The Lower Appellate Court considered the deed to be invalid for three reasons : (1) that the property, the subject of the gift, being capable of partition, had not been divided between the two donees ; (2) that part of it was not at the time of the execution of the deed in the possession of the donor himself ; and (3) could not therefore be transferred by him to them. As to the other portion of the property, which was admittedly in his possession at that time, the Lower Courts have not enquired or found, so carefully as they should have done, whether the deed took effect before Zahir-ud-din's death. If it operated immediately in respect of the property on the north side of the River Ravi, and the opinion

Nizam-ud-din v. *Zabida Bibi*—(concld.)

of the Lower Courts seems to lean to this view, which is also supported by good *primâ facie* evidence we should not be able to allow that it had failed to operate in respect of the property on the south side of the same river. The latter portion of the property was in the charge of a trustee, who was bound to pay out of its profits the whole of the revenue assessed on both portions. The person or persons in possession of the northern portion could scarcely be deemed to be out of possession of, and not to derive any benefit from, the other portion which paid the revenue due from him or them. At all events the donor gave to the donees such possession as he himself had, and could give, of the southern portion. But, although the soundness of the 2nd and 3rd reasons of the Judge's decision may be doubted, we are not prepared to say that his first reason is wrong. The general rule of the Mahommedan Law is that anything which is capable of division, when given to two persons, should be divided by the donor at the time of the gift, or immediately subsequent thereto and prior to the delivery to the donees, in order that the objection of confusion may be avoided and full and complete seisin obtained. But it is contended on behalf of the appellants that, although the gift of undivided property is contrary to law, it is not, if the donees have obtained possession of it, absolutely invalid. This contention is supported by the opinion of the two disciples, whilst it is opposed to that of Hanîfa. But it appears from a passage in the *Durr-ul-Mukhtâr* and a passage in the *Fatâwai-Alamgiri*, that in a special case like the present in which one of two donees is an adult, and the other an infant son, a gift of undivided property is absolutely invalid, not merely *fâsid* but *bâtil*. The reason of this rule is explained, and although the rule may, it is intimated, be evaded by a particular device, which is not quite clearly intelligible, there is no pretence that such device was employed by the parties to the deed in question in this case."

"The weight of authority appears then to be in favour of the conclusion at which the Lower Appellate Court has arrived, and that conclusion may be upheld upon the basis of Mahommedan Law. Had it been otherwise, it might have been our duty to consider whether we were bound strictly to apply Mahommedan Law to the case, or to deal with, and dispose of it according to the principles of equity, justice, and good conscience. Without entering upon such a discussion, we may content ourselves with remarking that, as the deed is found to be invalid under Mahommedan Law, justice, equity and good conscience do not, under the circumstances to which we have adverted, require us to maintain it. Twelve years have not elapsed since it was executed, and the heirs of Zahir-ud-din, who might, were he still alive, set it aside as not binding on himself, are fully competent to impugn its validity."

It is somewhat difficult to follow the reasoning in the latter portion of the judgment, and it would seem that the reason upon which the archaic Hanafî doctrine is founded, has been, to a considerable extent, missed. There can be no question that the principle owed its origin, as has already been pointed out, to the fear displayed by Hanafî lawyers regarding the enjoyment of a joint undivided property.

Regarding the validity, according to the Disciples, of a gift to two donees, one of whom is an adult and the other a minor, *but who is not in the guardianship of the donor*, there is no dispute. For in such a case the right to the possession of the minor donee's share devolves on a person other than the donor, and according to Abû Yusuf and Mohammed the defect of "confusion" does not arise. It is only when the minor donee is in the charge of the donor himself that the difficulty is supposed to arise.

Gift to an infant and an adult jointly.

For example, when a gift is made jointly to an infant and an adult son, the father would, *quâ* guardian, remain in possession of the infant son's share, whereas the adult son would take possession of the share given to him. t was supposed that under such circumstances the enjoyment of the property by the two donees would be likely to create confusion, not only among themselves, but also among them and the donor. And this confusion and difficulty would be enhanced, in case there happened to be creditors of the father, who alleged that the gift was in fraud of them. Looked at from this point of view, it would appear extremely probable the principle was originally framed, partly with the object of protecting creditors and partly with the object of avoiding all questions, on the part of the donor or his representatives, as to the completeness of the transaction. The donee takes under an act of bounty or mere *tabarr'u* (تبرع). As a mere volunteer, his title to the gift is not perfected, until the donor has completely manifested his intention to vest the property in him.(1) This intention

(1) Comp. *Kekewich* v. *Manning*, 1 De G. M. & G., p. 176.

is evidenced by his placing the donee in possession of the subject of the gift or by authorising him to take possession of it, and by so differentiating it from his other properties or those belonging to his co-sharers, as to leave no room for confusion. Until this is done there is no *kabz-ul-kâmil*, and the gift is a mere inchoate act of bounty. If the donee is an infant, the necessary possession should be delivered to his guardian.(1) This apparently was the reasoning on which the early lawyers based their views.

Mode of making a valid gift to an adult and a minor.

The Hanafî rule on this point appears to have undergone two modifications. Its extreme rigidity came to be recognised as early as the 14th century of the Christian era when the *Bazâzia* was compiled, and a procedure was laid down for avoiding the objection of "confusion," *viz.*, that *the entire property should be consigned to the adult, and then a gift of it made to both. In such a case, the adult donee would become a trustee for the minor, and possession being already vested in him as depositary, the objection of shuyû'u would not apply as to the gift of the share of the minor.*

The opinions of the legists developed still further, and by the time the *Radd-ul-Muhtâr* was compiled in the 17th century, it was plainly declared that "there was no difference between a gift to two adults or to two minors or to an adult and a minor jointly."(2)

It will thus be seen that even in its inception the rule did not regard there was any inherent illegality to a joint gift to a minor and an adult; the objection had its origin in a desire to prevent disputes. Where the interests of the two were sufficiently specified, and there could be no apprehension of confusion, the doctrine against *shuyû'u* did not apply.

Considering that in India the law regarding registration and mutation of names in respect of dispositions of immovable property coupled with other statutory provisions for evidencing *bonâ fide* transfers affords a sufficient guarantee against apprehensions of conflict in its enjoyment, the reason of the old rule seems to be non-existent.

The objection of *shuyû'u* only renders the gift invalid, but not void.

The objection of shuyû'u only renders the gift invalid, but not void. There is considerable difference between a *hiba* which is *bâtil*, that is, null and void, and a *hiba* which is *fâsid* or *ghair mu-*

(1) In the case of *Wajit Ali* v. *Abdool Ali* (Weekly Rep. 1864, p. 121), the Calcutta High Court held that the rule of *mushâ'a* does not apply to a gift by a father to a minor son.

(2) See *ante*, p. 100.

kammal, which is not complete or merely invalid. "According to the *Bazâzia*, an invalid gift is validated by possession and *decisions are passed according to this doctrine, and not the doctrine in the 'Imâdia.*" Accordingly, if a gift is to two individuals, possession taken by both removes its invalidity. In a gift of *mushâ'a* which is partible, if division is effected by the donees subsequent to the donation, it is valid.(1)

A gift of moiety of a house (which otherwise would be bad for *mushâ'a*) may validly be effected in this way (according to the *Bazâzia*), that is, the donor should sell it first at a fixed price, and then absolve the debtor of the debt, that is, the price.(2)

As already stated *shuyû'u* or confusion, in order to render a gift invalid, must exist at the time of the gift, and not be supervenient, and it must be such as is recognised by the law.(3)

The objection of indefiniteness carried to an extreme would often prevent the donee or donees from availing themselves of the power to take possession of the property, and thereby imparting to the act of gift that validity which was wanting to it initially. In order to obviate the difficulty arising from such a contingency the Arabian lawyers have devised the doctrine of *tahlîl*, which literally means "rendering lawful," but which, with reference to the subject under review, means the *legalisation* on the part of the donor, of the enjoyment of the subject-matter of the gift by the donee and thus rendering it a valid donation. The following examples will throw sufficient light on this branch of the law relating to gifts.(4)

The doctrine of *Tahlîl*.

"If a person were to say to another, 'Whatever of my property thou eatest, it is lawful for thee,' it would be lawful for the latter to eat thereof, but should there be any indication of dispute, he should not do so ; so it is stated in the *Multeka*."

"If a person were to say to another, 'Whoever has eaten out of my property, it is lawful for him,' the *Fatwa* is that it is lawful ; so in the *Sirâjia*."

"In a tradition reported by Ibn Makâtil, it is declared to be lawful for every person, whether rich or poor, to eat of the fruit

---

(1) *Radd-ul-Muhtâr*, Vol. IV, p. 783.

(2) *Ibid.*

(3) *Ibid.*

(4) *Fatâwai Alamgiri*, IV, p. 531.

of a tree, when the owner has said, 'it is lawful for all persons to eat of my tree;' so in the *Fatâwa-ul-'Itâbia.*"

Doctrine of *tahlîl* or legalisation —(contd.)

"If a person were to say to another, 'Make it lawful for me all the rights which thou possessest against me,' and he does so and discharges the speaker, in that case, if the owner was aware of his rights, then the speaker will be legally and conscientiously discharged. If, however, the *Sâhib-ul-hakk* (the owner of the rights) was not aware of his rights, the speaker will be discharged only legally. But Abû Yusuf holds that he will be discharged in conscience also, and the *Fatwa* is on this; so in the *Khulâsa.*"

"Where something belonging to one person was in the hands of another, who mixed it with his own goods, and believing fully that he would not be able to distinguish it from them, he asks the owner of the thing to make it lawful to him and he does so, it is lawful. But if he subsequently finds it, he must return it; so in the *Kinia.*"

"If a person were to say to another, 'It is lawful for thee to take from my property whatever thou findest and whatever thou likest;' according to Abû Yusuf this is restricted to *dirhems* and *dinârs*. Therefore it will not be lawful for him to take lands or trees or almonds or cow or goat; so in the *Bahîria* and *Khulâsa.*"

"If a person were to declare that he had made it lawful for another to eat of his *mâl;* and the latter person does not know it, —in such a case, if he were to eat of it, it would not be lawful, and it is stated in the *Muhît-i-Sarakhsi* and the *Tâtâr Khânièh*, that it is not lawful for him to eat thereof, until he knew of the permission."

"One man is a debtor of another, who is not aware of the amount of the debt; and the debtor says to him 'discharge me from what I owe thee'; and he replies, 'I discharge thee in both worlds'; the jurist Nasîr says that the debtor will be discharged only to the extent of the amount which the creditor believed the debtor owed him. But Mohammed ibn Sulma says that he will be discharged to the full extent of his debt; and the Jurist Abu'l Lais and others say that what Ibn Sulma has said is the decision of the Kâzi, and the saying of Nasîr has reference to the future world; so in the *Zakhîra.*"

"If a man were to say to another, 'It is lawful for thee what thou hast eaten of my property, or taken or given,' in such a case, the eating is lawful, but not the taking or giving; so in the *Sirâj-ul-Wâhâj.*"

* * * * * * * * * * *

"If a person turn loose a sick animal, saying, that whoever should take and use it, it would become his, and another man does take and use the beast, it would become lawfully his property. This is the *dictum* of Abu'l Kâsim."

"If a domesticated bird is let loose, it is in the position of a sick animal."

"If a person were to usurp a piece of property and the rightful owner were to say, 'I have made all my rights *halâl* to him,' the jurists of Balkh hold, that in this case the usurper is absolved from the liability for damages and not from the restoration of the specific property; so in the *Kinia.* It is, however, reported from Mohammed, that if one is liable to another for some property, and the owner says, 'I have made it *halâl* for thee,' it is a *hiba;* but if he had said *tahlîl*, it would be a discharge; so in the *Zakhîra.*"

"If a person were to say, 'I have made lawful (my debts) to all my debtors' this will be a discharge to the debtors, but not to a lessee; so in the *Khulâsa.*'"

* * * * * * * * * * *

"If a man were to say to his agent (*wakîl*), it is lawful for thee to 'eat' of my property from one dirhem to a hundred dirhems, it will not be lawful to the *wakîl* to take at once a hundred or fifty dirhems, but only so much as is reasonably necessary for his maintenance; so in the *Multeka.*"

Objection of *mushâ'a* not applicable to property devolving by inheritance.

It must be noted that the technical doctrine of *mushâ'a*, which owed its origin to a somewhat strained conception of the law relating to seizin and the undisturbed enjoyment of property, does not apply to property devolving by right of inheritance. But evidently a contention of that nature appears to have been raised before the Judicial Committee in *Ibrahim Golam Ariff* v. *Saiboo*.(1) In this case their Lordships say "assuming the law of *mushâ'a* which prohibits gifts of undivided shares of divisible property, applies to the succession of Mahommedans who reside in Rangoon, it does not apply to a gift by will of undivided shares in freehold land and of shares in Companies."

(1) [1907] L. R., 34 I. A., 167.

With reference to the view expressed in this case it is to be observed that the rule of *mushâ'a* does not amount to a prohibition of such gifts ; it only declares that they are invalid, which only means that the donor may at any time revoke the donation until possession has been taken by the donee. As "seisin perfects an invalid gift," the right of the donor's heirs to question the validity of a gift of an undivided share of a divisible property of which possession was delivered and taken does not seem to have been in the contemplation of any Mussulman jurist. Besides, shares in Companies hardly come within the category of divisible property in Mussulman Law.

Customary law among the Mahommedans of Southern India.

In Southern India a large number of the converts to Islâm have preserved many of their customs and institutions—especially the *tarwad* which is principally a joint family system based on the matriarchate. Among these people the Mussulman Law has been subjected to considerable modification. For example, in a gift made by a Mussulman governed by the *Maruma-Kattayan* (customary) law in favour of his wife and daughter and their female descendants, the condition excluding males has been held to be invalid.(1)

Similarly, where a gift is made by a Mussulman husband governed by the *Maruma-Kattayan* law to his wife, who is governed by the same law, and to her children, it has been held that the property becomes the exclusive property of the donees with the incidents of property subject to the *Maruma-Kattayan* law and that on the death of the mother it does not pass to her heirs under the Mahommedan Law, although the donation does not of itself constitute the mother and her children a separate *tarwad*.(2)

The marked divergence between the customary and the personal law is easily observable.

(1) *Mooriyat* v. *Kunhambi* [1908], I. L., 31 Mad., 315.
(2) *Pathumina* v. *Abdulla Haji* [1907], I. L., 31 Mad., 228.

CHAPTER II.

FORMALITIES RELATIVE TO GIFTS.

SECTION I.

WORDS OF CONSTITUTION.

Formalities relative to a gift.

GIFTS, under the Mahommedan Law, are not subject to any formality, or any special publicity; they can be made either verbally or in writing. But, when a gift of immovable property is made in writing in India, the provisions of the Indian Stamp and Registration Acts have to be complied with.

In order to create a gift, it is not necessary to make use of any express terms. Even where the declaration and acceptance are not expressed in words, so long as the intention is evidenced by conduct it would be sufficient.

"In the *Khazânat-ul-Fatâwa* it is stated that when a person makes over a thing to his son who deals with it, it still remains the property of the father, unless there is an indication that he made the son its owner (*i.e.*, transferred the ownership to him). I say, that the inference from this is that it is not a condition to use express words of declaration and acceptance, but that circumstances (قراین) indicating the intention to transfer ownership are sufficient. For example, a man gives a thing to a *fakîr* (a beggar), and he takes it, and neither of them use a word [it is enough]; similarly is the case with presents and such like."(1)

If the gift is made in writing or verbally, any word by which it may be presumed that the donor intended to give the substance

---

(1) و في خزانة الفتاوي اذا دفع لابنه مالا فتصرف فيه الابن يكون للاب الا اذا دلت دلالة التمليک ...... قلت فقد افاد ان التلفظ بالايجاب و القبول لا يشترط بل تكفي القرائن الدالة على التمليک كمن دفع لفقير شئيا و قبضه ولم يتلفظ واحد من هما بشيء و كذا يقع في الهدية و نحوها *

Radd-ul-Muhtâr, IV, p. 777.

of the thing, would convey the property in the thing itself. Intention, as gathered from attendant circumstances, must, in cases of doubt, furnish the governing principle. In short, if from the word used it can be inferred that the proprietary right in the *substance* of any object was intended to be conveyed that would be a gift. If, however, it should appear that what the donor intended to give was only the *munâf'aa* or the usufruct for a limited period, under the Hanafî Law, it would be an *'aâriat* (commodate loan).(1)

"The words," says the *Fatâwai Alamgiri*, "by which a gift can be effectuated are of three kinds; *first*, those by which a gift is expressly constituted; *second*, by which it is constituted by implication or custom (كناية , عرفا); and *third*, which convey the meaning equally of gift or loan." After giving examples of the different kinds of expression, it goes on to add—"the principle in all these cases is that when words are employed implying the transfer of the right of property in the substance (or corpus) of the thing, it is a gift; but where it has reference to the transfer of the ownership in the profits (*tamlîk-ul-manf'at*) it amounts to a loan; and if it is susceptible of either meaning, reference must be made to intention."(2)

The examples of express words by which a gift is constituted depend chiefly on the *nuance* of the language; and it is difficult to render in the English tongue the shades of meaning the different phrases convey. But some illustrations of a general character may throw light on the juridical conceptions on the subject. For instance, it is stated that "if a man were to say 'all my property' or all that I own is for so and so," that would amount to a *hiba*, but it will not be complete without possession....or "if he were to say 'all the property known to be mine or ascribed to me is for so and so,' that would be an acknowledgment according to the *Fatâwai Kâzi Khan*."(3)

"Where the father of an infant child plants a tree and says 'I have made it my child's', it is a *hiba*, and it would be the same if he said 'I have constituted it in my child's name.' This is the approved doctrine and most of our doctors have adopted it, so in the *Ghiâsia*."...."And if a man said 'all the properties I own

(1) *Fatâwai Alamgiri*, IV, p. 521.
(2) *Ibid*.
(3) *Ibid*, p. 522.

belong to this infant or child,' it would be an act of bounty (*karâmat*) and not a gift, unless he specified what he had given, when it would be a gift ; [for example], if he said, 'this shop of which I am the owner, or this house of mine is for my infant son,' it would be a gift, and it would become complete [immediately] if [at the time] in the hands of the father; so in the *Kinia*. And if he were to say 'this is for my son so and so' it would be a gift, and if he were to say, 'this thing is for any infant child of so and so' it would be valid ; and it will become complete without acceptance [by the donee]; so in the *Tâtâr-Khanièh.*"

"If a man were to give *dinârs* to his wife to spend on clothes to wear before him, and she employs them in trade, the profit arising therefrom as well as the money itself would be her property.(1) Clothes for children become their property, but not those made for apprentices or servants."

Conditions necessary for the validity of a gift.

The following are the conditions necessary for the validity of the act of gift :—

(1) Declaration expressed in any language which conveys the meaning, or expressed by conduct.

(2) Acceptance, expressed or implied.(2)

(3) And seisin by the donee of the subject of the gift, *i.e.*, if the property is not already in the hands of the donee.

Under the Mâliki Law the right of property is established in the subject of the gift before seisin, in other words possession is not necessary to complete a gift.(3)

In the case of *Nunda Singh* v. *Meer Jaffer Shah*,(4) which was decided under the Hanafî Law, it was held that a gift depends upon tender and acceptance, but seisin is necessary to make it complete.

To some extent the later decisions have overlooked the exact bearing of the question of seisin on the validity of a gift under the Mahommedan Law. It has been supposed that actual delivery or transfer of possession is intended by the rule which makes deli-

---

(1) *Fatâwai Alamgiri*, Vol. IV, p. 522.

(2) If a man give a thing to another, saying, "I give this to thee," and the donee take possession of it without saying a word, it is valid ; *Radd-ul-Muhtâr*, IV, p. 781.

(3) *Hed.*, III, p. 291.

(4) 1 Sel. Reports, p. 5.

very of seisin a condition to the validity of a gift.(1) In this view it becomes necessary to ascertain the exact meaning of the term *ikbâz* or seisin under the Mahommedan Law. It must be admitted that unless *ikbâz* (constructive or actual) can be presumed in the donee after the gift, it will not be operative. But a full consideration of the dicta on the subject shows that actual delivery of possession is not necessary. If the character of the possession changes, the mere retention of the subject-matter of the gift in the hands of the donor, would not affect the validity of the gift. He may continue to retain the possession of the property as a trustee or depositary, and such possession will not affect the legality of the transfer.(2) Similarly, if the thing given be in the hands of the donee in virtue of a trust, the gift is in that case complete, although there be no formal seisin, since the actual article is already in the donee's hands, whence his seisin is not requisite. "It is otherwise where a depositor sells the deposit to his trustee, for in this case the original seisin does not suffice, because seisin in virtue of purchase is a seisin inducing responsibility, and therefore cannot be substituted by a seisin in virtue of a trust, but seisin in virtue of a gift on the contrary, as not being a seisin inducing responsibility, may be substituted by a seisin in virtue of a trust." The law in cases of gifts to minors looks to the intention of the donor. When there is on the part of a father or other guardian a real *bonâ fide* intention to make a gift, transmutation of possession is not necessary, the subsequent holding of the property by the donor being considered to be on behalf of the minor. This principle was laid down with considerable distinctness in the case of *Abedunnissa Khatoon* v. *Ameerunnissa Khatoon*, where the Privy Council dealing with the question held that, under the Mahommedan Law, when there is on the part of a father or other guardian a real and *bonâ fide* intention to make a gift, the law will be satisfied without change of possession, and will presume the subsequent holding of the property to be on behalf of the minor donee.(3)

Meaning of *ikbâz* or seisin.

According to Kâzi Khân, the ability of the donee, if adult, or of his guardian if a minor, to take possession of the gift,—in

Ability to take possession is suffi-

(1) *Obedur Reza* v. *Mahomed Muneer* [1871], 16 W. R., 188 *Meherali* v. *Tajudin* [1888], I. L., 13 Bom., 156.

(2) *Radd-ul-Muhtâr*, Vol. IV, p. 785; *Majm'aa-ul-Anhar*; *Hed.* III, p. 295.

(3) *Ameerunnissa Khatoon* v. *Abedoonnissa Khatoon* [1875], L. R., 2 I. A., 87; s. c., 15 B. L. R., 67.

cient in many instances to validate the act of donation.

other words, to exercise the right of property over it, is sufficient to validate the act of donation. Accordingly, where a gift is made, and a direction is given to the donees to take possession of the subject of the gift and partition it among themselves, such a gift is held to be valid.(1) Power to take possession is equivalent in certain instances to actual delivery of possession. The meaning of this is, where the donor places the donee in a position to exercise the right of property over the subject of the gift, it is tantamount to delivery of seisin. For example, if *A* make a gift of his horse which is in his stables to *B* and give to *B* the key of the place, and authorise him to take possession of it, the seisin is sufficient in law.(2)

Thus a gift of immovable property in the occupation of tenants will be complete either by the delivery of the title-deeds or by requisition to the tenants to attorn to the donee,(3) and of zemindari rights by mutation of names in the Collector's Register.(4) So a valid gift may be made of property attached by the Collector for arrears of revenue by the *donor transferring such interest as he possesses at the time.*(5) In other words, a gift is completed if the donor does all he can to perfect the contemplated gift either by delivering actual possession of the property or placing the donee in a position to take possession of it.(6)

Possession must be with the permission of the donor.

But the possession of the donee must be with the permission of the donor. "If the donee," says the *Hedâya*,(7) "take possession of the gift in the meeting of the contract of gift without the order of the giver, it is lawful upon a favourable construction. If, on the contrary, he should take possession of the gift after the breaking up of the meeting, it is not lawful unless he have had the consent of the giver so to do. Analogy would suggest that the seisin is not valid in either case, as it is an act with respect to

---

(1) *Fatâwai Kâzi Khân*, Vol. II, p. 282.

(2) *Majm'aa-ul-Anhar, in loco.*

(3) *Shaik Ibrahim* v. *Shaik Suleman* [1884], I. L., 9 Bom., 146.

(4) *Sajjad Ahmed Khan* v. *Kadri Begum* [1895], I. L., 18 All., 1.

(5) *Anwari Begum* v. *Nizamuddin Shah* [1898], I. L., 21 All., 165.

(6) *Mahomed Bukhsh* v. *Hosseini Bibi* [1888], L. R., 15 I. A., 81; s. c., I. L., 15 Cal., 684. In *Mogul Shah* v. *Muhamad Saheb* [1887], I. L., 11 Bom., 507; and *Ismal* v. *Ramji* [1888], I. L., 23 Bom., 682, the Bombay High Court has held that registration of the deed was not sufficient to cure the want of delivery of possession. These rulings, however, are subject to the principles set forth in the text.

(7) *Hed.* (Hamilton's) III, p. 292.

what is still the property of the giver, for as his right of property continues in force until seisin, that is consequently invalid without his consent. The reason for a more favourable construction of the law in the instance in question is that seisin in a case of gift is similar to acceptance in sale, on this consideration that in the one the effect of the deed (that is, the establishment of a right of property) rests upon the seisin and in the other upon the acceptance. As, moreover, the object of a gift is the establishment of a right of property, *it follows that the tender of the giver is virtually an empowerment of the donee to take possession.* It is otherwise where the seisin is made after the breaking-up of the meeting, because our doctors do not admit of the establishment of the power over the thing, but when seisin is immediately conjoined with acceptance, and as the validity of acceptance is particularly restricted to the place of the meeting, so also is the thing which is conjoined with it. It is also otherwise where the giver prohibits the donee from taking possession at the place of meeting, for in that case the seisin of the donee at the place of the meeting would be invalid, as arguments of implied intention cannot be put in competition with express declaration."

In fact, the legal effect of a gift is not complete until transmutation of possession, actual or constructive, has taken place, and in this respect a stranger and the child of the donor are on the same footing when the child is adult.

Permission need not be express.

Although the possession of the donee must be with the permission of the donor, it is not necessary that such permission should be express. If the permission, or, in other words, the consent of the donor to the taking of possession, can be inferred by his conduct, it is sufficient. If the possession is taken immediately after the gift there can be no question as to the validity of the gift, but if after the gift the donor prohibits the donee to take possession, and if the donee nevertheless takes possession, it is not valid. Where a gift is made to two persons in succession, and is followed by possession to the second, the second gift is valid.

***Amina Bibi* v. *Khatija Bibi*.**

But the question of possession has such a practical importance in the discussion of cases arising under the Mahommedan Law relating to disposition of property, that an elucidation of the meaning attached to the word 'seisin', or its Arabic equivalent *kabz*, is of the

Amina Bibi v. *Khatija Bibi*—contd.).

utmost importance. The question came up for decision in the Bombay High Court in the case of *Amina Bibi* v. *Khatija Bibi*.(1)

In that case a husband had made a gift of his house and certain tenanted out-offices, &c., to his wife. He had made over the keys to his wife, left the house for a few days (to accentuate the fact of delivering possession), but had returned afterwards and lived with her in the same house until his death. During his lifetime he had collected the rents of the out-offices presumably on behalf of the wife. In a suit by his heirs against the widow to set aside the *hiba* on the ground that no possession had passed, Sausse, C. J., said as follows :—

" The acts essential for giving validity to a *hiba* or gift according to Mahommedan Law are tender, acceptance and seisin, but the manner in which seisin is to be effected must be considerably modified to suit the peculiar relations recognised as existing between husband and wife in the Mahommedan Law. The property of each is separate and independent of the other; either can make, and both are encouraged by law to make gifts to the other in order to promote mutual affection; and so strongly is this principle inculcated that retractation of such a gift is not allowed, although in many other cases it is lawful. A wife can make to her husband a valid gift of the house in which both are residing, although it contain her separate property, and though both continue to reside in it afterwards. Upon principle, I do not see why a husband should not equally be at liberty to bestow upon his wife the house in which both are living and in which they afterwards continue to reside, provided he have power to make the gift, and do make it *bonâ fide*, and not in contemplation of fraud upon creditors or others. The only difficulty is to comply with the exigency of the law, which requires ' seisin ' or exclusive possession to be given. If a husband, with full power to give, executes a deed of gift, and in accordance with its provisions hands over symbolical possession of a house or property by keys, &c., and also, to mark more strongly the *bonâ fides* of the intention, actually goes out of the house before witnesses in order to leave it and all within it, in the full and exclusive possession of his wife, I do not see what further

(1) [1864], 1 Bom. H. C. R., 157.

I give the judgment *in extenso*, as it is in every respect one of the most valuable decisions concerning the question of possession under Mahommedan Law.

act he could do to give effect to that gift consistently with exercising his other legal rights as a husband. The wife had at that time the power afforded to her of taking and keeping exclusive possession of the gift, and of continuing to reside in the house, but the Mahommedan Law gives the husband the right, and moreover makes it his duty, to reside with his wife. If, then such a clear expression of intention as is contained in the present *hiba*, accompanied by such an unequivocal act before the witnesses, be not held to give that seisin which is required by Mahommedan Law, it would amount to introducing a restriction as to the object of 'gift,' which is not found, so far as I have been able to learn, in any Mahommedan Law-book. The husband has a general power of making a gift to his wife, but were the present *hiba* to be held to be invalid, it would amount to declaring that a husband shall not under any circumstance make a gift to his wife of the house in which they are at the time residing, and in which they continue to reside down to his death. If such a restriction be unknown to Mahommedan Law, there must be some legal mode of effecting the gift of such a property of the husband's. The circumstance of possession once given being subsequently continued does not appear to be a necessary condition of a *complete seisin*, or its non-continuance to invalidate the *hiba*; see the case of *Jaffer Khan* v. *Hubshee Beebee*, 1 S. D. A. Rep. of Bengal, p. 12, referred to in Morley's Digest, Title 'Gift,' s. 55."

Amina Bibi v. *Khatija Bibi*—(contd.).

"The 'seisin' of the Mahommedan Law appears to be analogous to our livery of 'seisin' as formerly existing in England, and to have been effected much in the same way as by delivery of a sod or twig of the land, or the ring or hasp of a door, in the name of 'seisin.' In Coke on Littleton, 57*a*, it is laid down—" If the deed be delivered in the name of 'seisin' of the land, or if the feoffor (or donor) saith to the feoffee (or donee) take and enjoy this land according to the deed, or enter into this land and God give you joy," these words do amount to a livery of 'seisin.'"

"Two passages from the *Tohfa*, Vol IV, pp. 59 and 335, have been relied upon by the defendant to show that a delivery and acceptance of keys of a house is a sufficient seisin, or giving of possession in a case of sale and purchase, and also that gifts are in that respect to be treated as sales :—'The giving of the possession of immovable property to the purchaser depends upon the words expressed by the seller conveying the meaning that (the house) has been vacated, and in handing over the keys of the house,' *Tohfa*, Vol. IV, p. 59; and 'The thing of which a gift has been made does not become the property (of the donee) without possession, as in the case with things that are sold, and the declaration of a donor to the effect that he has given possession is sufficient to denote (real) possession;' *ib.*, p. 335."

"In the present case the deed of gift was delivered, and with it the keys of the houses and furniture mentioned in the *hiba*, which included the house in which the husband and wife were then living. No words can be stronger than those contained in this *hiba* to indicate the intention of the donor to complete the gift according to law;—'And I, having given up my possession, have given them (the houses and *chal*) into the possession of the above-mentioned woman (his wife), in whose favour the gift is made, and all the conditions respecting a gift, *viz.*, the mutual consent and taking possession in every way, together with the vacating of them, have been performed by me and the above-mentioned woman in whose favour the gift is made;' and again, "In future I have no claim to the property, nor can any of my heirs demand anything out of the above-mentioned property by way of inheritance."

"In my opinion, the relation of husband and wife, and his legal right to reside with her and to manage her property, rebut the inference, which, in the case of parties standing in a different relation, would arise from a continued residence in the house after the making of the *hiba*, and in the husband generally receiving the rents of the *chal* annexed to that house. It is also worthy of remark, that the husband mentioned to some tenants that he was receiving rent on account of his wife, to whom he had made a *hiba*."

"This is not a case of creditors claiming against a *hiba* set up to defeat their claims, but it is that of heirs or next-of-kin claiming in derogation of the gift of the person through whom they claim."

Azimunnissa v. *Clement Dale.*

The same principle was laid down in *H. H. Azimunnissa* v. *Clement Dale.*(1) In that case it appeared that the Nawab of Carnatic had made a gift of certain houses and gardens to his Begum (H. H. Azimunnissa), but had continued to reside in the houses as before, and to deal with the property as his own. Bittle-

(1) [1868], 6 Mad. H. C. R., 458.

that if the parties are present in the premises, it is sufficient that an intention on the part of the donor to transfer the possession has been unequivocally manifested."

In *Bibi Khaver Sultan* v. *Bibi Rukhia Sultan*(1), the donor (Bibi Begam Jan) a member of the Usuli division of the Shiah Sect had conveyed by way of gift to the defendant Bibi Rukhia Sultan (her widowed daughter-in-law) and to Rukhia Sultan's children the house in which she was residing with other property; after the execution of the document she had removed from the house leaving behind some of her effects; two days after she had returned and resided there as before the gift. It appeared also that at her instance some of the tenants who resided on a part of the premises attorned to Bibi Rukhia Sultan. On a suit by the plaintiff, a daughter of Bibi Begam Jan, to set aside the gift on the ground that the requirements of the Mahommedan Law regarding delivery of possession had not been complied with, the Bombay High Court held that the execution of a deed of gift of immovable property accompanied by a temporary abandonment of possession by the donor in favour of the transferee, and the attornment of the tenants to the transferee is a sufficient delivery of possession to make the gift valid under the Mussulman Law. In *Kandanath Veettil Bava* v. *Musalian Veettil Pakrakutti*(2), the Madras High Court laid down the obvious doctrine that the residence of the donor with the donee after the gift did not make the gift invalid.

When possession is already with the donee it need not be renewed; no formal transfer, therefore, is necessary, when the gift is to a depositary, bailee or trustee "or even a person who has obtained it by fraud (*ghasab*)" and who is already in possession of the property which forms the subject-matter of the gift.(3) In the case of *Vilayet Hussain* v. *Maniran*(4), the Calcutta High Court held, that when the subject of the gift has been in the hands of the donee as manager or agent of the donor, such possession by the donee was not sufficient to make it unnecessary to the validity of the gift, that

***Vilayet Hussain* v. *Maniram* wrongly decided.**

(1) 1905], I. L., 29 Bom., 46. The fact that the parties were Shiahs makes no difference in the principle, as the doctrine of seisin is the same in both schools.

(2) [1907], I. L., 30 Mad., 305.

(3) *Hed.* (Hamilton's) III, 295; *Radd-ul-Muhtâr*, IV, p. 783; *Durr-ul-Mukhtâr*, p. 635.

(4) [1879], 5 Cal. L. R., 91.

there should be actual or formal delivery of possession of the property. In this case the gift was made in death-illness. This case is clearly opposed to the Mahommedan Law.

In short, in considering the question of transmutation or delivery of possession, the relationship of the parties must be kept in view. The residence of the husband in a house of which he has made a gift to his wife, or the realisation by him of the rents and profits of a property he has given to her, is explainable by the relationship of the donor and the donee.(1) Similarly, if a father were to make a gift of his business to his minor son and continue to manage it for him, or an uncle were to give some property to a nephew and continue to be supported by the donee, the gift would not be invalid on that account.

As I have already pointed out, if the gift is made to a person, who is *sui juris*, the donor must evince his intention of making a complete transfer of the ownership in the property from himself to the donee, by placing the latter in a position to enjoy it beneficially or to make use of it consistently with its purpose. This, however, in the majority of cases, is a question of fact. In the case of *Agha Mohammed Jaffer Bindamin* v. *Kolsoom Beebee*(2), already referred to, the Judicial Committee considered that there was evidence of an intention to make a transfer but that the gift was incomplete. It would have been different if the notes had been endorsed over by the transferor.

The Bombay High Court has held that whether a property is conveyed directly to the donee or whether it is assigned to trustees for his benefit, transmutation of possession "actual, symbolical or constructive" is necessary for the validity of the disposition. As Mr. Justice Tyabji pointed out in this case, "ramifications of trusts" are to be found almost through every branch of Mahommedan Law; and it is therefore important to bear in mind that when a disposition is purported to be made by means of trustees for the benefit of a third person some indication of a transfer of possession is requisite to make the transaction complete.(3)

---

(1) *Amina Bibi* v. *Khatija Bibi*, supra; *Azim-un-Nissa* v. *Dale*, supra.
(2) [1897], I. L., 25 Cal., 9.
(3) *Moosabhai* v. *Yacoobbhai* [1904], I. L., 29 Bom., 267.

SECTION II.

GIFTS TO MINORS.

Gifts to minors.

IN the case of a gift by a father to his minor child, no acceptance is necessary. "The gift is completed by the contract, and it makes no difference whether the subject of the gift is in the hands of the father or in that of a depositary" [on behalf of the father]. When a father makes a gift of something to his infant son, the infant, by virtue of the gift, becomes proprietor of the same, provided the thing given be at the time in the possession either of the father or of any person who stands in the position of a trustee for the father, because the possession of the father is tantamount to the possession of the infant by virtue of the gift, and the possession of the trustee is equivalent to that of the father.

With regard to the validity of gifts to minors of property in the occupation of tenants the subject has already been discussed in a previous chapter.(1) And it has been shown that a father may make a gift to his minor child of immovable property in the occupation of tenants or in the possession of a lessee or mortgagee without any change of possession on the part of the persons directly holding the subject-matter of the gift. Nor, to make the gift complete, is any acceptance on the part of the donee necessary. The gift once made and the intention to convey the property unequivocally expressed, the donation is complete so far as the donor is concerned, though he may continue to hold the property in his own name in the same manner as before the gift.

The same rule applies to a gift by a mother to her infant child, whom she maintains and whose father is dead and there is no constituted guardian; and so also with respect to the gift of any person maintaining a child under similar circumstances.

"The law with respect to seisin in cases of *sadakah* or pious gifts is similar to that of gifts." This means that "a gift by way of a pious offering" stands in the same position as a simple gift or voluntary settlement so far as the question of seisin is concerned. Among Mussulmans, it is very frequent, or, perhaps, more correctly speaking it used to be so, to make donations to children and relations by way of a pious offering or *sadakah* "to obtain the nearness of God"—to deserve the Almighty's reward.

---

(1) See *ante*. p. 66. Comp. *Newazee Ferash* v. *Allussee*, 1 Sel. R., 41 [1800].

This recompense is regarded in the Mussulman Law as a meritorious consideration and bars the claims of creditors. But when a gift of this kind was made, delivery of seisin was to be effected in the same way as in the case of a gratuitous gift. If the donee was in possession of the subject-matter of the gift from before the donation, he became proprietor thereof "without the necessity of a new seisin." In the same way, if the father made a pious gift to his infant child of a thing in his possession or of somebody on his behalf, it is valid without actual delivery of seisin or change of possession.

Where a gift is made to an infant by a person other than the father "the gift is rendered complete by the seisin of the father of the infant."

When the father is dead, the possession of the person primarily entitled to the guardianship of the child is sufficient; the primary guardians after him being his executor, the grandfather, and the executor appointed by the grandfather.

Gift to a child by a non-relation.

"Where a *hiba* is made by an *ajnabi*" (a stranger) (1), says the *Fatâwai Kâzi Khân*, the right to take possession and accept [the donation on the child's behalf] belongs to the father, and in case he is dead or absent at a precluding distance(2), the right appertains to his executor for he is in the position of the father (بمنزلة الاب). He (the executor of the father) takes precedence of the grandfather. When there is neither the father nor his executor, the right of possession appertains to the grandfather, *viz.*, the father's father, and after him to his executor. Excepting these four the possession of any other person would not be valid unless the child is in his charge. Consequently some have said(3) that if the child is in the lap and charge of its uncle, and he makes a gift and takes possession when there is an executor of the father as he is *in loco parentis* such possession is not valid, and if the brother or uncle or mother were to take possession, when the child is in charge of a stranger, it would not be valid, but the

(1) Meaning a non-relative.

(2) *Ghîbat-ul-munkat'aa*, a distance which precludes his expressing his assent or dissent in time.

(3) قيل, showing that it is not accepted. The correct doctrine is stated a little beyond; comp. *Wajeed Ali* v. *Abdool Ali* [1864], W. R., Suppl. Vol., 121; *Gyazooddeen* v. *Fatima* [1866], 1 Agra H. C. R., 238; *Husain* v. *Mira* [1870], 7 Bom. H. C. R., 27; *Husain Khan Bahadoor* v. *Native Srinivasa* [1871], 6 Mad. H. C. R., 356.

possession of such stranger in whose charge it is would be valid. And when a minor girl is in the house of her husband, and a gift is made to her by an *ajnabi* (a stranger) [meaning a non-relative], the possession of the husband would be valid even though the father be present [*i.e.*, not dead or at a "precluding distance], and if the father were to take possession it would be similarly valid although she be in her husband's house."

"And when the child is in the charge of the grandfather, brother, mother or uncle, and a gift is made to the child [by any of them or some other person] and the person in charge of the child were to take possession whilst the father is present, the learned (the *Mashâikh*) have differed on its validity; some have said it would not be valid. But the correct doctrine is that it would be valid, similar to the case of a gift to a minor girl when the possession of the husband is valid even though the father is present ......" And if a child is in charge of an *ajnabi* (a stranger or non-relative), he would be entitled to take possession on behalf of the minor."

The *Radd-ul-Muhtâr* after stating the various views expressed by different jurists concludes thus—"if a person, in whose charge the child is, takes possession on its behalf of a gift made to the child, whilst the father is present, some have said it is not valid, whilst others have declared it is valid, and on this is the *fatwa* as is stated in the *Mushtamal-ul-Ahkâm*; and according to the correct doctrine it is valid as in the case of the husband taking possession [of a gift to a minor wife] in the presence of the father, as is stated in the *Khânièh*(1), and the *fatwa* is with respect to its validity. And this is the view (also) of Astarûshni."...."You know that the *Hedâya* and the *Jouhara* have considered it correct to hold that the possession of the person in charge of a child is not valid whilst the father is not absent, which the author of the *Badâya* has followed. But Kâzi Khân and others among the Masters of decisions(2), (*Ashâb-ul-Fatâwa*) have upheld the contrary doctrine that it is valid."

"Among the doctrines stated that declared to be correct by Kâzi Khân should not be departed from, for he is a jurist of the first order (*fakîh-un-nafs*—'jurist by spirit') especially as it is for the

---

(1) *Fatâwai Kâzi Khân*, Vol. IV, p. 191 (Cal., 1835).
(2) Jurisconsults.

benefit of the child. So consider this at the time of pronouncing decree (*fatwa*). And I have mentioned these various doctrines as they occur in the law-books." "A gift to an infant by a person in whom is vested the complete guardianship(1) [of the child], that is a person in whose charge the infant is, in which category are included a father and an uncle in the absence of the father provided he is in their charge—becomes completed by the mere declaration (*i.e.*, without acceptance of the donee and without possession) if the subject of the gift is *known*(2) [specified] and is in the hands of the donor or his depositary, for the possession of the guardian is equivalent to the minor's possession....."(3)

"And if a gift be made to the infant by an *ajnabi* (non-relative), in such a case it is completed by the possession of its *walî* (guardian); and he (the guardian) is one of four persons, first the father, then his executor, then the grandfather, then his executor; even though the infant is not actually in their *lap* (actual custody); and in their absence, the gift becomes completed by the possession of any one in whose charge the child is [that is, who takes care of him] as an uncle. And the gift by an *ajnabi* becomes completed [operative] by the possession of the mother or of a stranger or a *Multakit* (who has picked up a child) if it is in their *lap* not otherwise.... And it is completed also by the possession of the infant himself if he is possessed of discretion (مميزاً) and understands the acquisition of property"(4), "and the gift is to his advantage and not otherwise" (5).

The author of the *Durr-ul-Mukhtâr* goes on to add—"I say, in *Barjandi* it is stated that there is a difference of opinion [as to the validity] if possession is taken [of the gift for the child] by the person in whose charge it is whilst the father is present: *some have said* it is not valid but the correct doctrine is that it is valid; and Kahastâni has clearly preferred its validity, and he has ascribed it [the doctrine of validity] to the Fakhr-ul-Islâm contrary to the view on which the author [of the *Tanwîr-ul-Absâr*] has

---

(1) ولايت فى الجمله

(2) لو للموهوب معلوم

(3) *Radd-ul-Muhtâr*, Vol. IV, p. 784.

(4) *Durr-ul-Mukhtâr*, p. 635.

(5) Tahtâwi; the authorities referred to are Kahastâni, *Muzmirât*, *Fatâwai Sughra*, and *Fatâwai Alamgiri*.

relied in his commentary which he has ascribed to the *Khulâsa.* But the text of the author is open to the construction of validity for the qualifying phrase 'notwithstanding the father is present' is applicable to all cases." This is explained by Tahtâwi thus:— "As the author has stated that if the donee, though under age, can validly take possession of the gift notwithstanding the father is present, it is clear that the father's presence makes no difference if the child is in the charge of the mother or a stranger and either she or the stranger were to take possession of the gift."

"And the possession of a person in charge of the child is valid even though the father be present—and this is the accepted doctrine."(1)

"If the donee," says the *Fatâwai Alamgiri*(2), "is competent to take possession (*ahl-ul-kabz*) in that case he is entitled to take possession of the gift; but if he be a minor or insane (*majnûn*), then the right to possession belongs to his *walî* (guardian). And his *walî* is his father, and the father's executor, then the father's father and then the executor of his (the father's) executor(3), then the Kâzi and then any one appointed by the Kâzi whether the minor is in the charge of any one of them or not; so in the *Sharh-ut-Tahtâwi.*"

"So if the father or his executor or the father's father or his executor are absent at a precluding distance the seisin of one appointed to his guardianship would be valid according to the *Khulâsa.*" (This shows that an appointment may be made specifically for the purpose of taking possession on behalf of the minor of the subject of the gift.)

Possession may be taken by the person in whose charge the child is.

"But persons other than the father and father's father like the brother, the uncle or the mother and all kinsfolk are entitled on a liberal interpretation [of the law] to take possession of the gift if the child be in their charge (lit. in their family). Similarly their executor [would be entitled] on a liberal interpretation if the child be in his charge; and so also it is valid for any

(1) Kahastâni in the *Jâm'aa-ur-Ramûz.*

(2) Vol. IV, p. 547.

Executor of *his* executor, evidently meaning the executor of the father's executor, but immediately after comes a statement which indicates that after the grandfather comes *his* executor.

(3) ثم وصي وصيه

stranger who has charge of the orphan when he has no one else [to look after him] to take possession of the gift. And these principles apply equally whether the child is intelligent enough to take possession or not. All this refers to cases where the father is either dead or is at a *precluding distance*. But when he is alive and present, and the child is in the charge of any of the others, in such a case whether the possession of the latter would be valid there is no authoritative statement in the books, except with regard to a stranger that if a child is in his charge and it has no one else, the possession of that stranger on its behalf is valid. From this it follows that the possession of the others [*i.e.*, the kinsfolk] is not valid if the father is present. And it is also stated that the grandfather cannot take possession when the father of the child is alive; nor has any distinction been made whether the child is in his charge or not; so it is necessary to make the rule general that it is not valid in any case; so in the *Zakhira*."(1)

This statement, however, is qualified and placed on a reasonable basis a little later.

"So if the minor is in the *lap* and in the charge of his uncle, and he makes a gift to the infant whilst the father's executor is present, and the uncle takes possession of the gift for the infant, *some have said*(2) that his possession is not valid. And if the brother, uncle or mother were to take possession whilst the minor is in the charge of a stranger (*ajnabi*) it would not be valid; and if the stranger himself in whose charge the child is were to take possession it would be valid; so in the *Fatâwai Kâzi Khân*."

Gift to a married girl.

"If a married minor girl who has attained nubility is in the charge of her husband, either she herself or the husband on her behalf can validly take possession [of any gift made to her]... With reference to a girl who has not attained nubility some of our jurists (*ashâb*) have said the possession of the husband would not be valid, but the correct doctrine is that if she is in the husband's charge he can validly take possession of a gift made to her, but if the wife has not taken up her abode in the husband's home he is not authorised to do so, rather her guardian would be entitled to

---

(1) P. 548.

(2) قيل showing that the authority is weak and not accepted.

take possession on her behalf, as is stated in the *Zakhira*. And if the minor girl is in the charge of the grandfather, brother, mother or uncle, and any one of them make a gift to her, the possession of the husband is valid; so it is stated in the *Tâtâr Khanièh*. And when she has attained majority neither the father nor the husband is entitled to take possession except with her consent (*izn*); so in the *Jouharat-un-Nayyirèh*. If a minor girl is in the charge of a stranger with the consent of the father, and the father is absent, the stranger's possession is valid (*sahîh*, correct) and not of the brother, so in the *Sirâjia*.

"And if an infant is in the charge of the grandfather, or brother, or mother or uncle, and a gift is made to the child, and the person in whose charge it is, takes possession whilst the father is present (*hâzir*), our masters (*mashâikh*) have differed respecting it. But the correct doctrine is that it is valid as is stated in the *Fatâwai Kâzi Khân*, and the *fatwa* (decree) is pronounced according to it, as [is laid down] in the *Fatâwai as-Sughra*." **Recognised principle.**

"And if the youth himself takes possession and he has discretion (intelligence, *'akl*) it is valid, though the father may be alive, according to the *Wajîz l'il-kurdi*; and this is the opinion of one-third of our jurists according to the *Zakhîra*, but if he is not possessed of intelligence it is not lawful, according to the *Sirâj-ul-Wahâj*. Acceptance on the part of a youth is valid when the gift is for his benefit, but not if it is likely to damnify him."

"When a father makes a gift of a house to his minor child and the donor's things are in it, the gift is valid—and this doctrine is adopted and on this is the *fatwa*; so in the *Fatâwai-'l-'Itâbia*. And in the *Mocnteka* it is stated from Mohammed (may the peace, etc.) that if a person were to make a gift of his house to his infant child and continue to live in it as a tenant paying rent it would not be valid, but if the donor lived in it *without paying rent* it would be valid "(1)

Gifts to minors. The invalidity in the first case is due to the dual character in which the donor places himself by becoming a tenant in the house he gives to his infant child; for, as the guardian of the child, the posses-

(1) Abû Yusuf differs from his fellow-disciple as to the validity in either case, but Mohammed's rule is the accepted doctrine. But where a father makes a pious gift (*Sadakah*) of the house and continues to live in it, it is valid according to Abû Yusuf.

sion of the house vests in him, and if he continues to occupy it paying rent he becomes his own tenant. It is on the basis of such reasoning Imâm Mohammed holds that, although the father may validly continue to live in a house which he has given to his infant child, he may not do so as a tenant. But this objection would not apply if the subject of the gift be transferred to trustees, and the father were to rent the house from them. Nor would it apply where a gift is made by a person other than the guardian in whose charge the child happens to be.

If a fatherless child be under the charge of its mother, and she were to take possession of a gift made to him, it would be valid, because she has an authority for the preservation of him and his property, "and the seisin of a gift made to him is in the nature of a preservation of himself since a child cannot subsist without property." The same rule obtains with respect to the validity of the seisin of a non-relative who has the charge of an orphan. Thus where a gift is made to an orphan who is living in the guardianship of a stranger, if possession is taken by such guardian it is sufficient in law. In other words, the possession of a *de facto* guardian or of a guardian appointed by the Court, even where the father is alive, is sufficient.

Possession of a discreet minor.

If a person under age, who is able to understand what is to his advantage, were himself to take possession of a gift, it would be valid, provided it is a benefit to him. An example of an "injurious" gift is mentioned thus:—"If a man were to give to a youth a *blind* slave his acceptance would not be valid." The reason is obvious, for whilst the donee would be burdened with the slave's maintenance, he would not be able to derive any benefit from his services.

Gift to a minor wife.

As already stated, the possession of the husband of a gift made to his wife under age is valid, provided she has been sent from her father's house to his; and he is authorised to do so even though the father be living, because the father after sending the girl to her husband's house is held by implication to have resigned the management of her concerns to the husband. It is otherwise where she has not been sent from her father's house, because then the father is not supposed to have resigned the management of her concerns.

Where the father is alive and on the spot, the mother may not take possession, but as is abundantly clear from the passages quoted from the *Fatâwai Alamgiri* and other works it does not follow from this, that if she does, the gift is invalid.(1)

When a gift is made to an infant by a father or any other person in whose charge the child is, it is not necessary that the donor should divest himself of all interest in the subject-matter of the gift. For example, where a house is bestowed it is not necessary that the donor should not reside therein, or if it contains his effects, that he should remove them from it.(2)

Gift by the mother of her dower-debt to her infant child

"When a woman has her dower-debt owing from her husband and she makes a gift of it to her infant child by the same husband, the correct doctrine is that it will not be valid unless she invests the child at the same time with the power to realise it, and he (the child) will become the owner on realisation, so in the *Fatâwai Kâzi Khân*."(3) This evidently implies that at the time of the gift the mother should place the child in a position to recover the amount from the father, either by making over the dower-deed to some one on behalf of the child, or authorising him to make the demand on the child's behalf.

The above principles may be formulated as follows :—

If a stranger makes a gift to an infant, the right of acceptance and possession on behalf of the infant appertains, in the first place, to the father. If the father is dead, or is at such a distance as to preclude the possibility of his presence, in that case the executor of the father takes the place of the father. If there is no executor of the father, then comes the grandfather, and in his absence the grandfather's executor. Besides these, who may be regarded as guardians *de jure*, any person who happens to be the *de facto* guardian of the infant, that is, in whose custody the child is, may take possession of the subject-matter of the gift.

Musst. Banoo Bibi v. Fakhroddeen Hassan.

In the case of *Musst. Banoo Bibi* v. *Fakhroodeen Hassan*,(4) the Sudder Court held correctly on principle that a deed of gift by a female to a minor, whom she had received into her family as an adopted son, of property of which possession was not delivered at the time of the gift or during the lifetime of the donor, she having retained possession of it on behalf of the minor, was valid and complete in law notwithstanding that the father of the minor was alive.

(1) *Fatâwai Alamgiri*, Vol. IV, p. 546.
(2) *Ibid*, p. 547 ; Comp. cases cited *ante*.
(3) *Ibid*.
(4) Sel. Reports, II, p. 180.

If a minor girl be living with her husband after her marriage a gift of which possession is taken by the father or the husband is equally good.

But before the minor wife has been sent to the husband's house, or after she has attained her majority, the husband is not entitled to take possession. The guardianship in respect of a minor wife vests in the husband when she comes to his house.(1) As long as she has not been sent to his house, he has no right to take possession on her behalf of any gift made to her; when she has come to live with him he becomes her *walî*.

If the father is alive or present, but the child is being brought up by the uncle, grandfather or mother, their possession is sufficient.

If the minor is possessed of understanding, he may take possession of the gift, but in order to prevent any dispute, the Kâzi is authorised to appoint a curator for the same. When the donee is insane, the right to take possession belongs to his guardian.

If a gift is made to a *latîk* (foundling), the possession of one who brings up the child, or that of the Judge is sufficient.

An infant who has attained discretion has a right to reject as well as to accept.

It is lawful for parents in case of necessity (and where it can be shown that it was the intention of the grantor that they should do so), to make use of a gift made to the child but not to consume it.

Presents given to a bride follow the same rule, that is, if they are made by the relations of the husband they become the husband's property, unless they are distinctly mentioned to be given to the wife.

Things given in *jahâz* (by way of paraphernalia) to a bride taken to the house of the husband belong to her, unless the father says they were given by way of *'aâriat* (commodate loan), the *onus* being on him to prove his statement; usage will have to be considered in connection with the position of the father.(2)

---

(1) The custody of a minor wife does not belong to the husband, *in re Khatija Bibi* [1870], 5 B. L. R., O. C., p. 517, but it is not illegal, *in re Mahin Bibi* [1874], 13 B. L. R., O. C., p. 160.

(2) *Radd-ul-Muhtâr*, Vol. IV, p. 781. In the case of *Umes Chunder Sircar* v. *Mussamat Zuhoor Fatima* [1889], L. R., 17 I. A., 201, a Mahommedan husband had granted by a deed of settlement certain lands to his wife on condition

Nobody can make a gift of his child's property even for a consideration. This is a natural corollary of the principle which debars guardians from selling the property of a minor, unless under exceptional circumstances.

Presents given to a child at circumcision if suited for him become gifts to him. If not suited for him they become the property of the parents, according as they are made by the friends or relatives of the father or mother. But if the giver of the present distinctly specifies at the time that it is for the child, it will become his property.

A youth who has attained discretion but not puberty, and is able to understand what is to his advantage may accept a gift even after his *walî* has rejected it.

In the *Fatâwai Kâzi Khân* it is stated that if a person give a house to his minor child and subsequently purchase or acquire another house with the proceeds of the house of which gift has been made, this latter house will be the property of the child. According to the *Radd-ul-Muhtâr* this is the accepted doctrine. The doctrine, however, when analysed would seem to express in other words the principle that when a gift has been made by a father to his child, it becomes the property of the minor though it continues to remain in the possession and disposal of the father. And, accordingly, any dealing with the property by the father *dehors* the right of the infant would not change the character of the gift or destroy the right of the infant.

SECTION III.

GIFTS WITH CONDITIONS.

THERE is great difference between *contingent gifts* and *gifts with conditions attached to them*. The former are gifts which are made dependent for their operation upon the occurrence of certain contingencies, and are void according to all the schools.(1) Whilst

Contingent gifts and gifts with conditions.

that if she had a child by him the grant should be taken as a perpetual *mokurrari* and in case of no child being born as a life *mokurrari* with remainder to the settlor's two sons. It was held by the Judicial Committee that the two sons took definite interests under the deed similar to vested remainders, though liable to be displaced by the birth of a child to the wife.

(1) *Roushan Jahan* v. *Enaet Hassan* [1864], Weekly Rep., 3, and L. R., 4 I. A., p. 291; *Eusuf Ali* v. *The Collector of Tipperah* [1882], I. L., 9 Cal., 138; *Chekkone Kutti* v. *Ahmud* [1886], I. L., 10 Mad., 196.

with regard to gifts with conditions attached to them, there exists a certain divergence between the Shiahs and the Hanafîs. According to the Hanafî Law, any derogation from the completeness of the gift is null; and if the intention to give to the donee the entire subject-matter of the gift be clear, subsequent conditions derogating from or limiting the extent of the right would be null and void.(1)

Hanafî Law.

Accordingly, under the Hanafî Law, *whilst the gift is valid, the condition is void.* Under the Shiah Law, if the condition is subsidiary to the gift both the gift and the condition are valid. For example, if a man were to say, "I give you the debt due to me by *A*, on condition that you give to *B*, the interest thereon;" under the Hanafî Law the condition is void, but the gift valid.

Shiah Law.

Under the Shiah Law, if the gift depends on the condition attached, the entire gift is bad. If it does not and the condition is only subsidiary, then both the gift and the condition are valid.

Gifts dependant on condition.

In practice (*'urf*) there is no difference whether the gift depends on the condition attached, or whether the condition is only subsidiary. In both cases both gift and condition are valid.

Hanafî Law.

Under the Hanafî Law when it is clear that the intention is to make to *A* a gift of the *corpus* of a thing, and it is conditioned that he should take a limited interest in it or take it only for his life the condition would be void, and the gift would take effect absolutely. Similarly, if a man were to give a piece of land to another on the condition that he should give to him in *perpetuity* the whole produce of the land, the condition would be bad; for, in these cases, the condition defeats the object of the gift; in other words, although it purports to transfer the property to the donee, in one case it cuts down his interest, and in the other burdens him with a perpetual trust.

But even under the Hanafî Law only such conditions are invalid as render the gift nugatory or defeat its very purpose. The illustrations given in the *Fatâwai Alamgiri*, which are in accord with the social conditions of the times, leave no room for doubt as to the meaning of the jurists. "All our masters have declared that when a gift is made and an invalid condition is attached, the gift will be valid and the condition will be void. For example, if a person were to make a gift of a slave-girl to another and impose a con-

(1) Comp. *Nizam-ud-din* v. *Abdul Gafur* [1888], I. L., 13 Bom., 264; s. c. on app., I. L., 17 Bom., 1.

dition on him that he should never sell her or that he should make her the mother of his children," *i.e.*, he should have children by her which would have the effect of emancipating her, "or that he should sell her to so and so, or that he should return her to the donor after a month—in all these cases the gift is valid and the condition void, as is stated in the *Sirâj-ul-Wahâj*."

Examples of gift with nugatory conditions.

In the instances given the condition makes the donation absolutely nugatory; in fact it is opposed to the very purpose of the gift; it is a restriction on the rights purported to be transferred to the donee. And it is, therefore, held to be void. The other examples which follow further amplify the meaning of the jurists. "If a house is given to another on the condition that a part of *it* should be given back to the donor or that the donee should give something in return for it,(1) the gift would be valid and the condition void; so it is stated in the *Kâfi*. The rule in all these cases is that in contracts where [complete] seisin is a condition, nugatory provisions do not avoid the contracts but are themselves rendered void, such as gift or pledge, as is stated in the *Sirâj-ul-Wahâj*. Contracts which are avoided by nugatory conditions are thirteen in number, such as sale, partition, lease, discharge of a debt; contracts which are not avoided by such conditions are twenty-six, *viz.*, divorce...pledge, loan, *hiba, sadakah*, wills....; contracts which can be referred to a future time are fourteen in number ....and those which cannot be so referred are nine, *viz.*, sale, partition, partnership, *hiba*... A man makes a gift to another of a piece of land on the condition that whatever is produced thereon the donee should give the donor; Abu'l Kâsim Saffâr says if there are vines or other trees on the land the gift would be valid and the condition void; but if the land is unproductive the gift would be void; so in the *Fatâwai Kâzi Khân*. Similarly if a man were to give a vine to another, and were to condition that the donee should give him the crop thereof, the gift would be valid and the condition void; so in the *Muhît-us-Sarakhsi*. And Asbijâni says if a person were to make a gift to or *sadakah* for another of something and condition that the latter should return a third or fourth of the same......the gift would be valid, and the donee would make no return....so in the *Tâtâr-Khâniéh*."(2)

---

(1) This must not be confused with gifts for *consideration*.

(2) Vol. IV, pp. 553-4.

It will be noticed that in all these illustrations, the condition imposed on the donee is such as to defeat the whole purpose of the gift, for although the transaction purports to be a complete transfer of the *entire* thing, the right is so limited that it renders its enjoyment in some cases nugatory, in others only gives the *corpus* in part. And, therefore, effect is given to what is supposed to be the primary object, *viz.*, the gift is held to be valid whilst the condition is avoided.

This, in substance, is the meaning of the jurists.

Examples of valid conditions.

It is otherwise with a gift by *A* to *B* of a certain property without any restriction on the power of disposition, but subject to the condition that *B* should pay periodically to *A*, or to *A* and his heirs, a *part of the usufruct of the property*. In such a case both the gift and the condition would be valid. And if *B* should alienate the property, the assignee would take it subject to the condition.

In these cases the reason is obvious, for the reservation of an interest by the donor for himself, or for himself and his heirs, does not interfere with the right of property vesting in the transferee by the act of transfer.

An analytical examination of the principles with due regard to the main purpose of the Mussulman Law, shows that where the intention is clear to transfer the entire right of property in the *corpus* (*'ain*) of the gift, a mere reservation of interest in its rents and issues, or any profit accruing therefrom or a subordinate share in its enjoyment does not affect the validity. And this view is not restricted to the case of a minor donee.

Nawab Umjad Ally Khan v. Mussumat Mohumdee Begum.

In *Nawab Umjad Ally Khan* v. *Mussumat Mohumdee Begum*,(1) the Judicial Committee of the Privy Council deal with this principle with great amplitude and lucidity, and lay down, it is submitted, the correct doctrine applicable to such cases.

It is necessary to examine in some detail the legal aspects of this case.

The father of the appellant (Nawab Umjad Ally Khan) some years before his death transferred and endorsed a considerable number of Government Promissory Notes which then stood in his name into the name of his son. But the income of the notes was all along remitted to the father under the directions of the appellant.

(1) [1867], 11 Moo. I. A., 517.

Later the father conveyed to the son for a nominal consideration certain landed property reserving to himself only the use of the same during his life.

On the death of the father the respondent (one of the daughters) put forward a claim that, as regards the Government Promissory Notes, the late Nawab was the real owner and that the appellant was only a "nominal holder."

Their Lordships dealing with this part of the case said as follows:—"The first in order of these matters involves an important point of Mahommedan Law relating to gifts *inter vivos*.... Before the validity of this gift, as one *inter vivos* is determined, it must first be considered by their Lordships what the real nature of the transfer was. The legal title in the Promissory Notes was undoubtedly in the appellant in his father's lifetime, by virtue of an act of the father. But though the transfer of a legal title will satisfy that provision of the Mahommedan Law which relates to the point of seisin, in its legal and technical sense, yet that alone will not suffice where no intention exists to transfer the beneficial ownership, either present or future. The facts relating to the gift have been most carefully investigated by Mr. Fraser, the Civil Judge.... Mr. Fraser's observations as to the mode of dealing amongst natives living amongst themselves as a family, in a state of family union, and dealing in this state with the proceeds of property standing in the names of separate members of the family, to whom it has been transferred by the parent and head of the family and to the deference to his wishes and arrangements, and acquiescence in them commonly exhibited, are forcible arguments to exclude the notion of fraudulent concealment of design in a transaction circumstanced as the present. They strengthen the probability of an intended transfer of property in the life-time of the donor, with a reservation of the use or proceeds of the money transferred during the life-time of the donor only."

"It remains to be considered whether a real transfer of property by a donor in his life-time under the Mahommedan Law, reserving not the dominion over the *corpus* of the property, nor any share of dominion over the *corpus*, but simply stipulating for and obtaining the right to the recurring produce during his life-time is an incomplete gift by the Mahommedan Law. The text of the *Hedâya* seems to include the very proposition and to negative it. The thing to be returned is not identical but something different, see *Hedâya*, 'Gifts,' Vol. III, Book XXX, p. 294, where the objection being raised that a participation of property in the thing given invalidates a gift, the answer is, 'The donor is subjected to a participation in a thing which is not the subject of his grant, namely, the use (of the whole indivisible article) for his gift related to the substance of the article, not to the use of it.' Again, if the agreement for the reservation of the interest to the father for his life be treated as a repugnant condition, repugnant to the whole enjoyment by the donee, here the Mahommedan Law defeats not the grant but the condition; *Hedâya*, 'Gifts,' Vol. III, Book XXX, p. 307. But as this arrangement between the father and the son is founded on a valid consideration, the son's undertaking is valid and could be enforced against him in the Courts of India as an agreement raising a trust and constituting a valid obligation to make a return of the proceeds during the time stipulated. The contention of the parties therefore is not found to violate any provision of the *Hedâya*, and the transfer is complete."

This decision may, at first sight, seem to be in conflict with the doctrine of the Hanafî lawyer Abu'l Kâsim as-Saffâr(1), but it must be borne in mind that, in the Hanafî Law, much of the voidableness of conditions arises from the character of the Arabic expressions. As a general rule, it may be stated that, where the intention to make an absolute transfer *in præsenti* of all proprietary right is clear, any condition which derogates from the *immediate* completeness of the gift is regarded as void. Where the condition, however, may be given effect to without in any way interfering with or detracting from the immediate completeness of the gift, or rather the immediate transfer of the right in the substance of the gift, *the condition as well as the gift are valid.* If a man were to give absolutely his property to another and place the donee in possession thereof, so far as *its* nature admits, to use the language of the *Majm'aa-ul-Anhar*, with the condition that the whole or a portion of the income should be given to him, the donor, or to any body else *during his life-time*, such a reservation or condition would not prevent the property vesting immediately in the donee. The condition, therefore, would be valid. So also, if a person were to make a gift subject to the donee paying the

(1) *ante*, p. 135.

donor's debts, and place the donee in possession of the subject-matter of the gift, the condition would be valid. Or, if a donor were to make a condition that the donee should give a *part* of the income or pay an annuity to his heirs in perpetuity, and give effect to the donation by transferring the subject thereof to the dominion of the donee, as the condition in no wise interferes with the completeness of the gift, both the gift and the condition would become operative in law. In this view, the decision of their Lordships in the Privy Council seems to be in absolute accordance with the Hanafî Law.(1)

But where the donor continues to exercise rights of ownership over the property inconsistent with the transfer of proprietary interest, the gift has been held not to be operative.(2)

Contingent gift.

Gifts dependent upon contingencies are void, as stated before, according to both the schools. For example, a condition for the avoidance of a debt in words like the following :—" When to-morrow comes and thou happenest to die, then thou art discharged from my debt," is null and void. Or " shouldst thou die of this disease, this house is thine," in all these cases the gift is absolutely void. But a condition implying an immediate operation of the gift would be valid; for example, if a man were to say to another, " if you owe me any money, I absolve you of it," or " you will be absolved of my debt when I die."(3) (In the last case it becomes a legacy).

Hanafî doctrines.

When a person says to another, " that house is for thee; if thou diest before me it is mine, and if I die before thee it is thine," it is technically called a *rukba*. According to Abû Hanîfa and Mohammed, says Tahtâwi, such a transaction is void; according to Abû Yusuf, it takes effect as a gift. " But the former doctrine is correct. "

When a property is made over to another by way of a *rukba*, it will be held as an *'âriat*, that is, the donee shall have the loan of the thing without any disposing power over it, subject to the option of the donor to resume his gift or loan at any time.

---

(1) In this case the parties were Shiahs, and their Lordships could have maintained the gift as well as the condition on the basis of the Shiah Law without reference to the *Hedâya* which is a work on Hânafi Law.

(2) *Nawab Ibrahim Ali Khan* v. *Ummat-ul-Zuhra* [1896], L. R., 24 I. A., 1.

(3) *Radd-ul-Muhtâr*, IV, p. 794.

Under the Hanafî Law, a life-grant or *'umra*, if made in terms which imply an absolute gift, takes effect as a *hiba*, the condition limiting the gift being held void. A gift to *A* for life and remainder to *B* takes effect as an absolute gift to *A*,—to use an English expression, gives him an estate in fee.(1)

A mere grant of the usufruct of a thing however, is, in the eye of the law, simple *'aâriat* or commodate loan which implies on the part of the donee the obligation of returning the self-same thing.(2)

The gift of a thing, which has been lost, when "recovered," is bad, according to Abû Yusuf. For example, if a man were to say to another, "I give thee the pearl which I have lost, recover it and take it." It would be a void gift, being the gift of a mere speculation. Zuffar, on the other hand, holds it to be valid and his rule appears to be the law.(3)

But the gift of an enforceable right is valid by *consensus*. For example, *A* may be entitled to a property which is in the possession of *B*. A gift by *A* to *C* of the property or rather the right to the property is valid.

A gift of a building without the land on which it is situated is valid.(4)

If the gift is made with an option to the donee to accept it or not, the option must be exercised at the place where the offer is made or when it comes to his knowledge.

If the donor make a gift reserving an option to himself to recall it at his pleasure, the gift is good and the option void.

A gift not void for an invalid condition.

A gift does not become void on account of an invalid condition. Accordingly, when an arrangement is entered into between a husband and wife in regard to their respective rights, and property is conveyed thereunder by one to the other, it takes effect as a gift and does not become void for any invalid condition. "But sale, mortgage, and lease," adds Kâzi Khân, "would be void for invalid conditions."

---

(1) Ahmed bin Hanbal and others, says the *Durr-ul-Mukhtâr*, have held a *rukba* to be invalid and an *'umra* to be valid on the authority of a tradition of the Prophet who declared that when a grant is made for another's life he takes it for his life.

(2) "A mere grant of usufruct is an *'aâriat* in a thing which can be used without being destroyed, but things which must be consumed in use, imply gift except in the case of money;" *Fatâwai Kâzi Khân*, IV, p. 230.

(3) *Radd-ul-Muhtâr*; Vol. IV, 795.

(4) *Durr-ul-Mukhtâr*, p. 236.

Where a man purchases a house and after obtaining possession thereof makes a gift of it, and subsequent to the gift another person obtains possession of a moiety on the ground of pre-emption, the gift as to the remainder is invalidated so far as the donee is concerned. In other words, he may return the remaining portion of the gift or keep it.(1)

An acknowledgment of *hiba* is effectual as to possession.

An acknowledgment of *hiba* implies an acknowledgment that all the necessary formalities were complied with. If a man were to say, "I have made a gift of a certain property to Zaid," *such acknowledgment will be effectual also as to possession*; (2) in other words, that he had delivered possession according to law. In this view, where a gift is made in writing, and the donor acknowledges at the time the deed is registered under the Indian Registration Act, that he had complied with all the requirements of the law, it would imply that possession had been duly parted with. If this view be correct, then the ruling in *Mogul Shah* v. *Mohammed Saheb*,(3) can hardly be said to be in conformity with the Mahommedan Law.

At the same time, it must be noted that such an acknowledgment raises merely a presumption and is not a conclusive proof that seisin had been delivered. In this connection, however, two matters must be borne in mind; *first*, the relation of the donee to the donor, and *secondly*, the ability of the donor to give possession within the meaning of the Mahommedan Law. For example, if the donee is an infant to all intents and purposes under the guardianship of the donor, delivery of seisin will not be required. Again, if the subject-matter of the gift is landed property and the donor is too ill to send for the tenants to make them attorn to the donee, his mere handing over of the title-deeds together with the deed of gift ought to amount to a sufficient authorisation to take possession of the property.

If a man direct his partner to give his share of the partnership assets to his adult son, and at the same time authorise the son to receive the same, it would take effect as a complete gift.

---

(1) *Durr-ul-Mukhtâr*, p. 236 (2) *Nawâdir.*
(3) [1887] I. L., 11 Bom., 517.

SECTION IV.

SHIAH DOCTRINES—LIMITED ESTATES.

Shiah Law.

THE Shiah Law recognises, to the fullest extent, the validity of limited estates and deals with the subject under a special chapter.

For example, if a grant is made by *A* to *B* for *B's* life, *B* would take, under such a grant, an estate for life; and on *B's* death the property would revert to the donor or his heirs. Similarly, a grant to *B* for life and then to *C*, absolutely: or a life-estate to *B* and then to *C* for life, and thereafter to *D* absolutely, is valid under the Shiah Law. So also a grant may validly be made to *A* for his life and thereafter to *A's* children absolutely. In other words, an estate for life or for several lives in succession is valid under the Shiah Law.

Commenting on the passage in the *Sharâya-ul-Islâm*, "and if one say 'I have given this house to you and to your descendants by way of *'umra*, the same is "*umra*," the *Jawâhir-ul-Kalâm* says "the same (*i.e.*, the *'umra* or life-estate) shall, therefore, continue to be binding so long as the descendants may be existing, and on their extinction the benefit shall revert to the donor. But as regards the house itself, the same remains (always) the property of the owner."(1)

Shiah doctrines—life-estates.

It is a matter for consideration how far the principle of the *Tagore Case*(2) will apply to these provisions of the Shiah Law, which does not require that the ultimate donees should be actually or constructively in existence at the time of the gift. So long as the first "taker" is in existence at the time the gift is made, the disposition becomes operative under the Shiah Law; the subsequent donees being required to be in being only when the intermediate estates come to an end. And the delivery or transmutation of possession *in præsenti* effected in his favour enures to the benefit of the persons entitled to "take" after him, for the reason, as is stated, that the change in the character of the possession once made fixes upon the grant the indicia of a *bonâ fide* transaction.

---

(1) According to the *Jawâhir* there is no difference so far as the legal effect is concerned between an *'umra, sukna* or *rukba*.

(2) 9 B. L. R., Supp. 377; L. R., I. A., 47.

Temporary grants or limited estates under the Shiah Law.

Temporary grants or limited estates receive different names according to the object with which such grants are made or such estates are created.(1)

(*a*) *Hubs* signifies literally the tying-up of property; technically it means settlements or grants limited to a certain time. *Hubs* is an act by which the proprietor confers on another person "gratuitously," that is, without any consideration, the enjoyment of the use or usufruct of a thing with a reservation of the owner's right of property in it. The reciprocal consent of the contracting parties, expressed or implied, with transmutation of possession, suffices to render the contract valid. This is analogous to the *'aâriat* of the Hanafî Law.

(*b*) "The enjoyment of the use or usufruct created for life,"—in other words, a life-estate, is called *al-'umra.*

(*c*) The enjoyment of the use of a house, without any right of property in it, is called *as-sukna*, "right of habitation."

(*d*) The enjoyment of the use or usufruct of a thing for a fixed and determinate period is called *ar-rukba.* This word literally signifies *servitude* and is applicable to the condition, which derogates from the completeness of the gift and cuts down an absolute gift to a limited estate.(2)

There is no special formula for effecting such a contract, but it may be made in the following words, such as, "I have granted to such a one the enjoyment of such a house or such a land for his life or for such a time," or in any other words, which express the intention of the proprietor. When it is for the life of the grantee, it is also called an *'umra.* The execution of the contract becomes obligatory after the delivery of the property. The contract by which the enjoyment and use of a house or habitation is conferred upon any one is put an end to by the death of the grantor, unless there is any other period fixed for it.

When a grant is made in these terms, "when you die it will revert to me," the reversion will take effect by the death of the donee.

When the grant of the usufruct is made for a limited and determinate period of time, the contract becomes obligatory at the

---

(1) *Juwâhir-ul-Kalâm*, chapter on *Sukna*, p. 619; Comp. *Banoo Begam* v. *Mir Abid Ali* [1907], I. L., 32 Bom., 172.

(2) See the example given in the *Mabsut, the Ghunia, Jâm'aa-ush-Shittât*, &c.

moment of the delivery of possession, and the proprietor cannot resume the subject-matter of the grant until after the expiration of the term fixed. A grant made for the life-time of the donor does not terminate upon the death of the donee ; the right passes to his heirs who enjoy the same until the death of the grantor.

A grant of the usufruct without determination of period might be revoked at any time at the will of the grantor.

Shiah doctrines-limited estates.

A limited estate, or the grant of the usufruct of some property for a determinate period, does not terminate by the sale of the *substance* of the thing ; the grantee has the right of holding possession of the thing given and enjoying the usufruct until after the expiration of the term of the grant. "Of every thing of which a *wakf* is valid, the *'umra* or granting for life is valid also, and the grant is not invalidated by the sale of the thing, *for the purchaser must fulfil to the life-tenant whatever was conditioned on his behalf.*"(1)

(1) See also the *Kifâyet-ul-Ahkâm*, the *Hadâik-un-Nâdireh* and the *Tâzkiret-ul-Fukaha.* In the *Hadâik*, Vol. V, p. 514, occurs the following passage :—

"It is well known among Jurists that *sukna*, *'umra* and *rukba* do not become null and void by sale."

"Since you know that the sale [of the property] is valid in these cases, as the benefit accruing therefrom has already been granted to another [the person enjoying the *sukna* or *'umra*], the purchaser, if he be aware of the fact, has no option [to put an end to the grant] because of his having purchased a thing the profit of which has already been disposed of. It is therefore obligatory on him to wait till the expiration of the period or [the termination of] the life-interest, after which the benefit will revert [to him]. But it is lawful for him, pending the period and during the subsistence of the life-interest, to derive benefit out of the property by sale, gift, emancipation and such other acts as do not interfere with that particular interest of *sukna or 'umra.*"

In the *Tazkirat-ul-Fukaha*, Vol. II (Chapter on *Wakf*), the same rule is thus stated :—

"If Zaid makes a gift of his house to 'Amr by way of a *sukna*, *'umra* or *rukba*, it does not cease to be his property ; and it is lawful for him to sell the house. In such case the *sukna* or *'umra* does not become null and void ; nay the *sâkin* (person enjoying the *sukna*) is entitled to the right of residence, which is already made over to him ; consequently, if the purchaser were aware of the fact, he has no option to annul the contract, but if he was not aware, it is optional for him to cancel the sale or to confirm it at the full price with a view to derive any other benefit from the property.

The same doctrine is enunciated in the *Kifâyat-ul-Ahkâm* :—

"And whatever can be given away as *wakf* is lawful to be given away as *'umra* or *rukba*. An estate so settled does not become null and void by sale—nay the fulfilment of what is stipulated is obligatory and the purchaser shall wait till the expiration of the period or [termination of] the life-interest, after which the profit reverts to him."

In the *Jâm'aa-i-Abbâsi*, the rule is stated in the following terms :—

"If a person were to say to another 'reside in this house so long as you are alive,' then there are three conditions necessary for the same. *First*, proposal such

The right of *sukna* or habitation granted in general terms empowers the grantee to live in the house with his relatives and children; but he cannot transfer the right to any other person unless there is a special condition to that effect.

A grant of a *sukna* to *A* and his children will give to the grantee and his children, or the survivors, the right of residing in the house until the death of the last surviving child.

A grant limited to the donee and his *wâ-mundagân*(1) (those whom he leaves surviving), confers a life-estate on the donee and the persons existing at the time of his death, and reverts to the grantor or his heirs upon the death of the last surviving member of the grantee's family.

The passage in the *Sharâya*, that a grant to *A* and his *akab* only takes effect as a life-estate, as if the word *'akab* was not mentioned, refers to the case of an *'umra*, the author of the *Sharâya* being of opinion that the mention of the word *'ukab* (which signifies literally 'a person coming after') is not like the mention of descendants(2) and therefore does not convey an absolute estate.

as, 'I have given you room in such and such a house' or 'I have given you a life-interest [in such and such an estate]' or 'I have given you such and such a thing for such and such a time' and such other expressions as may be in keeping with the above; *secondly*, acceptance; *thirdly*, possession. And if the act of causing one to reside in a house is made contingent on his (the grantor's) own life or to that of the resident or if no time is fixed, it (the contract) becomes binding on his (the *sâkin's*) taking possession [of the house], and the same reverts to the owner after the death of any of them as stipulated. Hence, if one says 'you are to reside in this house so long as you are living, the same reverts to the owner on the death of the grantee [*lit. sâkin*, resident)]. And as to this case, if the owner dies it shall not be lawful for the heirs of the owner to eject the *sâkin*. And if one says 'reside in this house till the time of my death', then the *sâkin* should vacate the same on the death of the owner. But if the *sâkin* dies before the owner, it shall not be lawful for the owner to eject the heirs of the resident during his own lifetime. If the contract is not made contingent on death, he can eject the *sâkin* whenever he likes. And whatever may lawfully be given by gift may be given in *sukna* and *'umra*. The contract of *sukna* is absolute, and the *sâkin* is entitled to reside in it with his family (only) unless is stipulated for other people besides them in which case it is lawful for them [also to live there]."

In these excerpts, mention is made of one donee only for the purpose of illustrating the doctrine enunciated. But the principle is clearly applicable to several donees taking limited interests one after the other; See the *Jawâhir-ul-Kalâm*, Chap. on Gift.

(1) *Wâ-mundagan* includes such persons as the deceased leaves him surviving in his family, whether an heir or not, *e.g.*, a son and the son of a pre-deceased son widows, daughters, children's children, &c.

(2) *Jawâhir-ul-Kalam*, Chap. on Gift.

Limited estates, contd.

An *'umra* and *rukba*, for one life and for a limited period to his *wâ-mundagân* (those whom he leaves surviving), is valid; so also an *'umra* for several lives in succession.

A *rukba* for an *intermediate* period is valid, but is resumable at the will of the donor. A sale of the subject of the grant would put an end to the grant.

The grantee cannot let a house or mansion given to him for habitation without the special permission of the grantor.

All grants constituted in favour of definite individuals, *without specification of time*, terminate by the decease of the proprietor or grantor, and become a portion of his inheritance. A grant to *A* in these terms, "if you die before me, the property will revert to me; if I die before you, it will become yours," will take effect according to some, in case the donor predeceases the donee, as an *'umra* in favour of the latter; according to others, as an absolute gift (provided there is no other limitation.)

According to Makki, the Shaikh and others, a succession of life-estates is valid and lawful.(1)

Where a grant is to *A*, and *his children*, "generation after generation," or where a grant is made to *A*, with the addition of the usual expression which implies a perpetual descent in the grantee's line, *e.g.*, *naslan b'aad nasl batnan b'aad batn*, the grant conveys to the grantee an absolute estate, the terms used implying perpetuity of the grant. In fact, a grant to the donee and his descendants gives to the donee an estate in fee subject to no restraint of any kind upon alienation or otherwise.

Nasir Husain v. *Sughra Begum.*

In the case of *Nasir Husain* v. *Sughra Begum* (2) it appeared that the plaintiff's father, Zulfikar Husain, executed, on the 23rd of November 1868, a deed of gift, in respect of a certain house belonging to him, to his cousins, Ali Muhammud Muzaffar Husain and the defendant Abdul Muzaffar, and by another deed of gift duly registered and executed on the 14th of December 1872, he assigned his proprietary right in the same house to the plaintiff Nasir Husain. The right of Ali Muhammad, one of the above-named transferees under the deed, dated the 23rd of November 1868, was attached in execution of a decree against him held by the defendant Sughra Begum. The plaintiff objected in the execution depart-

---

(1) See *post*, p. 111.

(2) [1883] I. L., 5 All., p. 505.

ment, but as his objections were disallowed, he brought a suit to establish his right to the house in dispute and for a declaration that on the death of Ali Muhammad all his right in the property ceased and terminated. The main point for determination in the case, therefore, was whether under the terms of the instrument of transfer, dated the 23rd of November 1868, the proprietary right in the house had passed to the transferees. The material portion of that instrument was as follows :—

"I have of my own accord and free will given the house to my brothers Ali Muhammad Muzaffar Husain and Abdul Muzaffar for their residence and that of their heirs, generation after generation. I or my heirs neither have nor shall have any claim regarding the house in question, but if the said brothers or their heirs attempt to sell or mortgage the house, I or my heirs shall have a claim to the house; so long as a sale or mortgage is not effected, I or my heirs shall have no connection or concern with the house."

The Court of First Instance held that the right of Ali Muhammad, one of the donees, was heritable and transferable, and dismissed the suit. The plaintiff appealed to the High Court, contending *inter alia* that the parties to the suit being Shiahs were not governed by the texts of Mahommedan Law relied upon by the Lower Court which were applicable to Sunnis.

The High Court of Allahabad in affirming the judgment of the First Court made the following remarks :—

" We are of opinion that the Subordinate Judge has come to a right conclusion in this case, and that the house, the subject of the suit, was taken by the defendants not merely for the purpose of residence but absolutely. The operative words in the deed of gift are very clear and strong." (After stating these words the learned Judges continued as follows) :—" Now the meaning of such a conveyance is perfectly clear. The purpose and inducement of the gift of the house is residence, but the gift itself is to the donees and 'their heirs, generation after generation,' and what follows is merely in the nature of recommendation, and has not in law the effect of limiting the estate in the house itself. This is the construction of such an instrument under all systems of law, European or Indian. It is clearly conformable to the law of England, and the Subordinate Judge shows that it is in accordance with Mahommedan Law."

" It was argued at the hearing on behalf of the appellant that the parties in the present case are Shiahs, and that the text of the Mahommedan Law and of the other authorities referred to related *Nasir Husain v. Sughra Begum.*

to the more numerous Moslem sect, the Sunnis. The parties in the present case are undoubtedly Shiahs, and if their Imameea Law had contained any precept or provision inconsistent with the Sunni Law referred to by the Subordinate Judge, it would have been our duty to have given effect to such a state of things. But the careful examination which we have given to the doctrines of the Imameea Code as expounded by Mr. Baillie, 1869, page 226, *et seq.*, has convinced us that there is no difference on this subject between the two systems of Mahommedan Law. In fact, while the Sunni Law is very distinct, the Shiah or Imameea Law is silent on the subject; the intention in the latter system evidently being the adoption and application of the Sunni rule to Shiahs(1), where their own Imameea Law does not speak, the only cases of gifts of this nature alluded to in the latter being gifts plainly limited to a life-interest."

"There is a passage in Baillie's Imameea Law, pp. 226-227, which, if expressing undoubted Shiah doctrine, perhaps deserves some notice. The passage is this:—If one should say, 'I have given this mansion to thee for life, and to thy successor,' it would only be an *'umra* for his own life, and there would be no transfer to the life-holder according to the most approved opinion, just as if he had not said 'to thy successor.' If such is the Imameea Law, it is difficult to understand and still more difficult to appreciate a limitation of interest which necessitates the striking out from the words of gift its distinctly expressed 'extension to a successor.' The author does not explain what he is pleased to call 'the most approved opinion.' It is at least a most arbitrary construction of the gift confessing as it appears to do that it could not stand if the terms 'to thy successor' also remained part of the gift. In the present case, however, the estate given by the gift is conveyed in much larger terms giving the house to the donees 'for their residence and that of their heirs, generation after generation, I or my heirs neither have nor shall have any claim regarding the house in question,' words which, if they are capable of any legal meaning, clearly and distinctly bestow the right to the thing given absolutely."

(1) This view is founded on a clear misapprehension of the Shiah Law.

CHAPTER III.

THE REVOCATION OF GIFTS.

REGARDING the power of the donor to revoke a simple *hiba* or a gratuitous gift, there is considerable divergence between the schools.

Revocation—Shâfeï and Mâliki Law.

According to the Shâfeïs and Mâlikis, no gift (excepting such as have been made by parents to their children) can be revoked, whether change of possession has taken place or not. This, of course, is independent of the ground of coercion or want of comprehension.

The parents, however, may revoke gifts made by themselves to their children. But this right of revocation is not absolute. When the gift is in the nature of a *sadakah* (a grant or donation made with the object of securing happiness in future life, or for deserving the reward of God), the gift is irrevocable.

The parents are also precluded from revoking their donations to their children under the following circumstances :—

(1) When the subject-matter of the gift does not retain its original form, or has disappeared *in toto* or in part, or has been sold or exchanged ; mere increase or decrease in the value, from a fluctuation of the market, does not come under this head.

(2) When the donee has contracted a marriage and that marriage has taken place in consideration of the thing given.

(3) When the donee has died and the property has passed to his heirs.

Shiah Law.

According to the Shiah Law, " after possession has been taken of a gift, it cannot be lawfully retracted when made in favour of parents (according to general consensus), nor even when the donee is any other relative, by consanguinity, of the donor, though on this point there is some difference of opinion, which, however, is not approved." Nor can a gift made to the wife by the husband or to the husband by the wife be revoked according to the Shaikh (the author of the *Mabsût*) and an influential body of lawyers, if transmutation of possession has taken place. They hold that

Revocation of a gift.

husband and wife stand on the same footing in respect of their mutual gifts as kindred by consanguinity. These Shiah lawyers are in accord with the Hanafîs, who, as will be seen afterwards, hold that the marriage-relation prevents the revocation of gifts.

The author of the *Sharâya*, however, though he declares it to be abominable for a wife to revoke a gift made to the husband and for a husband to revoke a gift made to the wife, does not apparently consider it illegal. Considering, however, how much of the moral, or rather ecclesiastical, is mixed up in the *Sharâya* with the legal, I am inclined to think in the result he agrees with the Shaikh.

Gift to a stranger may be revoked.

A gift to a stranger may be revoked at any time so long as the substance of the thing given is in existence. After it has perished or changed ownership, there can be no revocation. In like manner, a gift cannot be revoked if anything has been received in exchange, though the exchange should be of little value. Mere use by the donee of the thing given is not sufficient to preclude the donor from revoking, unless in the use by the donee the subject of the gift has substantially changed its character. A question, however, arises whether when transmutation of possession has taken place, the donor can revoke the gift without the consent of the donee.

Hanafî Law.

According to the Hanafî Law, though the revocation of a gift is worthy of reprobation from a moral point of view, yet it is not illegal. The revocation of a gift, says the *Fatâwai-Alamgiri*, "is abominable under any circumstance, but is valid nevertheless." The consequence of this principle is that in every instance a gift may be revoked before delivery of possession, but after transmutation of possession has been effected, certain kinds of gifts cannot be revoked, whilst the others may be revoked under the decree of the Judge or with the consent of the donee.

When a gift is irrevocable.

When a gift is made to a blood-relation within the prohibited degrees *and delivery of possession has taken place*, the donor has no right of revocation.(1) In order to make a gift irrevocable, it will be seen that not only must it be to a blood-relation but such relation must be within the prohibited degrees. A gift to a cousin is not irrevocable, inasmuch as a cousin is not within the prohibited degrees. Similarly, a gift to the mother of one's wife is revocable as she, though within the prohibited degrees, is not a relation.

---

(1) See *Enaet Hossein* v. *Khoobunnissa* [1869], 11 W. R., 320.

Hanafi Law—Revocation of gifts.

In the case of gifts to persons other than relations within the prohibited degrees, *previous to delivery* the donor can revoke the gift of his own motion either in whole or in part. After delivery, he must obtain either the consent of the donee or the decree of the Judge to validate the revocation. *E.G.*, where a gift has been completed by delivery of the property to the donee, and the donor seeks to revoke it on grounds apart from fraud, misrepresentation or undue influence, such revocation can only be effectuated by the decree of the Court, unless the donee consents to return it to the donor without recourse to the Judge. Gifts obtained by fraud or compulsion are voidable in all cases.

All the jurists are agreed in holding that a revocation under a Judge's decree is a cancellation of the original gift, but there is some difference of opinion whether revocation by mutual consent is tantamount to cancellation. The tendency of precedents, however, is in favour of its being a cancellation. Thus, when one person has given a thing to another, who gives it to a third party and then revokes the gift, the power of revocation becomes re-vested in the first donor; but this would not be the case if the second donee was to return the thing to *his* donor by way of a gift; "for the second revocation being a cancellation, it follows that the thing given returns to the former state of property, and that the donor becomes again the proprietor without any necessity for taking possession anew." After revocation the subject of the gift constitutes an *amânat* or trust in the hands of the donee, so that if it should perish he is not responsible for the loss. But when the revocation is neither by a Judge's decree nor by mutual consent, and the donee gives back the subject of the gift to the donor who accepts it, he does not again become the proprietor of it till he has taken possession. When the donor does obtain possession, the gift by the donee takes effect as a revocation by the Judge's decree or by mutual consent, and the donee has no power to revoke it.

Power of revocation.

Abû Yusuf is reported to have held that, until an order has been passed by a Judge for cancelling a gift, the donee may use and dispose of the subject of it; but any such use or disposal, after the Judge has made his order, is unlawful; and the opinions of Abû Hanîfa and Mohammed are to the same effect. If the subject of the gift should perish in the hands of the donee, after the passing of the Kâzi's order and previous to the donor's retaking possession, the donee is not responsible for the loss, unless possession had been demanded of him and he had refused to give it. If, after a gift has been revoked but before any decree, the donee should give the subject-matter of the gift to the donor who takes possession, it would take effect as a revocation by order of the Judge.

Suppose the donor expressly foregoes the power of revocation, it still remains intact and does not "drop." But if the right of revocation is compounded by the donor for something given to him by the donee, the composition is valid and the thing becomes an exchange which extinguishes the right of revocation.

Revocation must be in express words.

The revocation must be effected in appropriate terms, such as, "I have revoked the gift," or "restored it to my own property," or "I have cancelled or dissolved it."

If without using any such expression, the donor contracts to sell the subject-matter of the gift or to give it in pledge, such act would not amount to a revocation. And if the revocation is conditional, it is ineffective. For example, if he should say, "I will revoke," or "this gift will stand revoked when such an event happens," or "on such a date," it would not be valid, because revocation can neither be suspended on a condition nor referred to a future time.(1)

Circumstances under which a gift is not revocable.

A gift is not revocable under the following circumstances :—

(*a*) When the subject-matter of the gift has passed out of the possession of the donee by gift, sale, or any other form of alienation by which the right of property is transferred ;

(*b*) When the donee is dead and the subject-matter of the gift has devolved on his or her heirs ;

(*c*) When the donor is dead—in other words, his heirs have not the power of revocation, the option of revocation being a personal right in the donor ;

(*d*) When the thing given is lost ;

(*e*) When the gift is for a consideration ;

(*f*) When the subject-matter of the gift has altered in substance in the possession of the donee ;

(*g*) When an increase or accretion has taken place in the thing given, and such increment or accretion is of such a nature as to be united with or inseparable from it. And it makes no difference in the irrevocability of the gift whether the increase be in

(1) *Fatâwai-Alamgiri*, IV, p. 537.

consequence of an act of the donee or without such act, and whether it has issued from the thing itself (such as fruit on trees) or be an accession to it (such as accretion by growth). But it must be incorporated with or form part of the body of the subject-matter of the gift and imply an addition to or enhancement in its value. Dyeing, sewing, porterage, &c., are considered as causes which extinguish the power of revocation ;

Mere transfer from one place to another, when it adds to the value and has occasioned expense, is sufficient to prevent revocation. A separate increase does not prevent the revocation of a gift nor any loss or damage sustained by the subject of the gift ;

Hanafi Law—Marital relationship bars revocation.

(*h*) When the donor and donee stand to each other in the marital relationship. But such a gift in order to be irrevocable must be made during the subsistence of the relationship. For example, a gift made prior to marriage may be revoked. But when a gift is made during marriage and the relationship is afterwards dissolved, the gift cannot be revoked. Difference in the creed of the married parties makes no difference in the irrevocability of the gift.

(*i*) Relationship of blood within the prohibited degrees is a bar to revocation, without any restriction as to the creed of the donor or the donee.(1)

(*j*) The natural growth of the subject-matter of the gift also debars the donor from revoking.

Where the power of revocation exists, it may be exercised either with reference to the whole or a part.

(1) *E. g.*, Parents and grandparents how high soever and children and their descendants how low soever ; sisters and brothers and their descendants, paternal and maternal uncles and aunts ; *Radd-ul-Muhtâr.*

" If a person make a gift of anything to his relation within the prohibited degrees, it is not lawful for him to resume it ; *Hedâya.*

Where an alien who has obtained the protection of a Moslem State, while living in the country of Islâm, makes a gift to his Moslem brother, and then goes away leaving permission to the donee to take possession which is done, it is valid in law ; but if the gift was made by the Moslem to the alien brother and he went to the *Dâr-ul-Harb* before acceptance, the gift would become void ; *Mabsût.* Where a gift is made to the mandatory of a brother, it cannot be revoked. And if the gift is rejected by the mandatory and accepted by the principal, it is valid ; *Kinia.*

See s. 126 of the Transfer of Property Act. But under s. 129, nothing in Chapter VII (Chapter relating to gifts) " shall be deemed to affect any rule of Mahomedan Law."

When a gift is revoked, the donor can exercise his proprietary rights from the time the subject of the gift comes into his possession; but he can give no antecedent effect to them. Thus, when a man has made a gift of a house and delivered it to the donee, and a house adjacent to it is sold, after which he revokes the gift, he has no right of pre-emption in regard to the second house.

No revocation in the case of a discharge of a debt.

When a debtor has been discharged from his liability, the donor or creditor has no power of revocation in regard to the debt so discharged.

According to the *Khazânat-ul-Muftiïn*, relationship arising from fosterage or affinity does not bar revocation.

Where one person makes to another the gift of a horse, and the donee has it trained, there is no power of revocation on the part of the donor. Approximate accompaniments acquired after the gift debar the right of revocation.(1)

The removal of the subject-matter of the gift from one place to another at expense or with labour bars revocation. If a man were to make a gift of clothes to another who has them washed by a washerman, the right is barred.

If a person make a gift of some dirhems to another, and then borrow them from the donee, the right of revocation is lost, the character of the subject having changed.

As after delivery of possession revocation does not take effect without the decree of the Judge or the donee's consent, if a person were to make a gift and deliver possession thereof to the donee, and after that were to take it back without the donee's consent, or the order of a Judge, and the thing be lost, the donor is liable for damages.

"If a woman make a gift to her husband and then allege that it was extorted from her by force or threats, her claim should be received."(2)

When a gift is made simultaneously or jointly to a relative within the prohibited degrees and to a person not so related, the gift to the latter may be revoked.

Sadakah not revocable—

(*a*) A *sadakah* or gift by way of a pious offering completed by possession cannot be revoked.

---

(1) *Fatâwai Kâzi Khân in locô.*

(2) Probably when supported by *prima facie* evidence—See *Moonshee Buzlur Rahim* v. *Shamsunnissa* [1865], 11 Moo. Ind. App., p. 310.

Any gift made with a view to recompense in future life is a *sadakah* and irrevocable. A *sadakah* may be made in favour of any individual, rich or poor, a relation or a stranger. The difference between *hiba* and *sadakah* consists in the object with which the donation is made, *viz.*, in the case of *hiba*, the desire is to increase the mutual affection of the parties or to evidence esteem(1); in the case of *sadakah* the object is, as the *Hedâya* puts it, "to acquire merit in the sight of the Lord." Vows for almsgivings, when actually carried out, take effect as *sadakah* and are governed by the same rules. "*Sadakah* requires seisin of the subject of the gift. Like gift, it is not valid unless attended by seisin, as it is gratuitous in the same manner as a gift. Neither is a *sadakah* lawful where it consists of an undivided part of a thing capable of division. Retractation of a *sadakah* is not lawful; because the object in making a *sadakah* is merit in the sight of God, and that has been obtained. If also a person make a pious offering to a rich man, it is not lawful to retract therefrom on a favourable construction of the law, because to acquire merit in the sight of God may sometimes be the object in making a pious donation to the rich. In the same manner also, if a person make a gift of anything to a poor man, it is not lawful to retract it, because the object in such gift is merit and that has been obtained." Its *raison d'être.*

(*b*) Before delivery of possession, a gift may be revoked without the order of the Kâzi or the consent of the donee. Summary rules as revocation

(*c*) If possession has been given to the donee, he is entitled to retain the gift and use its profits until the Kâzi has made his order.

(*d*) If a person were to make a gift of a house to another, and the donee subsequently has it painted or plants trees in or about it or in any way alters it, the gift is irrevocable.(2)

(*e*) When a portion of the gift is destroyed the remaining portion may be revoked.

(*f*) When a gift is made to two *ghair-mahram*(3) the portion of any one of them may be revoked, the gift as to the other remaining good.

(*g*) If a gift is made by two persons to one donee, any one of them may exercise the right of revocation in respect of his share without the consent of the other.

---

(1) *Mishkât; Fatâwai Kâzi Khân* and *Sharâya-ul-Islâm in loco.* For the meaning of the word *Sadakah*, see *post*.

(2) Comp. *Nunda Singh* v. *Meer Jaffer Shah*, 1 Sel. R. 6 note.

(3) A relation *not* within the prohibited degrees.

(*h*) Express withdrawal of the power of revocation does not destroy it.

Discharge of a debt cannot be revoked.

(*i*) There is no power of revocation in the case of a gift of a debt to a debtor. The debt becomes satisfied or cancelled by the gift and therefore does not exist to be revoked.

(*j*) If a person were to make a gift to another of a piece of land, which is unoccupied at the time and destitute of buildings and plantations, and the donee were to plant trees or erect buildings on it, the donor would not be entitled to revoke his gift. A small temporary erection, such as a shed, does not operate as a bar to revocation. Any actual and substantial improvement is sufficient to prevent the donor from exercising the right.

Acceptance of consideration a bar to revocation.

(*k*) The acceptance by the donor of a consideration or *ewaz, however small*, is a bar to revocation; and though the *ewaz* for the gift may have been made voluntarily by a third person on behalf of the donee, its acceptance by the donor would deprive him of his right of revocation.

(*l*) If the donee has given anything in exchange for the gift and a portion of the gift proves to be the property of some other person who recovers it from the donee, in that case the donee is entitled to receive from the donor a proportionate share of the exchange given by him. If, on the contrary, any portion of the consideration form the property of another person, the donor in such a case would not be entitled to resume a proportionate share of the gift, but he may return to the donee the remainder of the consideration or exchange in his hands and then resume his gift.

(*m*) When a person revokes his gift either by virtue of a decree of the Kâzi or with the consent of the donee, it is in effect a cancellation of the original gift and not a gift *de novo* on the part of the donee and therefore seisin by the donor is not, in such a case, a requisite condition.

(*n*) Revocation is lawful with respect to an undivided portion. If a revocation amounted to a gift *de novo* from the donee to the donor, seisin, say the Hanafî lawyers, would be a requisite condition, and consequently revocation with respect to an undivided portion would not be lawful.

The principles dealing with the power of a donor to revoke a gift are of importance in considering the question how far a transfer subsequent to a valid donation is effective or otherwise. For example, if a person were to make a gift to his child and then purport to sell it to another, such sale, though for a *bonâ fide* consideration, would not be valid. Similarly, if the gift were to a relative *not* within the prohibited degrees, who was put in possession of the property and who subsequent to the gift made some alteration or improvement in the same, a sale thereof by the donor would not be valid, for in both these cases the right of the donor had become extinguished and it was no more his to convey to another. The Transfer of Property Act (IV of 1882) leaves untouched the provisions of the Mahommedan Law on this point : (See *s.* 2, *cl. d.*)

CHAPTER IV.

RULES REGARDING CONSIDERATION OR *EWAZ.*

SECTION I.

THE DIFFERENT KINDS OF EWAZ.

Ewaz or considera- tion for a gift.

WE have so far dealt with gratuitous gifts; grants or donations for a consideration stand on a different footing. According to the original conception, which in itself was a development of the earlier rules, "*ewaz* or consideration was of two kinds; one which was subsequent to the contract (of gift), the other which was conditioned in it."(1) In other words, in the first case the consideration was delivered to the donor after his gift, and the transaction was treated as a case of mutual gift. There was no stipulation regarding the giving of *ewaz*, but the moment it was received by the donor his right of revocation dropped.

Hiba-b'il-ewaz.

This evidently was the earliest form of a gift for a consideration. The *Hiba-b'il-ewaz* of later times is clearly a development of this kind of gift.

Hiba-ba-shart-ul-ewaz.

In the other kind, the consideration was expressly stipulated in the contract, and when once it was received the transaction acquired the legal character of a sale. The modern *hiba-ba-shart-ul-ewaz* has unquestionably sprung from the above.

Dealing with the first kind of *ewaz*—a consideration which comes after the contract of gift—the *Fatâwai Alamgiri* says "that an *ewaz* of that kind requires discussion from two points of view, *viz.*, *first*, what are the conditions necessary for the validity of such consideration and when the thing [as *ewaz*] becomes such, and *second* what is its nature." It then proceeds to state the conditions. Summarised they amount to this—in the first place, it must be distinctly specified that the consideration is in lieu of the gift, and that the consideration should not form a portion of the subject-matter of the gift. If the consideration be a portion of the gift, it would not be valid

(1) *Fatâwai Alamgiri*, Vol. IV, p. 549.

and there would be no *ewaz*. But if such a change has taken place in the thing given, as would prevent revocation of the gift, part of it may be constituted a consideration or *ewaz* for the remainder. If two things are given by two different contracts, one of them may be given in exchange for the other. It is also a condition that the consideration must be secured to the grantor. If the grantor has to make over the consideration to anybody else, or if a right is established to the whole of it in anybody else then there is no exchange and the gift may be revoked. But if a portion of the *ewaz* becomes lost the remainder is a good consideration for the entire gift.(1)

As regards its "nature," the consideration which is given after the "contract" is regarded as a gift *ab initio*. But though the subject of the exchange is regarded as a gift, the giver (the original donee) has no power to revoke it after giving it. And after possession has been taken of the *ewaz* by the donor of the original gift, the donee's power to revoke the gift ceases absolutely. So that whether the *ewaz* was given by the donee or by a stranger, with or without his direction, neither the donor nor the donee can reclaim from the other what he has become possessed of. "All the conditions of gift are applicable to the *ewaz*; and the transaction does not come within the meaning of a contract of *m'uâwizat*, or mutual exchange, either in its inception or completion. Hence, it is not subject to *shufâ'a* [or the right of pre-emption]; nor can the thing given be rejected on either side on account of defect; so in the *Muhîi us-Sarakhsi*."

Hiba-ba-shart-ul-ewaz or gift with a condition of exchange

"The second kind of *ewaz*," says the *Fatâwai-Alamgiri*, "is what is stipulated in the contract." "When a gift is made on the condition that something should be given in lieu thereof, the conditions which apply to gifts shall apply to it, at its inception, so that an *ewaz* of property which is subject to the rule of *mushâ'a*, or anything that admits of partition, is not valid. Property is not established in the subject *before possession*, and each of the parties may refuse delivery. But after mutual possession has been taken, the effect is that of sale; and the donor cannot revoke his gift nor the donee the *ewaz*. *Shufâ'a* (right of pre-emption) is established by the transaction; and each of the parties may return the thing of which he

(1) Comp. Baillie's Dig., 2nd Ed., p. 541.

took possession for any defect." "According to *kyâs* (analogy),' says the *Fatâwai-Kâzi Khân*, "a gift on condition of an exchange ought to be a sale in its inception as well as in its completion." "When a man gives a mansion to two men on condition that they should pay an *ewaz*, or exchange of a thousand dirhems, the ***transaction amounts to a lawful sale after mutual delivery of possession***; so it is stated in the *Kinia*."(1)

Hiba-b'il-ewaz not revocable.

Where a person gives an *ewaz* for the whole of a gift, it bars revocation, ***whatever the amount of the consideration may be***; if the *ewaz* be for a part of the gift, the part for which there is no *ewaz* may be revoked, but not that part for which the *ewaz* was given.(2) It is not necessary that the donee himself should give the consideration, for an *ewaz* given by a stranger is lawful, whether by the direction of the donee or not. Where a person other than the donee gives the *ewaz*, he cannot recover it from the donee unless he (the donee) made himself specifically liable for it.

"The general principle in cases of this kind is," says the *Fatâwai-Kâzi Khân*, "that when anything is demandable of a person *in specie*, and is obligatory upon him, his direction to another to pay it is a cause of recourse against himself without any condition of responsibility, and that when a thing is not demandable from a person *in specie* and is not obligatory on him, his direction to another to pay it is not a cause of recourse against him, unless his responsibility is made a condition of the payment."

Circumstances under which a revocation may be made even when *ewaz* has been given.

If the father of an infant were to grant to another, by way of a gift, some property belonging to his child and receive from that person something in exchange, he may revoke the gift, or the donee may revoke his consideration, at any time they like. And when a person has given something to a minor, and his father makes an *ewaz* for it out of the minor's property, the exchange is not lawful though the gift were made on condition of an *ewaz*. The reason of both the above principles is obvious, for the father has no right to deal with the property of the minor, except for certain specific purposes.

Where a man, suffering from an illness to which he eventually succumbs, makes to another a gift of property of the value of a thousand dirhems, having no other property besides, and the donee gives an *ewaz* for the gift, of which the donor takes possession

---

(1) *Fatâwai Alamgiri*, Vol. IV, p 551

(2) *Sharh-i-Tahtâwi.*

and then dies, the *ewaz* being in his possession at the time of his death, if the *ewaz* be equal in value to two-thirds or more of the property given, the gift is valid, but if the *ewaz* be less than two-thirds of the value thereof, the heirs would be entitled to recover from the donee the difference between the value of the two-thirds of the subject-matter of the gift and the actual value of the exchange. For example, if the subject of the gift was worth 1,000 *dirhems* and the *ewaz* only 500 *dirhems*, the heirs of the donor would be entitled from the donee to one-sixth of 1,000 *dirhems*, "though the *ewaz* might have been stipulated for in the original gift." The donee, however, may, if he likes, return the whole gift taking back his *ewaz*, or restore a sixth of the gift and keep the remainder.

A condition for an exchange (*ewaz*) is valid if the subject of the exchange is sufficiently specified and not *majhûl* (unknown).(1) In other words, where a property is conveyed to another or a grant is purported to be made in lieu of a consideration moving from the transferee to the transferor, the consideration should be distinctly specified and must not be indeterminate.

The following examples taken from the *Fatâwai Kâzi Khân* will not be without value on this subject.

"Anything given in exchange for a gift bars revocation. Nor can the gift of an *ewaz* be revoked; it must be clear, however, that the consideration was given in exchange for the gift."

"Any person other than the donee, whether with or without the consent of the donee, may give an *ewaz* for a gift, thus destroying the right of the donor to revoke the gift, that is, if he has accepted the consideration."

"If the consideration is given by a person other than the donee, he may revoke the same unless the donee has made a bargain with such person that the consideration will be paid back to him."

"Even should there be any defect found by the donor in the thing given by way of an exchange, he cannot revoke his gift."

"When a gift is made to two people and one of them gives an *ewaz* for the share given to him, the donor may revoke as to the other share."

---

(1) *Radd ul-Muhtâr*, IV, p. 779.

"If a gift is made to a minor, and the father or his executors were to give an *ewaz* out of the property of the minor, such grant is not valid, and consequently the donor can revoke."

"If a person were to set up a claim to an *ewaz* and recover the same, the donor can revoke, but if he were to recover only a portion and there remained yet a portion thereof in the hands of the donor, he cannot revoke, *for the smallest consideration is sufficient to destroy the power of revocation.*"

"If the subject-matter of the gift is recovered by another person legally entitled to it, the donee may recover the whole of the *ewaz*; if a portion only is recovered by the rightful claimant, the donee can recover only a proportionate share of his *ewaz.*"

"If the donee were to convert a portion of the gift into another substance and give it in exchange it would be a good *ewaz.* If a person were to make a gift of one thousand dirhems to *A* who gives in exchange *out of the same* one dirhem, this is not a good *ewaz* according to 'us,' though Zuffar differs."

"If a Christian were to make a gift to a Moslem and the latter were to give in exchange any prohibited article the exchange is not good."

Where a gift is made by a minor to *A* who gives an exchange, the gift is null and inoperative nor does the *ewaz* vest in the minor.

Hiba-bi'l-ewaz. In all these cases the consideration is not a part of the contract. And the rules stated above do not, therefore, apply to what in modern times is called a *hiba-bi'l-ewaz*, which is a transaction of quite a different nature, and partakes to a certain extent of the second kind of *ewaz* mentioned in the *Fatâwai Alamgiri, viz.*, where it is stipulated in the contract. In this kind of *hiba-bi'l-ewaz* the consideration is directly opposed to the object of the gift both being *in esse;* there is no suggestion of one being subsequent to the contract. The grant and the consideration are parts of one transaction. A *hiba-bi'l-ewaz*, therefore, is a sale in all its legal incidents. In sale, mutual seisin is not requisite to render the contract valid and the terms in which a contract of this kind is entered into imply, "that the articles opposed to each other are present," and that there is no danger of either party suffering from the other's fraud. "I have given you this for that" implies that the consideration is present, and that the person will take care to receive it before parting with his property, and the law therefore annexes to it the quality of a sale both with regard to the condition and the effect.

Seisin not requisite in *hiba-bi'l-ewaz.*

Suppose, for example, a person in making a gift expressed himself to this effect, that he had made a gift to and conferred upon another the proprietary right in his entire property in exchange of something given by the donee,—this is not a gift in consideration of an exchange to be prospectively given, but it is a contract of mutual transfer or sale both as to the condition and the effect. In such a case, seisin is declared not to be a requisite condition.(1)

Hiba-ba-shart-ul-ewaz.

A *hiba-ba-shart-ul-ewaz* is a contract of a different description from a *hiba-bi'l-ewaz.* The terms used in the constitution of such a *hiba* imply a contingency. Thus :—" I have given you this *on condition* of your giving me such a thing." Now, it will be observed that in this contract, its legal operation depends upon the fulfilment of the condition, being the delivery and seisin of the *ewaz* or consideration ; otherwise, if it were valid and binding without such condition, the consideration might be withheld, and it might thereby become, as it were, a *nudum pactum.* As to the effect, this contract is declared to have the property of a sale, after the condition is fulfilled, that is to say, *after mutual delivery of seisin it becomes in effect a sale.*

Hiba-ba-shart-ul-ewaz—contd.

For example, if a person were to declare that he had made a gift to, and conferred on another, the proprietary right to his entire property on condition that the donee should give to him something in exchange for the gift, and the donee were to accept the condition, it would be a gift *ba-shart-ul-ewaz or a gift on condition of an exchange.* So long as the condition is unfulfilled, it is a gift revocable at the will of the donor under the same circumstances as a *simple* gift. And for the same reason delivery of seisin is necessary. But once the condition is fulfilled the contract becomes a sale. It is therefore stated in the *Sharh-i-Chalpi* that a *hiba-ba-shart-ul-ewaz* " technically, as regards the *shart,* is considered in the light of a gift, and sale as to the effect. Seisin is requisite to its validity and the gift cannot be said to be established until the parties shall have delivered seisin to each other, but the property conferred remains as formerly at the disposal of the donor."

---

(1) See *Meer Nujeeboolla* v. *Musst. Kuseema* [1795], 1 Sel. R., 10, where it was held that to give validity to a *hiba-bi'l-ewaz* or gift for consideration, seisin is not requisite in Mahommedan Law ; also *Chaudhri Mehdi Hassan* v. *Muhammad Hassan* [1906], 10 Cal. W. N., 706.

Ewaz may be of any kind and need not be in specie.

The stipulated consideration may take any shape or be of any kind. An *ewaz*, however small, is sufficient to make the gift effective. The examples given in the *Fatâwai Alamgiri* and other works show that it need not be of a specific character. For example, a woman may give her dower-debt to her husband, *i.e.*, release him from it, on condition that he should not ill-treat her. If he fulfils the stipulation, the gift takes effect; if not the right to the dower reverts to or re-vests in her. Or, she may release her dower on condition that he does not neglect her; in case of a breach of the stipulation the title to the *mahr* reverts to her.

Similarly, a man may make a gift on the condition that a certain payment should be made to him periodically by the donee; or that the donee should in lieu of the gift render some service to the donor at stated intervals.

The effect of a *shart* (condition) attached to a gift.

Where a gift is made with a condition attached to it, which condition is not a mere problematical contingency, but capable of being fulfilled by the donee, or of itself in the natural course of things, the condition is valid and so also the gift. Some examples of this are given in the *Sharh-i-Chalpi*:—It says, "in the *Bakâli* it is stated from Abû Yusuf that if a man were to tell another 'this thing is for thee if thou likest,' and make it over to him, and the person addressed reply, 'I like' or 'accept,'—the condition (*shart*) is good. So also it is reported from Mohammed, if a date-tree begins to bear fruit and the owner of the tree says to another, 'these dates are for thee, if they get ripe,' or 'if to-morrow comes,' it is lawful. But if he were to say, 'these dates will be thine, if Zaid enters his house,' it will not be valid."

Gift and release do not admit of the option of stipulation.

When a gift is made subject to a condition that the donee shall have an option for three days within which to accept or reject, the gift is valid if the acceptance be expressed before the separation of the parties; but if not accepted by him till after they have separated, it is not lawful. But when a gift is made on a condition that the donor shall have an option for three days, the gift is valid, and the option void; "because gift is a binding contract, and therefore does not admit of the option of stipulation." "When a person says to another, 'I have released thee from my right against thee, on condition that I have an option,' the release is lawful, and the option void."

"A man to whom a thousand *dirhems* are due by another, says to him, 'When to-morrow comes the thousand is thine'; or 'thou art free from it,' or 'when thou hast paid one-half of the property then thou art free from the remaining half,' or the remaining half is thine,' the gift is void. But if he should say, 'I have released you on condition that you emancipate your slave,' or 'Thou art released on condition of thy emancipating him by my releasing thee,' and he should say, 'I have accepted,' or 'have emancipated him,' he would be released from the debt."

Distinction between a conditional gift and a gift with a condition.

The subject of vitiating conditions attached to gifts primarily intended to take absolute effect, has already been discussed.(1) The principle is stated thus in the *Sirâj-ul-Wahâj*. "All our jurists agree in holding that when a gift is made, and a vitiating condition is attached to it, the gift in that case would be valid and the condition void. For example, if a person were to *give* something to another and stipulate that he should not sell it, the gift would be valid, and the condition void. It is a general rule with regard to contracts, in which seisin is necessary, such as *hiba* and *rahn* (pledge), that a condition *dehors* the absoluteness of the contract, would not avoid the contract, but drop itself." In other words, where a person intends to give *absolutely* and expresses his intention by the use of words which convey the meaning of an *absolute* gift, he cannot impose limitations on the enjoyment or devolution of the subject-matter of the gift so as to render the grant itself nugatory. But where the "condition" has not that effect, where it forms, in fact, the "consideration" for the grant, and the gift is made on the express stipulation that the donee should do something or abstain from doing something or should give something in return for the gift the contract is valid in its entirety. For example, if *A* were to convey to *B* a property in consideration of *B* maintaining him during his lifetime, or of paying him, and after his death, to his heirs a fixed allowance, there is absolutely nothing illegal in the contract as the condition does not make the contract nugatory; and if the grantee obtains possession of the property upon that contract, the grantor or his heirs would have the right to enforce the performance of the covenant relating to the consideration against the grantee and all persons deriving title under him.(2) In fact, once the transfer is given

Hanafi Law —an absolute gift cannot be subject to limitation.

(1) *Ante*, p. 133.

(2) See *Mozaffur Hossain Shaha* v. *Abdur Rahim Shaha*, App. from Original Decree, No. 197 of 1896, decided on 27th August, 1897.

effect to, the grantee takes the property subject to the trust. And any one taking the property from the grantee by sale, gift or inheritance, takes it burdened with the *trust* in consideration of which the grant was originally made. From the examples given in the *Radd ul-Muhtâr* it will be seen that a *hiba-ba-shart-ul-ewaz* is in the nature of an executory gift and the "grant" and "condition" are dependent upon each other; so that the moment the transfer is made the performance of the condition becomes obligatory, and if the consideration fails, the contract becomes voided.

Gift of the dower-debt by a woman to the husband.

"When a woman makes a gift of her dower on certain conditions which are not fulfilled, the gift is null. For example, if the dower-debt is released in consideration of the husband taking her on a *hajj*, or not treating her with cruelty, or not preventing her visiting her relations; and the condition or conditions are not fulfilled, there is no abandonment of the dower."(1)

"When a woman makes a gift of her dower on condition that the husband should give her something in return every year, and the husband fails to fulfil his part of the agreement, the gift fails also, for the gift in this case is a *hiba-ba-shart-ul-ewaz*, (that is an executory gift which is not completed and rendered perfect until the condition as to the *ewaz* is performed.) And consequently when the *ewaz* is not obtained the gift fails."

"A woman makes a gift of her dower on the condition that her husband divorces her, and the husband accepts the gift subject to the condition, but does not divorce her, he is not absolved from the dower-debt."(2)

The performance of the condition (*shart*) in a *hiba-ba-shart-ul-ewaz* may not be restricted to the actual donee or assignee; for the transaction may take the shape of a conveyance of the subject-matter to trustees for the benefit of a particular individual, subject to trusts in favour of others. For example, *A* may convey a property to *B* and *C* as trustees for *D* burdened with the condition of paying *E* and *F* certain allowances during their lives, or to them for their lives and to their descendants in perpetuity; in such case the beneficial title of *D* is subject to the performance of the condition by the trustees. Once it has been given effect to by delivery of seisin to the trustees it is a completed contract and enforcible by the persons acquiring interest under it.

(1) *Fatâwai Kâzi Khan* in loco.

(2) *Radd ul-Muhtâr*, throughout.

Gifts dependent upon the happening of a *contingency* are, however, void.

Examples of contingent gifts.

If a woman were to say to her sick husband, 'if you die of this sickness, you are released from my dower, or my dower is on you as *sadakah*,'—this is void because it is a contingent gift.(1) Or if a sick woman were to say to her husband, "if I die of this my disease, my dower is to thee as *sadakah*," or "you are released of my dower," and she does die of the disease the gift is void, and the dower remains due by the husband.(2) Similarly, if a person were to say to another who owes him money "if you do not pay me what you owe me till you die you are released" this is void according to the *Bahr ur-Râik*. But if he should say, "when I die, thou art released," it would be lawful, says Kâzi Khân. While if he were to say, "if I die, thou art free from this," there is no release, for this is contingent. Similarly, if he were to say, "if thou enterest the house, thou art free from what I have against thee."(3)

Illegal considerations for the discharge of a liability are wholly ineffective in making the discharge operative, *e.g.*, if a person were to say to another, "I would release you from my debt if you would settle an important matter for me with the Sultan,—he is not released, for this is a bribe."(4)

As already mentioned, an *ewaz* or consideration under the Mahommedan Law to constitute a *hiba-bi'l-ewaz* or to impart to a gift or a conveyance the characteristics of a "gift for a consideration," may take any form or consist of any kind of gratuity, corporeal or incorporeal. For example, in *Muhammadun-nissa Begum* v. *Batchelor*(5) the High Court of Bombay has held that the relinquishment by the uncle of his share in the property of a deceased Mahommedan to facilitate the action of the Collector to obtain a certificate of guardianship in respect of the minor niece's property under the Guardian and Wards' Act, was a good consideration under the Mussulman Law. Similarly, where a father and grandmother jointly executed a deed of gift in favour of the minor children relinquishing their shares in the grandfather's property, it has been

(1) *Fatâwai Alamgiri*, Gift of a debt, Vol. IV, p. 535.
(2) *Ibid* after the *Zahîria*.
(3) *Ibid* after the *Khazânat ul-Muftiîn*
(4) *Ibid* after the *Kinia*.
(5) [1905] I. L., 29 Bom., 428.

held that the document was not a voluntary settlement, but was a transaction supported by valuable consideration inasmuch as the relinquishment by one was the consideration for the relinquishment by the other.(1)

SECTION II.

Gift of a Debt.

The gift of a debt.

" The gift of a debt to the person from whom it is due," says the *Fatâwai Alamgiri*, " is valid both according to analogy (*kyâs*) and liberal interpretation (*istehsân*); and to any person other than the debtor, it is valid according to liberal interpretation, when he is authorised to take possession of it."(2)

" When a gift is made of the debt to the debtor and he is discharged therefrom it becomes complete without his acceptance; but should he reject it, the gift does not take effect, according to the generality of the jurists and this is the accepted doctrine according to the *Jawâhir-ul-Akhlâti*."

The above principle is applicable to a case where the debt is not cash. If it is, then it is dependent upon the debtor's acceptance. If he accepts it, he is discharged; but if he does not, he remains liable. This is not the case with other debts, which are discharged whether the debtor [expressly] accepts the release or not; but gift and discharge as regards other debts also become ineffective by rejection.

With reference to the donation of the debt to the surety, the matter stands upon a different footing from the discharge of the suretyship. The principle seems to be this:—The gift of the debt to the surety is not valid without his acceptance, and would be liable to a reversal on rejection; but a discharge is valid without acceptance and would not be reversed on rejection.

" When a *hiba* is made of a debt to the principal debtor who dies before rejecting the gift, he would (nevertheless) be discharged. Similarly, if the discharge is given after the debtor's death. But his heirs can reject such a discharge and the debt would be paid: this is according to Abû Yusuf. Mohammed, however, differs,

(1) *Ashid Bai* v. *Abdúlla Haji Mohammed* [1906], I. L., 31 Bom., 271.

(2) *Fatâwai Alamgiri*, Vol. IV, p. 535. The authority cited is the *Tátár Khâniéh*, but there is absolute consensus on this point.

and holds that the rejection would not be effective, for the past discharge operates as to the present, so in the *Zakhîra*."(1)

If a creditor were to discharge the principal debtor, and he accepts, then both he and the surety are discharged. But neither he nor the surety would be discharged if he should not accept.(2)

"If a man who is in debt to another were to die before payment, and the creditor were to make a gift of the debt *to the heir* of the debtor it would be valid whether the inheritance is immersed in the debt or not; so in the *Fatâwai Kâzi Khân*."(3)

"If a gift be made to some of the heirs of the debtor, it will be for all of them; similarly will a discharge to the heirs, so in the *Wajiz-l'il-Kurdi*."

"And in the *Fatâwai-Ahoo* it is stated that if the creditor discharges one of the heirs [of the debtor] from the debt, it is valid in respect of his share." This evidently refers to a discharge or release after partition of the debtor's estate when the share of each heir has been ascertained.

And in the *Khazâna*(4) it is stated that in the matter of the gift of a debt, the death of either the creditor or debtor is tantamount to acceptance."

* * * * * *

If the creditor dies leaving several heirs and one of them, before the partition of the deceased's estate, releases the debtor in respect of his share of the debt, the release is valid. The principle is thus stated in the *Kinia*. "One of the heirs of a creditor gives up his share in a debt to the debtor before partition, and in the deceased's estate there are both money and goods, the gift is valid in law, like a composition."(5)

There occurs the following passage in the *Fatâwai Alamgiri* as taken from the *Tâtâr-Khâniéh* :—"The gift of a debt to the infant son of the debtor is not valid." The meaning of this doctrine is that as the validity of the gift of a debt to a third person depends on the express direction to him by the creditor to recover the debt,

---

(1) This is the received doctrine according to all the Jurists (*Mashâikh*). *awâhir-ul-Akhlâti*.

(2) *Fatâwai Alamgiri*, Vol. IV, p. 535.

(3) *Ibid.*

(4) *Ibid.*

(5) *Fatâwai Alamgiri*, Vol. IV, p. 535.

and as the infant child of the debtor cannot be so authorised either personally or by its natural guardian (being the debtor himself), the gift cannot take effect. But this does not involve the conclusion that where a debtor is dead and the creditor chooses to make a gift of the debt to his child or to discharge him of any liability thereunder, it would be invalid. On the other hand, according to all the authorities, such a gift or discharge is absolutely valid. That the doctrine of the *Tâtâr-Khâniéh* given in the *Fatâwai Alamgiri* must be taken with qualification is clear from the rule which declares that a woman may validly make a gift of her dower-debt to her infant child by the husband from whom it is due, provided she places the child in a position to recover it. From this it follows that the objection to a gift of the debt to the *minor* child of the debtor springs from the apprehension that in such a case the donee being an infant the debtor would become, as the guardian of the child, entitled to recover the debt from himself. But as the mother can place her infant child in a position to recover her dower from the father, there is no reason why any other creditor may not adopt the same course by the appointment of a trustee or some person to recover the debt for the child.

In the case of *Tyani Begam* v. *Umrai Begam*(1) the Bombay High Court held, in accordance with the rules of Mahommedan Law, that the widow of a deceased Mahommedan may remit the dower-debt even without the acceptance of his heirs.

Gift of a debt.

"In the *Fatâwai-Astarûshni*,"(2) says the *Fatâwai Alamgiri*, "it is stated that where a woman sells a piece of stuff to her husband, and gives the consideration to her infant child by way of reward and gift, and the child dies thereafter, the whole consideration will be the property of the woman, and will not be treated as the inheritance of the child."(3)

When the gift of a debt is validly made to a debtor, he is entitled to recover from the creditor any property hypothecated for the debt.

* * * * * * *

"A creditor makes a gift of his debt to his debtor, who neither accepts nor rejects it at the meeting, and then comes after the

(1) [1908], I. L., 32 Bom., 612.

(2) *Fatâwai* Abi'l Fath Mohammad bin al-Mahmûd bin al-Hussain al-Astarûshni.

(3) *Fatâwai Alamgiri*, Vol. IV, p. 365.

lapse of some days and rejects the gift; there is some difference of opinion on the point, but the sound doctrine is that the gift is not reversed."

"When a debt is due to two persons, and one of them gives up his share to the debtor, the gift or release is valid."(1)

In other words when there are two creditors and one debtor, any one of them may discharge the debtor in respect of his share of the debt, or, to use the phraseology of the Mussulmen lawyers, may make a gift of his share of the debt to the debtor.

A release suspended upon the happening of a contingency is invalid. But where it is made dependent upon a condition which is immediately fulfilled, it is valid; for example, if a man were to say to another, "if thou owest me any debt, I absolve thee from it;" such a gift would be valid if the debt was existing at the time. So also if he were to say "when I die, thou wilt be discharged from my debt" it will be valid, the discharge taking effect as a bequest.(2)

In the case of a release from a liability, delivery of seisin is not possible, and therefore, it is laid down that "the gift of a debt to the debtor and his discharge from the liability takes effect without his acceptance, for the discharge of a debt is equivalent to its cancellation and therefore acceptance and possession on the part of the donee are not necessary."

Gift of a debt to a person other than the debtor—meaning of the word *hawâlât*.

The gift of a debt to a person other than the debtor is valid under the following circumstances(3):—

(*a*) When it is made by way of *hawâlât*, that is, the person to whom the assignment is made is constituted an agent for the creditor;(4)

(*b*) When it is bequeathed by way of a legacy;

(*c*) When the assignee is placed in a position to recover the debt.

As the assignment of a debt implies that the assignor vests the assignee (the donee of the Mahommedan Law) with the power to recover the debt—the required condition may be regarded as a legal refinement laid down *ex abundante cautela*.

(1) *Fatâwai Alamgiri*, Vol. IV, p. 565.
(2) *Fatâwai Kâzi Khân* in loco.
(3) *Hed.* III, p. 309.
(4) *Hed.* III, p. 606.

In fact, where a person places another in a position to realise the debt due to him, it amounts to a sufficient delivery of possession. But the mere handing over of deposit notes, signed by the Agent of a Bank, acknowledging the receipt of sums of money as deposit bearing interest and not in a form which would entitle the bearer of the notes to the debts created thereby as transferee thereof, has been held not to amount to a transfer of the debts so as to give the person to whom they were made over any dominion over them or to enable him to recover the money secured by the notes.(1)

Where a person is discharged or released from a liability upon any specified condition, the infraction of the condition revives the liability, *e.g.*, if a woman absolve her husband from her dower-debt upon any condition which is afterwards infringed by him, the liability would re-attach and he would continue liable for such debt.(2) "If she were to say to her husband, 'I absolve you from my debt *on condition* that you do not marry another woman,' and he were to accept the discharge and were subsequently to take a second wife, he would continue liable for her, *viz.*, the first wife's dower."

But, as already pointed out, when the discharge is made dependent upon a wholly uncertain contingency, it is inoperative: *e.g.*, if a man were to say to his debtor, "if I do not demand my debt from you until my death, it is yours," this is invalid.

A gift of a debt cannot be retracted if the debtor has once consented to the discharge.

SECTION III.

Further Rules as to the Law relating to Gifts.

Gifts by parents and *de facto* guardians to their children and wards.

As already stated a father may, in health, give his entire property to any one of his children.(3) It would be sinful, but if the gift is not invalid or void for other reasons, it would be legal.(4)

---

(1) *Aga Mahomed Jafter Bindamin* v. *Kolsoom Beebee* [1888], I. L., 25 Cal., 9; see also *Mumtaz-un-nissa* v. *Tufail Ahmed* [1905], I. L., 28 All., 234. In *Vahazullah Sahib* v. *Boyapati Nagayya* [1906], I. L., 30 Mad., 519, it appeared that the donor exercised rights of ownership over the property after the death of the donee.

(2) Comp. *Moonshee Buzlur Raheem* v. *Shamsunnissa Begum* [1869], 11 M. I. A., 511.

(3) See *ante*, p. 49; *Fatáwai Kázi Khán*, Vol. IV, p. 188.

(4) *Ibid.* See also the *Durr-ul-Mukhtár*, p. 636.

In the case of *Kandath Veetil Bava* v. *Musaliam Veetil Pakrukutti*,(1) where a mother had made a gift (*sridhanam*) to her daughter of certain property consisting of a house and lands, which was evidenced by a petition to the Revenue authorities by the donor and donee for the purpose of effecting a mutation of names, and the donor had continued to reside with the donee, the learned Judges of the Madras High Court held that *that* fact did not vitiate the gift.

"A gift by a father of a house, in which he lives or has his property, is good according to Abû Yusuf and the *Fatwa* is with him ;" that is decrees are passed according to his opinion.

A gift by a person *in loco parentis* to a child in his custody is completed by the simple declaration ; in such cases no transfer is necessary : " If a father," says the *Sharh-i-Vikâya*, " make a gift of something to his infant son, the infant in virtue of the gift becomes proprietor of the same. The same rule holds when a mother gives something to her infant son, whom she maintains and whose father is dead and no guardian is provided and so also with respect to the gift of any other person maintaining a child under these circumstances."

" If a stranger were to make a gift of a thing to an infant, the gift is rendered complete by the seisin of his father."

" Where the child is an orphan the possession on his behalf by his guardian, being either the executor appointed by his father or his grandfather, is sufficient. If a fatherless child be in the charge of his mother, and she were to take possession of a gift made to him, it would be valid. The same rule holds with respect to a stranger [*i.e.*, a non-relative] who has the charge of an orphan. If an infant should himself take possession of a thing given to him it would be valid provided he be endowed with reason."(2)

In the case of a gift by a parent to a minor child, no acceptance is necessary ; " the gift is completed by the contract and it makes no difference whether the subject of the gift is in the father's hands or in that of a depositary :" Nor is transmutation of possession necessary, for the possession of the parent is tantamount to that of the child.(3)

---

(1) (1907), I. L., 30 Mad., 305.

(2) See *ante*, p. 133.

(3) See *ante*, p. 123 *et seq.*

If a father makes clothes for his infant son with the express intention that they are for the child, he cannot give the clothes to another.

Gift by a wife of her dower.

A gift of dower obtained by the husband by force or misrepresentation is invalid,(1) *i.e.*, where a husband by force or misrepresentation induces his wife to release him from the dower-debt, such release or discharge is not valid.(2)

Gift of a debt.

In the *Bahr ur-Râik* it is laid down that "a person to whom there are debts outstanding can lawfully make them over by gift to another who is not indebted to him, directing the donee to realise such debts, and take them for his own use—and such gift is valid." And in the *Fatâwai Kâzi Khân*, as a consequence of the above principle, it is stated, that "a woman is entitled to convey her dower-debt to her infant child, and the child would be entitled to claim the same from the father on attaining majority. Similarly, a married woman has the power to compound her dower-debt with her husband and accept in lieu thereof anything else."

Bye-Mukâsa.

In India a conveyance between the married parties by which the husband conveys some property to his wife in lieu or satisfaction of her dower-debt is called a *bye-mukâsa*. A *bye-mukâsa* is a *hiba-bi'l-ewaz* and in its effect is tantamount to a sale in consideration of the dower.(3)

"If a woman compromise her dower for anything which has not been seen by her before delivery, and she subsequently become aware that it is defective, she is entitled to repudiate the contract, and her right to the dower remains intact."

"A woman may release her dower to her deceased husband," that is, the widow is entitled to exonerate or discharge the estate of her deceased husband from the liability for her dower-debt.

"When a woman who is ill makes a gift of her dower to her husband, the gift would be valid if she were to recover from her illness, and even though she should die of that illness, yet if it were not a death-illness the answer would be the same, but if it were a death-illness the gift would not be valid without the sanction of the heirs."

---

(1) *Fatâwai Kâzi Khân*, Vol. IV, p. 185.

(2) See *Moonshee Buzlur Rahim* v. *Shumsunnissa Begum* [1867], 11 Moo. I. A., p. 551.

(3) See *Suba Bibi* v. *Balgobind Das* [1886], I. L., 8 All., 178; *Mahamed Esuph* v. *Pattama Ammal* [1889], I. L., 23 Mad., 70.

A gift by way of a *rukba* is invalid according to all the Sunni schools, being a gift dependent on a contingency of a nature both uncertain and involving as it were a wager on one's life. A *rukba* is constituted by a person declaring "If I die before thee, this house of mine is thine, if thou diest before me it is mine." *Rukba.*

But when a *rukba* is made and the grantee is put in possession of the subject of the grant, it would amount to an *'aâriat* or commodate loan returnable to the grantor whenever he likes.

If a person is the proprietor of a building as well as of the land upon which it is situated, he may make a gift of the building without the land and it will be valid.(1) Gift of building without the land

(1) *Radd-ul-Muktâr*, IV, p. 780.

CHAPTER V.

THE SHIAH LAW RELATING TO *HIBA* OR GIFTS.

SECTION I.

MUSHA'A AND SEISIN ACCORDING TO THE SHIAH DOCTRINES.

According to the Shiahs, the gift of *mushâ'a* or a share in joint and undivided property is lawful,(1) "and seisin of it is to be taken," adds the *Sharâya*, "in the same way as seisin in sale," that is, "by mere surrender or vacating by the donor." And the *Mabsût* says "in our *mazhab*," *i.e.*, according to our doctrines, "the gift of a share of a property whether partible or not, is absolutely valid."

The character of the seisin, as stated before, when dealing with the Hanafî Law, must depend on the nature of the thing given.

And the same view is laid down by the Allâmah in his *Tahrîr-ul-Ahkâm*. Mere surrender or delivery of symbolical possession is sufficient in all cases of gift, where the subject is immovable; where it is movable, manual or physical possession seems to be required *so far as the nature of the article permits. Authority to take possession is equivalent to delivery of possession.*

Authority to take possession sufficient.

Under the Shiah Law there is no question, that if a thing is given to two persons *jointly*, and they take possession *jointly*, each donee becomes the proprietor of the portion given to him. If, again, only one of them should accept the gift and take possession while the other refuses, the gift to the acceptor would be valid.

As under the Hanafî Law, acceptance is a necessary condition to the validity of a gift. "The contract of *hiba*," says the *Sharâya*, "requires declaration and acceptance with seisin or taking possession."

Declaration is the expression of an intention or wish on the part of the donor to transfer to the donee the right of property by way of a *hiba*. But the contract is not valid, unless the person who makes the transfer is "of full age, sound understanding and

(1) *Mirza Kasim Ali* v. *Mirza Mahommed Hassan* [1832], 5 Sel. Reports, 213.

unrestrained in the use of his property," in other words, is *sui juris*, capable of understanding the nature of his act, and does not labour under any "inhibition."

Gift of a debt under the Shiah Law

A discharge or release given by the creditor to his debtor is equivalent to the gift of the debt, and this is valid both under the Sunni and Shiah Law. Owing, however, to the difficulty of obtaining physical or actual possession of a debt or *chose in action*, some Shiah lawyers, among them the author of the *Sharâya*, have held that a debt, or rather the right to recover a debt, cannot be assigned to a third person. Other jurists, especially the Shaikh, (the author of the *Mabsût*,) have held the contrary view, and there can be no question that upon the basis of correct analogy and the recognised practice, which has obtained for centuries among Shiah communities of making valid assignments of *choses in action*, a debt or a right depending on the obligation of another may validly be given or assigned by the obligee or creditor to a third party gratuitously, without any consideration, that is, by way of *hiba*.(1) In the case of *Nawab Amjad Ali Khan* v. *Mohamdi Begum*,(2) the gift was of Government Promissory Notes. Considered analytically, the gift of the notes amounted in fact to a gift of the right to receive the interest on the money, for which the notes formed the securities. Though the parties were Shiahs, there was no question raised in that case, that such a gift was invalid, because it was the gift of a right to receive periodically the accruing interest. The only ground upon which the gift was impugned, was, that the donor had reserved a life-interest in the income, and that such reservation was invalid under the Mahommedan Law. It follows, therefore, that the assignment of a *chose in action*, or a right in reversion, is as valid under the Shiah as under the Hanafî Law.

Seisin may be actual or constructive.

According to the Shaikh and the authors of the *Sarâir*, *Ghunia*, *&c.*, seisin may be either actual or constructive.

(1) Under the English Common Law, the benefit of a contract cannot be assigned (except by the Crown), so as to enable the assignee to sue in his own name. The origin of this restriction was attributed by Coke to a desire on the part of the founders of English Law to discourage maintenance and litigation; " but, " says Pollock, " there can be little doubt that it was in truth a logical consequence of the primitive view of a contract as creating a strictly personal obligation between the creditor and the debtor;" Pollock on Contract, p. 224.

The view held by some of the Shiah lawyers against the transfer of *choses in action* or the assignment of a contract may also be said to be a logical consequence of their view regarding the principle of seisin.

(2) Supra.

The authority to take possession in order to be effective must be such as would enable the donee to do so, or give some sort of dominion over the property. As already mentioned, the mere handing over to his wife by a person of certain deposit notes signed by the Agent of a Bank acknowledging the receipt of sums of money as deposit bearing interest and not in a form which would entitle the bearer of the notes to the debts created thereby as transferee thereof, has been held not to amount to a transfer of the debts so as to give the donee any dominion over them or enable her to recover the money secured by the notes.(1)

Release of a debt.

According to the author of the *Sharâya* and his disciples, who belong to the literal school of interpretation, a release or discharge does not require, for effectuation, the acceptance of the donee; whilst the progressive school, represented by the Shaikh, Ibn-Zuhra, Shaikh Murtaza and others, hold with the Hanafîs that the assent of the debtor or the obligor is necessary to the validity of the discharge. And this view seems conformable to the rules of equity. A discharge is a mere declaration on the part of the creditor of his intention not to enforce the obligation against the obligor. But the expression of an intention not to enforce a liability, which may have the effect of precluding the creditor from enforcing his claim, would not necessarily preclude the debtor from insisting upon the creditor to accept the payment of the debt. Obligation has been defined by an English writer to mean the relation that exists between two persons, of whom one has a private and peculiar right to control the other's actions, by calling upon him to do or forbear some particular thing.(2) The same definition may be applied to the term *'akd* of the Arabian jurists. It implies a relation which, whilst giving a certain right to one person over another, often creates a corresponding liability against him in favour of that other. Proceeding upon the basis of this conception, the Hanafî jurists have held that the "gift" of a debt, *i.e.*, the release of it, to the debtor is complete without his acceptance, though it is reversed by his rejection; but this is correct only with respect to the principal debtor, for the gift of a debt to the surety is not complete without his acceptance, though it is reversed by his rejec-

(1) *Agha Mahommed Jaffer Bindamin* v. *Koolsoom Beebee* [1897], I. L., 25 Cal., p. 9 supra.

(2) Pollock, p. 3.

tion. If the creditor releases the principal debtor from his debt, or gives it to him and he accepts, both he and the surety are released, but if he do not accept, he is not released.(1) This principle is enunciated with great clearness in the *Jawâhir* as well as the *Ghunia*.(2)

SECTION II.

LIMITED ESTATES UNDER THE SHIAH LAW

Although under the Hanafi Law, when the words of the grant purport to create an absolute estate in the grantee it cannot be cut down by subsequent words derogating from the original grant, the jurists of that school recognise the validity of limited estates in a qualified form(3) under the name of *'aâriat* (*commodatum*) which in effect is the transfer to the donee (called in such cases *musta'îr*) of the right to hold the property for the enjoyment of the usufruct. The lawfulness of such grants was accepted by the Allahabad High Court *in the matter of Khalil Ahmed and another*.(4)

The Shiah Law recognises to the fullest extent the lawfulness of limited estates.

Limited estates under the Shiah Law.

A grant to *A* limited to his life is valid, the subject-matter of the gift reverting to the donor or his heirs upon *A's* decease. So also a grant to *A* for life, and after him to another for his life will take effect as giving a life-estate to *A*, and after him a life-estate to the other person, after which the property would revert to the donor or his heirs. Similarly, a grant may be made to *A* for life and then to *B* absolutely, or a grant may be made to *A* for life and then to *A's* children absolutely. There is some difference of opinion as to whether only the children living at the time of the grant will take the remainder absolutely, or any children born to *A after* the grant will take also. The approved opinion seems to be that *all* the children will take, whether living at the time of the grant or born afterwards. But where a grant is to *A* for his life and to his children for *their* lives, only the children living at the time of the grant will take with rights of survivorship.(5)

---

(1) *Fatâwai Alamgiri*, IV, pp. 535, 536.

(2) See *post*, p. 187

(3) See *ante*, p. 54.

(4) [1908], I. L., 30 All., 309.

(5) *Jawâhir-ul-Kalâm*; none of these principles is affected by any dicta in *Tagore* v. *Tagore* [1868], 9 B. L. R., 377, or *Peake* v. *Robinson*.

A grant to *A* for his life and then to *B* for his life, and thereafter to *A's* children absolutely is equally valid.

According to the author of the *Sharâya* a grant to *A* and his (عقب) *'akab* ("one who comes after him") would give only a life-estate to *A*, as the term *'akab* does not indicate a person and conveys no definite meaning. According to the *Sarâir* and other works, such a grant would give an absolute estate to *A*.

Prince Suleiman Kadr v. Darab Ali Khan.

But when a gift is made to *A* for his life and after his death to his *heirs*, or if it is made in these terms, "the usufruct should be given to *A* during his lifetime and after him to his heirs,"(1) the grant would convey merely a life-interest to *A* and the absolute estate to *A's* heirs. In the case of *Prince Suleiman Kadr* v. *Darab Ali Khan*(2) their Lordships of the Privy Council gave expression to a *dictum* which might, perhaps, be supposed to imply a non-recognition of limited estates, but the view suggested was founded entirely on Sunni authorities and no reference appears to have been made to the provisions of the Shiah Law on the subject.

A gift to *A* and his children generally, *awlâd* or *farzandân*, or to his children *naslan b'ad nasl batnan b'ad batn*, "generation after generation, line after line," will convey to *A* an estate in fee the words "children after children, generation after generation," being words of description and not of limitation.

Definition of *Hiba*.

When a grant is made with the word *hiba* it implies, generally speaking, the grant of an absolute estate, for *hiba* is defined to be an act, by which one person transfers to another, gratuitously, without the motive of *kurbat*, i.e., of pleasing God, accompanied by immediate transfer, constructive or actual, the entire and absolute property (*milk*) in a certain thing. Such a transfer in the Arabic language is also constituted by the words *an-nahila* (a present) and *al-'atîa*. In Hindustani, the word *'atîa* is equivocal, and so are the words *dêna* and *bakhshnâ*. When grants are made with these words, the intention of the grantor must be examined from the context of the deed of gift and surrounding circumstances, *viz.*, whether he intended an absolute gift or to convey only a limited estate.

Powers of the life-tenant.

The life-tenant or the holder of an estate for a term has the right of letting the property for any period not exceeding his own

---

(1) *Jawâhir-ul-Kalâm.*

(2) [1881], L. R., 8 I. A., 117, see p. 122.

interest, provided there are no limitations on his power or his mode of enjoyment. He is bound, however, to return the property on the expiration of the period of his interest in proper order, natural deterioration and the lawful enjoyment of the same excepted.

As under the Hanafî Law, the donor may reserve a life-interest in the usufruct of the property, so long as that reservation does not interfere with the vesting of the property in the donee. For example *A* may grant a tenanted house to *B*, conditioning that during his lifetime he should receive the rent thereof. The principle enunciated in *Nawab Amjad Ali Khan* v. *Mohamdi Begum*(1) is in accordance with this rule.

Rukba.

As already explained, *rukba* is a generic name for all limited estates under the Shiah Law. It includes both an *'umra* (a life-grant) and a *sukna* (right of habitation). When the usufruct of a property is given to another limited to the life of the donee it is generally called an *'umra*. When a house is given for residential purposes, it is called a *sukna*. Under the Hanafî Law both these will come under the head of an *'aâriat*, but whereas an *'aâriat* is resumable at the will of the donor or his heirs, an *'umra* or *sukna* is operative for the fixed term and cannot be resumed. "And the grant is not invalidated by the sale of the property" for the purchaser takes it subject to the grant (2)

Servitudes in general.

A person is entitled under the Shiah Law to create other limited rights over his property. For example, a person may give to another a right of way over his land for a term, without giving rise to a perpetual easement, or may authorise him to take water from his cistern, &c. Such limited rights are also called *rukbas* in a restricted sense. The word *rukba* used in this connection implies a servitude.

Settlements in favour of individuals or any particular "purpose,"(3) either made without limitation of time or for a definite period are known as *hubs*.(4) They may be in favour of one individual or more, or in favour of a succession of individuals or purposes. When the *hubs* is for an indeterminate period, it comes to an end on the death of the settlor (*hâbis*). If it is for a determinate length of time, it comes to an end only on the expiration of the period

(1) [1867], 11 Moo. I. A., p. 517.

(2) *Sharâya-ul-Islâm*, chapter on *Sukna*.

(3) *E.g.*, *A* may settle his house on *B* or on *B* and after him on *C*, or on a mosque, or "assign his bondsman for the service of a family"; *Sharâya-ul-Islâm*, p. 241.

(4) *Hubs* means literally "tying up."

when it becomes part of the settlor's heritage.(1) A *hubs* may be created either directly or by means of trustees ; but the legal incidents are identical in either case.

In the case of *Banoo Begum* v. *Mir Abed Ali*(2), the High Court of Bombay emphatically recognised the validity of limited estates under the Shiah Law.

The settlor or grantor of a limited estate has the power during its subsistence of dealing with the deferred interest "by way of sale, gift and otherwise" provided there is no interference with the particular estate.(3) As already remarked, the purchaser's or donee's right is subject to the previously-created estate.

Gifts to infants.

Where a gift is made to a minor, according to the Hanafî Law, the possession of any person in whose protection the infant is living is sufficient. Among the Shiahs there are two divergent views. According to the author of the *Sharâya* possession should be taken on behalf of the minor by a person legally authorised to do so, or by the Judge. According to the Shaikh (the author of the *Mabsût*) and the Usûli jurists, the possession of any person who is a guardian *de facto* is sufficient. But even, according to the *Sharâya* where possession has been obtained and held on behalf of a minor by a person other than the father or the grandfather (or their executors) who are the guardians *de jure*, the Court will not allow the gift to be invalidated.(4)

Gift to minors.

The reciprocal consent of the parties and the delivery of the object into the hands of the donee suffice to validate a gift.

There is no particular formula prescribed for the purpose of constituting a gift. If the act or declaration of the donor unequivocally explains his intention it is sufficient. Thus the following words, "I have given," "I have made a present," "I have yielded the full proprietorship of such an object to such a person," may be used for the constitution of a gift.

The validity of a gift is established if the donor declares that he has made the gift and has delivered the thing to the donee, even if the object in question has remained in the possession of the donor.(5)

---

(1) *Sharâya-ul-Islâm*, p. 241.

(2) [1907] I. L., 32 Bom., 172.

(3) *Ibid.*

(4) The point has been decided in accordance with this rule by the Calcutta High Court.

(5) *Jawâhir-ul-Kalâm* chap. on *Hiba.*

If the thing given is in the hands of the donee at the time of the contract no further seisin is necessary.

Where delivery of possession not necessary.

Nor is express transmutation necessary in the case of a gift by a father or grandfather to an infant child, for their possession is tantamount to the minor's possession, such "persons being qualified to constitute a gift and receive it in the name of the infant donee."

Where the donee is a minor, and cannot himself take possession of the subject of the gift, the donor may nominate trustees to whom the property should be delivered in trust for the minor.

As under the Sunni Law, in considering the question of delivery of possession the relationship of the parties must be kept in view. For example, if a husband makes a gift of a house or landed property to his wife and continues to reside in the house or to realise the rents and profits of the estate, the gift will not be invalidated on that ground, for those acts are explainable by the relationship of the donor and the donee.(1) Similarly, if the father were to make a gift of his business to his minor son and to continue to manage it for him or an uncle were to give some property to a nephew and were to continue to be supported by the donee, the gift would not be invalid on that account.

Again, as under the Sunni Law the delivery of seisin must depend on the nature of the subject of the gift. For example, a gift of things contained in a box would be complete by delivery to the donee of the key of the receptacle, of immovable property in the occupation of tenants either by the delivery of the title-deeds or by requisition to the tenants to attorn to the donee,(2) of zemindari rights by mutation of names in the Collectorate Register.(3)

Gift of *mushâ'a* valid.

As already stated, the Shiah Law does not recognise the objection founded on *mushâ'a, viz.*, that the subject of the gift should form part of a property capable of division. Where a gift is made to two different donees, they do not become conjoint possessors; each becomes proprietor of the part that is given to him, when both have accepted the gift. Where the acceptance is by one of the donees

(1) See *Humera Bibi* v. *Najm-un-Nissa Bibi* [1905], I. L., 28 All., 147, and the cases cited there; see *ante*, p. 122.

(2) *Ibrahim* v. *Shaik Suleman* [1884], I. L., 18 Bom., 146.

(3) *Sajjad Ahmad Khan* v. *Kadri Begum* [1895], I. L., 18 All., 1.

only, the gift is valid with regard to him but inoperative as regards the one who has refused.

A father may validly give preference to one or more of his children over the others by making a gift, "but such gift constitutes an act from which it is recommended to abstain."

Power of revocation.

A gift made to the direct ascendants, in the first degree, of the donor and to one's descendants and accepted by them is irrevocable.

The irrevocability of a gift to blood-relations other than parents and children is likewise admitted. Married couples are in the same position as relations by consanguinity.

A gift made to a stranger is revocable, so long as the thing given is in existence in specie.

Where the object given has perished, the gift cannot be revoked. In like manner a gift cannot be revoked if anything has been received in exchange for it, though the exchange should be of little value.

A gift is also irrevocable, if the subject-matter of the gift has been sold for whatever price or otherwise alienated by the donee.

A sale by the donor of the subject-matter of the gift, after transfer of possession has taken place (expressly or constructively) is null, if the donee be a relative by consanguinity. Similarly, if the donee be a stranger (*i.e.*, not a relative by consanguinity) if he had given anything in exchange for the gift.

But where the gift is to a stranger without consideration even though possession may have been transferred, the gift is annulled by the sale. According to some jurists the gift remains valid with the donor's right to revoke it; but the former opinion, says the author of the *Sharâya*, seems more correct.

Sale by the donor of the thing given remains valid if the gift is annulled for illegality.

The two preceding principles are applicable to a sale by an expectant heir of property belonging to his ancestor, whom he believes to be alive, for the sale would be valid if it should appear that the ancestor was actually dead at the time.

A gift is constituted from the time of the seisin or transfer and not from the date of the contract, that is, all the legal incidents and the rights and obligations arising from the gift accrue from the date when the donee takes possession of the thing given.

This is contrary to the case of a bequest, the right to which accrues to the legatee at the moment of the testator's decease, though the transfer may take place afterwards.

Power of revocation —contd.

In case of a contest between the donor and the donee, the donor purporting to have in fact constituted the gift but alleging that he has not delivered it, his declaration will be accepted, but if the donee affirm that the object was legally delivered to him, the donor will have to establish his statement by proof.

So also if a person were to say "I gave him and made him the proprietor of it," and then deny having delivered possession. For, it is possible that he may have made the second statement (*i.e.*, "made him the proprietor of it") by way of re-affirmance of the first, (*i.e.*, "I gave it to him,") and may not mean to imply actual transfer.

In case of a revocation no indemnity is due to the donor, if the object constituting the gift has suffered any injury.

Where the donor revokes a gift after the thing given has attained in *itself* any increase in integral value, the augmentation accrues to him.

When the increase or accretion, after the gift, can be separated from the original subject of the gift, it belongs to the donee, but any accretion before the seisin of the donee is the right of the donor in case of revocation.

A gift made without any reserve is always presumed to be made gratuitously.

Should the donee on his side give anything to the donor, the gift would be irrevocable.

A gift made on condition that the donee should make some present or offer some gratuity or service to the donor, is valid; the gift will be revocable only if the donee do not fulfil the condition imposed.

Where the present or gratuity which the donee must give, or the benefit which he must render, is not definite, he is free to fix it according to his own wish, and the acceptance by the donor of such present or gratuity from the donee makes the gift irrevocable.

The donee in the cases mentioned in the preceding paragraphs cannot be compelled to give the present which has been fixed upon; he has the right to refuse it, but in that event the donor preserves the power of revoking the gift.

If in the preceding case, the refusal of the donee has caused the revocation of the gift, he is not held responsible for the destruction or depreciation of the object given; for he has dealt with a thing the proprietorship of which has been legally transferred to him.

There is some difference of opinion regarding the power of revocation possessed by the donor in the case of a gift of a piece of cloth, which, subsequent to the gift, has been dyed by the donee. Those lawyers who hold that the use by the donee of the subject-matter of the gift debars the right of revocation, are of opinion that the dyeing of the cloth puts an end to that right; others, who do not hold that view, think dyeing not to be an impediment to revocation, but that the donee only becomes entitled to the value of the dye and to retain a lien over the cloth for such value.

Gift in death-illness.

A gift made during a serious illness is valid if the donor recovers; if he dies it is valid only with the consent of the heirs, and if they refuse, it is valid only to the extent of one-third of his estate.

Section III.

Gift of a Debt under the Shiah Law.

As regards the gift of a debt to the debtor himself, I have already pointed out the difference between the author of the *Mabsût*, unquestionably the greatest of the Shiah jurists, and the author of the *Sharâya*. The difference is not a subject of mere antiquarian interest, for in one instance at least it has given rise to considerable practical results.(1)

The author of the *Mabsût* says—"When some person has a *mâl* owing from another, and makes a *hiba* of the same to that other, it is an *ibrâ* (release) by the word *hiba*. And whether, for the validity of a release, the acceptance of the person released is requisite or not, there is a difference of opinion. One body [of jurists] holds that for the validity of an *ibrâ*, such acceptance is necessary; and so long as the person released does not accept it the release is not valid; and when not accepted, the right remains intact. And this view is correct [*lit.* strong], in my opinion, for

(1) See Vol. II, p. 444.

when one person has a right against another, to discharge it is to confer an obligation; but nobody can be compelled to accept an obligation, otherwise [the result will be that] though he does not accept, he will be forced to accept. [For that reason also] in the case of a gift of *'ain* (specific property) it is required that there should be acceptance; and without acceptance a *hiba* is not valid. Another body says that the *ibrâ* is valid, whether the person who is liable accepts it or rejects it.''(1)

Gift of a debt —contd.

Similarly, the jurist Abû Zuhra states in the *Ghunia*, that "if a person were to make a gift to another of what is due to him, that is a release by the word *hiba*; it is necessary, however, that the person from whom the debt is owing should consent to such discharge, for a discharge is conferring an obligation on the debtor, and there is no compulsion in the acceptance of a mere obligation.''(2)

The author of the *Sharâya*, on the other hand expresses a different opinion. He states that the gift of a debt to the debtor himself is valid and operates as a release, and "in release (*ibrâ*), acceptance (by the donee) is not a condition according to the correct view.''(3) The "correct view" seems to be his own opinion. The author of the *Jawâhir*, after giving the dicta from the *Mabsût*, the *Ghunia*, the *Sarâir*, the *Intisâr*, and other works of high repute both among the Usûlis and the Akhbâris, says that the opinion of the Mohakkik(4) refers only to cases where the obligation is

---

(1) اذا كان له في ذمته لرجل مال فوهبه له ذاك كان ذلک ابرآء بلفظ الهبة و هل من شرط صحة الا برآء قبول المبراء ام لا قال قوم من شرط صحته قبوله ولا يصح حتى يقبل و مالا يقبل فالحق ثابة بحاله و هو الذي يقوي في نفسي لان في ابرآئه اياه من الحق الذي له عليه منة عليه ولا يجبر على قبول المنة فاذا لم يعتبر قبوله اجبرناه على ذلک كما نقول في هبة العين له انها لا تصح الا اذ يبدل و قال قوم انه يصح شاء من عليه الحق او ابى.*

(2) اذا وهب لم يستحقه فى الذمة كان ذلک ابراء بلفظ الهبة و يعتبر قبول من عليه الحق لانه في ابرائه منه منة عليه ولا يجبر على قبول المنة *.

(3) *Sharâya-ul-Islâm*, p. 242.

(4) The author of the *Sharâya-ul-Islam*.

Gift of a debt —contd.

one-sided; for example, where one person owes to another a sum of money, the creditor may release or discharge the debtor, and, in order to effectuate such a discharge, the acceptance of the donee (the debtor) is not a condition precedent. But when the creditor has also certain obligations to perform, his discharge of the debtor (without the debtor's consent) would not absolve him from the liability to which he is subject. For example, if *A* agrees to pay to *B* 500 dirhems, on the condition that *B* should supply him for five years with the fruit of his garden, unless the contract is put an end to by mutual consent, a release by *B* to *A* in respect of the 500 dirhems, would not absolve *B* from the liability of supplying the fruit for the period agreed upon. Again, suppose *A* contracts to serve *B* for five years on condition of receiving a monthly stipend of five dirhems, and *B* without the consent of *A* and before the expiration of the period, declares that he has no need for the service of *A*, in such a case he would not be absolved from the liability of paying the stipend fixed upon for the full period.

Viewed in the light in which the author of the *Jawâhir* puts it, the opinion of the author of the *Sharâya* would seem to be little different from that of his great predecessor; for the Shaikh and his disciples only say that a discharge cannot be given effect to against the will of the obligor; he may accept it or reject it; his acquiescence is tantamount to acceptance.

CHAPTER VI.

THE LAW OF GIFTS ACCORDING TO THE SHAFEI DOCTRINES.[1]

A GRATUITOUS transfer of property is called a gift. When such a transfer is made with the object of receiving reward in another world, it is a *sadakah ;* when made with the object of testifying respect for the donee, it is a *hadia* or present. The condition, essential to the validity of a *hiba*, is that there should be an offer on the part of the donor and acceptance on the part of the donee in terms, although in the case of a present, it is not necessary that the offer or acceptance should be express ; it is sufficient if the object is brought by the donor, and the donee takes possession thereof. A gift may be constituted by the use of the following expressions :—"I wish you to inhabit this house of mine, and after your death it will go to your heirs ;" "I wish you to inhabit it" (this is according to the doctrine embraced by Shâfe in his second period) ; or finally by saying "after your death it will revert to me." On the subject of the validity of a gift made in the following terms, Shâfeï held a different view in his second period from that which he entertained before ; "I grant you the usufruct of this house for life," or "I make a gift of it to you for life, that is to say, in case of your pre-decease, it will revert to me, and in case of my pre-decease, it shall be irrevocably yours." However, in our time both opinions of the Imâm are equally in force in "our school," and whilst some regard such gifts as valid, others hold them invalid. The former opinion is preferable. Shâfeï doctrines.

Anything which may form the subject of sale or barter may form the subject of gift ; but every object not subject to sale, such as a thing usurped or unknown, or an animal that has escaped is not capable of being made the subject of a gift. The gift of a debt involves the remission of the debt ; if it is made to the debtor it is What may form the subject of a gift.

(1) The following principles are taken chiefly from the *Minháj-ut-Tálibin* but are by no means exhaustive.

valid; but if made to a third person, it is open to question. According to some, it is valid.

As for the proprietorship of the object given, it is only transferred when the donee takes actual possession of the subject of the gift, with the donor's consent. When one of the parties dies between the making of the gift and the taking of possession, his heirs are placed in his position.

It is laid down by the traditions that parents, provided they are not notoriously bad characters, have the power to divide their property equally among their children by donations *inter vivos* without distinction of sex, though others hold that they should not thus destroy the effect of the rule relating to succession.

Revocation. A father has the right of revoking a gift made by him to his children, provided the donee has not irrecoverably disposed of the object received. So also other ascendants with respect to gifts made to grandchildren and their descendants. But where the donee makes a disposition which leaves the right of proprietorship intact, like mortgage, conditional gift (at least so long as possession has not passed), conditional enfranchisement, or even, according to "our doctrine," a contract of lease, the right of revocation is not lost. In case the donee should have lost the proprietorship of the object beforehand and should recover it subsequently, the right of revocation is not revived, and if, in the meanwhile, there has been an accretion to the subject of the gift, the revocation can only take effect if the increment has become incorporated with the object, but not where the increment exists separately. A revocation may be made in the following terms: "I revoke my gift," or "I reclaim the object," or "I wish the object to become my property again," or "I wish to break my gift," but it cannot be made impliedly by a subsequent disposition of the thing given, such as by sale, *wakf*, gift to another person or enfranchisement.

If a gift is made with the express stipulation that there should be no consideration, the right of revocation is not accorded to any one but the ascendants, whereas a gift with no such stipulation is supposed to have been made without hope of consideration if the donee is in any way inferior in social position to the donor, and even if he is superior. "Our doctrine" goes still further; it accepts the same principle if the two persons are quite equal. Where a consideration is obligatory, but has not been settled at the time of the contract, it must be of the value of the thing given ; and, under these circumstances, the donor has the right to revoke the gift if the donee neglects to pay the consideration.

The validity of a gift made on condition of a fixed consideration is permitted ; the gift must, however, be considered like a sale ; but, according to "our doctrine," a gift made on the especial condition of an unfixed consideration is null and void.

In the case of a present made to another, the thing in which it is delivered is considered as part of the present, and where it is customary need not be returned, *e.g.*, the basket that contains dates is not returned. Otherwise the package remains in the hands of the donor, and the donee can make no other use of it than in using it for that specific purpose.

CHAPTER VII.

THE HANAFI LAW RELATING TO *WAKF* OR TRUSTS.

SECTION I.

GENERAL OBSERVATIONS.

Origin of *wakf*.

THE law relating to Trusts or *wakf* is by far the most important branch of the Mahommedan Law. The doctrine has been recognised and enforced in the Mussulman system from the earliest times. Historically its origin is traced to the direct prescriptions of the Prophet.(1) "The validity of *wakfs*," says the *Ghâit ul-Bayân*, "is founded on the rule laid down by the Prophet himself under the following circumstances, and handed down in succession by Ibn 'Auf, Nâf'è and Ibn Omar as stated in the *Jâm'aa ut-Tirmizi*. Omar had acquired a piece of land in (the canton of) Khaibar, and proceeded to the Prophet and sought his counsel, to make the most pious use of it, (whereupon) the Prophet declared, 'tie up the property (*asl* or *corpus*) and devote the usufruct to human beings, and it is not to be sold or made the subject of gift or inheritance; devote its produce to your children, your kindred, and the poor in the way of God.' In accordance with this rule Omar dedicated the property in question, and the *wakf* continued in existence for several centuries until the land became waste." The author of the *Fath ul-Kadîr*, a work of great authority among the Sunnis, states that the law of *wakf* has its origin with the Prophet himself, who, besides having prescribed the above rule to Omar, is reported to have declared that all human actions end with the life of the individual, except such benefactions as are perpetual in their character; and that, in accordance with these principles, trusts or dedications were frequent in the lifetime of the Prophet and the early centuries of Islâm. The author gives examples of such

(1) "Imâm Shâfeí has stated that according to his knowledge the institution of *wakf* did not exist among the people of the *Jâhilyet* (the Ignorance);" (*Jâhilyet* is the designation applied to the pre-Islamic period); the *As'aâf*.

wakfs, some of which were in existence at the time when he was writing his work, *e.g.*, the *wakf* by the Prophet himself of a piece of land which he had acquired in the canton of Khaibar for the support of travellers ; the *wakf* of Omar of the land called *Sammâgh* in the same canton for his children, kindred, and the poor ; of Zubair ibn Awwâm(1) for his daughter ; of Arkam in favour of his son ; of Abû Bakr(2) in favour of his children ; of S'aad ibn Abî Wakkâs(3) of his lands in Medîna and Egypt for his children " which still exists ; " and of Osmân(4) of his lands called *Baruah*, " which still continues."(5)

The doctrine of *wakf* is thus interwoven with the entire religious life and social economy of the Mussulmans.

The classification of *wakf*

Trusts in the Mussulman system may, for the sake of convenience, be divided under three heads, *viz.*, public, *quasi*-public and private. This will probably indicate the division adopted by the Arabian jurists, who group *wakfs* or trusts under the following three heads, *viz.* :—

(*a*) Trusts in favour of the affluent and indigent alike.
(*b*) Trusts in favour of the affluent and then for the indigent.(6)
(*c*) Trusts in favour of the indigent alone.

Trusts for public works of utility which are dedicated to the public at large, though classed under the first head, have a distinctive name. They are called *wakfs* for *masâlih-ul-'aâmma*, and differ in one feature from other *wakfs*. For example, a bridge constructed by a private individual and dedicated as a public highway for the *people at large* without any restriction, comes under the direct control or supervision of the Sovereign (Sultan) and his representative, the Kâzi, whereas in the case of other trusts the Kâzi can interfere only at the instance of some of the beneficiaries. So is the case of a *Masjid-ul-Jâm'aa*, the public mosque, whether erected by the Sovereign or a private individual, which is peculiarly under the upervision of the Kâzi.

---

(1) A nephew of the Prophet.
(2) The first Caliph.
(3) The conqueror of Persia under the Caliph Omar.
(4) The third Caliph.
(5) See *post*, Chapter on the *Moukoof alaihim*.
(6) *Radd ul-Muhtâr*, Vol. III, p. 552 : according to the *As'aâf* the Prophet created seven *wakfs* in Medina.

These *masâlih-ul-'aâmma* I designate as public *wakfs*. But there is a large body of trusts which without being public trusts, partake something of that character. I have thought it expedient to include them under the head of *quasi*-public *wakfs*.

By *quasi*-public *wakfs*, therefore, I mean those trusts, the primary and initial object of which is, partly, to provide for a general pious purpose, and partly, for the benefit of particular individuals or class of individuals which may be the settlor's family.

By private *wakfs*, I mean those trusts, the primary object of which is to make a provision for private individuals, including the *wâkif's* family or relations.

Definition of *wakf*.

Wakafa literally means "I have bound up or detained" and is applied to the tying up of animals, such as a horse or camel. Technically or as the Arabian jurists put it, "in the language of the law," it signifies the dedication or consecration of property, either in express terms or by implication, for any charitable or religious object, or *to secure any benefit to human beings*.(1) To use the curt but expressive language of the Moslem lawyers a dedication to any good purpose [*wujûh-ul-birr-wa'l-ihsân* of the Shiahs, or *wujûh-ul-khair wa'l birr* of the Hanafîs(2)] is a *wakf*. The terms *birr* and *khair* include all good and pious acts and objects.(3) To make a provision for one's self is regarded by Hanafî lawyers as an act of *khair*, for the Prophet declared a man giving subsistence to himself as giving charity,(4) and settlements upon one's family are approved of and regarded as lawful by all the schools.

Hanafî Law.

Mohammed Sadik v. Mohammed Ali and others.

In the case of *Mohammed Sadik* v. *Mahommed Ali and others*,(5) the Law Officers of the Sudder Dewanny Adawlut stated that *wakf* according to the opinion of Abû Yusuf and Mohammed (which on this point is adopted as law) implies *the relinquishment of the proprietary right in any article of property such as lands, tenements and the rest*,(6) *and consecrating it in such manner to the service of God that it may be of benefit to men, provided always that the thing appro-*

(1) *Hed.* II (Ar.), p. 887 ; *Ghâit-ul-Bayan ; Fath ul-Kadir in loco.*
(2) *Durr-ul-Mukhtâr*, p. 410.
(3) *Hed.* II (Ar.), p. 888, see *post.*
(4) *Ibid*, p. 891.
(5) Sel. Rep. I., p. 17.
(6) *Waghaira* ; this does not mean such like things but other objects.

priated be at the time of appropriation the property of the appropriator.'' This definition I shall explain fully later on.

Abû Hanîfa's opinion.

According to Abû Hanîfa, the legal meaning of *wakf* is the detention of a specific thing in the ownership of the *wâkif* or appropriator, and the devoting of its profits in charity on the poor or other good objects(1) in the manner of an *'aâriat* or commodate loan,(2) but not being absolute in its nature, it is revocable by the *wâkif*, and he is at liberty to dispose of it according to his own will. Abû Hanîfa, further, thought that the right of the appropriator was extinguished only after the Judge had made his decree, and the mode in which such a decree could be obtained, as suggested by Abû Hanîfa, was for the dedicator to deliver the subject of the *wakf* to the *mutwâlli* or curator and then demand it back on the ground that the *wakf* was not binding [on him], whereupon the Judge would pronounce his decree holding the dedication to be obligatory, and it would then b come so.

This primitive and unpractical notion was never accepted as law among his followers. In the *Fâth ul-Kadîr*, Abû Hanîfa's notion on this point has been combated and refuted by *hadîses* (traditions) from the Prophet himself.(3)

Abû Yusuf's rule recognised as law.

According to Abû Yusuf, *wakf* is the detention of a thing in the implied ownership of Almighty God, in such a manner that its profits may be applied for the benefit of human beings, *and the dedication when once made, is absolute, so that the thing dedicated can neither be sold, nor given nor inherited.* Mohammed, the fellow-disciple of Abû Yusuf, agrees with him on this point, but he thinks that the right of the *wâkif* does not cease in the property until he has appointed a *mutwâlli* or curator and delivered it into his hands.

According to Abû Yusuf, the dedication becomes absolute and the right of the person making it becomes extinguished by the mere fact of his declaration that he dedicates it, or has dedicated

(1) *Hed.* II (Ar.), p. 891 ; see also the *Khazânat-ul-Mufiin.*

(2) *Ibid*, p. 887. *'Aâriat* is resumable at the will of the lender. Mr. Baillie's note on this subject is worth inserting here.

'' This does not mean that the profits are merely to be lent ; but that the objects of the *wakf* are to have the same benefit from it as if the subject of it were lent to them in the manner of an *'aâriat*, when they would have the use of it, or, in other words, its profits or usufruct, for their own benefit so long as it remained in their possession,'' Baillie's Dig., 2nd Ed., p. 557.

(3) *Fatâwai Alamgiri*, Vol. II, p. 454 ; *see post.*

it.(1) This rule of law laid down by Abû Yusuf is in force among all the Hanafî jurists. The great Digest prepared under the command of Aurangzeb expressly declares that, on the question of the completion of the *wakf*, "decrees in this country are given according to the doctrine of Abû Yusuf." Mohammed's views were adopted only by some of the Bokhariot schoolmen and have no application in any other part of the Sunni world.(2)

SECTION II.

CONDITIONS RELATING TO THE WAKIF.

Conditions necessary for creating a valid *wâkif*.

"The same conditions which are essential for the validity of mere acts of bounty," says the *Fath ul-Kadîr*, "are requisite to the valid constitution of a *wakf*, that is, the *wâkif* must be free, must be adult, and must be possessed of understanding." "It is also a condition," adds the author, "that it should not be dependent for its operation upon a contingency which may or may not happen."..."For example, if a man were to say 'this land of mine will become dedicated if my son arrives at home on such a day,' the land will not become dedicated even should the son arrive on that day."(3)

As a general rule, it may be stated that all persons who are competent to make a valid gift are also competent to constitute a valid *wakf*. The consecrator must be (*a*) free, *i.e.*, not a slave; (*b*) must be sane; and (*c*) must be adult, in other words, must

(1) In the case of *Doe dem. Abdoollah Barber* v. *Jaun Beebee* [1845], Fulton, p. 345, the learned Judges distinctly said that, according to the modern doctrine of Mahommedan jurists and lawyers, Abû Yusuf's opinion on this point is considered better Law.

(2) *Tas-hîl.* Mr. Baillie has entirely misconstrued the passage in the *Fatâwai Alamgiri* (Vol. II., p. 455), in saying that decisions are both ways. The passage in question affords no warrant for that construction. It runs thus :—"According to Abû Yusuf, the right of the *wâkif* becomes extinguished immediately on the declaration, and that also is the opinion of the three Imâms [Mâlik, Shâfeï and Ibn Hanbal] and of the bulk of the learned, and is followed by the Jurists of Balkh, and on that is the *Fatwa ;* so in the *Fath ul-Kadîr* and *Munieh*. And on that is the *Fatwa*, so says the *Sirâj-ul-Wahâj* also."

"Mohammed said that the right is not extinguished until the *wâkif* consigns the property to a trustee, and the *Sirâjia* says the *Fatwa* is thereon; and so also the *Khulâsa*." As I shall show later on, the law laid down by Abû Yusuf is in force universally among the Hanafî Sunnis.

(3) See *post*.

have attained that age when, according to his personal law, it would be presumed he has acquired sufficient discretion or understanding to comprehend the nature of his act.

All the schools are agreed respecting the capacity of the *wâkif*. "And of the *wâkif*," says the *Sharâya*, "it is required that he be of full age, sound understanding, and unrestrained in the use or disposition of his property." So the *Fatâwai Alamgiri*,—"among the conditions (of *wakf*) are understanding and puberty (on the part of the *wâkif*) as a *wakf* by a boy or an insane person is not valid." But the action of a mere imbecile is not absolutely invalid. "If a person who is imbecile," says the *Radd ul-Muhtâr*, "makes a *wakf* upon himself and after him upon some other purpose which does not fail, it is valid according to Abû Yusuf, but the latter will take effect only upon its being sanctioned by the Judge." Capacity of the *wâkif*.

Where, therefore, a person, who, without being absolutely *non compos mentis*, is so weak in intellect, that he cannot understand the nature of his acts, makes a *wakf* in his own favour with remainder in favour of others, such *wakf* is valid so far as the settlement on himself is concerned, and with regard to the remainder it would be valid with the sanction of the Judge.

Any person who is sane and adult may constitute a *wakf*. But the same circumstances which may avoid a gift, *viz.*, undue influence (*ikrâh*), fraud, or want of comprehension may avoid a *wakf*. In the case of *Nawab Asghur Ally* v. *Delroos Banoo Begum*,(1) the appellant had, in the year 1852, executed a *wakfnâmah* dedicating all her properties for certain pious purposes. Upon a suit by the respondents to remove her from the management of the *wakf* on the ground of misfeasance, the High Court held as follows :— *Nawab Asghur Alí* v. *Delroos Banoo Begum.*

"The Judge holds that the defendant cannot now be allowed to say that she misunderstood the effect of the words she used or of the acts by which she consummated the *wakf*, and under ordinary circumstances no doubt a person would be rightly presumed to have known the consequence of his own deliberate act, but in this case the matter is somewhat different. The defendant is a *pardanashin* Mahommedan lady, unable to read and write and

(1) [1875], 15 B. L. R., 167.

Nawab Asghur Ali—Delroos Banoo Begum v. contd.

generally ignorant as are most of her class ; she has been examined, and she swears positively that she did not understand the meaning of the deed which she executed. She admits her wish to keep her estate for the purpose of perpetuating certain ceremonies in memory of her mother, and out of the hands of her legal heirs, and that to this end she, by the advice of her confidential servant Ali Jameen, signed a deed which she was told would have that effect. She swears positively that the *tauliatnamah* was only read over to her in Persian, a language which she did not understand, and that she had no idea of divesting herself by it of her proprietary rights. No evidence has been given to rebut this statement ; only one witness to the *tauliatnamah*, Abdool Azeez (summoned by the defendant), has been examined, and he does not prove that the deed was ever read to the Begum, in Hindustani, a language which she understood, or that its purport was explained to her. Her own acts have been, from the first, absolutely inconsistent with a knowledge that she had divested herself of her rights as proprietor by the *tauliatnamah*. From a time shortly after its execution we find her dealing with the property just as if it were still her own, selling, buying, borrowing, granting mukurrari leases and exercising all the usual rights of ownership, and making everything as public as possible by registering the documents affecting these conveyances. I find, moreover, that long after the *tauliatnamah* was executed (namely, in 1871), the Collector of the 24-Pergunnahs gave pottahs to Delroos Banoo Begum, and treated her as the proprietor of her estate, and this is a further argument in favour of the property never having been considered an endowment for public purposes under Regulation XIX of 1810. It is, moreover, hardly likely that had Delroos Banoo Begum known what was the real effect of making a *wakf*, she would have headed her receipts for rents paid by the ryots with her name as mutwalli and a description of the estate as a *wakf* mehal, and still have gone on disposing of the property at her pleasure, and as if she had made no *wakf* at all. From first to last, as it seems to me, her acts denote a person endeavouring to make such an arrangement of her property as would defeat the claims of her heirs and permit of the estate being retained for particular purposes, but always considering that she stil' retained the right to do what she pleased with the property so lon as she lived."

But when a *wakf* has been created by a formally registered document by a person who is *sui juris*, and there is no reason to suppose that the settlement has been brought about by undue influence or fraud, it will not be set aside. Nor, when a *wakf* is created in express terms, can the *wâkif* turn round afterwards and say that he did not know the meaning of the word *wakf* or that he did not intend to create a *wakf*.(1) In *Fatima Bibi* v. *The Advocate-General*,(2) it appeared that the plaintiff, a Mahommedan lady of the Sunni sect, by an indenture dated the 16th of November 1866, conveyed all her properties in trust for the purposes set forth in the deed, primarily for herself and her children and other descendants and ultimately for the poor. In 1881 she desired to revoke the trust. Upon a case stated under section 527 of the Code of Civil Procedure, West, J., held as follows :—

A *wakf* by a *sui juris* person

Fatima Bibi v. *The Advocate-General*

"A *wakf* must be certain as to the property appropriated, unconditional and not subject to an option. It must too have a final object which cannot fail, and this object, it seems, must, according to the better opinions, be expressly set forth. In the deed now in question it is set forth, and the reserve to the plaintiff for her life of the annual profits does not invalidate it, as such a consequence arises only when there is a provision for the sale of the *corpus* of the property and an appropriation of the proceeds for the donatrix. In the case of *Delroos Banoo Begum* v. *Nawab Syud Ashgur Ali*, a dedication of property in *wakf* was declared invalid on the ground that the donatrix, an illiterate woman, though a wealthy one, had not really known what she was doing in endowing the imambarah. The imambarah was within her own house, she had appointed herself joint mutwalli and her co-mutwalli had died. The property had never been treated as dedicated to a public religious establishment within the meaning of Act XX of 1863. Everything went to show that there had not been a true dedication, but the learned Judge, who pronounced the decision of the Court, said that if the instrument of *wakf* had been 'really and knowingly executed by the lady defendant, it would have bound Delroos Banoo Begum without the power of revocation.' In the present case the direct ownership of the property was completely parted with. There was, it is said, a want of discretion on the part of the plaintiff,

(1) See *post*.
(2) [1882], I. L., 6 Bom., 42.

and certainly a dedication made by a girl of fourteen is not to be upheld without enquiry, but here the transaction was never questioned by the plaintiff's husband during his life, and the plaintiff herself has for fifteen years confirmed her own early act by a continued acceptance of the profits of the estate from the trustees. She cannot now say with any reason that the dedication was invalid on account either of its ceremonial defects or of a want of an effectual accompanying volition."

Islâm not necessary to create a *wakf*.

Islâm is not a necessary condition for the constitution of a *wakf*. Any person of whatever creed may create a *wakf*, but the law requires that the object for which the dedication is made should be lawful according to the creed of the dedicator as well as the Islâmic doctrines. Divine approbation being the essential element in the constitution of a *wakf*, if the object for which a dedication is made is sinful, either according to the laws of Islâm or to the creed of the dedicator, it would not be valid. Consequently, a Moslem cannot make a dedication in favour of an idol, a non-Moslem place of worship, or any other object which is held as unlawful or sinful in his law, nor can a non-Moslem validly make a dedication for a Moslem place of worship. But in either case the dedication may be effectuated by the consent of the heirs after the decease of the *wâkif*. The *Fatâwai Alamgiri* lays down the rule in a rather bald fashion:—" If a *Zimmi* should give his mansion as a *Masjid* or place of worship for Mussulmans and construct it as they are accustomed to do, and permit them to pray in it, and he should then die, it would become the inheritance of his heirs."(1) Stated in this form the rule is unintelligible, but the principle is explained, as I have mentioned above, in the *Fath ul-Kadîr*. No person has a right to withdraw a portion of his property which would devolve upon his heirs, for purposes considered as sinful in his creed without the assent of the heirs whose rights are interfered with. Such assent may be given either at the time of the dedication or after the inheritance has opened. But where an object is not sinful according to the laws of the dedicator (if non-Moslem) and is lawful according to the laws of the Moslems, the *wakf* is valid by *consensus*. For example, if a Christian were to make a dedication for a building, where the Almighty God may be worshipped according to the rites of Islâm (without

(1) *Fatâwai Alamgiri*, Vol. II, p. 526.

interfering in any way with his own residence), such a dedication would be valid. Similarly, if a Moslem were to make a dedication for Unitarian worship, such a *wakf* would (I submit), be in conformity with the principle enunciated in the *Fath ul-Kadîr*.

According to the *Bahr-ur-Râik*, it is lawful for a Moslem to create a *wakf* in favour of the non-Moslem poor and destitute. Similarly he can endow a school for the education of non-Moslem children and *vice versâ*.

Wakfs created by an apostate from Islâm

There is some difference of opinion about the validity of a *wakf* created by an apostate from Islâm. According to the jurist Ibn Shahna, all *wakfs* created by him in favour of the poor or for pious purposes of a *general* character remain operative. But *wakfs* created in favour of individuals, against the interests of heirs, are voided. According to others, all *wakfs* created previous to apostacy are avoided, and such property becomes on his death part of his inheritance to which the right of heirs attaches. Should he, however, return to Islâm before his death, the *wakfs* come into operation again.

But the *wakf* made by an apostate after his apostacy is valid.(1)

If a woman were to make a *wakf* and then apostatise, her *wakf* would not be voided.(2)

Section III.

The Subject-matter of the Dedication.

The subject-matter of *wakf* must be the property of the *wâkif*.

The subject-matter of the dedication must be the lawful property of the *wâkif* at the time the *wakf* is made, that is, he must be in a position to exercise dominion over it.(3) Consequently, if a *wakf* is made by a person of some property which he has unlawfully acquired, it would be invalid, although he may subsequently purchase it from the lawful owner.(4) So also, when a man makes a *wakf*, for certain good purposes, of land belonging to another, and then becomes the proprietor of it, the *wakf* is not lawful; but it would become validly dedicated if ratified by the

---

(1) *Bahr-ur-Râik*; *Radd ul-Muhtâr*, Vol. III, p. 557.

(2) *Sharh-i-Tahtâwi*.

(3) *Fatâwai Alamgiri*, Vol. II, p. 457; I construe المال المتقوم as meaning, property of which the person purporting to dedicate it is in lawful possession.

(4) *Sharh-i-Tâhtâwi*; *Fatâwai Alamgiri*, Vol. II, p. 457

proprietor. Accordingly, when a person purports to make a *wakf* of property which does not belong to him, and such *wakf* is subsequently ratified by the true owner, the dedication is valid.

When a person makes a bequest of some property to another, and the legatee, prior to the death of the testator and before the legacy has vested in him, makes a *wakf* thereof, it is invalid.

Similarly, if a person were to buy a property with an option on the part of the seller (to cancel the sale) and to make a *wakf* thereof, and the seller were then to confirm the sale, the *wakf* nevertheless would not be valid, according to the *Bahr-ur-Râik*, or, if the donee of a piece of land were to make a *wakf* of it before he has obtained possession, and were then to get possession, the *wakf* would not be valid according to the *Fath ul-Kadîr*.

In other words, a *wakf* of property before the full proprietary right has vested in the person appropriating is not valid. There are certain exceptions, however, to this rule.

Wakf of property in which the wâkif has not full proprietary title.

"If possession were taken of land given by an invalid gift, and it were then made a *wakf*, it would be lawful according to the *Bahr ur-Râik*, the donee being responsible for its value. And if one were to purchase a house by an invalid sale, take possession, and then make a *wakf* of the same in favour of the poor, the *wakf* would be lawful and operative according to the *Fatâwai Kâzi Khân*, with the responsibility for its value to the seller; but if the *wakf* were made before taking possession it would not be valid according to the *Muhît*."

"When a man buys land by a valid sale, and makes a *wakf* of it before taking possession and paying the price, the matter is in suspense until he pays the price and takes possession when the *wakf* is lawful; but if he were to die without leaving any property, the land would be sold and the *wakf* would be voided says Fakîh (the Jurist) Abu'l Lais. And if a right is established in the property after the creation of the *wakf*, or if it is claimed by a person under a right of pre-emption after the *wakf* by the buyer has been made, the *wakf* is void according to the *Nahr-ul-Fâik*."(1)

Wakf of property subject to a lease or mortgage is valid.

It is not necessary that the entire subject-matter of the *wakf* should be actually in the possession of the *wâkif* at the time of the *wakf*, for the consecrator may validly include in the *wakf* any

(1) *Fatâwai Alamgiri*, Vol. II. p. 457.

property which he may subsequently acquire.(1) Nor is it necessary that the property which is dedicated should be entirely free from the rights or claims of other parties. Accordingly, a property which is leased to tenants, or which is under mortgage, or held in pledge, can be validly dedicated.(2)

Freedom from rights of others not a condition.

It is not a condition, "says the *Fatâwai Alamgiri*," that the property dedicated should be free from the rights of others (*hakk-ul-ghair*) as in the case of pledge and bailment, so that if one were to give a lease of his land and were then to make a *wakf* of it before the expiration of the term, the *wakf* would be binding according to its conditions, and the contract of lease would not be voided, but on the expiration of the term the land would revert to the purposes to which it was dedicated. In like manner, if a man were to mortgage his land, and then dedicate it before redeeming it, the *wakf* would take effect (لزم الوقف), but the land would not be withdrawn in the same way from the mortgage and if it should remain for years in the hands of the mortgagee and then be redeemed, it would revert to the uses for which it was made *wakf*. And if the mortgagor should die before redemption, yet if he should leave sufficient inheritance to redeem the land, it is to be redeemed and the *wakf* would take effect. But if he should not leave enough for that purpose, the land may be sold and the *wakf* would become void. In the case of a lease, when either the lessor or lessee dies the lease becomes void, and the *wakf* immediately takes effect; so in the *Fath ul-Kadîr*."(3)

When the land is sold for the payment of the mortgage-debt, the *wakf* is not voided in its entirety; the *wakf* attaches to the balance of the sale-proceeds after the payment of the debt.

The passage in the *Durr-ul-Mukhtâr*(4) is as follows:—"And the *wakf* is void of a mortgagee who is insolvent (معسر) and of a person whose debts surround his assets and who consecrates his pro-

---

(1) *Sautayra*, p. 389.

(2) *Durr-ul-Mukhtâr*, p. 416; *Radd ul-Muhtâr*, Vol. III, p. 605; *Fatâwai Alamgiri*, Vol. II, p. 458; *Fath ul-Kadîr*, Vol. II, p. 460; *Durr-ul-Mukhtâr*, p. 419; *Tashîl*; *Ghâit-ul-Bayân*. The *Radd ul-Muhtâr* says:—"The *wakf* of leased property, according to the *Bahr*, is valid, and on the expiration of the term or the death of either the lessor or lessee it would be applied to the purposes of the *wakf*."

(3) *Fatâwai Alamgiri*, Vol. II, p. 458; *Fath ul-Kadir*, Vol. II, p. 638.

(4) *Durr-ul-Mukhtâr*, p. 417.

perty whilst suffering from a mortal illness, contrary to the case of one [a debtor] who dedicates in health if it is made before the issue of a fiat of inhibition. So if he has made a condition that his debts should be discharged out of the income of the *wakf* it is valid. And if he has made no such condition [even] then his debts would be paid out of the balance of the income which remains after discharge of his requirements without extravagance. Should the *wâkif* have made the *wakf* in favour of any person other than himself, the income will be specially for such person. So in the *Fatâwai-Ibn (u) Nujaim*....But in the *M'arûzât* (Ordinances of Mufti Abû S'aûd) it is stated that a question was submitted to him regarding the validity of a *wakf* made by a person who, in order to escape from his debts (هرب في الديدن)(1) made a *wakf* on his children, and he (the Mufti) answered such *wakf* is not correct and will not be operative, and the Kâzis are prohibited from giving effect to such a *wakf*."(2)

The same principle is stated in almost identical terms in the *Bahr-ur-Râik* and, according to Tahtâwi. there is absolute consensus on the subject. The rule enunciated was given effect to in the case of *Shahzadee Hazara Begum* v. *Khaja Hossein Ali Khan*,(3) where it was held that the existence of a mortgage at the time at which the endowment was made does not render the endowment invalid under the Mahommedan Law.

---

(1) In the *Majmu'a Jadida*, this is given as هرب عن الدين ; the *Zeitschrift*, &c., p. 528.

(2) "This edict," says Tahtâwi, "was issued by our Lord the Sultan" (of Turkey) "along with the one prohibiting the hearing of claims after the lapse of fifteen years." Evidently the council of the Sultan used to issue edicts for the better administration of the law.

(3) [1869], 12 W. R., 498. In this case, Peacock, C. J., after quoting the passage from the *Fatâwai Alamgiri* given in the text, said as follows:—"As I understand this passage, it is intended to point out that if after the mortgage the mortgagor endows the land and dies previously to redemption leaving sufficient assets, the heirs are bound to apply those asests to the redemption of the mortgage, so that the endowment may take effect free from the mortgage by the application of the other assets of the endower." Referring to the passage dealing with the circumstance of the mortgagor not leaving sufficient assets the Chief Justice said as follows:—"The meaning of that, as I understand it, is that the land will be liable to be sold by the mortgagee and the endowment rendered void, that is, the mortgagee will have power to enforce the mortgage by the sale of the land, if necessary, and the endowment will be rendered void as against the purchaser under the mortgage. It does not, as I understand, mean that the endowment will be rendered void as against the heirs of the endower."

The voidance of the lease on the death of the lessor or the lessee is a natural consequence of the principle of the Hanafi Law, which holds that a lease or *ijâra* cannot last beyond the lifetime of the lessor or the lessee. In India, however, where leases are often of a permanent character the principle stated in the text does not apply. It follows that where a piece of land which is already leased in perpetuity is dedicated, the *wakf* would at once take effect, and the rent reserved under the lease would be applied to the purposes of the *wakf* without interfering with the *mouroosi* right of the lessee.

Wakf of property subject to a lease.

Lands leased for a fixed period (*al-arz-ul-muhtak-kira*) stand on a different footing. In such cases the *wakf* would remain, as it were, in abeyance during the existence of the lease, without interfering with the possessory right of the lessee. For example, if a man were to dedicate a piece of land, which he has already leased to another, for the purpose of building thereon a mosque, or for any other purpose which would interfere with the possession of the tenant or lessee, the carrying out of that purpose would be postponed until the lessee has given up possession. But where the purpose has not that effect, in other words, where, though the property is dedicated, the rents and profits arising therefrom are only to be devoted to the objects of the *wakf*, there is no such postponement, and the *wakf* takes effect at once.

Wakf of a person placed under inhibition.

The *wakf* of a person who has been placed under "inhibition" by the Judge is not valid. The proceeding of "inhibition" may be likened to a proceeding in bankruptcy. The Kâzi is authorised, at the instance of the creditors of a person, or any of his relatives or friends, upon proof of prodigality, want of mental capacity, or reckless borrowing, to place him under "inhibition,"—to declare him incapable of contracting further debts or engaging in any transaction, and to appoint a curator of his estate or business or trade. When such a *fiat* has been made against a person, he is said to be a *mahjûr*. A *wakf* by a *mahjûr* is invalid. So long as a person has not been declared a *mahjûr* by the Kâzi, he has absolute power, if *sui juris*, to deal with his property in any way he likes.

The effect of a *wakf*.

The effect of a consecration or *wakf* of a property by its owner is to extinguish absolutely and for ever all his rights therein. The act of consecration, which is irrevocable in its character, transfers the property for ever into the legal ownership of the Almighty for the benefit of His creatures. Thenceforth the *wâkif* has no power to deal with it in any way or burden it or create any charge over it. In short, it is no more his to deal with. Should the *wâkif* constitute himself the *mutwalli*, any dealing of his, prejudicial to the interests of the *wakf*, is a misfeasance, and the Kâzi or Judge, on proof thereof, would be bound to remove him. He cannot even borrow for the benefit of the *wakf* without the sanction of the Judge.

Consequently, any liabilities contracted by the *wâkif after the wakf is created*, cannot affect the *wakf*, and subsequent creditors have no right to question the consecration.

But though no act of the *wâkif subsequent* to the *wakf* affects its validity, if any right was attached to the property *before* it was dedicated, the consecration would not defeat that right. If the property was already mortgaged, and the mortgagor has no other assets from which the debt can be satisfied, the property in question would be sold, and the proceeds would be applied to the payment of the debt.

The rule as regards the consecration or endowment of property held in mortgage or pledge has already been stated. But simple creditors for whose debts the property is not hypothecated or charged have no right to question the validity of a *wakf* created by a person "in health" and not in insolvent circumstances so as to give rise to the inference of fraud.

Wakf by a person who dies heavily involved in debt.

But when the *wakf* is made *in extremis*, or when the person is labouring under an illness which ends fatally, and the *wâkif* leaves no assets from which his debts can be satisfied, in other words, dies insolvent, the Kâzi has the power to direct the payment of the deceased's debts out of the *wakf* property.

With regard to the rights of those creditors, for whose debts no portion of the property dedicated is mortgaged, and the *wakf* is made by a person "in health," who is involved in debt the authorities to some extent differ.

According to the *Fatâwai Kâzi Khân*, the *Fath ul-Kadîr*, the *Zakhîra*, the *Anf'aa-ul-Wasâil*, the *Surrat-ul-Fatâwa* and other authorities [unsecured] "creditors have no right in the property of their debtors." And a person, who has only a money-claim against another and has not taken the precaution to get the property of his debtor hypothecated for his debt, has no right to question a *wakf* made by the debtor.

The text in the *Fath ul-Kadîr* is as follows :—

"In the *Fatâwai Kâzi Khân*, it is laid down, that if a man labouring under a death-illness make a *wakf* and his debts surround [exceed] his assets, the property will be sold and the *wakf* will be set aside ; this is contrary to the case of a *wakf* made by a person in health, although he may be immersed in debt, so that it exceeds his assets ; the *wakf* in such a case is valid nevertheless, and the creditors cannot ask it to be cancelled if the *wakf* has been made before the *fiat* of the Kâzi, declaring him to be a *mahjûr* ; such a *wakf* is valid by *consensus*, for creditors(1) have no claim in the property of their debtor whilst in health."(2)

The text in the *Surrat-ul-Fatâwa* is as follows :—

Wakf of a person who is involved in debt.

"In the *Durrar wa'l Ghurrar*,(3) Chapter on *Wakf*, it is laid down that if a person labouring under a death-illness make a *wakf* of his house, and it be found that his debts exceed his assets. [lit. he is surrounded in debt], the house will be sold and the *wakf* will break ; . . . . . . so it is stated in the Chapter on *Wakf* in the *Khazânat-ul-Muftiïn*."

"In the *Zakhîra*, it is laid down that when a man, who is largely indebted and has a piece of land worth 100,000 dirhems, makes a *wakf* thereof, and, with the object of throwing his creditors into difficulties, settles the produce of the *wakf* on himself, and witnesses prove that he is insolvent, the *wakf* will be valid, so will the testimony. The validity of the *wakf* is founded on the fact that the *wâkif* has a right over the property [in other words, if the property is not hypothecated, the creditors(4) have no right to question the disposition.] . . . .

(1) Meaning unsecured creditors.

(2) في فتاوي قاضيخان مريض وقف يد عليه ديون محيط بماله . يباع وينقض الوقف الى قوله و هذا بخلاف ما لو وقف المديون الصحيح و عليه ديون تحيط بماله - وقفه صحيح - لا ينقضه ارباب الديون اذا كان قبل الحجر بالاتفاق لانه لم يتعلق حقهم بالعين في حال الصحة *

Comp. The *Zeitschrift der Deutschen Morgenländischen Gessallschaft* (1891), p. 527, Art. by Prof. Kresmárik on *wakf*.

(3) An important and well-known authority.

(4) Unsecured.

. . . Any balance of the produce remaining over after providing for the subsistence of the *wâkif* can be taken by the creditors, for the produce is the property of their debtor(1) . . .

And in the Chapter on *Wakf* in the *Anf'aa-ul-Wasâil*, it is stated that if a *marîz* [person labouring under a death-illness] make a *wakf* of his house, and he be so heavily involved in debt that his liabilities *surround* his assets, the house will be sold, and the *wakf* will be set aside. But if the debtor makes a *wakf* in health, and he is so involved in debt that his liabilities *surround* his assets, the *wakf* is nevertheless obligatory, if made before an order of inhibition by the Kâzi. And this is by *consensus*, and the creditors will have no right to set it aside, for they have no claim in the property of their debtor in health [that is, in the case of a *wakf* made by a person in health]. So it is stated also in the *Fath ul-Kadîr*; and the reference in the *Anf'aa-ul-Wasâil* to the *Zakhîra* supports it."(2)

---

(1) من وقف الدرر و الغرر مريض وقف داره و عليه دين محيط بماله فانه يباع الدار و ينتقض الوقف * * * * * * * * *
* * * * * * * * * (كذا في) وقف خزانة المفتين و في الذخيرة رجل عليه ديون و له ضيعة تساوى عشرة آلاف درهم فوقفها و شرط غلاتها لنفسه قصداً منه المماطلة و شهد الشهود على افلاسه جاز الوقف و جاز الشهادة اما جواز الوقف لمصادفة ملكه و جواز الوقف مع هذا الشرط قول ابي يوسف و اما جواز شهادة فلانها صدق لان الرقبة خرجت عن ملكه فان فضل شي من قوته من هذه الغلات فللغرماء ان ياخذوه منه لان الغلات بقيت على ملكه *

(2) من. وقف انفع الوسائل مريض وقف داره و عليه ديون محيط بماله فانه تباع الدار و ينتقض الوقف و اما لو وقف المديون الصحيح عليه ديون تحيط بماله فان وقفه لازم لا ينقضه ارباب الديون اذا كان قبل الحجر بالاتفاق لانه لم يتعلق حقهم بالعين في حالة صحته كما في فتح القدير و يؤيده ما في انفع الوسائل معزياً الى الذخيرة *

According to the *M'arûzât* of Mufti Abû S'aûd, however, if a person is so heavily involved in debt as to be absolutely insolvent, and *with the object of defrauding his creditors consecrates his property*, the Kâzi has the power of not recognising the *wakf*, and of compelling him to sell the property and pay his debts, so far as possible, with the proceeds of the same.

After commenting on the statement in the *Durr ul-Mukhtâr*, "*that the wakf* of an insolvent mortgagor is void," the author of the *Radd-ul-Muhtâr* proceeds thus :—"This is a mistake ; such a *wakf* is not *bâtil ;* for in the *As'aâf* and other works it is laid down that if a person, after mortgaging a property and delivering it(1) to the mortgagee, were to dedicate it, it would be valid, and if he is possessed of [other] means, the Kâzi would constrain him to discharge the debt ; but if he have no means, then the Kâzi would declare the *wakf* cancelled, and the property would be sold for the payment of the debt. Similarly, if the mortgagor die and leave other assets from which the debt can be satisfied, the *wakf* will be maintained, otherwise the property consecrated may be sold, and the *wakf* cancelled. So it is stated in the *Fath ul-Kadîr* also."

Wakf by person involved in debt.

"And if a person make a *wakf* in *marz-ul-mout* and die so involved that his debts *surround* his assets, in that case the property will be sold and the *wakf* will be cancelled . . . . This is different from the case of a *wakf* made in health by a person against whom no inhibition has issued. The *wakf* of such a person is valid, though it may have been made with the object of throwing the creditors into delay, as he has dealt with his own property, so it is stated in the *Anf'aa-ul-Wasâil* from the *Zakhîra.* In the *Fath ul-Kadîr*, it is stated that such *wakf* is obligatory, when it is made before inhibition, and by *consensus* the creditors will have no right to set it aside, for creditors have no right in the property of their debtor during his lifetime unless hypothecated to them ; and in the *Khairiyeh* the *Fatwa* is given on this basis, and it is stated there that Ibn (u) Nujaim decreed accordingly. But as I shall show from the *M'arûzât* there is a difference [of opinion]"

. . . .

"If the *wâkif* has made a *wakf* on himself and made a condition that his debts should be satisfied out of the income, the

(1) There is no hypothecation under the Mahommedan Law without seisin.

wakf is valid *with* the condition,(1) as Ibn (u) Nujaim has decreed, and the author [of the *Durr ul-Mukhtâr*] says, that if the *wakf* is made on another with the same condition, both the *wakf* and the condition are valid." . . . . "Even if the *wâkif* make no such condition but the *wakf* is in his favour, any balance (over and above his necessary expenses) will be applied towards the payment of his debts. But if the *wakf* is on another, the produce will be given to him. So it is stated in the *Fatâwa* of Ibn (u) Nujaim(2) . . . . "In the *M'arûzât*(3) of Mufti Abû S'aûd it is stated that he was asked—'when a person makes a *wakf* on his children to escape his creditors and has no other property from which the debts can be satisfied, is such *wakf* valid,' he answered, 'no, it will not be valid or obligatory, and the Kâzi has the power of not recognising such a *wakf* by a person who is absolutely sunk in debt to the extent of his assets' . . . "What I have stated from the *Zakhîra* and the *Fath ul-Kadîr* is in conflict with this view, unless you restrict it to the *wakf* of a debtor making a *wakf* in death-illness. And in the *Fatâwa-ul-Ismâilia* it is stated that the Kâzi has the power of not enforcing such a *wakf* and of constraining him to sell the property and pay his debts, and this is what Moulâna Abû S'aûd states, and his enunciation seems approved."(4) This applies to the case of an insolvent debtor acting fraudulently.

Dedication by an insolvent *wâkif* acting fraudulently.

The rule enunciated in the *M'arûzât* of Mufti Abû S'aûd and the *Fatâwa-'l-Ismâilia* can be reconciled with the principle laid down in such high and recognised authorities as the *Fatâwai Kâzi Khân*, the *Fath ul-Kadîr*, the *Zakhîra*, &c., with the light of the statement contained in the *Tanwîr ul-Absár*, which is to this effect, "the *wakf* of a person whose debts *surround* his assets should be maintained either by giving him time to pay off his debts or appointing a manager to realise the rents and profits and to pay the debts therewith."(5) If it be wholly impossible to

(1) In the case of *Luchmiput Sing* v. *Shah Amir Alum* [1881], 9 Cal. L. R., 176, the *wakfnâmah* contained a provision to that effect, and it was held valid.

(2) Also called *Fatâwa-'z-Zainiyeh*; see Morley's Dig., Vol. I, Introd., p. cclxxxvii.

(3) Comp. the *Zeitschraft der Deutschen Morgenlandischen Gesallschaft* (1891), p. 528.

(4) *Radd ul-Muhtâr*, Vol. III, pp. 611-612.

(5) *Ibid*; *Durr-ul-Mukhtâr*, in loco.

discharge it by that process, the Judge in that case has the option of directing the sale of the property consecrated. It follows from this that the *wakf* of a person involved in debt is not *ipso facto* void; it is only voidable if he acts fraudulently to defeat his creditors.

The *wakf* of a person involved in debt is not void.

In this connection it must be observed that the poor, who are the ultimate beneficiaries of every *wakf* made in favour of individuals, cannot be parties to any fraud, and, therefore, if possible, should not be prejudiced.

27 Eliz., c. 4, did not apply to India beyond the limits of the Presidency Towns, and section 53 of the Transfer of Property Act, which embodies the rule contained in section 2 of the English Statute, does not affect the provisions of the Mahommedan Law.(1) And, consequently, when a person, who is not in insolvent circumstances, makes a *wakf* of any portion of his property, his subsequent creditors have no right to question that *wakf*, nor can a *subsequent* purchaser for consideration of the property in question, seek to set aside the *wakf*,—for, once dedicated, the property ceases to belong to the *wâkif*, and he can no more burden it or sell it than if he were an absolute stranger.

Principle.

It must be remembered also that a *wakf* is *not* a gratuitous transfer of property. It is a transfer to the legal ownership of the Almighty for substantial consideration, *viz*., His reward, which is obtained the moment the *wakf* is created. As will be seen afterwards, a *wakf* takes effect like the emancipation of a slave. *There is no power of revocation nor can there be any reserve;* and neither the *wâkif* nor any person deriving title from him can say afterwards that he had no intention to make a binding and irrevocable *wakf*.(2)

A *wakf* is a transfer of property for consideration.

In order that the *entire wakf* may be valid, it is necessary, however, that the *wâkif* should not be suffering from a mortal illness at the time of the dedication. In other words, the *wakf* of a person suffering from a mortal illness, from which he dies, takes effect as a bequest and operates with reference to one-third of his property. But the *wakf* of a person made during an illness from which he eventually recovers is valid with respect to the whole.

Wakf by a person suffering from a mortal illness.

---

(1) See s. 2, cl. d.
(2) *Ramz-ul-Hakâik.*

Principle.

"The *wakf* of a person suffering from a death-illness," says the *Radd ul-Muhtâr*, "takes effect like the *hiba*(1) of a person in that condition, *i.e.*, the *wakf* will operate as regards one-third of his estate. If the heirs, however, consent, it will take effect with reference to the whole. If some of the heirs consent it will take effect in proportion to their shares." So also in the *Fath ul-Kadir*, "'a *wakf* made in *marz-ul-mout*, takes effect,' says Tahâwi, 'like a *wasiat*'" (a testamentary disposition.)

Kâzi Khân following Imâm Abû Bakr Mohammed Ibn-ul-Fazl states that *wakfs* are of three kinds in relation to the state in which they are made:

(1) Those made in health (*i.e.*, to which operation is given in health).

(2) Those made whilst suffering from a mortal malady.

(3) Those made with the object of taking effect after death.

"Transmutation of proprietary right is necessary in the first, but *not* in the third, for that is testamentary in its nature; but the second is like the first, though it takes effect with reference to the third of the estate of the *wâkif*, like a gift made in death-illness."

Wakf made in death-illness.

If a person suffering from a death-illness were to make a *wakf* of his house, it would be lawful and valid if it does not exceed one-third of his estate, but if it exceeds one-third and the heirs consent, it would be valid in its entirety; but if the heirs do not consent, the *wakf* would be avoided as regards the excess over a third. If some of the heirs consent, and the others do not, the *wakf* in excess of the one-third would be valid in proportion to the shares of the assenting heirs. If one of the non-assenting heirs sells his share in the portion of the property respecting which the *wakf* is disallowed, and subsequently it is discovered that the *wâkif* has left other properties besides, so that the *wakf* can be valid in its entirety with reference to the property dedicated, owing to its forming less than one-third of the entire estate of the *wâkif*, the sale by the heir would not be set aside, but he would have to pay the price thereof for the purchase of other property to be added to the *wakf*.

Testamentary *wakf* revocable.

It has already been stated that a *wakf* is irrevocable. Once the dedication is made by word or in writing, the proprietary

(1) *Durr-ul-Mukhtâr*, p. 417.

right of the dedicator becomes extinguished for ever, and he cannot any more deal with the property in any shape.(1) The mere declaration of the owner that he dedicates the property or has already dedicated it is enough to divest his proprietary right therein. Thenceforth it is absolutely inalienable and unheritable.(2) *But a wakf made by a person to take effect after his death, or what is called a wakf by way of a wasiat (wakf-bi'l-wasiat) is revocable at any time before his death.* "And like all testamentary dispositions," says the *Fath ul-Kadîr* "a *wakf* declared to come into operation after the death of the *wâkif* may be revoked by him at any time before his death; but if not revoked, it will be operative in respect of a third of the estate unless assented to by the heirs, when it will take effect in its entirety." Principle.

This principle is stated in the clearest terms in the *Ghâit-ul-Bayân*. According to the Disciples "a *wakf* may be made in health or in sickness."..."If the person making it is suffering from an illness of which he dies, it will take effect in respect of one-third of his estate like a testamentary *wakf*."

SECTION IV.

Sadakah—ITS MEANING.

Sadakah or pious donations.

The word *sadakah* occurs so frequently in works dealing with Mahommedan Law, and has such an important bearing on the constitution of a *wakf* that an exact apprehension of its meaning is necessary to a proper understanding of the rules relating to dedications in the Islâmic system.

Richardson in his Dictionary translates it as meaning an "alms-gift" and also as "property dedicated to pious uses." Hamilton, the translator of the Persian version of the *Hedâyah*, evidently thought that the word meant 'alms,' to the poor; and this error has influenced all subsequent conceptions.

As a matter of fact, the word *sadakah* has a much larger meaning in the Mussulman system. It means, properly speaking, a *pious act*:—"a smile in a neighbour's face is *sadakah*; to help the weary is *sadakah*." Probably, the only expression by which it can be construed is the word *charity* in its broadest sense.

(1) *Ghâit-ul-Bayân*; *Fath ul-Kadîr*, Vol. II, p. 638.

(2) For other authorities, see *post*.

The legal meaning of *Sadakah.*

In the Mussulman Law, however, *it means an offering or gift made with the object of obtaining the approval of the Almighty, or a reward in the next world.* For example, a present to a friend is not a *sadakah* because there is no pious intention. But if a gift be made with the object of relieving his wants or to provide against his falling into indigence, it is a *sadakah.* A donation, therefore, with the object of obtaining the reward or approbation of the Almighty is a *sadakah.* If the purpose itself is pious, whether the gift is made primarily with the intention of obtaining the Almighty's reward or not, still it is *sadakah*, for the Almighty will bless the act whether the person doing it did it with that motive or not. For example, *the making of provision for one's self or for one's children against future want, is a pious act.* If one makes such a provision the Almighty will bestow His reward even if the person did not at the time think of such reward. As a matter of fact, among Mussulmans no dedication is created, or offerings made, without the intention (*niat*) being formulated in the mind, "I do this with the object of approaching the Almighty."

The meaning will be clear from the following examples :—

"To give to one's child or wife is a *sadakah* according to the Prophet's precept reported by S'aad ibn Abî Wakkâs."(1)

In the Mussulman system, there is an obligation, in some cases legal, in others semi-legal or moral, to provide for the maintenance of parents, descendants and kinsfolk in general. It is also an obligation that a person should so provide for himself that he may not fall into want and become a burden to society or his people. The principle underlying these conceptions, which are wholly foreign to all Western systems, are directly traceable to the rules enunciated by the Prophet.

Sadakah or pious donations—its meaning.

"It is reported by S'aad bin 'Aâffîr who received the tradition from al-Lais, who again received it from Abdur Rahmân bin Khâlid bin Musâfar, who again received it from Shahâb, who received it from Ibn ul-Mus'aib from Abû Huraira, that the Prophet of God (may the blessing, &c.), declared that the best of pious offerings is a provision for one's self, so that he may not fall into need, and the [giving of] *sadakah* should commence with those whose subsistence is obligatory on you."(2)

(1) Bokhâri, p. 806.

(2) Bokh ri, p. 806. I have omitted the authorities both here and in Muslim, tracing the Ordinances to the Prophet. Concerning Bokhâri's authority, see Morley's Dig., Introd., p. ccliii.

"The Prophet of God has declared that a pious offering to one's family [to provide against their getting into want] is more pious than giving alms to beggars."(1)

Pious offering to one's family.

"Said the Prophet of God, when a Moslem bestows on his family and kindred, with the object of earning the approval of the Almighty, it is *sadakah*, although he has not given to the poor, but to his family and children."

"The most excellent of *sadakah* is that which a man bestows upon his family." . . .

"The greatest *sadakah* in point of reward is that which you give to your family."

"To give money to free a slave, to give alms to the poor, to give to your children and kindred, are all *sadakah*."

"Giving alms to the poor has the reward of one alms; but that giving to kindred has two rewards."(2)

"The piety of all acts depends upon a pious motive, *viz.*, a desire to obtain the Almighty's reward . . . . A man who with a pious motive provides the means of subsistence for his family, is giving charity, and the Prophet of God has declared that it is a holy act."(3)

"And the Prophet has declared, that a man giving subsistence to his family is giving *sadakah*."

"And the Prophet of God declared that whatever subsistence you give to another will meet with God's approbation and reward from the Almighty; a provision for your wives will be rewarded."

"In giving charity, commence with those whose maintenance is obligatory on you."

***Sadakah* or pious donations—contd.**

"Support of one's self and his children and family is the first duty and necessity."

"The *Prophet of God declared, 'in giving charity begin with those who are bound to you and of whom you are in charge.'* "

"Zainab, the wife of Ibn Mas'aûd, came one day and asked the Prophet, who were the best entitled to receive her charity. The Prophet of God declared 'thy husband and thy children are most entitled to receive thy charity.' "

---

(1) Nis'i, Chapter on *Sadakah on one's relations*, p. 413.
(2) *Miskhât-ul-Masâbih*, Vol. II, p. 491.
(3) Bokhâri.

"Zainab, the daughter of Umm-i-Salma, says the Prophet directed her to support her relations, for that was charity, and God would give her His reward therefor."

In the *Sahîh-i-Muslim*,(1) occur the following traditions recognised as authentic and binding throughout the Sunni world.

"The Prophet of God declared, that whatever a man spends, the most pious of expenditure is that with which he provides for the maintenance of his children and family and against their future want."

"The Prophet of God declared, 'that which you spend to provide for the maintenance of your family and against their future want, has greater reward than that which you spend to provide for the maintenance of others.'"

"*The Prophet of God declared to one of the Faithful, 'in charity commence with yourself, and your family and your kindred and if there is a balance give to those round about you.'*"

"Abû Talha asked the Prophet upon whom or for what purpose should he dedicate a valuable property he possessed. The Prophet of God answered, 'consecrate it for thy kindred,' and he did so."

"The Prophet of God declared, that a Mussulman providing means of subsistence for his family is doing a pious act, and it is *sakadah*."

"A Moslem came and informed the Prophet that he had a *dinâr*, and asked what should he do with it? The Prophet answered, 'provide for thy wants with it.' He said he had another; the Prophet answered, 'provide for the needs of thy family therewith.' He said he had another. He was told to give it to the poor."(2)

It will be seen from these authorities, which are regarded as binding on the whole Sunni world, that provision for one's family and descendants is an absolute act of charity.

---

(1) A work of great authority, see Morley's Dig., Introd., p. ccliv.

(2) For further traditions, see *post*.

CHAPTER VIII.

THE CONSTITUTION OF A WAKF—HANAFI RULES.

SECTION I.

GENERAL PRINCIPLES.

THERE is no essential formality or the use of any express phrase or term requisite for the constitution of a *wakf*. Where a dedication is intended the law will give effect to it, in whatever language it may be expressed or in whatever terms the wish may be formulated. *And a wakf may be made either verbally or in writing.* How a *wakf* may be constituted.

When the word *wakf*, or any of its synonyms in vogue, is used in making the consecration, the law fixes upon it all the legal incidents of a permanent and valid dedication. It is only when such words are not used that reference is made to the intention of the donor. But when the intention to make a *wakf* is apparent, or can be inferred from the general tenor of the deed, or from the conduct of the donor, or from the nature of the object in favour of which the grant is made,(1) or from surrounding circumstances at large, it will constitute a valid and binding *wakf*, though the word *wakf* might not have been used.(2) Principles. Evidence of intention when necessary.

(1) *Piran* v. *Abdul Karim* [1892], I. L., 19 Cal., p. 203. In this case the dedication was made in these terms :—

و سيواي موضع مذكورا كه مختص براے خرچ خانقاه منها كرده
متعلق سجاده نشين گردانيديم *

"Excepting mouzah, &c., which having deducted I have made over to the *Sajjada-nashin* specifically for the expenses of the *Khankah.*" It was held that these words constituted a valid *wakf*.

(2) The paraphrase by Mr. Neil Baillie of a chapter in the *Fatāwai Alamgiri*, headed thus: "Words by which an appropriation is completed and those by which it is not completed," has given rise to an impression among English lawyers that there are set phrases or formulæ by which alone a *wakf* can be constituted, and if these expressions are not used, the *wakf* is not valid. It will be seen from the text that this idea is erroneous.

Some of the expressions by which a *wakf* may be constituted.

In the *Fatâwai Kâzi Khân* the subject is dealt with thus :—"Some of the terms by which *wakf* may be constituted are the following :—

"If a man were to say 'this my land is *sadakah*,' and add nothing more, the land would be dedicated as a charitable dedication for the poor." (Here the word *wakf* is not used at all, but as *sadakah* means a pious offering, and "the poor are always with us," it is sufficient to constitute a valid dedication).

"Or, if he were to say simply 'this land of mine is for a permanent object' (*wajjah abdi*), it would constitute a *wakf*." (*Wajjah* implying a pious or charitable purpose, and *abdi* meaning permanency, the intention of the donor is sufficiently evidenced). "Where the purpose is designated, and it is declared or implied that it should take effect in perpetuity, it is sufficient to constitute a valid dedication."

"Or, if he were to say 'this land of mine is consecrated, and I have consecrated it,' its effect is the same as if he had expressly said he had made it a *wakf*."

Principile.

No object need be mentioned when the term *wakf* used.

The *Siraj-ul-Wahâj* states that, "when a person constitutes a *wakf generally*, without designating the object to which it should be applied, it is lawful—and this is correct," and then goes on to add that there are several words which are express in their meaning, and the use of which clearly constitutes a *wakf*, because they convey in themselves the intention to dedicate, for example, *wakafto*, *haramto*, *habasto*, *sabalto*, &c. "I have dedicated," "I have consecrated," "I have tied up," "I have given in the way (of God)." These terms are express in their signification, and when a dedication is made by such words it is complete, as the intention is apparent.

Examples of express terms.

But where any expression is used which does not ordinarily convey the meaning of permanent dedication, it must be seen what the intention of the donor is, and this is to be gathered from the nature of the object in favour of which the trust is created or from surrounding circumstances. For example, if a man says "I give this property to this mosque," the fact that the grant is made to a mosque shows that it is for a permanent pious purpose, or if he were to say, "I give this property to the poor," the same result would follow.

This rule is given in almost similar terms in the *Fath ul-Kadîr*(1):—"If a man were to say, 'I give this land to the poor,' it would constitute a valid *wakf* for the poor are always existing, and hence the intention of the donor is clear that he means the income of the property should be applied permanently to the benefit of the indigent."

Constitution of *wakf* by expressions other than *wakf* and its synonyms.

According to the *Wajîz ul-Muhît*, "if a man were to say 'this my land is *mowkoofa* (dedicated)' or '*muharrama*' (consecrated) or '*mahboosa*' (tied up), it would constitute a valid *wakf* according to Abû Yusuf, and *this is most correct*, for he (the *wâkif*) has mentioned *wakf* unrestrictedly, and an unrestricted *wakf* is for the poor by custom and practice, and what is customary is as if conditioned, &c."

لو قال ارضي هذه موقوفة او محبوسة او محرمة عند ابى يوسف
رح تصير وقفاً و هو الاصح لانه ذكر الوقف مطلقا والوقف المطلق يكون
علي الفقراء عرفاً و عادةً و المعروف كالمشروط ٭

According to the *Fatâwai Alamgiri* "if a person were to say, 'I have made this my land consecrated,' or 'it is consecrated,' it would create, says the Jurist Abû J'aafar,(2) a valid *wakf*, according to Abû Yusuf, as if he had said *wakf*," (for the word "consecrated," *muharrama*, which may also mean "forbidden to others," carries with it the signification that the property is set apart for a charitable purpose).

In case of ambiguity the intention of the *wâkif* is to be enquired into.

The compilers of the *Fatâwai Alamgiri* add further, "and the Jurist Abû J'aafar says that 'detained and given as a *sadakah*' is equivalent to saying 'given as a *sadakah* and made *wakf*.'" And further—"if a person were to say 'this my land is a way, (*sabîl*) and he is in a place where such expressions are commonly known to imply *wakf*, the land would become *wakf*. If the expressions are not known to have that meaning, he shall be called upon to explain; and if he say that he meant *wakf*, they are to be applied according to his intention. If he say that he meant *sadakah*, or had no particular meaning, they are to be taken as a vow, and the land or its price should be given away as a pious gift."(3)

How intention is to be gathered.

(1) A work of great authority in India, frequently quoted in the *Fatâwai Alamgiri* and also by the Law Officers in the case reported in 1 Sel. Rep., p. 17, and referred to in Fulton's Reports, p. 345; see Morley's Dig., Introd., p. ccilxx.

(2) Often called Hindavi, the Indian.

(3) *Fatâwai Alamgiri*, Vol. II, p. 461.

In case of ambiguity, therefore, if the *wâkif* be alive, he would be the person to explain his meaning, but if he be dead, his intention is to be gathered from the surrounding circumstances, and the evidence of the manner in which the proceeds of the property have been applied.(1) If a man were to say simply, "Buy out of the produce of this my mansion every month ten dirhems worth of bread, and distribute it among the poor," according to the *Fatâwai Alamgiri* this is sufficient to constitute a dedication of the house for that purpose.

Use of the word *Sabîl* or *Râh-i-Khudâ* sufficient to create a *wakf*.

According to the *Hâwi*,(2) "if a man were to say 'this land and this house of mine is in the nature of a *sabîl* (path to God), and he is in a country where *sabîl* implies a *wakf*, it will become an absolute *wakf*.'" *Sabîl*, however, is now universally recognised to mean *wakf*. *Sabîl* or *sabîl-illâh* (way of God) is equivalent to the phrase, *Râh-i-Khudâ* (the path of God) in vogue in India.

A declaration to the effect, 'I have given the produce of this land to the poor' or any other charitable object, or 'I have given this house to the poor,' coupled with words prohibiting alienation and devolution by inheritance would, by consensus, constitute a *wakf*.(3)

No express words necessary to create a *wakf* so long as intention is clear.

The same principle is reiterated in the *Radd 'ul-Muhtâr*. "There are twenty-six expressions given by way of example in the *Bahr* [*ur-Râik*] by which *wakf* may be constituted; and many others are given in the *Fath ul-Kadîr*," . . . . . "but no express word is necessary to constitute a *wakf* so long as it is clear that the intention of the donor is to devote the usufruct of the property permanently to a good object; . . . . *e.g.*, if a man were to say, 'give so much out of the income of this my house to buy bread with for the poor,' that is sufficient to create a *wakf*." Similarly, if a man were to say 'I have set apart this property' or 'assigned it,' or 'deducted it from my other properties.'"

"In the thirteenth section of the *Jâm'aa-ul-Fusûlain*, it is stated that if a person were to say, 'this room or this house is for

---

(1) *Fatâwai Kâzi Khân*, Vol. IV, p. 74.

(2) A work of great authority, frequently quoted in the *Fatâwai Alamgiri*, by Kâzi Jamâl ud-din Ahmed bin Mohammed bin Nûh al-Kabisi of Ghazni, died in A. H. 600.

(3) *Fatâwai Alamgiri*, Vol. II, p. 461; *Bâhr-ur-Raik*; 2 Sel. Rep., p. 110.

lighting such a mosque,' and add nothing further, it would constitute a valid *wakf*, for such a purpose is sufficient."(1)

Jewan Dass Sahoo v. Shah Kubeer-ood-deen.

The decision, therefore, of their Lordships in the Privy Council in the case of *Jewan Dass Sahoo* v. *Shah Kubeer-ood-deen*(2) only gave expression to what is laid down and enunciated in the Mahommedan Law. In that case the grant or firman(3) by which the endowments were created contained no mention of the word *wakf*. On the contrary, the grant purported to be made as '*Inam Altamgha maddadmaâsh*,' which primarily conveys individual proprietary rights. It was accordingly contended on behalf of the defendant that the properties which formed the subject of the grant did not constitute an inalienable *wakf*. Their Lordships in the Privy Council in dealing with the case endorsed the views of the *Sudder Dewany Adawlut*(4) in the following terms :—

Mussumut Qadira v. Shah Kubeer-ood deen.

"After referring to this case and the opinions of the law officers, the *Sudder Dewany Adawlut* in the case of *Mussumut Qadira* v. *Shah Kubeer-ood-deen* (3 Mac. Sud. Dew. Ad., 407) appear to have determined that notwithstanding the use of the words "Inam" and "Altumgha" in the royal grants and the mention therein of the persons upon whose petition the grants were made, yet as these grants appeared clearly to have been made (as expressed in the petitions) for the purpose of maintaining a charitable institution, the persons named were not to be

---

(1) *Surrat-ul-Fatâwa*, p. 435 ; (MSS., Patna Oriental Library).

(2) [1840], 2 M. I. A., 390.

(3) The firman of Alamgir ran as follows :—

"As it has come to the knowledge of His Majesty that agreeably to a sunnud furnished by the Hakims, certain Mouzas situated in Sircar Behar have been appropriated for the purpose of meeting the charges of fakirs and students of the Madrassa, and the *Khankah* and Musjid of Moolla Dervish Hossain, son of Moolla Gholam Ali, and the aforesaid individual is hopeful for the royal munificence and favour, His Majesty's royal commands are that in the event of the aforesaid mouzas being in the occupation and enjoyment of that individual, the whole of these mouzas shall continue as they formerly were, at a jumma of 15,000 dams from (such a date) in the character of a *maddadmash* (aid for subsistence), according to the tenor of the grant, and in order that he may apply the produce of these lands to meet the charges of the students of his Madrassa and Musjid ; and the present and future Hakims, the Amils, &c., are enjoined to relinquish the mouzahs in question to that person's occupation, to deem them *maâfi* (exempt from taxes) and blotted with the pen in every respect, and not to require of him a fresh sunnud annually. Should that individual occupy anything in any other way, they are not to countenance him."

(4) [1845], *Musst. Qadira* v. *Shah Kubeer-ood-deen*, 3 Sel. Rep., p. 407.

considered proprietors; that the establishment (Khânkâh)(1) was the real donee and the persons named were only *Mutwâllis* of the Khânkâh; that a *Mutwâlli* has no right to alienate, and that, consequently, the transfer by gift or otherwise by Shah Shams-oo-deen was illegal.''

"This decision,'' their Lordships continued, "is in accordance with the doctrine laid down in the *Hedâyah*, Book XV, of *wakf* or appropriation, Hamilton's Translation, Vol. II, page 334, where it is said, '*wakf*,' in its primitive sense means 'detention.' In the language of the law (according to Hanîfa), it signifies the appropriation of any particular thing in such a way that the appropriator's right in it shall continue, and the advantage of it go to some charitable purpose in the manner of a loan. According to the two disciples '*wakf*' signifies the appropriation of a particular article in such a manner as subjects it to the rules of divine property, whence the appropriator's right in it is extinguished and it becomes a property of God, by the advantage of it resulting to His creatures. The two disciples, therefore, hold appropriation to be absolute, though differing in this, that Abû Yusuf holds appropriation to be absolute from the moment of its execution, whereas Mohammed holds it to be absolute only on the delivery of it to a *Mutwalli* (or procurator), and consequently, that it cannot be disposed of by a gift or sale, and inheritance also does not obtain with respect to it. Thus the term '*wakf*' in its literal sense comprehends all that is mentioned both by Hanîfa and by the two disciples.''

"Again (page 344) it is said, upon an appropriation becoming valid or absolute, the sale or transfer of the thing appropriated is unlawful according to all lawyers; the transfer is unlawful because of a saying of the Prophet, 'Bestow the actual land itself in charity in such a manner that it shall no longer be saleable or inheritable.' '' And their Lordships accordingly held that, "according to the Mahommedan Law, it is not necessary in order to constitute a *wakf*, or endowment to religious and charit-

---

(1) A *Khânkâh* is a religious monastery, a place where religious services are held, *dervishes* lodged, indigent travellers fed. It will be seen that the original grantee was a *mulla* or priest, and the grant was apparently made to him not only for his support and the support of his descendants, but also with the object of maintaining in perpetuity an institution for the lodgment of religious devotees, travellers and mendicants.

able uses, that the term *wakf* should be used in the grant, if from the general nature of the grant such tenure can be inferred.''

The word *wakf* used by itself *is sufficient in every case to constitute a valid permanent dedication, for that is its express meaning in law.* So that, as already stated, either where no object is designated, or where an object is mentioned, which is liable to failure, the *wakf* will, nevertheless, be valid and binding, and the property dedicated will, in the first case, be applied to the poor, and in the second case will be applied to them on failure of the object named, though they (the poor) may not have been mentioned in the deed nor the word *sadakah* used at all.

The word *wakf* sufficient by itself.

Principle.

The *Fatâwai Alamgiri* says—

" Though no mention be made of *sadakah* (اذا لم يذكر الصدقة) yet if *wakf* is mentioned as by a person saying ' This my land is *wakf*,' or, ' I have made this my land *wakf*,' the land would be a *wakf* for the poor according to Abû Yusuf...." " And Sadr ush-Shahîd and the jurists (*mashâikh*) of Balkh have declared that ' decrees are given on the opinion of Abû Yusuf; and *we*(1) *decree according to it, also from regard to custom.*' "(2)

" And if he should say, ' it is appropriated to Almighty God for ever,' it would be lawful, though the word *sadakah* be not mentioned, and would be a *wakf* for the poor. The word *wakf* alone or in combination with *habs*, establishes a *wakf* according to the approved opinion, which is that of Abû Yusuf."

So also in the *Fatâwai Kâzi Khân*;(3) " if a man were to say, ' this my land is made *wakf* ' (*mowkoofa*), and give its boundaries, and say nothing more, this, according to Abû Yusuf, is a valid dedication for the poor."

" Or, if he were to say, ' this land of mine is *wakf*,' the effect is the same."

" Or, if he were to say, ' this land of mine is *wakf*, for a pious object.' "

" If he says, ' this land is *mowkoofa* for God in perpetuity,' it will create a valid *wakf*, though he may not have used the word ' *sadakah*,' and it will be a *wakf* in favour of the poor; and should

(1) *i.e.*, the Jurists of India.

(2) This passage shows clearly that in India the rule laid down by Abû Yusuf on the point under discussion is the law applicable to the Hanafi Sunnis; see also Vol. II, p. 460.

(3) *Fatâwai Kâzi Khân*, see Vol. IV, p. 202.

Expressions by which a valid *wakf* is created.

he even not have used the words 'in perpetuity,' it will still be a valid *wakf* and the produce will be applied to the benefit of the poor."

"Similarly, if the *wâkif* merely said, 'this is *mowkoofa* for the sake of God,' or '*mowkoofa* for obtaining *sawâb* (reward) of God.'"

"So also if he say, 'this land of mine is *mowkoofa* for the sake of charity and piety (علی وجه البر و الخير)' or for both, it will be a valid *wakf* for the poor."

"If a man were to say, 'this land of mine is *wakf* for the purposes of *jehad* (religious fighting), or for supplying shrouds to the dead, or burying them, or digging graves, or for any act of charity or piety which may be perpetual,' it would form a valid *wakf* for that purpose."

"If a *wâkif* were to declare a particular property to be a *wakf* for travellers, it is lawful, for travellers never cease; and its benefits will be applied to those who are poor among them and not to the rich."

"Or, if he were to say, 'it is for the lame, decrepit or maimed,' it would be valid (for these people are never wanting in the world), and it will be applied to the poor among them."

The term *wakf* used by itself sufficient.

The *Durr-ul-Mukhtâr* says "if a man were to say 'this land or this house of mine is for the poor,' or is a *wakf* for so-and-so *in the way of God*, or 'for a good purpose' it is sufficient." "And according to Abû Yusuf the word *mowkoofa* [past participle of *wakf*] is sufficient, and [Sadr-ush] Shahîd says 'we give *fatwas* universally according to this.'"(1)

In India, in order to accentuate the fact of consecration, it has become usual to add the words "in the way of God" to the word "*wakf*," *e.g.*, to make the dedication in the following terms: "I make this *wakf* in the way of God for so-and-so."

"If a *specific* thing," says the *Tas-hîl* "be made *wakf* by the word *wakf*, it is valid, and upon the death of the *mowkoof alaih* its produce will go to the poor, and on this is the *fatwa*."

According to the *Wajîz-ul-Muhît*, if a man were to say, 'this my land is *mowkoofa*,' and do not use the words '*sadakah* in perpetuity' or 'on the poor,' it constitutes a valid *wakf* according to Abû Yusuf, and *this is correct*."(2)

---

(1) P. 410: See also the comment on this passage in the *Radd ul-Muhtâr*.
(2) *Wajîz-ul-Muhît*, p. 351.

Expressions by which a valid *wakf* is constituted.

According to the *Ghâit-ul-Bayân* also, "if the *wâkif* does not use the word *sadakah*, but simply uses the word *wakf*; for example, if he were to say, 'this land of mine is *mowkoofa*,' or 'this land of mine is *wakf*,' or 'I have made this *mowkoofa*,' or 'I have made this *wakf*;' such *wakf* according to Abû Yusuf, will be for the poor alone. And the Mashâikhs of Balkh decide according to Abû Yusuf's enunciations."

لولم يذكر الصدقة و ذكر الوقف فان قال ارضي هذه موقوفة او قال فارضي هذه وقف او قال جعلت ارضي هذه موقوفة او قال ارضي هذا وقفا فان هذا يكون على الفقراء في قول ابي يوسف رح خاصة فكان مشايخ بلخ يفتون بقول ابي يوسف رح *

Similarly, the word *sadakah* conjoined to the word *wakf* or its derivatives (like *mowkoofa*, i.e., dedicated) will constitute a valid and binding *wakf*. For example, if a man were to say, 'this my land is a *sadakah mowkoofa*, detained and perpetual during my life and after my death,' or 'this my land is a *sadakah*, detained and perpetual during my life and after my death,' or if he should say 'a *sadakah* dedicated and perpetual,' it would be lawful. Or if he should say, 'a *sadakah* dedicated or a *sadakah* detained,'(1) without saying 'perpetual,' the land would become a *wakf*, "according to all who consider *wakf* lawful, because a perpetual *sadakah* is established which does not admit of cancellation. The words, 'This my land is a *sadakah* dedicated to what is good,' or 'to good purpose,' also amount to a *wakf*."

Or, if a man were to say, 'my land is *sadakah* (charity) for God,' or '*wakf* to Almighty God,' it would become *wakf*. So also if he were to say, 'my land is assigned in the *way* of Almighty God,' or 'to seek the reward of Almighty God;' or if he were to say, 'my land is *wakf* for a good purpose,' it would be as lawful as if he had said a *sadakah wakf*."

"If he say, 'this land of mine is *sadakah mowkoofa* or *mowkoofa sadakah*,' and say nothing more, it will be a valid *wakf* (according to Abû Yusuf, Mohammed and Hillâl), and the benefit will go to the poor in perpetuity."

---

(1) *Mahboosatan* from *habasa*, means literally detained; its exact signification, however, is "being rendered inalienable;" *mowkoofa* is the participle of *wakafa*.

Expressions by which a *wakf* may be constituted.

" If a man say, ' this land of mine is *sadakah mowkoofa* for such a person,' it will be valid and the result will be that the ultimate beneficiaries will be the poor, for they are the lawful ultimate recipients of every pious offering, but the produce will be given to the person mentioned during his lifetime."

" If a person were to say, ' this my land is *sadakah mowkoofa* for such a person in perpetuity,' or that ' it is for my *child* in perpetuity," the same result would follow, the mention of the words ' in perpetuity ' not making any difference."

" And if a man were to say, ' this my land is dedicated, consecrated and detained,' or, ' dedicated, detained, and consecrated, not to be sold, inherited or given by gift,' all these words would create a *wakf* according to the received doctrine and the opinion of Abû Yusuf."(1)

Hamidulla Khan v. Budr-un-nissa Khatun.

Having regard to all these dicta on a point about which there is absolute *consensus* on the part of the jurists, one finds it difficult to understand whence the idea was derived which finds expression in the case of *Mahomed Hamidulla Khan* v. *Budr-un-nissa Khatun*(2) that a *wakf* in favour of one's children cannot be constituted without the use of the word *sadakah*.

In that case, the consecration was made in the following terms :—

" I have made *wakf* of the remaining 4 annas in favour of my daughter Budr-un-nissa and her descendants, and also her descendant's descendants how low soever, and when they no longer exist, then in favour of the poor and needy ; such *wakf* is good, legal, valid and effectual, and of the nature of a lasting permanent act of charitable endowment, the same being as good in my lifetime as after my demise, and the same being precluded from *tumulluk* and *tamlik*.(3) After payment of the Government Revenue and Collector's charges, etc., and after deduction of the Mutwalli's *towliut* right from the proceeds of all the above endowment properties, the surplus, whatever it may be, shall be divided as follows :—*i.e.*, 4 annas share be given to Jamila Khatun *alias*

(1) *Fatâwai Alamgiri* after the *Mabsût*.

(2) [1880], 8 Cal. L. R., p. 164. In this case the learned Judges seem to have thought that the *Hedâya* had been written by Abû Hanifa, *who had died nearly four centuries before the work was penned !*

(3) *i.e.*, from being owned (as private property) or being transferred.

Dhone Bibee and 4 annas to Budr-un-nissa, inasmuch as 4 annas has been endowed in favour of the said ladies, etc.''

So far as the constitution of the dedication went, nothing could be more distinct and explicit than the declarations contained in the above *wakfnâmah ;* the grantor expressly excluded all right of dominion over the property settled, which was intended to serve as a permanent provision for Bud un-nissa and her descendants so long as there were any in existe e ; and on their failure, he provided that the benefit of the *wakf* should accrue to the poor and the indigent. It will be seen that the terms of the settlement were in strict conformity with the provisions of the Mahommedan Law.

Erroneous conclusion of the High Court.

Upon a suit by Mahomed Hamidulla Khan to set aside a sale of a portion of the dedicated property in execution of a decree, on the ground that it was *wakf*, and consequently inalienable, the High Court held (*a*) that to constitute a valid *wakf* there must be a dedication of the property *solely* to the worship of God or to religious or charitable purposes ; (*b*) that when a settlement under the Mahommedan Law is made in favour of a particular person and his descendants in perpetuity, and on their failure in favour of the poor and needy, such settlement is only valid as a *wakf*, when the word *sadakah* is used in the deed of settlement.

As regards the first principle laid down by the High Court, I shall discuss it more fully in a later chapter.

As regards the second, *viz.*, the necessity for the use of the term *sadakah* where it is intended to create a trust for one's family or descendants, the question is set at rest by a reference to the express directions of the law.(1)

SECTION II.

CONDITIONS RELATING TO THE CONSTITUTION OF A WAKF.

Principle. Declaration extinguishes the right of the *wâkif* in the property.

As already stated, no formality is required to be gone through for the purpose of creating a valid *wakf*. It is enough if the donor declares that he constitutes a property *wakf* or has constituted it a *wakf*. That declaration fixes upon the property purported to be dedicated all the character of a legal and binding *wakf*, extinguishes the title of the donor, vesting it in the Almighty

(1) See *post.*

Wakf is completed by the mere declaration of the dedicator.

(whatever the object to which it is dedicated), and makes it irrevocably inalienable and non-heritable. In the *Sirâj-ul-Wâhaj*,(1) it is laid down as follows :—"Abû Yusuf has declared that a *wakf* is valid whether the property be *mushâ'a* (a share of a joint property) or whether it be consigned or not, whether perpetuity be mentioned or not, and the right of the donor becomes extinguished by his merely stating that he has made it *wakf* or makes it *wakf*, for *wakf* is on the same footing *as emancipation, and on this is the Fatwa.*"

فقال ابو يوسف يجوز مشاعاً كان لو مقسوما سلمة الى المتولى
و لم يسلمه اشترط او لم يشترط و يزول الملك بمجرد القول لان
بمنزلة الاعتاق و عليه الفتوى *

And in the *Ghâit-ul-Bayân* the same principle is given in the following words :—"The right of property is extinguished according to Abû Yusuf by the mere declaration, that is, according to him, by merely saying 'I have made this *wakf*,' the right of property [in the donor] becomes extinguished."

قوله يزول بالقول عند ابي يوسف رح اى يزول الملك عن
و قف بمجرد قوله وقفت عنده *

So also the *Fath ul-Kadîr* :—"According to Abû Yusuf the *wakf* becomes complete by mere declaration, and if no object is mentioned, it becomes a *wakf* for the poor . . . . and when the *wakf* has become valid for the poor by implication, no further mention of perpetuity is needed, for that purpose never fails, and Sadr ush-Shahîd says that all the jurists decide according to Abû Yusuf, and *we also decide according to him.*"(2)

Principle.

Perpetuity is a necessary condition to the constitution of a valid *wakf*, but it is not necessary that it should be expressly mentioned. In other words, the intention must be, either by implication or by express declaration, to dedicate the property permanently, but it is not necessary that the dedication should be primarily or expressly for a continuing object. If a dedication is made with the term *wakf, habs*, &c., the intention to part with the property permanently is apparent upon the face of the declar-

(1) A work of great authority in India; quoted by the Law Officers in the case in Fulton's Rep., p. 345; see also 1 Sel. Rep., p. 17, &c.

(2) *Fath ul-Kadir*, Vol. II, p. 632.

ation and whatever be the purpose named, the law will apply it, on failure of the objects designated, to other unfailing objects. If a *wakf* is not made in such express terms, the nature of the object must be taken into consideration and the intention gathered from circumstances.

The *Radd ul-Muhtâr* is very explicit on this point. "Abû Yusuf holds the declaration of *wakf* to be like a declaration respecting the emancipation of a slave. *Accordingly, he does not consider delivery or separation necessary.* According to him the *wakf* becomes binding and operative on mere declaration القول بمجرد like a declaration for emancipation, for the extinguishment of the right of property is common to both . . . It is stated in the *Durrar* [*ul-Ahkâm*] that 'it is correct that perpetuity is a condition by consensus, but according to Abû Yusuf its mention is not necessary'" . . . "and if a man were to say 'I make this dedication for my children' and add nothing further, *it is valid.*"

"Some have said that the mention of perpetuity is required in such a case by most jurists excepting Abû Yusuf; [but] according to him the mention of the word *wakf* or *sadakah* implies perpetuity, and consequently it is stated in the 'Book' [*Mukhtasar-ul-Kudûri*] that such a *wakf* is valid, and after the failure of the children it will be for the poor though they are not named, and *this is correct.*"

قوله و جعله ابو یوسف كالاعتاق ... فلذلک لم یشترط القبض و
الافراز الخ اي فيلزم عنده بمجرد القول كالاعتاق بجامع اسقاط
الملک قال في الدرر و الصحيح ان التابيد شرط اتفاقاً لكن ذكره
ليس بشرط عند ابي يوسف ..... لو قال وقفت على اولادي ولم يزد جاز
الوقف...الى قوله و قيل ان التابيد شرط بالاجماع الا ان عند ابي
يوسف لا يشترط ذكره لان لفظ الوقف و الصدقة مبني عنه و لهذا قال
وفى الكتاب و صار بعدها للفقراء و ان لم يسمهم و هذا هو الصحيح *

So also the *Ghâit-ul-Bayân.* "Abû Yusuf has said that *wakf* is valid whether it is *mushâ'a* or partitioned, delivered to the *mutwalli* or not, and whether he has mentioned perpetuity or not... and Abû Yusuf bases his view on the rule laid down by the Prophet, who only declared to Omar to tie up the property and apply

Abû Yusuf's rule on this point the recognised law.

its usufruct to human benefit, and did not make delivery a condition for the validity of the *wakf*."

قال ابو يوسف رح يجوز مشاعاً كان او مقسوماً سلمه الى المتولي لم يسلمه، شرط التابيد او لم يشترط • الى قوله و وجه قول ابي يوسف رح ان النبي صلى الله عليه و سلم امر عمر رض بالوقف ولم يامره بالتسليم فعلم ان التسليم ليس بشرطٍ *

"Perpetuity," says the *Fatâwai Alamgiri*, "is also among the conditions of *wakf* according to all opinions, though according to Abû Yusuf the mention of it is not a condition, and *this is correct.*(1) A man dedicates his mansion for a day, a month or any specified time without further addition, the *wakf* is valid and perpetual. But if he should say, 'This my land is a *sadakah mowkoofa* for a month and when the month has expired the *wakf* would be void,' the *wakf* would be void immediately according to Hillâl, because perpetuity being a condition, limitation to a particular time is not lawful.(2) If one should say, 'This my land is a *sadakah mowkoofa* after my death for a year,' without further addition, the *wakf* would be lawful in perpetuity for the benefit of the poor, for the words have the meaning of a bequest.(3) And if one should say, 'This my land is a *sadakah* dedicated to such an one after my death for a year, and when the year has expired the *wakf* is void,' it would be a bequest after his death to the person referred to for a year, and then it would become a legacy to the poor and its produce would be distributed among them. But if he should say, 'My land is dedicated to such an one for a year after my death,' without further addition, the produce would be to him for a year and then it would revert to the heirs."(4)

The recognised rule regarding the complete effectuation of a *wakf*.

The *Tas-hîl* is to the same effect :—"it (*viz.*, the subject of the *wakf*) can neither be sold nor given by gift nor inherited ; only its produce is to be spent ; and it will come out of [or be excluded from] the property of the *wâkif*, according to Abû Yusuf, by the

(1) After the *Kâfi* ; *Fatâwai Alamgiri*, Vol. II, p. 459.

(2) After the *Fatâwai Kâzi Khan*, Vol. IV, p. 83 (MSS. Copy belonging to the Asiatic Society.)

(3) After the *Muhît-i-Sarakhsi*.

(4) After the *Fatâwai Kâzi Khan*. The distinction between the two classes of cases arises from the use of the word *sadakah* in one and not in the other ; *Fatâwai Alamgiri*, Vol. II, p. 459.

mere declaration, for *wakf* means the extinguishment of the right of property of the *wâkif*, and it is not *tamlîk* [transfer of property]; it is therefore lawful without delivery, like emancipation. And the Jurists of Irâk decide accordingly . . . . Abû Yusuf has held a *wakf* to be valid without mention of perpetuity, so that when a person has made a *wakf* on some object that is liable to failure, according to Abû Yusuf, it will be lawful, and after failure of that object, it will be for the poor, and will not become the property of his heirs, and *this is correct*.''

لا يباع ولا يوهب ولا يورث ولكن لينفق ثمرته الى قوله فيخرج
عند ابو يوسف رح بمجرد القول لان الوقف اسقاط ملك الواقف
لا تمليك فصح بدون التسليم كالاعتاق وبه يفتي مشائخ العراق
الى قوله يجيز ابو يوسف رح بلا ذكر تابيد حتى لو وقف على جهة
يتوقف انقطاعها يصح عنده و يكون بعدها للفقراء لا ملكاً للورثة في
الصحيح *

And the *Ramz-ul-Hakâik*, after stating the origin of *wakfs* adds, ": Besides the incidents of a *wakf* are that it cannot be sold nor can it be given by gift, nor can it be inherited, and [if no other object is specified], its produce will be spent on the poor, and relatives and travellers, and the *wâkif* may also eat thereof. . . . And according to Abû Yusuf, merely saying that 'I have made this property *wakf*' is sufficient to extinguish the proprietary right of the *wâkif*, for by that the property is assigned over to God like the emancipation of a slave; and in this view the other three Imâms agree, [*viz.*, Shâfeï, Mâlik and Ibn Hanbal]. . ." "'And,' says Abû Yusuf, 'that even if an object is mentioned that is likely to fail, still the *wakf* will be valid, and after the extinction of the object named, the produce will be applied to the poor even if the poor are not mentioned.'"

General consensus on the point.

"Abû Yusuf has laid down that a *wakf* comes into operation, immediately on the declaration of the person making the dedication, that he has constituted a particular property *wakf* or constitutes it *wakf*, just like emancipation."

Wakf is like emancipation.

Thus, according to the principle laid down by Abû Yusuf, the declaration of *wakf* stands on the same footing as a declaration of emancipation, *and takes effect absolutely the moment the declaration is made.*

The recognised rule.

Elucidation of the principle.

The meaning of this rule has, it is submitted, escaped the attention of the Law Courts in India. The principle, however, is really this : when a person emancipates a bondsman, he cannot make any revocation, nor can he afterwards say that he had no intention to emancipate at all or to emancipate absolutely. The moment he pronounces the words or declares "I emancipate this slave," the law fixes the status of freedom upon the bondsman. Once the words are pronounced, neither the emancipator nor his heirs, creditors, or assignees can question the absoluteness of the emancipation. No question of intention arises ; for the law presumes an absolute and unqualified intention from the declaration.

Absolute and irrevocable.

Similarly, once a particular property is dedicated, the right of the *wâkif* is extinguished for ever. He cannot turn round and say afterwards that he had no intention of creating a *valid wakf ;* nor can his heirs, or creditors, or other persons deriving title from him say that it was a 'pretended' *wakf ;* that at the time of making the dedication he had no intention of making a 'real' *wakf.*

Perpetuity not necessary to be mentioned.

If the *wakf* is in favour of an object recognised as lawful by the Mahommedan Law and religion, the *wakf* is irrevocable, absolute, and beyond question.

This is emphatically the Mussulman Law according to all the sects and schools.

"The correct principle is that *mention* of perpetuity is not a necessary condition . . ." According to Abû Yusuf "if a dedication is made in favour of specific individuals, it is lawful, and upon their decease, the income would be applied for the benefit of the poor."

In India this rule is binding as laid down in the *Fatâwai Alamgiri,* for the Indian Jurists have followed the Jurists of Balkh who are in accord (according to the *Wajîz-ul-Muhît*) with those "of Khorâsân and Irâk," in other words, with the other Hanafî jurists all over the world, excepting the Bokhariots. According to the *Wajîz-ul-Muhît* also, "the mention of perpetuity" or of "a permanent object" is not necessary, for "if a man were to say 'this my land is *wakf* or *sadakah wakf* for some specific individual or for some specific object or for certain of his poor relatives or for certain orphans,' though he may not mention perpetuity, still, according to Abû Yusuf, it will constitute a legal *wakf.*"

"Or, if the *wâkif* were to say, 'this my land is *mowkoofa* for so-and-so, or for my child,' the *wakf* is valid, according to Abû Yusuf, although the word *abad* (perpetuity) is not mentioned, and so long as the specific individual is alive, the income of the property will be applied for his benefit, and after his death it will be spent on the poor."

و ان قال ارضي هذه موقوفة على فلان او على ولدي جاز الوقف
و ان لم يذكر عند ابي يوسف و الغلّة لفلان ما دام حيًّا فاذا مات
يصرف الغلة الى الفقراء *

But, if instead of simply, "*mowkoofa*" he were to say *sadakah mowkoofa*, it would be valid according to Abû Yusuf as well as Mohammed, though perpetuity (*i.e.*, a perpetual object) had not been mentioned.

So also in the *Jouharat-un-Nayyirèh*, "Abû Yusuf has declared that even where an object has been named, which is liable to fail, the *wakf* is valid, and after the failure of that object, it will be for the poor though they may not have been named, *and this is correct.*"

و قال ابو يوسف رح اذا سمىً جهة تنقطع جاز و صار بعده
للفقراء و ان لم يسمهم و هذا هو الصحيح *

According to Abû Yusuf, like the term *wakf*, the term *sadakah* implies perpetuity and the two are convertible, and he therefore holds that though the poor may not be mentioned, the profits will go to them on failure of other objects. The mention of *sadakah* is to mention perpetuity.

In short, any term which implies perpetuity is sufficient to create a *wakf*. For example, the mention of the poor, or *sadakah-mowkoofa* for God, *mowkoofa* for benevolence (*ihsân*), or charity (*khair*), or for *jehâd* (holy warfare), shrouds, cemeteries, etc., is sufficient. When a *wakf* is created for a specific individual or class of individuals by any term which, like *wakf* or *sadakah*, implies a dedication of the *corpus*, or shows that the property has been permanently parted with, it is valid and binding according to Abû Yusuf, and upon their extinction the produce will be applied to the poor, for the ultimate recipients of all *wakfs* are the poor, and they never fail—"and Sadar-ush-Shahîd has stated [that the *Fatwa* is thereon] and the Jurists of Balkh give *Fatwas*

The recognised rule.

according to this opinion, and *we* [*also*] *decide according to that view.*"(1)

Fatâwai Kâzi Khân.

According to Kâzi Khân, explicit declaration that a *wakf* is created is sufficient to constitute a *wakf*. When a *sadakah-mowkoofa* is made for a limited period without any mention that on the expiration of that period, the subject-matter of the *wakf* should revert to the appropriator, it takes effect as a *wakf* in perpetuity, for, according to custom, the term *wakf* implies and includes the poor, and that amounts to an actual dedication. But where a condition is made that it should revert to the donor, the condition is *bâtil* or void according to Abû Yusuf.(2) The *Raddul-Muhtâr* says—

Radd ul-Muhtâr—The recognised rule.

"The ultimate purpose of a *wakf* must, according to all, be for an object which never fails. According to Abû Yusuf such an object need not be mentioned, for when a *wâkif* makes a dedication for a *specific* object and does not mention to what purpose of a permanent character it should be applied, on failure of the initial trust, the property will go to the poor, as they are the ultimate recipients of all *wakfs* when no other purpose is specified, and the universality of jurists have adopted this view and the *Fatwa* is thereon . . . . and in the *Durrar* it is stated *this is correct* . . . ."

And again "if a *wakf* is made for a specific object (*e.g.*, one's descendants) and nothing further is mentioned, it is valid according to Abû Yusuf, and after the extinction of that object it will go to the poor—and this opinion is followed by the Sâhib-ul-Hedâya, as also in the *Muntaka*, the *Nikâya*, etc. .... and the Sadr-ush-Sharâya has stated that the *Fatwa* is thereon."(3)

Summation of the authorities.

To sum up the result of the authorities :—according to all the jurists "perpetuity is a necessary condition," but according to the acknowledged and accepted view, "on which the *Fatwa* is," *viz.*, the rule laid down by Abû Yusuf, it is not necessary to mention it at the time of dedication; in other words, though all the jurists insist that the property should be dedicated permanently and the right of the donor therein parted with for ever, accord-

(1) *Fatâwai Alamgiri*, Vol. II, p. 460.

(2) Hillâl holds that it will hold good for the period specified. This is in accordance with the Shiah doctrine.

(3) *Radd ul-Muhtâr*, Vol. III, p. 565.

ing to Abû Yusuf it is not necessary that the word *tâbîd* or *abad* (perpetuity) should be mentioned, or that the object in favour of which the dedication is primarily made should be of a continuing and permanent character—for

قال ابو يوسف رح اذا سمى جهة تنقطع جاز و صار بعدها للفقراء
ان لم يسمهم *

" Abû Yusuf has said that when he [the *wâkif*] has named a purpose liable to failure it is valid ; and after its failure, it will be for the poor, though they are not named.''

And

يجيزه ابو يوسف رح بلا ذكر تابيد حتى لو وقف على جهة
للوقف انقطاعها يصح عنده و يكون بعدها للفقراء لا ملكا للورثة
في الصحيح *

" Abû Yusuf holds a *wakf* to be valid without mention of perpetuity, so that when a *wakf* is made in favour of an object liable to failure it is lawful according to him, and after the failure of the object it will go to the poor and not become the property of his heirs, and *this is correct.''*(1) For, there are many objects that are liable to failure which are as pious in their nature as objects that are continuing. This is the real meaning of the following passage in the *Ghâit-ul-Bayân* :—

قوله و هو موفر عليه اى التقريب الى الله تعالى موفر على
جعل الوقف بجهة ينقطع كما هو موفر على جعله بجهة لا ينقطع يعني
يصل التقريب بهذا الوجه الى قوله كما يصل بذلك الوجه *

Dedication in favour of an object liable to failure.

But when a *wakf* is made in favour of " a specific object liable to failure,'' and any term is used in the dedication signifying that it is permanent in its character, *e.g.*, *sadakah* or *fi-sabîl-illâh* (" in the way of God ''), the *wakf* is valid not only according to Abû Yusuf, but also according to Mohammed, who considers the mention of perpetuity, or the mention of some object of a perpetual character necessary. The *Radd ul-Muhtâr* quoting the *Fatâwai Kâzi Khân* (cited as *Khânièh*) says :—" and if a man were to say that a property was dedicated as a pious offering (*mowkoofa-sadakah*), and add nothing further, it is lawful according to Abû

---

(1) *Ghâit-ul-Bayân.*

Yusuf as well as Mohammed and Hillâl . . . . and when an object has been specified, it is lawful according to Abû Yusuf, and after its extinction it will go to the poor, and the *Hedâya* has held this *to be correct*, and the texts are thereon, as in *Kudûri*, *Multeka* and *Nikâya*, and others.

و لو قال موقوفة صدقة او صدقة موقوفة و لم يزد جاز عند ابي يوسف و محمد و هلال .... و الصحيح الجواز لان محل الصدقة فى الاصل الفقراء فلا يحتاج الى ذكرهم و لان انقطاع لهم و لا يحتاج الى ذكر الابد ايضا الخ فهذا صريح في ان التصريح بالصدقة تصريح بالتابيد فيجوز عندهما بلا خلاف ...... فلو عين جاز عند ابي يوسف ثم بعد انقطاعه يعود الى الفقراء كما صححه فى الهداية و عليه المتون كالقدوري و الملتقي و النقاية و غيرها *

The *Sirâj-ul-Wahâj* states that, "Abû Yusuf says if a person make a dedication in favour of an object liable to failure, it is valid, and after its extinction, the *wakf* will be for the poor, though they may not be named, *e.g.*, if one were to say 'I have constituted this, *sadakatan mowkoofatan l'illah-ta'âla abadan* (*wakf as a pious offering for God in perpetuity*) on the child of so-and-so and his child's child,' and do not mention the poor or indigent, for when he has consecrated it to God, it is in perpetuity, as what is dedicated to God is spent on the poor; thus his saying as above is as if he had mentioned them."

قال ابو يوسف اذا سمى جهة تنقطع جاز و صار بعدها للفقراء و ان لم يسمهم و ذلک مثل ان يقول جعلتها صدقة موقوفة لله تعالى ابداً على ولد فلان و ولد ولده و لا يذكر الفقراء و لا المساكين او ذلک لانه اذا جعلها لله فقد ابدها لان ما يكون لله فهو ينصرف الى المساكين فصار كما لو ذكرهم *

Similarly, in the *Tas-hîl*—"if a man were to say 'I make this property *mowkoofa-sadakah* (a charitable *wakf*) for ('*ala, on*) so-and-so, its produce will be for such person for his life and after his death it will be spent for the poor."

موقوفة صدقة على فلان و الغلة له ما دام حياً فاذا مات يصرف الى الفقراء *

Upon the authorities it is perfectly clear that, under the Hanafî Law "perpetuity," express or implied, is a necessary condition to the constitution of a *wakf*, but its mention is not necessary at the time of dedication. Nor is it necessary that the dedication should be primarily for a *permanent* or *continuing* object. The term *wakf* and its equivalents imply perpetuity. And, accordingly, it has been laid down in the clearest terms that even when the *wakf* is, in the first instance in favour of an object which is likely to fail, the *wakf* is not void on that ground, *but the reversion would be applied for the benefit of the poor.* If a *wakf* is created for a *limited* period, the limitation as to time is void, and the *wakf* takes effect as a perpetual dedication. Principle.

SECTION III.

CONDITIONS RELATING TO THE CONSTITUTION OF A WAKF—(contd.)

Delivery of possession not necessary according to the Hanafî Law.

In order that a *wakf* should become operative or binding, it is *not* necessary under the Hanafi Law that the property should be actually delivered by the *wâkif* to a trustee. Delivery of seisin is not necessary in *wakf* as it is in *hiba*. The mere declaration of the *wâkif* is sufficient to constitute the property *wakf*, and the *wâkif* from that time forth is a mere trustee. He may be a trustee for himself, that is, he may reserve during his lifetime the income of the property for his own benefit; but whilst the law allows him, in case he makes a condition to that effect, to use the income of the property in whole or in part during his lifetime, the property is nevertheless a trust-property in his hands. He can neither sell it, nor mortgage it, nor burden it, nor deteriorate it in any way; and if he does so, the beneficiaries and reversioners would be entitled to have the property taken out of his hands and consigned to a *mutwalli*, to realise the rents and profits and to make over the balance to the *wâkif* after deducting expenses.(1)

"Though, according to Mohammed, consignment of the dedicated property and separation of it [from the other properties of the *wâkif*] are necessary to the completion of a *wakf*, according to Abû Yusuf, the *wakf* becomes absolute and binding, like emancipation, on the mere declaration of the *wâkif*, and his right therein

---

(1) *Fath ul-Kádir*, Vol. II, p. 640.

Fatwa according to Abû Yusuf.

becomes extinguished at once. And in the *Khulâsa* it is laid down that the jurists of Balkh decide according to the rule laid down by Abû Yusuf, and Sadr ush-Shahîd has stated that the *fatwa* is according to him; and in the *Fath ul-Kadîr* it is mentioned that Abû Yusuf's opinion is the accepted doctrine; and in the *Munièh* it is stated that the *fatwa* is with Abû Yusuf, and this is the rule accepted by the jurists of Balkh. But the Bokhâriots have adopted Mohammed's opinion. And in the *Sharh-i-Vikâyah* and the commentary of Mulla Khusru [the *Durrar-ul-Akhâm*] it is laid down that the *Fatwa* is with Abû Yusuf. In some places, it is mentioned in the *Khânièh* [*Fatâwai Kâzi Khân*(1)] that the *fatwa* is with Mohammed . . . . But in the *Muhît* it is laid down that the universality of our jurists have adopted the rule laid down by Abû Yusuf—and *this is correct.*"(2)

Hanafi doctrine—Delivery of possession not necessary to complete a *wakf*.

The question whether, in order to constitute a valid *wakf*, it is necessary to make over possession to a *mutwalli* was considered at great length in the case of *Doe dem. Jan Bibee* v. *Abdoollah Barber*, decided in the Supreme Court of Calcutta by Ryan, C.J., and Grant, J.

The judgment of the Chief Justice is of great importance, and I therefore give it *in extenso.*

"It is not necessary to state the facts of this case as proved at the trial; the whole matter in dispute between the parties being now narrowed to the construction that is to be put on this instrument of the 1st March, 1832. It is contended, on the part of the lessor of the plaintiff, that this instrument must be taken as a gift in contemplation of death, and that as such only one-third of the property can pass, and that the representatives of the plaintiff are entitled to recover the remaining two-thirds in the present action. It is also stated that, as an endowment or appropriation to religious uses, it is defective in several particulars, which the Mahommedan Law requires to make such instruments valid and binding.

Doe dem. Jan Bibee v. Abdoollah Barber.

"First.—It is said that, according to Mahommedan Law, an appropriator for religious uses cannot reserve for his life to his own use part of the property so appropriated as the present instrument purports to do.

(1) Kâzi Khân himself was a jurist of Bokhâra.

(2) *Surrat-ul-Fatâwa*, p. 430.

Doe dem. Jan Bibee v. Abdoollah Barber. (contd.)

"Secondly.—That a delivery to a *Mutwalli* is essential to the validity of an appropriation; that in this case there was no such delivery, but the appropriator constituted herself the *Mutwalli* during her life.

"Thirdly.—It has also been objected that a female, who is in this instance the appropriator and *Mutwalli* during life, cannot, according to Mahommedan Law, act as *Mutwalli*.

"For the defendant it is contended—

"First.—That the instrument is *wakf* and not a testamentary paper.

"Secondly.—That the whole of the property passed under it, and that according to Mahommedan Law, it is a valid endowment or appropriation of property to the service of God, and that consequently the verdict should remain as it now stands for the defendants.

"Upon the first question that has been raised, namely, whether this paper is to be considered as a *wakf* or consecration, or in the nature of a testamentary paper, the Court entertains no doubt. The reason given by the Moulvies is the commonsense view of the nature of the instrument. They say this paper is a deed of *wakf*(1) or consecration, because, say they, the *wâkif* or consecrator herself writes, 'she has consecrated certain lands in her lifetime,' and then states at the conclusion, 'These few words are, therefore, written, by way of a voucher of a pious donation to serve as a binding and decisive document when occasion requires.' The Moulvies add, this would have been a Will if she had said that the *wakf* should take place after her death, or if she had made the *wakf* when labouring under the illness which terminated life.

"It is equally clear and without dispute that a female may act as *Mutwalli*. It is hardly necessary to cite authorities for this proposition. The note in Mr. Macnaghten's book, p. 343, points out the distinction between the *Guddy Nasheen* (or superior of an endowment) and the *Mutwalli*, and adds, the office of trustee, *i.e.*, *Mutwalli*, may be held by a woman, and the duties may be discharged by proxy. In *Mussumaut Hyatee Khanum* v. *Mussumaut Koolsoom Khanum*(2) it is stated that it is legal for a female to be

(1) A translation of the deed of *wakf* in this case is given in the Appendix.
(2) 1 Sel. Rep., p. 285.

Doe dem. Jan Bibee v. Abdoollah Barber. (contd.)

a trustee according to all the authorities of the law. (See also the *Fatâwai Alamgiri*).

"Upon the two remaining points which have been raised, namely, that the appropriator and *Mutwalli* are one and the same person, and secondly, that the appropriator has reserved part of the property so appropriated to her own use, for life, more doubt and difficulty exists. It will be seen from the *Hedâya* that on both these points opposite opinions have been entertained by great authorities. The work to which I refer is, I think, worthy of more respect than Mr. Advocate-General is willing to bestow upon it. I think Mr. Hamilton in his preliminary discourse shows the value of the book as a guide to Mahommedan Law, and which appears to have been compiled about the close of the 12th century. The work principally leans to the doctrine of Hanifa, or his principal disciples. Two of the most distinguished of those disciples were Abû Yusuf and Mohammed, and it is their differences of opinion in the book of the *Hedâya*, to which I have already referred, that has given rise to the questions whether this instrument is a valid appropriation according to Mahommedan Law.

"Mohammed considers an appropriation with a reserve to the use of the appropriator during life illegal, and he also considers the assignment and delivery to the *Mutwalli* or procurator essential to the validity of an appropriation. Abû Yusuf, on both these points, is at variance with Mohammed. After obtaining all the information we are able to collect through the means of our Moulvies and a reference to authorities, we are of opinion that the opinion of Abû Yusuf on both these points must be considered as the law now prevailing and sanctioned by the more recent authorities.

"The translator of the *Hedâya* (who is some authority) seems to incline to Abû Yusuf's opinion by his note at page 351, and in the text, on the point whether an assignment and delivery to a *Mutwalli* is essential to the validity of the gift, it is stated that Abu Yusuf's is the more generally received doctrine.

"But we have directed our Moulvies to give their opinions on these points and to cite their authorities, which authorities, whether in print or manuscript, we have directed our interpreter to translate. From the authorities they have cited, although they commence with stating the difference of opinion between the two learned disciples of Hanifa, we] think it clearly appears according to the modern doctrine of Mahommedan decisions and lawyers that Abu Yusuf's opinion on this point is considered the better law.

"Some of the authorities which they cite are in print, and one in particular, which supports the doctrine of Abu Yusuf, I need hardly say, is of great authority in Mahommedan Law, I mean the *Fatâwa Alamgiri* which is a collection of opinions and precedents of Mahommedan Law compiled by Shaik Noyan and other learned men by command of the Mogul Emperor Aurungzebe. This compilation was made about, I presume, the close of the 17th century, and is of course received as an authority for the present state of the law."(1)

The following questions were referred to the Moulavies of the Court :—

1st Question.—Whether, according to Mahommedan Law, an endowment to charitable uses is valid, when qualified by a reservation of rents and profits to the donor himself during his life ?

2nd Question.—Whether delivery of the property is essential to render an endowment valid, according to the rule which governs other gifts ?

3rd Question.—Whether the endower can lawfully constitute himself Mootuwullee or trustee ?

4th Question.—Whether a female can lawfully be Mootuwullee ?

5th Question.—Whether the instrument in question is a will or a deed of endowment ?

To these questions the following answers were delivered by the Moulavies of the Court and duly filed—

To the first question—

There is a difference of opinion between Abu Yusuf and Mahommed touching the *wakf* or consecration of lands with a reservation, and setting apart of any portion of the profits and produce thereof for the support of the *wakif* or consecrator. Abû Yusuf considers the act legal, and Mahommed deems it illegal. The legal opinions of most of the learned uphold the opinion of Abu Yusuf, which is to be found in Chulpee or commentary of the Shurh Vekâyah, the Fatâwa Aulumgeeree, the Kâzi Khân, and the Kaffee.

To the second question—

Abû Yusuf does not consider the consignment and delivery of consecrated real property tô the Mootuwullee as necessary to render the *wakf* or consecration legal. In this opinion Mahommed differs, but the practice is in accordance with the opinion of Abû Yusuf, as written in the Mooneeah, Futhul Kuddeer, Seraj-ul-Wahaj, Hedâyah, and Veekyat-ul-Rawahij.

To the third question—

It is lawful for the *wakif* or consecrator to become Mootuwullee or Procurator, and to reserve the profits of part of the consecrated land for his own use and his descendants, as will be found in the Hedâyah, the Kâzi Khân, and the Alumgeeree.

(1) Grant, J., concurring, the rule obtained by the plaintiff was discharged.

To the fourth question—

It is lawful for a female to act as Mootuwullee, and qualified to become, as is to be found in the Fatâwa Aulumgeeree and other Fatâwas or text-books.

To the fifth question—

This paper is a deed of *wakf*, or consecration. From the tenor of this paper we are of opinion that it is an instrument of *wakf*, and not a testamentary paper because the *wâkif* or consecrator herself writes that "she has consecrated certain lands in her lifetime," and that she states at the conclusion of the instrument thus :—"Therefore I have delivered these few lines in the nature of an instrument of *wakf*." This would then have been a Will if she had said that the *wakf* should take effect upon her death, or if she had made the *wakf* with the illness that terminated her life,—in those cases this paper would have come under the guidance of the law touching Wills.

The following authorities were cited by the Moulavies on this occasion :—

In support of the first question—

From the Aulumgeeree in print, page 195, from line 10 to 12. "Whenever a *wakf* is made of land or other property and the party making the same reserves the whole of the profits thereof to himself, or a part only during his own life, and after that for the use of the poor, herein Abû Yusuf has said, " This *wakf* is right," and the learned of Bulluck (a town in Tooran) have decided conformably to this opinion of Abû Yusuf's and the decisions are in conformity therewith, for to induce persons to make *wakfs*. The like is to be found in the Sagrah and the Nesaub, and also in Moojmuraul—only.

From the Chulpee in print : the commentary of the Sharh Vekaya, page 245, from line 27 to line 28.

In the opinion of Abû Yusuf, it is right or lawful for the *wâkif* or consecrator to direct the profits to his own use and to make himself Mootuwullee, but not right in the opinion of Mahommed—only.

The Mooftee of Sakullian and Suddar Shaheed have said, the Futawas or decrees are in conformity with the words of Abu Yusuf's—only.

From the Kaffee in MSS. sheet 568 from the 5th to part of the 6th line.

The *wakif's* directing the profits of the *wakf* to his own use is right in the opinion of Abû Yusuf and the Masshâikh (Shaikhs) of Bulluck, and the decrees are consonant with that—only.

From the Kâzi Khân in print, page 251, from line 2nd to part of line 5th.

It is not right in the opinion of Heelall for the *wâkif* to stipulate in making a *wakf* that he shall appropriate the profits thereof to himself during his life, but it is right in the opinion of Abû Yusuf, and the Masshâikh of Bulluck have followed the opinion of Abû Yusuf, and said "such *wakf* and such reservation are both right," and Sudder Shuheed has said, the decrees are in conformity with the opinion of Abû Yusuf—only.

In support of the second question—

From the Kâzi Khân in print, page 212, from the 2nd to the 3rd line.

In the opinion of Abû Yusuf it is not necessary to deliver over possession to a Mootuwullee, therefore the *wâkif* is entitled to become Mootuwullee, although he does not expressly reserve that to himself, and the Masshâikh of Bulluck have followed this opinion of Abû Yusuf—only.

From the Aulumgeeree in print, page 455, from line 13th to line 14th.

The property of the *wâkif* in the *wakf* is severed from him by his saying, "I have made a *wakf* thereof," according to the opinion of Abû Yusuf and the opinion of the three Emaums (leaders) Mallick, Shafee, and Ahmud, son of Haumbul, and the opinion of most of the learned, is in conformity, with that and also with the Masshâikh of Bulluck, and it is written in the Mooneeah "that the decrees are consonant with that," and the like is to be found in the Futah-ul-Kuddeer, which says that the decrees are agreeable to that opinion, and also in the Seeraj-ul-Wahauj—only.

From the Veekahut-ul-rewahij in MSS., page 197, from the 7th to the 8th line.

In the opinion delivered by Abû Yusuf, the right is severed on bare declaration—only.

The authorities in support of the answer to the third question are to be found above.

The authorities in support of the fourth question are—

From the Aulumgeeree in print, page 504, line 15th.

In that respect men and women are equal.

Those in support of the answer to the 5th question are—

From the Aulumgeeree, page 455, from the 6th to the 7th line.

If a *wakf* is made to take effect upon the *wâkif's* death, saying, "upon my death I make a *wakf* of my house to so-and-so, and then the *wâkif* dies, the *wakf* is right as to one-third—only.

In the said book and page, from line 9th to line 10th.

"If the party appropriates the *wakf* to operate upon his death, during his illness, of which he eventually dies, the direction therein is that above—only."

The absence of uncertainty in the subject-matter of the *wakf* is also a condition,—not uncertainty in the object for which the dedication is made. Uncertainty in the object does not lead to the invalidation of the *wakf*, it only accelerates the application of the subject of the *wakf* to its ultimate object, *viz.*, the support of the poor, for they never fail. The subject of the *wakf* must be certain.

But the *subject* of the *wakf* must not be uncertain.(1) Accordingly, if a person were to dedicate a portion of his land without specifying it, the *wakf* would not take effect unless it can be gathered from attendant circumstances what he intended to convey, when the *wakf* will be valid upon the basis of *istehsân*.(2)

The doctrine of tanjiz.—The dedication must also not be dependent for its operation upon a contingency which may or may not occur. A condition, however, to which operation can be given immediately will not render a *wakf* void. Examples of the distinction between these two provisions of the law are given at great length in most of the law-books, and I would quote some passages here to render the meaning clear.(3) Principle. Must not be dependent on a contingency.

For example, "if a person were to say," says the *Fatâwai Alamgiri* quoting the *Fath ul-Kadîr*, "If my son arrives, my house is a *sadakah wakf* for the poor," and the son should arrive, never- Examples of a contingent *wakf*.

---

(1) *Fatâwai Alamgiri*, Vol. II, p. 458; *Radd-ul-Muhtâr*, Vol. III, p. 540.

(2) Liberal interpretation; *Fatawai Alamgiri*, Vol. II, 466.

(3) *Durr-ul-Mukhtâr*, p. 410; *Radd-ul-Muhtâr*, Vol. III.

theless, the house does not become *wakf*.(1) Or, if a person were to say, 'This my land is a *sadakah* if such an one please,' and the person referred to should indicate his pleasure, still the *wakf* would be void.(2)"

But when the condition is capable of immediate ascertainment or operation, the *wakf* is valid. For example, "if a man were to say, 'if this house be my property it is appropriated as a pious offering,' the appropriation is valid if the house be actually his property at the time of speaking, for the suspension is here on a condition that is actually fulfilled, and there is no contingency."(3) Another instance is thus given:—"A man loses his property and says, 'If I find it, by God I will make a *wakf* of my land,' and he finds the property, it is incumbent on him to make a *wakf* of his land for the benefit of those to whom it is lawful for him to pay *zakât* or poor rates, and if he should make it for those to whom it is not lawful for him to pay *zakât*, the *wakf* would not be valid nor would he be released from his vow."(4) And again:—"If a man were to say, 'if I die of this disease, I have made this my land *wakf*,' it is not valid whether he dies or recovers. But if he should say, 'if I die of this disease make this my land *wakf*,' it is lawful, for this amounts to the conditional appointment of a mandatory, which is legal."(5)

Testamentary *wakf* valid.

"But Shams-ul-Aimma Sarakhsi has stated at the end of his [chapter on] *Wakf*, that a *wakf* dependent on death is valid. And in the *Mukhtasar* [-*ul-Kudûri*] it is mentioned that where a *wakf* is made conditional upon the *wâkif's* decease, *e.g.*, if he were to say 'when I die this house will become *wakf* for this purpose,' it will be valid.(6)

But whilst a man can validly make a dedication in his own favour, he cannot reserve to himself the power of selling the property dedicated and applying the proceeds to his own use.

---

(1) So also in the *Surrat-ul-Fatâwa.*

(2) After the *Muhît.*

(3) *Fatâwai Kâzi Khân*, Vol. IV, p. 84.

(4) *Sirâjia.*

(5) *Jouharat-un-Nayerâh.*

(6) *Surrat-ul-Fatâwa*, 435: in fact this is a testamentary *wakf*.

(6) *Fatâwai Alamgiri*, Vol. II, p. 459, after the *Nahr-ul-Fâik*; *Durr-ul Mukhtâr*, p. 410; *Radd-ul-Mukhtâr*, Vol. III, p. 599.

Nor can a *wakf* be made for a determinate period.

Principle. A *wakf* cannot be revoked.

Where a *wakf* is made in favour of a lawful purpose and the *wâkif* reserves to himself the option of revoking the *wakf*, "the *wakf* is valid and the option void" by general consensus. According to Abu Yusuf, a short option, say, for three days, does not invalidate the *wakf*; if the option is not exercised within that time, the *wakf* becomes absolute.

CHAPTER IX.

THE SUBJECT-MATTER OF *WAKF*.

SECTION I.

GENERAL PRINCIPLES.

Principle. Everything capable of being reduced to possession or which may yield profit permanently, may form the subject of *wakf*.

UNDER the Mussulman Law there is absolutely no restriction on the dedication of any kind of property so long as it admits of yielding permanent benefit either in itself or by renewal from time to time or by conversion into something else which admits of the same possibility. Thus every kind of property, immovable as well as movable,—every object in fact which is capable of being possessed or being reduced to possession actually or constructively, equally with interest in trade, commerce, or investments—is a fit and lawful subject of *wakf*.

It will be seen, therefore, that the validity of a *wakf* does not depend on the nature of the property dedicated, but on the probability or presumption of permanent benefit being derived from it by any mode of dealing of which it is capable, or by converting it into something else. It is only where the object is absolutely unfit for being turned into profitable use, that its dedication falls to the ground. Land which is arid and waste, and cannot be cultivated or used for pasturage or any other purpose yielding a profit for the maintenance of the *wakf*—would be an unfit subject. But an object which was likely to be consumed in user and which, therefore, had no permanency in itself, can be sold and the proceeds invested in any manner customary among people in order to yield a permanent return, without any restriction to its renewal from time to time. For example, even eatables are fit subjects of *wakf* for they can be sold and the price so obtained laid out "in business." When a *wakf* is made of actual coin ("*dirhems* and *dinârs*"), it is to be invested with the like object.

Fatwa on this point according to Mohammed.

In two instances the British Indian Courts have lost sight of the root-idea underlying the principle, and have, therefore, failed to grasp the meaning of the jurists who had expressed themselves in favour of the *wakf* of certain kinds of moveable property as against others. It was thus that a canonical significance came to be attached in a Calcutta case(1) to the enunciations of the jurist Abû Yusuf, although by the consensus of Mussulman lawyers his doctrine is *not* adopted for judicial decisions (*fatwa*) in this matter. But even his *dictum* properly analysed, is merely illustrative but not restrictive. Nor must it be forgotten that when he speaks of invalidity in connection with any kind of property, he does not mean to imply that the *wakf* is unlawful on account of something in the nature of the property which forms the subject of the *wakf* but rather that it does not possess, on the basis of "analogy" (*Kiyâs*), in his judgment, the characteristic of yielding permanent benefit as being apt to be consumed in user.

Articles which Mussulmans cannot lawfully buy or sell—such as swine's flesh or intoxicants—cannot lawfully be dedicated, even though they can be sold to non-Moslems. The test, therefore, which was applied in early times to discover whether the property dedicated answered the root-idea was whether it was the "practice" in any particular locality to dedicate such objects, for the existence of the practice, to whatever extent, would indicate that they were the subjects of mutual dealing among the inhabitants of the place or people of the country, for otherwise they would not be capable of being bought or sold, or of yielding a permanent benefit by renewal or by the investment of the proceeds when sold.

These preliminary remarks will help to explain the authorities.

After dealing with the subject of *Mushâ'a*, the *Durr-ul-Mukhtâr* states the rules relating to the *wakf* of movables in the following terms:—"And similarly is valid the *wakf* of all movables [made] intentionally [*i.e.*, not as accessories to something else] which are the subject of mutual dealing among mankind (*tâ'amulun li'l-nâs*)(2) such as spades and axes and even *dirhems* and *dinârs*. I (3) say, that even an order has issued [from the sovereign(4)] to the Kâzis in that respect [*viz.*, to declare the validity of the *wakf* of *dirhems*

(1) *Kulsum Bibi* v. *Golam Hossain Cassim Ariff* [1903], 10 Cal. W. N., 499.

(2) The meaning of the expression *T'aâmul* will be further discussed later on, see p. 261 "Mankind" refers to the Mussulman people so as to exclude articles, the buying and selling of which is regarded unlawful by them.

(3) The author of the *Durr-ul-Mukhtâr*.

(4) Meaning the Sultan, see *ante*.

and *dinârs*] as is set forth in the Ordinances of Mufti Abû S'aûd; and of everything which can be measured or weighed; such things shall be sold and its proceeds shall be invested in *muzâribat* or *bazâ'at* (business or commerce). Thus if a person makes a *wakf* of several measures of wheat or barley on the condition that the *Mutwalli* should loan it to a cultivator for purposes of sowing, and after the crop has been reaped take back the measure, and then loan it again and so on, it is lawful as stated in the *Khulâsa*. . . . And it is lawful to make a *wakf* of cauldrons and biers and shrouds and the Koran and books (in general) for custom excludes analogy(1) according to the *hadîs* (traditional saying of the Prophet) that whatever the Mussulmans hold to be good is good in the estimation of the Almighty.(2) The *Bahr* has placed the *wakf* of boats and ships in the same category as the *wakf* of furniture, it not being customary."

Wakf of ships and boats valid.

With reference to this statement [quoted from the *Bahr-ur-Râik*], Imâm Halebi, the author of the *Multeka-ul-Abhar* distinctly lays down that "in our times the *wakf* of ships is customary."

As Tahtâwi points out in his *Sharh* (commentary) there is no difference of opinion among the Disciples regarding the validity of the *wakf* of horses and implements of warfare, "for with respect to them there are many traditions and proofs;" the difference relates to objects other than these. According to Mohammed the *wakf* of all movables is lawful provided there is a practice with regard to them, whereas Abû Yusuf holds otherwise. "But in the *Mujtaba* it is stated that according to Mohammed the *wakf* of all movables is valid *absolutely*, and according to Abû Yusuf when there is a practice. Although the language of the *Nahr-ul-Fâik* would give rise to an inference that the *wakf* of movables

(1) In other words when a certain mode of dealing or practice grows up among a people with the tacit approval of the community, the doctrine of "analogy" by which certain things, on pure hypothetical reasoning based on *à priori* considerations, are held to be invalid—does not apply.

(2) ما رآه المسلمون حسنا فهو عند الله حسن

This is the Moslem form of the ancient saying *Vox populi Vox Dei*. The difficulty is to find the *vox populi*. In the Mussulman system the practice or dealing of the community is the test. Professor Kresmárik in his article already referred to (*ante*, p. 207), says in any case it is necessary the subject of the *wakf* must not be *extra-commercium* and must be in the actual ownership of the consecrator, p. 529.

is valid only in places where the practice exists, Mufti Abû S'aûd has declared that there is no such limitation."

And the same writer dealing with the conditions of *wakf* says :—"Another condition is that the subject is suitable for dedication. According to the correct doctrine both immovable and movable property may be made *wakf*. [With respect to the latter] anything which by usage and practice it is customary [to dedicate] like the Koran and books of traditions may lawfully be made *wakf*. From this it follows that though in the neighbourhood of Egypt, it not being customary a *wakf* of current coins may not be valid, in the countries of Rûm [the Turkish Empire] the *wakf* of *dirhems* and *dinârs*, being customary, is lawful. When such a *wakf* [*viz.*, of actual money—*dirhems* and *dinârs*—or the equivalent of money] is made, it will be invested in *muzâribat* (business) and the income will be devoted to the purposes of the *wakf* "(1)

The development in the legal conceptions will become apparent from the fact that although in Tahtâwi's time the *wakf* of money was not customary in Egypt, it is now universally practised in that country as in the rest of the Moslem world. And not only money is dedicated in Egypt but shares in companies, stocks and bonds are commonly made *wakf*.

Even during the period which elapsed between the compilation of the *Hedâya* and that of the *Durr-ul-Mukhtâr*—a period of barely three hundred years—the legal conception appears to have made an advance. For the *Hedâya* regards the dedication of a bondsman as invalid, as the subject did not possess permanency, whilst the *Durr-ul-Mukhtâr* declares it to be valid—and adds that if the bondsman is intentionally killed by somebody the murderer should not be executed but should be made to pay as *wehr-geld* the full price of the bondsman so that another may be purchased in his place.(2) This shows that the idea of permanency by renewal had already grown up in the fifteenth century of the Christian era.

The rule relating to the *wakf* of movable property is enunciated in the following terms in the *Khazânat-ul-Muftiïn*(3) :—" If a

(1) Allâmah at-Tahtâwi's Commentary on the *Durr-ul-Mukhtâr*; See Morley's Dig., Introd., p. cclxxvlii.

(2) *Durr-ul-Mukhtâr*, p. 413, Hooghly Ed.

(3) The Treasure-house of the Muftis, (Jurists) frequently quoted by the law officers of the Sudder Dewanny Adawlat, and referred to in the *Fatâwai Alamgiri* and in the cases given in Macnaughten's Principles and Precedents of Mahommedan Law; See pp. 332, and 342; and Morley's Dig. Introd., p. cclxxxvii.

man makes a *wakf* of *dirhems* [here used generally for money] or food or whatever is weighed or measured, according to Imâm Zuffar it is lawful. When asked how such things can be made *wakf*, he answered the money should be invested in *muzâribat*,(1)and whatever profit is derived therefrom will be devoted to the purposes of the *wakf*; and what is weighed or measured will be sold and its price like money will be invested in business. And the jurists have held, and analogy is so, that if the *wâkif* provide thus—this measure of wheat will be loaned to the poor, for purposes of cultivation for themselves, and that after they have reaped the crops, the same measure will be taken back from them, and similarly for ever it should be loaned to other poor [people]; this will be lawful. And like this there are numerous *wakfs* in Damawand and the hilly tracts of Tabaristan [Northern Persia]

It must be noted in this connection that Imâm Zuffar is regarded in the Hanafî world as a *mujtahid* Imâm—a Jurist of the first rank entitled to lay down principles, standing next to Abû Yusuf and Mohammed.(2) And as I shall show abundantly later on, it is open to the Mussulman Judge to follow Zuffar's or any other principal jurist's rule, if, in his considered judgment, it appears more consistent with the needs of the times or the requirements of justice.

"According to the great Jurist Shams ul-Aïmma as-Sarakhsi," says Kâzi Khân, "*wakf* of movables is valid; custom and usage, however, regulate what movables can be made *wakf*. The *wakf* of shrouds, books, etc., are lawful according to all. The *wakf* of the milk of a cow is valid if customary. The *wakf* of *dirhems* (money) is valid. They would be applied in business, and the profit arising therefrom would be used for the purposes of the *wakf*. In the same way, a measure of wheat may be dedicated."

Commenting on the passage already quoted from the *Durr-ul-Mukhtâr*(3) the *Radd-ul-Muhtâr* says as follows:—"The dedication of movables subsidiary to immovable property (تبع للعقار) is lawful without divergence between them [Abû Yusuf and Mohammed]. Similarly, there is no divergence regarding the validity of a *wakf* of implements of warfare or horses, which are lawful according to well-

(1) *Muzâribat* is defined in Johnson's Arabic and Persian Dictionary to mean partnership business.

(2) See *ante*, p. 15.

(3) *Ante*, p. 247

known proofs. The difference [between the two] relates to the dedication of [movable property] other than these. For, according to Abû Yusuf, it [*viz.*, a *wakf* of every movable] is not valid; whereas, according to Mohammed, it is valid when dealing [or practice] pertains to such articles.

Imâm Mohammed's *dictum*.

And this rule has been adopted by the majority of the jurists of all countries(1) as is mentioned in the *Hedâya*; and *it is correct* as is mentioned in the *As'aâf*. And it is the doctrine of the majority of jurists as is mentioned in the *Zahîria*, for analogical reasoning is excluded where there is dealing.(2) And in the *Mujtaba*, it is mentioned, from the *Siyar*, that, according to Mohammed, the *wakf* of movables is unrestrictedly valid, and according to Abû Yusuf, the *wakf* of those movables as form the subject of dealing is lawful.

***Wakf* of movables unrestrictedly valid.**

And all this is mentioned in the *Bahr-u-Râik* and the first is well-known.... ....In the *Khulâsa* this doctrine relating to the validity of the *wakf* of *dirhems* and *dinârs* (money) is referred to Ansâri;(3) Ansâri was a disciple of Zuffar. And in the *Khâniéh* it is referred to Zuffar, where he hps said it is related from Zuffar on the authority of Sharnabalâlièh. And the author has stated in the *Manah* [*-ul-Ghuffâr*(4)] 'that the dealing is current in our days in the countries of Rûm [Turkey] and others;' thus the *wakf* of *dirhems* and *dinârs* comes within the dictum of Mohammed on which is the *Fatwa*, that 'every article which forms the subject of dealing a *wakf* thereof is lawful' and all this is patent.

***Wakf* of *dirhems* and *dinârs*. The *Fatwa* according to Mohammed.**

Consequently, it is not necessary to specify alone the dictum of Imâm Zuffar reported byAnsâri for its validity (*viz.*, the validity of a *wakf* of *dirhems* and *dinârs*).......Thus the Moulâna, the Sâhib ul-Bahr (the author of the *Bahr*), has given a *fatwa* that the *wakf* of *dirhems* and *dinârs* is lawful and has not stated any contrary doctrine."

"In the *Manah* [*-ul-Ghuffâr*] it is stated that Ramli(5) thought as doubtful the inclusion of *dirhems* and *dinârs* [money] in those articles to which dealing pertains, for [he said] they

---

(1) *Amsâr*, pl. of *misr*.

(2) (لان التعامل يترک به القياس) *Radd-ul-Muhtâr*, Vol. III p. 579;

(3) Mohammed ibn Abdullah al-Ansârî, a great jurist died about 830 A. C.

(4) The *Manah ul-Ghuffâr* and the *Tanwir ul-Absâr*, are by the same author (Shaikh Shams ud-din bin Abdullah al-Gazzi). The *Durr-ul-Mukhtâr* is a commentary on the *Tanwîr ul-Absâr.* whilst the *Radd-ul-Mukhtâr* is a commentary on the *Durr-ul-Mukhtâr*.

(5) A jurist of Egyp

dirhems and *dinârs*] are not such articles as one can derive profit from retaining [their character] in specie in the ownership [hands] of the *wâkif*; and that the *fatwa* given by the author of the *Bahr* without mention of any difference of opinion does not prove that the *wakf* of *dirhems* and *dinârs* comes within the meaning of Mohammed's dictum on which is the *fatwa*, that the *wakf* of all articles which form the subject of dealing is valid, for it is possible that he, the Sâhib ul-Bahr, has adopted the opinion of Zuffar and given *Fatwa* accordingly.......I [*viz.*, the author of the *Radd ul-Muhtâr*] say that money (*darâhim*, plural of *dirhem*) does not become specific because it is specified, and though it cannot yield profit retaining its specific character, yet because it cannot be retained in specie, its equivalent [what it is changed or converted into] stands in its place....Consequently, it may be taken as remaining for ever. And there is no doubt that it is movable property and, therefore, where the dealing [or practice] exists it will be included in what Mohammed has held to be capable of valid dedication. And it is for this reason that Mohammed referred to articles which were dealt with [or regarding which there was a practice] in his own time. The *Fath-ul-Kadîr* says that the Jurists proceeding on what was laid down by Mohammed extended the application of the principle to many other articles with respect to which they found the dealing [or practice] prevailing [in their times]......And in the *Khulâsa* it is stated that the *wakf* of a cow in order that its milk be distributed among the travellers, *abnâ-us-sabîl*, ('children of the road') will be considered lawful wherever the practice has come into existence."

"And Ansâri (who was a disciple of Zuffar) was asked, if a person made a *wakf* of *dirhems* and of such things as can be weighed and measured, whether it would be valid? He answered, 'yes;' on being questioned how that could be done, the reply was—the money would be invested in *muzâribat*, and its income would be devoted to the purposes of the *wakf*; and things which are capable of being weighed or measured would be sold and the proceeds invested in *muzâribat* or *bazâ'at*."

"The author says, it is upon this analogy that the *wakf* of a measure of wheat with the condition that it should be given to the poor (peasantry who are unable to procure seedlings) and they after reaping their crops, should return the wheat, and this measure of wheat should be again given to others who are in the same condition, in this way for ever—is lawful and valid. There are many such [*wakfs*] in Rai(1) and in the vicinity of Damâwand.(2) From this is clear the correctness of the principle stated by the author [of the *Tanwîr*] that the *wakf* of *dirhems* and *dinârs* is included in the rule of Mohammed on which is the *Fatwa, viz.*: "That whatever movable it is customary (3) (بالمنقول المتعارف) to make *wakf* it is valid..........'The reason for ascribing to Zuffar specifically the validity of a *wakf* of moneys was that in his time it was not generally in vogue, and he orginally enunciated the doctrine.' In the territories of Rûm [Turkey] it is customary to make a *wakf* of money," (وقف الدراهم و دنانير تعورف فى الديار الروميه).(4)

"According to all the jurists," says the *Fath ul-Kadîr*, "the *wakf* of all movables in ordinary use among mankind is valid." "Shâfeï says that everything the sale of which is valid, and which can be renewed from time to time by its usufruct or otherwise, can be validly dedicated, and this also is the opinion of Mâlik and

---

(1) Ancient Rhages.

(2) See *ante*, p. 250.

(3) From *'urf*, (custom); *Radd ul-Muhtâr*, Vol. III, pp. 578-9.

(4) *Fath ul-Kadir*, Vol. II, p. 636; also the *Surrat ul-Fatâwa*, p. 427. See also the *Hâwi*.

The above doctrines will explain the following passage in the *Hedâya*:—

"The appropriation of things which are consumed in using, such as gold and silver, or eatables and drinkables, is not unlawful according to the generality of the lawyers, but by gold and silver are not to be understood *dinârs* and *dirhems*, or what is not ornament. And if one should make an appropriation of *dirhems* or things estimated by measure, or of clothes, it would not be lawful. *But it is said that in places where this is customary, decrees are given in favour of the legality of the appropriation.*"

"If it be asked how, that is, how can the money be applied? It is answered that the *dirhems* may be lent to the poor and taken back again or given in *muzâribat*, and the profit laid out in charity, and wheat may be lent to the poor to sow and then taken from them, and clothes lent them to wear when necessary and then taken back."

"It is not lawful to appropriate movables, the appropriation of which is unusual or uncommon according to our doctors. The argument of our doctors is, that appropriation requires perpetuity, according to what has been already stated, and this cannot exist in movables since these are not of a lasting nature; analogy therefore suggests that the appropriation of movables in general is unlawful; it is admitted, however, in some articles (although contrary to analogy), because of the traditions already recorded and in other articles (such as axes, saws, and so forth) because of utility, but the appropriation of furniture, clothes and slaves is unlawful as being contrary to the suggestions of analogy, because they have neither tradition nor utility to support the legality, and therefore resemble *dirhems* and *dinârs*;" Hed. II (Eng. Tr.), p. 344. Since the *Hedâya* was indited the *wakf* of money has been expressly recognised; *Fath-ul-Kadir*, Vol. II, p. 636.

Ahmed ibn Hanbal "......" ornaments can be dedicated, for Hafsa, the daughter of Omar (the Caliph), dedicated her ornaments and such has been the practice." . . . . . . "Ansâri, who was a disciple of Imâm Zuffar, was asked if the *wakf* of money (*dirhems*) and whatever can be weighed or measured is valid or not. He replied—yes, a valid *wakf* may be made thereof. Asked how such things can be made *wakf*, he replied—such money should be invested in some partnership business and its profit applied to the purposes of the *wakf*. And if it is an article it should be sold and its price invested similarly."(1)

The same principle is enunciated in other authorities. For example, in the *Ramz ul-Hakâik* of Allamah 'Aini it is laid down in clear terms, "and the *wakf* of movables also is valid, as horses, and utensils of war, cauldrons, and shrouds and copies of the Koran, law-books, &c., for the *wakf* of these things is the result of necessity and recognised by the conditions of society."

So also in the *Wajîz ul-Muhît*, "every movable property which it is the practice to make *wakf* of, may be legally dedicated. . . . . Accordingly where a *wakf* of *dinârs* and *dirhems* (money) is in vogue it is lawful." And further, "according to Imâm Shâfeï, everything which may lawfully form the subject of bargain and sale may validly form the subject of *wakf*." And on this point there is not only a *consensus* among the Sunni Imâms, but also an agreement with the Shiahs who hold the *wakf* of both movables and immovables to be valid.

These authorities were evidently not placed before the High Court of Calcutta in the case of *Fatima Bibi* v. *Ariff Ismailjee Bham*.(2)

---

(1) *Radd-ul-Muhtâr*, Vol. III, 579.

Professor Kresmârik states that Mohammed Ibn Abdullah al-Ansâri is the usual authority relied upon regarding the validity of a *wakf* of money, food-stuffs and movable objects which are measurable by weight or bulk. He emphatically declares that he holds such objects as lawful subjects of *wakf*. When he was asked how money can be dedicated to fulfil the purpose of a permanent *wakf*, he answered money should be given to merchants for commercial purposes and the profits divided among the poor. Similarly, grain can be applied in the interests of the *wakf* by loaning it to poor peasants who have no seeds; when they pay back, it should be given to others, and so on; *Zeitschrift der Deutschen Morgenländischen Gesellschaft* (1891), p. 529.

(2) [1881] 9 Cal. L. R., 66.

The Allahabad High Court has, in a considered judgment, in which the authorities were carefully reviewed, dissented from the decision in the above case, and held that according to the Mahommedan Law a *wakf* of movable property including money may be validly constituted.(1) The same view has been taken by the Calcutta High Court in *Sakina Khanum* v. *Luddun Sahiba*.(2) In the case of *Banubi* v. *Narsingrao*.(3) the High Court of Bombay (Jenkins, C. J., and Beaman, J.), dealing with the question whether the dedication of movable property including money was valid under the Mahommedan Law, expressed itself in the following terms :—"As to whether property of this kind can legitimately form the subject of a *wakf*, we need only say that movables, in our opinion, may ; and if movables, there seems no sound reason in these days to exclude from that category funded moneys."

Wakf of Government securities, etc., valid.

The Sunni doctrine as to the validity of a *wakf* of movables including money is repeated in the same terms in the *Tas-hîl*, the *Jouharat-un-Nayyerèh*, the *Ghâit-ul-Bayân* and other works. From these principles it will be seen that, under the Hanafî Law, the *wakf* of Government Securities, Shares in Companies, Debentures and other stock, is perfectly lawful and valid. The doubt, which one or two of the ancient Hanafî doctors had expressed as to the validity of the *wakf* of certain kinds of movable property in contradistinction to certain other things, was the outcome of the primitive and archaic conditions of society, and was founded on the notion that as perpetuity was essential to the validity of *wakfs*, it could hardly be secured by the dedication of movable things generally. But as the Mussulman communities progressed in material civilisation and commerce developed, it came to be universally recognised that the *wakf* of everything, "to which practice appertains among mankind (تعامل للناس) or which it is customary in any particular locality to do so, is valid." The observant reader will not fail to see that "custom" or "usage" (*'urf*) is an important factor in Mahommedan Law. Like *istehsân* (liberal interpretation), it expresses the spirit of development. It enables com-

---

(1) *Abu Sayid Khan* v. *Bakar Ali* [1901], I. L., 24 All., 190.

(2) App. from O. D. No. 110 of 1900, decided on 10th June 1902 [1905] ; 2 C. L. J., 218.

(3) [1906], I. L. 31 Bom., 250.

munities to progress and develop in spite of the strict letter of the law.(1)

Principle.

When a *wakf* is made of articles which are "capable of being weighed or measured," like corn or cloth, they will be sold, and the proceeds will be invested in commerce or partnership business. The *wakf* of such articles as grain-seeds will have effect given to it by being loaned to the poor. The *wakf* of cauldrons to cook food for distribution to the poor, and other utensils of the like nature is lawful. "In ordinary practice," to paraphrase the Arabian rule, "analogy (*kyâs*) has no application." In saying that practice excludes analogy, the jurists mean to say, that analogy declares that when perpetuity is an essential condition of *wakf*, and a movable property cannot exist perpetually, a *wakf* of movable property *primâ facie* cannot be valid. But, according to present usage, "wherever it has become customary to make *wakf* of any kind of movable property," says the *Radd-ul-Muhtâr*, "it will be held valid notwithstanding that, in the time of the Companions, the custom may not have existed." From this it is evident that the appropriation of movables depends purely upon the circumstances of the age and the conditions of society and the usages of the people. According to this principle, the appropriation of mere rights and *profits à prendre* would be valid.

Wakf of books.

Similarly, the *wakf* of books is lawful. When a *wakf* is made of copies of the Koran for the use of students in a particular mosque, they can be studied only in that mosque and cannot be removed anywhere else. Nor, when a *wakf* is made of books for the people of a particular locality *exclusively*, can the books be taken to another locality.

Wakf of clothing.

A *wakf* of warm clothing for the poor to be worn in winter and then returned is lawful.

It must be noted, however, that the word "usage" or "custom" when used in connection with the dedication of movable property does not connote the idea conveyed by the term "custom" in English law; nor would the evidence required to prove "custom" under the rules of English law be required to establish the question of practice in the Mussulman system. The Kâzi is not called upon to see how long the "custom" of making such dedication has existed; what he has to determine primarily is whether the article dedi-

(1) *See ante* p. 17.

cated is capable of yielding permanent benefit by any mode of dealing usual among mankind; and secondly, whether its *wakf* is recognised or has become common among the people of the place where the dedication is made. Even where it is an uncommon *wakf*, he has the unquestioned authority to declare it to be a valid dedication if he considers that it is directly or indirectly for a pious object, and that the subject-matter is capable of yielding permanent benefit to the purposes of the *wakf* by any mode of user recognised among human beings.

SECTION II.

THE WAKF OF MONEY AND MOVABLE PROPERTY IN GENERAL

In the case of *Kulsum Bibi* v. *Golam Hossain Cassim Ariff*,(1) the High Court of Calcutta in the exercise of its original jurisdiction has held that "the *wakf* of shares in Companies is not valid under the Mahommedan Law." **Wakf of money.**

It is respectfully submitted that this conclusion proceeds upon an erroneous and strained construction of the principles, is not warranted by the authorities and has the effect of unsettling a settled and recognised rule of Mussulman Law; whilst in adopting the dictum of Abû Yusuf it ignores the doctrine in force among the Hanafîs; for the *Hedâya* itself lays down that "the majority of the jurists of all countries (اكثر فقهاء الامصار) act according to the rule of Mohammed (may the peace, etc.)"

There can be no question that funded moneys and shares in Commercial Companies constitute property (*mâl*) within the meaning of the Mahommedan Law; they are capable of being renewed and are, therefore, *mâl mutakawwim*, something over which the rights of ownership can be exercised; and as they form the subject of common dealing they are not *extra-commercium*. Again, they yield, or can yield permanent benefit either as shares or by other forms of investment. Then it may be asked how is it that a *wakf* of shares in Commercial Companies is invalid? The reasoning on

(1) [1903], 10 Cal. W. N., 499, *supra*. This case has been followed without examination of the authorities by the Bombay High Court in *Bai Fatmabai* v. *Gulam Husen* [1907], 9 B. L. R., 1337, and the Madras High Court in *Kadir Ibrahim Rowther* v. *Mahomed Rahumatulla Rowther* [1909], I. L., 33 Mad., 118.

which the Calcutta High Court in the case referred to has proceeded requires, therefore, serious consideration.

In the first place, it is evidently supposed that in stating that the *wakf* of actual money or money invested in business was lawful under the Mahommedan Law,(1) the present writer had enunciated some novel doctrine and assumed the functions of *Ijtihâd.* There seems to be some misapprehension regarding the meaning of *Ijtihâd.* This word signifies the evolution of principles. The privilege of evolving new principles ceased, according to Hanafî ideas, in the third, fourth and fifth centuries of the Hegira ; but there is absolutely no warrant for holding that any limit is imposed on the interpretation of the old rules and doctrines to bring them into accord with social progress and the requirements of the times.(2) On the contrary the Kâzi (Judge) is authorised to construe "liberally" the legal principles and to apply them in a manner most consistent with justice and expediency.(3)

The next submission is that it is a mistake to suppose that in the Hanafî system the views of Imâm Abû Yusuf are more authoritative *in all matters* than those of Imâm Mohammed.

Rule of law when there is a difference of opinion among the principal expounders.

In dealing with the Hanafî Law it should always be remembered that when there is a difference of opinion between Imâm Abû Yusuf and Imâm Mohammed, "the Mussulman Judge is at liberty to adopt either of the two decisions which seems to him the more consonant with reason,"(4) or consistent with the requirements of the times.(5) And this rule applies to divergence of opinion among all the jurists.

In the *Durr-ul-Mukhtâr* it is stated first that the Hanafî Judge is authorised to decree either according to Abû Yusuf or Mohammed ; and again that when there are two "correct" doctrines in respect of any particular question, it is lawful to pass a decree and give a *fatwa* according to either of them.(6) On this the comment of the *Radd-ul-Muhtâr* is both instructive and important. After explain-

(1) *Ante*, p. 246.

(2) See the authorities cited in the Introd., p. lii.

(3) The chapter on "the Duties of the Kâzi" in the *Radd-ul-Muhtâr* and similar works deserve careful study.

(4) Sir William Jones' Works, Vol. III, p. 540; also *ante*, p. 17.

(5) *Fatâwai-Hamâdia.*

(6) *Durr-ul-Mukhtâr*, p. 413.

ing(1) that it is allowable for a Hanafî Judge to pass a decree according to the opinion of either Abû Yusuf, Mohammed or any other Hanafî Imâm, as they are all followers of *the* Imâm (Abû Hanîfa, the founder of the School)—it proceeds thus :—"With reference to his(2) statement that when there are two 'correct' doctrines, etc., it means that when they are declared to be correct in an equal sense [*i.e.*, the Judge may decree in accordance with either doctrine], but if it be not so, it is best(3) to adopt the one which is stronger in correctness. For example, one doctrine [*Kawl, saying*] is declared to be 'correct,' whilst the other is declared to be one on which is the *fatwa*,(4) the latter is the stronger (*akad*) of the two. And if one is mentioned in the Texts or in the Approved Traditions or it is said that there is an agreement of a majority on it or that it is most in accord with the [needs of] people, then it is best to adopt it instead of the other opposed to it, although it may be said to be also 'correct' as I have already stated in the beginning of the book(5)........"

Judge to decide according to what is just and consonant with the requirements of the times.

"Although it is allowable to the Judge to decide according to one or other of two 'correct' doctrines [as explained above], when he has decided a particular case (*hâdisa*) according to one doctrine, he is not authorised to decide the same case again according to the other doctrine, but he may do so in some other case. And these rules apply also to the *Mufti* [the jurist who has to expound the law for the Court to act upon]. He should carefully consider(6) what is most in accord with the times or the needs of the people or what is most expedient (اصلح), and this is their meaning [*i.e.*, the meaning of the learned] that the *Mufti* can deliver *fatwas* according to what he considers most expedient; from expediency is meant not mundane expediency but that which is pious."(7)

Primary rules relating to *wakf*.

In the law relating to *wakf* there are certain primary rules on which the principal doctors are in agreement. With regard to the subsidiary principles there is considerable divergence. The primary rules are, (*a*) that the subject of the *wakf* should be dedi-

(1) *Radd-ul-Muhtâr*, Vol. III, p. 577.

(2) Namely, the author of the *Durr-ul-Mukhtâr* on which the *Radd-ul-Muhtâr* is commenting.

(3) اولى *Awla*, pre-eminent, most excellent, proper, fit.

(4) عليه الفتوى

(5) *Radd-ul-Muhtâr*, Vol. III, p. 578.

(6) Lit. "view with raised eyes."

(7) *Radd-ul-Muhtâr*, Vol. III, p. 578.

cated in perpetuity; (*b*) that all human right should be divested therefrom; and (*c*) that it should be made non-heritable and inalienable.

With regard to these there is *consensus*. When we come to the subsidiary principles, *e.g.*, how and for whom a *wakf* may be made, what expressions should be used in its constitution, what things are fit subjects for *wakfs*, we find a difference of opinion between Abû Yusuf and Mohammed. On some "the *fatwa* is with Abû Yusuf," that is, decrees are passed according to his views; on others, according to Mohammed. Mohammed insists that for a *wakf*, to be valid, an unfailing object should be expressly designated; Abû Yusuf does not consider that essential. The jurists of Bokhâra adopted Mohammed's view; those of Balkh, Abû Yusuf's. In India this was the recognised rule. But the British Indian Courts have chosen to follow Mohammed's principle.(1)

Difference between Abû Yusuf and Mohammed.

Mohammed considered consignment to a trustee essential; Abû Yusuf did not, and his views were adopted by the jurists of Balkh, and were followed in India.(2)

Abû Yusuf considered that, save certain kinds of movable property which it had already become the practice to dedicate, the *wakf* of others was not valid, being inconsistent with the main purpose of a dedication, namely, *perpetuity*, as they were likely to be consumed in user. Mohammed was of opinion that every kind of movable property which formed the subject of common dealing among men, or which it was the practice anywhere to dedicate, may lawfully be constituted as *wakf*. The rule of Mohammed is now the universally recognised doctrine; and in every treatise it is laid down that on this point "the *fatwa* is with Mohammed," that "*fatwas* (decisions) are given according to his rule."(3)

Zuffar, a contemporary and disciple of Abû Hanîfa, who is classed with Abû Yusuf and Mohammed(4) as a *mujtahid* Imâm of the first rank, that is, entitled to *ijtihâd*, i.e., to evolve principles, agreed with Mohammed and declared the *wakf* of movables, *including money*, to be absolutely lawful. "And Zuffar (may the peace, etc.),

---

(1) See *Amrut Lall Kalidas* v. *Shaikh Hussein Mahomed Ibrahim* [1887], I. L., 11 Bom., 492.

(2) See *Doe dem. Jaun Beebee* v. *Abdoollah Barber*, supra.

(3) *Radd-ul-Muhtâr*, Vol. III, p. 578.

(4) See the *Multcka* and d'Ohsson, *Tableaux General de l' Empire Ottoman*.

has declared that when a man has dedicated money (*darâhim*, pl. of *dirhem*), or comestibles (*at-ta'âm*) or anything else which can be weighed or measured, it is valid. On being questioned how that could be, he answered, the *dirhems* would be laid out in *muzâribat*(1) and the income devoted to the purposes of the *wakf*; and similarly things measurable or weighable should be sold and the proceeds invested like money in *bazâ'at* or *muzâribat*."(2) The same view has been expressed by another mujtahid Imâm, Zuhri.(3)

The rule of Mohammed the recognised law.

The author of the *Radd-ul-Muhtâr* emphatically states that as the rule of Mohammed, *according to which is the Fatwa*, covers all kinds of movable property, it is not necessary to refer to Zuffar.(4)

It is a fundamental error, therefore, to suppose that on this point the opinion of Abû Yusuf supplies the principle for decision. Such an assumption is at variance with the recognised rule of Mahommedan Law.

With regard to movable property, as already stated, the jurists require that the article dedicated should be the "subject of mutual dealing among mankind," as, if it were not so, it would hardly be possible to renew it or derive permanent benefit therefrom. For example, unless a cow dedicated for supplying milk to the poor, the validity of which is recognised, could be sold when it ceased to give milk, the benefaction would come to an end.

Exception has been taken to the rendering of the passage(5) from the *Radd-ul-Muhtâr* on the ground that the word (تعامل) (*t'aâmul*) means the "practice of making *wakf*," and not as construed by the writer "dealing". This view confuses the two expressions, *t'aâmul* and *t'aârûf*, on the assumption that they are synonymous. Both these words occur in the passage translated in this work.

The word *t'aâmul* is defined in Catafago's Arabic Dictionary, and in Johnson's "Arabic and Persian Dictionary" as meaning "dealing, acting together;" whilst *t'aârûf*, according to Johnson,

---

(1) Partnership business, in which one partner supplies capital and the other labour.

(2) *Fatâwai Kâzi Khan*, Vol. IV (Cal. Ed.), p. 240.)

(3) Allâmah Aini's *Umdat-ul-Kâri*, a Commentary on the *Sahîh-ul-Bukhâri*, Vol. VI, p. 516.

(4) *Radd-ul-Muhtâr*, Vol. III, p. 578, see also the *Fath-ul-Kadîr*, Vol. II, 636.

(5) In p. 178 of the previous Edition ; pp. 251-2 of the present.

signifies "practice, custom, fashion." *T'aâmul* is emphatically *not* synonymous with *t'aâruf*.(1)

The same definition is given in the Arabic *Tâj-ul-Arûs* and Lane's Arabic Lexicon which explain the words (تعامل) (*t'aâmul*) and (معاملة) (*m 'uâmilat*) both derived from the same root as meaning "dealing together, as buying and selling" . . "for example, one says (تعامل الناس بالدراهم) 'people dealt together in buying and selling with *dirhems*'; (يتعامل به) business of buying and selling is transacted with it (فليس, coin).' "

Dozy defines the meaning of تعامل in the same terms, "(عامل بالدراهم), employér des dirhems dans à commerce : (عامل في دراهمة) faire un remplacement d'argent un emploi utile." And in the *Kashshâf-ul-Istilahât il funûn*, an identical explanation is given. تعامل (*t'aâmul*) does not appear to be ever used synonymously with تعارف (*t'aârûf*) nor does تعامل or معاملة convey the same meaning as تعارف (custom or practice).

The *Ghâit-ul-Bayân* has the following passage in which the two words occur together in the same sentence, excluding the suggestion that they both convey the same meaning.

صح ايضاً وقف منقول كالكراع و السلاح و الفاس و القدر و القدوم
و المنشار الجنازة وثيابها والمصاحف وكتب الفقه والحديث و الادبية
غير ذلك مما فيه تعامل و تعارف لوقفه *

Wakf of movables

"Similarly is lawful the *wakf* of movables (*mankûl*), such as implements of husbandry and war, hatchets, saws (*manshâr*), biers and shrouds, copies of the Koran, books on jurisprudence, traditions, and literature, and *other things which people deal in* (*t'aâmul*) *and which it is the practice* (*t'aâruf*) *to make wakf of.*"

Assuming that *t'aâmul* does not mean dealing, as all the great lexicographers, European and Arab, declare it does, but the practice of making *wakf*, it makes no difference, it is respectfully submitted, in the settled principle relating to the validity of all kinds of movable property including money. It would only mean that the *wakf* of every article which people are in the practice of making *wakf* is lawful; and considering that the practice of making a *wakf* of money or anything else in which

(1) تعامل is derived from عمل *'aml* or act; whilst تعارف comes from عرف *'urf* or usage.

it is invested has become universal since the edict of the Sultan mentioned above,(1) there can be no question as to its validity.

It is evident that the enunciation of Mufti Abû S'aûd already mentioned(2) was not brought to the notice of the learned Judge in *Kulsum Bibi* v. *Golam Hossein Cassim Ariff*,(3) nor the fact that, as stated in the *Durr-ul-Mukhtâr*,(4) the Kâzis had been directed by sovereign authority (clearly, with the object of putting an end to casuistical discussion as common then as now), "to declare the validity of the *wakf* of moneys." This edict which gave expression to the developed rule of Mussulman Law and which appears to have been promulgated about the middle of the 15th century, and the enunciation of Mufti Abû S'aûd, one of the greatest Hanafî Jurists, leave no possible room for doubt as to the correct rule of law.

Since the days of Abû Yusuf, the legal conception regarding articles that may validly be made *wakf* has made a great advance. He did not recognise the validity of the *wakf* of buildings and trees apart from the land; *that* is now universally admitted by the Hanafî jurists. The *wakf* of money (*dirhems* and *dinârs*) which he discountenanced on the ground of *analogy* (*kyâs*), as likely to be consumed in use, is now admitted as lawful, wherever it is in vogue, and it is declared that where money is dedicated its value should be laid out in *muzâribat* (business) or *bazâ'at* (commerce).(5) (This is not even referred to in the judgment in *Kulsum Bibee* v. *Golam Hossein Cassim Ariff*.) If any other object likely to perish in its use is made *wakf*, the direction is that it should be sold and its proceeds similarly invested. Even where a thing is dedicated the *wakf* of which is not common, the Kâzi is authorised to declare its validity, if he considers it suitable for its purpose.(6)

No sacramental value or significance is attached to the *wakf* of any particular kind of property in contra-distinction to another. What the Judge has to see is whether the article dedicated is capable of yielding *permanent* benefit by renewal from time to time, or by investment of the proceeds, when sold, in business or commerce,

(1) Ante, p. 247.
(2) See *ante*, p. 247 and following pages.
(3) Supra.
(4) See *ante*, p. 247.
(5) See *ante*, p. 248.
(6) *Radd-ul-Muhtâr*, Vol. III, p. 579.

(*muzâribat* or *bazî'at.*) It is a mistake to attach canonical importance to the statements and arguments in the *Hedâya*, for many of the doctrines set forth in it are long since exploded, or have been considerably modified.

feï and ih doc- es iden·

The validity of the *wakf* of movables including moneys is accepted without question among the Shâfeïs, the Mâlikis, the Hanbalis, and the Shiahs. "And Shâfeï has held," says the *Hedâya*, "that the *wakf* of everything from which benefit can be derived consistently with the retention of the *corpus* is valid; and whatever can be lawfully sold(1) may be lawfully dedicated, for what is capable of yielding profit [from changes of form] resembles lands, horses and arms."

The *wakf* of money is now common everywhere among Mahommedans from Algeria to India and Burmah. The Shrine at Mecca and at Kerbela, the endowments at Ajmere, Hossainabad (Lucknow), and many of the mosques and religious institutions all over the country, are largely supported by the income of moneys invested in Government Securities, which people have come to regard as safer and more permanent than even land. In Egypt, the income of many important endowments created in modern times is, for the most part, derived from shares in commercial companies.

Money invested in Government or Municipal stock is employed by the State or local authorities, as the case may be, generally in productive work, and a share of the profits derived therefrom is received by the investors under the name of dividends or interest. The income derived from money invested in commercial companies stands in the same category. And the *wakf* of moneys invested in trade or commerce (*bazâ'at*) has been recognised as lawful for centuries.

SECTION III.

THE WAKF OF BUILDINGS AND MUSHA'A PROPERTY.

The rule relating to the dedication of a building without the land on which it is situated is thus given in the *Durr-ul-Mukhtâr*(2):—"a person builds a house on [some] land and dedicates it with intention without the land, [in that case] the *wakf* is

---

(1) This gives an indication to the sense in which the word *t'uâmul* is used in this connection.

(2) P. 416.

not correct [according to some], whilst others have held that it is correct (valid) *and on this is the fatwa.* The Kâri-ul-Hedâya(1) was asked regarding the validity of *wakf* of buildings and trees without the land, and he answered that *fatwas* are given (decrees passed) in favour of the validity of such *wakfs.* The author of the *Sharh-i-Wahbânieh* has preferred this view; and the author [of the *Tanwîr-ul-Absâr*] has enforced the doctrine by declaring that as buildings and trees are movable property, and it is the practice to make *wakf* thereof, it is established that *fatwas* should be given in favour of its validity."

Wakf of a building without the land.

As regards the *wakf* of a building without the land on which it is built, although there seems to have been some difference of opinion on the part of the ancient jurists, its validity is now clearly recognised. Allâmah al-Kâsim thought such a *wakf* was not valid, and he appears to have adopted the views of Mohammed and Hilâl ibn Yahya Basrî on this point. But, says the *Radd-ul-Muhtâr*, "it is stated in the *Bahr* (*ur-Râik*) from the *Zakhîra* that where it is customary to dedicate a building without the land upon which it is erected, the dedication of the building without the land is valid; but where it is not customary to do so, the dedication is not valid."

In connection with this point the *Radd-ul-Muhtâr* mentions a memorable disputation which took place in the presence of Sultan Malik uz-Zâhir,(2) at a Convocation held for the purpose, between the Allâmah and his celebrated disciple 'Abdu-bar Ibn Shahna, who held in opposition to his master, that the *wakf* of a building without the land was valid, that this doctrine had been recognised for over two hundred years, and repeated decisions had been passed in accordance therewith by learned Kâzis. This view of Ibn Shahna was combated by Allâmah Mohammed ibn Zahîra, but has been universally accepted in recent times. The author of the *Radd-ul-Muhtâr* lays down the proposition broadly, "that the *wakf* of a movable thing of which it is customary to make *wakf* is valid; so the *wakf* of a building without the land, when it is customary, is

(1) The Kâri-ul-Hedâya's real name is Sirâj-ud-din. He was a disciple of Shaikh Akmal-ud-dîn (the author of the *Inâya*, and master of the author of the *Fath-ul-kadîr*). As he read the *Hedâya* eighteen times with his master, he received the designation of Kâri-ul-Hedâya (Hedâya-reader); Tahtâwi.

(2) The Great Sultan Baibars.

valid, and this doctrine is not in conflict with the views of those who hold that such a *wakf* is not valid, *for the question of validity turns upon the custom recognised in the locality where the wakf is made. If people are in the habit of making such wakfs, the law will recognise them as valid.*"(1)

Modern doctrine. The *wakf* of land subject to a mortgage.

The doctrine now in force is, that the *wakf* of a building without the land on which it is situated is valid and the *fatwa* is accordingly.(2)

As already stated the *wakf* of land which is in lease or which is subject to a mortgage is valid.(3)

"And if the land is dedicated to the same purpose as the building [lit., for which the building is being appointed] it is valid as subsidiary to the *wakf* of the land. [But] if the land has been dedicated to a different purpose, there is a difference of opinion, and the correct doctrine is that it is valid [*i.e.*, the *wakf* of the building], so in the *Manzûma ul-Mujiba.*"

"Ibnu Nujaim was asked regarding the *wakf* of trees without the land and he answered that it is valid, although the two *wâkifs* may be different."

"He was further asked regarding the *wakf* of buildings and trees on land held on lease by another on a monthly or yearly tenancy,(4) and he answered 'it was valid.'"

But the *wakf* of a building on land belonging to another, of which the dedicator is in possession as bailee or lessee is not valid. The *Durr-ul-Mukhtâr* states the rule thus—"the *wakf* of a building on land held in *'aârîat*(5) or *ijâra*(6) is not valid." The *Radd-ul-Muhtâr* commenting on this passage states as follows:—"from this must be excluded cases such as have been mentioned by Khassâf, that is, lands in which the dedicator has a limited permanent interest;(7) the *wakf* of a building on such land is valid; so in

(1) *Radd-ul-Muhtâr*, Vol. III, p. 604.

(2) *Jouharat-un-Nayyerèh.*

(3) See *ante*, pp. 203-205. *Zakhîrat-ul-Akhyâr*; see also the case of *Khaja Hossain Ali* v. *Hazara Begum* [1869], 12 W. R., 498.

(4) الارض المحتكرة lit. land leased for short periods.

(5) Bailment.

(6) Lease.

(7) متقررة الا حتكار. I construe these words to mean that the person dedicating has a permanent *limited* interest in the land on which the building is situated. *Ihtikâr* literally means accumulating grain for selling, but the legal meaning is different.

the *Bahr* [*-ur-Raik*]. And it is stated by Asa'ât and it is also mentioned in the book on *wakf* of Khassâf that if a person were to make a *wakf* of shops(1) situated in the market—place (*aswâk*, pl. of *sûk*) it would be lawful, if the land has been held in *ijâra* by the builders of the shops, without any attempt by the Sultan to eject them, and has been inherited and been partitioned without objection."(2)

In other words where the lease is of a permanent character and the lessee cannot be ejected from the land without process of law, the lessee is entitled to dedicate any building on such land.

When the land and the building belong to the same person he is entitled to dedicate them separately to different purposes. But the *wakf* of the building would carry with it the right of way over the land whether the dedications are made at one and the same time or separately.(3)

What is included in a *wakf* of a house.

Where a house has been made *wakf*, everything that would be included in its sale would be included in the *wakf*, whether it be mentioned or not that the house is made *wakf*, "with all its rights and everything, small and great, belonging to it, or in it, or of it." So also in the *wakf* of shops everything is included that would be included in the sale thereof.

In the *wakf* of lands, the buildings and trees standing thereon are included, but not the fruit then on the trees, nor the crop if the land has already been sown. Canes and other plants that are cut annually are not included, but such as are cut biennially are included in the *wakf* of the land.

"Khassâf mentions in his Book on *Wakf*, that when a dedication is made of land for specified purposes with the ultimate reversion in favour of the poor, the buildings on the land, and the palm and other trees are included in the *wakf*. He also mentions that existing fruit is not included in an appropriation of trees, and most of our Shaikhs are of that opinion, and *it is correct*." "When a *wakf* is made in the following terms :—'I consecrate this my land as a *sadakah* with its rights, and all that is in it, and of it,' and there happens to be at the time fruit on the trees, he ought to bestow the fruit in charity on the poor, though not by way of *wakf* but by

(1) *Hawânit*, pl. of *hânût*.

(2) *Radd-ul-Muhtâr*, Vol. III, p. 605.

(3) *Ibid*.

virtue of his vow, on a favourable construction, and what is subsequently produced is to be applied to the purposes specified in the *wakf*. Similarly, when a *wakf* is made in the following words, 'my land is consecrated as a *sadakah* after my death, to the end that what produce God may cause to come out of it shall be for the servants of God,' upon the death of the *wâkif* the fruit actually on the trees are not included in the bequest by virtue of the *wakf*."

Rent already accrued due is not included in the *wakf* of land.

It follows from these principles that when a property or land occupied by tenants is made *wakf*, the rent that has already accrued due will not be included in the *wakf* unless expressly declared to be so, and the *mutwalli* will not acquire a right to collect the same unless specially authorised.

It is not necessary for the validity of a *wakf*, that the boundaries of the land or house appropriated should be specifically set forth. It is only requisite that what is constituted as *wakf* should be ascertainable. Where, therefore, a house or land is well-known, it may be made *wakf* without specifying the boundaries. "And though the witnesses may testify that the land was not bounded in their presence and they did not know it," the *wakf* will not be invalid on that account.

Mills in a field whether turned by water or hand, and Persian wheels and buckets used for raising the water are included in the *wakf* of the land.

When a man has made a *wakf* of his land without mentioning a right of water or way, both are included "on a favourable construction," because land is not dedicated except on account of what it will produce and for that purpose both rights of water and way are included.

***Wakf* of *mushâ'a* valid.**

The *wakf* of *mushâ'a*, in other words, the *wakf* of an undivided share of a property which is capable of partition, is valid according to Abû Yusuf. Mohammed differs from him, and bases his difference on the difficulty of delivering possession of a property, which was not specifically divided off or apportioned from the rest. Abû Yusuf, however, holds delivery of possession wholly unnecessary in the case of a *wakf*. Kâzi Khân says, "the opinion of Abû Yusuf has been adopted by the jurists of Balkh, whilst that of Mohammed by the Shaikhs of Bokhâra." And the *Fatâwai Alamgiri* adds, "the moderns decide according to the opinion of Abû Yusuf, who held that [the *wakf* of *mushâ'a*] was lawful, and *this is approved.*"

According to the *Siraj ul-Wahâj* the *wakf* of *mushâ'a* is valid by *consensus*.

But where the property is incapable of partition, Mohammed agrees with Abû Yusuf and holds that the dedication of a share thereof is lawful. For example, the dedication of a moiety of a public bath or *hammâm* is valid according to Abû Yusuf as well as Mohammed, " for a *hammâm* is not partible."

Wakf of Mushâ'a.

Both Abû Yusuf and Mohammed, however, agree in holding that where a piece of land is dedicated for *erecting* a mosque or *building* a tomb thereon, that piece of land ought to be divided off. The reason of this is apparent. But no division is necessary according to Abû Yusuf, if the dedication is in *favour* of a mosque or for the maintenance of a mausoleum.

As a consequence of the rule laid down by Abû Yusuf regarding the validity of the *wakf* of a partible *mushâ'a*, and which has been adopted by the majority of the Hanafî jurists, it is held that where a person purports to make a dedication of the whole of his property, but for some reason it cannot operate as to the whole, the *wakf* of the undivided share would be valid, *e.g.*, if a person were to make *in his death-illness* a *wakf* of his house in favour of his children and after them for the poor, and to leave no other property but this house, and no other heir besides the children, according to Abû Yusuf, the *wakf* would take effect with reference to one-third unless all the children consent.(1) " In case of any dispute regarding the *wakf* of undivided property, the Kâzi can decree partition."

A *wakf* by two or more individuals of a joint property is valid according to all the jurists.

When two persons are in joint possession of a piece of land and one of them dedicates his share for his children (*i.e.*, his descendants) in perpetuity, so long as any one of them happens to exist, and, upon their failure, for the poor; and the other partner dedicates his share for his *brethren* and the *people of his family* (*ahl-ul-bait*), and on their failure, for the performance of pilgrimages, and both of them consign the trust to one and the same *mutwalli*, such a *wakf*

Wakf by two joint owners.

---

(1) *Fatâwai Alamgiri*, Vol. II, p. 455; a *wakf* intended to operate after the death of the *wâkif* takes effect with regard to one-third of the estate of the appropriator; Comp. *Doe dem. Jaun Beebee* v. *Abdoollah Barber*, Fulton's Reports, p. 345.

is valid. Similarly, if one of the partners were to dedicate his moiety for the poor, and the other his moiety for another purpose, it would be valid. This is according to both Mohammed and Abû Yusuf. But the latter does not insist upon consignment to a *mutwalli* as an absolute essential. "And as he does not insist upon consignment or delivery of possession for the validity of a *wakf, so according to him partition is not necessary*. And this is the accepted doctrine."(1)

It is not necessary that the property dedicated or the share dedicated should be ascertained at the time. If a person were to dedicate his share in a certain property, intending that the dedication should take effect as to the whole of his share, and subsequently his share is found to be larger than what he had supposed, the whole would become *wakf; e.g.*, "if a person were to declare 'I make a *wakf* of my share in this house which is one-third,' and it afterwards appears that his share amounts to half or two-thirds, the entire share would become *wakf*." Similarly, "if a man were to say in his will, 'I leave to so-and-so one-third of my property, *viz.*, 1,000 dirhems,' and it turns out subsequently that the one-third of his estate amounts to 4,000 dirhems, the legatee would get the latter sum." This is different from sale, in which the vendee would only get the amount specified.

Where two persons are jointly entitled to many houses, or where a land is jointly held by two partners, and one of them dedicates his share in all those houses or in that specific land for a pious purpose, and afterwards desires to have a partition of his share effected by the Kâzi, and the Kâzi in effecting the partition allots to the *wâkif* one house or one specific plot for his interest in all the houses or in the entire land, the *wakf* will take effect with reference to that house or that specific plot of land.

When two persons jointly own a piece of land, either of the co-sharers may make a valid *wakf* of his own share.

When a *wakf* is made of land which is leased to another person, the lease is not cancelled; it continues in force until the end of the term, the rent paid by the lessee being applied during that term to the purpose of the *wakf*, but on its expiration the entire income arising from the leased property is to be applied to such purposes.

(1) *Fath ul-Kadir*, Vol. II, p. 642.

Similarly a dedication or *wakf* of property subject to a mortgage or in the possession of tenants is valid. When a property is dedicated which is subject to a mortgage, its income will be devoted to the discharge of the debt, and after it has been paid off, it will be applied to the purposes of the dedication. A *wâkif* may lawfully make a dedication with the condition that the income of the property should be applied for his maintenance or in the payment of his debts and afterwards be devoted to the poor or any other unfailing object.

As regards the *wakfs* of *jâgîrs* or grants made by Kings and Ameers :— *Wakf* *jâgîr*

Jâgirs (*ikt'aât*) are of two kinds, one where the land has been granted in fee, that is, first the sovereign has purchased it from the *Bait-ul-mâl* and presented it to the grantee, or it is a portion of the royal domains; 2nd, where the usufruct is only granted and the jâgir is vested in the Crown. In the former case, the grantee may make a *wakf*, in the latter case not.

In the *Fatâwai Alamgiri* occur the following remarks on this subject :—

"It is a branch or consequence of property being a condition, that the dedication of *ikt'aât*, or royal grants, is not lawful, except when the grant is of waste land, or of land belonging to the Imâm [Sovereign] himself, which he has granted to the person making the *wakf*. Nor is the *wakf* of *houz* land in the possession of the Imâm lawful, for it is not his property. And by *houz* is to be understood land which the owner is unable to cultivate and pay its *kharâj* or land-tax, and has surrendered it to the Imâm [Sovereign] that the yearly profits may be applied in payment of the *kharâj*." Meaning of *houz*.

"If the land has been validly purchased from the *Bait-ul-mâl* the *wakf* thereof is lawful whether the purchaser be the Sultan or any private person, and the *wakf* will be governed by the conditions which the *wâkif* may validly impose on the *wakf*."

"If the Sultan has even without purchasing it, set apart any portion of the public land, *i.e.*, land which yields revenue to the public treasury, by way of *wakf* of a permanent inalienable character for any charitable or pious purpose, such *wakf* is valid. And the Allâmah Kâsim has given *fatwa* according to this principle when he was asked regarding the dedication made by Sultan Fârûk.

who had set apart a portion of the public lands for the purpose of a mosque ; and he also held that no future Sultan could set aside the *wakf*."

Wakf by the Sultan lawful.

The principle then is, that if the Sultan makes any *wakf* from the *Bâit-ul-mâl* for any purpose of public utility, such as a mosque, caravanserai, a madrassa, etc., it is valid, for it is lawful to set apart from the public revenue an allowance to maintain such objects ; and the King is authorised to set apart land sufficient to pay the allowance in question, instead of disbursing the expenses periodically from the public treasury. But he cannot make a *wakf* of *public* lands in favour of his children, even though the ultimate reversion may be reserved for the poor. But he may make a *wakf* for any object from which benefit accrues to the generality of Mussulmans, for the *Bait-ul-mâl* is for the benefit of Moslems at large.

CHAPTER X.

THE MOWKOOF ALAIHIM; OR, THE OBJECTS OF A *WAKF.*

SECTION I.

GENERAL OBSERVATIONS.

THE subject of this chapter forms one of the most important branches of the law relating to *wakf*. In the Mussulman system, law and religion are almost synonymous expressions, and are so intermixed that it is difficult to dissociate the one from the other; in other words, generally speaking, what is *religious* is lawful: what is *lawful* is religious.

A *wakf* may be created for any object of piety or charity.

According to *all* the schools of Mussulman Law, a *wakf* may be created for the benefit of any person or class of persons, or for any object of piety or charity. It may even be for children that are *unborn*. If the person or object in whose favour it is created is not in existence at the time of the creation of the trust, it will be applied "for the poor," who are the ultimate recipients of all *wakfs*, unless any other object is named.

Definition of charity.

The words "piety" and "charity" have a much wider signification in Mussulman Law and religion than in any other system. *Khair*, *birr*, *ihsân*, &c., include every purpose which is recognised as *good* or *pious* under the Mussulman religion and the Mussulman Law; and the test of what is "good" or "pious" or "charitable" is *the approval of the Almighty*. Every "good purpose" (*wajah-ul-khair*) which God approves, or by which approach (*kurbat*) is attained to the Deity, is a fitting purpose for a valid and lawful *wakf* or dedication. *A provision for one's self, for one's children, for one's relatives is as good and pious an act as a dedication for the support of the general body of the poor.* The principle is founded on the religion of Islâm, and derived from the teachings of

Hanafî Law.

the Prophet, and therefore any variation of the rule is a direct interference with the Mussulman religion.(1)

Wakf for any purpose is for the benefit of human beings.

Another point worthy of attention in the Mussulman Law is that every trust for whatever purpose created is *really* and in fact for the benefit of human beings. *The religious and legal system of Islâm is founded essentially on the service and well-being of humanity.* A dedication may be made for a mosque,—but the mosque is intended for human beings to pray in; it may be for a school, intended for the instruction of students; for *khânkâhs*, where a particular class of people congregate for religious exercises, and so forth. Every object, therefore, is intended for the spiritual, religious, moral, or material good of human beings. This is the meaning of the terse and sententious rule pronounced by the Prophet "tie up the property and leave its usufruct free for mankind." A *wakf* once made for whatever object, has the effect of "detaining" the property in the custody of the Almighty, its produce alone being applicable for the good of human beings. This is the meaning of the definition given by the law officers in the case of *Mohammed Sadik* v. *Mohammed Ali and others*,(2) that *wakf* implies "the relinquishment of the proprietary right in any article of property such as lands, tenements, &c., and consecrating it in such manner to the service of God that *it may be of benefit to men*." This definition was not invented by them but borrowed from the law-books, and must be read with the explanations given in them.

In the Islâmic system there is no such thing as a dedication "solely to the worship of God." A dedication "solely to the worship of God" is an unmeaning phrase in Islâm. The service of man and the good of humanity constitute pre-eminently the service and worship of God. Everything which is dedicated to God is in reality for the good of mankind; and everything which is dedicated for the good of human beings, individually or collectively, is for the service of God. Every pious act is *'ibâdat* (worship), "the service of God:" to provide maintenance for one's parents, for one's children, for one's poor relations are acts of *'ibâdat*. The essence of

(1) See Zailye's *Takhrij-ul-Hedâya*, Book on *wakf* where the traditions (*hadises*) and the *sanads* (authorities) on which the Hanafi doctrine of *wakf* is based, are set forth. A translation of the principal passages will be found in the Appendix.

(2) 1 Sel. Rep., p. 17.

every *wakf* is *kurbat*, approach to the Almighty; prayers are one form of *'ibâdat* and *kurbat*.

I have dwelt on this subject at some length in consequence of the erroneous view taken in the case of *Abdul Gane Kasim* v. *Hussan Miya Rahmatulla*,(1) in which the learned Judges enunciated the somewhat startling proposition that a *wakf* in order to be valid must "be solely to the worship of God." It is difficult to understand the meaning of this comprehensive dictum. If that view were correct, a *wakf* to an *Imâmbara*, to a *Khânkâh*, to a *Dargâh*, &c., would be invalidated. It is impossible to gather from the report upon what basis the view was founded, for no single original authority appears to have been cited. As will be seen afterwards, it is in absolute contravention of the Mussulman Law.

SECTION II.

THE CLASSIFICATION OF WAKFS.

Wakf divisible into three classes.

The Mussulman lawyers divide *wakfs* into three classes, *viz.* :—

I. *Wakfs* for the affluent (اغنيا) first and then for the indigent.

II. *Wakfs* for the affluent and indigent alike, in other words, *wakfs* in the benefit of which both the affluent and the indigent are entitled to participate.

III. *Wakfs* for the indigent exclusively.

The *Kinia't-ul Muniah*(2) says, "in the Book on *wakf* by Hillâl [*lit.* in the *wakf* of Hillâl] [it is stated] *wakf* may be of three kinds, one kind being *wakf* for the poor exclusively; another kind being for the affluent and *after them* for the indigent; and the third being for the rich and poor alike such as *rubâts* (monasteries), *khâns* (caravanserais), cemeteries, mosques, acqueducts, bridges, etc. for both rich and poor have their needs attached to them."

The *Durr-ul-Mukhtâr* states the classification in similar terms:—"there are three kinds of *wakf*—(*a*) in favour of the poor; (*b*) in favour of the rich, and *then* in favour of the poor; and (*c*) in favour

---

(1) [1877], 10 B. H. C. Rep., p. 10.

(2) P. 201. The *Kinia't-ul-Munieh* is by a distinguished jurist of the name of Mukhtâr bin Mahmûd bin Mohammed az-Zâhidi, surnamed "The Imâm of the Learned" (*al-Imâm ul-'Ullâma*), also "the Star of Religion" (*Najm-ud-dîn*), d. 658 A. H. (A. C. 1259). The *Kinia't-ul-Munieh* is a commentary on the *Nafis-ul-Kudûri*.

of both equally, such as rest-houses for wayfarers, reservoirs of drinking water for the use of travellers, burial grounds, bridges, and such like things, as mosques, water-mills, and basins, inasmuch as every one is in need of them."

All these *wakfs* are valid and lawful. The first class includes all trusts or consecrations in favour of individuals, or one's descendants, or relations, or friends, with the ultimate remainder for the poor, either expressly provided at the creation of the trust, or affixed by the law. If the reversion is expressly provided for at the time of consecration, the *wakf* is valid *without any difference of opinion.* But if the poor are not mentioned at the time when the *wakf* is constituted, still it is valid and binding according to the accepted doctrine, the remainder being for the poor by implication of law upon the extinction of the people named.

Hanafi Law

The second class includes *wakfs* in favour of objects in the benefit of which both rich and poor may participate, *e.g.*, mosques, caravanserais, rest-houses, reservoirs, shrines, hospitals, colleges, cemeteries, &c.

The third class includes *wakfs* in which the poor are solely interested, *e.g.*, *lungar-khânahs*, where the poor alone are fed; charities for distributing doles of food, supplying raiment to the living, or shrouds for the dead, poor-houses, hospitals for paupers, &c.

Wakf lawful in favour of any person or class of persons.

Dealing first with class I, it may be stated shortly that a *wakf* can be validly made in favour of any person or class of persons subject to the exception immediately following.

It can be made in favour of—

(*a*) a Mussulman or a *Zimmi*, but not in favour of an alien or *harbi* (an inhabitant of the *Dâr ul-Harb*); (1)

(*b*) one's children and descendants, male and female, born or unborn;

(*c*) similarly, other people's children and descendants;

(1) *i.e.*, an inhabitant of a country with which the State is at war. The Moslem jurists, like the jurists of Christendom, until very recent times, divided the world into two portions, one the *Dâr ul-Harb*, the country of warfare, and the other the *Dâr ul-Islâm*, the country of peace. Juridically, all Mussulman nations were at peace with each other. As a matter of fact, no Mussulman Sovereign could declare war against another without first pronouncing him to be a heretic and beyond the pale of Islam. The non-Moslem subjects of Moslem States are called *Zimmis*. The non-Moslem subjects of non-Moslem Sovereigns at peace with Islamic States are called *Mustâmins*.

(*d*) heirs as well as non-heirs;
(*e*) one's kindred, neighbours, &c.
(*f*) strangers;
(*g*) one's dependants, servants, &c; and
(*h*) *under the Hanafî Law* in favour of the *wâkif* himself first, and then for other objects, in other words, a *wâkif* may constitute himself the first beneficiary of the trust.

Ultimate reversion. The ultimate reversion may be *expressly* reserved in these cases for any specific object of *general* benevolence, charity or piety, of a permanent character, such as a mosque, a madrassa, the *rouzah* (mausoleum) of the Imâm, an imâmbara, &c., or for the poor at large. Where no such express reservation has been made, the law supplies the deficiency and declares that on failure of the primary object of the *wakf*, it will continue for the benefit of the ultimate recipients of all charity, *viz.*, the poor. *The wakf can under no circumstance fail.*

A *wakf* can never fail.

Principle. Hanafi Law. The *Fath ul-Kadîr* (1) after stating that "there is an analogy between *wakf* and *mushârikat* (partnership) . . . and its great excellence is that it enables mankind to perpetuate good actions," goes on to say, "it is necessary to define its literal signification and its technical meaning, its essentials, and its rules. Literally it signifies *detention* . . . in law . . . according to the Disciples, the tying up of the substance of a thing in such a manner that it does not become the property of any one excepting that of God. . . . The *wâkif* may give the produce to whomsoever he likes, and the reason of it is that though a desire to approach the Deity should form the ultimate motive of all *wakfs*, yet, if, without such an [immediate] desire, a person were to consecrate a property in favour of the *affluent*, the *wakf* would be valid, in the same way as a *wakf* in favour of the *indigent* or for the purposes of a mosque, for in giving to the affluent there is as much *kurbat* (nearness) as in giving to the poor or to a mosque, and though the profits may not have been [expressly] given in charity [to the poor] on the extinction of the affluent, yet it is *wakf* and will be treated as *wakf* before their extinction. This principle is founded on the reason that the motive in all *wakfs* is to do good to the living in this world and to approach the Almighty in the next."

Meaning of *wakf*.

---

(1) For the authority of this work see *ante*, p. 219, footnote.

Wakf dependent on a contingency.

" And the conditions which are requisite for all acts of bounty or generosity are also required for the valid constitution of a *wakf*, that is, freedom, puberty and understanding. In order to be operative it must operate at once and not be dependent on a contingency; for example, if a man were to say ' this house of mine would be *wakf* for the poor *if* my son comes back,' the house will not be *wakf* even if the son comes back."

Wakf in favour of one's posterity.

" In *wakf*, Islâm is not a condition. Consequently, if a *Zimmi* were to make a *wakf* on his children and his posterity and give it at the end to the indigent, it is lawful [equally with that made by a Moslem]. And it is lawful in such a case to give the usufruct (conditioned for the indigent) to the poor of both Moslems and *Zimmis*. The *wâkif* may lawfully condition to give the usufruct solely to the poor of the *Zimmis* and in that will be included the Jews, Christians and Magians; and if he condition that a special body of them should get the produce, such special body will then be entitled to it . . . . whatever condition the *wâkif* makes if it is not contrary to the *Shar'aa*, will be lawful. And the *wâkif* may give to whomsoever he likes so long as it is not sinful . . . . And there is no doubt in this that charity for *Zimmis* is *kurbat* . . . but it is necessary in the case of a *wakf* (in favour of *Zimmis*) that the object should be *kurbat* according to them as well as ourselves (Moslems). . . . . So a *wakf* by a *Zimmi* to promote *Hajj* or *'Umra* to Mecca is not valid, for *Hajj* is not lawful according to them. But a *wâkf* to the mosque at Jerusalem is valid because both Christians and Moslems regard it as holy."

A *wakf* goes into the ownership of the Almighty.

Then, after dealing with the terms by which a *wakf* may be constituted, which I have explained already, the author goes on to say, " if a man were to say ' this property of mine is for God' it is equivalent to saying ' it is *sadakah-mowkoofa*.' . . . . According to the Disciples *wakf* means the tying up of property so as to subject it to the rules governing property belonging to God, and accordingly the right of the *wâkif* in the property becomes extinguished and it goes to God, and its benefit is applied for His creatures. According to ' us,' it is clear that the right of the proprietor becomes extinguished if he ties it up for the good of God's creatures, for every property belongs always to God, and so it is written in the lucid language of Kâzi Khân." In other words, " a dedication or consecration of property, means only its preservation in the custody of God not to be descendible or alienable". . . . . "That a *wakf* once made cannot be inherited nor sold nor be given by way of gift is clear from the recorded sayings of the Prophet."

Then, after quoting the sayings of the Prophet and giving the examples of the *wakfs* created by the early Disciples and Companions, the author states that it is conclusively established that when a *wakf* is once created, it is thenceforward absolutely inalienable and non-heritable and neither the *wâkif* nor his heirs have any right or title to it, excepting what may have been specially provided for them in the usufruct. "And like all testamentary dispositions, a *wakf* which is to come into operation after the death of the donor may be revoked by him at any time before his death, but if not revoked, it will be operative in respect of a third if not assented to by the heirs." . . . . .

A testamentary *wakf*.

"According to both Abû Yusuf and Mohammed the proprietary right of the *wâkif* is extinguished for ever when once the property has been constituted *wakf*. According to Abû Yusuf the right becomes extinguished by his merely declaring that he has made a particular property *wakf*, and this also is the opinion of the three [other] Imâms, *viz.*, Shâfeï, Mâlik and Ahmed [ibn Hanbal], and of the universality of jurists, because the extinguishment of the right of property in a *wakf* is like that in emancipation. Mohammed says that the *wâkif's* right becomes extinguished on his consigning the property to a *mutwalli*. . . . . The rule laid down by Abû Yusuf is most approved by the universality of the learned, and in the *Kinia* it is stated, *that decrees are passed in accordance therewith*, and this is the opinion of the *Mashâikh* of Balkh . . . . The *Mabsût* has thus answered Mohammed's objections, 'Consignment is only intended to evidence the fact that the *wâkif* has parted with all interest in the property; it is not intended for completing the *wakf*. Its object is the protection of the *wâkif* by his withdrawal. When a *mutwalli* is appointed, it is to show that the *wâkif* has no further interest in it.'"

Consignment not necessary. *Fatwa* with Abû Yusuf.

Declaration sufficient for the completion of a *wakf*.

"According to Abû Yusuf the *wakf* of *mushâ'a* is valid. Owing to the difference of opinion on the question of consignment, Mohammed thinks that when a share of a property capable of division is made *wakf*, it ought to be divided off. According to Abû Yusuf such consignment not being necessary, the *wakf* of a *mushâ'a* becomes complete by the mere declaration of the *wâkif* that he constitutes it *wakf*. The opinion of Abû Yusuf has been followed by the jurists of Balkh, whilst that of Mohammed by some lawyers of Bokhâra."

The opinion of Abû Yusuf, as already stated, has been adopted by the Hanafî jurists in India.

The author then proceeds to lay down his own view—" in *wakf* there is no *tamlîk* or assignment of a right of property (to another) so as to require delivery of seisin or consignment, and therefore without consignment, the right of the *wâkif* becomes extinguished on the declaration." . . . " When the property is not capable of partition, both Abû Yusuf and Mohammed are agreed in holding the *wakf* valid without partition." " When a piece of land is dedicated as a cemetery or to build a mosque on, it must be divided off from the other property of the *wâkif*." . . .

" If a house be dedicated for the residence of a body of people or for the children and posterity of the *wâkif*, so long as they are in existence, with the condition that on their extinction the rents and profits arising therefrom should be given to the poor, the *wakf* will be valid, and after the extinction of his posterity the house will be let out to tenants and the rent received from them will be expended on the poor. None of the *mowkoof-alaihim* (beneficiaries) will be entitled to let it; . . . . if his descendants are so many that the house has not sufficient accommodation for all of them, they may occupy it in rotation." . . . . . .

Mention of perpetuity not necessary.

" According to Abû Yusuf the mention of perpetuity or dedication to an object of a permanent nature is not necessary to constitute a valid *wakf*, for the words *wakf* and *sadakah*, either conjunctively or separately, convey the meaning of perpetuity." . . . In the *Barâmika*(1) it is stated that according to Abû Yusuf when a *wakf* is made in favour of specific individuals, on their extinction, the profits of the *wakf* will be applied to the poor." . . . .

Wakfs of the Companions of the Prophet.

" A large number of the Companions of the Prophet (may God's blessings be with him), made *wakfs*, and an authentic account of such *wakfs* made by men and women, I have given already.(2) And

(1) A collection of *Fatwas* made under the orders of the Barmekides during the Caliphate of Hârûn ar-Rashid.

(2) The author mentions them, beginning with this remark :—" In the traditions there are repeated statements about them, and all the Disciples, the Tâbiîns and their immediate successors have always acted in conformity with them,

the *sanads* (authorities) thereof are given by Khassâf. Among these, which we regard as *sanad* (authority for our rules), are the *wakfs* of [the Caliph] Omar (may God be pleased with him) of his land called *Samagh* at Khaibar; . . . . that created by Zubair bin Awwâm for (the support of) his daughter who had been divorced [by her husband]; the *wakf* of Osmân bin Arkam Makhzûmi on his children and descendants of his house called *Dâr ul-Islâm* at *Safa* (near Mecca), where the Prophet used to preach Islâm and where many of the disciples (among them Omar) accepted the Faith. . . . . Baihaki in his *Khilâfiât* has stated upon the authority of Abû Bakr Obaidullah bin Zubair al-Humaidi that [the Caliph] Abû Bakr had a house in Mecca which he made *wakf* of in favour of his children, and that it is still in existence. . . . and S'aad ibn Wakkâs made a *wakf* of his houses in Medîna and in Egypt in favour of his children and that *wakf* is still in existence; and [the Caliph] Osmân made a *wakf* of his lands on his descendants and that *wakf* also is still continuing."

Then, after stating that all articles which form the lawful subjects of common dealing among mankind may be validly dedicated according to tne approved doctrine, in which the other "Imâms are agreed," and giving the opinion of Ansâri on the subject of a *wakf* of movables, the author proceeds to state, "according to Abû Yusuf, the *wâkif* may lawfully retain the governance of the trust or *reserve the profits for himself during his life*. These two subjects have been fully dealt with by Kudûri. . . . The Jurists Ahmed Ibn Abî Laila, Ibn Shabarna, Zuhri and others agree with Abû Yusuf. . . . Mohammed holds a contrary opinion. . . . Abû Yusuf bases his rule upon the practice and recorded precepts of the Prophet himself, who used to participate in (*lit.* eat out of) the produce of the lands dedicated by him. . . . . Another proof in support of Abû Yusuf's rule is that the meaning of *wakf* is to extinguish the right of property in one's self and consign it to the custody of God. Therefore, when a person reserves the whole or a portion of the profits for himself, . . . it does not inter-

Wakf of movables.

The *wâkif* may reserve the profits for himself —Hanafi Law.

---

and of these are the *wakfs* of the Prophet (God's blessing, &c.), [the Caliphs] Abû Bakr, Omar, Osman, and Ali, of Zubair, of M'uaz ibn Jabal, of Zaid ibn Thâbit, of 'Ayesha [the daughter of Abû Bakr], of her sister Asma, of Umm Sulma, of Umm Habîba, of S'afiya, of S'aad ibn Wakkâs, of Khâlid bin Walîd, of J'aabir bin Abdullah, of Okba bin 'Amir, of Abdullah bin Zubair (may God be pleased with them all)."

fere with the consecration, for that also implies the approval of the Almighty and is lawful. Nor is the providing of subsistence for one's self contrary to it. For example, if a man were to dedicate a caravanserai and make a condition that he may rest in it, or a cistern, and condition that he should take water from it, or a cemetery, and say that he may be buried there, all this would be lawful. [Further] our Prophet (may the blessings of God be with him) has declared that a man making a provision for his (future) subsistence is doing a pious act and giving charity. This *Hadîs* has been substantially handed down by a large number [of people] and is authentic, and Ibn Mâja reports from Mikdâm bin M'aadi Karib that the Prophet declared that no gain of a man is so meritorious as that which is earned by the labour of his hands, and his making a provision for the maintenance and support of himself, his family and his dependents, is *sadakah*. And Imâm Nisâï from Bakia and he (Bakia) from Buhair has given the same tradition in these words :—'Whatever thou providest for thyself is a *sadakah.*' Ibn Hâbân in his *Sahîh* states that Abû S'aîd reports from the Prophet that any one who acquires property in a lawful manner and provides therewith a subsistence for himself and for other creatures of God or clothes himself and them out of it, gives alms in the way of the Lord. . . . . And Dâr-Kûtni reports from J'aabir that the Prophet (may God's blessings be with him) declared that a man providing subsistence for himself, his children and his people and for the maintenance of his and their position, is giving charity in the way of God. . . . Tibrâni has reported from Imâma that the Prophet of God declared that a man making a provision for his [own] maintenance or that of his wife, his family or children, is giving *sadakah*. And in the *Sahîh* of Muslim it is stated from J'aabir that the Prophet told a man to make a beginning with himself and give the remainder to his family. All these traditions support Abû Yusuf's rule. And Sadr ush-Shahîd has laid down that decisions are passed according to Abû Yusuf's rule, . . *and we all decide according to that rule.* And the *Mashâikh* of Balkh have adopted the same. And it is also approved in the *Hedâya*, as is evident from the author mentioning the opinion of Abû Yusuf at the end, though he does not deal with it in detail."(1)

Principle.

Provision for one's self, family and children lawful.

The *Hedâya.*

(1) *i.e.*, after mentioning the opinion of Abû Hanifa and Mohammed; *Fath ul-Kadir*, Vol. II, pp. 630—638 (*b*). For the conditions the *wâkif* may lawfully make in his own favour, see *post*.

Similarly, in the Chapter "On the *wakf* of a man on himself, his children, his kindred, or his neighbours" in the *Fatâwai Kâzi Khân*, the authority of which cannot be disputed, the principle is stated thus, "says Fakîh Abû J'aafar (may the mercy of God be with him), if a person were to make a *sadakah wakf* on himself on condition that he should eat the whole or part (of the income) during his lifetime it is valid according to Abû Yusuf, and the *Mashâikh* of Balkh (may the peace, &c.) have adopted his rule and have held that both the *wakf* and the condition are valid and Sadr ush-Shahîd has laid down that decrees should be passed according to the rule of Abû Yusuf."(1) *Fatâwai Kâzi Khân Principle.*

Again, "a person makes a *wakf* for the poor and conditions that the entire [produce] will be for him, and says that it will be lawful for him to eat out of it, Abû Bakr Askâf holds such [*wakf*] to be valid."(1) General consensus.

And further "if a man were to say 'I have made this *wakf* on myself,' it is valid according to Abû Yusuf, and on his death it will be for the poor."

"Or if he were to make a *wakf* on 'the mothers of his children' it would be as valid as the *wakf* on himself."

And again "Ansâri has stated in his work on *wakf* that when a person constitutes a *wakf* in the following term—'This my land is *wakf* for the sake of God in perpetuity and its produce will be applied to my uses as long as I live' and adds nothing further, it is valid; and when he dies, its benefit will go to the poor."(2)

The same principle is laid down in the *Radd ul-Muhtâr* in identical terms:—"If a person were to make a *wakf* and reserve the produce or the governance of the trust for himself, it would be valid according to Abû Yusuf, and on that is the *Fatwa*," that is decisions are passed in accordance with that rule. "And that is

---

(1) رجل وقف على الفقراء و شرط لنفسه الكل و قال على ان لي ان اكل منها قال ابوبكر الاسكاف رح يجوز ذلک و لو قال وقفت على نفسي عن ابي يوسف رحمه الله انه قال يجوز ذلک و اذا مات يصير للمساكين *

(1) For the authority of Kázi Khân (Imâm Fakhr-ud-din Hassan) see Introduction, and Morley's Digest. His decisions have been frequently quoted in the Sudder and Supreme Courts, *e.g.*, see *Doe dem Jaun Beebee v. Abdoollah Barber*, supra. 1 Fulton's Rep., 345.

the opinion of Sadr ush-Shahîd, and it is the authority among text-writers, and the same has been preferred by the author of the *Fath* [*ul-Kadîr*], and has been adopted by the jurists of Balkh. And in the *Bahr* [*ur-Raik*] it is stated from the *Hâwi* that this rule has been adopted for the *fatwa*, &c.(1)

A *wakf* for the payment of the debts of the *wâkif*, or for other purposes beneficial to him.

"When a man," says the *Fatâwai Alamgiri* quoting the *Zakhîra*, "has made a *wakf* of land or something else with a condition, that the whole or part of it shall be for himself while he lives and after him for the poor, the *wakf* is valid according to Abû Yusuf, and the jurists of Balkh have adopted his opinion and ruled accordingly, and the *Fatwa* is in conformity with that opinion as an inducement to the making of *wakfs*. There are several ways in which this may be done, as for instance, by a person saying 'on condition that he will pay my debts out of the produce,' or 'when death happens to me, if I should be in debt, that he will begin with the payment of my debts,' or 'when death happens to such an one, meaning the *wâkif*, take every year one-tenth share of the produce and apply it to the performance of the *hajj* or pilgrimage to Mecca on his account or on the expiation of his vows and so-and-so' (naming something); 'or take every year out of this *sadakah* so many *dirhems* and expend them in such a manner and the remainder on so-and-so.' *In all these cases the wakf is lawful.* And if the *wâkif* were to say 'This is a *sadakah-mowkoofa* to Almighty God and he, the *mutwalli*, will pass its produce to me while I live,' without adding anything more, it would be lawful, and after his death, the benefit will go to the poor. So also if he should say, 'This my land is a *sadakah-mowkoofa*, he (meaning the *mutwalli*) will pass the produce to me while I live, then after me to my child and my child's child and their *nasl* for ever, while there are any and when they cease, to the indigent.' *This is lawful.* So also if he should make it a condition, 'That he may maintain himself and his child and pay his debts out of the produce and that when death happens to him the produce of the estate is for such an one, the son of such an one, and his child and child's child and his *nasl*.' Or, if he should

Principle.

***Wakf* in favour of descendants, valid.**

---

(1) جاز جعل غلة الوقف او الولاية لنفسه عند الثاني و عليه الفتوى كذا قاله الصدر الشهيد و هو مختار اصحاب المتون و رجحه فى الفتح و اختاره مشائخ بلخ و فى البحر عن الحاوي انه مختار للفتوي •

begin by saying 'for such an one and then for himself,' it would be lawful as conditioned, the putting himself, first or last, says Khassâf, making no difference. A person makes a *wakf* for the poor with a condition 'that he may eat and feed others (out of its produce) so long as he lives and that after his death it is to be for his child and in like manner to his child's child for ever while there are any descendants,' the *wakf* is lawful with such a condition."(1)

So also in the *Ramz ul-Hakâik* of Allâmah 'Aini; "If the *wâkif* reserves the produce of the *wakf* for himself, that is, if he makes it a condition in the *wakf-nâmah* that during his lifetime the produce should be applied for his benefit, and after his death to the benefit of so-and-so or any specific object, such a *wakf* is valid according to Abû Yusuf and the *Mashâikh* (jurists) of Balkh have decided on that rule, &c."(2)

Authorities proving absolute consensus.

In the *Fatâwai Alamgiri* the section dealing with this subject runs thus:—" Section II on *wakfs* on one's self, and on one's children and descendants: A man says, 'This land of mine is a *sadakah-mowkoofa* on myself,' that *wakf* is valid by consensus, so in the *Khızânat ul-Muftiïn*. Or, he says 'this land is *wakf* for myself and after me on so-and-so, and after him for the poor,' such a *wakf* is valid according to Abû Yusuf, so in the *Hâwi*. Or, 'that it is a *wakf* for so-and-so, and then for me, or for me and after me for so-and-so, or for my slaves and after them for so-and-so, ' it is valid according to the most approved authorities, so in the *Ghyâsia*."(3)

---

(1) *Fatâwai Alamgiri*, Vol. II, p. 495; I have omitted the authorities cited.

(2) و ان جعل الواقف غلة الوقف لنفسه فان قال فی کتابه یصرف الریع الیه مدة حیاته ثم من بعده الی فلان و فلان او علی جهات عینها جاز ذلک عند ابي یوسف رح و علیه مشائخ بلخ ترغیبا للناس علي الوقف *

(3) *Fatawai Alamgiri*, Vol. II, p. 471. Comp. Baillie's Digest (Second Ed.). p. 576.

...

"There is a passage," says the author of the *Radd ul-Muhtâr*, "in Kâzi Khân, to the effect that 'when a person makes a *wakf* on himself and another, the *wakf* so far as regards that person will be valid and not with reference to himself; and if he says that *that* person shall take after him, the whole *wakf* will be void." "This statement," continues the author of the *Radd ul-Muhtâr*, "is founded upon *weak* authority, and is evidently an interpolation; in fact it is not recognised as law, and so it is stated in the *Bahr* [*ur-Raik*];" *Radd ul-Muhtâr*, Vol. III, p. 598.

Similarly, in the *Ghâit ul-Bâyân* :—

"And if a man reserve the income of the *wakf* for himself or the governance thereof, it is valid according to Abû Yusuf. And Ulu'l w'alji has stated in his *Fatâwa* that the jurists of Balkh have accepted the rule laid down by Abû Yusuf; and Sadr ush-Shahîd also decided in accordance therewith....."Therefore, if he conditioned the whole for himself during his lifetime and after it for the poor, it will be valid."(1)

And the *Tas-hîl* lays down the principle in the same terms :—

"Abû Yusuf has held it lawful for the *wâkif* to make a condition that the profits either in whole or in part should be for himself for his life, and on this is the *Fatwa*; and the Prophet (may the blessing, &c.), used to eat himself out of his *wakf*, but the *wâkif* cannot take any share therefrom (*lit.* eat therefrom) unless he so conditions."(2)

So in the *Wajiz ul-Muhît* :—"According to Abû Yusuf no such conditions [as are required by Abû Hanîfa or Mohammed] are necessary; so that if a person makes a *wakf* for himself, or for the mothers of his children (*i.e.*, bondswomen who have borne him children), or for his own children, or makes a *wakf* of *mushâ'a*, it is lawful."(3)

The rule laid down by Abû Yusuf was recognised as the law in force among the Hanafîs in the case of *Doe dem Jaun Beebee* v. *Abdoollah Barber*.(4)

---

(1) فان جعل الواقف غلة الوقف لنفسه او جعل الولاية اليه جاز عند ابي يوسف رح *

قال الو الوالجي ى فتاواه و مشائخ بلخ اخذوا بقول ابي يوسف رح والصدر الشهيد كان يفتي به ايضاً ترغيبا للناس فى الوقف الى قوله فا ما اذا شرط الكل لنفسه ما دام حياً ثم على الفقراء فانه يجب *

(2) يجيز ابو يوسف رح بشرط المنفعة كلها اوبعضها...... لنفسه و فيه به يفتي ترغيبا للناس ...... و اكل عم من وقف نفسه و لم يحل لاكل بلا شرط *

(3) و عند ابي يوسف شي من ذلک کله ليس بشرط حتى لو وقف علي نفسه او على امهات اولاده او اولادة او وقف مشاعاً يصح عنده *

(4) Fulton's Repts., p. 345, supra.

Shiah and Shâfeï Laws.

The Shiahs and the Shâfeïs differ from the Hanafîs on one point. According to the recognised and accepted Hanafî doctrine, the *wâkif* may reserve the entire produce of the *wakf* property for his benefit during his lifetime—may, in fact, constitute himself the primary beneficiary of the trust. According to the Shiahs and the Shâfeïs, the *wâkif* can, if he be the *mutwalli*, receive only the allowance reserved for the trustee. Mohammed agrees with the Shiahs and the Shâfeïs in holding that the *wâkif* cannot reserve for himself the entire produce of the *wakf* during his lifetime.

Principle—*Wakf* in favour of one's descendants valid without difference among all the schools.

But as regards the lawfulness of *wakfs* in favour of one's descendants there is absolutely no difference of opinion. All the schools and all the jurists recognise the validity of such *wakfs*.

The *Durr-ul-Mukhtâr* citing the *Mawâhib* says "if a person makes a *wakf* on himself, his children, descendants and posterity, and reserves the income for himself during his lifetime, and similarly *thereafter* and *thereafter*, it is valid according to Abû Yusuf and on this is the *fatwa*."(1)

The *Radd ul-Muhtâr* is most explicit on this point. "It is lawful," it says, "to reserve the produce of the *wakf* for one's self according to Abû Yusuf; the words *thereafter* and *thereafter* which the *wâkif* mentions have no connection with the present discussion; for example, if a person makes a *wakf* on himself and thereafter on *his* children and thereafter on *their* children *there is no difference as to the validity of this wakf on such children;* whatever difference there is refers to the reservation by the *wâkif* of the whole of the produce for himself during life, but none as to the lawfulness of the dedication in favour of the *wâkif's* children."(2)

General consensus.

This was indited in the middle of the 17th century. The author of the *Majm'aa ul-Anhar*, writing at the end of the eighteenth century, *states in positive terms that the principle is acknowledged by all the schools and sects.* He lays down emphatically that "there s *no difference* if a person condition the profits of a *wakf* for his

---

(1) *Durr-ul-Mukhtâr*, p. 427.

(2) جاز جعل غلة الوقف لنفسه عند الثاني قوله ثم و ثم حكاية لما
يذكره الواقف من العطف بثم فى وقفه كقوله ثم من بعدي على اولادي
ثم على اولادهم و هذا لا مدخل له فى نقل الخلاف لان الخلاف فى
جعله الريع لنفسه لا لاولاده * Vol. III, p. 676.

children, and, accordingly, in such a *wakf* male and female [children] will take together, unless he condition for the male alone."(1) From the time of the Founder of Islâm, until the present day, this has been the acknowledged rule of law among Mussulmans.

Acknowledged rule.

As pointed out in the *Radd ul-Muhtâr* there is absolutely no question about the lawfulness of *wakfs* in favour of one's children. Whatever difference of opinion exists among the several schools or between Abû Yusuf and Mohammed, relates to the reservation by the *wâkif* of the income of the *wakf* for himself during his lifetime.

I have already given some of the texts in which the validity of *wakfs* in favour of the *wâkif's* descendants is recognised. I now proceed to give the rule as laid down in the leading authorities. A special chapter is devoted in every work on law to the subject of these *wakfs*.

In the *Fatâwai Alamgiri* it is headed thus :—" Second section relating to *wakfs* on one's self, on one's children, and on his *nasl*."

In the *Radd ul-Muhtâr*, it runs thus :—" Section relating to all that pertains to *wakfs* in favour of one's children."

And similarly in every other law-work.

Zailye.

According to Zailye, one of the greatest of Hanafi jurists whose authority is recognised as undisputable throughout the Sunni world, " if a man constitute a *wakf* with these words, 'this my land is a *sadakah-mowkoofa* for my children or my *nasl* (descendants),' it is valid according to both Abû Yusuf and Mohammed, for the mention of the word *sadakah* [according to Mohammed] shows that the *wakf* is perpetual, and that on the extinction of his children it would go to the poor who never fail. But if he said ' this my land is *mowkoofa* on my children or *nasl*, the effect would be the same according to Abû Yusuf and *this is correct*."(2)

Fath ul-Kadîr.

The passage in the *Fath ul-Kadîr* dealing with the subject, has already been given, but it may be quoted again with advantage here.

" Islâm," says the author, " is not among the conditions of *wakf* ;" in other words, it is not necessary that the object in whose

---

(1) *Majm'aa ul-Anhar* (Constantinople Ed.), Pt. II, p. 640.

(1) *Takhrij-ul-Hedâya.* MSS. copy belonging to the Patna Anglo-Oriental Library ; see Appendix where the part of the chapter dealing with a *wakf* in favour of the *wâkif* and his descendants has been translated in *extenso*.

favour the *wakf* is made should be a Moslem nor that the *wâkif* should belong to the faith of Islâm; and then the author proceeds to state the rule as follows: "so if a man were to constitute a *wakf* for his children and his *nasl* (posterity), and destine it after them for the poor, that will be lawful."(1)

"And when any one of the recipients of the benefaction dies, and the *wâkif* has made no mention what would become of his share upon his decease, in that case the usufruct will be divided among his surviving children every year, and will be given both to the affluent and the indigent of them, unless he [the *wâkif*] has provided that the *wakf* is for the needy [of his children] . . . . it must be known [*lit.* know] that when he [the *wâkif*] mentions [in the *wakf*] his children and kindred [in other words, when the *wakf* is for them], the *wakf* is valid for the affluent and indigent among them, unless he has specified that it is for the needy [of them alone] as I have already stated. But if it [the *wakf*] is for others than they [*viz.*, if it is for strangers] in such a case the Shams-ul-Aïmma [Sarakhsi] has stated that if he [the *wâkif*] has specified its application for purposes of necessity, it is valid whether the persons in whose favour it is made are limited or unlimited in number, for the object of a *wakf* is to obtain the approval of God, and when its application is provided for, both the affluent and indigent are equal in it. If no purpose is specified and the *wakf* is for a limited body of people, it is valid in respect of them; but not, if they are unlimited in number, unless the *wâkif* has used some expression which ordinarily or customarily or *in fact* implies *need*, *e.g.*, if the *wakf* is for orphans generally it is valid, and its benefit shall be applied to the poor among them and not to the affluent."(2) All this, *viz.*, what the Shams-ul-Aimma says, is applicable to a *wakf* in favour of strangers, and not to *wakfs* in favour of one's children and kindred.

In the *Ramz ul-Hakâik* the following passage is to be found in regard to the same principle:—"If a *wâkif* constitute the proceeds of the *wakf* for his benefit, that is, if it be written in the deed of *wakf* in this way, that the income of the *wakf* should be applied *Ramz ul-Hakâik.*

---

(1) اما الاسلام فليس بشرط فلو وقف الذي على ولده نسله و جعل خره للمساكين جاز •

(2) *Fâth-ul-Kadir*, Printed Ed., p. 858.

to his *jihat* (benefit) [during his life] and after his death to so-and-so, or any specified object, such a *wakf*, is valid according to Abû Yusuf . . . . and the jurists of Balkh have decided in accordance therewith. . . And Abû Yusuf bases his rule on the practice of the Prophet who used to eat out of his *wakfs*." There is no mention of children here, but there is no restriction whatsoever; the word *jihat* including a dedication in favour of one's posterity.

Fatâwai Alamgiri. In the *Fatâwai Alamgiri* the principle is laid down in similar terms.

First of all "everything that is said in respect of a *wakf* in favour of one's own children, applies to a *wakf* in favour of another's children."(1) So that there is no distinction between the validity of a *wakf* in favour of one's children, and of that in favour of strangers.

"When a man has made a *wakf* of his land in favour of his children and after them on the poor, the child [or children] who may be in existence at the time the produce comes into existence will take it, whether he was born at the time of the *wakf* or thereafter."(2)

"And in like manner if he said 'on my child and what child may be born to me and when they fail, upon the poor . . . in such a case the *wakf* is valid."(3)

"And if a man should say, 'I have made a *wakf* on my children,' males and females are included in its benefit."

"If a man were to say 'this my land is a *wakf* on my child, and the child of my child, and the child of the child of my child,' mentioning three generations, the income is to be spent upon his descendants for ever so long as there are any, and is not to be applied to the poor; while one remains the *wakf* is for him [or her] unto the very lowest of the descendants,—the nearer and more remote being equal [in the share of the produce], unless the *wâkif* declared in making the *wakf* that the 'nearer was nearer' or said, 'on my child and then after them on the child of my child,' or said, 'generation after generation' when a beginning must be made with them with whom the *wâkif* had begun."(4)

---

(1) *Fatâwai Alamgiri*, Vol. II, p. 474.

(2) *Ibid*, p. 471.

(3) *Ibid*.

(4) *Ibid*, p. 474; *Fath ul-Kadir*, Vol. II, p. 643 (*b*). Comp. Baillie's Dig. (2nd Ed.), p. 577.

" If a man were to say, 'This my land is a *wakf* on my child and my *nasl* (posterity),' the *wakf* is valid."(1)

In the Commentary of Allâmah at-Tahtâwi(2) the principle is given in almost identical terms:—" And according to Abû Yusuf it is lawful for the *wâkif* to reserve the usufruct of the *wakf* or its governance for himself, *and on this is the fatwa*(3)". . . .

" If a man makes a *wakf* of his land on his children and children's children for ever so long as his posterity lasts, the produce will be divided equally among his descendants, and no preference will be given to males over females, for the *wâkif* established an equal right for all of them; in the *Zâhir-ur-Rawâyet* the approved traditions) it is stated that in such a *wakf* the descendants through females [*lit.* daughters] will not be included; on this is the *fatwa*.(4)

"And in the *Hindièh* (the *Fatâwai Alamgiri*) it is stated that when a *wakf* is made on one s *nasl* (progeny) and *zurriyèt* (posterity) in that are included one's descendants through males as well as through females, whether near or remote."(5)

" When a person says this land of mine is *wakf* on my *walad* [child in the singular] in that case the produce will be for the child [or children] of his loins male or female."

It will be seen that in these statements the validity of benefactions in favour of one's self and one's descendants is taken for granted.

The *Khazânat-ul-Muftiin* states the rule thus:—" If a man say 'this land is a *mowkoofa* or *sadakah-mowkoofa* on myself' this is as lawful as if he had made a condition that during his lifetime he should feed himself out of it and feed others. Therefore, it is approved as authority that this *wakf* is valid."

Again "a man makes a *wakf* on the poor and makes a condition that he should eat out of it, saying that it will be lawful for me to eat of it; this is lawful." " And if he says 'this land of mine is a *sadakah-mowkoofa* or *mowkoofa* in perpetuity for Almighty God, that so long as I am alive its produce should be [*lit.* remain current] for me,' and adds no more, it will be lawful. And when he dies, the *wakf* will be for the poor."

---

(1) *Fatâwai Alamgiri*, Vol. II, p. 475

(2) See *ante*, p. 249.

(3) P. 544.

(4) P. 562.

(5) P. 568.

"And if he says 'whilst I am alive its produce will be for me and after me for my child and child's child and their *nasl* (progeny) so long as their *nasl* exists, it will be for them, and when they cease to exist it will be for the poor;' this will be lawful." "And when the *wâkif*, besides his maintenance, has made this condition that his debts should be paid out [of the produce], this condition will be lawful."

The same rule is enunciated in the *Durrar ul-Ahkâm* and the *Mawâhib*(1) "if a person appoints [*lit.* fixes] the usufruct for himself during his lifetime and thereafter, and thereafter, it will be lawful according to the second [*viz.*, Imâm Abû Yusuf]; and on this is the *Fatwa*, etc.(2)

The passage in the *Bahr-ur-Râik* which is more detailed is equally important.(3)

Majm'aa ul-Anhar. The *Majm'aa ul-Anhar* written towards the close of the 18th century thus sums up the result of the authorities :—A *wakf* in favour of one's self is valid according to Abû Yusuf, and on this is the *fatwa* (in other words, this is the law). A *wakf* in favour of one's children and *nasl* with the ultimate benefit for the poor in case of the failure of the *wâkif's nasl* is valid by *consensus*. If the poor are not mentioned, but the word *sadakah* is used with the term *wakf*, it is valid both according to Abû Yusuf and Mohammed and on the extinction of the *wâkif's* descendants it will be for the poor. Even if the poor are not mentioned and the word *sadakah* is not used, the *wakf* is valid according to Abû Yusuf, and its produce on the extinction of the *wâkif's nasl* or posterity will be spent on the poor, and on this is the *fatwa*."

Sirâj ul-Wahâj. In the *Sirâj ul-Wahâj* it is taken for granted that a *wakf* in favour of the *wâkif's* children and thereafter in favour of the poor is valid :—"And according to the *Wâkiât*(4) if a man were to make a *wakf* of his land in favour of his children and after them destine it for the poor, and some of the children die, the [proceeds of the] *wakf* would be applied to the survivors of the children, and

(1) The author of this work, commonly called the Sâhib-i-As'aâf (the author of the *As'aâf*) is placed by D'Ohsson on the same footing with the author of the *Hedâya*, *Tableaux Generale de l'Empire Ottoman*.

(2) Tahtâwi, Vol. II, pp. 569-70.

(3) See Appendix.

(4) A work of great authority among the Sunnis; Morley's Dig., Introd, p. cclxxxv.

when they [all] die, the *wakf* will be expended towards the poor."(1)

Wajiz ul-Muhît.

In the *Wajiz ul-Muhît* the principle is laid down in similar terms : " Chapter relating to *Wakfs* in favour of one's children and *nasl* and *then* on the poor,"—" where a person makes a *wakf* on his *awlâd* (children), all his *own* children and the children of his sons(2) will be included therein ; but there are two opinions regarding the inclusion of the children of daughters . . . . and when a man makes a *wakf* of his land on his *awlâd* (children) and then on the poor, upon the death of any one of the children the interest devolves upon the survivors, and if they were all to become extinct the *wakf* would be applied for the poor. This is different from the case of a *wakf* on so-and-so and so-and-so, naming them specifically among his (the *wâkif's*) children, and then on the poor, in such a case upon the death of any of the specific individuals so named, the share of such deceased would be for the poor, etc."(3) Here it is assumed that a *wakf* in favour of children with an ultimate reversion in favour of the poor is valid.

The *Fatâwai Kâzi Khân* is conclusive on the point :—

---

(1) و فی الواقعات رجل وقف ارضا علی اولاده و جعل آخره للفقراء فمات بعضهم یصرف الوقف الی الباقي و ان ماتوا صرف الوقف الی الفقراء *

(2) *Viz.*, all lineal male descendants

(3) باب الوقف علی الولد و النسل ثم علی الفقراء و لو وقف علی اولاده یدخل فیه اولاده لصلبه و اولاد لصلبه و فی اولاد البنات روایتان فی ظاهر الروایة لا یدخلون کما فی الامان و لو وقف ارضه علی اولاده و جعل اخره للفقراء فمات بعضهم یصرف الوقف الی الباقین فان ماتوا صرف الی الفقراء بخلاف ما لو وقف علی فلان و فلان و فلان و سمّاهم تعینهم من اولاده و جعل آخره للفقراء ثم مات واحد منهم بعینه یصرف نصیبه الی الفقراء لانه لو وقف علی کل واحد منهم بعینه فنصیب بلمیت لا یستحقه الباقون و فی الاول وقفه علی کل اولاده قل او کثر و بعد موت بعضهم بقي اولاده فاستحقه الباقون *

Fatâwai Kâzi Khân.

"And Khassâf(1) has laid down that when a man makes a *wakf* in these terms, 'this my land is a *sadakah-mowkoofa* or *mowkoofa* and its produce will remain current for me so long as I live, and after me it will be for my children and children's children and their descendants in perpetuity so long as my posterity exists, and on their extinction, it will be for the poor,' it is lawful."(2)

Hâwi.

In the *Hâwi*, a work of great authority, frequently referred to in the *Fatâwai Kâzi Khân* and the *Fatâwai Alamgiri*, the principle is thus stated—"If a person make a *wakf* of a piece of land or garden on the condition that should he be in need of the income, it should be applied to meet his wants, the *wakf* will be valid with the condition; or, if he reserves the entire produce or the governance for himself, it will be lawful; similarly, if he makes a *wakf* with the condition that so long as he is alive he shall eat out of it and feed others therewith, and that upon his death, his children will have the same power and after them his children's children in perpetuity so long as his posterity lasts, *viz.*, that they should eat of the same and feed others too, this *wakf* is valid with the condition. This is according to Abû Yusuf and it is authoritative and the *Fatwa* is thereon."

Hâwi.

"If a person says 'this land of mine is dedicated for me,' Hillâl says it would not be valid, but all the [other] jurists hold that according to Abû Yusuf it would be valid, and the *Mashâikh* of Balkh have adopted this rule of Abû Yusuf. And they have laid down that both the *wakf* and the condition are valid; and Sadr ush-Shahîd has held that . . . the *Fatwa* is on the rule of Abû Yusuf. And if the *wâkif* were to say 'this land of mine is *mowkoofa*, and so long as I am alive the produce is for me, and on my death for my children, and my children's children and their posterity so long

---

(1) Of Khassâf, the author of the *Radd ul-Muhtâr* speaks thus—"Khassâf is an Imâm, whose worth has been testified to by Shams-ul-Aimma Halwâni, who has declared that Khassâf's views are adopted everywhere:" *Radd-ul-Muhtâr*, Vol. III, p. 672.

(2) و ذكر الخصاف رح لو قال ارضي صدقة موقوفة او موقوفة تجري غلتها علي ما عشت ثم بعدي على ولدي و ولد ولدي و نسلهم ابدا ما تناسلوا فاذا انقرضوا فهي على المساكين جاز *

as any of them exists, and on their extinction, it will be for the poor,' such *wakf* is lawful."(1)

In the *Fatâwa'l Ankirawia*,(2) the principle is laid down thus : *Fatâwa'l Ankirawia.*

"Q. What is the rule in a case where a man makes a *wakf* in these terms, 'this my land is a *sadakah-mowkoofa* on my child and my child's child and their children ?"

"A. It is lawful, and it will be applied to all of them."

"Q. Would its produce be given to others lower in degree?"

"A. Yes, because such a dedication amounts to a dedication for his descendants so long as his *nasl* (posterity or line) exists, and here three generations are mentioned, and whenever three generations are mentioned the right construction is that the *wakf* is for the *wâkif's* posterity so long as they exist."

Be it noted that the word *sadakah* is used here in conjunction with the word *wakf*, and accordingly the *wakf* is valid by *consensus*, though the poor are not mentioned as the recipients of the usufruct upon the possible contingency of the *wâkif's* posterity becoming extinct; for, as stated already, according to Mohammed the word *sadakah* implies a dedication to the poor. Nor is there any difference of opinion where the word *sadakah* is not used, but the poor(3) are expressly mentioned. According to Abû Yusuf, however, the use of the word *sadakah* is wholly immaterial; and in the above case, even if the word had not been used, the dedication would have been perfectly valid.(3)

And in the *Jouharat un-Nayyerèh*, there occurs the following passage: "When a man makes a *wakf* in these terms, 'this land of mine is for ever a *sadakah* or *wakf* for the sake of God for my children,' then upon their extinction, the poor will become entitled to its produce." Here it will be noticed there is nothing certain as to the time when the children will become extinct, and yet the *wakf* is held to be valid. *Jouharat un-Nayyerèh.*

In the case of *Rosamaya Dhur Chowdhuri* v. *Abul Fata Mohammad Ishak*,(4) the Calcutta High Court enunciates a proposition for which, it is submitted, there is not the least warrant in the Mahommedan Law. It says "that a dedication must not depend upon an uncertain contingency, such as the possible extinction of *Rosamaya Dhur Chowdhuri v. Abul Fata Mohammad Ishak.*

(1) *Surrat-ul-Fatâwa*, pp. 443, 444.
(2) See Morley's Dig., Introd., p. ccxc.
(3) *Sirâj-ul-Wahâj.*
(4) [1891]. I. L., 18 Cal., 399.

the family, has recently been well laid down by the Madras High Court in *Pathukutti* v. *Avathalakutti*."(1) Speaking with respect, this dictum seems to be based on an erroneous apprehension of the Mussulman Law. A *wakf* dependant for its operation upon the happening of a contingency is undoubtedly held to be invalid. Examples of such contingent *wakfs* are given in the law-books, and a reference to any treatise will show what is meant by this rule. For example, if a man were to say, "if my son arrives to-morrow, or if my ship arrives from Basra on Friday next, this house of mine will become *wakf*," the operation of such a dedication is dependant on the happening of a contingency which may or may not occur; the son may arrive to-morrow or may not; the ship may arrive on Friday or may not. The *wakf* is *not* intended to have any effect until the event, upon the happening of which it is made dependant, has actually occurred: but as its happening is wholly uncertain and contingent, the *wakf* is held to be invalid, for it is one of the conditions of a *wakf inter vivos* that it should be immediately operative in favour of some object not deemed *sinful* under the Mahommedan Law; or if it is testamentary, it should be similarly operative upon the death of the *wâkif*. A

The rule relating to *wakfs* depending on uncertain contingencies has no bearing whatsoever on the question of a *wakf* in favour of one's descendants, but it seems to have been introduced into the judgment on a complete misapprehension of the Law of *Wakf*. provision for one's children and descendants—nay, for one's self in the Hanafî system—is regarded as a pious duty by which "nearness" (*kurbat*) to God is attained. The mention of the poor is required by Mohammad (not by Abû Yusuf "with whom is the *Fatwa*") *not to give validity to the wakf but to ensure perpetuity*; and as human beings are liable to become extinct and as a *wakf* must be a *permanent* dedication, Mohammad required that the poor should be expressly "named," or "implied" by the use of the word "*sadakah*." Abû Yusuf, on the other hand, held that whether the poor were named or not, or whether the word "*sadakah*" was used or not, the word *wakf* implied *perpetuity*, and, therefore, unless some other object was named, on failure of the *wâkif's* posterity, the income would be applied for the poor

(1) [1888], I. L., 13 Mad., 66. This case has absolutely no bearing on the point in issue.

There is no question about the validity of the *wakf;* the mention of the poor does not make the *wakf per se* more or less valid; it only ensures perpetuity insisted upon in the law.

The view expressed by the High Court in the case above referred to is evidently founded, *firstly*, upon a misapprehension of the law relating to *contingent wakfs;* and *secondly*, upon the notion that the ultimate dedication to the poor was the real dedication. There is no indication, however, in the judgment of the authority upon which this notion is founded.

In order to understand the nature of the conflict between this decision and the principles of Mussulman Law, it is necessary to state the facts of the case as appearing in the authorised report.

By a deed dated the 21st December 1868, duly registered and purporting to be a deed of *wakfnâmah*, two brothers named respectively, Abul Hossein Mohammad Abdur Rahman and Abu Mohammad Abdul Kadir, made a settlement of all their immovable properties in the following terms:—

"For perpetuating the names of our father and forefathers and for protecting our properties, we, leaving ourselves to the mercy and kindness of God and relying upon the bounty of Providence, and being in possession of sound health of body and mind as enjoined in the Mahommedan Law and fully capable of performing and observing all the religious rites and ceremonies, and of our own free will and accord and without reluctance or compulsion, make this permanent endowment (*wakf*) of all our shares and rights in the immovable properties, that is, all our pergunnahs, zemindaris, talooks, segas, rent-free lands, and all ancestral and self-acquired properties such as purchased at private or auction-sale, and all properties, either standing in our own names or in the names of others, and all our rights and interest in connection with the same, that are in our possession and enjoyment, *for the benefit of our sons and children and the members of our family from generation to generation and in their absence for the benefit of the poor and beggars and widows and orphans.* We two brothers take upon ourselves the management and supervision of the same in the capacity of *mutwallis* for such time as we may live, and as *mutwallis* we enjoy all rights and interest in the *wakf* properties.* * * * * * * We shall deal in the following way with the net profit that will come to our hands. If it be necessary to bring any suit or put in any answer or objection or claim in respect of these *wakf* properties or the profits, etc., of the same in the Civil Courts* * * * * * * * then we, the *mutwallis*, shall do those acts according to the laws and rules for the time being, and we shall pay the expenses for the same from the profits of the *wakf* properties. In order to maintain the name and prestige of our family, we, the *mutwallis*, shall make reasonable and suitable expenses according to our means and position in life. We shall, according to our choice, fix allowances for the support and maintenance of the persons who are now living or may be born afterwards for whose benefit the *wakf* is made, and we shall pay the same to them every month, and also the expenses of their marriage and the mourning ceremonies whenever they may be required. It will be competent for us, the *mutwallis* and our successor *mutwallis* to enhance or reduce the allowances of the persons who are now living or who may hereafter be born for whose benefit the *wakf* is made, in consideration of course of their position and circumstances and the state of the income of the *wakf* properties * * * * * to use the *wakf* properties as security and grant *putni and durputni* and permanent and temporary *ijara* settlements, and to purchase some other properties with the money to be received as *salami* for the aforesaid settlements, and to exchange any of the lands in this *wakf* with some other lands or to include the lands so acquired by purchase or in change, in the *wakf*, to spend the profit of the same towards the expenses of the *wakf* and keep the surplus profit in stock in the *tahvil*, and to try to increase the *wakf* properties and the amount in cash. Whatever properties may be acquired by us the *mutwallis* or our successive *mutwallis* after execution of this document shall be in this way *wakf*. * * * * * * * None of the persons for whose benefit the *wakf* is made shall be able to make any claim for taking any of the *wakf* properties or to sell or mortgage or to make any gift of his allowance, and the allowance shall not be attached and sold in execution of any money decree against any of those persons because the *wakf* properties have been settled only for the support of our sons, grandsons, etc., from generation to generation. It will not be competent for any of the persons for whose benefit the *wakf* is made to call upon the *mutwalli* or *mutwallis* to submit any accounts in respect of the *wakf* properties, or to bring any suit in any Court against the *mutwalli* or *mutwallis* for increasing his allowance or for taking possession of the *wakf* properties, o for any accounts in respect of the same, and if any such suit is brought it will be rejected by the Court, but it will be competent for any of the persons for whose benefit the *wakf* is made to ask the *mutwallis* for increasing his allowance or for any occasional expenses and if the *mutwallis* are satisfied that he is actually in need or want, then the *mutwallis* will increase his allowance or meet his demands. The principal object of this *wakf* is that there is to be no loss to the properties, and that the profits of these properties be appropriated towards the maintenance of the name of the family and the support of the persons for whose benefit the *wakf* is made. * * * * * * Be it known here that up to the time of executing the document we are not indebted to any one, that, without keeping in our possession even a very small portion of the properties that are in our possession, we make a *permanent wakf* of all our properties and take in our possession and custody the documents and other papers in connection with the *wakf* properties, that will furnish sufficient information and description regarding the *wakf* properties, and so no schedule thereof is given below."

The deed undoubtedly purported to create an absolute and immediate dedication in favour of the settlors and their descendants with an ultimate reversion for the poor. It thus fulfilled all the conditions required by the Hanafî Law to which the settlors were subject. The provisions regarding the appointment of new Mutwallis were not contrary to the rules of Mussulman Law. The power, however, which the executants of the deed attempted to reserve to themselves for reducing the allowances without any right of question on the part of the beneficiaries, and the provision excluding the obligation of accountability were, like some others, vicious and opposed to the directions of the law. But if the dedication became absolute immediately the *wakf* was created by the execution of the document, which the Mussulman Law declares is the case, conditions contrary to its rules do not destroy or invalidate the *wakf* but are themselves voided. The obligations which attach to a *wakf* are the creation of the law; and a man making a dedication cannot cut down its operation, or by any subsequent conduct affect its character.

This, it is respectfully submitted, is the rule of Mussulman Law.

Examination of the case of *Rasamaya Dhur Chowdhry* v. *Abul Fata Mohammad Ishak.*

The terms of the deed show an absolute and immediate dedication of the properties, whilst it contains provisions regarding the appointment of new *mutwallis*, and for the appointment of any of the settlors' male descendants as *mutwallis*.

After the execution of the deed, Abdur Rahman and Abdul Kadir dealt with the properties as *wakf* properties. They held themselves out as *mutwallis* and for some years described themselves as such in collection and other papers connected with the management of the properties. In 1874 Abdur Rahman became involved in difficulties; and on the 7th November of 1874 he executed an *ijara putta* for Rs. 4,200 per annum of his share in the properties in favour of his brother, Abdul Kadir, and Abdul Kadir executed a *kabuliat* or counterpart thereof in favour of Abdur Rahman on the 1st of June 1875. Both the deeds were duly registered, and in them the two brothers declared that by reason of their necessities they had revoked the *wakf* of the 21st December 1868, which under the Mussulman Law they had absolutely no power to do.

In 1881 Abdur Rahman and Abdul Kadir made a formal partition of all the *wakf* properties. In this deed of partition, which was executed on the 11th of September 1881, it was stated that the *wakf* of 21st December 1868 was invalid, as the *wakfnâmah* did not contain the word *sadakah* or charity, and was not made according to the provisions of the Mahommedan Law.(1) After the execution of the deed of partition, Abdul Kadir and Abdur Rahman each dealt with his share as exclusively his own. And Abdur Rahman, who had now become heavily involved, mortgaged and alienated several parcels of the property. If the *wakf* was, in its inception, valid, none of these acts, which amounted to mis-

(1) This was evidently in consequence of the decision in 8 Cal. L. R p. 154.

Rasamaya Dhur Chowdhry v. *Abul Fata Mohammad Ishak*—contd.

feasance on the part of the trustees, could affect the validity of the dedication or of the trusts of the deed.

On the 6th March 1881, Abul Fata Mohammad Ishak, on behalf of himself and his minor brothers, the sons of Abdur Rahman, instituted this suit as beneficiaries under the *wakf*, *inter alia* to have it declared that all the properties were *wakf*, to recover from the transferees the properties alienated by their father, Abdur Rahman (defendant No. 1), and to have him removed from the post of *mutwalli*.

The material issues in the case were the following :—

11*th*.—Whether the *wakf* deed propounded by the plaintiffs was valid ? If so, what relief the said plaintiffs were entitled to ?

12*th*.—Whether the *wakf* deed in dispute was bad in law, fraudulent and collusive and whether it was ever acted upon ?

13*th*.—Whether the disputed *wakf* was cancelled by the subsequent acts and conduct of the defendants Nos. 1 and 2 ?

The Subordinate Judge found that Abdur Rahman and Abdul Kadir had executed the *wakfnâmah ;* that at the time of its execution they were joint-owners in possesson of the *wakf* properties, that they were *free from debt*, sound in mind and body, and had of their own accord and free will and in good faith made the *wakf* for the purpose of dedicating their properties to the service of God ; that after the execution of the deed they had acted as *mutwallis*, supported the beneficiaries, kept up a Madrassah for teaching the Koran and other religious books of the Mahommedans, and had described themselves as *mutwallis* in collection papers, *chittas, terij taujee*, and other documents connected with the management of the *wakf ;* that five or six years after the execution of the *wakfnâmah*, Abdur Rahman was much involved in debt, and on the 11th of September 1881 had partitioned the *wakf* properties with his brother, Abdul Kadir, that shortly after the partition Abdur Rahman, without the knowledge or consent of Abdul Kadir, had transferred, mortgaged and granted leases of some of the *wakf* properties, and that he had been guilty of waste and misconduct. The Subordinate Judge held that the deed was valid and irrevocable under the Mahommedan Law ; that Abdur Rahman should be removed from the office of *mutwalli ;* that defendant No. 2 should be appointed sole *mutwalli ;* and that the transfers, mortgages, and leases, etc., executed by the defendant, Abdur Rahman, were invalid and should be set aside. He accordingly gave the plaintiffs a decree.

Rasamaya Dhur Chowdhry v. Abul Fata Mohammad Ishak—contd.

The defendant appealed to the High Court. The learned Judges, who decided the case, after setting out the above facts, said as follows :—

"The learned Advocate-General contended that the decisions in *Abdul Ganne Kasam* v. *Hussein Miya Rahimtulla*(1) and *Mahomed Hamidulla Khan* v. *Lutful Haq*(2) were wrong upon the authority of *Doe dem Jaun Beebee* v. *Abdoollah Barber*,(3) a case tried in the Supreme Court of Calcutta before Ryan, C. J., and Grant, J. He also relied upon *Fatima Bibee* v. *The Advocate-General of Bombay*,(4) and *Amrutlall Kalidas* v. *Shaikh Hussein*,(5) and upon the authorities cited by Mr. Ameer Ali in the Tagore Law Lectures for 1884, including Mr. Baillie."

"The judgment of Ryan, C. J., based as it was upon the opinions of the Moulvies to whom the questions of Mahommedan Law were referred, is certainly entitled to very great weight, but all that the judgment decides in respect of the validity of a *wakf* is that an endowment to charitable uses is valid, though qualified by a reservation of the rents and profits to the donor himself during his life, and that the donor may appoint himself *mutwalli* and need not deliver possession to another. It does not declare that a *wakf* which on the face of it is not an endowment to religious or charitable uses is valid, and that is the question now before us. That judgment does show that the decision in *Abdul Ganne Kasam* v. *Hussein Miya Rahimtulla* and *Mahomed Hamidulla Khan* v. *Lutful Haq* went too far in holding that a valid *wakf* must, from its creation, be solely and exclusively for religious or charitable purposes, but it does not show that they were wrong in laying down that the primary and substantial objects must be of that nature. And in the case of *Doe dem Jaun Beebee* v. *Abdoollah Barber* the benefit to the religious purposes indicated in the deed were not wholly and indefinitely postponed to the interests of the donor and his descendants so long as any of the latter should con-

(1) [1873], 10 Bom. H. C., 7.
(2) [1881], 8 Cal. L. R., 164.
(3) [1838], Fulton's Repts., 345.
(4) [1881], I. L., 6 Bom., 42.
(5) [1887], I. L., 11 Bom., 499.

tinue to exist; but the reserve was in favour of the donor himself and of certain persons only who were already in existence."

Rasamaya Dhur Chowdhry v. Abul Fata Mohammed Ishak— **contd.**

"The other two cases relied upon by the Advocate-General, *Fatima Bibee* v. *The Advocate-General of Bombay* and *Amrutlall Kalidas* v. *Shaikh Hussein*, seem to lay down practically that a perpetuity in favour of the donor and his descendants is a valid *wakf*, if an ultimate dedication be made in favour of some religious or charitable object upon the occurrence of a contingency, however remote and improbable. And we are not prepared to follow this ruling unless we find it irresistibly supported by unquestionable authority. Baillie, no doubt, as well as the learned Tagore Law Lecturer of 1884, seem to favour this interpretation of the law, but the *Hedâya* as translated by Hamilton, and most of the cases laid before us, seem to us to establish the fact that a *wakf* must be in favour of a religious or charitable purpose, although there may be a temporary intermediate application of the whole or part of the benefits to the appropriator's family. All the cases that expressly sanction this latter arrangement were cases in which at least the ostensible and principal object of the *wakf* was religious or charitable. And that the dedication must not depend upon an uncertain contingency such as the possible extinction of the family, has recently been well laid down by the Madras High Court in *Pathukutti* v. *Avathalakutti*."(1)

"We have the authority of the Privy Council in the case of *Mahomed Ahsanulla Chowdhry* v. *Amarchand Kundu*(2) cited by Mr. Evans for refusing to recognize as a valid deed of *wakf*, an instrument which uses a particular form of words as a veil to cover arrangements for the aggrandisement of the family and to make their property inalienable.

"Precisely such, in our judgment, is the deed before us, and notwithstanding the fact that for a few years after its execution the owners of the property dealt with it nominally as *mutwallis*, it is certain that they had not really intended to give up their proprietary rights in it. And before very long they abandoned even the semblance of mere trusteeship. We cannot believe that the authors of Mahommedan Law intended that, under cover of a pretended dedication to Almighty God, owners of property should

(1) [1888], I. L., 13 Mad., 66.
(2) [1889] I. L., 17 Cal., 498.

be enabled to secure it for their own use, protect it for ever from their own and their descendants' creditors, and repudiate alienations in respect of which they have received full consideration." *Kasamaya Dhur Chowdhry v. Abul Fata Mohammed Ishak—contd.*

Unfortunately, no original authority appears to have been discussed at the Bar. Certainly there is no reference to any in the judgment. Even Mr. Baillie's Digest is dismissed with a passing remark; nor is any endeavour made to explain or reconcile the principles stated there with the views expressed in the decision of the case. Hamilton's *Hedâya* is referred to as supporting the proposition that a "*wakf* must be in favour of a religious or charitable purpose, although there may be a temporary and intermediate application of the whole or part of the benefits to the appropriator's family." It has already been shown from the recognised authorities that this view is utterly opposed to the principles of the Mahommedan Law, and that there is no warrant for cutting down *wakfs* in the way suggested. Whether there is anything in the *Hedâya* which countenances the view taken will be discussed later on.

One cannot help remarking that in former times the Courts of Justice took every pains to acquaint themselves with the law they had to administer. For example, in *Doe dem Jaun Beebee* v. *Abdoollah Barber*,(1) neither of the parties appears to have cited original authorities, but the Supreme Court of its own motion had the available works carefully translated. In later times, the citation of original authorities has been to some extent discouraged.

It is submitted that the main idea which underlies the judgment under discussion is founded on an inaccurate application of the words "religious" and "charitable." Referring to the judgment of Ryan, C. J., in *Doe dem Jaun Beebee* v. *Abdoollah Barber*, the learned Judges say "it does show that the decisions in *Abdul Ganne Kasam* v. *Hussein Miya Rahimtulla*(2) and *Mahomed Hamidulla Khan* v. *Lutful Haq*(2) went too far in holding that a valid *wakf* must, from its creation, be solely and exclusively for religious or charitable purposes, but it does not show that they were wrong in laying down that the primary and substantial objects must be of that nature." And again, "all the cases that expressly sanction this latter arrangement (*i.e.*, application of the

(1) Supra. (2) Supra.

Kasamaya Dhur Chowdhry v. *Abul Fata Mohammed Ishak*—contd.

whole or part of the proceeds to the appropriator's family) were cases in which at least the ostensible and principal object of the *wakf* was religious or charitable."

Now in both these passages there is a clear misapplication of the terms "religious" and "charitable." The words are unquestionably used in the *English*, and *not* in the *Mussulman*, sense. These terms were introduced by Mr. Hamilton into a note in his translation of the *Hedâya*, and are not found in the Mahommedan Law. Under the Mussulman Law, every "object of piety" is a fitting purpose for a dedication. It is expressly declared in the Hanafî Law, with which the learned Judges were dealing, that making a provision for one's self, is a pious act. As regards a provision for one's children or kindred there is *absolutely no difference among the jurists of the several schools*. Such a provision in the Mussulman religious and legal system is as much a "religious and charitable purpose" as a dedication for the poor. To confine the word "charitable" to objects which would be called such in the English legal system is, it is submitted, a mistake. In the case of *Meer Mahomed Israil Khan* v. *Sashti Churn Ghose*(1) Mr. Justice O'Kinealy very pertinently observed that in interpreting a deed of *wakf* "we must naturally look to what is really meant by the words 'religious or charitable' among Mahommedans. As an example we know that the words 'charitable purpose' in Scotland have quite a different meaning from that in which they are used in England. And so in India, in judging of what is really meant by the words 'religious and charitable' by a Mahommedan we must take the view which their law takes, and not what is to be found in the English Dictionary."

As already stated, a *wakf* has been defined to mean the detention of the *corpus* in the ownership of God *in such a manner that its profits* may be applied for the benefit of His servants; (تعود منفعته على العباد). It is nowhere laid down that these *must* be the poor and the indigent. The idea that, as in *Doe dem Jaun Beebee* v. *Abdoollah Barber*, "the reserve was in favour of the donor himself and of certain persons only who were already in existence," it consequently made a difference in the validity of the *wakf*, is founded on an absolute misapprehension of the authorities referred to by the Law-Officers of the Court. A more

(1) [1892], I. L., 19 Cal., 412, 437.

careful study of the Mahommedan Law will show that whether a *wakf* is made in favour of persons in existence or not, it has nothing to do with the validity of the *wakf*.

Examination of *Rasamaya Dhur Chowdhry v. Abul Fata Mohammad Ishak*—concld

There is another passage in the judgment which deserves some notice :—"We cannot believe that the authors of Mahommedan Law intended that, under cover of a pretended dedication to Almighty God, owners of property should be enabled to secure it for their own use, protect it for ever from their own and their descendants' creditors, and repudiate alienations in respect of which they have received full consideration." Speaking again, with respect, it is difficult to follow the exact meaning of this sentence, which shows some misconception of the nature and legal effect of a *wakf* under the Mahommedan Law. In using the word "pretended," the whole question for decision is begged.

Under the Mussulman Law, a provision for one's self or for one's posterity or kindred is an act of piety, and a fitting purpose for a *wakf*. The word "pretended" used in connection with a transfer, whether by sale, gift or dedication, implies that though there is an appearance of a transfer,—in reality, the transferor does not part with his proprietary interest. A "pretended" gift means, that whilst the donor purports to give the property to another, he retains it all the while as his own. If possession is transferred in such a case, it is subject to a secret trust for the donor. Similarly, in the case of a "pretended" sale or dedication, the vendor or dedicator never parts with the property. It continues his all the while. The words "pretended" or "ostensible" or "colorable" can hardly have any application to a *wakf* in the Mahommedan system, for when a *wakf* is once made, the *wâkif's* proprietary right in the *property* "drops" altogether,—in other words, becomes extinguished by *operation of the law*. The property is thenceforth "in the custody of God." If the *wâkif* is in debt *at the time of the dedication*, the law lays down rules as to how, under the circumstances, the *wakf* should be dealt with. But if he was *not in debt at the time*, or had other property from which the debt could be discharged, his creditors have no right to look to the property for the satisfaction of their debts, for the property is no more his. If he has any interest in the usufruct, such usufruct may be available *during his lifetime* for the payment of his

The rule of Mussulman Law.

debts.(1) If his descendants are the beneficiaries and any of them contracts a debt, his allowance *during his lifetime* may be available for the payment of the debt. But neither the *wâkif* nor his heirs can in any way burden or alienate the property, whether for consideration or not. Any dealing with the property contrary to the conditions of the deed of *wakf* is a breach of trust. This, it is submitted, is the Mahommedan Law; and the importation of the word "pretended" cannot in any way affect the legal consequences resulting from the conduct of a person, competent at the time to make a valid and binding dedication which becomes, under the law, immediately operative and irrevocable.

The rule of Mussulman Law—contd.

Mahomed Ahsanullah Chowdhry v. Amar Chand Kundu.

In the case of *Mahomed Ahsanullah Chowdhry* v. *Amar Chand Kundu*,(2) which is referred to by the learned Judges and which undoubtedly lends some colour to the view expressed by them, their Lordships of the Privy Council had declined to enunciate any general principle and had carefully guarded themselves against laying down "any precise definition of what will constitute a valid *wakf*, or to determine how far provisions for the grantor's family may be engrafted on such a settlement without destroying its character as a charitable gift."

Certainly, so far as that case is concerned it does not appear that the Judicial Committee intended to go beyond the facts before them which were somewhat peculiar, and calculated to give rise to doubts and prejudice in the minds of English lawyers.(3) Paragraph 8 of the deed of *wakf*, which gave to the *mutwallis* the power of increasing their own salaries at their own discretion, was objectionable and, perhaps, invalid. But, as already observed, under the Mahommedan Law an invalid condition in the *wakfnâmah* does not invalidate the *wakf* but is itself void. This, however, does not seem to have been brought to the notice of their Lordships, for they say: "On the other hand, they (their Lordships) have not been referred to, nor can they find any authority that, according to Mahommedan Law, a gift is good as a *wakf* unless there is a substantial dedication of the property to charitable uses at some period of time or other." No authority appears to have been cited in support of the validity of such *wakfs*, a point

(1) *Surrat-ul-Fatâwa*, 425.

(2) [1889], I. L., 17 Cal., 498.

(3) Their Lordships have since explained their meaning in *Abul Fata Mohammad Ishak* v. *Rasamoya Dhur Chowdhry* [1895], I. L., 22 Cal., 619.

on which there is absolute *consensus;* no Arabic law-work was referred to, and the case both in the High Court and before the Judicial Committee was discussed upon the wholly erroneous notion that a *wakf* in order to be valid must be a substantial dedication to what is called "charitable uses" in English Law. The word "charity," as understood in the Mahommedan system, was not explained; nor was it pointed out that, under the Mussulman Law, a provision for one's family is the highest act of charity, and a "tying-up" of property for the support of one's descendants as substantial a dedication "to charitable uses," as "if the beginning had been made with the poor," to use the language of the *Radd ul-Muhtâr*. Nor does it appear to have been shown from well-known authorities, that when a *wakf* is created in express terms, the non-mention of the poor as the ultimate beneficiaries upon the failure of the primary object or objects, does not affect the validity of the *wakf*, for the law implies as a necessary incident of the *wakf* that the reversion is for the poor, "who are the ultimate recipients of all charities whether named or not," as is expressly stated in the *Ghâit-ul-Bayân*. It was not shown that a *wakf* in favour of unborn children is valid, nor was it pointed out that when the primary object or purpose fails or is for some reason void, the property does not revert to the donor or become the property of his heirs, but is applied to the next succeeding object, or, if none such is mentioned, to the poor. For example, if a *wakf* is created in favour of *A*'s children and *A* has no children, the proceeds of the *wakf* would be given to the poor so long as *A* has no children; and, if children are subsequently born to him, to them;(1) or if a *wakf* is created in favour of *A*, and after him in favour of *B*, and after him for the poor, if the *wakf* in favour of *A* cannot take effect either because he is not existing or because he is incapable of taking, being, for example, a *Harbi* (an alien enemy, in whose favour a *wakf* by a Moslem is invalid), the *wakf* does not fail but takes effect in favour of *B* and the poor.

Examination of *Ahsanullah Chowdhry* v. *Amar Chand Kundu.*

There is one other matter in connection with this case which seems to have escaped attention—and perhaps naturally because it is connected with the religious system and the inner life of the Moslems. In most *wakfnâmahs*, whereby property is dedicated for the benefit of the *wâkif's* family and beggars and *wârid-sâdir*

(1) See *post;* even Macnaghten gives this principle.

(travellers and mendicants), there is no sum fixed for the latter purposes. This is by no means an indication of a motive to leave more for the family. On the contrary, it is owing to the fact that when a fixed sum is specified, no more need be spent, so that whilst a few receive help, the majority are turned away. Under the general provisions all who seek help *must* receive help—and if they do not, the Kâzi's door is open and they get redress either by the removal of the *mutwallis* or by a stricter control.

The administration of the Mussulman Law.

From the year 1798 downwards the Courts of Justice have uniformly applied the Mussulman Law to the determination of questions affecting the validity of dispositions made by Mahommedans. In the case of *Jewan Das Sahu* v. *Shah Kabiruddin Ahmed*(1) the appellant was a Hindu, and the question was whether the property which formed the subject-matter of the suit was *wakf* or not. Their Lordships in the Privy Council decided the case on the basis of the Mahommedan Law. And every case before and since has proceeded upon the same principle.(2)

Apart, therefore, from the question whether a *wakf* in favour of the endower's family is a religious institution or not, it is submitted with respect that it would be contrary, not only to the principles of "justice, equity and good conscience," which the British Indian Courts have to administer, but also to "immemorial and recognized practice," to apply to its consideration any principle other than that of the Mahommedan Law. And their Lordships of the Judicial Committee have condemned in express terms the idea that the validity of dispositions made by Mussulmans should be decided from any other point of view than that of their own laws and customs.(3)

The Mahommedan Law, therefore, must be sought in authorities recognised by the Mahommedans as such, for it would hardly be right to profess to decide a case according to Mahommedan Law, and yet wholly to ignore the works in which that law is to be found.

Mr. Morley points out in his Digest(4) the sources from which the Mahommedan Law is derived. He shows that the Mussulman Law is founded (*a*) on the Koran; (*b*) on the precepts of the Prophet; and (*c*) on the decisions of the leading disciples. The

(1) [1840], 2 Moo. I. A., 390.

(2) See also *Zohoruddin Sircar* v. *Baharulla Sircar*, W. R., 1864, 187.

(3) See *post*.

(4) See *ante* Introd., p. cxxvii.

direct precepts and practice of the Prophet form part of what may be called the Statutory Law of Islâm, being regarded as supplementary of the divine ordinances in the Koran. Mr. Morley also repeatedly mentions how closely connected religion and law are among the Mussulmans, and how impossible it is to dissociate the one from the other. His remarks on this subject are worthy of consideration.

"In considering the propriety of altering or abrogating the Hindu or Mahommedan Laws, all preconceived notions of the relative excellence of the English and native systems of jurisprudence should be taken as secondary consideration. Nor should it be called in question whether such systems are in themselves good or bad, for it should never be forgotten . . . . that they are an integral part of the faith of that people, and that though we may not be bound by absolute treaty, we have virtually pledged ourselves to preserve them by repeated proclamations and enactments."(1)

The institution of *wâkf* in favour of the *wâkif's* family.

The institution of *wakf*, in which the endower's family and descendants are the immediate recipients of the benefaction, owes its origin to the direct ordinances of the Prophet. Not only did he declare that a provision for one's family was the best of alms-giving, but he encouraged members of his household and his companions to create such *wakfs*, and himself set the example by consecrating certain lands at Khaibar. As I have said before, in dealing with the Mussulman Law the meaning attached by Mussulmans to the words "charitable purposes" has been, unfortunately, often lost sight of. Charity has been construed to mean "charity to the poor," irrespective of the endower and his descendants; and piety and religion to mean such acts as would, in practical Europe, be regarded as pious or religious. This is *not* the Mussulman Law, which will be best explained by the following passages from the *Mishkât*,(2) showing what the Prophet considered "piety and charity" to mean:—

"The Apostle of God said, 'When a Mussulman bestows on his family and kindred, hoping for reward in the next world, it becomes alms, although he has not given to the poor, but to his

(1) Morley's Digest, Introd., p. cliii.

(2) For the value and authority of this work, see Morley's Digest, Introduction, p. cclviii; I quote from Capt. Mathew's Translation, Vol I. p. 453 (1823). See Morley's Digest, Introd., pp. ccliii and ccliv.

family and children.' " "The Apostle of God said, 'There is one *dinâr* which you have bestowed in the way of God and another in freeing a slave, and another in alms to the poor, and another given to your family and children; that is the greatest *dinâr* in point of reward, which you gave to your family.' " "The Apostle of God said, 'The most excellent *dinâr* which a man bestows, is that which he bestows upon his own family; and a *dinâr* spent upon quadrupeds, in the way of God, and a *dinâr* which a man bestows upon his friends, in the way of God.' " "Umm-i-Salma says, 'I said to the Prophet, is there any good tiding for me of rewards, for my bestowing on the sons of Abû Salma? His sons are no otherwise than mine.' " "The Prophet said, 'Then give to them, and for you are the rewards of what you bestow upon them.' "

"The Apostle of God said, 'Giving alms to the poor has the reward of one alms, but that given to kindred has two rewards; one the reward of alms, the other the reward of relationship.' "(1)

These precepts are also given by Kâzi Khan in his Decisions known as the *Fatâwai Kâzi Khân*, and by Imâm Zailye in substantially the same terms as in the *Fath ul-Kadîr* and are considered as binding on Mahommedans.(2)

In Muslim and Bokhâri the precepts of the Prophet are given in detail. I shall quote here only two:—

"The Prophet of God declared that a pious offering to one's family [to provide against their falling into want] is more pious than giving alms to beggars. The most excellent of *sadakah* is that which a man bestows upon his family."

"To give money to free slave, to give alms to the poor, to give to your children and kindred are all *sadakah*."

Meaning of the words "charitable purposes" in Mussulman Law.

It is unnecessary to multiply these quotations. A reference to any book on Mahommedan religion or law will show that the expression "charitable purposes" is not used in the Mussulman Law in the restricted sense in which it has been attempted to be used in the British Courts of Justice. It has already been pointed out that according to the Founder of their religion, it is a pious duty among all Moslems to make a provision for their family and descendants; among the Hanafîs all over the world a provision

(1) See also *ante*, p. 215. (2) See *post*.

for one's self comes in the same category. The notions, therefore, derived from other systems of law or religion form no index to the understanding of the Mussulman Law. The words "piety" and "charity" have a much wider signification in Mussulman Law and religion than perhaps in any other. Every "good purpose," *wajah-ul-khair* (to use the language of the *Kifâya*), which God approves or by which approach (*kurbat*) is attained to the Deity, is a fitting purpose for a valid and lawful *wakf*. A provision for one's children, for one's relations and, under the Hanafî Sunni Law, for one's self, is as good and pious an act as a dedication for the support of the general body of the poor. The principle is founded on the religion of Islâm and derived from the teachings of the Prophet.

Examination of the authorities.

The *wakfs* created in the lifetime of the Prophet, under the sanction of his sacred authority, are set out at length in the *Fath ul-Kadîr*;(1) and Imâm Zailye, one of the greatest expounders of the Mahommedan Law, has preserved for us a copy of the deed of Osmân bin Arkam (an immediate disciple of the Prophet) by which he dedicated his house in charity upon his children without any reference to the poor.(2)

Fatâwai Barâmika.

In the earliest collection of decisions called the *Fatâwai Barâmika* (those delivered by Imâm Abû Yusuf, who was the Chief Judge of Bagdad under the Caliph Harûn ur-Rashîd), it is laid down that a *wakf* is lawful in favour of any object, and will, after its extinction, enure in favour of the poor,—the ultimate beneficiaries of all benefactions.

---

(1) See *ante*, p. 280.

(2) "He [Osmân bin Arkam] had a house close to Safa. This was the house dwelt in by the Prophet, peace and safety be unto him, at the time of the promulgation of Islâm, and it was in this house that he invited people to embrace Islâm. A large number of people accepted the Faith in this house, of whom Omar Ibn-ul-Khattâb was one, and the house was therefore called (the house of Islâm). Arkam dedicated the said house to his child [meaning, children], and the deed of *wakf* was as follows :—

'In the name of God the most Merciful. This relates to how Osmân bin Arkam disposed of the usufruct of his property which lies close to Safa, that is to say, he has consecrated it in charity to his child [meaning, children], together with the place where it lies, *viz.*, its environs, so that it may neither be sold nor inherited.'

"This was witnessed by Hishâm, son of 'Aâs, and by the slave of Hisham, son of 'Aâs. This house all along continued to be a permanent *sadakah* (a thing given in charity), his descendants living in it, letting it out on hire, and they alone appropriating its proceeds. No one raised any objection."

Fatâwai Hâwi.

The next collection of decisions now extant, in order of date, is the *Fatâwai Hâwi*, quoted in the *Fatâwai Alamgiri* as "the *holy Hâwi.*" Its author Kâzi Jamâl ud-din Ahmed,(1) who died in A. H. 600, was a celebrated lawyer and Kâzi of Ghazni (in Afghanistan). In it we find the following rule:—

Wakf in favour of one's self and posterity

"If a man makes a *wakf* of a piece of land, or of an orchard, on condition that whenever he should be in want of the produce thereof, he should have it, the *wakf* will be valid according to the said condition. If he reserves for himself the whole of the produce of the *wakf* property, or makes himself *Mutwalli*, it will be valid according to *istehsân ; and this also will be the case when a man makes a wakf on the condition that he should eat out of it and feed others with it, during his lifetime, and, upon his death, his child shall have the same privilege, and such will be the case with his child's child also, for ever, so long as his posterity continues, who would eat out of it, and feed others with it ; the wakf will be valid with these conditions*. The whole of the above is what Abû Yusuf says, and *fatwas* are given in accordance with the same."

Kiniat-ul-munièh.

The opinion of Kâzi Khan who was his contemporary has already been given.(2) In the *Kiniat-ul-munièh*(3) (A C. 1259) the principle is laid down in almost identical terms.

Zakhîrat-ul-Fatâwa.

In the *Zakhîrat-ul-Fatâwa,*(4) a collection of decisions prepared about the end of the 13th century, and frequently referred to by the Law-Officers of the Sudder Court, there is the following:—

"It is laid down in the book *Ajnâs* by Nâtiki(5) that if a man makes a *wakf*, and lays down in it with respect to himself that he should, during his lifetime, eat out of it, and feed those whom he likes; that after him it should go to his child, his child's child and to his posterity for ever, so long as it may continue, and that upon its becoming extinct, it should go to the poor; this is valid according to Abû Yusuf, may the mercy of God be on him, and it is not a disposition in the nature of a will in favour of his child, the child eating out of a property belonging to God, the Most High. *Do you not see that when a man makes a wakf in favour*

(1) A distinguished Kâzi of Irâk who flourished about the latter half of the 12th century; see Morley's Digest, Introd., page cclxv.

(2) See *ante*, p. 293.

(3) See Morley's Digest, Introd., p. cclxxxvi.

(4) *Ibid*, p. cclxxxv.

(5) A celebrated Kâzi of Irâk, recognised as a great authority in India

of his children and their children so long as their posterity may continue, and gives it afterwards to the poor, it is valid. Now this case is just like it."

In the *Khazânat-ul-Muftiïn*, an important collection of decisions of the year 1339, frequently referred to by the Law-Officers in India,(1) the *Fatwa* is given thus :— *Khazânat-ul-Muftiïn.*

"If any one says 'I make a *wakf* of this land of mine in favour of my child and child's child and afterwards in favour of the poor,' the income thereof would go to his child and his child's child till they be dead and none of them be alive, and even if the third generation be forthcoming, the income would go to the poor, and not to the third generation. If he says : 'In favour of my child, my child's child and the child of my child's child,' making mention of three generations, the income would be spent by his descendants for ever, so long as his posterity continues, and not by the poor till any of his descendants be alive, be he of a degree howsoever low."

The *Fath ul-Kadir* by Kamâl ud-dîn Siwâsi who died in 1456 A. C. has already been referred to. *Fath ul-Kadîr.*

The *Bahr ur-Râik*(2) (1562), a work of great authority in India states that "there is no difference [of opinion] regarding a *wakf* in favour of one's descendants." *Bahr ur-Râik.*

In the *Durr-ul-Mukhtâr* (1660), the principle is enunciated in these words :— *Durr-ul-Mukhtâr.*

"If one should declare the income of it [*i.e.*, the *wakf* property] to be for [*i.e.*, receivable by] himself during his lifetime—and thereafter—and thereafter [*i.e.*, then for his children, and then for his children's children], it is lawful according to the Second [Imâm Abû Yusuf], and the *Fatwa* is in accordance with it. And if he should add (thereto) a third generation, it would include his *nasl* in general."

The *Radd ul-Muhtâr* (written about the end of the 17th century) commenting on the above passage, *viz.*, "if a person fixes the usufruct for himself during his lifetime and *thereafter* and *thereafter*, it will be lawful according to the Second [Abû Yusuf], and on this is the *Fatwa*," says as follows :— *Radd ul-Muhtâr.*

---

(1) See Macnaghten's Principles and Precedents of Mahommedan Law, pp. 332, 342, etc.

(2) See *Mohammud Sadik* v. *Mohammud Ali and others*, 1 Sel. Rep., 17.

"It is lawful to reserve the produce of the *wakf* for one's self. According to Abû Yusuf, the words (thereafter and thereafter) which the *wâkif* mentions have no connection with the present discussion. For example, if a person makes a *wakf* on himself and thereafter on his children, and thereafter on their children, there is no difference as to the validity of the *wakf* on such children; whatever difference there is, refers to the reservation by the *wâkif* of the whole of the produce for himself during life, ***but none as to the lawfulness of the dedication in favour of the wâkif's children.***"

Majm'aa-ul-Anhar.

The passage from the *Majm'aa-ul-Anhar*, compiled towards the end of the last century, showing that there is absolutely no difference among lawyers about the validity of *wakfs* in favour of one's *awlâd* (children or descendants), has already been quoted;(1) as also the principle enunciated in the *Fatâwai'l-Ankirawia* of the Shaikh-ul-Islâm Mohammed bin-al-Hussain, who died in A. H. 1098 (A. D. 1686), a work of great authority among the Hanafîs.

Fatâwai'l-Ankirawia.

But of all the works on Mahommedan Law, which possess an interest for those who are charged with the administration of justice in India, the most important is the great Code which was compiled in that country, in the reign of the Emperor Aurungzeb Alamgir, by Indian Judges and Muftis, barely a hundred years before the establishment of British rule.

The Fatâwai Alamgiri.

The *Fatâwai Alamgiri* has been cited and followed not only in the old Sudder and Supreme Courts, but also in the High Court of Calcutta. Kemp, J., decided the case of *Khaja Hossein Ali* v. *Shahazadi Hazra Begum*(2) upon the law laid down in that work; and in *Mullick Abdul Guffur* v. *Mussummat Muleka.*(3) Garth, C. J., referred to it frequently. In it the subject of *wakfs* on one's self and on one's children and posterity is treated in two aspects. In one part the recognised law as to the validity of *wakfs* in favour of one's self and one's children and descendants is discussed in detail.(4) In the other part relating to *conditions in wakfs*, the subject is dealt with by way of reservations or

Discusses the law in two aspects.

(1) See *ante*, p. 287.

(2) [1869], 12 W. R., 344.

(3) [1884], I. L., 10 Cal., 1112.

(4) In Section II, Chapter III, Volume II, p. 471 (Calcutta Edition) Baillie's Digest, 2nd Ed., p. 576.

conditions.(1) The first establishes that a man may make a *wakf* directly constituting himself and his descendants the recipients of the benefaction with an ultimate reserve for the poor; the second that he may create a *wakf* in general terms, or expressly in favour of the poor, and reserve the usufruct for himself and his family so long as they exist. The dedication is valid in both cases. A cursory study of Baillie's Digest would show what is laid down in the *Fatâwai Alamgiri*, *viz.*, that there is absolutely no question about the validity of a *wakf* in which one's descendants are the recipients of the benefaction; and further, that the view expressed by Mohammed, the second disciple of Abû Hanîfa that the endower could not reserve any benefit for himself, was never followed among the Hanafîs, and that decisions on this point have always been in accordance with the rule laid down by Abû Yusuf.

The *Fatâwai Alamgiri* is substantially the Mussulman Code of India, and it is submitted that the law derived from it, or from authorities quoted in it, has been recognised and given effect to by the Courts of Justice ever since the establishment of British power in that country.(2)

From the promulgation of Islâm up to the present day there has been an absolute consensus of opinion regarding the validity of *wakfs* on one's children, kindred and neighbours. Practical lawyers, experienced judges, high officers of every sect and school under Mussulman sovereigns, are all in unison on this point. There are minor differences, *viz.*, whether a *wakf* can be created for one's self, whether the unfailing object should be designated, whether the property should be partitioned or not, whether consignment to the *mutwalli* is necessary or not; but so far as the validity of a *wakf* constituting one's family or descendants the recipients of the benefaction, in whole or in part, is concerned, there is absolutely no difference. Absolute consensus.

A *wakf* is a permanent benefaction for the good of God's creatures; the *wâkif* may bestow the usufruct, but not the *corpus*, upon whomsoever he chooses and in whatever manner he likes, only it must endure for ever. If he bestows the usufruct in the first instance upon those whose maintenance is obligatory on Principle.

(1) In Chapter IV, p. 459; Baillie's Digest, 2nd Ed., p. 596.
(2) For additional authorities, see Appendix.

him, or if he gives it to his descendants so long as they exist to prevent their falling into indigence, it is a pious act,—more pious, according to the Prophet, than giving to the general body of the poor. He laid down that one's family and descendants are fitting objects of charity, and that to bestow on them and to provide for their future subsistence is more pious and obtains greater reward than to bestow on the indigent stranger. And this is insisted upon so strongly that when a *wakf* is made for the *indigent* or *poor* generally, the proceeds of the endowment are applied first to relieve the wants of the endower's children and descendants and kindred in the first place.(1) When a *wakf* is created constituting the family or descendants of the *wâkif* the recipients of the charity so long as they exist, the poor are expressly or impliedly brought in *not* for the purpose of making the *wakf* charitable (for the support of the family and descendants is a part and parcel of the charitable purpose for which the dedication is made), but simply to impart permanency to the endowment. When the *wâkif's* descendants fail, it *must* come to the poor. So it is an enduring benefaction—an act of *'ibâdat* or worship, to use the language of the (Shîah) *Jawâhir ul-Kalâm*,—an act by which *kurbat* or nearness is obtained to the Deity, according to the (Hanafi) *Bahr-ur-Râik*.

Doe dem Jaun Beebee v. *Abdollah Barber.*

Coming now to the cases decided by the British Indian Courts, we find that the first directly bearing on the subject is that of *Doe dem Jaun Beebee* v. *Abdollah Barber*(2) (1838). In that case, the ultimate benefit was not given to the poor in express terms. The lady dedicated the property in general terms as is customary among Mussulmans. In the first paragraph, she provided that after paying the revenue and taxes she should appropriate as much of the produce as was required for her own use, and the remainder to "hereditable and charitable purposes." She provided further that her several relatives should receive their maintenance as heretofore; that she should have the power of increasing or decreasing the number of incumbents; and that the repairs of the mosque, etc., and other expenses connected therewith in Ramazân and the Id festivals should be defrayed from the produce. By para-

---

(1) See Baillie's Digest, 2nd Ed., p. 593.

(2) Fulton's Reports, page 345; the *wakfnâmah* in that case is set out in this Appendix.

graph 2 she constituted herself the *mutwalli* during her lifetime; after her death, her daughter's son Abdollah was to be the *mutwalli*, and after him some one among her relations most deserving of the office; and she declared that the property was to be for ever inalienable.

It will be seen that the usufruct was, after paying the revenue, to be appropriated to the endower's own use and towards the maintenance of the members of her family. The amounts disbursable for the repairs of the mosque and for the performance of the festivals were postponed until after the maintenance of the family. But neither the decision of the Judges nor the opinion of the Law Officers turns upon this provision and it was stated by no one that the provision for the maintenance of the family invalidated the *wakf*. The word "hereditable" in the first paragraph, the power of increasing the persons receiving maintenance, the appointment of *mutwallis* one after another for the purpose of carrying out the directions in the *wakfnâma*, coupled with the answer of the Law Officers to the third question, all show that the provision for maintenance did not refer to "specific individuals then existing," but to the endower's descendants at large. It was never attempted to be argued in that case that the *wakf* was bad, because it was wholly or mainly for the support of the endower's family, or because it was not wholly, or mainly, or substantially for a mosque or for the poor. It was impugned on the only ground open under the Mohammedan Law that the *wâkif* had reserved the usufruct for herself. And the case was decided on the *Fatwa* of the Law Officers founded on well-known authorities, following the rule laid down by Abû Yusuf, whose doctrine on the point in question has always been recognised as the binding authority.

Bibi Kuneez Fatima v. Bibi Saheba Jan.

In the case of *Bibi Kuneez Fatima* v. *Bibi Saheba Jan*(1) (1867) the question was whether certain properties which had been conveyed by one of the defendants to the others were or were not *wakf* and consequently inalienable.

In dealing with the case the Judges (Kemp and Glover, JJ.) considered two points—(*a*) the right of the plaintiff to sue, and (*b*) the meaning of the grants in the case. There was no mention of the word *wakf* in any of the *sanads* put forward by the

(1) [1867], 8 Weekly Reporter, 313.

plaintiff; they were all in fact *Madad Maash* grants.(1) Kemp, J., in discussing the first point, said "the grants of the lands in dispute make no mention of any provision for the maintenance of the plaintiff or any other member of the grantee's family." There is no suggestion that, had there been any such provision, it would have been invalid or that there could be no *wakf* for that purpose. Then after pointing out that the alleged endowment did not come under the provisions of Act XX of 1863, Kemp, J., proceeded to show that the plaintiff had no interest to entitle her to sue.

He first gives the substance of one of the *sanads* :—

"That the grantee, *i.e.*, Syud Mahomed Mir, had a large family to support, and had to defray the expenses of a 'Khânkâh,'(2) for travellers and the benighted, for students and mendicants who beg at his door; that the said grantee found it difficult to discharge all these duties which involved considerable expense; that in consideration of this the villages detailed in the grant were given to him at a fixed annual *jama* of Rs. 896. The *abwabs* and other cesses hitherto levied upon the grantee were remitted, and the aforesaid *jama*, which had all along been paid, was declared to be fixed. It was further recited that the grantee, after paying the said *jama*, was to enjoy the profits of the property, to support himself therewith, and to pray for the grantor."

The learned Judge then goes on to say—"Now, it is very clear, that this is not a grant constituting a *wakf*. There is *no dedication of the properties solely to the worship of God, or to any religious or charitable purposes.* The grant recites that the grantee and his predecessors have hitherto held the lands at a *jama* of Rs. 896, which *jama* is declared to be fixed at that rate henceforth. In consideration of the charitable disposition of the grantee and the expenses which he apparently voluntarily incurred in supporting poor students, in giving alms to mendicants, and food and shelter to travellers, the grantor remits the payment of *abwabs* and other cesses, which in the days of the Nawab Nazims were a heavy impost, and directs the officers of the *tehsil* to refrain from exacting the same from the grantee. For this indulgence, the

(1) Grants made by Mussulman Sovereigns or chiefs for the maintenance of the grantees and their descendants.

(2) See *ante*, p. 222.

grantee was requested to give the grantor the benefit of his prayers. The grantee was to enjoy the profits after paying the *jama* fixed, *viz.*, Rs. 896. In short, the grants were grants to an individual in his own right and for the purpose of furnishing the means for the subsistence of the grantee, and nothing further."

It seems to be perfectly clear that in using the term, "religious" or "charitable" in the passage above quoted, Mr. Justice Kemp used them in the Mahommedan sense, that is, as meaning a purpose which is regarded as religious or charitable by the people among whom the question arose. He had already observed that there was no provision for the maintenance of the grantee's family. He then pointed out that there was no provision for the support of the *khânkâh* or travellers, or students or mendicants; that, on the contrary, in consideration of the charitable disposition of the grantee, who apparently voluntarily incurred expenses in the performance of good acts, the grant was made personally to him, in return for which he was to give the grantor the benefit of his prayers. He accordingly held that such a grant could not be regarded as a *wakf* under the Mussulman Law. To imagine that in using the term "charitable," he meant to confine it to a dedication solely for the poor, would be going against the whole purport of his judgment.

Khaja Hossein Ali v. Shahzadee Hazara Begum.

In the case of *Khaja Hossein Ali* v. *Shahzadee Hazra Begum*(1) (1869) the only question for determination, as pointed out by Kemp, J., was whether the subsistence of a mortgage, at the time the endowment was made, rendered such endowment wholly invalid under the Mahommedan Law or not. In the course of his judgment the learned Judge (who differed from his colleague, Markby, J.) made various observations pertinent to the case before him in support of his views. Kemp, J., as well as the Appellate Court which affirmed his judgment, took the law on the subject bodily from the *Fatâwai Alamgiri*. Mr. Justice Kemp also showed, quoting Harington's Analysis, that *Fatwas* or law decisions "are given primarily according to Abû Yusuf, and next according to Imâm Mahomed."

Mr. Justice Markby's judgment contains the following reference to the *wakfnâma* in this case:—

(1) [1869]. 12 W. R., 344; *ibid* (on appeal), p. 398.

"In this document," says the learned Judge, "after referring to the duty which he felt it incumbent on him to perform of making provision for the assistance of travellers and the maintenance of the heirs of his late son, he (the endower) states as follows :—

'Consequently, for the sake of the maintenance of Khaja Hossein Ali, I do hereby appoint him (who is my grandson) as a *mutwalli* of the aforesaid *Astana* or sepulchre under the following conditions : that the said Hossein Ali shall neither be competent to transfer the aforesaid property under a sale, gift, or mortgage, nor to transfer the *wakf* property in any other way. He is hereby authorized to take care of and to assist the travellers and the poor. He is to attend to the Fatihas of Shabebarat, the Mohurrum, and the Eeds, and to allow such expenses as are for solemnizing the above festivals. He is to appropriate such amounts as would remain in hand, after the payment of the *sudder jama*, from the nett proceeds of *taluq* Lot Billissur and from the produce of gardens, for his personal expenses as well as for his family, *i.e.*, his grandmother and mother.'

It will be seen, therefore, that the endowment was for the maintenance of the endower's grandson, and that the proceeds went after the payment of the *sudder jama* towards his support and that of his family. The provisions relating to the travellers and the poor and the festivals were mere recommendations. He was authorised to take care of and to assist the travellers and the poor. He was "to attend to the Fatihas of Shabebarat, the Mohurrum, and the Eeds, the usual Mahommedan festivals, and to allow such expenses as are for solemnizing the above festivals." There was no specific dedication for those purposes.

Mr. Justice Kemp, dealing with one of the objections of the Lower Court to the *wakf* in that case, says as follows :—

"As to the endowment being uncertain and conditional, I do not find, on perusal of the *towliutnama*, that such is the case.

"The performance of certain ceremonies at the great Mahommedan festivals is provided for, the festivals are distinctly enumerated, the poor who are always with us are to be relieved, and travellers looked after. The Government revenue, or in this case the rent, is to be paid, and the residue is to be expended in the maintenance of the relatives (who are also specified) of the endower, that is, of his mother and grandmother. The sister of the endower is also to be maintained and a small marriage portion given to her. It will be seen that the poor are provided for, which is the primary object of every *wakf*. Settlements in favour of relations who are specifically named are made. Such an endowment is in every respect a lawful one under the Mahommedan Law.''

The learned Judge was explaining the several particulars *in the document before him*, which went to establish that the endowment was neither uncertain nor conditional. And in doing so he pointed out that the poor were also provided for. And he added, what is no doubt true in one sense, but not so in another, that the primary object of every *wakf* is to provide for the poor, for it is unquestionable that there are many *wakfs* which have not the remotest connection with the poor, *e.g.*, a *wakf* for a mosque. But as I said before, his observation is correct in one sense ; in every *wakf*, the benefaction of which is bestowed upon any individual or on one's descendants, the charity is continued, upon their extinction, expressly or by implication of law, to the general poor. The poor are thus always present in the mind of a Mahommedan making a *wakf*. That Mr. Justice Kemp did not mean to hold that only such *wakfs* were valid as were intended for strangers or to provide for the general body of the poor, is apparent, *first*, from the fact that in that very deed, which he held to be valid, the poor formed a secondary object of the *wakf*, and, *secondly*, from his reference to Baillie's Digest,(1) where the subject of *wakf* on one's descendants is treated.

Whatever interpretation may be sought to be put upon the words of Kemp, J., the broad fact remains that the immediate recipients of the benefaction in that case were Khaja Hossein Ali and his family, though the deed contained discretionary directions about helping the poor and performing the usual family festivals. That case, instead of being an authority *against* the institution of *wakf* constituting the endower's family as the recipients of the benefaction, is an important authority in support of it.

Muzhurul Huq v. Puhraj Ditarey Mohapattur.

In the case of *Muzhurul Huq* v. *Puhraj Ditarey Mohapattur* (1870),(2) the plaintiff sued to obtain possession of certain lands which he had purchased with notice that they were *wakf*. The

(1) Pp. 585—586.

(2) [1870] 13 W. R., 236.

special appellant had intervened in the suit alleging that he was the *mutwalli* under the *wakfnâma*. The Judge in the Court below had decreed the suit on the ground (*a*) that the lands had not been endowed by the plaintiff's vendor, and (*b*) that the deed not being registered could not be admitted in evidence, and that therefore the intervenor had no *locus standi*. Dealing with the first ground, Kemp, J., examined the terms of the deed in order to show that they all constituted a valid endowment :—

Muzhurul Huq v. Puhraj Ditarey Mohapattur.

"Looking to the terms of the deed," he said, "it has all the characteristics of a valid endowment under the Mahommedan law. The primary objects for which the lands are endowed, and which are the objects which all Mahommedans have in view in endowing lands, are to support a mosque and to defray the expenses of the worship conducted in that mosque. The mosque had admittedly been in existence for a long period on the endowed land. It is first provided that from the profits of the endowed lands the mosque is to be repaired and lighted and furnished on certain festivals; that travellers are not to be allowed to go away hungry; that an establishment, including a Muezzin, or caller to prayers, and other necessary servants of the mosque are to be kept up; that mendicants are to have alms given to them; that a certain number of poor scholars are to be educated in Arabic, which necessitates the employment of a teacher; and, lastly, that from the remaining profits the expenses for the marriages, burials and circumcisions of the members of the family of the *Mutwalli* Muzhurul Huq were to be defrayed. This was to be done after the primary objects for which the endowment was made, and which objects have been already detailed above, were fully accomplished."

In this case, it will be observed the learned Judge calls an endowment in favour of a mosque as the primary object of a *wakf*, whereas in the previous case he had stated the poor to be the primary object. It is evident, therefore, that Kemp, J., could not have intended in either of these cases that his words should be taken as exhaustive, for he had already spoken of a *wakf* being in favour of *any religious* or *charitable* purpose; and he was well aware, that, under the Mussulman Law, one's family were objects of charity in a higher degree than indigent strangers and, therefore, entitled to be classed among the poor in the sense in which it is understood in the Mussulman system. The learned Judge then proceeded to say :—

"We are of opinion that the mere charge upon the profits of the estate of certain items which must in the course of time necessarily cease, being confined to one family and for particular purposes, and which, after they lapse, will leave the whole profits intact for the original purposes for which the endowment was made, does not render the endowment invalid under the Mahommedan Law. A person may make an endowment settling lands on himself and enjoying the profits during his lifetime, and after his lifetime devoting the profits to the support of the poor, the main object of the Mahommedan Law being that the profits of the land endowed should be endowed for a purpose which always remains in existence. Now the poor are always with us, and therefore a man making an endowment and enjoying the profits during his lifetime, to go to the poor after his death, does not make the endowment for an uncertain or non-existent object." *

Considera-tion of Mr. Justice Kemp's ex-pressions.

Here again the learned Judge was dealing with the question by way of an example, and there is no shadow of a ground for suggesting that the illustration is exhaustive or exclusive ; on the contrary, the very fact that he contemplated a provision for the members of a particular family for particular purposes would show that it never entered his mind to suggest that a *wakf* in which the proceeds are applicable towards the maintenance of the members of the endower's family was invalid. The views enunciated by Kemp, J., in the passage last quoted, have received the approval of their Lordships of the Privy Council in the cases of *Mahomed Ahsanullah Chowdhry*(1) and *Abdul Fata Mohammed Ishak*,(2) but that passage appears to me to deal with the question, which he was discussing, from the two aspects, to which reference has already been made(3) both of which are provided for in the *Fatâwai Alamgiri*, an authority upon which that learned Judge relied considerably. With reference to the first it is laid down that "when a man has made an appropriation of land or something else, with a condition that the whole or part of it shall be for himself while he lives, and after him for the poor, the appropriation is valid according to Abû Yusuf

Wakf for the poor with a condition.

(1) [1889], I. L., 17 Cal., 498. (2) [189]2 I. L., 22 Cal., 619.

(3) *Ante* p. 284.

and the Shaikhs of Balkh have adopted his opinion, and the *Fatwa* is in conformity with it."(1) The instances in which this may be done are given. And then comes this passage :—

"So also, if he should say, 'this my land is a *sadakah mowkoofa*(2) (pious *wakf*) he (the *mutwalli*) will pass the produce to me while I live; then after me, to my child and child's child and their *nasl* for ever, while there are any, and when they cease, to the indigent,' this also would be lawful. So also, if he should make a condition 'that he may maintain himself and his child and pay his debts out of the produce, and that when death happens to him, the produce of this estate is for such an one, the son of such an one and his child and child's child, and his *nasl.*' . . . A person makes a *wakf* for the poor with a condition 'that he may eat and feed others (out of its produce) so long as he lives, and that after his death it is to be for his child, and in like manner for his child's child for ever, while there are any descendants,' the *wakf* is lawful with such a condition."

Here, the dedication is either in general terms or is expressly for the poor, subject to the condition that the benefaction should be bestowed wholly or partially on the endower and his family so long as they exist as part and parcel of the charitable purpose for which the dedication is made, the proceeds going to the poor (meaning indigent *strangers*) only on the extinction of the endower's descendants.(3)

The second aspect deals with a dedication primarily in favour of the *wâkif* and his family.

"A man says 'my land is a *sadakah mowkoofa* on myself'; such an appropriation is lawful according to approved traditions. So also, if he should say 'I have made a *wakf* of it on myself, and after me on such a one and then upon the poor' it would be lawful according to Abû Yusuf. And if one should say 'my land is *mowkoofa* on such a one, and after him upon me' or should say

(1) Volume II, p. 495; see Baillie's Digest, 2nd Ed., p. 595.

(2) *Mowkoofa*, past participle of *wakf*; Mr. Baillie translates this word as "settled," but I prefer to follow the original, as the word "settled" is misleading.

(3) In p. 474, Volume II of the same work; Baillie's Digest, 2nd Ed., p. 576.

'upon me and upon such a one, or upon my slave and upon such an one' the accepted doctrine is that it would be valid.''

* * * * * * *

Dedication primarily in favour of one's self and family and descendants with a reversion for the poor.

'' If a man should say 'I have made a *wakf* of it on my children (*awlâd*),' males and females are included.''

'' If one should say 'this my land is a *sadakah mowkoofa* on my child, and child of my child,' the child of his loins, and the child of his child in existence on the day of the consecration and those who are born afterwards are included, and the two generations participate in the produce, but none below them are included, nor the children of daughters according to the *Zâhir-ur-Rawâyèt* (approved traditions); and the *Fatwa* is in accordance with it. And if he should say, 'upon my child and child of my child, and child of the child of my child,' mentioning three generations, the produce is to be expended upon his children for ever, so long as there are any descendants, and is not to be applied to the poor; while one remains the *wakf* is to them, and the lowest among them; the nearer and more remote being alike unless the appropriator say in making the *wakf* 'the nearer is nearer,' or say 'on my child, then after them, on the child of my child,' or say, 'generation after generation,' when a beginning must be made with them with whom the appropriator has begun.''

In these cases the *wakf* is primarily in favour of the *wâkif* or of his children and *afterwards* of the poor.

Mr. Justice Kemp, it is submitted, *affirms both these principles.* In the first part of the passage under reference, he recognises the Mussulman Law given in page 596 of Baillie's Digest. The words '' the mere charge upon the profits of the estate of certain items, which must in the course of time necessarily cease, being confined to one family and for particular purposes '' (be it for the payment of the endower's debts or the maintenance of his family or the payment of their marriage expenses), '' and which after they lapse will leave the whole profits intact for the original purposes for which the endowment was made,'' show that the learned Judge recognises the validity of the *conditions* which may be superimposed by the endower upon the application or enjoyment of the property dedicated, as laid down in the *Fatâwai Alamgiri.* In the second part, he points out that '' a person may make an endowment settling lands on himself and enjoying the profits during his lifetime, and after his lifetime devoting the profits to the support of the poor," and mark these words "the main object of the Mahommedan Law being that the profits of the land endowed be endowed for a purpose which always remains in existence." Here there is no reference to the charge of any items upon the profits of an estate dedicated for some specific purposes. The principle is stated in the clearest terms that a person may make an endowment "settling lands on himself" with the reversion for the poor "who are always with us," who are, in other words, a perpetual object of bounty. Reference is made to the case of the endower himself, because on that point Abû Yusuf and Mohammed were disagreed, and the learned Judge enunciated the rule laid down by the former. There is no reason for suggesting that he intended cutting down the Mahommedan Law. If his words are studied with some care, it will be found that he enunciated the accepted rules of Mahommedan Law, *viz.*, that the endower may make an appropriation and *condition* that he and his family or children shall enjoy the usufruct so long as they last, the whole going to the general poor after they have ceased to exist; *or* that he may directly endow the lands for himself or his children or descendants, and in the end for the poor, in other words, constitute himself and his children the recipients of the charity in the first instance, the general poor taking their place on the extinction of the family.

Mahomed Hamidulla Khan v. Lutful Haq.

The case of *Mahomed Hamidulla Khan* v. *Lutful Haq*(1) is, as I have already ventured with all respect to point out, in absolute conflict with the Mahommedan Law, and displays some confusion of ideas. The substantial portion of the *wakfnâmah* was in these terms:—"I have made *wakf* of 4 annas in favour of *Jamela Khatun alias Dhone Bibi*, daughter of my daughter, and her descendants as also her descendants' descendants, so long as they may continue to have offspring, and, when they no longer exist, then in favour of the poor and needy." It will be seen that this dedication complied with all the essential requisites of the law. The learned Judges held, however, as follows:—

"There has been much argument before us as to the real signification of the term '*wakf*.' There is no doubt that there is a conflict of authority between Baillie and other writers on Mahom-

(1) [1881] 8 Cal. L. R., 164.

medan Law, Macnaghten and Hamilton, on this subject. But looking to the principal authority, the '*Hedâya*' as read by Abû Hanîfa, (*sic*) who was undoubtedly a Sunni, to which sect the family of Gholam Sharuff belong, and looking to the doctrines of his disciples, it seems to us that the balance of authority is strongly in favour of the view as stated by the Bombay Court in the case of *Abdul Ganne Kasâm* v. *Hussein Mirza Rahimtullah*, 10 Bom. H. C. R., 13, *viz.*, that 'to constitute a valid *wakf*, there must be a dedication of the property solely to the worship of God, or to religious or charitable purposes.' Abû Hanîfa undoubtedly in 2 *Hedâya*, p. 334, points out that the appropriation that is *wakf*, must be to some 'charitable' purposes."(1)

"Now here it is manifest that this appropriation in favour of Budrunnissa is not in the nature of a charity. It is simply in the nature of a settlement upon the daughter, a settlement of property which was to be heritable and to be taken by Budrunnissa's descendants in certain shares.(2) The words are clear, each daughter is to take four annas and in the terms of the deed, 'four annas share has been endowed in favour of each of the said ladies.' If, therefore, the principle underlying a *wakf* is charity, and if the ultimate application of the property, the subject of '*wakf*,' must be to objects which never became extinct, and those objects are all of a religious and charitable character, then this particular appropriation fails to answer to this description. Consequently, the appropriation of the one-fourth share, which is the subject of this appeal, is invalid and cannot be held to be a *wakf*."

Mahomed Hamidulla v. *Lutfu Haq*—contd.

"There is, however, some force in the argument which has been addressed to us, that appropriation in the nature of settlement of property upon a man and his descendants have been treated by various exponents of Mahommedan Law as legitimate appropriation under the designation of *wakf*, but these settlements are all under Mahommedan Law termed *Sadakah* and in the view

(1) The learned Judges evidently thought that the *Hedâya* was the work of Abû Hanîfa, whereas Abû Hanîfa had died four centuries before the *Hedâya* was written. He neither read nor wrote it!

(2) Here the learned Judges have clearly misconstrued the document. It did not provide that the property dedicated should be "heritable" and "taken in certain shares." It only provided (as the Mussulman Law permits) that the descendants of the first recipients of the benefaction should take the usufruct in "certain shares."

apparently of Baillie, when a settlement of property is made in this way by a man in favour of his descendants, the term *Sadakah* must be used ; but we do not gather that this term is employed in the deed of 1st Bhadro 1248. But further, even admitting that under Mahommedan Law appropriations or rather settlements of this character can be made, it seems to us clear that the present appropriation falls outside the principle of '*wakf*.' As explained in the case already referred to in 10 Bom. H. C. R., the doctrine of settlement rests entirely upon a saying attributed to the Prophet. 'A man giving subsistence to himself is giving alms,' but this doctrine only holds good according to Hamilton (2 *Hedâya* 351, note), where a man appropriates the whole of the property and so reduces himself to poverty, in which case the charity is as effectual with respect to him (where he necessarily reserves a sufficiency from the product for his own sustenance) as with respect to any other pauper. So that to validate a '*wakf*' by making a settlement of his property on himself, or his descendants, a man must, in the view taken by the Prophet, reduce himself to a state of absolute poverty. In the present case it is clear, and it is admitted by both sides, that there are other properties vested in the appropriator besides those which are the subject of this deed. Consequently, it cannot be said that Budrunnissa has received this property as a pauper."

Speaking with respect, not only does this judgment proceed upon patent erroneous assumptions, but shows an extraordinary confusion of ideas. It is by no means clear who is to reduce himself "to a state of absolute poverty" the endower or the recipient of the benefaction in order that the *wakf* may be valid. Again it is assumed that "there is a conflict between Baillie and the other writers on Mahommedan Law, Macnaghten and Hamilton." Macnaghten never pretended to write an exhaustive treatise on Mahommedan Law ; he collected a few general elementary principles, many of which have been found to be incomplete.

Principle 4, Chapter X of Macnaghten's Principles and Precedents of Mahommedan Law, however, shows that an endowment may be made in favour of the children of a person and on their failure for the poor.(1) Cases are also given which refer

(1) Pp. 338 and 341.

distinctly to *wakfs* for the support of particular families.(1) The quotation from the *Khazânat-ul-Muftiïn* is emphatic.

The rule stated in the *Hedâya*.

Nor is there anything in the *Hedâya* to warrant the view taken by the learned Judges. It must be remembered that the English version is a rendering of a Persian translation of the original Arabic *Hedâya* with many interpolations and omissions. Mr. Hamilton in translating the Persian version into English rendered the word *wakf* by "appropriation;" but as every "appropriation" cannot be regarded as *wakf*, he took care to add in a footnote that it meant appropriations of a pious or charitable nature. *The learned Judges decided the case before them upon the authority of that footnote, construing it in the strictest English sense.*

There is absolutely no warrant in the *Hedâya* itself for that view. In the *Hedâya*, a *wakf* is defined thus: "in law, it signifies, according to Abû Hanîfa, the tying-up of the substance of a property in the ownership of the *wâkif* and the devotion of its usufruct, amounting to an *'aâriat* . . . .

The *Hedâya*.

. . . . . According to the Two Disciples, it means the tying-up of the substance of a thing under the rule of the property of God, whereby the proprietary right of the *wâkif* [therein] becomes extinguished and [it] is transferred to Almighty God for any purpose by which its profits may be applied to [the benefit of] His creatures."

The definition given by the Disciples has been adopted for the *Fatwa*.(2) This has been explained over and over again in all the commentaries, in all the works of law, in decisions, and in *Fatwas*, to include every object of a meritorious character, by which 'reward' is obtained or 'nearness' sought; and a dedication for one's children is placed in the same category as one for a mosque.

The statement that "to constitute a valid *wakf* there must be a dedication solely to the worship of God, or to religious or charitable purposes," is unsupported by any authority. In the *Hedâya*, the subject of *wakfs* in favour of children is not discussed, as there was no difference of opinion on the point between Abû

(1) P. 242.

(2) *Mohammud Sadik* v. *Mohammud Ali and others*, 1 Sel. Rep., 17 *supra*.

Yusuf and Mohammed.(1) On the question whether a *wakf* in favour of one's self is valid or not, there was a difference between Imâm Abû Yusuf and Mohammed, and consequently the author goes fully into it, and proves on the authority of the Prophet that a *wakf* may validly be created with a reservation by the settlor of the primary interest for himself The doctrine again is misconstrued upon the authority of a footnote by the translator, and it is supposed that a man must, in order to create a valid *wakf*, reduce himself to absolute poverty. It is a gloss by Hamilton upon the text and upon the precept of the Prophet which has not been recognised by the Mahommedan lawyers themselves.(2) "A provision for one's self," said the Prophet, "is tantamount to an act of charity," whether he dedicates the whole of his property, or only a portion thereof. The reservation of the income of the *wakf* in whole or in part is considered as a pious and meritorious act. The word *sadakah* has been translated into *alms-giving*, and it is chiefly due to this that the Courts of Justice have been misled. The ground upon which a dedication in favour of one's self is held to be valid is that it is a pious act, *viz.*, to provide the means of support for one's self. Considering how unstable fortunes and wealth have been at all times in the East, it was laid down by the Hanafî Jurists as a precept that when a man placed his property in the custody of God for the benefit of mankind, he might constitute himself as one of the beneficiaries or the sole beneficiary of that of which God was the trustee. The learned Judges further thought that a settlement in favour of children could only be made by the word *sadakah*. It is clear from the authorities already cited that this view is absolutely opposed to the recognised and accepted principles of the law.(3)

Misconstruction of the word *sadakah*.

---

(1) The *Hedâya* is not a work of *fatâwa* or decisions, but only deals with principles of general Mussulman jurisprudence and questions on which Abû Hanîfa, Abû Yusuf and Mohammed were in disagreement. *It does not discuss the subject of wakfs in favour of one's children as there was absolutely no difference on that point;* see Arabic *Hedâya* (printed with the *Rifâya*), Vol. II, p. 900, where the validity of such a *wakf* is taken for granted.

(2) See Baillie's Digest, p. 593, which shows that a man need not make himself a pauper before he can reserve the usufruct for himself.

(3) See *ante*, pp. 217-224.

The case of *Fatima Bibi* v. *Ariff Ismailjee Bham*(1) was not argued at all, and was decided by the learned Judge on the authority of *Abdul Ganne Kasam* and *Mahomed Hamidulla Khan*. *Fatima Bibi* v. *Ariff Ismailjee Bham.*

One of the learned Judges (Tottenham, J.) who decided the case of *Mahomed Hamidulla Khan* had afterwards to consider a similar question in *Lachmipat Sing* v. *Amir Alum*,(1) in which he seems to have, to some extent, modified his former opinion. In *Lachmipat Sing's* case the *wakfnâmah* provided for the payment of the settlor's debts, for the support of a mosque, for the performance of certain funeral ceremonies of his ancestors and for the maintenance of his descendants. It was not, therefore, "a *wakf solely* and *exclusively* for the worship of God." The learned Judge in dealing with this *wakf* expressed himself in these terms:— *Lachmipat Sing* v. *Amir Alum.*

"The next question is, whether or not the *wakf* is a valid one according to Mahommedan Law. There has always been a good deal of controversy in the Courts as to what is essential, and as to what will invalidate a *wakf*. On the one hand, it has been contended that no *wakf* is valid unless it is solely and wholly for pious and charitable purposes enduring throughout all time, and, on the other hand, there have been those who considered that what is practically a perpetual provision for the dedicator's family may be a valid *wakf*."

"The fact that the Subordinate Judge, who tried this case, is himself a Mahommedan gentleman of considerable attainments in Arabic learning, entitles his opinion to peculiar weight in a case of this nature, and he appears to have entertained no doubt, whatever, as to this *wakf* being of a thoroughly legitimate character as to its constitution and objects. And singularly enough, the only matter which strikes us as one in respect of which, with reference to the decisions of the Courts, makes [*sic*] the character of this alleged *wakf* at all doubtful, is the very one which the lower Court has treated as one as to which there could be no dispute as to its being a proper object of *wakf*. For, in the *wakfnâmah*, there is express provision for the maintenance of the dedicator's male descendants, in addition to the strictly pious and religious objects for which the *wakf* purports to have been made. But the Bombay High Court has, by a Full Bench, decided that, to constitute

(1) [1882] 9 Cal. L. R., 74.

a valid *wakf*, there must be a dedication of the property solely to the worship of God, or to religious or charitable purposes; see *Abdul Ganne Kasam* v. *Hussein Miya Rahimtulla.*(1) The view has been endorsed by a Division Bench of this Court in the case of *Mahomed Hamidulla Khan* v. *Budrunnissa Khatun.*''(2)

''This definition might seem to exclude from judicial recognition a *wakf* of which one object is a provision for the family of the creator of it.''

''The lower Court, however, easily disposes of this question by the observation that 'it is quite evident, and there is no necessity to quote any authority on the subject, that a *wakf* for one's self and for one's children is valid.' ''

''In the Bombay case, the Judges, after considering all the available authorities on this question, held that the balance was in favour of the dictum to which they gave effect; and this too was what the Division Bench, of which one of us was a member, decided in the case of *Mahomed Hamidulla Khan* v. *Budrunnissa Khatun.* In that case the alleged *wakf*, which we declined to recognize, had for its object nothing connected with the worship of God or religious observances, and provided only in a very remote contingency for the poor. It was simply a perpetuity for the benefit of the dedicator's daughter and her descendants so long as any should exist.''

Lachmipat Sing v. *Amir Alum.*

"The *wakfnâmah* now before us is of a very different character, and having regard to the passage in it reciting the fact of dedication, we think that without saying whether or no we are prepared on further consideration to adopt to the full the ruling above mentioned, we can treat this *wakf* as actually fulfilling the condition described, for the maker of the *wakf*, after reciting the whole of his property of every kind, proceeds to declare that all has been endowed by him for the expenses of the *musjeed* and the tombs of the holy personages of his family, the servants of the *Asthánâ*, and for performing the *urs* and *fateha* at the tomb. ''

"These are the objects of the *wakf*, and they are all distinctly religious. They also involve to some extent charity to the poor. ''

---

(1) [1882] I. L., 9 Cal., 176; for the *Wakfnâmah* see *Appendix*.
(2) [1881] 8 Cal. L. R., 167.

"We are disposed to hold this, therefore, to be a valid *wakf* within the purview of the rulings quoted."

The distinction which was drawn between the case in question and *Mahomed Hamidulla Khan* was more apparent than real. In the main the dedication was for the descendants of the *wâkif*, coupled with the payment of certain expenses for the *masjid*, *etc.*, and yet the *wakf* was held to be valid. It was supposed that the provision in respect of the latter lent substance to the provision as to the former.

The Subordinate Judge, however, who was a Mahommedan versed in his own law, had held that the very provision which appeared to the High Court doubtful was the one about which there could possibly be no dispute.

Amrutlall Kalidass v. Shaik Hussein Mahomed Ebrahim.

The authority of these three cases has been discussed with considerable clearness and ability by Mr. Justice Farran in the case of *Amrutlall Kalidass* v. *Shaik Hussein Mahomed Ebrahim and another*.(1) That learned Judge very properly observes:—

"The authority of the cases of *Mahomed Hamidulla Khan* v. *Lutful Haq* and of *Fatima Bibi* v. *Ariff Ismailjee Bham*, is much weakened by the fact of the Judges, who decided those cases, treating what, at most, is but an expression of opinion in *Abdul Ganne Kasam* v. *Hussain Miya Rahimtulla* as a decision, and by the doubt thrown upon them by the Court in deciding *Lachmipat Sing* v. *Amir Alum*, in which one of the Judges, who decided the former of the two cases, sat. The case of *Fatima Bibi* v. *The Advocate-General* was not referred to in either of them, nor in the later case."

Abdul Ganne Kasam v. Hussein Miya Rahimtulla.

I now come to the case of *Abdul Ganne Kasam* v. *Hussein Miya Rahimtulla*. Neither in that case, nor in the Calcutta cases which have followed it, was there any reference to Ryan, C. J.'s decision in the case of *Doe dem Jaun Bibi* v. *Abdollah Barber*. No original authority was cited. Various analogies derived from other systems of law were imported into the discussion, but the principles of the Mahommedan Law, deducible from recognised law-works, were noticeable by their absence.

The learned Judges drawing a conclusion from the decision of their Lordships of the Privy Council in *Jewan Dass Sahoo* v. *Shah Kubeer-ood-deen Ahmed* (which had nothing to do with the ques-

(1) [1887] I. L., 11 Bom., 499.

tion under discussion in the Bombay High Court) say as follows :— "In that case it was held that according to the Mahommedan Law, it is not necessary, in order to constitute a *wakf* or endowment to religious and charitable uses, that the term *wakf* be used in the grant, if from the general nature of the grant such tenure can be inferred. We think that the converse of this proposition holds good, namely, that it is necessary, in order to constitute a *wakf*, that the endowment should be to religious and charitable uses, and that it is not sufficient that the mere term *wakf* should be used in the grant. To hold otherwise would be to enable every person by a mere verbal fiction to create a perpetuity of any description." With respect it must be stated that the reasoning is fallacious and ignores the express provisions of the Mahommedan Law.

Nizam-ud-din Gulam and others v. Abdul Gafur and others.

In the case of *Nizamuddin Gulam and others* v. *Abdul Gafur and others*,(1) the Bombay High Court (Birdwood and Parsons, JJ.) apparently accepted the principle that a Mahommedan could make a valid *wakf* of his property in favour of his descendants, but they held that inasmuch as there was "no express provision at all for the ultimate application of the property to any religious or charitable object," the settlement was invalid. Here, again, not a single original authority is referred to. The real question is lost sight of, the principle of the Mahommedan Law is misunderstood, and the case is decided upon inferential reasoning founded upon two earlier decisions which hardly support the view taken by the Judges.

Ayesha Bibi v. Gholam Hyder Khan.

The case of *Fatima Bibi* v. *The Advocate General*(2) was followed in the Calcutta High Court in the cases of *Ayesha Bibi* v. *Gholam Hyder Khan*,(3) and *Phudia Bibi* v. *Haji Mahommed Kazim Isphahanee*.(4)

Pathukutti v. Avathalakutti.

In the case of *Pathukutti* v. *Avathalakutti* (5) the *wakf* was to take effect on the contingency of the settlor having no issue. If she had issue the property was to go to them absolutely; if not, it was to be *wakf*. It might be said that in this case there was no valid dedication under the Mahommedan Law.

(1) [1889] I. L., 13 Bom., 264.
(2) [1881] I. L., 6 Bom., 42.
(3) Decided, 19th Novr. 1883.
(4) Decided 31st March 1884.
(5) [1888] I. L., 13 Mad., 66.

In the case of *Murtazai Bibi* v. *Jumna Bibi*,(1) the parties were Shiahs and the endower was a Shiah. Under the Shiah Law when a *wakf* is in favour of a specified class of people, such as the *wâkif's* family or descendants, the ultimate unfailing purpose must be expressly designated. This is one of the points of difference between the *recognised* Hanafî law and the *recognised* Shiah law. In the *wakfnâmah* in *Murtazai Bibi's* case the poor were not mentioned, and the case could have been decided on that point. But the learned Judge who decided the case was probably not aware of this difference, and derived the law from Hanafî cases. *Murtazai Bibi v. Jumna Bibi.*

The *Hedâya* is held responsible for all the present confusion on the subject of *wakf*. But it must be remembered that Hamilton did *not* translate the original work as it exists in the Arabic language. At his instance the Arabic *Hedâya* was rendered into Persian by somé Moulvis of Calcutta, who interpolated passages into the Persian version probably with the object of elucidating the meaning of the author, the effect of which, however, has been to confuse the subject. Often, important sentences have been left out, which wholly detracts from the value of the translation. It is upon this so-called translation that the decisions are based. With reference to Hamilton's rendering and gloss, Mr. Neill Baillie, the paraphrasist of the *Fatâwai Alamgiri*, speaks thus:—"Mr Hamilton has unnecessarily restricted the legal meaning [of the word *wakf*] to appropriations of a 'pious or charitable nature.'" *Hedâya.*

And having regard to the meaning usually attached by English lawyers to the words "charitable" and "pious," nobody who has studied Mahommedan Law will question for a moment the correctness of Mr. Baillie's comment.

Critically examined, however, there is no difference between the *Hedâya* and any of the other works on Mahommedan Law. In the *Hedâya*, the law of *wakf*, as already stated, is dealt with most meagrely; and the subject of *wakfs* on one's "children and *nasl*" is not discussed at all; for with regard to the validity of such *wakfs*, there was no dispute between Abû Yusuf and Mohammed. The matter on which they were at issue, *viz*., the validity of a *wakf* in favour of one's self, is considered at some length. But all the commentaries, like the *Fath-ul-Kadîr*, the *Ghâit ul-Bayân*, etc., treat fully of the subject.

(1) [1891] I L., 13 All., 261.

The text is as follows :—

The text of the *Hedâya*.

" Abû Hanîfa (may the mercy of God be with him), has said that the right of the *wâkif* is not extinguished in the property dedicated unless the Judge makes a decree or the *wakf* is made dependant on the death of the *wâkif;* therefore [according] to him the *wâkif* should say thus, ' when I die, my house will become *wakf* in this way.' According to Abû Yusuf (may the mercy etc.), the right [of property] is extinguished by the mere declaration of the *wâkif*.(1) Mohammed (may the mercy, etc.) says the right of the *wâkif* is not extinguished until a *mutwalli* is appointed and the property delivered to him."

The recognised rule.

" [And] the author (God be pleased with him) says that *wakf* literally means detention, as when they say when tying-up an animal, ' I have tied it up,' the [two] expressions meaning the same. In law, it signifies according to Abû Hanîfa, the tying-up of the substance of a property in the ownership of the *wâkif* and the devotion of its usufruct, amounting to an *'aâriat* (commodate loan). [Then] it is said(2) that as the usufruct of a thing is non-existing and as the giving in charity of a non-existing thing is not valid, *wakf* is not lawful according to Abû Hanîfa, and this is mentioned in the *Asl*."

" But it is most correct, that *wakf* is lawful according to him [Abû Hanîfa] though not absolute—same as an *'aâriat*.(3) According to the Two [disciples] it means the tying-up of the substance of a thing under the rule of the property of Almighty God, so that the proprietary right of the *wâkif* [therein] becomes extinguished and [it] is transferred to Almighty God for any purpose by which its profits may be applied to [the benefit of] His creatures. Consequently a *wakf* is absolute, nor can it be sold, nor given, nor inherited."

" And [thus] the word [*wakf*] comprehends both meanings [*i.e.*, that put upon it by Abû Hanîfa and that put upon it by his disciples]. Accordingly, preference should be given to the one which is founded on proof. The Disciple's views are based [*firstly*]

(1) That is "I have constituted this as *wakf*"; see the *Bahr-ur-Râik*, Appendix.

(2) *i.e.*, "some have said."

(3) The words in the translation of Hamilton " the appropriator is held to be at liberty to resume it, and the sale or gift of it is consequently lawful," do not occur in the original.

on the precept of the Prophet, who told Omar when he was desirous of consecrating his land of *Samâgh*, 'consecrate its substance, and it will not be sold, nor given, nor inherited.' *Secondly*, on the necessity that a *wakf* should be absolute, so that its reward may accrue in perpetuity to the *wâkif*; and this can be attained [only] by the extinguishment of the *wâkif's* property [in it], and constituting it Almighty God's,(1) example of which is given in the *Shar'aa* [the law] like that of a mosque. Therefore, it will be constituted like that."(2)

It will be noticed that throughout this passage there is not a single word justifying the inference that "the dedication must be *solely to the worship of God*." Hamilton translates (جعله لاله تعالى) which means "constitutes it Almighty God's [property]" by the words "dedicating it *solely* to God." The Arabic expression has been freely paraphrased in the Persian version from which his translation was made, but even his rendering does not warrant the conclusion arrived at by the learned Judges in *Abdul Ganne Kasam*, that a *wakf* means a dedication "solely to the *worship* of God."(3)

In page 911, at the end of the Gloss, in the Chapter on *Wakf*, the author of the *Kifâya*(4) distinctly lays down that "the *Fatwa* in all these matters is according to the Disciples [and not with Abû Hanîfa] by notoriety and custom, and on this is the *Ijmâ'a-ul-ummat*(5) (concordance of the universality of the people.)" Comment of the *Kifâya*.

It is unnecessary to quote authorities in support of the proposition that the views of Abû Hanîfa on these questions have never been recognised as law among the Hanafîs. I shall give only the references to some, such as the *Fatâwai Alamgiri*

(1) Or, "to Almighty God"

(2) *That is*, the legal consequence is the same.

(3) In the Persian translation (Mss. copy in the Calcutta High Court) the Arabic expression has been rendered thus:—

از ملک خود بیرون کند و صرف برای خدایتعالی گرداند

"should take it out of his own ownership and make it over absolutely to God the Great." Hamilton has omitted the first part of the sentence and only translated the second and has thus wholly missed the meaning of the Persian version, which points to absolute transfer of the right of property from the endower to God and not to the purpose of the dedication.

(4) See Morley's Dig., Vol. I, Introd., p. cclxix.

(5) For *Ijmâ'a-ul-ummat* as one of the fundamental bases of jurisprudence see Introduction, *ante*.

Fatâwai Kâzi Khân, Himâdia, Fathul-Kadîr, Ghâit ul-Bayân, Sharh-i-Tahtâwi, etc.

Commenting on the passage in the *Hedâya* where Hamilton has introduced the words "dedicating it solely to God," the author of the *Kifâya* has this:—"The Disciples say that examples of the absoluteness of *wakf* are given in the *Shar'aa* (the law) such as a mosque; for they say the constitution of a mosque is absolute by *consensus;* and that is withdrawal of the right [of property] for some beneficial purpose from one's self without [the subject of the *wakf*] entering into the property of anybody else. But whatever purpose of divine approbation he may have intended, it will be tied up for that purpose. It is so in all *wakfs.*"(1)

And again, according to the Disciples, "the meaning of *wakf* is the extinguishment of the right of property towards God Almighty; consequently the thing dedicated will be tied up in the ownership of God on condition that its usufruct will be applied to His creatures. So that a dedication of property to Almighty God means a constitution of its profits for human beings."(2)

Misconstruction of the *Hedâya.*

Even according to Abû Hanîfa, a *wakf* does not mean "the dedication of property to the *worship of* God" or to "charity," in the English sense of the word, solely or otherwise, for according to the *Kifâya*, Abû Hanîfa held *wakf* to mean, "the tying-up of the substance in the ownership of the *wâkif*, and the devotion of its profits on the poor *or on any purpose among good purposes.*"(3)

I will give here another passage from the *Hedâya* which has been subjected to misconstruction. "According to Abû Hanîfa and Mohammed (may God's mercy be with them), a *wakf* is not completed until the *wâkif* constitutes its ultimate benefit (*lit.* its end) for an object not liable ever to failure. But Abû Yusuf (may the mercy of God be with him) declares that if the *wâkif* names an object which is liable to failure, the *wakf* would [nevertheless] be lawful, and after the extinction of that object it would be for the poor, though they may not have been named [at all]. The contention of Abû Hanîfa and Mohammed is that, as *wakf* means the extinguishment of the right of property [of the *wâkif*] without

(1) *Hedâya* printed with the *Kifâya,* Vol. II, p. 889.

(2) *Ibid,* p. 895.

(3) إن الوقف حبس العين على ملک الواقف و التصدق بالمنفعة على الفقر او على وجه من وجوه الخير *

a transfer to anybody else permanently, like emancipation, if an object is named likely to fail, it will not answer the purpose intended thereby; like a temporary sale, a temporary *wakf* is invalid." "Whilst Abû Yusuf (may the mercy of God be with him) contends that the motive of [creating] a *wakf* is to obtain the approval of the Almighty, and that may be obtained in many ways, for it may be obtained sometimes by dedicating to an object which is liable to become extinct and sometimes by dedicating to an object which may continue for ever *so that a wakf in either case is lawful.* Some have said *perpetuity* is a condition required by *consensus.* But Abû Yusuf has declared that it is not necessary, to mention perpetuity [or a continuing object] [at the time of *wakf*] for he says the words *wakf* and *sadakah* [pious offering] convey the meaning of perpetuity, as I have already stated, and [also] because in *wakf*, like emancipation, there is an extinction of right without a transfer of right [to anybody also]. AND it is, therefore, laid down in the Book [*Mukhtasar-ul-Kudûri*] that though the poor be not named in a *wakf* yet they will take [on failure of the objects named]. AND THIS IS CORRECT."(1)

Hamilton's translation of the *Hedâya* partial and incorrect.

The whole of the last few lines has disappeared in Hamilton's translation.

That the rule laid down by Abû Yusuf is the accepted doctrine has already been shown from quotations from all the recognised works of law, such as the *Fatâwai Alamgiri*, *Fatâwai Kâzi Khân*, *Fath ul-Kadîr*, *Radd ul-Muhtâr*, *Ghâit ul-Bayân*, *Tas-hîl*, &c., and it is unnecessary therefore to go over the same ground again at any length.(2) It may be convenient, however, to recapitulate as briefly as possible the accepted principles on this branch of the question :—

(1) That a *wakf* is valid and lawful by *consensus*.

(2) That it becomes absolute and operative, according to Abû Yusuf, immediately on the declaration of the *wâkif*, in other words immediately upon his signifying the *factum* of the dedication.

(3) That no particular words are necessary to create a *wakf*. So long as it is evident from the context or the conduct of the *wâkif* that a permanent dedication or settlement is intended, it is enough.

---

(1) *Hedâya* printed with the *Kifâya*, Vol. II, p. 895

(2) See *ante*, pp. 282-288.

4) That a *wakf* may be made by a Moslem in favour of any object whether terminable or otherwise not regarded as sinful in the Mussulman Law.

(5) That where a *wakf* is made for objects that are terminable or liable to extinction, the ultimate benefit will continue for the 'poor,' even though it may not have been destined for them expressly.(1)

Principle underlying the law of *wakf*.

It would seem from the language used in some of the cases that it is thought the introduction of the word 'poor' in the case of a *wakf* in favour of one's posterity, is for the purpose of giving a "semblance of charity" to the dedication. This conception appears to underlie almost all the decisions under review. That notion, however, it will be seen, is founded on an erroneous apprehension of the principles of Mahommedan Law. Under that Law, perpetuity, express or implied, is a necessary condition in a *wakf*. The *wâkif* must relinquish his right in the property *for ever*. And it must be consigned to the custody of God *for ever*. But it is not necessary that either the word *perpetuity* should be mentioned, or that it should be stated in express terms that the dedication is for ever. If the *wakf* is in favour of an object of an unfailing or permanent character, the dedication is valid and binding without the mention of the word *perpetuity*. If it is in favour of an object or objects, which, in the course of nature, must come to an end at some time or other, and if the dedication is made with the word *wakf* or any of its equivalents like *sadakah*, then according to the recorded and recognised doctrine, the law will presume that the ultimate reversion is to the poor "who never fail," unless some other object of a permanent character is mentioned. According to Mohammed, if the purpose is of a failing character, such as a *wakf* for one's *nasl* (posterity), then either the word *sadakah* (which will necessarily give the reversion to the poor) or the poor should be expressly mentioned. The object, therefore, of introducing the word 'poor' is not to give validity to a *wakf* in favour of descendants, *but to fulfil the requirements of permanency*. If the poor are mentioned in a *wakf* in favour of descendants, as the ultimate beneficiaries, the *wakf* is valid not only according to Abû Yusuf and Mohammed, but according to all the schools, Hanafî, Shâfeï, Mâliki, and the Shiah. If the poor are *not* mentioned, the law presumes it

(1) See the *Bahr-ur-Râik*, *post*, p. 785.

and supplies the omission according to the accepted Hanafî doctrines. Thus, according to the recognised Hanafî Law, a *wakf* in favour of objects liable to fail is as lawful as a *wakf* in favour of permanent objects ; the former as much secure *kurbat*, "approach to God," as the latter.

Wakf in favour of one's self.

And a provision for one's children and kindred is considered so pious, that where a dedication is made for the poor, "commencement should be made with the *wâkif's* descendants, then his kindred, then the neighbours, and then his fellow towns-people."(1)

I come now to another passage of the *Hedâya* which has been subjected to an equal degree of misconstruction, namely, where the difference between Abû Yusuf and Mohammed about the validity of a *wakf* in favour of one's self is discussed.

"If the *wâkif* constitute the income of the *wakf* for himself or reserve the governance of it for himself, it is valid according to Abû Yusuf (may God's blessings be with him)."

"I (may God be pleased with me) say that there are two [distinct] subjects [or sections] mentioned, *viz.*, the reservation of the usufruct for one's self, and, secondly, constituting one's self *mutwalli* thereof."

"The first is valid according to Abû Yusuf, though not so by analogy according to Mohammed. Such is the opinion of Hillâl of Rai, and has been adopted by Shâfeï. Some say that this difference between the two is founded on the difference between them as to the necessity of seisin and separation ; whilst others say that their difference is with respect to the present case only. And this difference exists whether the *wâkif* reserves a part of the income only for himself during his life, and after his death for the poor, or the whole for himself during his life to go to the poor after his death.(2) If, also, a man were to make a *wakf* reserving the whole or part of the income for his *ummahât-ul-awlâd* [pl. of *umm-ul-walad*, mother of his child, *viz.*, a bondswoman who has borne him a child], or his *muddabars* [slaves to whom he has given a conditional grant of freedom] during their lives, and after their death to the poor and indigent, some say that this is lawful by *consensus*. Whilst others say that in this case also there is the same differ-

(1) *Fath-ul-Kadîr*, Vol. II, p. 641 ; Comp. Tahtâwi (Egypt. Ed.), Pt. II, p. 533.

(2) That is to say Abû Yusuf holds it valid, whilst Mohammed apparently does not.

Wakf in favour of one's self.—contd.

ence [between Abû Yusuf and Mohammed], and this is correct,(1) for his reserving the income for their use for their lives is the same as if he conditioned it for his own use. Mohammed's argument is this: a *wakf* is an act of bounty in the shape of a transfer of the property [to God], as I have stated before, and consequently to reserve the whole or part of the income [of one's *wakf*], for one's self would make that transfer void, as a *tamlîk* [transfer] to one's self is not right,(2) as if a man made a *conditional sadakah*(3) [pious offering] or reserved a part of a mosque for himself. Abû Yusuf bases his opinion upon what is related from the Prophet (may God's blessings be with him), that is, that he used to eat out of the income of his own pious offerings, in other words, his own pious *wakfs*; as the *wâkif* cannot lawfully eat the same without a condition to that effect [the Prophet's consuming the same], shows that it is lawful for the *wâkif* to reserve the produce for himself. *Secondly*, as I have said before, *wakf* implies the extinguishment of the proprietary right in the *wakf* by its transfer to Almighty God with the object of approaching Him, so if one conditions that a part or the whole [of the income] should be for him [during life], it would mean his obtaining for himself [an interest] in what belongs to God; and not that he reserves to himself what [before] was his own; and it is lawful to reserve an interest in the property which is transferred to God; thus, if a man were to build a *khân* (caravanserai) or a reservoir, or [dedicate] a piece of land for a cemetery, and condition that he should reside [in the *khân*] or drink water out of the reservoir or be buried in the cemetery, it would be lawful. *Thirdly*, the motive in *wakf* is a desire to approach [God], and to expend the income of the *wakf* upon one's self is an act of piety by which an approach is obtained, for the Prophet has declared 'a man's provision for himself is an act of charity.'"

Kifâya.

The *Kifâya* commenting on this passage says, "if the *wâkif* constitute the produce or the governance of the *wakf* for himself, it is lawful. As regards the first, *viz.*, the reservation of the income by the *wâkif*, it is lawful according to Abû Yusuf, and the Jurists

---

1) The author means to say that the fact of there being a difference is correct.

(2) The property being already his, he cannot transfer it to himself.

(3) *Sadakah-munfaza*, charity given to a poor man with a condition that a portion will be the giver's property.

of Balkh are agreed thereon, and Sadr us-Shahîd has declared that the *Fatwa* is in accordance with the rule of Abû Yusuf.''(1).

No difference regarding the validity of a *wakf* in favour o one's descendants.

Throughout all these discussions in the *Hedâya* or anywhere else there is not the least trace of a difference of opinion as to the validity of a *wakf* in favour of one's descendants. There is a difference as to a dedication with a reserve of interest in favour of one's self; there is also some slight difference of opinion on the question whether a man may lawfully make a dedication in favour of his slaves (for that is tantamount to a dedication in favour of one's self), *but there is no difference of opinion as to the validity of a wakf in favour of one's children and descendants. All the Jurists, all the schools, are agreed thereon.*

Fatima Bibi v. *Advocate-General.*

The principles of the Mussulman Law, it is submitted, were rightly apprehended in the case of *Fatima Bibi* v. *The Advocate-General.*(2) In this case, West, J., said as follows :—'' If the condition of an ultimate dedication to a pious and unfailing purpose be satisfied, a *wakf* is not made invalid by an intermediate settlement on the founder's children and their descendants.'' [It must be noted that this is by consensus, without any difference of opinion between Abû Yusuf and Mohammed; according to Abû Yusuf, the law will presume the ultimate dedication to an unfailing purpose from the use of the word *wakf.*]

The learned Judge then goes on to say that '' the benefits they [the descendants] successively take, may constitute a perpetuity in the sense of the English Law, but according to the Mahommedan Law that does not vitiate the settlement, provided the ultimate charitable object be clearly designated.'' This, again, is accord ing to Mohammed and not Abû Yusuf. Apparently, the learned Judge overlooked the difference between the two, and the fact that Abû Yusuf's rule is the recognised law in the Hanafî world. Still there is some basis for the view which he has expressed in the passage last quoted, whereas the other cases are in conflict with the whole body of Moslem jurists and the principles contained in Mahommedan law-books.

---

(1) *Hedâya* printed with the *Kifâya*, Vol. II, p. 901.

(2) [1881] I. L., 6 Bom., p. 42 ; In the case of *Jugutmoni Chowdhrani* v. *Romjani Bibee* [1882], I. L., 10 Cal., 533), it was also thought that the ultimate purpose should be *expressly* mentioned.

Perpetuity, the essence of a *wakf*.

As a matter of fact, no analogy drawn from English Law with regard to trusts and settlements can assist in the comprehension of the Mahommedan Law relating to *wakfs*. The Mussulman Law relating to trusts or consecrations is founded on the ordinances of the Prophet, and the practice of his Companions and early Disciples based on those rules. Under the English Law a perpetuity is bad. Under the Mussulman Law, *without any difference*, perpetuity is an essential element in the constitution of a *wakf*. A consecration for one's family and posterity is, in the Mussulman religion and law, a charitable and pious purpose in the strictest sense of the term. But as one's descendants are liable to become extinct at some time or other, the law requires that, in order to ensure perpetuity, the reversion should be to an unfailing object. Under the recognised Hanafi Law, such reversion need not be in express terms, for if no other object is mentioned, in whose favour the *wakf* will take effect upon the extinction of the *wâkif's* descendants, the law itself will supply the omission, and the *wakf* will be for the poor.

English doctrine of perpe tuity inapplicable to the Mussulman Law.

Having regard to the difference in the standpoints of the English and the Mussulman lawyer, it is not surprising that the former, imbued with the doctrine of the English Law against perpetuities, should find it difficult to comprehend the Mahommedan Law relating to *wakf* in favour of one's family or the principle upon which it is founded.

The whole experience of judicial administration justifies the above observations: whilst the Government is acutely anxious to protect and preserve, in the public interests, family *wakf*, the Courts of Justice have taken an exactly opposite course.

The judgment of the Calcutta High Court in *Abul Fata Mahomed Ishak* v. *Rasamaya Dhur Chowdhry*(1) has been affirmed by the Judicial Committee of the Privy Council. The authorities in support of family benefactions were brought on this occasion to their Lordship's notice. With regard to them they remark as follows:—"The opinion of that learned Mahommedan lawyer (referring to the dissenting Judge in the case of *Bikani Mia*) (2) is founded, as their Lordships understand it, upon texts of an abstract character, and upon precedents very imperfectly stated.

---

(1) [1894] I. L., 22 Cal., 619; s. c. L. R., 22 I. A., 76.
(2) [1892] I. L., 20 Cal., 116.

For instance he quotes a precept of the Prophet Mahomet himself to the effect that 'a pious offering to one's family, to provide against their getting into want, is more pious than giving alms to beggars.' 'The most excellent of *sadakah* is that which a man bestows 'upon his family.' And by way of precedent he refers to the gift of a house in *wakf* or *sadakah*, of which the revenues were to be received by the descendants of the donor Arkan. His other old authorities are of the same kind."

"As regards precedents, their Lordships ought to know a great deal more in detail about them before judging whether they would be applicable at all. They hear of the bare gift and its maintenance, but nothing about the circumstances of the property except that in the case cited the house seems to have been regarded with special reverence—or of the family, or of the donor."

Examination of the judgment of the Judicial Committee in *Abul Fata Mahomed Ishak* v. *Rasamaya Dhur Chowdhry.*

It is submitted that those very precedents, which appeared meagre or imperfect to their Lordships, form, as has already been attempted to be shown in these pages, the foundation on which the Mahommedan Law relating to *wakf* is based; and it is upon those precedents that Mussulman communities throughout the world(1) have moulded their practice and their religious and social life for centuries.

(1) In the Art. by Professor Kresmárik (already referred to) in the *Zeitshrift der Deutschen Morgenländischen Gesellschaft*, p. 554, §§. 24, the validity of *wakfs* in favour of the founder's children and descendants is expressly recognised. Professor Kresmárik says "we have several times alluded to the lawfulness of a *wakf* in which it is conditioned that the income shall belong to the founder during his life time, and after his death to his children and their descendants, and after the extinction of his posterity shall be devoted to pious purposes. This class of *wakf* is in Turkey called *awlâdiyyêh-wakf* from the Arabic word *walad*, plural *awlâd* meaning children." Then after giving the opinions of Mohammed and Hillâl, and the doctrine of Abû Yusuf recognised as law on the point, he goes on to say, "it would be a mistake to assume that there is any legal difference between *awlâdiyyeh wakf* and *wakfs* for other pious purposes; or that the descendants of the *wâkif* are vested with any other rights over the *wakf* than the right to the income or benefits." "The Mahommedan Jurists," adds the Professor, "also insist that the *wakfs* in favour of children and children's children and ultimately for the poor are not to be regarded as legacies; they are ordinary *wakfs*; and the beneficiaries, they declare, live on God's property. The holder (inhaber) of an *awlâdiyyeh-wakf* is equally obliged to guard the integrity of the *wakf* as any other *mutwalli* and is responsible for any damage thereto." He cites authorities both Arabic and Turkish to show that such *wakfs* are absolutely valid in the Mussulman Law. A passage from the *Bazâzia* is of special importance. "When a person makes a *wakf* in favour of his *awlad* and the *awlâd* of his *awlâd* in perpetuity so long as the posterity lasts, and after them for the poor it is lawful, and it is not a legacy for his children for they only eat out of the property of Almighty God, according to the condition in the *wakf*."

Their Lordships observe :—" As regards precepts which are held up as the fundamental principles of Mahommedan Law, their Lordships are not forgetting how far law and religion are mixed up together in the Mahommedan communities; but they asked during the argument how it comes about that by the general law of Islâm, at least as known in India, simple gifts by a private person to remote unborn generations of descendants, successions that is of inalienable life-interests, are forbidden; and whether it is to be taken that the very same dispositions, which are illegal when made by ordinary words of gift, become legal if only the settlor says that they are made as *wakf*, in the name of God, or for the sake of the poor. To those questions no answer was given or attempted, nor can their Lordships see any. It is true that the donor's absolute interest in the property is curtailed and becomes a life-interest, that is to say, the wakfnama makes him take as mutwali or manager. But he is in that position for life; he may spend the income at his will, and no one is to call him to account. That amount of change in the position of the ownership is exactly in accordance with a design to create a perpetuity in the family, and indeed is necessary for the immediate accomplishment of such a design."

Difference between *hiba* and *wakf*.

The keynote to their Lordships' judgment is to be found in this passage; they cannot understand the difference between "simple gifts," to use their expression, and "*wakfs*," nor were counsel able to explain it to them. One important point of difference may be pointed out. Under the Hanafî (Sunni) Law, when a gift is made the donee takes an absolute interest in the subject of the grant; he has absolute power of disposition over it and can enjoy it in any way he likes and deal with it in any manner he chooses. And accordingly any restriction on, or derogation of, his right by the creation of life-interests is held to be invalid. In a gift or *hiba*, the donee is a human being; in a *wakf* (for whatever purpose made so long as it is not immoral), the donee is the Almighty God. In *hiba*, the object is to pass the property from one human being to another; in a *wakf*, the object is to keep the property in the custody of the Almighty(1) for the benefit of mankind; and, therefore, if the original purpose named at the consti-

(1) See the case of *Mohammed Sadik* v. *Mohammed Ali*, *supra*, 1 Sel. Reports, 17

tution of the *wakf* fails, the benefit is applied to other purposes of a like nature. If a *wakf* is for specific individuals, and they come to an end, it is applied to the relief of the poor and needy. Again, in the case of a *hiba* the dominion over the subject passes from one human being to another; in the case of a *wakf* the right of property is absolutely extinguished. If the grantor or appropriator were to remain in possession, it would be only as a trustee. He may be turned out any moment for breach of the conditions of the consecration. The beneficiaries have no right in the property; they are only entitled to the benefit of the trust to the extent specified in the *wakf*.(1)

Difference between *hiba* and *wakf*—contd.

"Their Lordships," the judgment continues, "have endeavoured to the best of their ability to ascertain and apply the Mahommedan law, as known and administered in India, but they cannot find that it is in accordance with the absolute, and as it seems to them extravagant, application of abstract precepts taken from the mouth of the Prophet. Those precepts may be excellent in their proper application. They may, for aught their Lordships know, have had their effect in moulding the law and practice of *wakf*, as the learned Judge says they have. But it would be doing wrong to the great law-giver to suppose that he is thereby commending gifts for which the donor exercises no self-denial, in which he takes back with one hand what he appears to put away with the other; which are to form the centre of attraction for accumulation of income and further accessions of family property; which carefully protect so-called managers from being called to account; which seek to give to the donors and their family the enjoyment of property free from all liability to creditors; and which do not seek the benefit of others beyond the use of empty words."

In making these remarks their Lordships, it is submitted, did not sufficiently keep in view the principle underlying the Mahommedan doctrine of family benefactions, that a provision for one's family and descendants is an act of piety, more pious than giving to strangers. And it is very probably owing to this circumstance that the law enunciated in the works of Mussulman writers seemed

Error in the comprehension of the underlying principle.

(1) The remarks of Professor Kresmárik (see *ante*) have an important bearing on the author's view of the law.

to their Lordships an "extravagant application of abstract precepts taken from the mouth of the Prophet."

The above quoted passages give rise to the following considerations, which are submitted without in any way impugning the authority which must always attach to the utterances of the Judicial Committee :—

Are Courts of Justice competent to inquire into the origin of, or reason for, any law recognised and accepted among any community subject to British rule, the enjoyment of which has been guaranteed to them as well by statute as by Royal Proclamation? Are they not bound to administer the law as they find it? Is it not their duty to ascertain what the law is as received, recognised and acted upon by the general body of the community? And if they are entitled to consider what was in the mind of the Lawgiver, are they competent to rely upon their own *à priori* reasoning and pre-conceived notions, without any regard to his recorded sayings and acts as understood by his followers all over the world?

In the cases to which reference have been made in this chapter, the Courts had to find what the developed Mahommedan Law of Wakf was, as accepted by the generality of Mussulman lawyers and jurists, and to administer the same, although it might have appeared to them that in some respects it was inconsistent with the law on the subject of *gift.* It is respectfully submitted it is not competent to Courts of Justice to refuse to administer the law as they find it, until it is ascertained to be in direct contravention of the statutory enactments of the State.

If the enunciation means that a *wakf* purely in favour of one's descendants is not valid, then it must be respectfully submitted that the views expressed by their Lordships are opposed to the Mahommedan Law and the general *consensus* of Mahommedan nations.

Recognition of the Mussulman Law by the Judicial Committee.

The Mahommedan subjects of His Majesty are, however, grateful to their Lordships for condemning in express terms the contention that cases relating to *wakf* should not be governed by the Mahommedan Law. Their Lordships say :—"Among the very elaborate arguments and judgments reported in *Bikani Mia's* case, some doubts are expressed whether cases of this kind are governed by Mahommedan Law; and it is suggested that the decision in *Ahsanullah Chowdhry's case* displaced the Mahommedan Law in favour of English Law. Clearly the Mahommedan Law ought to govern a purely Mahommedan disposition of property."

Although in the judgment in *Abul Fata Mahomed Ishak* v. *Rasamaya Dhur Chowdhry* there are many observations of a contentious character and in conflict with the Mussulman Law which have naturally caused a widespread feeling of alarm among the Mussulmans as a *direct* interference with their religious institutions, it is respectfully submitted that those observations are limited, and were in fact intended to be limited, to the special facts of the case. For some of the provisions of the deed were of such a vicious character that it was easy to presume that the *wakf* in question was not for the maintenance of the family, or to prevent them from falling into poverty, but was created only with the object of forming a centre for accumulation of income and aggrandisement; that in reality the founders had no pious object in its constitution.

Principle deducible from the judgment.

Taking their Lordships' judgment as it stands, two principles are deducible from it. The first of these appears to be that for the constitution of a valid *wakf* it is not necessary that the property should be *solely* dedicated for pious uses. Under this head their Lordships say as follows :—"Some authorities go so far as to hold that for a valid *wakf* the property should be solely dedicated to pious uses. On that point, however, this Board in *Ahsanullah Chowdhry's case* adopted the opinion of Mr. Justice Kemp to the effect that provisions for the family out of the grantor's property may be consistent with the gift of it as *wakf*." When a *wakf* of this kind is attempted to be created, there must be some present provision of a substantial, and not merely of an illusory, character for some pious uses, but those pious uses presumably need not be of a character which would be considered as such by a non-Moslem.

According to the enunciations of the Judicial Committee, therefore, where it is proved that a substantial portion of the income is devoted to or is likely to be spent on purposes, which, according to the law or customs and usages of the Mahommedans, are pious and meritorious, or in the performance of ceremonies and the distribution of charities on occasions regarded as sacred, the dedication will be valid.(1)

---

(1) *Phulchand* v. *Akbar Yar Khan* [1896], I. L., 19 All., 211.

As a necessary corollary from the above, it follows that when the portion of income set apart for religious or general pious purposes is such as to indicate that the *wakf* was not altogether illusory, nor designed merely for the aggrandisement of the *wâkif's* family, the consecration will be valid, though the rest of the income may be devoted for the maintenance of the *wâkif's* descendants.(1) In another case where the *wakfnâmah* provided in the first instance for the support of the descendants and kindred of the grantor who might be in want and in need of support, and directed that the surplus of the income of the property dedicated should be applied to purposes regarded as "undoubtedly religious," the dedication was held to be valid.(2) Of course the application of this principle will depend on the idiosyncrasies of individual judges, and it remains to be seen how it will work in practice.

The views expressed in *Abul Fata Mahomed Ishak* v. *Rasamaya Dhur Chowdhry* have more or less been adopted in subsequent decisions with the result that the administration of the Mussulman Law of *wakf* has become a matter of some difficulty not depending on recognised rules but on individual opinions proceeding on hypothetical considerations.(3)

For example in *Deoki Pershad* v. *Inaitullah*(4) the Allahabad High Court held that the fact that the grantor of a *wakf* (meaning thereby the *wâkif* or endower) has in the deed constituting the same made some provision for the maintenance of his kindred and descendants will not render the *wakf* invalid. Whilst in another case, the same Court held that a mere charge for some charitable purposes on the profits of an estate strictly settled on the family of the settlors in perpetuity and not dedicated in substance to charitable uses is not sufficient to constitute a good and valid *wakf*.(5) As I have already pointed out, this view proceeds upon the notion that a *wakf* in favour of the settlor's family is not valid, a notion wholly opposed to the Mahommedan law.

---

(1) See *Mahommed Israil Khan* v. *Sushti Chunder Ghose*, supra.

(2) *Deoki Pershad* v. *Inaitullah* [1892], I. L., 14 All., 375.

(3) See *Fazlur Rahim Abu Ahmud* v. *Mahomed Obedul Alim Abu Ahsan* [1903], I. L., 30 Cal., 666, and *Mahommad Anwar Ali* v. *Razia Bibi* [1904], I. L., 21 All., 320.

(4) [1892] I. L., 14 All., 375.

(5) *Mohammed Munawar Ali* v. *Rasulan Bibi* [1904], I. L., 21 All., 329.

In a case(1) which has already been cited in connection with another branch of the subject, the Allahabad High Court laid down, if I may venture to say, very correctly, that in determining whether a disposition of property made by a Mahommedan is or is not a valid *wakf*, the intention of the *wâkif* may be interpreted by reference to custom prevailing at the time the *wakf* was made, and proceeding upon the cases decided by the Judicial Committee,(2) it added that if there is found to be a substantial dedication of the property dealt with to charitable uses, that dedication will constitute a valid *wakf*.

In *Mohammed Azizuddin Ahmed Khan* v. *The Legal Remembrancer, N.-W. P. & Oudh*(3) a Mahommedan apparently belonging to the Hanafî sect (though in the report he is called by the general and vague term of "a Sunni Mohammedan") had executed and registered a document which purported to be a deed of *wakf*, but never acted upon it and retained possession until his death of the property dealt with by the deed, which property subsequently passed to his two sons by inheritance. The learned Judges held that under the circumstances no valid *wakf* of the property mentioned in the deed was constituted.

They also laid down that, according to the "law of Sunni Mahommedans," it is essential to the validity of a *wakf* that he *wâkif* should actually divest himself of possession of the *wakf* property.

This latter view, as I have already pointed out, is opposed to the recognised Hanafî doctrine. If the intention to create a *wakf* is clear from all the surrounding circumstances the mere fact that the *wâkif* retained possession of the property dedicated will not affect the validity of the *wakf*.

Dedication for the maintenance of a tomb

Under the English law, a dedication for the purpose of maintaining a tomb has been held to be invalid as being in contravention of the rule against perpetuities.(4) This doctrine has been imported by the Madras High Court into the decision of cases arising under the Mahommedan law which recognises, in distinct terms, the validity of dedications for the maintenance of tombs, sepulchres and mausoleums. In the case referred to, a Mussulman lady by an instru-

(1) *Phul Chand* v. *Akbar Yar Khan* [1896], I. L., 19 All., 211, supra.

(2) *Mohammed Ashanulla Chowdhry* v. *Amar Chand Kundu*, supra, and *Abul Fata Mahommed Ishak* v. *Rasamaya Dhur Chowdhry*, supra.

(3) [1895] I. L., 15 All., 321.

(4) *Neo* v. *Neo*, L. R., 6 P. C., 381.

ment in writing dedicated certain movable and immovable properties for the up-keep of her husband's tomb and "for the daily, monthly and annual expenses of the aforesaid mausoleum, such as lighting, frankincense, flowers, and the salaries of repeaters of the Koran and readers of benedictions, etc., as well as for the annual *fateha* ceremonies of the deceased," and after her own death for her annual *fateha* ceremony. It was found that a traveller's inn was erected by the endower of the property as an appurtenance to the tomb, and that the performance of the ceremonies necessarily involved the distribution of charity, and that the lights at the tomb were of use to passers-by. Under the Mahommedan Law there could not be the faintest doubt that the *wakf* in this case was absolutely valid. The Madras High Court, nevertheless, held that the instrument did not create a valid *wakf*, and that it was void as contravening the rule against perpetuities.(1)

In *Bibi Jan* v. *Kalb Hossain*(2) it appeared that a Mahommedan lady of the Sunni sect had dedicated certain properties "to God and charitable and religious purpose" and provided out of the income for the celebration of the birth of Ali Murtaza (the fourth Caliph of Islam), the observance of the Moharram and the death-anniversaries (*Fateha Barsi*)(3) of the members of the *Wâkif's* family, the upkeep of the *tazias*(4) and the repairs of the Imambara. In a suit by her heirs to have the *wakf* declared invalid, the High Court of Allahabad held that the dedication was not illusory; that there was an intention of creating a substantial *wakf* for pious and charitable purposes and that the objects for which the *wakf* was created were valid. The learned Judges added that the keeping of *tazias* was a pious and religious ceremony not restricted solely to the Shia sect.

---

(1) *Kaliloola Rakib* v. *Nuseeruddeen Sahib* [1894], I. L., 18 Mad., 201.

(2) [1908] I. L., 31 All., 136.

(3) Annual ceremonies observed both among Shias and Sunnis at the anniversaries of the death of people at which prayers are offered and blessings invoked for the soul of the deceased.

(4) Symbols of the biers of the Imam-martyrs.

CHAPTER XI.

THE OBJECTS OF A WAKF.—(Continued.)

SECTION I.

WAKF IN FAVOUR OF ONE'S CHILDREN AND DESCENDANTS.

Principles of construction

ACCORDING to all the jurists, when a *wakf* is constituted in favour of the *wâkif's* descendants, and they are mentioned in general terms, or when three generations are mentioned, the trust takes effect in their favour so long as they exist. For example, if a man were to say, 'this land of mine is a *wakf* for my children,' using the term *awlâd* or *farzandân*, the term being general, it will endure for the benefit of his descendants so long as they are in existence. And so long as a single descendant of the *wâkif* is in existence, no portion of the usufruct will go to the poor.

Similarly, if he were to say, "this *wakf* is for my child and the child of my child and the child of the child of my child" (using the word in the singular, but mentioning three generations), the effect would be the same.

This is clear from the following passage in the *Fatâwai Alamgiri* :—

"And if a man should say 'this is a *wakf* for [original, *upon*] my child and for the child of my child and for the child of the child of my child,' mentioning three generations, the income is to be expended upon his *awlâd* (children) for ever, so long as there are any descendants, and is not to be applied to the poor; while one remains, the *wakf* is to them, and the lowest among them, the nearer and more remote being alike, unless the *wâkif* say in making the *wakf*, 'the nearer is nearer,' or say, 'on my child, then on the child of my child,' or say, 'generation after generation' (*batnan-b'aad-batn*), when a beginning must be made with them with whom the *wâkif* has begun."(1)

"Or if he should say, 'this my land is a *wakf* or a pious *mowkoofa* on my children' (*awlâd*), all generations are included on

(1) After the *Fatâwai Kâzi Khân ; Fatâwai Alamgiri*, Vol. II, p. 474.

account of the general character of the name; but the whole is to the first generation while any remains, and when they are exhausted, to the second, and, when they are exhausted, to the third and fourth and fifth, all these generations participating in the division, and the nearer and more remote being alike.''(1)

This principle is given in identical terms in the *Fath ul-Kadîr*.

It would be otherwise if he said 'this is a *wakf* for my child (*walad*),' using the singular expression, or even if he said 'my child's child,' unless he extended his meaning by other expressions, indicating that though the term was used in the singular, or though only two generations were mentioned, his intention was to give the proceeds to his descendants so long as they happen to be in existence.

Principles of construction.

The *Fatâwai Alamgiri* states further that if a person were to say, 'this my land is a *mowkoofa* as a pious offering on my child (*walad*),' the produce is for the child of his loins, males and females taking equally, and so long as there is in existence one child of his loins, the produce is to him or her only. When there no longer remains one of the first generation (*batn*), the produce is to be expended on the poor, nothing being allowed to the child of a child. But if he had no child of his loins at the time of the settlement, and there was then a child of a son, the produce is to the son's child, none of the generations below him participating with him; the child of a son, in the event of there being no child of the loins, thus coming into his place. The child of a daughter is not included, according to the approved traditions,.....which is correct; this is according to the *Fatâwai Kâzi Khân*. If, after this, he should have a child of his loins, the future produce is to be expended on such child according to the *Zakhîra*. And when there is no child of the first and second generations, but there happens to be a third, a fourth and any lower generation, according to the *Muhît* the third generation, and those below them, participate together, even though there should be many of them."

And then comes the significant passage, "all the rules stated in respect of a *wakf* in favour of his child" [meaning the child

(1) *Fatâwai Alamgiri*, Vol. II, p. 474; after the *Muhit-us-Sarakhsi*.

of the endower] are applicable to a *wakf* in favour of the 'child of such an one' [meaning another person]."(1)

So also in the *Radd ul-Muhtâr*:—

"But if a man were simply to say that it was a *wakf* for his *walad*, then the daughter's children will not be included, for *walad* by itself means his own child,....though it includes in the language of custom the son s children, owing to the fact that the son's children are descended from the *wâkif*."(2).

But there is considerable divergence of opinion regarding the exclusion of daughter's children when two generations are mentioned.

The *Fatâwai Alamgiri*, quoting the *Muhît-us-Sarakhsî*, states that "If one were to say, 'this my land is a pious offering and a *wakf* (*sadakah-mowkoofa*) on my child and the child of my child,' the child of his loins, and the child of his child in existence on the day of the settlement, and those who are born afterwards, are included, and the two generations participate in the produce, but none below them are included, nor the children of daughters, according to the approved traditions (*Zâhir-ur-Rawâyèt*); and the *fatwa* is in accordance with it."(3)

According to Imâm Mohammed, the term *walad-ul-walad*, "child's child" or "children's children" includes daughter's children. The subject has been discussed at some length in the *Radd-ul-Muhtâr*(4) where the author states that eminent jurists like Khassâf, and Ibni Himâm have held the contrary, *viz.*, that in such a *wakf* the children of daughters are not to be excluded. Khassâf, in fact, says there is no warrant for the doctrine of exclusion except a statement of Abû Hanîfa which is applicable to the case of a bequest. Kâzi Khan(5) also says that Khassâf has held in accordance with the opinion of Imâm Mohammed that daughter's children are included in the benefit of such a *wakf*. In another place he lays down the following rule:—When a person says this is [*a wakf*] for my *awlâd* and their *awlâd*,

(1) *Fatâwai Alamgiri*, Vol. II, p. 474. the authority cited for the last enunciation being the *Zakhîra*.

(2) *Radd ul-Muhtâr*, Vol. III, p. 672.

(3) *Fatâwai Alamgiri*, Vol. III, p. 474; after the *Muhît-us-Sarakhsi*. Comp. the *Bahr-ur-Râik*; see Appendix. The word "*awlâd*" is a general term and includes all descendants whether descended through males or females.

(4) Vol. III, p. 672.

(5) *Fatâwai Kâzi Khân in loco*.

in all such cases it will include the children of sons and the children of daughters, and *this is correct.*"(1)

"Allâmah Shaikh Ali al-Mukaddasi [the author of the *Hâwi*, who died A. H., 600], has laid down that if a man were to make a *wakf* in favour of his *walad* and the *walad* of his *walad*, in such a case his own children, the children of his sons and the children of his daughters will be included. And Khassâf and Kâzi Khân have adopted this view."(2)

So in the *Fath ul-Kadîr*, "if a person were to say 'this is a *wakf* on my *walad* and the *walad* of my *walad* (child of my child) and then on the poor,' in this all the children of his loins participate, the children of his daughters alike with the children of his sons. And Hillâl and Khassâf have accepted and Kâzi Khân has held it to be correct."(3)

It may be taken, therefore, that the view expressed in the *Fatâwai Alamgiri* represents only one set of opinions, whilst Khassâf's doctrine appears to be supported by a greater weight of authority.

Kâzi Khân states these principles shortly thus:—If a person make a *wakf* of his land for his *walad* (issue of his loins), and after him or her for the benefit of the poor, without mentioning that upon his or her death, it will go to his or her issue, in such a case, according to the jurist Abu'l Kâsim, upon the death of such *walad*, the produce will go to the poor. If he says, "this is a *wakf* for my *walad* and my *walad's walad* and after them for the poor," according to Abu'l Kâsim, the produce will be applied to his children and children's children, and on the death of the last surviving of the *wâkif's* children's children, the produce will go to the poor and not to the descendants in the third degree. But if he were to say "for my *walad* and my *walad's walad* and my *walad's walad's walad*," so that the third generation is [expressly or impliedly] included, the produce would be applied to his descendants in perpetuity, as long as any of them be surviving, and it will not be given to the poor so long as any

Mention of three generations equivalent to perpetuity.

(1) *Fatâwari Kâzi Khan*, Vol. II, p. 253.

(2) "Khassâf is an Imâm whose worth has been testified to by Shams-ul-Aimma Halwâni who has declared that Khassâf's views are adopted everywhere." —*Ibid*, p. 672.

(3) *Fath ul-Kadir*, Vol. II, p. 643.

of his descendants, however low, may be in existence. *When the wâkif has mentioned three generations, it will be applied to his descendants always, so long as they are in existence, and the near and remote will be equally entitled to the benefit thereof, unless the wâkif has provided that the nearer shall be preferentially entitled, or has said " line after line " or " for my children and after them for their children,"* and so on. In such cases the commencement of the division will be made as provided for by the *wâkif*."(1)

In other words, when a man makes a *wakf* for his (or anybody else's) child (*walad*)(2) and does not mention that after the death of that child it will enure to the benefit of succeeding generations, on the extinction of the first generation, the *wakf* will go to the poor. But if he uses the term *awlâd*, *farzandân*, *nasl*, *'akab* or *khalaf*, the *wakf* is for his descendants, male as well as female, in perpetuity. When a *general term of this character is used, no further condition is necessary.* Similarly, if he mentions three generations as the recipients of the benefit of the *wakf*, it is tantamount to his declaring that it is a perpetual *wakf* in favour of his descendants, and will be applied to their benefit as long as any of them is alive.(3)

A general term is equivalent to saying 'so long as his posterity lasts.'

If a *wakf* is made in favour of children specifically named, the others not named will be excluded.

Wakf in favour of children specifically named.

A *wakf* in favour of *A*, and after him for his children (generally) will include all the children, both male and female. Similarly, if a person make a *wakf* for his own children (*awlâd*) both males and females will be included.

If a man were to say, " this *wakf* is for my children and *their* children and *their* children's children" those of his children who were living at the time of the creation of the *wakf*, or who are born afterwards, and their children would take, but not the children of those children who had died before the *wakf*.

But if he said, " the *wakf* is for my child or children and for my child's child or children's children and for *their* children's children," then the children of those children who had died before

(1) Same in the *Hâwi* and the *Durr-ul-Mukhtâr ; Radd ul-Muhtâr*, Vol. III, p. 677, see *post*.
(2) *Walad* has usually a collective signification and means children.
(3) Comp. the *Majm'aa ul-Anhar*, Part II, p. 641.

the creation of the *wakf* would participate; for the term "my children's children" refers to all his grandchildren, not merely to the children of those children who are entitled to participate in the *wakf* at its inception.(1)

Validity of a *wakf* in favour of one's descendants.

It must be noted that these principles proceed on the validity of *wakfs* in favour of one's family and descendants and show the utter untenability of the position assumed by the Indian tribunals in declaring against them. The application of the rules depend on the intention of the *wâkif* as deducible from the language used by him.

When a *wakf* is made in the following terms, "This *wakf* is in favour of my children that are born and for my *nasl*," any children born afterwards will be included; but if the term, *their nasl*, had been used the after-born children of the *wâkif* would not have been included.(2)

If the *wâkif* were to say, "it is for my *walad* who are born and for their *nasl* and for all my *walad* who may be born hereafter," his after-born children will take but not their children. If he were to say, "it is for my *walad* who are born and their *nasl* and for the *nasl* of those that are born subsequently," the children of the after-born children will take though not their parents.

Wakf in favour of the children and the poor.

When a *wakf* is in favour of children without any right of survivorship, as each child dies his interest goes to the poor, for the interest of each is separate. But the case is different where there is a right of survivorship or joint tenancy implied from the nature of the grant. For example, if a man were to make a *wakf* in favour of his children and then for the poor; it is clear that the intention of the donor was that the *wakf* should continue for the benefit of the *wâkif's* children so long as any one of them was living, and it is only on their failure that the *wakf* should go to the poor; consequently when each child dies his interest goes to the survivors, or his or her child as the case may be.(3)

Right of survivorship.

If a man were to make a *wakf* in favour of his wife and his children, upon her death her interest will not devolve upon his child by her alone but will go to all his children, unless there is any

---

(1) *Radd ul-Muhtâr*, III, p. 678. (2) *Fath ul-Kadir*, Vol. II, p. 644.

(3) *Radd ul-Muhtâr*, Vol. III, p. 680.

provision to the contrary making her interest descendible to *her* children.(1)

If the *wakf* is made "for my sons," or "for my brethren," the females will be included. If a man were to say, "the *wakf* is for my daughters," and he has only sons, the *wakf* will be applied to the benefit of the poor, until a daughter is born to him, or it is shown that the expression had been used by mistake, and though he used the term daughters he meant sons or both.(2)

If a *wakf* is made generally without any specification regarding the proportion in which the males and females of each line should take the produce, the distribution should take place in the usual proportion of two for each male and one for each female.(3)

The word *nasl* includes all descendants on the male as well as the female side.(4)

'Akab and khalaf

The word *'akab* or *khalaf* includes descendants through males; *âl*, *jins*, and *ahl-ul-bait* of the *wâkif* include those persons who are related to him through the father or grandfather or any other male ancestor. And *kârâbatdâr*, *arhâm* and *ansâb* of the *wâkif* include all those people who are related to the deceased from any ancestor, male or female. The highest ancestor to which the line would be carried is the person who first adopted Islâm.

If a man were to say, "this is a *wakf* for my *walad* and for my *nasl* in perpetuity and that should any one of them die, his or her share should go to his *nasl*," in such case the entire produce would be divided among all the *wâkif's* children and *nasl*; and the shares of those among them who are dead will go to their children.(5)

If a person were to make a *wakf* in favour of his children, and make no provision declaring that upon the death of any one of them his or her share should go to his or her children, such share or interest will merge in the general produce and will be divided among

---

(1) *Wajiz ul-Muhit.*

(2) From the *As'âf.* The reason given is that according to the Arabic idiom when males and females both co-exist the use of the plural form of the masculine noun includes the feminine, so that though the word 'son' in the singular refers only to a male child, the word 'sons' includes female children as well, when both sons and daughters co-exist. The converse case, however, does not hold good.

(3) *Radd ul-Muhtâr*, Vol. III, p. 679.

(4) *Ibid*, p. 682; *Majm'aa ul-Anhar*, Part II, p. 611.

(5) *Ibid*, p. 679.

the beneficiaries for the time being.(1) If the *wâkif* were to make a condition that upon the death of any of his descendants, his or her share should go to his or her *nasl*, in that case it would devolve upon all the children of such deceased descendant, and should any of the children be dead, the children of such child would take his or her share. Should he say nothing about the devolution of the share of deceased descendants, or should he say that the share of such deceased descendant should go to a higher class, and one of that class is surviving, in both these cases, the entire produce will be divided among the surviving beneficiaries for the time being among the descendants of the *wâkif*, and will not go to the poor so long as any of the posterity of the *wâkif* is living.(2)

Preference to propinquity.

If a man were to say that when one of his descendants dies, his share should go to other descendants of the same degree, in that case the nearest in blood would be preferred to one more remote; and if there be none of that degree, the share would merge in the general produce. For example, if a person die leaving him surviving sister's children and paternal uncle's children, the latter would take his share in preference to the former, being of the same degree though remoter in blood.

If a person were to make a *wakf* in favour of his children according to their number and their legal shares, and were also to provide therein that the female children should get no share, unless they are widows, and that after the children, the *wakf* should be for their children, and their children's children and their descendants, *on condition, that if any one of them should die leaving children, his or her share should go to such children*, the aforesaid condition would refer to all.(3)

Farzand includes daughters.

If a man were to say "this is a *wakf* for my *farzand*,"(4) and he also has daughters living at the time, the daughters will be included; because when a person has got sons and daughters they are mentioned in the masculine gender, "and, so also, even should the children be all daughters."

(1) *Radd ul-Muhtâr*, Vol. III, p. 679.

(2) *Ramz ul-Hakâik; Radd ul-Muhtâr*, Vol. III, p. 679; see *post*.

(3) *Radd ul-Muhtâr*, Vol. III, p. 671.

(4) The Persian word *farzand* means a son, but in the common acceptation of the term, especially in its plural form, it applies to both male and female offspring.

When a masculine term is used collectively it includes females.

If a person were to make a *wakf* in favour of his children, and after that upon their children and so on, generation after generation and provide also that should any one of them die leaving children, then his or her share should go to his or her child, and if such person should die before becoming entitled to a share in the rents and profits, leaving him surviving a child, the latter will take his place and become entitled at the distribution of the profits to the share of his parent.

If the *wâkif* were to die leaving him surviving several children, *A*, *B*, *C*, *D*, and *E*, and then *A* were to die leaving certain children, the share of *A* would go to his children, in accordance with the conditions laid down by the *wâkif*. But supposing *B* were then to die, leaving several children and grandchildren by a predeceased child. The question arises would such grandchildren be entitled to share in the interest of *B* along with his children ? Sabki has answered this question in the negative. He holds that *B's* share should go entirely to the children, and the grandchildren should be excluded. On this point Khassâf agrees with him. But Khassâf holds that upon the death of the last surviving member of the first group, *viz.*, the children of the *wâkif*, the rule will cease to operate ; that is, if *E*, the last surviving son of the *wâkif*, were to die leaving a child, his share will not go to his child, but the entire income will be divided among the grandchildren of the *wâkif*, that is, members of the second class, the same rule applying as in the previous case, *viz.*, the share of each member of this class upon his death, will descend to his children until the class is exhausted, when the distribution would take place according to the number of the third class. According to Khassâf, therefore, the members of each class take *per capita*. According to Sabki, the distribution is *per stirpes*. He holds that, as the members of each class die, their shares descend to their children respectively. Jalâl Suyûti differs from both Khassâf and Sabki. He holds that when any member of one class dies, leaving children and grandchildren by a deceased child, the grandchildren and children share in the interest of their grandparent, that is, the grandchildren take the share of their parents, the distribution being *per stirpes*.(1)

Distribution *per stirpes*.

(1) *Radd ul-Muhtâr*, Vol. III, p. 672 ; *Majma'aa ul-Anhar*, Part II, p. 641.

The author of the *Ashbâh* agrees with Sabki, and is followed by all moderns.

Principle.

The result is, that when the adjunct '*waw*' ('and') is used between the lines, then after the extinction of each line the distribution begins again, but when the word *summa* ('then') is used the division continues *per stirpes* throughout. And this view is apparently adopted by the majority of Shâfeï lawyers and some of "our own (Hanafîs)." The consensus of opinion is, that when a person dies during the lifetime of his father, leaving him surviving a child, that child takes his father's share in the interest of the grandfather but acquires no interest in that of his uncle.(1)

Wakf for lineal descendants

If a person were to make a *wakf* for his *lineal* descendants, the children of daughters will not be included, unless those children are the offspring of husbands, who are the lineal descendants of the *wâkif*. If a woman were to make a *wakf* for her *ahl-ul-bait* or her *jins*, her children will not be included unless the father of the children belongs to her *kowm* or tribe.

Principle.

If a man were to make a *wakf* for his or anybody else's descendants, without mentioning the order in which they should enjoy the income of the *wakf*, the near and the remote will take equally, in other words, the division will be *per capita*. For example, if a man were to say, "I make this *wakf* in favour of Zaid's descendants in perpetuity as long as his line lasts," Zaid's children and grandchildren will be entitled to share equally, and there will be no difference between son's children and daughter's children; they will take equally.

This principle applies where no order of succession is indicated by the specification of the line or generation (*batn*). Where the order of the line is not given, by mentioning "generation after generation" (*batnan-b'aad-batn*), the rents and profits will be divided equally among all the descendants, male as well as female, living at the time of the distribution, the one lower in degree getting the same share as the one nearest. And as each person among them dies his share merges in the *wakf* estate, and the entire usufruct is divided among the beneficiaries living at the time of the division. If the succession of lines is given, that is, the *wakf* is in favour of the descendants, "generation after generation" (*batnan-b'aad-batn*),

(1) *Radd ul-Muhtâr*, Vol. III, p. 672; *Maj'aa ul-Anhar*, Part II, p. 641.

in that case it would imply that the nearer line or class takes first and after them the "line" next after.(1)

If a man were to declare that the *wakf* was in favour of the sons of his *awlâd*, or his *akriba* or his brethren, the females will be included. Inclusion of females.

Where a *wakf* is constituted in favour of a child (*walad*), and after him for the poor, the child who may be in existence at the time the produce comes into being enters into the benefit of the *wakf*, whether he was born at the time of the creation of the *wakf* or after it.

Similarly, if the words were to this effect, "this is a *wakf* for my child, and any other child that I may have, and when they fail, upon the poor." And the *Fatâwai Alamgiri* goes on to add, "when a man has made use of these words, though he have no child at the time, the *wakf* is valid; and the produce, when there is any, is to be divided among the poor. If a child should be born to the *wâkif* after the division, the subsequent produce is to be expended on this child so long as he lives; and when there is no surviving child, it is to be expended on the poor."

When a trust is created in favour of one's children (*awlâd*), a right is established only in favour of "children of known paternity" (*nasab*). "Hence if there be a child who is not of known paternity, but whose paternity is known on the word of the appropriator, such child is not included." Children of known paternity included.

"As already stated, if one should say 'I have made this *wakf* on my *children*,' and he has only one child at the time of the produce, half of it will be for that child and half for the poor.' But if the words were 'on my child,' and he has only one, the whole of the *wakf* is for the child. So also when he has had several children, but only one is surviving."

---

(1) Khassâf; Mr. Baillie's note will be of interest in this connection.
"It appears from these cases that when two or three generations are mentioned separately and then joined by the word 'and,' all the generations participate together unless there is something to indicate that one generation is to take in succession to another when the first would have an estate for life in possession and the other estates in tail, as it is termed in England. There seems to be no reason for a different construction if the settlement were on a person and his children. But "with" denotes conjunction as well as 'and.' A settlement on a person with children, or *bafurzundan* as it would be in Persian, ought therefore, it would seem, to be similarly construed, that is, to him and them jointly." See S. D. A. Reports, Calcutta, for 1853, p. 648.

Reservation of a right of survivorship.

Shaikh Imâm Abû Bakr Mohammed ibn Fazl has declared that when a *wakf* is in favour of two children *and when they die then on their children*, upon the death of one of them leaving issue, his share of the profits will be given to the poor until such time as the other son of the *wâkif* also is dead, when the entire *wakf* will be devoted to the benefit of the grandchildren, *unless the wâkif has provided that, upon the death of any one of the immediate beneficiaries, the produce will go to the surviving issue of the deceased.*(1) So also in the *Fatâwai Alamgiri.*(2)

Principle.

When a person makes a *wakf* of his land for his descendants (*awlâd*) and destines its ultimate appropriation for the poor, upon the death of each beneficiary the entire produce will go to the survivors, and it is only upon their failure that the benefit of the *wakf* will accrue to the poor. *So long as any of the descendants are surviving nothing will be given to the poor.*

" When a man has made a *wakf* for his son and for his children and for his children's children in perpetuity so long as any one among his descendants is alive. Abu'l Kâsim says the produce will be divided among the *wâkif's* son's children *per capita*, the female and male taking equal shares. And when he was asked regarding the children of daughters, he said they would be entitled, because they are the *awlâd* of his *awlâd*."

Wakf in favour of *awlâd* or descendants.

If he should say, " This my land is a pious *wakf* on my children (*awlâd*)," all generations are included on account of the general character of the name; but the whole is to the first generation while any remain; and when they are exhausted, to the second and when they are exhausted, to the third and fourth and fifth, all these generations participating in the division, and the nearer and more remote being equal.(3) If he should say, " I have dedicated it on my children," and he has only one child at the time of the produce, half of it will be for that child and half to the poor. But if the words were " on my child," and he has only one, the whole of the *wakf* is for that child. So, also, when he has had several children and they have failed leaving only one remaining.

" If a man were to make a *wakf* with the words, ' a *wakf* on my two children, and when they fail then upon the children of both,

(1) Kâzi Khân. (2) *Fatâwai Alamgiri*, Vol. II, p. 470.
(3) *Fatâwai Alamgiri*, Vol. II, p. 470.

and the children of the children of both for ever so long as there are descendants,' and one of the children were to die leaving a child, half of the produce is to be expended on the surviving child and half on the poor; but when the second of the children of the *wâkif* dies, the whole of the produce is to be expended on the children of the two, and the children of the children of the two. If he were to say, 'This property is a pious *wakf* on the needy of my children,' and there is only one needy child among them, the half of the produce is to be expended on him and half on the poor."

In all these instances the conclusion turns on the intention of the *wâkif*. If he intended that the benefit should go to several children, in that case if there is only one child, he would only receive half the income. But if his intention were that his children should be the primary beneficiaries, the entire benefit would go to the one child.

In connection with this subject, however, it must be remembered that "the object of the *wakf* depends on custom (*'urf*), and if a person were to make a *wakf* for his children, and his children's children with the intention that whosoever among them may be surviving should take the whole of the produce, the entire produce would go to his descendants, though there be only one."(1)

If a person were to create a *wakf* in favour of his *nasl*, or *zurriat* (both words meaning progeny), the children of his sons and the children of his daughters would be included, whether near or remote.

In the case of *Shaikh Kasimodin* v. *Nawab Mir Sayad Alam Khan*,(2) the Bombay High Court held that the term *ahfâd* being a term of the largest and most general signification, included the descendants of males as well as females.

When a *wakf* is made by a person who is not suffering from a mortal disease and the *wâkif* declares that the distribution of the income should be according to the *Faràizullah* (the divine law) among his children, the division will take place among all the beneficiaries, without distinction of sex, in equal proportions.

When a *wakf* is made in favour of consanguine and uterine brothers, they take equally.

---

(1) *Radd ul-Muhtâr*, Vol. III, p. 672.
(2) [1880], I. L., 10 Bom., 110.

Principle relating to distribution of the proceeds of a *wakf*.

When a *wakf* is made in favour of children, the income is to be divided among them equally. This is according to Abû Yusuf and "the *Fatwa* is with him." A condition in the *wakfnâma* giving to one child a greater interest than the other, or to the sons more than the daughters is sinful, as it is sinful to make any difference in gifts. This is the opinion of all leading jurists.

Shaikh Nûr ud-dîn Mukaddasi, Mufti of Cairo, and Shaikh ul-Islâm Mohammed Tahtâwi, Shâfeï Muftî of Egypt, have given decisions to the same effect, that is, when the *wâkif* makes a *wakf* in favour of a class, all persons belonging to that class take equally whether they belong to the same sex or not, or whether they differ in their "roots." For example, when it is in favour of brothers, consanguine and uterine brothers take together and not according to their shares under the law of succession. Similarly, if a man were to say that in case of his dying without issue, the *wakf* would endure to the benefit of his relatives belonging to the class nearest to him in degree, and he dies leaving only one paternal uncle's son and two paternal uncle's daughters, the male and female cousins take the income in equal shares. The meaning, therefore, of the expression *Farâiz-ullah* is not that the division should be according to their shares under the law of inheritance, but according to the rule laid down by the Prophet in which he declared that no preference should be shown in gifts; and consequently the donees will take equally.(1)

Principle.

When a man makes a *wakf for the sons of A, excepting the sons residing abroad*, and then some of the sons leave the city or country, they lose the right and do not recover it on their return to the country. Similarly, if a *wakf* is made for the children of *A*, engaged in the pursuit of learning, and some of them give up their studies, they lose all interest in the *wakf* and do not recover it on resuming their studies, unless in all these cases the *wâkif* has declared that they would get back their interest on their return.

The beneficiaries not entitled to partition.

When a *wakf* is made in favour of two or more individuals, they are not entitled to a partition of the property in proportion to their share of the profits. The *mutwalli*, however, has the power to make such arrangements as he deems necessary, consistently with the provisions of the *wakf*, for the due cultivation of the *wakf* lands or occupation of the *wakf* premises.

---

(1) *Radd ul-Muhtâr*, Vol. III, p. 672.

When a *wakf* is created in favour of one's children and on their extinction in favour of the poor, it is lawful. Hillâl(1) declares that the children of the children will participate in the benefit of the *wakf* if they be in existence at the time when the produce or income becomes distributable, whether they were or were not in existence at the time of the dedication. This view has been accepted by the jurists of Balkh.(2) Accordingly, when a person declares the *wakf* to be in favour of his children and grandchildren *all of them who happen to be in existence at the time the produce comes into being or becomes distributable, will participate in its benefit.*

A *wakf* in favour of the *wâkif's* progeny valid.

When a *wakf* is constituted in favour of the *wâkif's* child and his *nasl* (progeny), the "*wakf*," says the *Fatâwai Alamgiri*,(3) "is valid, and the males and females of his children and children's children are included: the near and the remote, the children of sons and the children of daughters, the free and bond, being all equal, although the shares of the bondsmen belong to their masters."...

"And if he should say, 'I have made it a *wakf* on my child and my *nasl*,' and he has a grandchild at the time, but a child of his loins is born to him after the *wakf*, they both enter into the right. So also if he should say, 'this my land is a pious *mowkoofa* on my children that have come into being,(4) and on my *nasl*,' a child subsequently born would enter by means of the word *nasl* according to the *Fatâwai Kazi Khan*. If he were to say this land is a pious *wakf* 'on my children that have come into being and *their nasl*,' the children in being and their *nasl* would enter, whether the *nasl* were in being or not, but none of his children who are not in being, nor their *nasl*, would be included. So also if he were to say, 'upon my children in being, and their children,' and should there afterwards be born to him a child of his loins, that child would not be included. And if he were to say, 'upon my

(1) Hillâl ibn Yahya ibn Muslim Basri died in the year 456 A. H. He was a disciple of Yusuf ibn Khâlid Basri who himself was a disciple of Abû Hanîfa Some say he received his legal education under Abû Yusuf and Zuffar. He was called Râwi because he followed implicitly the usages of the people of Kûfa; *Radd ul-Muhtâr*, Vol. III, pp. 676-680.

(2) Whose views are adopted in India.

(3) P. 475, quoting the *Hâwi*.

(4) In the original (مخلوقين) meaning "created," which includes a child in the womb, see *post*.

children that have come into being, and on the children of their children, and their *nasl*,' his children in being and their children and the children of their children forever, while there are any *nasl* or descendants, are included.".......

Principle. Again—"If a man not suffering from death-illness were to say 'I have made this my land a pious *mowkoofa* to Almighty God for ever, for my children and the children of my children, and the children of their children, and their *nasl* for ever, so long as there are *nasl*,' every child that he had at the time of the *wakf* and every child born to him thereafter before the existence of the produce, and every child of the child for ever, enters into the benefit of this consecration, and if any of them should die before the existence of the produce, the share of the person so dying becomes extinguished; but if the death should not occur till after the existence of the produce, the person dying would have acquired a right to his share, which would pass to his heirs; the higher and lower generations sharing equally, unless it had been said in making the *wakf* that a beginning was to be made with the higher generation, and then the generation below it. In that case, if all of the higher generation but one person should die, the whole would go to that person alone, to the exclusion of the generation below. "......(1)

And if one were to say, 'for my child and child of my child for ever so long as there is any *nasl*,' without saying *batnan-b'aad-batn*, but adding 'as often as one dies his share of the produce is to his child,' the produce would, before the death of any of them, be among the whole of the children and children's children and their *nasl* equally, and if one of them should die leaving a child, the share of the person so dying would go to his child, who would thus have his father's share in addition to that appointed for himself by the *wâkif*."(2)

It is clear, therefore, that when a dedication is made in favour of "the children and the progeny" (*walad* and *nasl*), and at the time there is only one grandchild but subsequently a child is born to the *wâkif*, both will participate. Similarly, if a person were to declare a *wakf* to be in favour of his children who are in existence, and for his *nasl*, children born after the *wakf* will be included as his *nasl*.

---

(1) *Fatâwai Alamgiri* Vol. II, p. 476, after the *Zakhira* and *Muhit*.
(2) *Ibid*, according to the *Khulâsa*.

When a person makes a *wakf* in favour of his *infant* (*saghîr*) children, in that case such of his children alone will be entitled to share as were infants at the time of the *wakf*, for though infancy is a quality which ceases, yet it is such a quality which never comes into existence again, and it is therefore tantamount to specifying the children by name. Principle.

If a dedication is made for a child, and there is born to the *wâkif* another child, within six months from the date when the produce of the *wakf* came into existence,(1) this latter child will share with the former in such produce. If the child is born after six months, it will not share with the first in the produce, as the presumption is that it was not in being at the time the produce came into existence. If a person were to make a *wakf* for his child at a time when he has no issue and no child is born to him within six months from the time the produce came into existence, such produce also, as already stated, would go to the poor, though subsequent accretions would go to the child. Principle.

"When a *wakf* is made for the indigent, upon whom should the produce be spent?" Nâtiki has declared that 'if the *wâkif's* children or descendants happen to fall into indigence it should be first applied for them; then upon his relations; then upon his emancipated bondsmen; then upon his neighbours; then upon the inhabitants of the city where the *wâkif* lived having regard to the nearness and proximity of their residence to where the *wâkif* lived' and children and females will be included in the distribution among neighbours."(2) **A *wakf* in favour of the poor how to be applied.**

"If a man were to make a *wakf* on so-and-so (naming him) and his children, and he rejects, his rejection does not affect the right of the children whether they be minors or adults."(3)

SECTION II.

WAKF IN FAVOUR OF THE KINDRED OF THE WĀKIF.

The term *âl*, *jins* and *ahl-ul-bait* of the *wâkif* include those persons who are related to him through the father or the grand- **_Wakf_ in favour of the *akriba* or kindred.**

(1) The time when cultivation takes the shape of grain is regarded as the time when the produce is in existence.

(2) *Fath ul-Kadir*, Vol. II, p. 649.

(3) *Ghâit ul-Bayân*, Chap. on *wakf*.

father or any other male ancestor. And *karâbatdâr*, *zu-karâbat*, *arhâm* and *ansâb*, include those people who are related to the deceased through any ancestor male or female. The highest ancestor to which the line would be carried is the person who first adopted Islâm.

Abû Yusuf and Mohammed have said, that by *karâbat* is to be understood every one related to a person through a common ancestor "up to the farthest back in Islâm" either on the father's or the mother's side, and whether within the prohibited degrees or not, and that the near and the remote are alike in this respect, whether the word be in the singular or the plural. But according to Abû Hanîfa, when the settlement is made in the singular, as for instance, "on my *karâbat* or on a person of my *karâbat*," it is the nearest of the relatives within the prohibited degrees that enters into the benefit of the *wakf*, while if the settlement be in the plural, as for instance, "on persons of my *karâbat* or on my *akriba*" (relatives), the whole of those above-mentioned are included as the words are applicable to two or more. With regard to the meaning of the words "most remote ancestor in Islâm," some say that it is the most remote who adopted the Mussulman religion, but others, the most remote ancestor since the promulgation of Islâm whether he adopted the faith or not. *The views of the Disciples are recognised as the law on the subject.*

If a man were to say, "this is a *wakf* for my *akriba*, *ahl-ul-bait*, etc., according to the Disciples, even if there be only one of this class the trust will take effect."

Poverty has reference to the time of distribution.

When a man makes a *wakf* for his poor relatives, the poverty has reference to the time when the income becomes distributable. But the recipient of the benefaction must be one who has no relation legally liable to maintain him or her, for example, a husband, a father, or any other person subject to the same obligation.

Principle.

When a *wakf* is made in favour of one's children or relations, all those who are existing at the time when the produce comes into existence, though born after the creation of the *wakf*, are entitled to share.

What has been said as to a person's *akriba* and *zav'-il-karâbat* is equally applicable to his *arhâm* and *zav-il-arhâm* and *ansâb* and *zav-il-ansâb*—all these terms implying the same thing.

When a person has said, "This is a pious *mowkoofa* on the poor of my kindred or the poor of my children and after them on the indigent," the settlement is valid, and the persons entitled are those of them who are poor at the time when the produce comes into existence, according to Hillâl, whose opinion "we" (the Hanafis) approve and the *Fatwa* is in accordance with it. Similarly, if instead of "the poor," the words of dedication were "the indigent and the needy of my kindred." "If one after making a *wakf* on the needy of his *kindred*, and then on the poor, should die leaving a poor son, Abû Yusuf holds that the son would not come within the meaning of kindred, and this seems correct When there are poor of a *wâkif's* kindred in another city than that in which he resides, the produce is not to be sent to them, but is to be divided wholly among those of his own city, though if the superintendent should send any of it away to them he would not be considered as committing a breach of trust."(1)

The meaning of the word *sâleh*.

A *wakf* to those who are *sâleh* (pious) includes those men who are pure, and nobody doubts them or makes any imputation against them, and they follow the path of rectitude, use no evil expressions, are not drunkards and do not revile good women, and are truthful and honest, "these are the *sâleh*, men of purity and goodness."

A *wakf* to the "nearest" among all mankind.

If a man were to make a *wakf* for "those who are nearest to him among all mankind," and after them for the poor, and he has a child, a father and a mother, or a father or a mother, *then the produce will go to the child*, though it be a female, for she is nearest to the *wâkif*. And after the child to the poor, and not to the parents, because the *wâkif* did not state "to the nearest and then to the nearest." If the *wâkif* has no child, but only parents, the produce will go to them equally. If the *wâkif* left a mother and brothers, the produce will be given entirely to the mother. If he leaves paternal and maternal grandfathers and brothers, the brothers will take the whole produce.(2)

---

(1) See Baillie's Dig., p. 587.

(2) Some jurists hold the paternal grandfather would take the entire produce, being supposed to stand in the place of the father.

"When a person has made a settlement on the nearest of men to him and after that to the indigent and has a son or a father, he enters into the benefit of the *wakf*, though if his words were 'on the nearest of men among my *karâbat*' they would not enter into it. And if he has a son or a daughter and both parents,

If the *wâkif* has a daughter's daughter and son's son's son, the daughter's daughter as the nearest will be entitled to the benefit solely.

But when a man makes a *wakf* on the nearest of his *karâbat*, in that case his parents and children will not share as they are not included in the term *karâbat*.

If a person were to declare, "I make a *wakf* for my *akârib* on condition that the distribution should commence with the one nearest in the *nasab* (consanguinity) or *karâbat* (relationship), and after him for one who is nearest to him and so on," and the *wâkif* has two brothers and two sisters, the distribution will commence with the brothers or the sisters of the full blood and then with those who are uterine. And if one of them is consanguine, and the others uterine, the uterine will take first. This is according to Abû Hanîfa. According to the Disciples they will share equally. A maternal uncle and aunt are preferred to a consanguinous or uterine brother of the father. So a full paternal uncle is preferred to a consanguine or uterine brother or sister of the mother. A full paternal uncle and aunt are preferred to a maternal uncle and aunt. This is according to Abû Hanifa. According to the Disciples, they take equally. *In both these cases the views of the Disciples are accepted as law.*

The same rule is applicable to the offspring as to the "roots," bearing in mind that, according to the Disciples, there is no difference whether they are connected through males or females or through one side or the other, *viz.*, the father's side or the mother's side.(1)

The word *karîb* (near) is not confined to the *karâbat* alone. Therefore, if a man, instead of saying "the *wakf* is for one nearest to me among my *karâbat*," were to say "the *wakf* is for one *nearest*

the son or daughter alone is entitled and on their death the produce belongs to the indigent and not to the parents; while if he leave his parents only, the produce is to them in halves, and if either should die his or her half would pass to the poor. In like manner, if he have ten sons and one of them should die, his share goes to the indigent. And if he has a mother and brothers or a mother and grandfather, the produce is to her alone to the exclusion of the others, she being the nearer. The same is true of the father also. And a father is nearer than a son's son, but a son's son is preferred to a full brother and a daughter's daughter to a son's descendant in a lower grade. So also a daughter's daughter's daughter is preferred to a full sister;" Baillie, p. 588.

(1) *Fatâwai Kâzi Khân in loco.*

to me among all people,'' this would include both *karâbat* and *ghair karâbat*, and consequently parents and children will be included in the *wakf* as they do not fall in the category of *karâbat*.

If a man were to say, " this *wakf* is for my children, and if any of them should die, his share shall go to one of his degree, the nearer being preferred to the one more remote,'' and there are *wâkif's* sister's children and paternal uncle's descendants, the share of the deceased beneficiary would go to the *wakif's* paternal uncle's descendants and not to the children of the *wâkif's* sisters. This is contrary to the *Fatwa* in the *Khairiyèh* in which the *wâkif's* sister's children are preferred.

A person may create a *wakf* lawfully in favour of his kindred (*karâbatdâr* or *karâbat* or *zû-karâbat*), and no preference will be given to males over females. And in the *Ziâdât* it is stated that the grandparents and grandchildren will participate in the benefit of the trust.(1) A wife, however, is not included in the term *karâbat* or *akriba*.(2)

If a person declare his property to be *wakf* for his *nearest* kindred and he has a consanguine sister and daughter's daughter's daughter, the *wakf* will be in favour of the latter, for she is nearest in blood to the *wâkif* being his own descendant, however low in degree.

When a *wakf* is in favour of the poor kindred, such kindred as are in indigent circumstances will alone be entitled to share in its benefit. With reference to the question who are indigent and who are not, the *Fatâwai Alamgiri* states the principle in the following terms :—

Test of indigence according to the *Alamgiri.*

According to the *Hâwi* the approved doctrine is that all persons who are the legitimate recipients of the *zakât* or the poor rates, must be regarded to be *poor* (for the purposes of the *wakf*). A person possessed of only a dwelling-house and a servant (in the original, bondsman) is held to be poor, and properly entitled to receive the *zakât*, as well as the benefit of a *wakf* for the poor.(3) "So also when with this, he has a sufficiency of clothes without

(1) *Radd ul-Muhtâr*, Vol. III, p. 681.

(2) [1872] *The Advocate-General* v. *Fatima Sultani Begum*, 9 B. H. C. R., 19.

(3) *Fatâwai Alamgiri*, Vol. II, p. 484, "according to the *Zakhira*."

anything superfluous, or house-furniture that cannot be dispensed with."(1)

But if he have an excess above his clothes and furniture, which excess equals 200 dirhems, he is to be accounted rich (*i e.*, not a pauper) and will not be held entitled either to the *zakât* or to the benefit of a *wakf*.(2)

So also if he have two dwelling-houses or two slaves and the superfluous house or slave is of the value of 200 dirhems, he is to be accounted rich with regard to the illegality of participating in *zakât* or *wakf*, but not so as to render him liable to the former. And, though the surplus above his dwelling-house, or the surplus above his clothes, or his furniture should not each by itself be of the value of 200 dirhems, yet if all taken together are of that value, he is rich, and cannot lawfully participate either in *zakât* or in *wakf*.(3) And if he have land of the value of 200 dirhems, though the income from it be insufficient for his maintenance still he is "rich," according to what is approved.(4) Though he should have plenty of property not immediately available, or debts owing to him by other persons, he may be allowed to take of the *zakât* or the *wakf*, for he is in the condition of a way-farer (*ibn-us-sabîl*); yet if he can borrow, it is better for him to do so than to receive from a charity."(5)

Test of indigence.

"Every one who is entitled to maintenance from another, and who may take it without his consent or the order of a Judge, or to whom the Judge may award it out of the property of an absent person,—and every person, the profits of whose property are so mixed up with those of another that neither can be accepted as a witness for the other, is accounted rich in respect of *wakf*, on the strength of the wealth of his maintainor or person with whom he is so connected, and of this, parents and children and grand-parents are examples. But persons, who though entitled to maintenance from another, yet cannot take it without his consent, or the order of a Judge, and to whom the Judge cannot assign maintenance against another during his absence, and persons,

(1) According to the *Fatâwai Kâzi Khan*.

(2) "This is the doctrine of our masters (may the peace, &c.) according to the *Muhît*."

(3) According to the *Fatâwai Kâzi Khân*.

(4) According to the *Khazânat-ul-Muftiïn*.

(5) *Fatâwai Alamgiri*, Vol. II, p. 485.

ston, J., held that the gifts were valid and conveyed a good title to the donee.

So in *Emma Bai and others* v. *Hajira Bai*(1), Sargent, C. J., following the views expressed by Sausse, C. J., in *Amina Bibi* v. *Khatija Bibi*, held that where a gift was made by a husband to his wife, it would not be invalid even if he continued in reception of the rents and profits after the date of gift, if it could be inferred that he was doing so as his wife's manager.

In the case of *Jaffer Khan* v. *Habshi Bibi*(2), it was held that where the technical requirement of delivery of seisin is complied with, continued possession is not necessary.

The question whether for the purpose of completing a gift of immovable property by delivery and possession, a formal entry or actual physical taking of possession is necessary, was also discussed before West and Nanabhai Haridas, JJ., in the case of *Shaikh Ibrahim* v. *Shaikh Suleman.*(3) Mr. Justice West laid down the principle of the Mahommedan Law on the question of seisin with considerable distinctness. The learned Judge said :—

"As to the law of the case, the Courts below are to bear in mind that when land is occupied by tenants a request to them to attorn to the donee is the only possession that the donor can give of the land in order to complete a proposed gift. Such a possession would, according to the case of *Khajooroonissa* v. *Rowshun Jehan*, be sufficient. As to the delivery of the house, the principle is to be borne in mind that when a person is present on the premises proposed to be delivered to him, a declaration of the person previously possessed puts him into possession. He occupies a certain part, and this occupation becoming actual possession by the will of the parties extends to the whole, which is in immediate connection with such part where the possession is rightfully, though not where it is wrongfully taken, *Ex parte Fletcher*. An appropriate intention where two are present on the same premises, may put the one out as well as the other into possession without any actual physical departure or formal entry, and effect is to be given as far as

(1) [1868], I. L., 13 Bom., 352.

(2) 1 Sel. Reports, p. 12; *Mir Azmatullah Saheb* v. *Boyapato Nagayya* [1906], I. L., 30 Mad., 519, seems to have been decided from a rather narrow point of view. Besides it lays down no principles.

(3) [1884], I. L., 9 Bom., 146, wherein the cases bearing on this point are referred to.

possible to the purpose of an owner whose intention to transfer has been unequivocally manifested."(1) This is in accordance with the principle stated in the *Majm'aa-ul-Anhar.*

Humera Bibi v. *Najm-un-nissa Bibi.*

In the case of *Humera Bibi* v. *Najm-un-nissa Bibi*(2) the plaintiff (Humera Bibi) had formally conveyed a house and other immovable property by a registered document to her nephew (the husband of the defendant) who lived with her. After the execution of the deed of gift, mutation of names in the Collector's records in favour of the donee was effected at the instance of the donor, and rent-receipts given to the tenants were thenceforth in the donee's name. But the plaintiff all along continued to live in the house included in the gift, and was practically maintained by the donee out of the rents and issues of the immovable property.

On the death of the donee the plaintiff brought a suit against his widow to have it declared that the deed of gift was invalid inasmuch as there had been no delivery of possession within the meaning of the Mahommedan Law and that the donor had not vacated the premises at the time of the gift and removed with her effects therefrom. The High Court of Allahabad, in a careful judgment, expressed themselves in the following terms:—"We are not prepared to hold that in a case such as the present actual physical departure of the donor from a house which is the subject of a gift evidenced by a written instrument is necessary in order to complete the gift by delivery and possession. On the contrary, we think

---

(1) In a case among Hindus, *Kalidas Mullick* v. *Kanhyalal Pundit* [1884], I. L., 11 Cal., 121, the Privy Council had occasion to refer to the principle, which, it is submitted, ought to be carefully borne in mind in dealing with the subject of gifts among Mahommedans. Dealing first with the question what interest is conveyed to the donee when the terms of the gift are indefinite, their Lordships said: "It appears to their Lordships that the indefinite words of a gift must be limited by the purpose of the gift, and it was Romasunderi's intention that Ruttonmoni should take the property only for her life."

With reference to the validity or invalidity of the gift on the basis of non-possession, their Lordships used the following language:—"A gift where the donor supports it, the person who disputes it claiming adversely to both donor and donee is not invalid, for the mere reason that the donor has not delivered possession, and that where a donee or vendee is under the terms of the gift or sale entitled to possession, there is no reason why such gift or sale though not accompanied by possession, whether of movable or immovable property (where the gift or sale is not of such a nature as would make the giving effect to it contrary to public policy) should not operate to give the donee or vendee a right to obtain possession." This principle is applicable also to cases arising under the Mahommedan Law.

(2) [1905], I. L., 28 All., 147.

the profits of whose property are so distinguishable from those of another that each may be accepted as a witness for the other—are not to be accounted rich on the strength of the wealth of their maintainors; and of this, brothers and sisters and other relations within the prohibited degrees are examples."(1)

"When a poor woman has an affluent husband she is not to *receive* from a *wakf* constituted for the poor, but a poor man although he has an affluent wife may participate in its benefits."(2)

Kâzi Khân lays down the following rule on the subject, which, however, he says, must vary with the changing circumstances of the times. A person is called *fakîr* (indigent) who has only a lodging (and nothing more), and he would be entitled to *zakât* (poor's rate or religious alms) as well as to the benefit of a *wakf* (for the poor). Similarly, a person who has only a lodging, but no wherewithal for subsistence, though he may have an attendant, is a *fakîr*. A person, who has only a few necessary raiments and nothing else, is a *fakîr*. Kâzi Khân.

According to Abû Yusuf, the owner of a piece of land which is worth 200 dirhems, though its income may not be enough for his support, is not indigent; but Mohammed ibn-Shahna, and Mohammed ibn Makâtil of Rai would regard him as a *fakîr*. "The words of Abû Yusuf, however, are words of caution, and the saying of Ibn-Shahna contains much elasticity." The author goes on to say, that a person ostensibly possessed of means, but who, through having been overtaken by some calamity, cannot have the immediate use of such property, may be regarded as an indigent. He also adds that a person who, with the exception of a debt owed by an insolvent, owns no other property, will be regarded as an indigent. *Radd ul-Muhtâr.*

From these statements it is clear that the question whether a person is or is not an indigent, is dependent upon special circumstances and cannot be answered without reference to the requirements and exigencies of the society among whom the question arises. Conclusion.

When a *wakf* is made for the indigent kindred of the *wâkif* and one of his kinswomen gives birth to a child within six months

---

(1) *Fatâwai Alamgiri*, Vol. II, p. 485, after the *Muhit*.
(2) *Ibid.*

of the date upon which the produce of the *wakf* comes into existence, such child will not be entitled to a share in it, for a child *en ventre sa mère* cannot be regarded as coming under the category of indigent kindred. Such child will be treated in the same way as a kinsman, who was *ghanî* (affluent) at the time the produce came into existence and became indigent afterwards. This person though not entitled to a share in that produce, will participate in all future income.

When a *wakf* is clearly intended for more than one person comprehended in a class, and there is only one person of that class existing, he will take half of the produce and the remainder will go to the general poor. If, however, it appears *primâ facie* that the whole benefit is intended for persons of that class, independently of their number, such person will take the entire benefit. For example, if a *wakf* is made for the benefit of the indigent among

Principle.

the posterity of *A*, and there is only one such person in existence, the entire income of the *wakf* will go to that person. But if the *wakf* was created for the paupers among the posterity of *A*, and there happens to be only one, he takes half of the produce, while the remainder goes to the poor in general.

Meaning of the term. "orphan."

A *wakf* made for the orphans of one's kindred is subject to the same principles. An orphan or *yateem* means an infant child who has no father living, though the mother and the grandfather may be alive. The condition of orphanage ceases on the attainment of puberty. In the absence of any indications of puberty, the completion of the 15th year is regarded by Abû Yusuf as the age of majority. Abû Hanîfa holds that the completion of the 19th

Age of majority.

year is the age of majority for men and the 17th year for women, whilst Zuffar is of opinion that the age of majority should be the same in both cases, namely, the completion of the 18th year.

If a person make a *wakf* of his property for his poor kindred, will the *mutwalli* be authorised after the *wâkif's* death to give a share of the produce to his indigent grandson? Most of the jurists have answered this question in the affirmative and the Fakîh Abû Lais has stated that in the *Ziâdât* Imâm Mahommed has held the same view, though apparently Abû Hanîfa and Abû Yusuf have held otherwise.(1)

---

(1) In the *Fatâwai Alamgiri*, preference is apparently given to the views of Abû Hanîfa and Abû Yusuf :—

Where a *wakf* is made for the benefit of the *wâkif's* kindred residing in a particular locality and after them for the poor, would the kindred be deprived of the benefit of such *wakf* if they leave their residence? Fakih Abû Bakr of Balkh has declared that if the *wâkif's* kindred, who are constituted the beneficiaries of the *wakf*, are limited in number and capable of being specified, in that case their right to the benefit of the *wakf* is ambulatory and will go with them wherever they go. But if they cannot be specified and are not limited in number, in that case the right of any one of the kindred who leaves the locality will drop and the entire produce will be distributed among those living on the spot, and when none of them is in existence, it will go to the poor. And Abû Lais has stated that should any one of the kindred (so leaving the place), return to that locality, the right would revive.

A *wakf* for the kindred residing in a particular locality.

Should a *wakf* be made for one's *akriba* but the words *their descendants* be not added, still they would be included, as the descendants of *akriba* are also *akriba*.

If a person make a *wakf* for his *akriba* and after them for their descendants, these will not share in the benefit of the *wakf* until the first stock is exhausted.

A person makes several dispositions by will and creates a *wakf* of his land for the poor and authorises his executor "to give to whomsoever *he* likes and whatever *he* likes," in such a case it is lawful for the executor of the *wakf* to give to his parents, his wife and kinsmen, if they are poor or in need, and it will, in the main, be regarded as a *wakf* for the poor.

A *wakf* with a discretion to the trustee.

When a man has made a *wakf* for his neghbours, the produce ought to be expended, according to analogy, on all who live adjacent to him, but, on a liberal construction, it is for those who assemble together with him and come to the *masjid* or place of worship of the *mahallah* or quarter, and *this is approved*. "Re-

Wakf in favour of neighbours.

Principle.

"In a *wakf* on '*karîb*' the produce is divided according to heads, the young and the old, the male and the female, the poor and the rich being all alike, because the noun is equally applicable to all. But neither the father of the appropriator nor the children of his loins are included, nor his grandfather, according to the approved traditions (*Zâhir-ur-Rawâyât*). A man makes a settlement on the needy of his *karâbat* and then dies. Question.—Can the *mutwalli* give any portion of the produce to a son of the *wâkif's* son when poor? According to Abû Hanîfa and Abû Yusuf he cannot, for the child of a child according to them is not included in the term *karâbat*." There can be no question that the views of Abû Lais are accepted by the Hanafis.

sidence is the condition, according to the plain doctrine of Abû Hanîfa, whether the resident be proprietor or not, and this also is correct. When the resident is not the proprietor, the benefit of the *wakf* is to the resident and not to the proprietor." The neighbours, whether Moslem or infidel, male or female, free or *mukâtib*, minor or adult, are entitled, and the produce is to be divided among them according to the number of heads, the superintendent being responsible if he give more to some than to others.

If, among the endower's neighbours, there are some who have gone to another *mahallah*, selling their houses to other persons who have come into them after the ripening of the crops, but before they are gathered, these are to be regarded as neighbours who are such at the time of the division of the produce. And if a person should make a *wakf* on his neighbours when residing in one house, but should remove to another even though it be a merely rented house, and *reside* therein until his death, the produce will go to his last neighbours. "And if a man, after making a *wakf* on his neighbours, should remove to Mecca and die there, the produce would belong to his neighbours in Mecca if he had taken a house there, but if he had gone on a pilgrimage only, it would belong to his neighbours in his own city." If a man have two mansions, in one of which he resides and in the other of which he keeps his merchandise, the produce is for the neighbours of the house in which he lives. If he have two mansions and a wife in each, the neighbours of both are entitled to the produce, though he should die in one of them. So also, though one of the houses be in Basrah and the other in Kûfa, he having a wife in each. And if a person should make a *wakf* for the poor of neighbours without referring to himself, as, for instance, by omitting to say, "my neighbours," it would be the same as if he had said "my neighbours." If a man should fall sick and be removed by his son to another *mahalla* or village and die there, his first neighbours would be entitled, this being no proper removal. But if a woman inhabiting a mansion should make a *wakf* on her neighbour and afterwards marry and be taken to the house of her husband and die there, her neighbour are those of her husband. So also, when a man has married a woman and removes to her house, his neighbours are changed to hers, unless he has left his furniture in his own house, when they say his neighbours are those who were so before his removal.

When it is not known who are a man's neighbours, the produce is not to be divided until witnesses testify to the house in which he died and then a distribution is to be made among the neighbours of that house. "And if a neighbour should claim as being poor and the fact of his poverty is not known, he must be put to the trouble of producing witnesses to prove it."

SECTION III.

GENERAL PRINCIPLES OF CONSTRUCTION.

When a man makes a *wakf* and constitutes himself *mutwalli* thereof during his lifetime, and declares that after his death his son *A* shall be the *mutwalli*, and after him the fittest and worthiest of his children, the latter "his" refers to *A*, and not to the *wâkif*.

If the *wakf* is for Zaid and 'Amr and his children, the pronoun "his" refers to 'Amr.

If a man constitute a *wakf* for his children and *such of his children's children as are male*, the qualification refers to the grandchildren and not to the children. Principle of construction.

"*Q.*—A person makes a *wakf* for his son named Hassan and for his children (*awlâd*), that may be born subsequently, and after them for their children that may be male, and after them for his children that may be female and for their children. After the constitution of the *wakf*, another son is born to the *wâkif* whose name is Mohammed, and subsequently Hassan dies. Does the first *his* refer to Hassan or to the *wâkif*, so as to include Mohammed in the *wakf*?"

"*A.*—The Hanafî Mufti of Egypt, whose name is Moulâna Shaikh Hassan Sharnibilâlièh, anwsers the question thus, 'the pronoun 'his' refers to the *wâkif*, and the *Khairiyèh* adds this is most consistent with the intention of the *wâkif*; and it has been decided that when a word is equivocal in its meaning and is capable of a double construction, the construction most consistent with the intention of the settlor should be adopted; for in the case put, if the pronoun is held to refer Hassan, the *wâkif's* own child will be excluded.' "(1)

---

(1) *Radd ul-Muhtâr*, Vol. III, p. 669.

"The expression *inshâ-Allah* 'if God pleases' is a proviso, an '*istisnâ*,'(1) but it is not equivalent to *illa* (unless)." According to the Shâfeïs, a proviso refers to the whole document and not to the immediate provision only. According to the Hanafîs, it refers only to the last condition, provided it can be separated from the other conditions, *otherwise to all*. For example, if a man were to say "I make my house *wakf* for my children and my garden for my brothers, but should they go away it shall cease," the proviso refers to the condition regarding the brethren.

But if he had said, "I make this house *wakf* for my children and children's children, but if they go away it will cease to be *wakf*," the proviso would be general. Among the Hanafîs, if a person were to make the possession of a qualification a necessary condition to receive the benefits of a *wakf*, the qualification would refer to the persons in immediate connection with whom the condition is mentioned. But, if it is clear that the qualification refers to all, it will have effect given to it generally. For example, if a person were to make a *wakf* for his indigent children and his children's children, the qualification of indigence is restricted to the children alone. But if he said the *wakf* is for his children's children who are indigent, it refers to both.(2)

According to the Shâfeïs, the qualification would refer to all in any case.

If a person should constitute some portion of his property a *wakf* by way of a pious offering for Abdullah and Zaid, the income will go to these as tenants in common, and when one of them dies, his share would go to the poor, and upon the demise of both of them the entire rent and profits would be given in charity. Similarly when a *wakf* is in favour of a class (*kowm*), the rents and profits will be divided among them, according to their number as tenants in common. And on the death of any one of them his share will be given in charity to the poor. When the appropriation is made in favour of "the children of Abdullah," without mentioning a number, the children of Abdullah will take as joint-tenants, and so long as there is any issue of his living, nothing is to be given in charity to the poor. When two persons are named, *e.g.*, Zaid and

(1) When the settlor makes use of the expression "Inshâ-Allah," in connection with any provision, it must be regarded as precatory.

(2) *Radd ul-Muhtâr*, Vol. III, p. 669.

Amr, and it is provided that Zaid should get a half and 'Amr two-thirds, the whole is to be divided into seven parts, as in the case of the increase (*awl*) in inheritance, of which three are to be given to Zaid and four to 'Amr. When a settlement is made in the following terms:—"to Zaid a half and to 'Amr a third," each is to have the portion mentioned for him and the remainder is to be divided equally between them. When the *wâkif* makes the settlement in these words—"My land is a *wakf* for Zaid and 'Amr and to Zaid out of it a third or a hundred dirhems," and is silent as to the other, Zaid shall get what is mentioned for him, "and the remainder is for him of whom nothing has been said." And so in all other cases where one is named and silence is preserved with regard to the other. When the *wâkif* has provided that each of the beneficiaries should get a specific sum, and owing to loss of income none of them can get the exact amount, the actual income will be divided in proportion to their respective allowances. But, when the income more than covers the allowances, the excess shall be shared by them equally.(1)

Principle.

When the dedication is for a class of persons (*kowm*) and they all reject it, the produce is for the poor.(2) But where only some reject it, the whole of the produce shall go to those who do not reject, if the designation under which the settlement is made is generic and the term applies to them all; but if the name is inapplicable to them, the share of those who reject passes to the poor. Thus when the *wâkif* has said "to the children of Abdullah" and some of them reject, the whole is for those that accept. But if he were to say "to Zaid and 'Amr," and Zaid rejects, his share passes to the poor.(3)

A person claiming an interest in a *wakf* created for the poor relatives of the *wâkif*, on the ground that he (the claimant) is a poor relation, is bound to prove his right, ***first***, that he is a ***karâbatdâr***, and ***secondly***, that he is poor. He cannot subject the ***mutwalli*** to affirmation.(4)

---

(1) *Radd-ul-Muhtâr*, Vol. III, p. 670.
(2) *Ibid.*
(3) *Ibid*, p. 671.
(4) A wife is not included in the term *akriba*; *Advocate-General* v. *Fatima Sultâni Begum* [1872], 9 B. H. C. R., 17 supra.

The principle, upon which persons who leave a certain locality are precluded from participating in the benefit of a *wakf*, does not apply to a case like the following :—"A man makes a *wakf* for his poor relations residing at Bagdad, and some of them go and live at Kûfa and after a while they come back to Bagdad, [on their return] they regain their right to share in the benefits of the *wakf*." The reason of this is that their condition should be regarded at the moment when the distribution takes place, as their poverty forms the basis of their claim and the object of the *wâkif* is to help his poor relatives.

Principle.

When a man makes a *wakf* for his descendants, and after the *mutwalli* has been dividing the produce among certain of his descendants, another person establishes his right also to a share as one of the descendants of the *wâkif*, he will be entitled to recover the past share if the *mutwalli* has divided the shares without the sanction of the Kâzi. The *mutwalli's* position in such a case is like that of an executor who, after paying some of the creditors, divides the remainder of the testator's estate among the poor, and subsequently thereto arises another creditor who establishes his claim. Such creditor is entitled to proceed against the executor for the satisfaction of his debt.(1)

The *Mutwalli's* liability.

When a *wakf* is made by a person in favour of the people of his *bait* or house, every one is entitled who is connected with him by ancestry "to the most remote of them in Islâm," without distinction of creed or sex, or the nature of the relationship. "The Moslem and non-Moslem, the male and female, the prohibited and the unprohibited, the near and the remote, are all alike in this respect. The remotest ancestor, however, is not included. But the child and parents of the *wâkif* are included, though not the children of his daughters and sisters, nor the children of any other females besides these, except when married to paternal nephews of the *wâkif*." As-Sarakhsi has stated in his commentary on the *Siyâr Kabîr*, that the words "people of the house" when they occur in deeds of *wakf* or wills are to be construed according to the intention of the testator. If by "house" he intended his residence, "the people of his house" should be taken as meaning those who reside in family with him and are maintained by

Principle.

"People of the house."

---

(1) *Radd ul-Muhtâr*, Vol. III, p. 672.

him, though there may not be any of his *karâbat* or kindred among them; and if by "house" he meant *nasab*, then the people of his house are all the recognised children of his father. Imâm Ali as-Sugdi, however, maintains that if the person has a house of *nasab* like the Arabs, the words "people of his house" would mean the descendants of his ancestors, (lit. the children of his fathers,) though they should not be residing in family with him: "but if he have no house of *nasab*, they are those living in family with him and maintained by him and none others, though they should be of his kindred, and this is approved." When a *wakf* is made on the "people of the house," "those in existence are included, and those who may come after them, of their children and children's children."(1)

When a person uses the expression *âl* or *jins*, it is in effect the same as "on the people of my house," and there is no speciality in favour of the poor, unless the *wakf* is made specially for them. The phrase "on the poor of them" is like "on those who become poor," and consequently "the produce is for him who is poor at the time, though he were rich when the settlement was made and it is not restricted to those who were rich and have become poor." If a woman should make a settlement "on the *ahl* (people) of her house" or "on her *jins*," her mother and her child would not be included.(2)

If a man should say "on the *ahl* of 'Abdullah," it would be for his wife specially, according to Abû Hanîfa. Hillâl, however, has said, "We think it better to make it include all free persons of his family living together with him in his house: *and this is approved*. But slaves are not included, nor 'Abdullah himself nor persons of his family living in another house." Approved doctrine as to the meaning of *Ahl*.

A'yâl comprehends every one maintained by a person whether living in his house or not, and *hasham* is synonymous with *a'yâl*. By *'akab* are to be understood all those who are connected with a person through his father, and the children of daughters are not included except females whose husbands are among these. And if one should make a *wakf* on Zaid and his *'akab*, Zaid himself being

(1) *Fatâwai Alamgiri*, Vol. II, p. 490.

(2) The *dictum* in the *Fatâwai Alamgiri* that "when a woman makes a settlement on the *ahl* (people) of her house or on her *jins*, her mother and her child would not be included, is explained further on.

alive and having children, these would have nothing, for the child of a man cannot be called his *'akab* except after his death.(1)

Application of a *wakf* in favour of the indigent.

The following rules are laid down in the *Alamgiri* relating to the distribution of the income of a *wakf* for the poor kindred :— 1. It is to be expended in the first place on the poor of his children and his kindred and the surplus only given to strangers. 2. Poverty on the day of the produce coming into existence is not to be regarded but rather poverty on the day of distribution. 3. The nearest in kindred are first to be supplied, and then the more remote, that is, the child of the loins has priority, and after him the child of a child, then the third generation, and then the fourth and lower generations. If none of these remain, or there is a surplus after satisfying them, it is to be bestowed on the more remote of the poor kindred beginning here also, with the nearest among them. 4. That to each person to whom a portion is given something less than 200 dirhems be given, that is, when the *wakf* is for the poor generally and some of the kindred are in need. But if the *wakf* be for the poor of a person's kindred, the whole produce is to be distributed among them, though the share of each should exceed 200 dirhems.

Beginning must be with the *wâkif's* descendants and kindred.

When an appropriator has appointed the produce for debtors or travellers, or "in the way of God," as for pilgrimage, and some of his children or kindred fall into want, no part of it is to be given to them, unless the child or the relative be a debtor, or a traveller or a pilgrim when also a beginning is to be made with them.

When a man makes a *wakf* on some of his children, and mentions that the *wakf* should be during his life and after his death, the words, "after his death" does not, according to the most authentic report, constitute a legacy to an heir, but bears the construction of a perpetuity.(2)

---

(1) *Fatâwai Alamgiri in loco.*

(i) *Karâbat literally means* relationship, but is often used to imply related.

(ii) *Karâbatdâr* and *zu-karâbat* mean one who is related.

(iii) *Zavi*, plural of *zu*.

(iv) *Akriba*, plural of *karib*, next of kin, people nearly related.

(v) *Arhâm* plural of *rahm*, womb ; technically means uterine relations.

(vi) *Fakir* and *miskin*, both words are applicable to indigent people, but a *fakir* may be possessed of some property, the whole of which must not amount to more than a *nisâb* ; a *miskin* has no property or habitation ; *Hed.*, Vol. I, p. 54.

(2) *Fatâwai Alamgiri*, Vol. II, pp. 474-475.

When a *wakf* is made in favour of Zaid and his children and after them in favour of the poor, and Zaid were to declare that the *wakf* was in favour of 'Amr and the poor, his declaration would not affect the interests of the children or the poor. But the rents and profits will be divided equally among Zaid and the children in existence at the time, and half of Zaid's share would be given to 'Amr.

If 'Amr died before Zaid, his share would be given during the lifetime of Zaid to the poor. Should Zaid die before 'Amr, his interest in the profits would cease.

If the *wakf* be for Zaid and the poor, and Zaid were to make a declaration in favour of 'Amr instead of himself, in that case the rents and profits will be divided equally between Zaid and 'Amr, and when Zaid dies, the entire rents and profits will go to the poor. If 'Amr dies during the lifetime of Zaid, half of Zaid's share will be given to the poor. For when Zaid has declared himself entitled only to a moiety and 'Amr to the remaining moiety, in that case 'Amr's half only goes to the poor.(1)

When a *wakf* is in favour of *A* and his descendants, on the extinction of *A's* posterity the *wakf* will be for the poor as already stated, whether they are expressly named or not. If *A* refuses to take any benefit under the *wakf*, the produce will be given to his children existing at the time. If he has no children, the *wakf* will be applied in relieving the needy. If afterwards any child is born to *A*, the profits will be given to such child.(2)

If *A* as well as his children existing at the time refuse to take any benefit under the *wakf*, it will go to the poor; but their rejection does not bind the succeeding generations.

If a *wakf* is in favour of *A* and after him for *B*, and they both reject, it will go to the poor absolutely.(3)

Principle.

As a general rule, it may shortly be stated that the poor form by necessary implication of the law, the ultimate beneficiaries of every trust created in favour of individuals or classes of individuals. The failure of the primary object or objects of the trust does not avoid the trust, but only accelerates its ultimate application to the poor.

---

(1) *Radd ul-Muhtār*, Vol. III, p. 669.
(2) *Ibid.*
(3) *Ibid*, p. 670.

The Madras High Court in view of the Privy Council rulings(1) declaring that a *wakf* in favour of the *wâkif's* descendants is "illusory" and, therefore, not valid has held in effect that a *wakf* partly for "charitable" purposes and partly for the *wâkif's* heirs will not be void, because the latter is not a legal purpose of a *wakf*; but the *wakf* will be valid and the whole income will be devoted for the valid purposes.(2)

Meaning of the word *fakîr*.

I have already explained the meaning of the word *fakîr* according to the various authorities. The definition which is adopted for the *Fatwa* is one not derived from any particular authority, but generally from a comparison of the meaning of all; and the effect is, as stated in the *Anf'aa-ul-Wasâil*, that any person who according to the exigencies of the society in which he lives is in poor and needy circumstances, or has not the wherewithal to support himself and his family for more than a few days, is indigent. Kâzi Khân puts it tersely, that a person entitled to the *zakât* (obligatory alms) is also entitled to the benefits of a *wakf* for the poor.

Principle.

A *wakf* created for the purpose of relieving the needs of the *wâkif's* descendants, &c., when they fall into indigence, is lawful.(3)

A *wakf* generally for the poor or for the indigent, or for the relief of those of the *wâkif's* kindred or descendants who fall into want, will be applied in providing them with food and raiment; and if homeless, in housing them.

Kâzi's discretion.

If there are no provisions in the *wakfnâmah* for carrying out the purposes of the trust, the Kâzi or Judge has absolute discretion to frame a scheme.(4)

When a *wakf* is made for an undefined number of people, such as for the poor generally, Mohammed says, at least, 10 must be fed or supported; according to Imâm Abû Yusuf, 100; others, again, have held that the number ought to be 40 or 80. But the *Fatwa* is that the fixing of the number should be left to the Judge with due regard to the circumstances of the *wakf*.

---

(1) See *ante*, p. 344.

(2) *Muthukana Ana Ramanadhan Chettiar* v. *Vada Levvai Marakayar* [1909], I. L., 34 Mad., 12.

(3) *Radd-ul-Muhtâr*, Vol. III, p. 670.

(4) *Kiniat-ul-Munia*.

SECTION IV

A *Wakf* CREATED IN DEATH-ILLNESS.

When a *marîz* (a person labouring under a death-illness) makes a *wakf* of his property in favour of his children and children's children in perpetuity so long as his *nasl* exists, upon the death of the testator (according to all the jurists), the *wakf* will not be valid in favour of the heirs, but will be valid (according to Abû Hanîfa, Abû Yusuf, Zuffar and Hassan), in favour of the non-heirs, *i.e.*, the grand-children, in respect of one-third of the estate, "for the *wakf* of a *marîz*, is like a will and is valid so far as the third of the estate extends when it is in favour of a non-heir."(1) *Wakf of a marîz.*

"When a person in death-illness makes a *wakf* of his land for his child and his child's child and leaves no other property besides it, one-third of the land becomes *wakf* for the benefit of the child's child, whether assented to by the heirs or not, and the other two-thirds form the property of the heirs, if the *wakf* is disallowed by them, but if it is allowed by them the produce of the two-thirds will be divided between the child and the child's child equally."(2)

Example.—A woman in a death-illness makes a *wakf* for her two daughters and after them for their daughters and their daughter's daughters and so on, and on failure of their issue for the purposes of a mosque. She dies leaving her surviving the said two daughters and a sister(3) who does not consent to the *wakf*. In such a case the *wakf* will be valid respecting one-third of her estate and the remaining two-thirds will be divided among the heirs, in proportion to their legal shares. The income of the one-third, which is *wakf*, will also be divided among the heirs in proportion to their shares until the death of the two daughters, when the produce will go exclusively to their children. Similarly, if the *wâkif* had said, "I devise by way of *wakf* the produce of this land after fifty years to my children's children,' it would be valid. The reason is that, though a testamentary *wakf* in favour of an heir is not valid, it is A *wakf* in favour of heirs during death-illness. Testamentary *wakf*. Principle.

(1) *Radd ul-Muhtâr*, Vol. III, p. 610; *Durr-ul-Mukhtâr*, p. 410; practically there is *consensus* of opinion on this point.

(2) *Ibid*.

(3) The sister takes a share with the daughters under the Sunni Law, but not under the Shiah doctrines.

valid in favour of his or her children, and accordingly when the other heirs do not consent,—the one-third, with reference to which the *wakf* would be valid, if not made to an heir, will be set apart and its produce will be distributed among all the heirs, the immediate beneficiary included, and upon his or her death, the produce of this one-third will be divided among his or her children.

Wakf during last illness.

As already stated, a dedication by a person during his last illness is valid to the extent of one-third of his estate, unless it is assented to by his heirs. When the *wakf* exceeds the one-third and is not assented to by the heirs, it is void as to the excess. If some of the heirs assent to it, it is valid to that extent beyond the third.(1) Accordingly, when a person makes his land "a pious *wakf* to Almighty God, for his child and child's child and his *nasl* for ever, so long as there are any, and after them for the necessitous," and this land falls within a third of his property, its *produce* will be divisible among all his heirs according to their shares in his heritage; and, accordingly, if he leave a wife and children, an eighth will be given to his wife, or if he leave both parents and children, a sixth is to be given to his parents,—the remainder, in either case, being divisible among the children, in the proportion of two shares to a male and one share to a female. This is the case when the *wâkif* has left children of his own and no grandchildren. But when he leaves him surviving both children and grandchildren, the other circumstances of the case being the same, the produce is to be divided according to the number of the children and grandchildren, *i.e.*, *per capita*, and the portions of the children in this division are to be divided among them according to the rules of inheritance, and the portions of the grandchildren are to be divided among them equally. And when "the children of the loins" are exhausted, the produce will be divided among the grandchildren and their *nasl*, the widow and parents taking nothing. If the land in question "does not come out" of the third of the *wâkif's* estate, but the *wakf* thereof is assented to by the heirs it is lawful in respect of the whole property dedicated, and its income will be divided among the children in equal shares (without any preference of the male over the female), to the exclusion of the wife and the parents who will take nothing. But if the heirs do not assent to the dedi-

If assented to by heirs, valid as to whole.

Otherwise as to one-third.

(1) *Surrat-ul-Fatâwa*, p. 418 (Mss.).

cation, it will take effect with respect to the portion forming one-third of the *wâkif's* estate, and the income will be divisible among all the heirs according to the rules of inheritance; and on the extinction of the *wâkif's* descendants the produce of that portion will be given to the poor.(1)

Wakf during last illness with legacies.

When a *wakf* is created during the last illness and legacies are also made, they will have operation given to them out of one-third of the estate.(2)

If one should say "The produce of this my land is to be given after my death to the child of 'Abdullah and his *nasl*," it is a bequest of the produce. And in like manner, when one has said "Detain it after my death on the child of 'Abdullah," this expression constitutes a bequest of the produce.

A death-bed wakf in favour of descendants.

To summarise—When a *wakf* is made by a man in his *death-illness* in favour of his own child, and the child of his child, and their posterity (*nasl*), the *wakf* in favour of his own children is not valid (they being his heirs), but it is valid as regards the grandchildren. So long as there is a child of the *wâkif* living, the produce is to be divided *per capita* among the children and the grandchildren. The shares falling to the lot of the children being, however, given to all the *heirs* of the *wâkif*, so that if besides children there is any other heir of the *wâkif*, he or she would participate in the children's share. For example, the *wâkif* leaves four sons, two grandsons and a wife, and the income from the *wakf* is 600 dirhems, it will be divided "according to the number of heads." The children's share will be 400 dirhems. This sum will be divided among all the *wâkif's* heirs, including the widow. [It must be remembered that the grandchildren are not heirs.] Should some of the children of the *wâkif* die, the income will be divided among the surviving children and grandchildren *per capita*, and the shares of the surviving children will be given to all the surviving heirs of the *wâkif* and to the heirs of those heirs of the *wâkif* who were alive at the time of his death.

Similarly, if a *wakf* is made by a person to take effect after his death in favour of his children, children's children and their *nasl*,

---

(1) *Surrat ul-Fatâwa*, p. 416 (Mss.); *Fatâwai Alamgiri*, Vol. II, p. 480. These provisions show that *wakfs* in favour of one's family or descendants are absolutely valid under the Mahommedan Law.

(2) *Radd ul-Muhtâr*, Vol. III, p. 671.

the *wakf* in favour of the children will not be valid, they being heirs, but will be valid in respect of the others. The division will be as in the case of a death-bed *wakf*.

In these cases the *wakf* does not take effect in favour of the children in consequence of its being made either in death-illness or as a testamentary disposition. But where the *wakf* is made "in health," as a disposition *inter vivos*, it takes effect in favour of the children, as stated before.(1)

(1) By a person "in health" is meant a person not suffering from a fatal malady which ends in death.

CHAPTER XII.

PUBLIC AND QUASI-PUBLIC WAKFS.

SECTION I.

GENERAL OBSERVATIONS.

AMONG *wakfs* in which the affluent (*aghniâ*) and indigent (*fukarâ*) are equally interested may be mentioned the following :—

(1) Mosques and prayer-grounds (*musallas*).
(2) *Imâmbaras.*
(3) *Rouzahs* (mausolea) and *dargâhs.*
(4) *Khânkâhs.*
(5) *Caravanserais* and *musâffir-khânèhs* (travellers' houses).
(6) Colleges and schools (*madrassas* and *maktabs*).
(7) Hospitals and dispensaries.
(8) Reservoirs, cisterns, aqueducts, roads, bridges, &c.
(9) *Rubâts* or hostels and rest-houses.
(10) Cemeteries.(1)

In these *wakfs*, the rich and the poor, the affluent and the indigent, are equally entitled to participate. But the *wâkif* may specially consecrate such institutions or places for the poor, in which case these alone would be entitled to derive benefit therefrom. For example, a school may be dedicated for the education of the children of the poor, or a hospital for the relief of the sick and ailing among them, and so on.(2)

In the case of *lungar-khânèhs*(3) and similar institutions which are primarily intended for the poor, the affluent have, *primâ facie*, no title to benefit therefrom. But the *wâkif* may condition otherwise.

Mosques are too well-known to require any detailed description. The word *masjid* is derived from *sijda*, devotion, and **Mosques.**

(1) This is by no means exhaustive.
(2) A burial ground for the poor or homeless strangers is called *gôr-i-gharibân*
(3) A place where doles of food are distributed to the poor.

means a place of devotion or a place where prayers are offered to the Almighty.

A very fair description of an ordinary mosque is given by Herklot in his *Qanoon-i-Islâm.* *Musallas* are prayer-grounds, and the word is derived from the word *salât*, or prayers. In India. they are generally called *Idgâhs* or *namâz-gâhs*, and consist of a plot of ground set apart for the performance of the daily prayers or the Id prayers.

An *Imâmbâra* literally means the house of the *Imâm.* It is a building consecrated to services held in honour of the martyrdom of Hussain, and is generally a Shiah institution, though many Sunnis also erect and maintain *Imâmbâras.* In Persia, an *Imâmbâra* is generally called an *Imâmzâda* or *mash-had.*

In India, the tombs of saints or holy personages are generally called *dargâhs.* In Persia and Western Asia they are called *rouzahs*, like the *rouzah* of the Caliph Ali, that of Imâm Ali bin Mûsa ar-Razâ at Meshed, and so on.

Khânkâhs. A *Khânkâh*, sometimes also called *Khângâh*, is defined by Richardson to mean a monastery or religious structure built for the Eastern Sûfis or Dervishes.

Meninski defines the word thus, "*domus propter Deum extructa in usum sophorum aut religiosorum, cœnobium.*"

In the *Burhân-i-Kâté* and the *Majâlis-ul-'Aârifin* it is defined as a place where *dervishes* and other seekers after truth congregate for religious instruction and devotional exercise.

It is, ordinarily speaking, an institution for the lodgment of religious devotees, travellers and mendicants.

In Western Asia, they are sometimes called *rubâts* and are used generally for housing pilgrims, dervishes, &c.

In India, *Khânkâhs* have generally sprung up in the following way :—A *dervish* or a person who, by leading a pious life, has won the esteem and veneration of the neighbourhood, or a *sûfi* of particular sanctity has settled down in some locality. So long as he has not attained sufficient importance, his place of abode is called a *takia.* But when he is a man of importance or has attained sufficient eminence, it is designated an *âstâna.* His pious life and religious ministrations attract public notice, disciples gather round him, and a place is constructed for their lodgment. And the humble *takia* grows into a *Khânkâh.* After the death of the holy

Khânkâhs and Tombs.

personage, the spot where he is buried becomes a shrine and an object of pilgrimage not only for his disciples, but for people of distant parts, both Mussulmans and Hindoos, and is designated either as a *dârgâh* or *âstâna* or *rouzah*. Such are the shrine and *Khânkâh* of Shah Kubeer Dervish, to which I shall refer again later.

And grants have been made by pious chiefs and sovereigns to these holy men for their maintenance and the maintenance of their descendants in perpetuity and the performance of pious acts.

There are a number of *dargâhs* in India. Some of the most noted ones in Southern India are mentioned by Herklot.(1) Of the others, the most important are those at Ajmir(2) and at Futtehpur Sikri (near Agra). There is a celebrated *dargâh* in the suburbs of Calcutta called *Moula Ali ki dargâh*, where votive offerings of all kinds are made. The tomb of the famous poet, Shaikh Ali Hazîn, is also regarded as a shrine not only by Mussulmans but also by Hindoos

Rest-houses for *ghâzis* or soldiers engaged in holy warfare are also called *rubâts*.

SECTION II.

MOSQUES AND MUSALLAHS.

"The proprietary right of the *wâkif* in a building or ground set apart for prayers becomes extinguished either on the declaration of the *wâkif* that he has constituted it a mosque or *musallah* or consecrated it for worship, *or* on the performance of prayers therein or thereon."(3) Prayer-grounds.

Every ground set apart for prayers is not necessarily a *musallah* and subject to the rules governing a mosque. A *musalla* is a place where funeral prayers or the prayers of the two Ids are usually offered. In such cases only the place where the congregation gather and the worship is performed that is governed by the rules governing a mosque. But a piece of ground may be specially dedicated for the performance of public prayers, and though there is no building thereon, if prayers have been habitually performed

(1) Herklot's *Quanoon-i-Islam*. (2) The mausolea of Muin ud-dîn Chishti.
(3) *Radd ul-Muhtâr*, Vol. III, p. 571.

thereon, it is *wakf* and subject to the rules governing a mosque.(1)

Dedication of a mosque.

According to the *Multeka*, the performance of prayer is equivalent to consignment. But in the *Zakhîra* it is stated that the prayer must be congregational, *salât-bi'l-jamâ'at*, which is unanimously regarded as tantamount to delivery. So that when a person erects a building with the object of dedicating it as a mosque and permits people to offer prayers therein, without declaring that he has constituted it into a mosque, and prayers are offered there *bi'l-jamâ'at* (congregationally), the mosque becomes irrevocably dedicated.

The approved doctrine.

"When a mosque is erected or set up inside a dwelling-house or residence (*dâr*), and permission is granted to the public to come and pray, and a pathway is also made or set apart for their egress and ingress, the dedication is good by general consensus. If a pathway is not indicated, in that case, according to Abû Hanîfa, the dedication is not sufficient. But according to Abû Yusuf and Mohammed, it is good, and the pathway will be implied by the permission to pray, and *this is correct.*"

The public do not acquire any right in a private mosque without special permission. Need not be express

Accordingly, if a man were to build a mosque inside his house, it will not become a public mosque, subject to the rules governing a *public* religious institution, *unless permission has been once granted to outsiders to come and pray.* It is not necessary that such permission should be given in *express* terms, but, without an actual or constructive permission, a mosque created within a private building will not become a public mosque so as to entitle the public, or any section of the public, to claim the use of it. At the same time, though the public may have no right in a private mosque, it may constitute a good *wakf* so as to exclude the rights of the heirs over it. *Where prayers have been once offered it is not necessary to prove an express dedication.* The very fact of the prayers being offered in it will imply a valid and good dedication.

Acknowledgment or declaration of the *wâkif* sufficient evidence of a *wakf*.

According to Abû Yusuf, the *kawl* alone of the *wâkif*, or a declaration on his part that the land or premises is dedicated, is sufficient :—For example, if he were to declare that a particular building is constituted into a mosque, it would be a valid dedication, even though prayers may not have been offered in it "This

(1) *Sharh-Multeka.*

is the accepted doctrine,'' says the author of the *Radd ul-Muhtâr* "as stated in the *Durr-ul-Munteka*, the *Durrar*, the *Vikâyah* and other authorities, and we decide according to it.''(1)

Principle.

When the structure does not bear the shape of a mosque, or when there is no evidence of a declaration on the part of the *wâkif* that he has constituted the building into a *masjid*, and the evidence of dedication depends on the performance of prayers within it, some lawyers have held such prayers should be with *azân*(2) and *ikâmat*.(3) The reason of this condition is stated in the following terms :—" As delivery of possession in the case of a *wakf* is deemed necessary, though Abû Yusuf holds a contrary opinion, the nature of the delivery depends in each case upon the nature of the specific thing, for example, the delivery of a cemetery is by the burial of *one* person ; of a tank or reservoir by *one* person drinking there ; a guest-house (*musâffir-khânèh*, traveller's house) by *one* wayfarer or traveller alighting there. Similarly, as the purpose of a mosque is that people should pray there in *jamâ'at*,(4) it is required that where there is no express dedication, prayers should have been offered there with the *azân* and *ikâmat*.''

Prayers offered once in a mosque constitute a valid dedication.

But when one man acts both as *muezzin*(5) and *imâm*(6) his praying alone is sufficient.

If prayers are offered once in a mosque it is sufficient to constitute a good dedication. But should the *wâkif* alone pray in it, that would not be sufficient unless there is a declaration.

Accepted doctrine.

In the *Fatâwai Kâzi Khân* it is stated that, " the delivery of possession as regards a *masjid* is complete when only one person has prayed in it with *azân* and *ikâmat*. Prayers offered by one person in a mosque is sufficient to constitute it a public mosque devoted to the worship of God, for a mosque belongs to the Deity and there affixes to it a right of the Mussulmans in general, and one person can be a proxy for the establishment of the right of the Creator and the public......According to Abû Yusuf consignment is not necessary for the validity of any dedication, whether it be a mosque or any other *wakf*. Therefore, if a person erect a

(1) *Radd ul-Muhtâr*, Vol. III, p. 572.
(2) The call to prayers.
(3) The standing-up for prayers.
(4) In assemblies.
(5) The person who calls to prayers.
(6) One who leads the prayers.

mosque and give permission to people to pray therein, it becomes complete."(1)

Consignment without prayers sufficient.

Should a mosque be consigned to a *mutwalli* but no prayers be offered therein, it would be a valid dedication.

Dedication of a cemetery, &c.

When a person has erected a public reservoir, fountain or cemetery according to Abû Yusuf, "whose opinion we follow," the *wakf* cannot be revoked. The burial of even one man in a cemetery is sufficient to constitute it a *wakf*, so the staying of one *musâffir* (traveller) *in a musâffir-khânèh* makes the *wakf* irrevocable.(2)

General result of the principles.

The general result of the above principles may be summed up in the following terms:—Where effect has once been given to a dedication in the mode which is natural to the particular dedication, the *wakf* is complete and irrevocable. For example, the special purpose of a mosque is that people should perform their devotions there; of a cemetery, for dead persons to be buried there; of a reservoir or tank, to supply water to those who use it, &c., so according to the accepted doctrine of Abû Yusuf, even where there is no evidence of an express dedication in words, if it appears that one single individual (other than the consecrator) has offered his prayers at the place, or one single person has been buried in the cemetery, or one person has drunk at the fountain, the dedication for the specific purpose must be regarded as complete. Such use of the subject of the *wakf* being in conformity with its avowed or ostensible object should be considered as conclusive of the dedication.

"A person has a piece of land and permits people to pray thereon without any restriction or limitation as to the time of prayer, or the number of people who should pray there. After his death that land will not form a portion of his inheritance. But if the permission was limited to a particular occasion or to a fixed period of time, the land will continue to be his inheritable property, for the limitation of time or occasion rebuts the presumption of absolute *wakf*."(3)

---

(1) *Fatâwai Kâzi Khân*, Vol. II, p. 206.
(2) *Radd ul-Muhtâr*, Vol. III, p. 572.
(3) *Ibid*, p. 571.

A place where the *namâz-Id*(1) or *namâz-i-janâza*(2) is usually performed is subject to the rules of a *masjid* according to Kâzi Khân and the author of the *As'aâf*.(3)

Principle.

If a person were to say "this room of mine I have set apart for supplying oil to the lamps of a certain mosque," and add nothing further—then, according to Fakîh Abû J'aafar, the room becomes *wakf* for the mosque in question, if it is made over to the *mutwalli*, and the *Fatwa* is according to this opinion.(4)

If a person were to make a *wakf* of his land to a mosque and consign it to the *mutwalli* of the mosque, it is lawful and cannot be revoked. If a person were to bestow money for building a mosque or for the "affairs" or for the support of the mosque it is valid upon its delivery to the trustee.

If a person were to consecrate his house for a mosque or for the benefit of Mussulmans, it is lawful, and the *Fatwa* is according to this.

A *wakf* for the repairs of mosques and graves is lawful, for it implies perpetuity.

A *wakf* for the repairs of mosques, &c.

A sovereign cannot give any portion of the land acquired by treaty and negotiation to be converted into a mosque without the consent of the owners, but he can give any portion of the land acquired by war, provided it does not interfere with the right of way possessed by any individual.

If a person erect a mosque but appoint nobody as the *mutwalli* thereof, the *towliat* or governance remains vested in him. This is according to Hillâl and Nâtiki and is the accepted rule.

The *Ahl-i-mahalla*, *i.e.*, the people of the quarter may lawfully enlarge or reconstruct a mosque and supply it with better articles at their own expense, but not at the expense of the mosque unless the Kâzi's permission is obtained to that effect. Should the *Ahl-i-mahalla* wish to improve the mosque, with or without the consent of the Kâzi, the heirs of the *wâkif* will not have any right to object unless it is patently contrary to the wishes of the *wâkif*.

Rights of the congregation.

(1) Prayers offered on the occasion of the two Id festivals, being, *viz.*, the *Id ul-fitr* and the *Id-ul-uzha* or *Bairam*.

(2) Funeral prayers.

(3) *Radd ul-Muhtár*, Vol. III, p. 571.

(4) *Ibid.* p. 572; *Surrat-ul-Fatâwa*.

Private places of worship.

Frequently, rooms are reserved in private residences for family prayers, or for the performance of the Moharram ceremonies. Such rooms cannot be regarded as specifically consecrated so as to constitute a *wakf* to exclude the rights of the heirs. In many cases, however distinct apartments are set apart for the performance of the religious ceremonies, like Kerbelai Mohammed's Imâmbara in Calcutta. Often, they have an entrance separate from that of the private residence, and in all respects fulfil the conditions laid down by Kahastâni, who declared that, where the mosque was so intermixed with the private property or residence of the *wâkif* as to render differentiation necessary, the *wakf* premises should be distinctly indicated. In these cases, there can be no question as to the apartments constituting a valid *wakf*. As a matter of principle, however, the law disfavours the dedication by way of *wakf* of one portion of a private residence, whilst the other portion is in the occupation of the *wâkif*. For example, the dedication of the upper or lower storey of a building as a mosque is not considered valid, *unless owing to the crowded condition of the locality, it has become customary to constitute such mosques.* Both Abû Yusuf and Mohammed recognised the lawfulness of such dedications in Bagdad and Rai, on account of the dense population of those cities in that century. It must not be inferred from the above, that there is any bar to the temporary conversion, or use, by any person, of a portion of his private residence as a place for family prayers or religious worship. The rule is, that unless certain conditions are complied with, the apartments will not be subject to the law of *wakf* and will continue to form the private property of the individual, the one condition chiefly requiring attention being that the portion dedicated is capable of being differentiated from the rest of the residence ; when such can be done, the *wakf* is valid.

But where the whole building is constituted *wakf* for a mosque, imâmbara or madrassa, and a portion of the building is used for the specific purpose of the *wakf*, and the remainder for the use of the servitors of the institution, or for letting out to people as a source of income to the *wakf*, the dedication is valid. The mere fact of the *wâkif* occupying some portion of the building as *mutwalli* will not affect the validity of the *wakf*.

In the *Hedâya* it is stated that Abû Yusuf and Mohammed have held the dedication of the central hall of a house for the purpose of a mosque to be valid. In the *Radd ul-Muhtâr* the statement is subjected to the condition that in order to be valid means of egress and ingress should be provided.

The existence of secular buildings attached to the mosque does not affect the religious structure.

In many places it is usual to build mosques or mausoleums so as to be able to let the ground-floor or the outer portions to shop-keepers, the rent being applied for the maintenance of the institution. In fact, in such instances, the shops form the only endowment attached to the mosque or mausoleum. The existence of these secular buildings does not affect, as has been sometimes supposed, the validity of the *wakf* or the nature of the religious structure.

The right of the servitors.

When any portion of the building is allotted for the residence of the survitors, such servitors have no right to let their rooms to others. They can reside in such rooms so long as they are in the service of the mosque; but they cannot allow another person to reside in those rooms for hire or otherwise without the permission of the *mutwalli*. If the service is hereditary, their successors have the same right and no more. The *Radd ul-Muhtâr* says that "as the servitors of a mosque or *madrassa* cannot assign their allowances to others, so they cannot assign their rooms."

A mosque open to all sects of Moslems.

A mosque does not belong to any particular sect. It is open to all Mussulmans to go in and offer their adoration to the Almighty. Suppose a Hanafî erects a mosque; the Shâfeïs, the Mâlikis and the Hanbalis may pray there equally with the members of the Hanafî sect. Nor is there any objection to a Shiah going and praying there according to his own ritual. The Hanafî *mutwalli* cannot prevent any person, so long as he is the worshipper of God, and does not interrupt or disturb the worship of others from coming and offering his adoration to the Almighty. This view of the law was given effect to in the case of *Ata-Ullah* v. *Azim-Ullah*,(1) where the Allahabad High Court held that a mosque, being dedicated to God, is for the use of all Mahomedans, and cannot be lawfully appropriated to the use of any particular sect.

(1) [1889], I. L., 12 All., 494.

A Sunni Mahomedan belonging to any one of the four sects(1) may validly perform his devotions under the leadership of a member of another sect.(2)

Leadership in prayers of a free-thinker valid.

According to the *Fatâwai Alamgiri*, "the *imâmate* (leadership in prayers) of freethinkers and heretics is valid."(3) The same principle is laid down in the *Radd ul-Muhtâr*.(4) But the *Alamgiri* adds that it is not lawful to offer prayers behind a *mushabbaha* (one who believes God to be like a man, in other words, an anthropomorphist), a Jahmi,(5) or a Râfizi."(6) In short, freethought (*hawa*), which does not amount to *kufr* (denial of the unity of God and the messengership of the Prophet) does not disqualify one from *imâmate*, "and it is lawful to pray behind a freethinker . . . . so it is stated in the *Khulâsa*, and that is correct, and the *Badâye* says the same."(7)

There is no prohibition, therefore, to a Sunni praying behind a Shiah, and *vice versâ*, but practice does not recognise it; and among the Shiahs some of the legists have gone so far as to declare praying behind a Sunni illegal. Nor is this exclusiveness confined to some Shiah legists, for *ultra*-Sunnis hold a similar opinion regarding a Shiah officiating at their prayers. In spite of the barriers created by bigotry between the two sects, it is frequent for a Shiah to go into a mosque dedicated by a Sunni, or a Sunni to go into a mosque where Shiahs usually pray, and perform his prayers according to his own ritual, even when the Sunnis or the Shiahs, as the case may be, are engaged in their prayers. There is nothing illegal in his so doing, nor can the *mutwalli* of the mosque turn him out *so long as he does not interrupt or disturb the worship of the others*.

Every Moslem entitled to pray in a mosque according to his own ritual.

According to the Hanafis and the Shiahs, the prayers of the congregation are not commendable unless the imam (the person who leads the prayers) is well-conducted and leads a pure life.

---

(1) See Introd., p. 13.

(2) See the observations of Mahmood, J., in *Queen-Empress* v. *Ramzan* [1885], I. L., 7 All., 461. See also *Fazl Karim* v. *Haji Mowla Buksh* [1891], L. R., 18 I. A., 59; s. c., I. L., 18 Cal., 448; and *Abdus Subhan* v. *Korban Ali* [1908], I. L., 35 Cal., 294.

(3) *Fatâwai Alamgiri*, Vol. I, p. 116.

(4) *Radd-ul-Muhtâr*, Vol. I, pp. 585-586.

(5) A follower of Jahm-ibn-Safwân, who denied all free will.

(6) *Lit. a deserter*, name given to a body of Shiahs who deserted Zaid bin Ali bin Hussain; See *Short History of the Saracens*, p. 156.

(7) *Fatâwai Alamgiri*, Vol. I, p. 116.

According to the Shâfeïs, Mâlikis and Hanbalis, the imâm's conduct has no effect upon the prayers of the congregation.

But though some members of one sect may go and pray in a mosque whilst members of another sect are engaged in their devotions, there cánnot be two *azâns* (calls to prayer) nor two *jamâ'ats* (assemblies) at one and the same time in that mosque.

But there cannot be two *azâns* or two congregations.

The Sunnis offer their prayers with the hands folded in front, whilst the Shiahs perform their devotions with their hands held straight down by their side. Both practices are based upon certain traditions accepted by one sect and rejected by the other.

Mode of performing prayers.

The Shâfeïs, Mâlikis and Hanbalis raise their hands when pronouncing the *takbîr* (*viz.*, the words "*allaho-akbar*, God is great") during a certain part of the prayers. This gesture is called *raf'aa-ed-dain*, 'raising of the hands.' They also pronounce loudly the word *âmîn* or amen after the first chapter of the Koran has been recited by the imâm, which is not regarded as correct by the Hanafîs. This practice is called *âmîn-bi'l-jahr*.

The Hanafîs regard both these practices as irregular. They pronounce the word *âmîn* softly, and raise their hands during the *takbîr* not higher than above the ears.

These small differences in ritual have given rise to considerable disputes in India. A large section of the Sunnis in India have, chiefly on doctrinal matters, become non-conformists or *ghair-mukallid* (from *taklîd*, conformity). They profess to follow no particular Imâm, but to act according to all four. They incline, however, towards Shâfeïsm, and call themselves *'Aâmil-bi'l-Hadîs*, "followers of the traditions." In practice, they adopt *raf'aa-ed-dainisim* and *âmîn-bi'l-jahr*. The ignorant Hanafîs object to these innovations, and hence the disputes. They refuse to pray after an *'aâmil-bi'l-hadîs* imâm, or to allow the *'aâmil-bi'l-hadîs* to offer prayers in a mosque, usually used by Hanafîs. Both these points have been settled in favour of the *'aâmil-bi'l-hadîs*.

In the case of *Fuzlul Karim* v. *Haji Moula Buksh*,(1) their Lordships of the Privy Council have decided that an imâm does not become disqualified from leading at prayers owing to his having adopted the *'aâmil-bi'l-hâdîs* doctrines.

(1) [1891], L. R., 18 Ind. App., 59; s. c., I. L., 18 Cal., 448, *supra*.

The *'aâmil-bi'l-hadîs* support their practice by a reference to certain *hadîses* given in the *Sahîh-ul-Bokhari* and *Sahîh-ul-Muslim*.(1)

Colleges, schools, hospitals, dispensaries, &c., stand on the same footing as mosques and other religious institutions. From an English point of view, they would be regarded, generally speaking, as secular endowments. But, in the Mussulman Law there is no distinction between purely religious institutions and others. All are treated on the same footing.

Application of the endowment of a mosque which has become deserted.

"In the *Khulâsa*, Chapter on *Wakf*, third section, it is stated that the Sâhib-i-Manah [the author of the *Manah*] was asked with regard to such a *wakf* as this: 'a mosque has become ruined and part of it has come down, and the people of the *mahalla* (where it is situated) do not need it, and near to it is a mosque, can the remaining portions of the ruined mosque be sold and applied for the benefit of the other mosque?' The answer was, 'the matter must be referred to the Kâzi.'"

"In the *Kinia* it is laid down that when a reservoir or a mosque has become ruined, and people have abandoned it, the Kâzi has the power of authorising the application of the proceeds arising from the sale of the materials to another reservoir or mosque. And it is also stated there, that when there are two ruined mosques, and nobody knows who were the dedicators of the two, the Kâzi has the power of directing the application of the one to the other for the purpose of reconstruction. If the consecrators are known and have left their heirs, they might give the sanction themselves."

"In the *Khânièh* (*i.e.*, *Fatâwai Kâzi Khân*) it is laid down that when the mosque has become ruined, and the people of the locality do not require it, the matter should be taken before the Kâzi that he may authorise the sale of the materials and the application of the proceeds to another mosque." . . . . . .

"When a *wakf* [building] has become ruined, and there is no income forthcoming to repair or re-erect it, some have said the *wâkif*, and if he be dead, his heirs, may resume it, but Sadr-ush-Shahîd in his *Fatwa* has stated that this opinion is questionable and against principle."(2)

---

(1) *Bokhari*, pp. 19 and 108; *Jâm'aa-ul-Tirmizi*, p. 38; see Appendix.
(2) *Surrat-ul-Fatâwa*, p. 432.

According to the *Radd-ul-Muhtâr*, where a mosque has fallen into ruin, and it is not known who had erected it, the *ahl-i-mahalla* can sell the materials, presumably with the sanction of the Kâzi, and apply the proceeds to the building of another mosque. A well can be dug in a mosque if it is to its benefit. The *wâkif* cannot let for hire for his own purposes any portion of the mosque premises. When a mosque has ceased, the *wâkif* cannot make use of it for any other purpose. "No profit should be derived from a mosque, nor can it be leased or turned into a private abode."

According to Abû Hanîfa and Abû Yusuf, the land which has once been dedicated to a mosque continues *wakf* even though it has become waste and the building has fallen into ruin; and the *Fatwa* is according to their opinion.(1) And Abû Yusuf further holds that, with the permission of the Kâzi, the ruined or waste portion may be sold and applied towards the construction or maintenance of any other mosque nearest to the disused mosque. "And the same principle is applicable to every other religious or charitable institution."(2) According to the *Surrat-ul-Fatâwa*, the *Fatwa* is according to Abû Yusuf.

The *cy-près* doctrine.

"According to the *Sharh-Multeka*, when the purpose of a trust fails, it is lawful to apply the income of the trust-property to an object nearest in its nature to the original purpose, *jins-i-karîb*. For example, if the object of a *wakf* is a reservoir, the income may be applied to a tank or canal; if it is a mosque, the income is to be applied to another mosque, or to fasting, prayers, etc."(3)

Shams ul-Aïmma al-Halwâni has declared that when a *hauz* (reservoir) or mosque becomes ruined, and nobody uses it, the Kâzi can direct the application of its materials to another *hauz*, or mosque. "In these times," says the author of the *Radd*, "it is essentially necessary to adopt the views of Imâm al-Halwâni, who authorises the Kâzi to give permission to apply the materials belonging to a mosque, which has fallen into ruin, to another which is in use."(4)

(1) *Hâwi*. By *consensus* the *Fatwa* is with Abû Yusuf.

(2) The *Bahr* explains thus the difference between Abû Hanîfa and Abû Yusuf on one side and Mohammed on the other :—"According to Mohammed the articles in the disused mosque go to the *wâkif*, but the mosque and land remain *wakf* perpetually as Abû Yusuf holds, and cannot revert to the *wâkif* or his heirs to become their heritable property."

(3) *Radd-ul-Muhtâr*, Vol. III, p. 574.

(4) *Ibid*.

"When there are two *wakfs* and of both the *wâkif* is the same and the purpose the same, but owing to certain calamities the income of one has diminished, whilst from the other a balance is left [over and above the expenditure], the Judge has the power to direct that the allowances of the servants of the first *wakf* may be made up from the balance of the income of the second." But the Kâzi is not invested with this power, if the purpose of the two *wakfs* is different. "For example, if a man make two dedications for a mosque, one for its building and the other for the imâm and the muezzin, and, owing to a decrease in the profits of the second *wakf*, the imâm and muezzin cannot be employed, then it is lawful for the Hâkim, in consultation with the leading people of the *mahalla*, to direct that the allowance of these officers should be paid out of the balance left from the *wakf* for the building, provided the *wâkif* is one and the same." The *mutwalli*, though he be the trustee of both endowments, cannot of his own motion apply the balance of the proceeds of one *wakf* for the maintenance of the people provided for in the other. He must apply for and obtain the sanction of the Judge.

"In the thirteenth section of the *Jâm'aa-ul-Fusûlain*, it is laid down that when a person says his house or his room is for lighting such a mosque, and no more—that house or room will become *wakf* for the mosque." . . . . . "In the *Wâkiât-ul-Hisâmi* it is stated that if there are already funds for the lighting of the mosque, and it be considered desirable to apply the income of the house or room dedicated to building a minaret for giving *azân*, so that people may hear the call to prayers better, they may do so, but if it is not needful it should not be done."(1)

Where several *wakfs* are attached to one mosque, the *mutwalli* or manager may keep the income of all together, in fact keep a joint account, and if one shop attached to the masjid has fallen into disrepair, there is no objection to its being repaired with the income of another shop belonging to the same mosque.

If a person were to make a *wakf* or a piece of land for the purpose of erecting a mosque, he cannot afterwards resume or sell it, neither can it be inherited, because this ground is altogether alienated from the right of the individual and appertains solely to God. The reason of this is, that all things whatever are originally

(1) *Surrat-ul-Fatâwa*, p. 435.

the property of the Almighty. When, therefore, the individual relinquishes his right in the ground, it reverts to its original state, and his power over it terminates in the same manner as a master's power over a bondsman terminates in consequence of emancipation and cannot be resumed.

SECTION III.

DEDICATION FOR AQUEDUCTS, INNS, &C.

Dedications for aqueducts, inns, cemeteries, &c.

According to Abû Yusuf, a dedication to any object of utility is effectuated by the *kawl* or word of the *wâkif*, as in the case of a mosque. For example, when a person erects an aqueduct for Mussulmans, or an inn for the occupation of travellers, or a caravanserai or constitutes his land into a cemetery, the dedication becomes complete upon the declaration of the *wâkif*, and all his right of property ceases therein.(1) "According to Mohammed, it abates when people have used the aqueduct or have occupied the inn or caravanserai, or buried in the cemetery, and it is sufficient if one person do so."(2) The rule is the same as to wells and cisterns, and if they are delivered to a superintendent, the dedication is valid in like manner. It is stated in the *Mabsût* that the *Fatwa* is according to the Disciples by general consensus, in other words, the dedication may be effectuated in either way, *viz.*, by the actual declaration of the *wâkif* or by delivery, in other words, by the use of the place by a single person.

Any one can drink from the wells and cisterns and water his cattle and camels at them, and also use the water for ceremonial ablutions. In the use of all such objects of utility as abovementioned, there is no difference between the rich and the poor, and it is lawful for all alike to put up at inns and caravanserais and to drink from aqueducts and bury in a cemetery. But the income of a mansion appropriated for *ghâzîs* or religious warriors can be taken only by those of their number who are necessitous. When a mansion is dedicated for the residence of pilgrims, mere wayfarers have no right to occupy it, and when the days of the season have

---

(1) According to Abû Hanîfa, the right of the *wâkif* ceases, on the Judge making a decree, or, if the appropriation is by way of a bequest upon the death of the *wâkif*. This is not accepted.

(2) *Fatâwai Alamgiri*, Vol. II, p. 554.

passed, it should be let and kept in repair out of the rent, and the surplus, if any. distributed among the poor.

Dedication of a road or way.

A road or way is validly dedicated by the owner of the land declaring in the presence of witnesses that he has constituted it as such. But those lawyers who consider consignment necessary to the completeness of a *wakf* require that one person should pass over the way, in order that it may serve as evidence of user. According to Hillâl, the same rule applies to a bridge. Declaration alone (according to Abû Yusuf), or user by one individual extinguishes the right of private property over such objects.(1) And the *Fatwa* is on this.

A burial-ground.

"When a body has been buried in the ground, whether for a long or short time, it cannot be exhumed without some excuse. But it may lawfully be exhumed when it appears that the land was usurped, or another is entitled to it under a right of pre-emption.

" Auzjundi being asked with regard to a masjid for which there no longer remained a congregation and all around it had gone to decay, whether it was lawful to convert it into a cemetery, answered 'No :' and being asked with regard to a cemetery, in a village, where it had gone to decay, and there remained in it no traces of the dead, not even bones, whether it was lawful to sow the land and take its produce, answered 'No,' for in legal effect it is still a cemetery."

Cemeteries.

" A man makes his land a cemetery or an inn—the *kharâj* abates, if the land were *kharâji*, and this is correct."

" When a woman has made a cemetery of part of her land, divesting herself of the property and has buried her son in it, but the piece of land is unfit for a cemetery by reason of an overflow of water upon it, and she wishes to sell the land, if it be still in such a state that people desire to bury their dead in it, she cannot sell it, but if they have no such desire she may."

A cemetery or graveyard is consecrated ground and cannot be sold or partitioned. Even lands which are not expressly dedicated but are covered by graves are regarded as consecrated and consequently inalienable and non-heritable. But when a place is found not to be a *makbara* (a burial-ground), but only one or two bodies are buried there, the actual spot where the bodies lie buried is con-

(1) *Fatâwai Alamgiri*, Vol. II, p: 556.

secrated.(1) Whether a place is a *makbara* or not depends on the number of persons buried there, or evidence of dedication derived from the testimony of witnesses or reputation.

" When there is no fund or other means to repair a mosque with, a portion of the land or the outer premises may be leased for a term to raise money for the repairs."(2)

Application of the funds of a mosque.

" No portion of the funds of the mosque should be spent for its ornamentation unless a provision to that effect has been made by the *wâkif*.(3) But the *ahl-ul-mahalla* (*i.e.*, people of the locality where the mosque is situated), may do so at their own expense."(4)

The Ahl-ul-mahalla.

" The paraphernalia of the K'aaba is a *wakf* on the K'aaba, even until they are torn to pieces, so that no article can be removed unless lawfully disposed of by the *mutwallis* for the purposes of the shrine. And this principle applies to [all] mosques, &c."

" It is lawful to make a *wakf* of lands or property for the maintenance and preservation generally of mosques, *rubâts*, and other pious charitable institutions."(5)

" A dedication in favour of a mosque is absolutely lawful according to Abû Yusuf, for a mosque exists forever until the Day of Judgment, and can never revert to private proprietorship even though it be ruined and wholly disused, nor can its material be taken to any other mosque, and on this is the *Fatwa*."(6)

" It is allowable for *Zimmis* [non-Moslems] to enter the holy shrine of the K'aaba, the sacred temple at Jerusalem, and all mosques for the purposes of work and other proper purposes, but their going to the *mihrâb*(7) of the mosque or the *maiza*(8) is objectionable."(9)

" All acts of indecency within the precincts of a mosque are forbidden, nor must one wash himself or expectorate or indulge in indecent talk or take instruments of war inside it. But a soldier may go in and offer his prayers and leave directly."(10)

---

(1) See *Mir Nur Ali* v. *Majidah* [1831], 5 Sel. Report, p. 136.

(2) *Radd-ul-Muhtâr* after the *Hâwi*.

(3) *Ibid.*

(4) *Ibid.*

(5) *Ibid.*

(6) *Ibid*, see *post*.

(7) The principal place in a mosque where the imâm stands, a kind of high altar.

(8) The place for religious ablutions.

(9) *Radd-ul-Muhtâr* after the *Hâwi*. (10) *Ibid.*

"It is not proper for any person to enter a mosque unless he is clean. The gate of a mosque should not be kept closed at any time. If there is fear of theft, and there is no gate-keeper, there is no objection to keep the doors closed at other than prayer-times."(1)

Compulsory acquisition of land for enlarging a mosque.

"If a mosque requires enlargement, and there is a piece of land adjacent to it which the owner refuses to sell, it is lawful to take it from him on payment of its proper price, whether he be willing or not."(2)

"Nothing belonging to a mosque should be given away, not even grass or old articles, such as mats (unless they can fetch no price), but should be sold for some value to be applied for the purposes of the mosque."(3)

The *ahl-ul-mahalla* or "people of the quarter."

The *ahl-ul-mahalla* can pull down a mosque and reconstruct it in better style, or improve it in any other way, and supply superior articles; but this they can only do with their own money, but *not* with the money of the *wakf*, unless the sanction of the Kâzi is obtained beforehand. This is stated in the *Khulâsa*. The *ahl-ul-mahalla* can also construct reservoirs for drinking and washing (*Wuzû*) provided the consecrator is not known; otherwise his prior permission must be obtained. His heirs, however, cannot raise objections to any improvement which the *ahl-ul-mahalla* may propose to effect in the mosque."(4)

"The *ahl-ul-mahalla* can, with the sanction of the Kâzi, sell the materials of a disused and ruined mosque and build another with the proceeds thereof."

"A mosque is the property of God. The statement in the *Hedâya* is founded on weak authority." A mosque, therefore, cannot be resumed or treated as private property.

"In the *Bazâziah* it is laid down that the *wâkif* cannot derive any benefit from the hire of any portion of the building of the mosque."

"Though a mosque may be ruined and be never used, still it is a mosque, for ever consecrated to the eternal worship of God until

---

(1) *Radd-ul-Muhtâr*, Vol. III, p. 575.
(2) *Ibid.*
(3) *Hâwi.*
(4) *Ibid.*

the Day of Judgment, according to Abû Hanîfa and Abû Yusuf, and on this is the *Fatwa*, as is stated in the *Hâwi-ul-Kûdsi*."(1)

"When a mosque is so utterly ruined that it cannot be used or the people have abandoned praying in it, according to Abû Yusuf, it and all articles appertaining to it will be applied *with the sanction of the Kâzi* to another mosque."

Application of the funds of a disused *wakf*.

"The same principle applies to all such institutions. In other words, when no benefit can be derived from a disused *langar-khânèh*, well, cistern, &c., the materials or any thing appertaining to them will be applied to the nearest mosque, *langar-khânéh*, &c. This doctrine is universally accepted as stated in the *Durrar*."

Application of the funds of a disused mosque.

"But whether a mosque has become ruined or dilapidated, or the people have no further need, owing to another mosque close by, still it will not revert to the ownership of the *wâkif*, nor will it be lawful to take it or its property to another mosque and on this is the *Fatwa* as stated in the *Hâwi-ul-Kûdsi*."(2) "And so it is in the *Mujtaba*, in the *Bahr* and in the *Fâth-ul-Kadîr*. And in the *As'aâf* it is stated that Abû Hanîfa and Abû Yusuf are in accord."

Discussion of the rule.

The author of the *Radd-ul-Muhtâr* discusses more fully the doctrine enunciated in the *Hâwi* that, according to Abû Yusuf's views, the ruined mosque or articles devoted to it, or property dedicated for it, cannot be applied to another mosque. He states first, that in the *Bahr ur-Râik*,(3) the *Multaka* and the *As'aâf*, it is expressly laid down that when a building or cistern or reservoir is ruined or abandoned, it may be applied with the leave of the Kâzi to another object nearest in character, *e.g.*, a mosque to a mosque, a well for a well, &c. Then he goes on to say, that this may seem inconsistent with the views of Abû Yusuf on which is the *Fatwa*, but he says in Abû Yusuf's rule there is no *restriction*. "And in the *As'aâf* and the *Fatâwai Kâzi Khân* it is laid down that it is permissible. And Syed Imâm Abû Shujâ'a was asked 'whether it was lawful to apply the income of a *langar-khânèh* which had become disused to another close by?' He answered, 'yes, as in the case of a mosque which has become ruined and the people of the

(1) *Radd-ul-Muhtâr*, Vol. III, p. 574.
(2) *Ibid.*; the Kâzi has the power to permit these acts to be done.
(3) P. 575.

village have given up praying there. The matter should be taken to the Kâzi and his leave obtained, and thereupon it would be lawful.' In the *Zakhîra* it is stated from Shams-ul-Aimma al-Halwâni that he was asked a similar question as to an abandoned mosque, and he answered in the affirmative. And Shaikh ul-Imâm Amîn ud-din ibn Abd-ur-'ulaâ, Shaikh ul-Imâm Ahmed ibn Yunus ash-Shibli, Shaikh Zain ibn Nujâim, Shaikh Mohammed al-Wafâi and others have given *Fatwas* to the same effect"

The *Fatwa*.

. . . . "It is sufficient to rely on the *Fatwa* of Imâm Abû Shujâ'a and Imâm Halwâni, especially in these days when it is frequent for the care-takers, embezzlers, and other dishonest people to steal and usurp the property of disused mosques, &c."(1)

In the *Hâwi* it is stated (by way of an example) that when one reservoir has become destroyed and there exists no need for it, the *wakfs* attached to it will be applied in support of other reservoirs.

Application of the endowment of a disused mosque, &c.

It is laid down in the *Khulâsa*, that when a mosque or reservoir has fallen to ruin and there is no further need for them, the inhabitants having left the neighbourhood, the *wakfs* attached to them will be applied to other mosques or reservoirs.(2) For the same reason, if the sovereign or his delegate were to withdraw a piece of land from the *Bait-ul-Mâl* and grant it to an individual for the construction of a canal for the use of the public, and subsequently, owing to the depopulation of the country, there exists no need for such a canal, the grantee does not acquire the land as his private property ; he will hold it subject to the condition of storing water for the use of flocks and cattle. According to the Shâfeïs he would take it absolutely.

The *Nahr* states thus the result of the above principles :— According "to us"(3) when the beneficiaries of a particular appropriation have ceased to exist, the proceeds arising therefrom will be applied to a *wakf* of the same nature. Consequently, the *wakfs*

(1) *Radd-ul-Muhtâr*, Vol. II. p. 642.

(2) When the Sovereign or Imâm (the chief of the commonwealth) withdraws a piece of land from the Public Treasury (*Bait-ul-Mâl*), that is, makes it revenue free and *designates the purpose to which the income derivable from it should be applied*, it becomes *wakf*. Mere withdrawal of land from the *Bait-ul-Mâl*, or declaring it rent-free, does not render it necessarily *wakf*, though it resembles in its nature a *wakf*.

(3) Meaning the Hanafis.

Application of the endowment of a disused mosque, &c.–contd.

of one mosque will be applied to the support of another mosque and of a reservoir to another reservoir. To withdraw land from the *Bait-ul-Mâl* is analogous to the creation of a *wakf*. And, therefore, when land is thus withdrawn and given to a person for the construction of a canal for the use of the public, it will on the failure of the canal be applied to the watering of the flocks and cattle and similar objects.

If the cattle belonging to a *wakf* become unfit for work, the *mutwalli* is entitled to remove and sell them.

Things belonging to the mosque but not needed may be sold by the *mutwalli* with the sanction of the Judge where there is one.

When a village, in which there exists a brick-built well or reservoir, has become completely depopulated, the materials of that reservoir or well may, with the sanction of its *wâkif*, or, in his absence, of the Kâzi, be used for the building of another well or reservoir in a contiguous village.

When anything is dedicated to a mosque which afterwards becomes ruined, the subject of the dedication does not revert to the grantor or his heirs, but will be used for the nearest mosque.

When the subject of the *wakf* is unfit for the purpose for which it is intended, the *wakf* will be avoided. For example, if a piece of land be dedicated for a cemetery, and a corpse be even buried in it, but if it afterwards appear that the place is unfit for a burial-ground, and people are unwilling to use it as such, the dedicator may sell it, for the place is not suited for the purpose for which it is intended, and that circumstance would avoid the *wakf*.

If a land dedicated to some "good" purpose has become uncultivated, and owing to its distance from town no person is willing to take a lease thereof, and no profit can be derived from it, nor can any building be raised upon it, such land may be sold according to Kâzi Khân, with the sanction of the Kâzi and its proceeds applied to other meritorious purposes.

If a road or path which leads to a mosque becomes dilapidated, it can lawfully be repaired with the funds of the mosque, when it is the only mode by which the members of the congregation can gain access to the mosque. Similarly, if a *langar-khânèh* is created on the banks of a river and people have access to it only by means of a bridge, and the bridge becomes dilapidated, it may be repaired out of the funds of the *langar-khânèh*.

SECTION IV.

PRINCIPLES APPLICABLE TO CASES WHERE THE PRIMARY OR INTERMEDIATE OBJECTS HAVE FAILED.

In connection with the foregoing subject, it must be remembered that the failure or non-existence of the initial or primary object of a *wakf* does not, under the Hanafî Law, affect the operative character or validity of the *wakf*, or avoid it. So also the failure or extinction of the intermediate objects only accelerates the ultimate reversion, but does not cancel or avoid the *wakf*.

The *cy-près* doctrine in Mussulman Law.

Consequently, when a *wakf* is made in favour of children that are unborn, or of any other non-existing object, it is valid.(1)

"When a *wakf* is made in favour of Zaid's children (and Zaid has no children existing at the time), or to a *masjid* which has not been erected, the appropriation is valid, and the rents and profits will be applied to the support of the poor, until children are born to Zaid, or the mosque is erected. This is according to the *'Imâdia*. In the *Nahr ul-Fâik* it is stated further, that when the object for which the consecration is made has not come into actual existence, but the purpose can be carried into effect, the rents and profits will be applied to that purpose so far as it is possible to do so. For example, when a man makes a grant for the support of the students of a madrassa which has not been erected, if lectures are given to students in any other building, such students will be entitled to support from the *wakf*."

"The object of a *wakf* may be non-existent," says the *Radd-ul-Muhtâr*, "in two ways :—*Firstly*, the beneficiary may be non-existing when the *wakf* is made, when it is called *wakf munkat'aa-ul-awwal* (*cut off initially*) ; and *secondly*, the persons, for whom the *wakf* is made, may cease to exist after the creation of the *wakf*, when it is called *wakf munkat'aa-ul-wasat* (*cut off in the middle*). Examples of both classes of cases are given by Kâzi Khân, *e.g.*, a man makes a *wakf* for the children born of his loins, if he has no children at the time, it is a *wakf munkat'aa-ul-awwal*, and the rents and profits will be applied to the benefit of the poor." "If children are born to him afterwards, then the rents and profits will be paid to them."(2)

(1) *Radd-ul-Muhtâr*, Vol. III, p. 641 ; *Fatâwai Kâzi Khân*, Vol. IV, p. 87.
(2) *Radd-ul-Muhtâr*, Vol. III, p. 641.

"Similarly, as stated in the *As'aâf*, when a settlement is made in favour of one's *walad* (child), and there is no *walad* existing at the time, but there is a grandson, the income of the *wakf* will be given to the grandchild until a child is born to the *wâkif*."

"An example of the second or *wakf munkat'aa-ul-wasat* arises in this way :—a *wakf* is made in favour of two sons and *after them* in favour of their children and children's children, and subsequent thereto one of the sons dies leaving him surviving the other son, it is a *wakf munkat'aa-ul-wasat*. In this case, half of the rents and profits will go to the surviving son and the remainder to the poor and indigent, and when the surviving son dies the entire rent and profits will be given to *his* children,(1) for the *wâkif* has reserved the interest of the *wakf* for the grandchildren only after the demise of both the sons. But should it appear that the intention of the *wâkif* was that the surviving son should take the entire benefit, or the interest of the deceased son should descend to his issue, effect would be given to such intention."

Intention of the *wâkif* to be strictly regarded.

"The *Khairiyèh* states the law somewhat differently, *viz.*, where the object of the *wakf* is not existing or ceases to exist, the rents and profits will be applied to purposes nearest the object for which the donor intended the *wakf*. This view, however, is not according to 'us' (that is, Hanafî doctors), but represents Shâfeï doctrines. According to the Shâfeïs, where a *wakf* is made in favour of lineal descendants and they fail, the *wakf* will be applied to other people 'nearest' to the *wâkif*."(2) According to the Hanafîs, it will be given to the poor.

"When a man makes a *wakf* of his property,—a moiety in favour of his poor kindred, and a moiety in favour of the indigent generally, it has been held that the relatives, in case of indigence, will be entitled to a share in the other moiety."

"Ibrâhîm ibn-Yusuf and Ali ibn-Ahmed al-Fârsi and Abû J'aafar Hindwâni are in agreement on the point. And it is stated in the *Nahr*, that the same is the view of the Kâzi ul-Kuzzât Maulâna Ali al-Halabi, who wrote his *Risâlat-ul-Kubrâ* about the period when Maulâna Mohammed Shah Bâderna's rule came to an end. And in the *Fatâwai Kâzi Khân* it is laid down that, according to the approved doctrine, when a *wakf* is made in favour of an

(1) *Radd-ul-Muhtâr*, Vol. III, p. 641.
(2) *Ibid.*

individual *and* the poor generally, if that person subsequently becomes poor he is entitled to participate in the *wakf* for the poor."

Hanafi Law—Distribution of a *wakf* to a wife and son.

"According to Kâzi Khân, if a man were to make a *wakf* of his land, a moiety in favour of his wife and the other in favour of his son Zaid, with a condition that upon the wife's death, her moiety should be *wakf* for his (the grantor's) children, Zaid would be entitled to participate in that moiety also as one of the children. The wife's moiety would therefore go to Zaid and the rest of the *wâkif's* children, and Zaid's moiety would be for him alone. There is no difference of opinion on this point."

The *cy-près* doctrine in the Mahomedan Law.

Mere vagueness or uncertainty will not lead to the failure of a *wakf*, for in such a case the law does itself supply the defect by declaring that the trust should be in favour of such objects as approach nearest in character to the intended object of the *wakf*; or, even when that is not expressed, be applied to the support of the poor and needy. In the absence of explicit directions on the part of the *wâkif*, the Judge has the power of framing a scheme by himself or in consultation with the beneficiaries, for the administration of the *wakf*. The principle, therefore, laid down in *Morice* v. *The Bishop of Durham*,(1) which has been occasionally endeavoured to be applied to *wakfs*, is not applicable to trusts or consecrations under the Mahomedan Law. For the *cy-près* doctrine is carried to the utmost limit in the Moslem system, and the failure of the original purpose does not in any case cause the failure of the *wakf*.

The poor are the ultimate beneficiaries in every *wakf*.

The poor form, by necessary implication of the law, the ultimate beneficiaries of every *wakf* created in favour of individuals or the descendants of the *wâkif*. Where, therefore, the primary object fails, such failure instead of voiding the *wakf* "only accelerates" the ultimate application.

Again, where the dedication is to a religious or charitable institution, which, in course of time, ceases to exist, the property so dedicated, instead of reverting to the grantor or his heirs, should be applied, as already pointed out, to some other religious or pious institution, similar in character to the one which has failed, or to any other object by which benefit may accrue to human beings.

(1) 10 Vesey, p. 399.

CHAPTER XIII.

THE INCOME OF THE WAKF ESTATE, HOW TO BE APPLIED.

THE *Fatâwai Alamgiri* citing the *Hâwi li'l-Kudsi*, says (1) "the income of the *wakf* property is to be expended, in the first place, on necessary repairs, whether the *wâkif* has made it a condition or not, and next, if nothing else has been specified, on such things as are nearest to the principal object [*lit.* the building], in other words, on such objects as are most essential to the general purpose or policy of the dedication, as, for instance, in providing an imâm for a mosque and a professor for a college, to the extent of their needs, then on the attendants (*lit.* man for lighting lamps and spreading carpets), and so forth, to carry out the purpose. But if anything else has been specified, the income must be applied to that immediately after the repairs."

The *Durr-ul-Mukhtâr* states the rule in identical terms.

Similarly, in the *Hedâya* it is laid down, "that it is incumbent that the income of the *wakf* should, in the first instance, be expended in its repairs [or maintenance], whether the *wâkif* has made a condition to that effect or not, inasmuch as his object was that the income should form a perpetual fund, and as a perpetual income cannot be derived from the *wakf* property unless it is maintained in proper condition, this is a necessary concomitant to it."

Application of the income of a *wakf*.

The *Radd-ul-Muhtâr* states as follows:—"The rents and profits arising from a property which is constituted *wakf* must first be applied towards its preservation and maintenance and the payment of the wages of the care-taker or custodian."

"The income of the *wakf* must be first applied in keeping the property in a proper condition so as to yield a permanent income. If the *wakf* property consists of fruit-bearing trees, a portion of the income must be spent in buying new plants. So, also, if it is land, which without irrigation will not yield any crops, the first charge

---

(1) *Fatâwai Alamgiri*, Vol. II, p. 468.

on the income must be to do the needful for that purpose ; so it is stated in the *Muhît* and the *Fatâwai Kâzi Khân*.''(1)

In case of immovable property, therefore, all expenses incidental to its due maintenance in proper condition according to its nature, must be first paid out of the income ; the wages of persons entrusted with its preservation and management stand on the same footing. The balance is to be applied for the purposes of the *wakf*. If the *wakf* is in favour of individuals, such as the *wâkif's* children, it is to be applied to their benefit or given to them as the case may be, in accordance with the provisions of the *wakfnâmah*. If there are no express provisions, the application will be in accordance with the general design of the *wakf*. If the intention of the *wâkif* was that his children should be supported with the income of the *wakf*, it will be done according to his wishes.

Similarly, in the case of a *wakf* for any other purpose. The general design of the trust should be kept in view, even when the particulars are not sufficiently defined.(2)

Disbursements from *wakf* property.

'' For example, if a dedication is made for a *madrassa* and nothing further is said, the residue of the rents and profits after deducting the cost of maintaining the building shall be applied to maintain the proper staff of teachers. When the dedication is to a mosque, the balance shall be applied to the employment of the usual servants and the supply of the usual articles of furniture, &c., necessary for the performance of the worship, even though the *wâkif* should not have mentioned it.''

The primary object should be to maintain the purpose for which the dedication is made. If a dedication is made to a mosque and the salary set apart for the imâm is not sufficient to employ one, the provision made by the donor should be set aside and a reasonable allowance should be made for that purpose. A mosque once dedicated should not be allowed to lie useless. The result is that, in the first place, the cost of maintaining the *wakf* should be defrayed from the income, and after that, each object should take precedence in accordance with its relative importance. But if the expenses are specified by the *wâkif*, care will be taken to carry out his wishes with due regard to the primary object of keeping up the *wakf*.

---

(1) *Radd-ul-Muhtâr*, Vol. III, p. 598.

(2) *Durr ul-Mukhtâr in loco.*

"In the application of the proceeds, the first thing to which attention should be directed is the maintenance of the *wakf*. Should the entire income be necessary to put the *wakf* buildings or property in repair, it may be so applied, and in the case of a mosque, no person, not even the imâm or muezzin should get any salary until the repairs are made." [This passage shows the importance which is attached to the maintenance and preservation of the *wakf*. The primary object of the *wakf* being the perpetual consecration of the property for meritorious or pious purposes, the law insists that the first duty of the curator should be to preserve the building in a state of repair, and if it is in such a condition that it is likely to fall into ruin, the income is to be applied primarily to its restoration and repair.] "If anything remains over after defraying the cost of repairs, it should be given to those whose discharge would cause injury to the *wakf*. After this has been done, the other matters connected with the *wakf* should be carried into effect with due regard to their relative importance. Those people from whose dismissal no injury would accrue(1) will not get any portion of their allowance until the absolutely necessary repairs are completed. But when those people do work for the *wakf* they will get their proper wages, though not the allowance fixed in the *wakfnâmah*."(2) This refers to a case where the income is not sufficient to defray the cost of urgent repairs as well as the full allowance of the servants of the *wakf* or of the beneficiaries.

Maintenance of the *wakf*.

"When the *wâkif* has provided that after defraying the cost of repairs and maintaining the institution, the surplus should be distributed among the poor or the beneficiaries, it is nevertheless incumbent on the *mutwalli* to deduct every year a certain sum from the income for repairs, even though there is no immediate need for it—so as to enable him to provide a fund therefor; for it may so happen that, owing to some unforeseen contingency, there may not be any income at the time."

The mode in which a *wakf* building ought to be used.

"If a house is made *wakf* for another person, he is entitled only to the income arising therefrom but not to occupy it. Similarly, the person for whose occupation the house is made

(1) Such as the supervisor, the *kâtib* (writer) and rent-collector.

(2) According to the *Nahr-ul-Fâik*, the *Ashbâh* holds they ought to get their fixed salary.

wakf is not entitled to its income." The correctness of this doctrine appears to have been doubted, and in any case the Kâzi would have it in his discretion to authorise any act which may be beneficial to the *wakf*. The principle, however, which is deducible from the above doctrines is, that the beneficiaries cannot, of their motion under any circumstance, change the nature of the dedication.

Kazi's discretion.

In the *Sharh-Wahbânieh* by Sharnibilâlièh, it is stated that among the persons considered necessary for the maintenance of a *wakf* are included, the superintendent, the *imâm* (who leads the prayers), the *khatîb* (who reads the *khutba*), the *muezzin*, whether the *wâkif* has made a condition to that effect or not, after the repairs. The *Bahr-ur-Râik* holds the door-keeper and care-taker of a mosque whose duty it is to keep it clean as necessary adjuncts of a mosque.

If there are any debts on the *wakf* property, the *mutwalli* should, either by leasing the property or in any other reasonable manner, liquidate such debts.

If there is no income at all accruing from the *wakf*, and the endowed property is going to ruin, the Kâzi has the power to authorise the *mutwalli* to let temporarily the whole or any portion of it, and with the proceeds thereof to repair it. Where the income of the *wakf* premises is not sufficient to cover the outlay on its maintenance, or when the *wakf* is falling into ruin, and there is every probability of its dissolution, and the income is not sufficient to cover the cost of repairs, the Kâzi has the power of directing that it may be sold and with the proceeds thereof certain other property may be purchased subject to the same trust.

This doctrine is laid down by Abû Yusuf and it will be acted upon as long as it is possible to do so. If it is impossible to sell the *wakf* property or to apply the proceeds of the sale for the beneficiaries or for the benefit of the poor, in that case only effect would be given to the doctrine of Mohammed, that where the purpose has failed absolutely, the property should revert to the heirs of the donor.

"When a *wakf* is made for students *and the wakf is small*, only poor students will be supported. But generally the word 'student' implies want, and when a *wakf* is made for students in general, it is confined to indigent students alone, for students are almost all in straitened circumstances. Similarly, the *wakf* of a Koran in a masjid and books in a madrassa is generally confined to the poor, unless it can be shown that the books are not available.'' According to the *Khulâsat-ul-Wakniëh,* however, in the case of a *wakf* of books or of a *wakf* to students, the poor stand in the same category as the well-to-do. It further lays down the principle that such *wakfs* may be looked upon from two points of view :—that the poor and rich are equal as in the case of *mussâffir-khânëhs,* cemeteries, tanks, &c., the benefit of which is shared by all alike. ''In respect of the benefit arising out of these objects of *wakf,* custom makes no difference in the position of an indigent and a well-to-do person. In the case of a *wakf* of books, the rich student stands in the same position as the poor regarding the difficulty of obtaining some of the books ; and it must be remembered that the object is to benefit all.'' This seems to be the generally accepted doctrine.

Wakf in favour of students.

If a *wakf* is made of books for a specified place, their use will be restricted to that place, and the books will not be allowed to be taken away from there. And if it is for students, then every student is entitled to make use of them, but cannot remove them from the place. In matters relating to the use of a *wakf* the provisions made by the *wâkif,* if legal, should be followed. The jurists look upon the conditions imposed by the *wâkif* as conditions imposed by the law (the *Nass*). But in order that any restrictive condition may be binding, it must be satisfactorily proved that the *wâkif* really and intentionally imposed the same.

" When the *wakf* is in favour of individuals, the building cannot be enlarged without their consent.'' In other words, the beneficiaries of a trust have a right to be consulted in any alteration in the character of the *wakf* as may be likely to entail serious expenditure.

House dedicated for the residence of another.

" If a house is made *wakf* for the dwelling of another, the duty of keeping it in repairs devolves on him. If he has no means, the Kâzi may let it for a while, and with the rent thereof repair the same.''(1)

If the person for whose residence the house has been dedicated agrees to pay rent whilst it is undergoing repairs, the

(1) Comp. the *Durr-ul-Mukhtâr*, p. 414.

Kâzi may leave him in occupation. If it is the *mutwalli* himself who is entitled to reside in the *wakf* and he fails or cannot keep it in repairs, the Kâzi has the power to compel him or to appoint another curator *pro tem* to carry out the repairs. But after the work has been done and its cost fully disbursed, the house should be restored to the person for whose habitation it was dedicated.(1)

When a *wakf* building is falling into ruin, the *mutwalli* is not entitled of his own authority to sell the trees planted within it for the purpose of repairing the house, but he can hire out the house, and with the rent thereof repair the building.

(1) Comp. the *Durr-ul-Mukhtâr*, p. 414.

CHAPTER XIV.

GENERAL PRINCIPLES.

SECTION I.

THE POWERS OF THE WÂKIF.

IT is lawful for the *wâkif* to reserve the governance of the *wakf* for himself during life; this is by consensus. He can also lawfully reserve for himself the usufruct for life according to Abû Yusuf "and the *Fatwa* is thereon."(1)

It is also lawful for the *wâkif* to make a condition to the effect that the *wakf* premises may be exchanged for other property or that it may be sold, and the proceeds thereof invested for the purposes of the *wakf* in other lands or investments with the income of which the objects of the trust may be carried out. And the new property will become subject to the same rules as the former whether he has made a condition to that effect or not.(2)

The power of altering invest-ments or changing the pro-perty.

As regards the power to exchange the *wakf* property for other property, in other words to alter the investment, the rule is divisible under three heads: (i) if the donor has reserved to himself or to the *mutwallis* generally the power of making the exchange, in such a case, the exchange may be made without any question; (ii) if no power is reserved, but the property yields no profit, in that case an "exchange" may be made with the sanction of the Kâzi; (iii) if it is merely for the advantage of the *wakf* to make the exchange, in such a case the "exchange" is not lawful unless the exchange or alteration is necessitated by altered conditions of the locality or it is to the manifest advantage of the *wakf*. The main object to be kept in view is the permanent maintenance of the dedication.

(1) *Durr-ul-Mukhtâr*, p. 415; *Radd-ul-Muhtâr*, Vol. III, p. 598; Comp. *Doe dem. Jaun Beebee v. Abdollah Barber*, supra.

(2) Baillie, p. 597; *Fatâwai Alamgiri*, Vol. II, p. 494.

With regard to the question whether the property dedicated yields any profit or not, the test generally laid down is whether it yields enough for its "repairs" or upkeep.

The early lawyers attached great importance to the dedication of land or immovable property (*'akâr*) for the purposes of a *wakf* as ensuring perpetuity, and it is often declared, therefore, that when land is "exchanged" it should be for land. But there is no rule of law to prevent, under the conditions of modern life, the investment of the proceeds of a *wakf* property in other forms of "trust securities."(1)

The *wâkif* can lawfully reserve for himself the power of altering the investment, and in the *Fatawâi Kâzi Khân* it is laid down that "this is correct, and in another place that it is correct, *bi'l-ijmâ'a* (by consensus)."

Condition of exchange lawful.

When there is a condition in the *wakf* "that the *wâkif* may exchange the land for other land as he pleases and that the land so obtained shall become *wakf* instead of the first," both the dedication and the condition are lawful according to Abû Yusuf, and so also when there is a condition "that he may sell and make an exchange for the price;" and the *Fatwa* is in conformity with it.

When the *wâkif* reserves to himself the power of altering the investment he may appoint an agent for the purpose, but if he should bequeath the power to an executor, the executor of such executor cannot exercise it. And if the power is reserved to another and himself, the other cannot exercise it singly, but the endower himself may lawfully do so. When the power to "exchange" is given to "every one that may preside over this *wakf*," it is lawful, and every president (*mushrif*)(2) may exercise the power. But when the endower has declared "on condition that such an one shall have the power of exchanging," the person authorised cannot exercise the power after the death of the *wâkif* without an express condition to that effect. The *kyyum*

(1) The following passage in the *Nahr-ul-Fâik* quoted in the *Durr-ul-Mukhtâr* shows in fact that there is no limitation to the discretion of the Judge: "if the order for change is made by a just Judge (*Kâzi-ul-jinnah*), even if it be for [investment in] *dirhems* and *dinârs* (money) there is no fear of loss [to the *wakf*.]"

(2) The *mushrif* is the person who is vested with supervisatorial functions over the *wakf*; his powers are larger than those of the ordinary *mutwalli* or *Kyyum*.

or administrator has no power to exchange unless expressly authorised to do so. And when it is made a condition that *he* may exchange, the endower may also exercise the power without a similar condition in his favour.

Ordinarily, after the "exchange" has once been made in accordance with the power specifically reserved, it cannot be made a second time, unless there are words indicative of an intention that the *wâkif* or the person to whom he reserves the power may alter the investment according to his discretion whenever he thinks fit.

When there is no provision in the *wakf* regarding *istibdal* or alteration of the trust-property or even when the *wâkif* has made a condition against it, the Judge has the power of directing a change. And this is one of the exceptions to the rule that the prescriptions of the *wâkif* are absolute and must be strictly carried out.(1)

When a man has said, "My land is a pious *mowkoofa* to Almighty God for ever, on condition that I may *employ* the produce as I please," he may lawfully do so. But if he should give it to the indigent, or employ it in pilgrimage, or bestow it upon a particular individual, he cannot reclaim it. And in like manner, if he should say, "I have given it to such a one," he has no power to reclaim it. He may give it to one set after another, but he cannot apply the proceeds to his own purposes. It would be different if he had said "on condition that I may *give* it to whomsoever I please."(2)

Conditions made by the *wâkif*.

Where a *wakf* is made subject to a condition that the *wâkif* shall have the power of giving the produce to whomsoever he pleases, the *wakf* is lawful; and he shall have the power of doing whatever he likes with the income during his lifetime, but he cannot make any disposition respecting it to continue binding after his death, nor can he apply the income to his own purposes (*lit.* cannot eat of the produce himself). His doing so, however, will not *avoid* the *wakf*. But he may bestow it on anybody he likes. A man makes a *wakf* of his estate on condition that the

(1) *Durr-ul-Mukhtâr*, p. 415; see *post*.

(2) The difference lies in the Arabic expressions. What has to be borne in mind is the condition relating to the application of the proceeds laid down by the *wâkif* at the creation of the *wakf*, as even he cannot depart therefrom.

administrator may give the produce as he pleases, this is lawful; and he may give it to both rich and poor If the *wâkif* at the time of dedicating his property were to say, "on condition that such an one (some other person, generally referring to the *mutwalli*) may give the produce to whomsoever he pleases," it is lawful; and the power may be exercised by that person either during the lifetime of the appropriator or after his death, and the person so authorised may give the income to his own child and descendants, and also to the child and descendants of the *wâkif*, but not to himself.

[It is not clear what the effect would be, if the person authorised were to take the profits of the *wakf* estate himself. The *Fatâwai Alamgiri* goes on to say that "the power does not pass out of his hands on his saying 'I have given the produce to myself.'" A mere declaration may not have the effect of destroying the power, but will not an unlawful application of the income to his own use amount to breach of trust?]

The *Radd-ul-Muhtâr* adds that, according to those jurists(1) who hold a man cannot make a *wakf* in his own favour, if the *mutwalli* were to give the proceeds of the property dedicated to the *wâkif*, it would not be lawful. But this doctrine is not now recognised as the law; for the rule universally observed is that a person may validly make himself the first beneficiary of the trust. According to this rule "upon which is the *Fatwa*," the *mutwalli* may give the usufruct lawfully to the *wâkif*.

"If a person were to say, 'my land is a pious *wakf* for the sons of such a one on condition that I may select of them whom I please,' it would be as he has said, and he may select as he pleases or give the whole to one; and if he were to say, 'I make no selection this year,' it would be lawful, and the produce would be [divided] among them all equally. And if he were to say 'on condition that I may deprive whom I please among them,' and he were to deprive them all but one, it would be lawful; and though *by analogy* he should not be able to deprive them all, he has that power also, *on a favourable construction*. But he cannot restore those whom he has deprived and the *wakf* would be for the poor. If he were to say 'I have deprived them of the produce of this year,' they have no right in that year's produce and it passes to the poor."(2)

Conditions that may be imposed by the *wâkif*.

(1) Those who follow the doctrines of Imâm Mohammed.

(2) See *Fatâwai Alamgiri*, Vol. II, pp. 495 to 504; Baillie, p. 595, *et seq.*

If a man were to constitute a *wakf* in favour of the mother of his children (*umm-ul-walad*),(1) subject to the condition that if she marries after his death she is to have nothing, and she does marry but is subsequently divorced; in these circumstances she has nothing, unless it were provided that in the event of her being divorced, she should be restored to the benefit of the *wakf*. In like manner, when a *wakf* is for the sons of such a one except those who go out of the city, and some of them go out but return again, or when it is for the benefit of the sons of such a one who are acquiring knowledge, and some of them abandon their studies which afterwards they resume, the parties continue to be deprived of the benefit of the *wakf*, in the absence of any condition to the contrary. And if one should make his land a *pious wakf* on his child and *nasl* forever, and after them on the poor with a condition that any of them, who may leave the sect or doctrine of Abû Hanîfa for that of Shâfeï shall lose the benefit of the *wakf*, those abandoning the sect will be deprived of its benefit.(2)

Similarly, if he had said when any one of them shall leave the doctrine of the Sunnis and become a heretic he shall be excluded and one of them does so, he is to be excluded. A man and woman are on the same footing and when it is made a condition that if one should depart from the established doctrine he is to be excluded; and one of them does so and then returns, he is not to be restored to the benefits of the *wakf* without an express condition to that effect. In like manner, when a particular doctrine has been specified and there is a condition that if anyone should depart from it, he is to be deprived of the benefit of the *wakf*, regard must be had to the condition. So also, when the condition is "that if any of my kindred go from Bagdad he is to have nought," respect must be had to the condition, except that in this case if he were to return to Bagdad, he would be restored to the benefits of the *wakf*.(3)

Among the prescriptions of the *wâkif* that must be respected, Khassâf has mentioned a condition that the *mutwalli* shall not let the lands, and if he does let them, (without the sanction of the Kâzi) the lease shall be void. If the *wâkif* makes a condition Prescriptions of the *wâkif*.

(1) *Umm-ul-walad* is the designation given to a female bondswoman who bears a child to her master, and thus becomes enfranchised.

(2) *Fatâwai Alamgiri*, Vol. II, p. 504.

(3) *Ibid.*

that he shall not enter into an agreement for gardening or cultivation on the basis of a division of produce, or provides that when the *mutwalli* lets the land he shall be removed from the office, in such cases if he should act contrary to the conditions he is to be removed and the Kâzi shall appoint another, whom he can trust to carry out the condition.

Power to alter the beneficiaries.

The *wâkif* can reserve to himself, at the time of the dedication, the power to alter the beneficiaries of the trust by either adding to their number or excluding some, or to increase or reduce their interest in it. He cannot do so afterwards. "The *wâkif*," says the *Radd ul-Muhtâr*, "has no power to alter or change the conditions (provisions) of a *wakf*, unless he has expressly reserved to himself the power of doing so."(1) If he has reserved to himself the power of adding to the beneficiaries or removing any person from that category, or of removing the *mutwalli* from his office, it would be lawful for him to do so. No alteration, however, can be made in the nature or character of the *wakf*. Similarly, it is not lawful for the *mutwalli* to go beyond the conditions laid down in the *wakfnâmah*.

A condition in the *wakfnâmah* to the effect that the *mutwalli* shall have the power of increasing the allowance of anybody or reducing it or adding anybody or removing anyone is lawful. "At the same time, the *maslahat-ul-wakf* (the policy of the *wakf*) is to be kept in view."(2) "If a person," says Kâzi Khân, "in good health were to make a *wakf* of land for the indigent and deliver it over to a *mutwalli*, and at the time of his death direct his executor to pay out of the proceeds thereof so much to so-and-so, that would not be valid, for he had parted with his right over the proceeds at the time of the *wakf*. But he can do so, if at the time of dedication he reserved to himself the power of giving directions for the application of the proceeds."

The powers of the *wâkif*.

Nor can the *wâkif*, who devotes property to any meritorious or pious uses and transfers the proprietary right therein to the Almighty, take it back at his pleasure from the *mutwalli* whom he has constituted God's proxy and give it to another person, unless on

---

(1) Comp. *Hedaitoonnissa* v. *Afzal Hossain*, 2 All. H. C. R., 420.

(2) *Maslahat* here means the policy or purpose. What is intended to be conveyed is undoubtedly this, that in any alteration which may be made, the original purpose or object or policy of the trust shall not be ignored.

the creation of the trust he reserved to himself in express terms the right to do so.

If a person were to declare, that if necessary the *wakf* land may be sold and the proceeds invested in other property, all the incidents of *wakf*, as already stated, would attach to the new property, which will be subject to the same conditions as the original property.(1)

Conditions laid down by the *wâkif* are equivalent to the prescriptions of the Law.

In carrying out the provisions of the trust the intention of the consecrator must be solicitously regarded, and in case his meaning is not distinct, recourse should be had to evidence to explain the meaning, and the inferential shall be considered equally with the actually expressed.(2)

When the language is upon the face of it unequivocal and unambiguous, no outside evidence will be let in for the purpose of altering or modifying the intentions of the *wâkif*. For example, if the *wâkif* has declared in unequivocal language that he endows certain property for his children who are females, no evidence will be admitted to show that he also intended to include males. But where, from the language of the *wakf* itself, it can be inferred that he meant to include the males, though using the word 'females,' they would participate with the female children: In understanding, however, the meaning of the donor from the actually expressed words, consideration should be paid to the circumstances of the particular case and the customary use of language among the people.

If the words are capable of two meanings, the construction most consistent with the intention of the *wâkif* should be adopted.

SECTION II.

THE SUPERVISORY FUNCTIONS OF THE KÂZI.

The Kâzi's authority to interfere with the *wâkif's* directions.

"IN the Chapter on *Wakf* in the *Inâm-ul-Mufti 'aala Jawâb ul-Mustafti*, it is laid down that the observance of the provisions laid down by the *wâkif* are obligatory, for the jurists hold such rules to be equivalent to the *Nass*, *viz.*, rules laid down by the Lawgiver."

(1) *Radd-ul-Muhtâr*, Vol. III, p. 599.
(2) *Ibid*, Vol. II, p. 644.

Conditions inconsistent with the nature of the *wakf.*

But the Kâzi, and, in certain cases, the *mutwalli*, are entitled to override any condition made by the *wâkif* which is inconsistent with the nature of the *wakf* or opposed to the requirements of the very object for which the *wakf* is constituted. For example, if there is a condition to the effect that the Kâzi shall not remove the *mutwalli* appointed by the *wâkif* or his successors in office, the Kâzi would nevertheless be entitled to remove any *mutwalli* who proved himself unfit or committed misfeasance or misbehaved himself in the trust. Or, if it is stated in the *wakfnâmah* that the *mutwalli* shall not grant a lease of the *wakf* property for more than one year, and it appears that no person is willing to take a lease for a year, the Kâzi has the power to authorise the *mutwalli* to let the land for more than a year. Or, if the *wâkif* has declared that no alms should be given to the indigent who derive their subsistence from a certain mosque, the *mutwalli* is empowered nevertheless to give alms to such people. Or, if he has provided that the person for whom the *wakf* is constituted shall get fixed rations daily, the *mutwalli* may, with the consent of the beneficiaries, commute the same into money payment.(1) The beneficiaries may even ask for commutation.

The Kâzi is also authorised to increase the pay of the imâm, if it is insufficient, and if the officer is learned and religious, *i.e.*, deserving.

The several exceptions to the rule declaring that the prescriptions of the *wâkif* must be strictly carried out, are stated at length in the *Ashbâh-wan-Nazâir*. Their purport has already been given, but they may be summarised here with advantage.

The Kâzi's supervision.

"(1) Should the *wâkif* make a condition that the Kâzi shall not have the power of dismissing the *Nâzir* or *mutwalli*, the Kâzi nevertheless will have the power of dismissing a *mutwalli* who has been found to be untrustworthy or incompetent. And in the *Bahr-ul-Râik* it is laid down that even if the *wâkif* were to make a condition that the King or Kâzi shall not interfere in the management of the *wakf*, still the Kâzi will have his superintendence over it, for his supervision is above everything.

"(2) If the *wâkif* has made a condition that the *wakf* property shall not be leased for more than a year, and it appears that nobody

---

(1) *Radd-ul-Muhtâr*, Vol. II, p. 601.

is willing to take a lease for one year only, or if it appears that it is to the advantage of the beneficiaries that the property should be let for a longer term, the Kâzi has the power of authorising the grant of a lease for a longer term, but the *mutwalli* has no power to do so of his own authority.

"(3) If he has made a condition that so much grain should be bestowed on the beggars asking for alms at the door of his mosque, the condition may be varied, and the alms may be bestowed on such beggars as do not ask for alms there.

"(4) If he has made a condition that cooked food should be bestowed on the recipients, the *mutwalli* will have the power of giving them the value thereof, and the recipients can even ask for payment in cash.

"(5) If the *imâm* is a learned and pious man, and the allowance fixed by the *wâkif* for him is not sufficient, the Kâzi has the power of increasing it.

The power of increasing the emolument of the *imâm* includes the salary of all such persons whose withdrawal would be to the injury of the *wakf*. For example, if a *mutwalli* or a *muezzin*, or a professor in a college, or door-keepers and such like cannot be entertained for the remuneration fixed, the Kâzi has the power of increasing their salaries or wages; and this view is supported, says the author of the *Radd-ul-Muhtâr*, by the statement in the *Bazâziah* that when an *imâm* or *muezzin* cannot be employed on the prescribed salary, the judge can increase the emolument from the profits of the *wakf* (1) in consultation with people of integrity (or respectable people) of the neighbourhood (*ahl-us-salâh min ahl-ul-mahalla*).(2) But in fixing all emoluments he should keep in view the customary remuneration (*ujr-ul-misl*).

The Kâzi, however, cannot create a (new) *wazifa*, in other words new offices in respect of a trust-property, without a condition to that effect by the *wâkif*.

This, again, is subject to an important qualification. The author of the *Radd-ul-Muhtâr*, commenting on the text in the *Durr-ul-Mukhtâr*, says, "be it noted(3) that the invalidity regarding the creation of new offices is confined to the absence of

(1) *Radd-ul-Muhtâr*, Vol. III, p. 647. (2) After the *Kinia*.

(3) In the original, "Know."

necessity ((مقيد بعدم ضرورة)), as is stated in the *Fatâwai* of Shaikh Kâsim; for whenever necessity arises, and it becomes advisable to employ the services of a new officer for any work such as the collection of tithes or rent or giving evidence before the *Diwân*,(1) the matter should be placed before the Kâzi, and the need (for such employment) should be established before him, and he would appoint a fit and proper person for the purpose, and fix for him the customary remuneration, or give the *nâzir* (the *mutwalli*) permission to the same purpose."(2)

Although the *mutwalli* has no power to appoint new servants or to increase the stipends of those already in service, yet where the consecrator has not fixed the stipends or allowances, he has a general discretion subject to the control and direction of the Judge. In this connection the following passage in the *Fatâwai Kâzi Khân* is of importance. It says, "if a person were to make a *wakf* of rest-houses for the poor (travellers), and it becomes necessary to appoint a servitor to keep them clean and open the doors, the *mutwalli* may engage one even allotting a room for his services."(3)

"(6) If there is a condition to the effect that the *wakf* property shall never be changed, should the Kâzi deem it advisable he has the power to authorise the same."(4)

The Judge's discretion regarding the alteration of the *wakf* property is controlled by the consideration that the new property or investment ensures the permanent maintenance of the consecration and is to its benefit. At one time this discretion seems to have been so capriciously exercised as to give rise to serious abuse; and accordingly, says Mufti Abû S'aûd in his *M'aarûzat* "in 951 of the Hegira an august Edict (*al-amr ush-sharîf*) was issued with the approval of the Sadr-ush-Sharîyàh(5) declaring that no alteration (exchange) of *wakf* property should take place without the sanction of sovereign authority."(6)

[All this is by way of example and is by no means exhaustive.]

---

(1) The Exchequer or Court.

(2) *Radd-ul-Muhtâr*, Vol. III, p. 646.

(3) *Fatâwai Kâzi Khân*, Vol. IV, p. 222.

(4) *Surrat-ul-Fatâwa*, p. 420; Comp. the *Ashbâh-wan-Nazir*, p. 308, 7th exception.

(5) The Chief Justiciary, prototype of the modern Shaikh-ul-Islâm.

(6) *Durr-ul-Mukhtâr*, p. 416; *Radd-ul-Muhtâr*, Vol. III, p. 603.

Wakf in favour of one's children and descendants valid.

(7) The author of the *Zawâhir-ul-Jawâhir*, which is a commentary on the *Ashbâh-wa'n-Nazâir*, adds another exception to the general rule regarding the absoluteness of the *wâkif's* prescriptions. He says, "if the *wâkif* were to declare that the superintendent (*mushrif*) appointed by him should have sole charge of the *wakf*, and the Judge were to consider it expedient to associate some one else with him, it would be lawful to do so," as in the case of an executor.(1)

(8) Tahtâwi states on the authority of Sirâj Hanouti(2) that there is a further exception; *viz.*, if the *wâkif* were to lay down that the *wakf* property was not to be leased for more than a certain rent fixed by him, and the ordinary rent was higher than what he had fixed, his direction must be departed from.

(9) In early times, the reading of the Koran over the graves of deceased persons was, in accordance with the views of Abû Hanîfa, regarded by some as objectionable. And, accordingly, it is stated in the *Ashbâh-wa'n-Nazâir* that if the *wâkif* made a condition that the Koran should be recited over his or any body else's grave, that condition should not be obeyed.

Imâm Mohammed, however, has held it to be permissible that the Koran should be read over graves; and its lawfulness is "the accepted doctrine."(3)

In India, it is the common practice to employ readers of the Koran to recite it over the graves of deceased persons.

One jurist has attempted to lay a restriction on the power of altering the investment, by imposing a condition that the thing for which the *wakf* property is exchanged, or the new investment should be of the same nature as the former property. The author of the *Radd-ul-Muhtâr*, however, holds that there should be no such restriction, as it is essential to see which investment is most profitable. For example, a man may have made a *wakf* of shops, and it may be more profitable to invest in land the proceeds arising from the sale of such shops, as yielding

(1) *Viz.*, as the Judge has the power, when he deems it expedient, of associating a co-executor with an executor appointed by the testator, he has the power of joining a *co-mutwalli* with a *mutwalli* appointed by the *wâkif*; *Durr-ul-Mukhtâr*, p. 416; *Radd-ul-Muhtâr*, Vol. III, p. 602.

(2) A well-known jurist flourished in the 16th century of the Christian era.

(3) *Radd-ul-ul-Muhtâr*, Vol. III, p. 602; Comp. *Biba Jan* v. *Kalu Hossain* [1908], I. L., 31 All., 136.

a larger income for the purposes of the *wakf*. Or he may have consecrated a piece of land for cultivation; but in the course of time owing to change of conditions it may be more profitable to build houses or shops on it. In such cases the *mutwalli* is empowered to alter the mode of user.(1)

Hence, when the power is vested in the *mutwalli* or the *wâkif* to dispose of the *wakf* property and invest the proceeds in other property similarly subject to the conditions of *wakf*, there should be no such restriction as to insist that the new property should be of the same character or nature as the former property.

The proceeds of *wakf* property may be invested in *dirhems* and *dinârs*.(2) It must be remembered, however, that when an investment takes the form of actual money, there is a possibility of the fund being wasted, and therefore it is undesirable to keep the proceeds of a *wakf* in that shape. If, however, it is in a shape from which profit can accrue without loss to the *corpus*, as in the case of Government Securities, the investment is lawful.

Not only has the *wâkif* the power of reserving to himself the power of removing beneficiaries but he may validly make at the time of dedication conditions for excluding, in certain eventualities, particular beneficiaries or class of beneficiaries from the benefit of the trust; or he may provide that certain persons or class of person for reason assigned by him shall not participate in it or be appointed as *mutwalli*.(3) For example, if he were to declare that abjuration of Islâm should cause a divestment of interest in the *wakf* or a particular person should not derive any benefit from it, owing to his misconduct, it would be valid; and his wishes will have effect given to them.

As the right to participate in the benefits of a *wakf* is not acquired by virtue of inheritance, Act XXI of 1850 does not affect these provisions of the Mussulman Law.

---

(1) *Fatâwai Kâzi Khân*, Vol. III, p. 222.
(2) See the *Radd-ul-Muhtâr*, Vol. III, p. 600.
(3) *Radd-ul-Muhtâr*, Vol. III, p. 600; *As'âf*, p. 89, Cairo Ed. See *Khajah Salimullah* v. *Abul Khair Mustafa* [1909], I. L., 37 Cal., 263.

SECTION III.

THE CONDITIONS IN WAKF.

When a dedication is made subject to the exercise of an option on the part of the *wâkif*, according to Abû Yusuf, "the *wakf* as well as the condition" are valid, provided there is a determinate period fixed, within which the option should be exercised. For example, if a man were to say, "I constitute this house as *wakf*, but I shall have an option to set it aside within three days," if the option is not exercised, the *wakf* becomes absolute after three days, but if the time is uncertain and wanting in specificness, the *wakf* is invalid. **A *wakf* with an option.**

The jurist Abû J'aafar holds that in such a case the *wakf* should be considered as valid, and the condition void (*bâtil*). Hillâl and Mohammed hold that the reservation of an option invalidates the *wakf* itself, whilst Yusuf ibn Khâlid declares that the *wakf* is valid in all cases, the condition alone being void. And this seems to be the generally received doctrine.(1)

If a person were to make a dedication for a specific period of time, say, for a day, or a month, without any additional words, it would take effect as a lawful *wakf in perpetuity*. But if he were to say that it will be a *wakf* for a particular month, and on the expiry of that month, the *wakf* will be void—in such a case, the dedication would be void *ab initio*.

If a man were to say "when to-morrow comes my land will become a pious *wakf* (*sadakah-mowkoofa*)" or "when I become its *mâlik*, the land will be *wakf*," it is unlawful, for the creation of a *wakf* cannot be made dependent on the happening of a contingency. **Contingent *wakf* void.**

If a person were to say, "my land will be *wakf* after my death for a certain number of years," it will take effect after the death of the declarant as a *wakf in perpetuity*. **A *wakf* for a limited period takes effect as a *wakf* in perpetuity.**

If a man were to say, "my land is a pious *wakf* (*sadakah-mowkoofa*) on this condition, that I shall have the power of revoking it whenever I chose," according to Hillâl, such a *wakf* is invalid. Yusuf ibn Khâlid, however, holds that the *wakf* is valid, and the condition void. And Abû Yusuf is of opinion that where the time for the exercise of the power is prolonged and undefined, the *wakf* itself is invalid.(2)

(1) *Fatâwai Kâzi Khân*, Vol. IV, p. 199.
(2) This view is adopted as law by the sect.

Similarly, if a man were to say, "I consecrate this land on the condition *that it remain my property*, and I shall have the power of selling it whenever I like, and of dedicating the proceeds thereof,"—such a *wakf* is invalid.

A conditional *wakf*.

When a *wakf* is created conditionally, it is valid, *e.g.*, if a person were to say, "this land is *wakf*, if it is mine," in that case if the land was his property at the time, it would constitute a valid *wakf*.

Divergence between Hanafî and Shâfeï doctrines.

According to the Hanafîs, the *wakf* of property belonging to another is validated by the ratification of the real owner; not so according to the Shâfeïs.

Power of conversion reserved at time of dedication.

If a man were to say, "this land of mine is *mowkoofa* for God in perpetuity on condition that I shall have the power to sell it, and with its price to buy another piece of land which will then become *wakf*, subject to the same incidents as the original *wakf*," both *wakf* and condition are valid according to Hillâl and Abû Yusuf. *And this is correct*."(1)

Kâzi may authorise sale when advantageous for the *wakf*.

The *wâkif* can alter the investment only when the power of sale has been expressly reserved. In the absence of any such power, the Kâzi, if he deem it expedient, may authorise the sale of the *wakf* property and a re-investment of the proceeds in any shape conducive to the proper maintenance of the *wakf*.(2)

"The author of the *Manah* was asked regarding a house consecrated in favour of a mosque, whether it would be lawful for the Kâzi to direct its sale if he was of opinion that with the price thereof another piece of land may be purchased, which would bring considerably more profit to the *wakf*. The author of the *Manah* answered 'the question is for the Kâzi to decide judicially, so that if he considers deliberately that such sale and investment are for the benefit of the *wakf*, it is lawful,' and this is according to the opinion of Kâzi Imâm Abû Yusuf."(3)

Sale or exchange of *wakf* property when authorised.

"In the *Fatâwa's-Sirâjia* it is stated that when the sale or exchange of a *wakf* property is distinctly advantageous to the *wakf*, the Kâzi may direct it. For example, if no income is derived from the property, and somebody is anxious to purchase it, and in lieu thereof is willing to give such land or house as would yield an

(1) *Radd-ul-Muhtâr*, Vol. III, p. 600.
(2) *Ibid.*
(3) *Surrat-ul-Fatâwa*, pp. 420, 421.

income for the *wakf*, in that case the exchange is authorised according to Abû Yusuf as well as Mohammed."

"Where the *wakf* property yields an income, but some person is desirous of exchanging it for another property yielding a much larger income, *e.g.*, if the *wakf* property is a *bazaar* situated in a lane and the person anxious to take it is willing to exchange it for a *bazaar* situated in a better place, in such a case, but not otherwise, the exchange is lawful according to Kâzi Abû Yusuf, &c.; on this is the practice."(1)

"In the commentary of Nâzim-Wahbâni it is stated upon the authority of the *Muhît* and Kâzi Khân, &c., that according to Imâm Mohammed the *mutwalli* is authorised to exchange for a better and more productive piece of land the one dedicated, if it has deteriorated in productive powers."(2)

"In the *Tâttima* it is reported from Hishâm and Mohammed, that when a *wakf* [property] is in such a condition that the beneficiaries cannot derive benefit therefrom, the Kâzi is authorised to sell it and with its price to buy another, and this power nobody else can exercise excepting the Kâzi."(3)

"And in the *Siyar-i-Kabîr* it is stated that although some jurists have held the change of *wakf* property not to be lawful, according to Abû Yusuf it is lawful; and in the *Muhît* it is stated that the following question was put to Shams-ul-Aïmma Halwâni, 'whether when the *wakf* of a mosque [property consecrated to a mosque] becomes useless and cannot yield an income, the *mutwalli* can sell it and in its stead buy another?' He answered, 'yes, it is lawful.' He was then asked, 'whether it would be lawful to do so when the property does yield an income, but with its price a better property can be purchased.' He answered, 'yes, it would be lawful.' Though some of the jurists hold against exchange or sale of *wakf* property, I have already stated that we conform to the rule laid down by Abû Yusuf."(4)

---

(1) *Surrat-ul-Fatâwa*, pp. 420, 421.

(2) In all instances where a *mutwalli* is spoken of as having the power of selling or exchanging a property which does not yield an income or of making a better investment, unless such power is reserved in the *wakfnâmah*, it must be exercised with the sanction of the Judge.

(3) *Surrat-ul-Fatâwa*, p. 421.

(4) *Ibid*, pp. 422, 423.

"If the *wâkif*," says the *Fath-ul-Kadîr*, "has made a condition to the effect that he should have the power of exchanging the land dedicated, and the land for which it is exchanged would become dedicated in place of the other, such a condition is valid according to Abû Yusuf, Hillâl and Khassâf, and this is *istehsân* (a liberal or equitable interpretation of the law)."

"If he has made a condition to the effect that the *mutwalli* should have the power of changing the investment during his (the *wâkif's*) own lifetime, the *mutwalli* will not have the power of making the change after the *wâkif's* death."

Alteration of the subject of a *wakf*.

"In the *Fatâwai Kâzi Khân* it is stated that the rule laid down by Abû Yusuf and Hillâl is correct. So has Ansâri declared that such a condition is lawful, but it cannot be sold [by the *mutwalli*] without the sanction of the Judge. And when this matter is brought before the Judge, and it appears to him necessary for the benefit of the *wakf* (that the investment should be changed), he should give the sanction"......"A condition for the alteration of the investment is lawful according to Abû Yusuf, and *this is approved*; and in the *Fatâwai Kâzi Khân*, it is stated that there is *Ijmâ'a or consensus* on the part of the universality of jurists on the lawfulness of a reservation of power to the *wâkif* to change the investment, both condition and *wakf* being valid. Without such condition he will not have the power to make the change [unless authorised by the Kâzi]. In other words, if he has reserved the power at the time of dedication, by *consensus* he can exercise the power at any time himself; but when he has not reserved such power, then he must have recourse to the Kâzi for the necessary permission.....In the *Mukhtasar-ul-Kudûri* it is stated the *nass* (express dictum of Law) is on the rule laid down by Abû Yusuf."(1)

The general result of the authorities seems to be that the *wâkif* may lawfully change the *wakf* property, in other words, alter the investment provided he has reserved, at the time of dedication, power to that effect. Otherwise, no alteration can be effected without the leave of the Kâzi or Judge, who has the power to authorise a change of investment whenever he considers it beneficial for the *wakf*.

(1) *Fath-ul-Kadir*, Vol. II, p. 639.

Among the conditions which the *wâkif*, under the Hanafî Law, may lawfully make at the time of dedication is one which has already been given at another place, *viz.*, that the *wâkif* may provide for the payment of his debts with the income of the property.(1)

Powers of the *wâkif* regarding the governance of the trust.

"In the Chapter on *Wakf* in the *Khazânat-ul-Fatâwa* it is stated that the Sâhib-ul-Manah (the author of the *Manah-ul-Ghuffâr*) was asked about a deed of *wakf* in which there was a condition to the effect that the *wilâyèt* of the trust should appertain only to the *wâkif's* male descendants, but now a deed has been discovered bearing a prior date, in which the *towliat* was given to his male as well as female descendants; the question was which deed should be acted upon [in regard to the *towliat*]. The Sâhib-ul-Manah answered, if the *wâkif* in the first deed or at the time of dedication reserved to himself the power of altering any of the provisions regarding the management, &c., of the *wakf*, in that case the second deed should be acted upon, that is, the deed in which the *towliat* is restricted to his male descendants. But if he reserved to himself in the original *wakf* no such power, in that case the first deed of *wakf*, *viz.*, in which there was no restriction, should be acted upon."(2)

"In the *As'aâf* it is stated that the *wâkif* cannot go beyond the conditions laid down at the time of dedication."

"In the *Fawâid* it is stated from Khassâf that when there are two contradictory conditions made by a *wâkif*, the second is to be acted upon, unless it is beyond his powers."

"When there are two contradictory provisions in a *wakfnâmah*, the one which follows will be given effect to, according to us [Hanafîs] as the last condition overrides the first."

With reference to the principle that when there are two contradictory conditions in a *wakfnâmah*, the second has effect given to it, in preference to the first, the *As'aâf*(3) gives examples of it. For example, if in the beginning of the *wakfnâmah*, the *wâkif* declares

---

(1) *Fath-ul-Kadîr*, Vol. II, p. 638.

(2) *Surrat-ul-Fatâwa*, p. 425.

(3) The *As'aâf* is the work of Allâmah Burhân-ud-dîn Ibrâhim Trâbulusi, *i.e.*, of Tripoli. Of this work Moulâna Mohammed Amin, the author of the *Radd-ul-Muhtâr*, speaks thus:—"Should the exigencies of this world make it necessary for any individual to study the law of *wakf*, he should study the *As'aâf*, as it is the greatest authority on the subject."

Powers of the *wâkif*—contd.

that the subject-matter of the *wâkf* shall not be "sold nor given in gift or become the property of anybody," and subsequent to that declares that it will be lawful for the *mutwalli* to sell the property, and with the proceeds thereof to purchase another property, which will be substituted for the original *wakf*, in such a case the sale of the *wakf* will be valid, and the second condition will override the first. Or, if he were to say first, that the *mutwalli* may sell the *wakf* property and purchase something else in its stead and afterwards declare that it shall not be sold or given in gift, then it will not be sold. But, whent he two conditions are not contradictory, and it is possible to give effect to both of them, then it will be incumbent to carry out both, for the conditions of the *wâkif* are like the *nass* (express dictum of the Law). When there are general provisions and after them come the details, these (unless otherwise apparent on the document) will apply to the last condition, according to "us."

According to the Shâfeïs, these details refer to all the conditions, if the connection is with an "and" (*waw*); but only to the last condition, if the connection is with "then."

The Kâzi's powers.

As already stated, the Kâzi has the power of associating a *mutwalli* with the one appointed by the *wâkif* even though the *wâkif* may have made a condition against it, should the Kâzi consider it would be beneficial for the trust to do so.

Miscellaneous.

When a person makes a dedication by a deed, and afterwards says he does not know what is contained therein, or that he did not intend to create an irrevocable *wakf*, in such case, if it appears from the evidence of witnesses or otherwise, that the document was either read by or explained to the person, and that he fully understood its purport, his denial will be of no avail. "And this principle does not apply to *wakf* alone but to sales and all other transactions."(1)

A *wakf* created with a knowledge of its effect absolutely binding.

A person, intending to make a *wakf* of his lands in a particular village, gives instructions at the time of his death for the preparation of a document therefor. The writer, however, by mistake leaves out certain plots of lands. If at the time of reading the document, the *wâkif's* attention is not called to the omission, but he says that

---

(1) و هذا لا يختص بالوقف بل البيع و سائر التصرفات يكون كذلك *Fatâwai Kâzi Khân in loco*; see *Fatima Begum* v. *The Advocate-General* [1881], I. L., 6 Bom., 42.

he dedicates all that is contained in that village, the *wakf*, according to the jurist Abû Lais, will take effect with reference to all the lands. The same principle applies to a dedication made in health. The essential point to consider is whether he intended to adhere or not to his expressed intention of dedicating all his lands.(1)

In the *Khazânat-ul-Muftïn*, it is stated that when a person has made a *wakf* in favour of certain specific individuals, without designating any ultimate trust of a permanent character, and has not had the document (*sick*) of *wakf* sealed by the Kâzi, he may, if he falls into poverty, apply to the Kâzi to allow him to revoke the *wakf* "so as to relieve him of his poverty." The impressment of the seal of the Kâzi is equivalent to the registration of a document in British India.

When a *wakf* is made of land, everything appertaining to the land, such as tenements, roads, ghauts, trees, &c., attached to, or on the land, passes under it, but not partible produce. When land is dedicated for a cemetery, whilst big trees and buildings are on it, they will not be included in the *wakf*, although it may have been stated in the *wakfnâmah* that the dedication is "with all appurtenances and rights."

If there are fruit-bearing trees on the land or a *hammâm* attached to the premises dedicated, and the dedication is made with the expression "with all appurtenances and rights belonging thereto," they will be included in the *wakf*.

Wakf for digging graves for the poor.

A *wakf* for digging graves for the poor and providing shrouds is valid.

An opinion has been expressed by Imâm Ali as-Sughdi that a *wakf* in favour of Sufis is not valid. But this view is contradicted by other jurists. And the Shams-ul-Aïmma has stated that a *wakf* is valid for all who are needy and indigent, and that when a *wakf* is made for a large body of people, it should be taken as referring to the poor and indigent among them; and if the *wakf* is general in its terms so as to include both rich and poor alike, the persons or the class of persons for whom the benefit is intended should be distinctly indicated, or it must appear from the words of the *wâkif* that though the terms are general, the intention is that indigence should furnish the claim to share in the benefit. For example, if the *wakf* is for orphans generally, it is valid, and its benefit shall

(1) *Fatâwai Kâzi Khân in loco.*

be applied to the poor among them. Hence, a *wakf* is valid for the lame and paralytic and the blind, the readers of the Koran, lawyers, traditionists, &c., and it will be expended on the poor among them, for indigence is clearly inferrible from these words. As the blind, the lame, those who devote themselves to study and such like, cannot apply themselves to obtain a livelihood, hence, indigence or want is their normal condition. And, accordingly, a *wàkf* in favour of Sufis also is valid, for they are generally very poor and lead a life of austerity.(1)

(1) *Radd-ul-Muhtâr*, Vol. III, p. 665.

CHAPTER XV.

THE GOVERNANCE OF THE WAKF.

SECTION I.

THE MUTWALLI.

"THE *wâkif* may lawfully reserve the *wilâyèt* (the management of the trust) for himself; this is according to Abû Yusuf; and Hillâl also has said the same. And the Sâhib-ul-Hedâya [the author of the *Hedâya*] states this is the approved doctrine."(1)

"In the *Fatâwai Kâzi Khân* it is stated that, according to Mohammed as given in his *Siyar-i-Kabîr*, the *wâkif* will not be the trustee unless he has reserved the trusteeship for himself at the time of consecration; but according to Abû Yusuf consignment is not necessary in the case of the *wâkif*, so even when he does not [expressly] reserve the trusteeship for himself, he will still be the trustee. What I have stated is also laid down in the *Zakhîra* and *Tâtimma*,(2) and the Sâhib-ul-Hedâya has mentioned that this is the approved doctrine in our *Mazhab* [school]."(3)

Wâkif may reserve the governance for himself.

"The *wâkif* is primarily entitled to appoint a *mutwalli* for the management of the trust. If he is honest and just, he has a title superior to that of the Kâzi to nominate a trustee, for though he has parted with the property, and his right in it has become extinguished, still he has a right to see that its proceeds are applied according to the terms of the consecration."

"He has a better title to appoint a *muezzin* and *imâm* for a mosque than the congregation, unless his appointment is objectionable on the ground that the persons nominated by him are unfit.

(1) *Fath ul-Kadir*, Vol. II, p. 640; see also the *Durr-ul-Mukhtâr*, the *Fatâwai Alamgiri*, &c.

(2) Two works of great authority; see *Doe dem. Jaun Beebee* v. *Abdollah Barber* [1838], 1 Fulton's Reports, p. 345.

(3) *Fath ul-Kadir*, Vol. II, p. 640.

So it is stated in the *Nawâzil* and Abû'l Lais says the *Fatwa* is thereon."(1)

Similarly, in the *Radd-ul-Muhtâr* :—It is lawful for the *wâkif* to reserve the *towliat* (the governance of the trust) for himself. And where a *wakf* has been created, but the *wâkif* has appointed no trustee or *mutwalli* for the administration of the *wakf*, nor has expressly reserved the *towliat* for himself, the office would nevertheless appertain to him *quâ wâkif*.(2)

Power of appointing the *mutwalli* rests primarily with the *wâkif*.

He has the power of appointing a *mutwalli* during his lifetime whenever he likes. Should he die without making any express appointment, the power devolves upon his executor. "If there is no executor, then the right of appointing a *mutwalli* is in the hands of the Judge."(3)

"If the *mutwalli* appointed by the *wâkif* dies in his lifetime, the power of appointing another *mutwalli* rests with the *wâkif* and not in the Kâzi."(4)

So also in the *Fusûl-ul-'Imâdia*. "In the *Sughra* it is stated that when the *mutwalli* is dead, and the *wâkif* is alive, the power of appointing another *mutwalli*, appertains to the *wâkif* and not to the Kâzi. And if the *wâkif* is dead, it appertains to his executor in preference to the Judge. But if the *wâkif* leave no executor, then the Kâzi is empowered to appoint a *mutwalli*. . . . So in the *Khassâf*."(5)

Women eligible for a *towliat*.

Any person who is trustworthy and otherwise qualified to discharge the duties of the office may be appointed *mutwalli*. "In this respect men and women are alike," *i.e.*, a woman may be appointed a *mutwalli* in the same way as a man.(6) Sectarian and religious differences form no disqualification, and accordingly, the fact that a person is a Shiah does not disqualify him for the super-

---

(1) *Surrat-ul-Fatawa*, p. 425.

(2) *Radd-ul-Muhtâr*, Vol. III, p. 594 ; *Fatâwai Alamgiri*, Vol. II, p. 543 ; *Advocate-General* v. *Fatima Sultani Begum* [1872], 9 Bom. H. C. R., 19.

(3) *Radd-ul-Muhtâr*, Vol. III, p. 594 ; *Durr-ul-Mukhtâr*, p. 241.

(4) *Surrat-ul-Fatâwa*, p. 425.

(5) *Fusûl-ul-'Imâdia*, p. 237.

(6) *Radd-ul-Muhtâr*, Vol. III, p. 595 ; *Doe dem. Jaun Beebee* v. *Abdollah Barber*, 1 Fulton's Reports, 345 ; *M. S. Hyati Khanum* v. *M. S. Kulsum Khanum*, 1 Sel. Rep., 217 ; *Hussaini Bibee* v. *Hussain Sharif* [1868] 4 Mad. H. C. R., 23. When a woman is appointed a *Mutwalli* and a salary is attached to the office, "she will not be required to do more than her sex permits ; and she is entitled to discharge the duties to which she cannot personally attend by deputy or proxy."

intendence of a *wakf* made by a Sunni.(1) So long as a person can discharge the duties of the trust personally or through a deputy, he or she is qualified to hold the office of *towliat*.

"The office of *mutwalli* is an office of personal trust, and a person who cannot discharge the duties of the trust personally, nor be responsible for their due discharge, cannot appoint a deputy."(2)

Where the *mutwalli* has to perform religious duties.

But where the *mutwalli* has to perform religious duties or spiritual functions in connection with the *wakf*, which, as regards men, can only be performed by a man, a woman cannot be appointed to the office. For example, if the *mutwalli* is also the superior of a religious establishment, and, as such, has to officiate on occasions of religious festivals, a woman is precluded by her sex from holding the *towliat*.(3) Such superiors in India are called *sajjâda-nashins*. [*Sajjâda* is the carpet on which prayers are offered; and *nashîn* is the person seated thereon.] "The *sajjâda-nashîn* is not only a *mutwalli* but also a spiritual preceptor. He is the curator of the *dargâh* where his ancestor lies buried, and in him is supposed to continue the spiritual line (*silsila*). These *dargâhs* are the tombs of celebrated *dervishes*, who, in their lifetime, were regarded as saints. Some of these men had established *khânkâhs* where they lived, and their disciples congregated. Many of them never rose to the importance of a *khânkâh*, and when they died their mausolea became shrines or *dargâhs*. These *dervishes* professed esoteric doctrines and distinct systems of initiation. They were either *sufis* or the disciples of Miân Roushan Bâyezid, who flourished about the time of Akbar, and who had founded an independent esoteric brotherhood, in which the chief occupied a peculiarly distinctive position. They called themselves *fakîrs* on the hypothesis that they had abjured the world, and were humble servitors of God: by their followers they were honoured with the title of *shah* or king. Herklot gives a detailed account of the different brotherhoods and the rules of initiation in force among them. The preceptor is called the *pîr*,—the disciple, the *murîd*. On the death of the *pîr* his suc-

Dargâhs.

(1) *Doyal Chund Mullick* v. *Syud Keramat Ali* [1873], 16 W. R., p. 116. A person convicted of any ordinary offence, as defamation, abusive language, &c., is not considered unfit.

(2) *Piran Bibi* v. *Abdul Karim* [1891], I. L., 19 Cal., 203.

(3) *Shah Imam Bukhsh* v. *Beebee Shahee* [1835], 6 Sel. Reports, 22; see also *Mujawar Ibram Bibi* v. *Mujawar Hossain Sharif* [1880] I. L., 3 Mad., 95.

cessor assumes the privilege of initiating the disciples into the mysteries of *dervishism* or *sufism*. The relationship which exists between a *pîr* and his *murîds*, as I understand the theory and practice of *dervishism*, is a spiritual and personal one."(1)

The appointment of a *sajjâda-nashîn*.

Accordingly, the appointment of a child of tender years as *sajjâda-nashîn* would seem to be opposed to the constitution of the office. There is one instance, however, in which a boy of nine or ten years of age was appointed a *sajjâda-nashîn* by the last holder of the office, the work of initiation, &c., during his minority, being entrusted to a disciple or *khalîfa* (vice-gerent). In this case the office was hereditary in the family, and apparently there was no other member qualified to perform the spiritual duties. "The appointment of a *sajjâda-nashîn* of a *dargâh* must, to a large extent, however, be regulated by the practice followed in the particular *dargâh* or neighbouring *dargâhs*. Herklot describes the custom in vogue in the *dargâhs* existing in Southern India. And, so far as I am aware, that is consistent, with the practice prevailing in other parts of India, *viz.*, that upon the death of the last incumbent, generally on the day of what is called the *sium* or *teja* ceremony (performed on the third day after his decease), the *fakîrs* and *murîds* of the *dargâh*, assisted by the heads of neighbouring *dargâhs*, instal a competent person on the *gaddi*; generally the person chosen is the son of the deceased, or somebody nominated by him, for his nomination is supposed to carry the guarantee that the nominee knows the precepts which he is to communicate to the disciples. In some instances the nomination takes the shape of a formal installation by the electoral body, so to speak, during the lifetime of the incumbent. But in every case the person installed is supposed to be competent to initiate the *murîds* into the mysteries of the *tarîkat* (*the holy path*)."(2)

Similarly, if the *wakf* relates to an institution where services special to one sect or one religion are held, a member of another sect or creed would not ordinarily be appointed for the *towliat* of such an institution.

" A *mutwalli*," says the *Hâwi*, "can delegate the trust to another on his death-bed like an executor."(3)

---

(1) *Piran Beebee* v. *Abdul Karim*, supra.
(2) *Ibid.*
(3) Comp. the *Durr-ul-Mukhtâr*, p. 421.

In the absence of any provision in the trust-deed as to the mode of succession, or of any evidence of usage, the *mutwalli* may, on his death-bed, nominate his successor, and such nomination will be valid without any judicial order. But in order that the nomination may be effective, it is necessary that the person so appointed should be adult and possessed of understanding. All the authorities are agreed that a minor cannot lawfully be appointed a *mutwalli*. The *Fatâwai Alamgiri* lays down the principle thus:— Succession to the *mutwalliship*.

"And it is a condition to the validity (of the appointment of a *mutwalli*) that he should be adult and possessed of understanding; and thus it is stated in the *Bahr ur-Râik*." A *mutwalli* must be *sui juris*.

So also in the *Radd-ul-Muhtâr*; "the conditions necessary to the validity [of the appointment] are puberty (*bulûgh*) and understanding (*'aakl*)."(1)

But when the office of *mutwalli* devolves upon a minor by virtue of a provision in the trust-deed, for example, if the *wakf-nâmah* provides that the *towliat* should be confined to the male descendants of the *wâkif* or the members of a particular family, and it happens that at some time the person on whom the office devolves by virtue of this provision is a minor, in such a case the appointment will remain in abeyance until he attains *majority*, when the *wilâyèt* (*mutwalliship*) would be transferred to him.(2) Devolution of *mutwalliship* under the provisions of the trust-deed.

So, also, when the *towliat* is hereditary in a family, and the last incumbent appoints his minor son on his death-bed to be the *mutwalli*, the Kâzi shall not remove him, but appoint another to discharge the duties of the office during his minority.(3)

"In the *Anf'aa-ul-wasâil* it is written from the *Wakf* of Hillâl that if the *wâkif* has said thus, 'the *wilâyèt* is for my children,' and he leaves both adult and minor children, the Kâzi should appoint somebody in the place of the minors, or he may place the adult to represent the minors." Appointment of a minor.

But a minor cannot be appointed by a *sanad* [of the Kâzi] whether he is appointed by himself or with another, for by his incapacity he is unable to superintend the affairs of the *wakf*, nor can he appoint a deputy in his place.

---

(1) *Radd-ul-Muhtâr*, Vol. III, p. 505.
(2) *Ibid.*
(3) *Ibid.*

"If the *wâkif* appoints a minor as *mutwalli*, and no adult is associated with him, the Kâzi shall appoint some person to do the work until the minor attains majority. If there is an adult associated with the minor, the Kâzi may appoint some person to represent the minor and act jointly with the *co-mutwalli*, or may empower the adult *mutwalli* to act for the minor."(1)

Freedom and Islâm are not necessary conditions.(2)

Appointment of a bondsman and of a non-Moslem.

The *Radd-ul-Muhtâr*, after stating that puberty and understanding on the part of the *mutwalli* are necessary qualifications to a valid appointment, goes on to say "freedom and Islâm are not requisite. So if a minor is made an executor, according to *kyâs* (analogy),(3) it would be absolutely void; according to *istehsân* (liberal interpretation of the law), it would remain inoperative only so long as he is a minor; and when he attains majority the *wilâyet* (trusteeship) would revert to him. If the person appointed be a bondsman, the appointment would be valid both according to *kyâs* and *istehsân* for he possesses the personal capacity....... which the minor does not. The same is the case of a *zimmi* (non-Moslem fellow-subject). And should the Kâzi remove the bondsman from the *wilâyet*, he would not recover it on emancipation, nor the other on his adopting Islâm," which is different from the case of a minor.

It will be seen from this that although a bondsman or a non-Moslem fellow-subject may be appointed a *mutwalli*, it is in the discretion of the Kâzi to remove him if he considers that the appointment is prejudicial to the interests of the trust or is opposed to the wishes of the beneficiaries or that it is not expedient to have a person professing another faith as administrator of the endowment.

So also in the *Fatâwa-'l-Ankariwia* :—

When the *towliat* has devolved on a minor, an adult should be appointed to discharge his duties.

"Q.—If the *wâkif* has made a *wakf* with this condition that its governance shall belong to his children, and among his children are both major and minor, to whom is the *towliat* to be given.

A.—The Kâzi shall appoint somebody in place of the *saghîr* (the infant) and if he likes he may appoint the adult children as the *kâim-mukâm* (deputy) of the minors."(4)

(1) *Radd-ul-Muhtár*, Vol. III, pp. 595, 596.

(2) *Ibid*, from the *As'aáf*.

(3) *i. e.*, Logically.

(4) *Fatâwa-l-Ankariwia*, Vol. II, p. 217.

"If the *towliat* has been entrusted [by the *wâkif*] to a boy, his *towliat* will remain in abeyance [or ineffective] until he attains majority when the trust will be made over to him."(1)

"If the *wâkif* appoints as *mutwalli* a person who is absent, the Kâzi has the power of nominating in his place another for the time-being, and when the *mutwalli* appointed by the *wâkif* arrives the trust will revert to him."(2)

As already mentioned it is only when the *wâkif* has made a condition at the time of dedication before the delivery of the property to the *mutwalli*, that he reserves to himself the power of removing the *mutwalli* or changing the property, that he may do so, but not otherwise.

If a person create a *wakf* and appoint another as the *mutwalli* thereof, and also make it a condition that such *mutwalli* shall not have the power of appointing by *testament his successor*, *such condition* would be valid.(3)

When a person makes a *wakf*, and at the time of his death appoints a person to be his executor without mentioning anything about the *wakf*, such executor shall nevertheless be the *mutwalli* of the *wakf*.(4)

If a man in health(5) were to make a *wakf* of his land for the poor and consign the same to a *mutwalli*, and subsequently at the time of his death, were to tell his executor to give out of the produce of the land, certain shares to so-and-so, and to do whatever the executor thinks best with it, and the executor acts up to the *wâkif's* instructions it will not be valid, for the *wakf* was complete from the outset, and the *wâkif* had no power to make any alteration unless he reserved the power to himself.

SECTION II.

THE APPOINTMENT OF THE MUTWALLI.

As already observed the power of appointing a *mutwalli* rests primarily with the *wâkif* and, in his absence, with his

Appointment of the *Mutwalli*.

(1) *Surrat-ul-Fatâwa in loco.*

(2) *Fatâwa-'l-Ankariwia*, Vol. II, p. 217, from the *As'aâf*.

(3) *Ibid*, Vol. III, p. 636; so also in the *Wajîz-ul-Muhit*, see *post*.

(4) *Durr-ul-Mukhtâr*, p. 421, and *Radd-ul-Muhtâr*, Vol. III, p. 634; *Fusûl-ul-'Imâdia*, p. 226.

(5) *I.e.*, when not suffering from any fatal illness which causes his death.

wasî or executor, "*because he is the wâkif's locum tenens.* It is only in the absense of an executor that the power of appointing a *mutwalli* to the *wakf* devolves on the Judge,(1) and a derivative executor or in other words the executor's executor has the same powers as the executor.(2)

A *mutwalli* appointed in general terms or whose appointment is not limited to the life-time of the *wâkif* stands in law in the same position, so far as the *wakf* is concerned, as an executor. And it is in consequence of this view that he is given the power of appointing on his death-bed or when suffering from a mortal illness, a successor.(3)

If the *wâkif* were to appoint two persons to be *mutwallis* of a *wakf* after his death, and one of them were to die appointing the other as his executor in the matter of the *wakf*, the survivor would be entitled to act as the sole *mutwalli*.(4)

An executor appointed only with reference to, or in respect of, the *wakf* properties would be a general executor, though Abû Yusuf differs in this view from the other jurists. According to the *As'aâf*, if a man were to appoint first a *mutwalli*, and then an executor (in respect of the same *wakf*), both would be *mutwallis* unless their duties are specified. The mode of specifying the functions is stated in this manner :—" The *wâkif* says, 'such piece of land of mine is *wakf* and so-and-so is the *mutwalli* thereof, and, as regards the rest of my property, so-and-so is the *wasi*.' In such a case the persons appointed have separate functions."

Advocate-General v. *Fatima Sultani Begum.*

In the case of the *Advocate-General* v. *Fatima Sultani Begum*(5) it was held that, according to Mahommedan Law, the appropriator has a right to reserve the superintendence of the *wakf* to himself or appoint some one else. But when he has specified the class from whom the manager is to be selected, he cannot disregard his own trust-deed and appoint a person not answering the proper description he has indicated by the provisions of the *wakfnâmah*, and his right of nomination of the person to succeed to the management on his death must be confined to the class mentioned in the *wakf*-

(1) *Durr-ul-Mukhtar*, p. 421.
(2) *Radd-ul-Muhtar*, Vol. III, p. 633.
(3) *Durr-ul-Mukhtar*, p. 421.
(4) *Fatawai Kazi Khan*, Vol. IV, p. 276.
(5) [1872] 9 Bom. H. C. Reports, 19, *supra*.

nâmah. This *dictum* must, however, be accepted with some qualification. If the *wâkif* at the time of dedication has reserved to himself the power of altering the class from whom the manager should be selected, his appointment of a person "not answering the description in the *wakfnâmah*" will not be invalid. The term *akriba*, though more properly confined to relations by blood, will, when the context shows that it was intended to be used in a wider sense, be so extended as to include relations by affinity, but the wife or widow of the founder is not included among his *akriba*.

Meaning of the term *akriba*.

Abû Yusuf holds that if a *wâkif* were to appoint a *mutwalli* during his lifetime, without mentioning that such appointment should continue in force after his death, the *mutwalli* would vacate his office on the death of the *wâkif*. The rule of law, however, is, that when an appointment is made without mentioning its duration, it does not cease on the death of the appointor.

If a person make a *wakf* during his lifetime, but do not appoint a *mutwalli* thereof even when death comes upon him, but appoint an executor, such executor will be the executor as well as the *mutwalli* of the *wakf*. This is according to Abû Yusuf and the *fatwa* is according to him. If, however, the *wâkif* appointed a *mutwalli* for the *wakf* during his lifetime, his executor will not be the *mutwalli* of the *wakf*.

In *Shah Ghulam Rahmutullah Sahib* v. *Mohammed Akber Saheb*,(1) the Madras High Court enunciated the recognised principle of Mahommedan Law, that when property is devoted to religious charitable purposes, it is usual for the appropriator to lay down rules for succession to the office of trustee, and upon those rules whether they are in writing or have to be inferred from evidence of usage, the question of succession depends. Should no rules be laid down, the power of appointing is vested in the appropriator during his life, and upon his death, it is vested in his executor; or, should he have left no executor, in the magistrate and sovereign power, that is to say, in the Court.(2)

(1) [1864], 1 Mad. H. C. R., p. 63.

(2) *Mohammed Sadik* v. *Mohamed Ali*, 1 Sel. Rep., p. 17; *Mohammed Kessori* v. *Mohammed Shah Kiyamuddin*, 5 Sel. Rep., p. 133; *Advocate-General* v. *Fatima Sultani Begum*, supra; *Phate Sahib Bibi* v. *Damodar Premji* [1879], I. L., 3 Bom., 84; *Agha Mahomed Eusoof Mushadee* v. *Abdool Hossain Khan*, S. D. A., 1857, p. 640; *Het Koonwar* v. *Chutterdharee Singh* [1870], 13 W. R., 396.

When the *wâkif* has provided that the appointment to the *towliat* shall be made by his children,—and among his children, there are some who are minors, the Kâzi may authorise those who are adults to make the appointment on behalf of the minors as well as their own, or may associate some person with them to represent the minors.

In the *Anf'aa-ul-Wasâil* it is stated from Khassâf, that when a person has made a *wakf* of two pieces of land, and appointed two *mutwallis*, and subsequently at the time of his death appoints Zaid as his executor, Zaid will be a *mutwalli* with them; and if Zaid appoints 'Amr as his executor, 'Amr's position will be the same as that of Zaid.

If a person were to appoint two executors one after the other without removing the first, both of them would become executors, for "among us" (meaning the Hanafîs), an executorship does not fall to the ground of itself. The appointment of a second *mutwalli* by the Kâzi is different from the appointment of a second *mutwalli* by the *wâkif*, for in the latter case both appointments are valid; but when two appointments are made by the Kâzi, the second appointment invalidates the first provided the first *mutwalli* becomes aware of the second appointment. "It is not expedient to appoint to the office of *mutwalli* one who is a seeker after it, but it is not unlawful."

If the *wâkif* has appointed no *mutwalli*, and the Kâzi has appointed one, the *wâkif* has no power to remove the person appointed by the Kâzi.

The Kâzi's power to appoint a *mutwalli*.

When the *wâkif* dies without appointing a *mutwalli* or leaving an executor, in that case the Kâzi will have the power of appointing the superintendent of the *wakf*.

Similarly, if the last incumbent in the office of *mutwalli* dies without appointing his successor or an executor, the appointment rests with the Kâzi; the *fatwa* is according to this principle and the Allâmah Kâsim has decided according to it.

The last *mutwalli* has the power of nominating his successor only when the *wâkif* has made no provision regarding the office. If the *wâkif* has declared that the office shall descend in the lineal male line in a particular family, none of the incumbents will have the power of changing the course of descent. Or, if the *wâkif* has declared that after *A*, *B* shall succeed to the office, *A* has no power to appoint *C*.(1)

" So long as there is a relative of the *wâkif* qualified for the office, a stranger should not be appointed *mutwalli*,(2) for a relative is more benevolently disposed [towards the *wâkif*], and it is [generally] the intention of the *wâkif* that a relative should be appointed."

The right of members of the *wâkif's* family to the office of *towliat*.

" This dictum is from Hâkim in the *Kâfi*, and he has made it *Nass* (absolute) thus :—' So long as among the descendants of the *wâkif* or among the people of his family (*ahl(u)-bait*) there is to be found any qualified [for the office] a *mutwalli* shall not be appointed from strangers. When no qualified person is found among them, and the *towliat* is entrusted to a stranger, and subsequently a member of the *wâkif's* family is forthcoming who is qualified for the office, it shall be given to him.' The result of this is, that the descendants of the *wâkif* shall be preferred (for the office of *mutwalli*) even though the *wakf* may not be for them, as in the case of a *wakf* for a mosque or for others."

Preferential right of the members of the *wâkif's* famify.

Similarly, it is laid down in the *Wajiz-ul-Muhît* :' So long as a descendant of the *wâkif* or a member of his family (*ahl(u)-bait*) is living and is qualified for the *towliat*, the Kâzi should not appoint a stranger. If there is no one among his descendants or his family qualified for the office, in that case the Kâzi may appoint an outsider. But when after such appointment, a qualified person among them is forthcoming, the trust should be assigned to him." The principle is repeated in similar terms in the ***Fatâwa'l-Ankarawia***, the ***Fusûl-ul-Imâdia*** and the ***Fatâwai Alamgiri***. The author of the ***Radd-ul-Muhtâr*** goes on to add :—

" In the *Hindièh*(3) it is stated from the *Tahzib*, that when there is any one among the descendants or kindred of the *mowkoof-alaih* qualified [for the office] it is preferable to appoint him. From the term *mowkoof-alaih* are clearly meant the descendants of the *wâkif* [as the objects of the trust] and therefore this dictum is not contradictory of the one above [from the *Kâfi*]. Again, the use of the word ' preferable,' shows that the appointment of a stranger in the pre-

(1) *Mohammad Sadik* v. *Mohamed Ali*, supra ; *Jâm'aa-ul-Fúsulain.*

(2) *Durr-ul-Mukhtâr*, p. 421, also *Advocate-General* v. *Fatima Sultani Begum*, supra ; *Radd-ul-Muhtâr*, Vol. III, p. 636.

(3) The *Fatâwai Alamgiri* is so-called having been compiled in India.

sence of a descendant of the *wâkif* is not invalid. This view is not contradictory to what is stated in the *Jâm'aa-ul-Fusûlain*, which amounts to this, that should the *wâkif* make a condition to the effect that his children and children's children should be the *mutwallis* of the *wakf* in succession to each other, in that case the Kâzi has no power to appoint an outsider without finding any breach of trust on the part of the *wâkif's* descendant, and should the Kâzi appoint an outsider to the office of *mutwalli*, in supersession of a descendant of the *wâkif* without any lawful reason, such person shall not become *mutwalli*. This refers to a case where the *wâkif* has made such a condition, but the present discussion relates to a case where the *wâkif* has made no such provision." "And what is stated from the *Khairiyèh* at the end of the chapter on *wakf* leads to the result that such an appointment [*i.e.*, the appointment of a stranger] will be absolutely invalid, and this (no doubt) is the meaning of *la-ej'aalo*, so this must be considered. And in the *Khairiyèh* there is also a *Fatwa* that it is not necessary for a person among the *ahl-ul-wakf* [people from among whom a *mutwalli* should be selected] to be qualified thus; if his disqualification is removed afterwards, it is sufficient [that is, he should then get the office]. And this is clear. [But] then it must not remain concealed, that all this relates primarily to a case where any of the descendants of the *wâkif* or his *ahl-ul-bait* is found to be fit."

In the *Fusul-ul-'Imâdia* it is stated that the author's father(1) was asked whether, if the *wâkif* had made a condition that the *towliat* should be confined to his descendants, the Kâzi could appoint a stranger—he answered, 'no.'

When an outsider may be appointed as *mutwalli*.

But when there is no fit and proper person to be found among the descendants or relatives of the *wâkif* an outsider may be appointed; and a descendant or relative of the *wâkif* succeeding to the office of *towliat*, if he proves himself unworthy or commits a breach of trust. can be removed, and, in the absence of any other member of the *wâkif's* family qualified to take his place, an outsider can be appointed, "for when the *wâkif* himself can be removed for breach of trust, *à fortiori* other people can be removed also for misbehaviour."(2) In a case where a descendant or relative or a neighbour of the *wâkif* is not willing to accept the office without

(1) Himself a great jurist. (2) *Fatâwai Alamgiri*, Vol. II, p. 505.

a salary, and an outsider is willing to accept it without remuneration, the Kâzi should see whose appointment would be most beneficial to the *wakf*, and who is fittest for the appointment.(1)

The law distinctly lays down that so long as a fit and proper person can be found among the members of the *wâkif's* family or among his relatives, the Judge should not appoint a stranger. Is the same rule applicable to an appointment by a *mutwalli* who holds the office with general powers. The Calcutta High Court has answered it in the negative. It has held that when a *mutwalli* suffering from a death-bed illness appoints a successor, his nomination is not necessarily restricted to the founder's family.(2)

The appointment of the *mutwalli*.

If an appointment has once been validly made, no other person can be appointed so long as the former appointment lasts.

A *mutwalli* cannot give up the office of *towliat* of his own motion; he must obtain the permission of the Kâzi to retire from his office. Some jurists appear, no doubt, to have expressed an opinion that a *mutwalli* can resign his post in favour of another, but they have also held that the latter will not become *mutwalli* until his appointment has been sanctioned by the Kâzi, who is not bound to appoint him to the office.

The appointment of the *mutwalli*.

If a *mutwalli* resigns his post in favour of another in lieu of some pecuniary consideration, and the latter is not appointed by the Kâzi, he can proceed against the quondam *mutwalli* for the money paid to him, though such "payment was illegal." Those who hold such payments to be legal are a few modern jurists, but it is against the true construction of the law and absolutely immoral.(3)

It would appear, that at one time attempts were frequent on the part of the servitors of charitable endowments to discharge their duties by substitutes. The allowance fixed for the officers were drawn by them, whilst a small honorarium was given to their substitutes. The legality of such conduct seems to have given rise to considerable discussion among the early Mussulman

(1) *Radd-ul-Muhtár*, Vol. III, p. 636.

(2) *Sheikh Amir Ali* v. *Syed Wazir Hyder* [1915], 9 Cal. W. N., 876. This ruling, however, does not seem quite consistent with the principles of the Mussulman Law.

(3) *Radd-ul-Muhtâr*, Vol. III, 636. See *Shah Mohinuddin* v. *Elahee Buksh* [1866], 6 W. R., 277.

jurists; but the more modern lawyers are generally agreed in opinion that the appointment of a substitute is not lawful unless there is any just reason for it. A female *mutwalli*, who is, by reason of her sex, unable to discharge all the duties of her office, is authorised to appoint a deputy. Similarly, where the disqualification is temporary, and is caused by illness or absence "on lawful grounds," the work may be performed by a substitute appointed by the superintendent or the Kâzi. Where such appointment is made, the substitute is entitled either to the whole allowance or a portion thereof in accordance with the arrangement made between him and the incumbent. Ibn Shibli has stated in his *Fatâwa*, that when a *mutwalli* has become incapable from weakness to superintend the work personally, he may appoint a substitute or deputy to help him in the management, but the responsibility will continue to rest with him, and the substitute will only obtain his allowance from the *mutwalli*.(1)

The power of the *mutwalli* to appoint his successor.

The *mutwalli* cannot, however, assign or transfer the office to any one, or appoint another during his lifetime, unless his own powers are "general."(2) Should he in his lifetime and in health appoint another in his place, the appointment will not be lawful and valid, unless the *mutwalli* has obtained the *towliat* with that condition, "in a general manner." In that case the *mutwalli* so appointing another person in his place will not be able to remove the latter, unless the *wâkif*, whilst confiding the trust empowered him to assign the same to another, *and also to remove the trustee.*

The restriction mentioned above refers to the appointment of a permanent and substantive successor, who would occupy the position and exercise the full powers of the *mutwalli*, in fact succeed him in the office. And not to the appointment by the *mutwalli* of a *kâim mokâm* or substitute in his place. The appointment of a successor to take his place absolutely can only be made by the *mutwalli* on his death-bed or in death-illness.(3) "This restriction does not apply to the appointment of a deputy or agent." And in the *Fath* [*ul-Kadîr*] it is stated that the *mutwalli* is empowered to

---

(1) See also *Mohimuddin Ahmed* v. *Elahee Buksh*, supra.

(2) *Radd-ul-Muhtâr*, Vol. III, p. 637. In the case of *Wahid Ali* v. *Ashraf Hossain* [1882], I. L., 8 Cal., 732; s. c., 10 C. L. R., p. 529, the meaning of the word "general" was not considered at all.

(3) *Durr-ul-Mukhtâr*, p. 421.

appoint such persons as deputies, as are able to discharge the duties connected with the office, or which are incumbent on the *mutwalli*. The *mutwalli* has the power of removing his deputy and appointing another in his place. If the *mutwalli* becomes insane, the appointment of his deputy becomes vacated of itself; and the Kâzi becomes entitled to appoint a substitute for the *mutwalli*. This applies to all cases, both where the *mutwalli* has been appointed by the Kâzi or by the *wâkif*.

Where the appointment of the *mutwalli* is "general" the *mutwalli* has the power of assigning the trust to another, not otherwise. In the *Fatâwai Alamgiri* the principle is given thus:—"A *mutwalli* may at his death commit his office to another in the same way as an executor may commit his to another. But when the appropriator has assigned some particular property for the *mutwalli*, it does not belong to the person to whom the office has been bequeathed; and the matter must be submitted to the Judge in order that he may assign for him the hire or salary of similar work, unless the *wâkif* had assigned the allowance for every *mutwalli*; so in the *Fath-ul-Kadîr*. And if the *mutwalli* were to intend to appoint another in his place in *his own lifetime and in good health*, it would not be lawful, unless the consignment (*tafwîz*) was made to him in a general manner (علي سبيل التعميم); so in the *Muhît*."(1)

As regards the meaning of the expression "in a general manner" the author of the *Radd-ul-Muhtâr* explains it as follows:—"It means that if the *wâkif* or Kâzi were to make a condition at the time of appointing the *mutwalli*, that he should have the power of transferring the trust to another and substituting that other in his own place by a *sanad-i-wakf* or *wasiat*, should necessity arise for it, such a condition would carry with it the power, on the part of the *mutwalli*, to appoint another *mutwalli* during his lifetime, or in death-illness."(2)

Meaning of the term "general."

If the appointment of the *mutwalli*, or the assignment to him of the trust, is not general in its nature (علي سبيل التعميم) as stated above, in other words, when the *mutwalli* does not possess general powers, he cannot assign the trust to another "in health," whilst capable of discharging the functions of the office; but if there

(1) *Fatâwai Alamgiri*, Vol. II, p. 508. (2) *Radd-ul-Muhtâr*, Vol. III, p. 637.

are no provisions in the *wakfnâmah* regulating the mode of succession, he can appoint a successor in death-illness.(1) The reason of this is stated by Kâzi Khan to consist in the fact that the *mutwalli* is in the position of an executor, and like an executor he has the power of appointing on his death-bed another executor in his place to perform the functions which appertain to him. As an executor has no power to resign the executorship which he has once accepted, without the permission of the Kâzi, so a *mutwalli* cannot withdraw from a trust without such permission. The appointment of another *mutwalli* by one who does not possess general powers, without the leave of the Kâzi, is tantamount to a withdrawal of the incumbent from office, yet he remains responsible, unless the appointment or transfer of the trust is subsequently confirmed by the Kâzi.

A *mutwalli* possessing general powers can alone appoint a successor "in health."

"With reference to a *mutwalli* appointed in a general manner," it is further explained "the meaning of the term (التعميم) 'general' is thus explained in the *Anf'aa-ul-Wasâil* :—'that the *wâkif* appoints a *mutwalli* and places him in his own place and constitutes him his successor, and authorises him to assign the trust to whomsoever he likes, in such a case the *mutwalli* can transfer the trust either in health or death-illness.'"

"If the *nâzir*, (supervisor, meaning the *mutwalli*) without the condition, during *marz-ul-mout* entrusts the *towliat* to another, it is valid; but if he assigned it in health, it would not be valid, as is stated in the *Tattima*, &c., and the reason of this is, that he is in the position of an executor, ... and as an executor can assign the executorship by testament, a *mutwalli* may also do so. And it is right to hold that the powers of a *kyyum* (curator) and executor are co-extensive. And this is different from an act done in health, for a *kyyum* in health is like a deputy (*wakîl*), and a *wakîl* has no power of delegating his powers."

With reference to this subject, the *Surrat-ul-Fatâwa* is distinct. "If the *wâkif* has provided that the *mutwalli* shall have the power of assigning the trust to another, in such a case an assignment of the *towliat*, whilst the *mutwalli* is in health, is valid, otherwise not. But even without such power, if the assignment is made in *marz-ul-mout* it is valid; so it is stated in the

(1) Taken from the *Anf'aa-ul-Wasâil*.

Kinia and *Tattima*. And if the *mutwalli* has once appointed another in his place by virtue of the power reserved to him by the *wâkif*, he cannot remove the person so appointed, unless the *wâkif* gave him the power of appointing as well as discharging. Tarṭûsî in his *Anf'aa-ul-Wasâil* has laid down the same rule . . . . I was asked with reference to a *mutwalli* who had been appointed by his predecessor by virtue of the power given to the latter, and who had died leaving the trust in the hands of a third person, whether the *hâkim* could give the *towliat* to somebody else. I answered that if the *mutwalli* had assigned the trust *in health*, the appointee would hold the trust for the lifetime of the *appointer ;* but upon his decease the Kâzi would have the power of appointing."(1)

I take it that this refers to a case where the *mutwalli*, who had been appointed by virtue of a power given to his predecessor by the *wâkif*, did not possess the power himself also ; in other words, if the power was only personal to the first *mutwalli*. But whether he had the power or not, if he appointed a successor on his death-bed it would be lawful.(2)

An appointment made on death-bed.

If the *wâkif* on his death-bed was to say to another, " You shall be in my place with reference to this *wakf*," or if he was to say that " my children will have the same powers as myself with respect of this *wakf*," this in fact would be vesting them with all the powers he possesses. And I take it that in such cases the executor of the *wâkif's* children will have the power of appointing a *mutwalli inter vivos*. This question was not considered properly in the case of *Wahid Ali* v. *Ashraf Hossein*.(3)

" But the *wâkif* may condition that so-and-so is the *mutwalli* of this *wakf*, but that he will not have the power of

(1) *Surrat-ul-Fatâwa*, p. 440.

(2) *Ibid ;* See also *Fatâwai Kâzi Khan*. Vol. IV, p. 219. In the case of *Khajah Salimullah* v. *Abul Khair M. Mustafa*, supra, the Calcutta High Court has laid down that when a *mutwalli*, who did not appear to possess such general powers as would enable her to appoint a successor whilst physically fit to carry on the duties of the trust, did in fact transfer it to another, the Statute of Limitation ran from the date of such appointment against a person claiming a preferential right to the governance of the *wakf ;* and " his title to the office " would become barred under Article 120 of the second schedule of the Limitation Act if the office was not hereditary. If it was hereditary, it would become barred under Article 124.

(3) Supra.

leaving the trust by *wasiat* to another ; and such condition is lawful."(1)

"The *wâkif* may lawfully condition that so-and-so will be the *mutwalli* of the *wakf*, but that neither he nor any other *mutwalli* shall have the power of leaving the trust by *wasiat* to another."(2)

When a condition is made in the *wakfnâmah* that upon the death of each *mutwalli*, the power of appointing his successor shall rest with the Judge, a *mutwalli* cannot appoint a successor to himself either in health or in illness. And upon the decease of each incumbent, the Kâzi shall appoint a successor.

The *wâkif* has the power of removing the *mutwalli* only when he has reserved a power to that effect.

As regards the power of the *wâkif* to remove a *mutwalli* whom he has appointed there is a difference of opinion between Abû Yusuf and Mohammed. Abû Yusuf holds that the *wâkif* is absolutely entitled to remove the *mutwalli* appointed by himself, whether he has reserved the power or not. Mohammed differs, holding that it is only when the *wâkif* has reserved the power that he can remove the *mutwalli*, without any misfeasance, and the *Fatwa* is according to Mohammed's view.(3)

The difference between Abû Yusuf and Imâm Mohammed is fully stated in the *Fatâwai Alamgiri*. "A person having made a *wakf* of his property and after having transferred it to the curator (*Kyyum*) desires to take it back from his hands ; if he made a condition for himself in the *wakf* that he should [have the power to] discharge the curator and take back the property, in that case he may do so according to Mohammed and not otherwise. But according to Abû Yusuf he may do so [in either case, *i.e.*, whether he has reserved the power or not]. And the *Mashâikh* (Jurists) of Balkh decide according to Abû Yusuf and the Jurist Abû Lais has adopted the same view. The *Mashâikh* of Bokhâra decide according to the rule of Mohammed, and the *fatwa* is thereon ; so in the *Muzmirât* "(4)

The *Radd-ul-Muhtàr* explains the reason of the difference. Abû Yusuf holds the *mutwalli* to be a deputy (*wâkil*) of the *wâkif*

(1) *Wajiz-ul-Muhit.*

(2) *Ibid.*

(3) *Radd-ul-Muhtâr*, Vol. III, p. 638. See the case of *Hidayatunnissa* v. *Afzal Hossein*, 2 N.-W. P. Rep., p. 240 ; also *Golam Husain* v. *Aji Ajam Tadallah*, 4 Mad. H. C. R., 44.

(4) *Fatâwai Alamgiri*, Vol. II, p. 505.

and consequently the *wâkif* has the power at any time to discharge him. According to Mohammed the *mutwalli* is a deputy of the beneficiaries, and that, therefore, the *wâkif* has the power to discharge him only when he has reserved it expressly at the time of the dedication.(1)

And it adds, that according to the *Tashîh-ul-Kudûri* of Allâmah Kâsim this is the rule on which decisions are passed.

The doctrine which is given in the *Durr-ul-Mukhtâr* on the authority of the *Ashbâh* that "the *wâkif* has *absolute* authority to discharge the *mutwalli*,(2) and the *Fatwa* is thereon," does not represent the view recognised as binding by the compilers of the *Fatâwai Alamgiri* or the author of the *Radd-ul-Muhtâr*.

The officers of the *wakf* have no power to remove the *mutwalli*.(3)

The *mutwalli* may resign his office with the "knowledge" of the *wâkif* or of the Kâzi;(4) in other words with their sanction but he can not do so of his own accord.

The *wâkif* may give the power to the *mutwalli* to increase or reduce the allowance of the *wazîfadars*(5) (persons receiving stipends) according to his discretion or to remove or add to the *wazîfadars*.

Directions of the *wâkif* regarding the devolution of the trust.

If a person were to make a *wakf* and appoint 'Abdullah the *mutwalli* thereof and declare that upon 'Abdullah's death, Zaid shall be the *mutwalli*, 'Abdullah has no power to devise the *mutwalliship* to another, and Zaid will be the *mutwalli*, notwithstanding any appointment made by 'Abdullah. And Allâmah al-Hanouti has held that when a person has declared that the *towliat* of any *wakf* should be given to the "most discreet of his descendants, and one of them, being the *mutwalli* for the time, appoints his son-in-law as the *mutwalli* and dies, the *towliat* shall nevertheless go to such person among the descendants of the *wâkif* as fulfils the condition in the *wakfnâmah*." Any appointment contrary to the terms of the *wakf*, or conditions laid down by the *wâkif*, is invalid.

---

(1) *Radd-ul-Muhtâr*, Vol. III, p. 63.
(2) *Durr-ul-Mukhtâr*, p. 421, Hooghly Ed.
(3) *Ibid*; Comp. *Meher Ali* v. *Golam Nujuff* [1870], 11 W. R., 333.
(4) *Ibid*; *Radd-ul-Muhtâr*, Vol. III, p. 638.
(5) *Radd-ul-Muhtâr*, Vol. III, p. 639.

As already stated the servitors of the mosque cannot remove the *mutwalli*, though the *mutwalli* can remove them for unfitness or misconduct or other fault.(1)

Mussulman jurists draw a distinction between public and private trusts. For example, in the case of a mosque, the congregation, according to the accepted rule, have no power to appoint a *mutwalli* whereas in the case of a private trust made in favour of specific individuals, the beneficiaries are permitted to nominate a trustee.

This is the rule I gather from the statements in the *Fatâwai Kâzi Khan* and other works of authority.

In the *Fatâwai Kazi Khan* occurs first the following passage :— "A person makes a valid *wakf* in favour of a particular mosque and [appoints] a *kyyum* (superintendent) for it; and then the *kyyum* dies, whereupon the *ahl-ul-masjid*(2) assemble and appoint in his place a *mutwalli*(3) without the order of the Kâzi; and this *mutwalli* proceeds [in the original, stands up] to repair the mosque with the income of the *wakf;* the *mashâikh* (the jurists) have differed regarding this *towliat.* But the most correct doctrine is that it is not valid, for the power of appointing a *kyyum* appertains to the Kâzi. But if this *mutwalli* (so appointed) had spent any money out of the income of the *wakf* over the repairs of the mosque he would not be liable; if he, however, leased the *wakf* and spent the money himself, it would not be lawful and he would be guilty of breach of trust."(4)

Wakf in favour of specific individuals.

"But where the *wakf* is in favour of specific individuals (*arbâb-m'alumain*, or known persons) limited in number, and they appoint a proper person of integrity without the order of the Kâzi, it would be valid but it is preferable to lay the matter before the Kâzi to appoint a *kyyum*. They (the jurists) or some of them say, however, that in these times it is preferable not to bring the matter before the Kâzi, as the Kâzis of our times have betrayed avarice (*atmâ'a-ul-fâsila*). Nevertheless, the congregation of the

---

(1) This is the approved doctrine; *Zâhir-ur-Rawâyet*; *Tâtâr Khânieh.*

(2) The people of the mosque, *i.e.*, congregation.

(3) *Towliat* is the office; it means governance, trusteeship, superintendence.

(4) In the original, "if this *mutwalli* belongs to the category of people of integrity (*Ahl-us-Salâh*) and is not a *fâsik* (a man of bad behaviour)." *Ahl-us-Salâh* really means virtuous people, worthy of trust.

mosque have not the power to appoint a *mutwalli* or *kyyum*, without informing the Kâzi and obtaining his sanction to the appointment."(1)

The author of the *Radd-ul-Muhtâr* says, " the result of what is stated in the *Tâtâr Khâniêh* is that if the devotees or congregation of a mosque agree in appointing a man as *mutwalli*, for the administration of the mosque (*li-masâlih-il-masjid*), it is valid according to the ancient jurists, but it is most preferable to obtain the sanction of the Kâzi. The moderns, are, however, unanimously of opinion that 'in these days' it is preferable not to inform the Kâzi, for it is known how covetous they are of the property of *wakfs*. In the same way, when a *wakf* is in favour of individuals limited in number they may appoint a *mutwalli* from among people of integrity."

As I understand the principle, the *dicta* which prohibit the appointment of a *mutwalli* by the congregation, refer to endowments of a public nature like a *masjid* and similar institutions in which the public at large or the Mussulman public generally are interested. But when a dedication is in favour of particular people whose number is ascertainable, the modern Moslem jurists have recognised the validity of an appointment by the beneficiaries. The *Fatâwai Alamgiri*, after stating the views of the older jurists concerning such appointments, says :— Principle.

"It is stated from Shaikh ul-Islâm Abûl Hasan that all the *mashâikhs* (jurists) declare that if the beneficiaries were to appoint a *mutwalli*, it would be as valid as if the appointment was made with the permission of the Kâzi."

The same principle is given in the *Radd-ul-Muhtâr* and the *Wajîz-ul-Muhît*.

---

(1) *Fatâwai Kâzi Khan*, Vol. IV, p. 216. In later times during the convulsions which afflicted the Islâmic world consequent upon internecine struggles and the invasions of the pagan Mongols and the Christian Crusaders, the high standard of judicial morality certainly declined. But the lofty ideal of Moslem justice and the adequacy, not to say elasticity, of its conceptions can be gathered not only from the treatise of Mâwardi—"the Hugo Grotius of Islâm"—on political law called the *Ahkâm-us-Saltanat*, but also from the chapters on "the Duties of the Kâzi" in recognised works of authority, which well deserve translation. In one respect the Mussulman Jurists appear to be in advance of the modern thinkers of Christendom, for the founder of the Hanafî school admitted the right of women to hold judicial office.

When the *wâkif* has appointed *nâzirs*(1) to exercise a supervisory control over the *mutwalli*, and vested them with the power of removing him for misfeasance or misconduct, they will have also the power of appointing his successor, although this latter power may not be expressly given to them in the deed of *wakf*.

If the *wâkif* were to appoint a *mutwalli*, but there is no indication that the appointment should continue in force even after his (the *wâkif's*) death, the *mutwalli* would be discharged upon the happening of the *wâkif's* death.

The *Mutwalli*.

The *Radd-ul-Muhtâr* states the principle thus :—When a *mutwalli* is appointed by the *wâkif*, he will become discharged on the death of the *wâkif*. This is according to Abû Yusuf's rule on which is the *fatwa*, for such a *mutwalli* is merely an agent on behalf of the *wâkif*. But when the *wâkif* appoints a *mutwalli* "for his life and after his death," such *mutwalli* will not become discharged in consequence of the *wâkif's* death.

When the *wâkif* himself holds the office of *mutwalli*, and is found guilty of misfeasance or breach of trust, he can be removed, whether there is a condition to that effect in the *wakfnâmah* or not. Unfitness to carry out the duties of the trust is a cause for removal from office.

Wâkif may be removed from the governance of the trust if guilty of misfeasance.

" If the *wâkif* has reserved the *wilâyèt* in his own hands, and he proves himself dishonest, the Kâzi has the power of removing him in the interests of the *cestuis qui trustent*, just in the same way as he has the power of removing a dishonest executor."(2)

Ā fortiori he has the power of removing a *mutwalli* for breach of trust, and he may do so even though the appropriator should have made a condition that there should be no such power.

But the malversation or breach of trust must be proved; mere imputation is not sufficient to justify his removal. If a *mutwalli*, with funds in his hands, neglects to repair the *wakf* premises and allows it to fall into disrepair, it amounts to a breach of trust, for if he knowingly and intentionally causes damage or loss to the *wakf*, or if he misdeals with the trust-property he must be removed from his office.

---

(1) Supervisors.

(2) *Radd-ul-Muhtâr*, Vol. III, p. 596; *Surrat-ul-Fatâwa*, p. 420; *Fatâwai Alamgiri*, Vol. II, p. 505.

The *Fath ul-Kadîr* is very distinct on the point. "The Kâzi has the power of doing so even if the *wâkif* has made a condition to the effect that in case of breach of trust on his part, neither the Kâzi nor the Sultan will have the power of removing him."(1)

In the *Jâm'aa ul-Fusûlain*, it is stated that "when a *mutwalli* has been appointed by the *wâkif* or by any of the constituted Judges, he cannot be removed without any of those causes which justify his removal, that is, manifest breach of trust or misfeasance and the like causes. In the terms 'like causes' appear to be included incapacity to discharge the duties of the office as well as immorality."(2)

The dismissal of the *mutwalli*.

The Kâzi cannot remove a *mutwalli*, whether appointed by the *wâkif* or himself, merely on the complaint of the beneficiaries but can do so upon proof of misfeasance or breach of trust.(3)

But though the Kâzi has no power to remove the *mutwalli* merely upon the complaint of the beneficiaries, yet upon receiving a complaint, if he consider it to be *bonâ fide* and reasonable, he can associate another trustworthy person with the *mutwalli* and fix a remuneration for him, either out of the allowance of the *mutwalli* or from the general funds.

Similarly, the Kâzi has no power to remove an executor appointed by the deceased merely on the complaint of anybody without proof.

Responsibility of the *mutwalli*.

Any loss sustained by the *wakf* through the wilful neglect of the *mutwalli* shall be made good by him. It is doubtful, however, whether a gratuitous *mutwalli* would be liable for any loss which is occasioned, merely through neglect, to the *wakf*.

"The *mutwalli*," says the *Fath-ul-Kadîr*, "is also liable to be removed if he is proved to be addicted to drunkenness and such like vices."(4)

If a *mutwalli* takes up his abode in the *wakf* building without any provision to that effect in the deed of dedication or without the permission of the Judge, his conduct amounts to misfeasance.

The *mutwalli* should ordinarily be chosen from among the relatives of the *wâkif*. If, among his relatives or neighbours, no

---

(1) *Fath-ul-Kadîr*, Vol. II, p. 640.
(2) *Radd-ul-Muhtâr*, Vol. III, p. 597.
(3) *Jâm'aa ul-Fusûlain*; *Radd-ul-Muhtâr*, Vol. III, p. 597.
(4) *Ibid*, Vol. III, p. 640.

person can be found willing to undertake the work of *towliat* without a remuneration, and there is an outsider willing to do so, then his appointment would depend upon the Kâzi's discretion, and he must judge who is the best person to be appointed.(1)

Persons who get an allowance from the *wakf* shall not be deprived of their *wazifa,* unless they are proved to be guilty of some offence which entails this penalty.(2)

It has been held by the Calcutta High Court that the sale of an office to which are attached religious duties is void under the Mahommedan Law.(3)

An attempt to "sell or alienate the allowance or to create a charge upon it has been regarded as misconduct sufficient to pass the *wazîfa* or allowance, if hereditary, to the children of the *wazîfadar.*"(4) Upon this principle, the insolvency of the *wazîfadar* would lead to the same result.

If a person, who is allowed to reside in the *hujra* or a room of the mosque either in lieu of his services or in addition to his salary, lets it without permission of the *mutwalli,* he renders himself liable to dismissal.

Beneficiaries can not assign their interest.

When an allowance is fixed for a person in the *wakfnâmah* and it is declared that upon his death such allowance shall go to another, if the person for whom the allowance is fixed assigns his interest to a third person, upon the decease of the original beneficiary, the allowance shall go to the person appointed by the *wâkif,* and not to the assignee of the original beneficiary.(5)

No beneficiary is entitled to substitute another in his place, but he may appoint another person to receive his allowance.(6)

A student who has been absent for three months may not be deprived of his room and allowance on account of his absence alone.

In the *Ashbâh* it is laid down that if the sovereign himself were to appoint a person as a teacher who is not competent, he may be removed, *for the act of the Sultan must not be unreasonable or improper.* "A king appointing an incompetent person," says the

(1) *Radd-ul-Muhtâr,* Vol. III, p. 636.

(2) *Ibid,* 597.

(3) *Sarkum Abu Torab Abdul Waheb* v. *Rahaman Buksh* [1896], I. L., 24 Cal., 83.

(4) *Radd-ul-Muhtâr,* Vol. III, p. 597.

(5) *Ibid.*

(6) *Ibid.*

Bazâziah, "does two wrongs, *first,* that by appointing an incompetent person, he does an injustice to a competent person; and, *secondly,* that he does an injustice to the public by appointing one who was not entitled to the office."

"In the *Fath-ul-Kadîr* it is laid down that when a *mutwalli* becomes totally insane, and the insanity lasts for a year, he will become discharged of himself; but when he recovers, he will get back the *towliat.* The *Nahr* says on this point, that, he will get back the appointment only in case the *mutwalli* is one who holds the appointment by virtue of the provisions of the deed of *wakf;* but this rule does not apply to a *mutwalli* appointed by the Kâzi." In other words insanity will lead to his removal, and he will not get back the post on recovery.

"A *mutwalli* who is trustworthy and has not been proved to be guilty of any fault, cannot be removed even by the Sultan."

"When a *mutwalli* has been lawfully appointed by the Kâzi and subsequent thereto the Sultan appoints another, the former appointment will take effect and not the latter."

"If the *wâkif* has empowered the *mutwalli* to appoint a successor, the Kâzi has no power to interfere with an appointment made in virtue of that authority, and the *fatwa* is on this."

"In the Book on *Wakf* by Nâsihi it is stated that where a *wakf* is created in favour of a body of people, and the *mutwalli* does not or cannot fulfil the provisions made by the *wâkif* for the benefit of the *cestuis qui trustent,* he ought to be removed and another appointed in his place."(1)

Powers of the *wâkif's* descendants.

In the absence of a *mutwalli,* the power of nomination and appointment of an *imâm* and *muezzin* to a mosque, is given to the *wâkif's* descendants and the members of his family preferentially to others. This is the view stated in the *Ashbâh.*

In the matter of building and repairing a mosque the person who has erected the mosque and his descendants, are preferred to the congregation or outsiders. This is according to the *Anf'aa-ul-Wasâil.*

---

(1) The author adds that if the *mutwalli* is addicted to *alchemy,* that is a desire to convert a baser metal into gold he should be removed, for this avarice might lead to breach of trust. Generally, the purport of this passage is that if the *mutwalli* is given to gambling or habits of a kind which might be prejudicial to the interests of the *wakf* he should be removed.

If the *wâkif* makes a condition that the administration should devolve on " the most intelligent " (رشد) it implies the most intelligent among his descendants; and according to a *Fatwa* of Moulâna Abû S'aûd, if there are two of them equally intelligent, both should be associated together in the office. In the *Nahr*,(1) however it is stated from the *As'aâf* that if the *wâkif* has declared that the *towliat* should be for the most qualified (فضل) among his children, and there are two equally qualified, the *towliat* shall go to the one who is the oldest in age, and in this there will be no distinction of sex. And if among the two, one is very pious and the other is best acquainted with the affairs of the *wakf* and its management, the *towliat* should be given to the latter, if he is trustworthy. The author of the *Radd-ul-Muhtâr* adds that the *dictum* in the *Nahr* particularises the view of Abû S'aûd, for it declares that when excellence is required to be joined with intelligence, and there are two equally intelligent and virtuous, regard is to be paid to age. And according to the *Bahr* (after the *Zahîria*) if all the descendants are equal in integrity and piety, in learning and uprightness and age, the one who is best acquainted with the affairs of the *wakf* and is most capable of discharging the duties connected with the trust, whether male or female, is to be preferred. According to the *Bahr*, *rushd* or intelligence refers to the ability to perform the work and honestly to discharge the duties of the office.(2) In the *As'aâf* also it is stated that when two of the descendants are equally qualified, so far as the qualities of the mind are concerned, the *towliat* will go according to seniority; and the fact that one is a male and the other a female will make no difference. But the person best acquainted with the business of the *wakf* will be preferred, though in the *Fatâwa-'l-Ismailia* there is a *dictum* to the effect that where two people are equally qualified in all respects a male is to be preferred to a female.(3)

Competency in the person to be appointed.

---

(1) *Nâhr-ul-Fâik.* (2) *Radd-ul-Muhtâr*, Vol. III, p. 666.

(3) In the case of *Wahed Ali* v. *Ashruf Hossain* [1882] (I. L., 8 Cal., 732; s. c., 10 C. L. R., 529), the Calcutta High Court has held that " the office of a *mutwalli* is a trust which a woman, equally with a man, is capable of undertaking, but it is a personal trust, and the office may not be transferred, nor the endowed property, to any person whom the *mutwalli* for the time being may select," unless, as already stated, the *wâkif* has vested the *mutwalli* with general powers of appointing another in his stead; see also *Piran* v. *Abdul Karim, infra.* But although a woman may become a *mutwalli* and discharge the duties connected with the office by a deputy, it has been held by the Madras High Court in *Muja-*

When the *wâkif* declares that the *towliat* should be vested in the "fittest" among his children, and there is no fit person to be found among them, the Kâzi has the power to appoint a stranger to the office until such time as a proper person among the *wâkif's* descendants can be found. If among the children there is a properly qualified person and he is absent, and there is no one else among them to take his place until his return, the Kâzi has the power to appoint a stranger to be his substitute until he returns to take up the office. If there are two children, one more qualified than the other, the one who is the fitter of the two should take the office, and after him should come the other.(1)

The words *nâzir*, *kyyum* and *mutwalli* used separately, convey one and the same meaning, *viz.*, the administrator of a trust. But it often happens that at the time of appointing a *mutwalli*, the *wâkif* also appoints a *nâzir* or a supervisor over the *mutwalli*. The *nâzir*, however, has no power to spend any portion of the money of the *wakf*, for that work is entrusted to the *mutwalli*; his duties are simply of a controlling and supervising character, and the *mutwalli* cannot make disbursements, without the knowledge or permission of the *nâzir*. The same principle applies to a *nâzir* appointed over an executor; as a matter of fact, the principles which apply to the duties of *mutwallis* and *nâzirs* in the case of *wakfs* are taken from the principles of the law relating to the duties of executors.

The powers of the *Nâzir*.

The builder of a mosque is the person who has a preferential title to appoint the officers, such as *imâm*, *muezzin*, &c., for the service thereof, and this is the approved doctrine. If the person appointed by the *wâkif* is incompetent or unfit, the congregation have a right to select a more fit person. Will their appointment, however, take effect without the sanction of the Kâzi? I take it that an application should have to be made to the Kâzi for the removal of the incompetent servitor and the appointment of the person selected by the congregation.

In a case where the plaintiff as the *de facto sajjâdanashîn* of a *durgah* sued to recover possession of certain property alleged

---

war Ibram Bibi v. *Mujawar Hossain Sheriff*, I. L., 3 Mad., 95, that she is not competent to perform the duties of a *mujâvir* of a *durgah* which are not of a secular nature; see also *Hussaini Bibee* v. *Hussain Shariff*, 4 Mad. H. C. Reports, 23.

(1) *Radd-ul-Muhtâr*, Vol. III, p. 666; the same principles are given in the *Fatâwa-'l-Ankariwia*, &c. Fitness includes piety says the *Fusûl-i-Imâdia*.

by him to have been improperly alienated by his predecessor, and it was contended by the defendant that the plaintiff was not entitled to maintain the action as he was not appointed either by the last incumbent or the Kâzi, and his appointment was invalid, it appeared that he had been installed in office by a large body of Mussulmans including the disciples and *sajjâdanashîns* of neighbouring shrines. The Calcutta High Court held that the appointment was valid, being in accordance with the Mahommedan law as also the general practice.(1)

Property purchased by the *mutwalli* out of the *wakf* funds becomes *wakf* without any express declaration, subject to the same conditions as the original trust-property. But it may be sold or exchanged for some other property, in case there is any need for it, and such other property, would be *wakf* similarly.

The stipends of the servitors and students.

The salaries of the *imâm*, *khatîb*, *muezzin*, &c., which have already become due, will be paid on the death of any one of them to their heirs. In the case of a *wakf* in favour of children, the heirs of the deceased beneficiaries are entitled to share in the rents and profits, which have been realised and are therefore distributable, or which are accruing.

If a student absents himself from the Madrassa, he does not lose his former allowance which has already accrued due, nor his future allowance, "if he has absented himself in the pursuit of learning (with the permission of his master without severing his connection with his *madrassa*), or has been absent for fifteen days only on lawful grounds, that is, in search of livelihood ; or has gone on *hajj*, but has not been away for more than three months."

Leave is allowed to the servitors of a *wakf* on lawful grounds, and they do not lose their allowance whilst on leave unless a deputy is appointed to officiate for them during their absence.

The Kâzi has no power to fix allowances not provided for by the *wâkif*, but he can determine the amount of the allowances provided for by the *wâkif*. If there is a provision that the *mutwalli* should fix the amount, the Kâzi has no power. The Khair ur-Ramli has stated in his commentary on the *Bahr*, that the restriction on the powers of the Kâzi refers to a case where the *wâkif* has expressly stated that the *wakf* is not public in its nature, and the Kâzi shall have no authority over it. "This, of course, refers to *wakfs*

(1) *Piran* v. *Abdul Karim* [1891], I. L., 19 Cal., 203, *supra*.

created by private individuals. Royal *wakfs* are clearly subject to the jurisdiction of the Kâzi."

In fixing the salary of the *mutwalli*, regard should be paid by the Kâzi to the customary allowance at the time.

In the *Durr-ul-Mukhtar* it is stated that "by the tenth to the *mutwalli* the customary allowance is meant "(العشر للمتولي اجر المثل المراد من). On this passage the comment in the *Radd-ul-Muhtâr* is as follows :—" Some jurists have explained that the allowance (or remuneration) which should be given to the *mutwalli* is a tenth [of the net income], but the correct view is that the tenth (عشر) means اجرالمثل (customary remuneration, *lit.* remuneration of his like) so that if what is customary is more than the tenth, he should receive it ;" *viz.*, that the remuneration should be fixed on that basis. In other words, the customary remuneration would be the standard for fixing the allowance of the *mutwalli*, but generally speaking it should not exceed the one-tenth of the income. But this rule restricting the remuneration ordinarily to one-tenth of the income does not apply to cases where the *mutwalli* or *sajjâdanashîn* has a beneficial interest in the income of the endowed properties.(1)

The *wâkif* can fix any amount for stipend.

Of course, the *wâkif* can fix any amount, and even if it be more than one-tenth it would be valid ; but if he fixes too low a sum, the Kâzi has the power upon the application of the *mutwalli* to fix a proper salary.

Powers of the Judge to increase the salaries of officers.

The *mutwalli* has no power to increase the allowance of the *imâm* or *khatîb*. The Kâzi has the power to increase the allowance, provided in his discretion it is necessary to do so for the benefit of the mosque, or when it is impossible to obtain a proper man to discharge the duties on account of the low salary fixed by the *wâkif*. And this principle applies to the appointment of every servant, *e.g.*, a *muezzin*, *mudarris* (teacher), &c. If these men cannot be had on the salaries fixed by the *wâkif*, the Judge has the power of increasing their salaries from the balance of the fund. The Kâzi has also the power of making provisions regarding the application of the balance

(1) *Mohiuddin* v. *Sayiduddin* alias *Nawab Meah* [1890], I. L., 20 Cal., 810. In the *Secretary of State for India* v. *Mohiuddin Ahmad* [1900], I. L., 27 Cal., 674, it was held that the *Sajjadanashin* was not liable to income-tax in respect of such moneys as he draws from the *Khankâh* properties for his own maintenance and that of his family.

of the income, in consultation with the members of the *wâkif's* family or the beneficiaries.

If a person is appointed *mutwalli*, and he acknowledges another to be the *mutwalli* instead of himself, the latter will be entitled only to a share in the income of the acknowledgor during his lifetime. Upon the death of the acknowledgor the effect of the acknowledgment ceases, and the *towliat* goes with all its adjuncts to the person designated by the *wâkif*.

The *mutwalli* cannot encumber *wakf* property.

The *mutwalli* is not entitled under any circumstance to create any incumbrance by way of mortgage upon the *wakf* property without the sanction of the Kâzi, nor can the beneficiaries hypothecate the *wakf* property. Accordingly, if the *mutwalli* mortgages the *wakf* property and the mortgagee takes possession of the same, he will be liable for the customary rent thereof.

In the same way, if a *mutwalli* sells certain *wakf* lands, and subsequently the sale is set aside by the Kâzi, the purchaser, if he takes possession of the said lands, will be liable for mesne profits, calculated upon the customary rates.

"If a *mutwalli* were to mortgage a *wakf* property, his act would amount to a breach of trust and he ought to be removed. The mortgagee should not take possession of the property mortgaged to him, and if he does so he will be liable for damages."

"In the *Kinia* it is laid down that it is not lawful for the *mutwalli* to borrow for the purposes of the *wakf* even in case of necessity without leave of the Kâzi. If he is away from the Kâzi, he must borrow on his own credit. So also in the *Khazânat-ul-Muftiin*."(1)

"In the *Ashbâh-wan-Nazâir* it is stated that the Sâhib-ul-Manah [*i.e.*, the author of the *Manah*] was asked regarding a *nâzir* (*i.e.*, *mutwalli*) who had borrowed money on the *wakf* property and spent it over the beneficiaries (*lit.*, those deriving sustenance from it), and he had been since dismissed, and the debts were still due, whether the second *mutwalli* was bound to pay such debts out of the *wakf* property. The Sâhib-ul-Manah answered that a *mutwalli* has no power to borrow money to spend on the beneficiaries; but he can for necessities, such as repairs and such like matters, borrow with the leave of the Kâzi. . . . And, therefore, the dismissed *mutwalli* will be liable (personally) for the debts contracted and not the *wakf* property."(2)

(1) *Surrut-ul-Fatâwa*, p. 436. (2) *Surrut-ul-Fatâwa*, p. 440.

Similarly, in the *Radd-ul-Muhtâr*;—a *mutwalli* cannot contract debts for the *wakf* unless they are made in consequence or in pursuance of the directions given by the *wâkif*. The *mutwalli* cannot create any charge on the *wakf* estate or incur liabilities for which the *wakf* estate might be liable, unless such charge is created or debt is incurred under express powers given by the *wâkif*. This restriction does not apply to the powers of the executor, for it is lawful for him to contract debts for the necessaries of the minors confided to his charge, and the infant and his estate would be liable for such debts as are incurred *bonâ fide* by the executor for the infant. But the *wakf* cannot under any circumstance, in the absence of a provision in the *wakfnâmah* to that effect, be made liable for any debt contracted by the *mutwalli* on his own responsibility. A debt contracted by the *mutwalli* is his personal debt. Should it become necessary to incur a debt for the *wakf* or to create a charge on the estate, the *mutwalli* can only do so with the sanction of the Kâzi previously obtained.(1) This principle does not refer to such debts which owing to the exigencies of society, must necessarily be contracted from day to day for the due discharge of the work of the trust; for example, a debt to the oilman for the oil to light the mosque, to the baker to supply bread for the students of a *madrassa*; all these can only be paid at periodical intervals. Such necessary debts must be paid out of the income of the *wakf*.

Debts contracted by the *mutwalli*.

Section III.

Powers of the Mutwalli.

If the *mutwalli* has advanced money to the *wakf* estate for the purpose of protecting the interests of the *wakf*, he can repay himself out of the profits of the *wakf* property coming into his hands. But when the *mutwalli* has any claim against the *wakf* estate for advances made by himself, he has to establish such claim by valid proof, otherwise it will not be maintainable. The *mutwalli* is, therefore, bound to keep clear and distinct accounts of his expenses with vouchers and other proofs; in which case a claim for any credit given by the *mutwalli* to the *wakf* would be maintainable, and such advances will be liquidated out of the rents and profits of the *wakf*

(1) *Radd-ul-Muhtâr*, Vol. III, p. 649. According to Abû Lais: See *seq.* On The Creation of Incumbrances on Wakf Property.

property. But the *wakf* estate cannot be *charged* with any debt either to the *mutwalli* or anybody else, without the sanction of the Kâzi previously obtained.

It is lawful for a *mutwalli* with the income of a *wakf* to erect shops, houses, &c., which may yield profit to the *wakf*, as all this is for the benefit of the *wakf*. All properties purchased by the *mutwalli* out of the proceeds of the *wakf* become part of the *wakf* and are subject to the same legal incidents as the original *wakf* estate. And the *mutwalli* will not be entitled to dispose of them without the sanction of the Kâzi.

If the rules laid down by the *wâkif* are not ascertainable, *mutwalli* must follow the practice of his predecessor.

If the directions of the *wâkif*, or the rules for the administration of the trust cannot be ascertained, the *mutwalli* should ascertain the practice of his predecessors and act accordingly. The *mutwalli* is not entitled to undertake any expenditure utterly inconsistent with the original character of the *wakf*, for example, a *mutwalli* of a mosque is not entitled to purchase cloth from the funds of the mosque and distribute the same among the poor ; and if he does so, he will be liable to pay the money from his own pocket.

If a *mutwalli* contracts a debt for the purchase of necessary articles for the mosque, when there is no money of the mosque in hand, in other words, if he has purchased goods for the *wakf* intending to pay for the same on realising the rents thereof, or if he has paid for the same from his own pocket, he is entitled to pay the debt when the rents come into his hands or recoup himself as the case may be.

If a person find a " trove " belonging to the *wakf*, the *mutwalli* may give something out of the same to the finder if he is poor

If some portion of the building of the *wakf* is so dilapidated as to endanger the safety of others, and the neighbours insist upon the *mutwalli* repairing the same, and it happens that the *mutwalli* has no funds wherewith to repair the building, he can, with the permission of the Kâzi, contract a debt for that purpose. Debts can be incurred by the *mutwalli* only when there are no *wakf* funds in his hands to meet the requirements of the *wakf*. The *mutwalli* is authorised to deduct from the *wakf* income any sums spent by him legitimately for the purposes of the *wakf* out of his own pocket.

If a person make a *wakf* of his lands for the poor, without specifically providing for the cost of repairs or cultivation, the income will nevertheless be first employed in paying the *kharâj* or tax, and then for the payment of the cost of collection, maintenance, repair, cultivation and such like matters, and the residue (after defraying the said costs) will be applied for the poor, *e.g.*, if the *wākf* consists of lands covered with date-trees, the *mutwalli* should first pay the expense of planting new date-trees and keeping up the old ones, for making walls and dams, so that the fruit-trees may not be exhausted or killed. If any portion of the land dedicated is unculturable, the *mutwalli* should take from the income the expense of rendering it fertile. If barns for storing grain, or reservoirs for storing water be necessary for the irrigation of the lands, the *mutwalli* is entitled to spend a portion of the income for that purpose. If the *wakf* land is contiguous to the city, and it is more profitable for the *wakf* that it should be let to tenants than be used for cultivation, the *mutwalli* may erect buildings for tenants or let the land to them without the buildings.(1)

Mohammed says, that if the *wakf* lands become unculturable and cease to yield any income, and the *mutwalli* can, with its price, get another piece of land yielding more profit, it is proper that he should do so; that is, he should [with the requisite permission,] sell the land and with its price buy another piece. But if the land is far away from towns, so that buildings will not yield any profit, he may not erect buildings. Abû J'aafar has held that when the *wâkif* has made no provision regarding the mode in which the land should be used, the *mutwalli* is authorised to use the land to the best advantage for the *cestui qui trust*, but he cannot give a long lease without the sanction of the Kâzi.

Discretionary trusts.

If a man were to make a *wakf* of some property and declare that the *mutwalli* may give the income thereof to whomsoever he likes, or may apply the proceeds thereof according to his discretion, it is lawful,—and the *mutwalli* may give it to both rich and poor. Though in the case of these discretionary trusts, the administration of the *wakf* is left to the discretion of the trustee, still "the power is accompanied with a duty and meant to be exercised," and the Kâzi will compel the *mutwalli* to apply the income properly.

Mode of disbursement when proof of custom wanting.

"In the *Manah* it is stated from the Jurist Zain ibn Nujaim that where there is an old existing *wakf*, but its deed is lost and the *mutwalli* is unable to find out the mode in which the produce

(1) *Fatâwai Kâzi Khân*, Vol. IV, p. 216.

should be spent on the beneficiaries, he should ascertain the usage of his predecessors and how they made the application, and proceed in accordance therewith."(1)

If there is no proof forthcoming as to who are entitled to the benefit of a *wakf*, or as to the mode of disbursement followed by the *mutwallis* of former times, the *wakf* should be applied for the benefit of the poor.

In the *Anf'aa-ul-Wasâil* it is stated from the *Zakhîra* that where there is an old existing *wakf*, but the person dedicating it is not known, and some person is in possession of it under the title of being *mutwalli* and he asserts that the *wakf* in question is for a particular purpose, and he produces witnesses in support of his assertion, and there is no proof to the contrary, that assertion will be accepted. But when the purpose is known or the conditions laid down by the *wâkif* are ascertainable, such testimony will not be admitted.(2)

"A *wakf*" says the *Radd ul-Muhtâr* "may be established without any evidence of the *wâkif's* declaration. This is the doctrine laid down by Abû Yusuf; and the jurists of Balkh, such as Abû J'aafar and others, follow this view; Khassâf also has adopted it. In the *Khairiyéh*, it is stated that where there is an old *wakf*, known by reputation to be *wakf* and the *wâkif* is unknown, should a wrongdoer get possession of it, the *mutwalli* can establish his claim, according to the approved doctrine, by the testimony of two witnesses; and the *Jâm'aa-ul-Fusûlain* has followed this view."(3)

Evidence of reputation may establish a *wakf*.

So also in the *Fatâwai Kâzi Khân*: a *wakf* may, according to the jurists of Balkh, be validly established by evidence of reputation. If the dedication is one within the knowledge of the general public, as a matter of notoriety, "like the *wakf* of 'Amr ibn al-'Aâs" (the Amru of European history), it can be established by the testimony of witnesses, or it may be established by the evidence of user for the purposes of dedication.

It is not necessary that the endowment should be in writing, or that the property should be delivered over. A verbal declaration of the intention to create an endowment is sufficient if made in the

(1) *Surrat-ul-Fatâwa*, p. 442.

(2) *Ibid.*

(3) *Radd-ul-Muhtâr*, Vol. III, p. 645.

presence of witnesses.(1) Although the witnesses to the fact depose vaguely, yet their evidence, if corroborated by circumstances, is legally sufficient.(2)

The *wakf* of a property which is wrongly described in the *wakfnâmah is operative*, if it is clear what was intended to be conveyed in trust. If the description, however, is so uncertain and indefinite as to render it impossible to find out what was intended to be conveyed, the *wakf* will not take effect.

"The Sâhib-ul-Manah was asked the following question with reference to the effect to be given to a *wakf*: A man makes a *wakf* in favour of the poor and indigent and executes a deed of *wakf* properly sealed and signed and attested. After his death a number of people testify to the effect that the ultimate purpose was destined [by the *wâkif*] for a specified purpose (and not for the poor). Will such testimony be accepted and acted upon? The Sâhib-ul-Manah answered—'If the deed of *wakf* purports to be prior in date to the condition alleged by the witnesses no effect should be given to such testimony. But if the *wâkif* had reserved to himself in the *wakfnâmah* the power of altering and cutting down the terms, then regard is to be paid to the credibility of the witnesses.'"(3)

A person makes a *wakf* for the habitation of his *wife* in the *wakf* building, and then dies. The widow afterwards re-marries. She loses her right of habitation, and even if the second husband divorces her, she does not recover the right.

When a house is dedicated for the habitation of certain individuals they cannot partition the dwelling among themselves. But when a dedication is made for the residence of the members of a certain family, only those who are *mahram*(4) to each other may reside in it, unless the dwelling is divided into apartments or rooms with doors, where a female may live with her husband without being subjected to the intrusion of a *ghair-mahram* living in the same house. For example, if a house is dedicated for the

(1) *Doe dem. Jaun Beebee* v. *Abdollah Barber*, supra: *Sharbo Narain Singh* v. *Ally Buksh Shah*, 2 Hay, 415; *Abul Hasan* v. *Haji Mohammad Masih Karbalai*, 5 Sel. Rep., 8. See also *Dalrymple* v. *Khoondkar Azeezul Islam*, S. D. A., 1858, p. 586; *Shoojat Ali* v. *Zumeer-ooddeen* [1865]. 5 W. R., 158.

(2) *Surrat-ul-Fatâwa*, p. 424.

(3) *Radd-ul-Muhtâr*, Vol. III, p. 650.

(4) People within the prohibited degrees.

residence of a family consisting of two married sons and two married daughters, in order that the husbands of the married daughters may be able to live in the same house, there must be separate rooms set apart for the sons and daughters respectively.

Case Law. Breach of trust does not alter the nature of the trust.

A breach of trust on the part of the *mutwalli* cannot alter the essential nature of the trust, or convert endowed property into the personal property of the manager (1) A grant should be construed according to the intention of the founder, and not according to the strict interpretation of any particular word: the word "inam" being indiscriminately applied to personal grants and religious endowments.(2)

A religious office.

Under the Mahommedan Law a religious office cannot be claimed by right of inheritance. Where a grant has been made for the maintenance of a religious office the members of the grantee's family have no right at his death to a division amongst them of the income derivable from the land. The right to the income of such land is inseparable from the office for the support of which the land was granted.(3) They may, however, under the provisions of the grant be entitled to maintenance out of the income.

Succession to the management of an endowment.

Where property has been devoted by a Mahommedan to religious and charitable purposes, the determination of the question of succession depends upon the rules laid down by the *wâkif* on the constitution of the *wakf* whether such rules are embodied in writing or are to be inferred from evidence of usage. Where the custom has always been for the incumbent to appoint a successor, thus indicating the will of the endower on the subject, the Court should not find in favour of any rule of succession by primogeniture solely from the circumstance that the persons appointed were usually the eldest sons.(4)

The Bombay High Court has, in conformity with the Mahommedan Law held that, although a *wâkif* has a right to reserve the management of the *wakf* in his own hands or to appoint some one else thereto, yet when he has specified the class from amongst which the manager is to be selected he cannot afterwards name a person

(1) See *Asheerooddeen alias Kalla Miah* v. *Drobomoyee* [1876], 25 W. R., 557.

(2) *Ibid.*

(3) *Jaafar Mohiuddin Sahib* v. *Aji Mohiuddin Sahib*, 2 Mad., 19.

(4) *Gulam Rahmutulla Sahib* v. *Mohammed Akber Sahib*, 8 Mad., 63. See also *Syed Abdulla Edrus* v. *Syed Zain Sayad Hussan Edrus* [1888], I. L., 13 Bom., 555.

as manager not answering the proper description. After the death of the *wâkif* the right to nominate a manager vests in his executors, or the survivor of them for the time being.(1)

SECTION IV.

THE LEASE OF WAKF PROPERTY.

Lease of *wakf* property.

The limitation with regard to the duration of a lease imposed by the earlier jurists in respect of *wakf* property has been, says the *Radd-ul-Muhtár*,(2) departed from by the moderns (*mutâkherîn*). And the rule now stands in a much more elastic form than when it was first enunciated.

The power of the *mutwalli* to grant leases.

In the *Fâtawai Kâzi Khân*(3) which is one of the earlier authorities, it is stated(4) in substance that "where the *wâkif* has made no provision in the document of *wakf*(5) [about the grant of leases in respect of the *wakf* property] the *mutwalli* has a discretion to do what is proper and to the advantage of the poor(6) [in other words the beneficiaries] subject to the condition that he should not lease a house for a longer term than one year, for a long lease is apt to give rise to the idea that the lessee is the owner. And he may not give a longer lease of land than is necessary for purposes of cultivation. Should the *wâkif* have imposed a condition that the land shall not be leased for more than one year and people are not willing to take such a short lease, and it is to the advantage of the beneficiaries to lease the property for a longer period, the *kyyum* (the *mutwalli*) cannot act contrary to the condition in the *wakf* and give a longer lease unless he submits the matter before the Kâzi who can sanction a longer lease on the ground that it is to the advantage of the *wakf*, for the Kâzi is the supervisor over [the interests of] the poor, the absent and deceased persons."

"And should the *wâkif* have provided in the document of *wakf* that the *mutwalli* shall not grant a lease for more than a year un-

---

(1) *The Advocate-General* v. *Fatima Sultani Begum*, supra.

(2) Vol. III, p. 614.

(3) Vol. IV, p. 273.

(4) On the authority of the Jurist Abû J'aafar.

(5) *Sikk-ul-wâkf*.

(6) This is explained in the *Radd-ul-Muhtâr*, as applicable to all beneficiaries, see *post*.

less it is for the advantage of the poor [the beneficiaries], in which case he [the *mutwalli*) may do so himself [*i.e.*, of his own authority] if he considers it expedient, and it does not require being taken to the Court of the Kâzi, for the *wâkif* has [already] given him the power."

"In case the *mutwalli* has created a lease for five years,(1) Shaikh Abu'l Kasim of Balkh has declared that it would not be valid over a year unless some need has arisen for expediting the rent;(2) but says the jurist Abû Bakr Mohamed bin al-Fazl that he does not consider such a lease should be held to be void, but the *Hâkim* (Judge) should take note of it and if it is to the injury of the *wakf* he should cancel it."

"Abu'l Hassan Ali as-Sugdi has expressed the same view. And it is stated from the Jurist Abû Lais that where the *wâkif* had imposed no condition against a lease being granted for more than a year, he permitted it to be given for three years irrespective of the question whether the property was house or land. It is reported from Imâm Abû Hafs Bokhari that he permitted the lease of land for thee years. But there is a difference of opinion regarding [the effect of] a lease for more than three years; the majority of the jurists of Balkh have held that such a lease is not valid, whilst others have declared that it is to be submitted to the Kâzi so that he may cancel it and this doctrine the Jurist Abû Lais has adopted."(3)

In the *Durr-ul-Mukhtar*(4) the rule is given in a more compendious form. "Any condition imposed by the *wâkif* regarding the leasing of *wakf* property must be followed and the *kyyum* (*mutwalli*) cannot act contrary to it, but the Kâzi may, for to him appertains the supervision over the interests of the poor, the absent and deceased people. So where the *wâkif* has left indeterminate the period for which a *wakf* property may be leased, some (jurists) have said the *kyyum* has a general discretion as to the length of the term; whilst others have said the limit should be one year in

(1) This assumes, I take it, that the power of leasing is reserved in the deed of *wâkf*.

(2) *T'aajil-ul-ujrat*, evidently meaning that the whole rent for the period is paid in advance.

(3) *Fatawâi Kâzi Khân*, Vol. IV, pp. 273-4.

(4) P. 418.

all cases. And the *fatwa* (1) is with regard to a year for [the lease of] houses and three years in respect of land unless expediency is opposed to this, and expediency varies according to time and locality."(2)

The author of the *Radd-ul-Muhtâr* in commenting on the above passage makes an important statement on the authority of the *Fatâwai Kâri-ul-Hedâya*, "when the repairs of the *wakf* premises cannot be effected without letting [some portion of] it, the matter must be placed before the Judge who can direct the grant of a lease long enough for that purpose."(3)

If the *wâkif* has made a condition that no lease shall be granted for more than one year, and it appears that a longer lease is good for the trust-estate, in that case, as already stated, the *mutwalli* should apply for leave to the Kâzi to grant a longer lease and should act according to the Kâzi's directions.

Similarly, where the *wâkif* has made a condition that the *mutwalli* shall not grant a long lease of the *wakf*, and people are not willing to take a short lease thereof, and it is to the advantage of the *wakf* that a long lease should be given, the *mutwalli* should prefer the matter before the Kâzi, who, if he deems necessary, can make an order to that effect, "for the Kâzi is the guardian of the poor." If the *wâkif* has made a condition that the *mutwalli* shall not grant a long lease unless he deems that it would be productive of great benefit to the *cestui qui trust*, the *mutwalli* can give the lease in case of necessity, without reference to the Kâzi.(4)

Discretion of the Kâzi.

Thus the Kâzi, as the general superintendent of all charities, in his capacity of the representative of the Sultan, has the power of empowering the *mutwalli* to grant leases for a longer period than provided for by the *wâkif*. But where the *wâkif* has given no directions he can authorise the grant of a lease for any term which may, in his discretion, be advantageous to the *wakf*.(5)

Jurisdiction of the Civil Courts.

The principal court of original civil jurisdiction under the British Government in India, is vested, generally speaking, with

(1) *I.e.*, Decrees are made in accordance with this view.

(2) *Durr-ul-Mukhtâr*, p. 418.

(3) Vol. III, p. 614.

(4) *Hedâya*, Vol. II, p. 888; *Fath-ul-Kadir*, Vol. II, p. 6; *Ramz-ul-Hakâik*; *Fatâwai Alamgiri*, Vol. II, p. 641.

(5) "The Kâzi is the curator and guardian of the interests of persons who are dead or absent or unborn, of the poor, the indigent, as well as the custodian of the property of a deceased person and of things which are picked up."

the powers exercised by the Kâzi, though in a recent case(1) the Calcutta High Court has extended the power to the Court of a Subordinate Judge.(2) Accordingly, the application for sanction should be made to the District Judge, if the property is situated in the mofussil, or to the Judge on the Original Side of the High Court, if it is within a Presidency town. It is not necessary to bring a suit for obtaining such sanction; it will be granted upon a proper application made by the *mutwalli*. If there are *Nâzirs*, their consent should be obtained as a condition precedent to the application.(3) If the *wakf* is of a public nature, notice should be given to the beneficiaries in any mode the Judge directs, either by advertisements in newspapers or by posting it up at the institution to which the *wakf* property belongs.(4)

Where the trustees of a certain mosque without obtaining the sanction of the Judge sold the lands in dispute, which formed part of the trust-property, to the plaintiffs in order to raise money to meet the expenses of litigation and the repair of the mosque, it has been held that the sale was not merely voidable but void.(5)

As the Indian Trustees' Act (XXVII of 1866), and the Trustees' and Mortgagees' Powers Act (XXVIII of 1866), are not applicable to Mahommedans, the following additional rules need attention.

" If an executor or guardian leases the property belonging to his ward without the proper customary rent, or if a *mutwalli* acts in that manner in respect of *wakf* property, in all such cases, according to the illustrious Imâm Abû Bakr Mohammed bin Fazl, the lessee will be regarded as a *ghâsib* (embezzler); but Khassâf

---

(1) *Nimai Chand Addya* v. *Golam Hossein* [1909], I. L., 37 Cal., 179.

(2) *Shama Churn Roy* v. *Abdul Kabeer* [1898], 3 Cal. W. N., 158; *In the matter of Woozatunnessa Bibee* [1908], I. L., 36 Cal., 211. The Mussulman Jurists themselves restrict this jurisdiction to the Chief Kâzi (the Kâzi-ul-Kuzzât). For example, it is stated that the power of sanctioning alteration of investments or change of *wakf* property, granting longer leases than ordinarily allowed by law or provided for in the *wakfnâmah* and similar acts is vested only in the Chief Kâzi.

(3) In the matter of the Act XXVII and Act XXVIII of 1866, and in the matter of a *wakfnâmah*, dated the 30th of May 1896, before Stephen, J., 14th and 25th August, 1902 Calcutta.

(4) *Ibid.*

(5) *Shama Churn Roy* v. *Abdul Kabeer*, supra. For the liability of the superintendent of a mosque and board of directors respectively, see the *Advocate-General of Bombay* v. *Abdul Kadir Jitaker* [1894], I. L., 18 Bom., 40.

holds that he will not be treated as a wrong-doer, but will be liable for the proper customary rent. And the *Fatwa* is according to this latter view." So also in the *Surrat-ul-Fatâwa* ; " If a *mutwalli* leases a *wakf* property for below its real rent, the tenant will be liable to pay the proper rent (*ujr-ul-misl*, customary rent), and on this is the *Fatwa*."(1)

A lease given by a *mutwalli* is not cancelled by his death.

The lessee of *wakf* properties can plant trees or make erections on the land leased to him, provided such act does not in any way injuriously affect the property, but he cannot dig a reservoir or tank ; even the *mutwalli's* permission would justify his doing only such acts as are beneficial to the trust-property.(2)

The lessee of a *wakf* property.

The lessee can remove such erections as he has built with his own money, provided their removal does not damage the property. If it does, the lessee will not be entitled to remove such erections.

Regarding erections on *wakf* lands, the following rules are applicable :—

" If the *mutwalli* of the *wakf* erects the building, with the property of the *wakf* or the income of the trust-property, the building becomes the property of the *wakf*, whether the erection be for the *wakf* or for himself, or whether it was erected generally without any specific purpose. If the erection was made with his own money or materials for the *wakf*, or *generally*, then also it belongs to the *wakf* property, unless the *wâkif* himself is the *mutwalli* and the erection is made without any expressed purpose, in which case it remains his property, as is stated in the *Zâkhira*. If the *mutwalli* erects the building with his own money *for his own especial purpose and keeps evidence of the fact that it is erected for such purpose out of his own funds*, it will remain his property, and this is what is stated in the *Kinia* and *Mujtaba*."

When a person, other than the *mutwalli*, erects a building on *wakf* property, for the use of the *wakf* (though temporarily and with the object of taking it back), if the erection is made with the permission of the *mutwalli*, it becomes *wakf*. The same is also the case when the erection is made without the *mutwalli's* permission, but for the use of the *wakf* ; but, where the building is erected for

---

(1) *Surrat-ul-Fatâwa*, p. 436. (2) *Radd-ul-Muhtâr*, Vol. III, p. 616.

the private purposes of the person erecting it, or where it is made generally without any expressed object, it will be lawful for him to remove it, provided no loss accrues to the *wakf* property in the removal. In the *Fatâwai Kâzi Khân*, it is stated that if a person were to plant trees in a mosque they become the property of the mosque. If a *mutwalli* were to lease the *wakf* lands to his father or son,(1) it would not be valid unless the rent is higher than is usually current, as in the case of an executor, who cannot sell the property of a minor unless at a higher price.

"In the Chapter on *Wakf* in the *Manah* it is stated, that where a man has dedicated a house in favour of his children in perpetuity so long as his posterity lasts, and one of his sons gives a long lease of it to another, and that person under colour of that lease erects a building in the house, if the person giving the lease is not the *mutwalli*, then the lease is void, and the lessee would be entitled to recover from him any money spent on the premises. If the person granting the lease is the *mutwalli* then the lessee would be liable to pay the *proper* rent for such period as the Kâzi may fix."

Section V.

The Creation of Incumbrances on Wakf Property (Istadânat.)

When once a dedication has been duly effected, the right of the person making the *wakf* in the property dedicated "drops" absolutely. Thenceforth the property is "tied-up" in the ownership of the Almighty, and nobody has a right to deal with it in any shape—neither the *wâkif*, nor his heirs, nor the beneficiaries under the *wakf*.(2) In other words as *wakf*, all right of proprietorship ceases, and the property cannot be alienated or transferred by sale or gift, nor is it subject to the rights of inheritance.(3)

Alienation of *wakf* property illegal.

(1) The principle includes any relation or connection.

(2) *Fatâwai Alamgiri*, Vol. II, p. 454; *Radd-ul-Muhtâr*, Vol. III, p. 656; *Hedâya*, Vol. II, p. 888; *Fath-ul-Kadîr*, Vol. II, p. 454. "Where property is endowed, that is made *wakf*, by the proprietor and as such devolves on his widow as trustee or *mutwalli*, it cannot be sold in satisfaction of a claim against him"; *Fegredo* v. *Mahomed Mudessur* [1871], 15 W. R., 75.

(3) *Hedâya*, Vol. II, p. 888; *Fatâwai Alamgiri*, Vol. II, p. 454; *Fath-ul-Kadîr*, &c., &c.

A *wakf* made *inter vivos*, that is, which is not dependent for its operation upon the death of the testator, cannot be revoked, nor is it affected by the subsequent misconduct or misdealing of either the *wâkif* himself, or those responsible for carrying out his behests, so as to render the property alienable, or to destroy the character of inalienability impressed on it by the constitution of *wakf*.(1)

As regards the power of borrowing on account of the *wakf* so as to make it liable, the Mussulman Law is absolutely clear and explicit. Once the dedication has been made, neither the *wâkif* nor the *mutwalli* has any power to burden the property in any shape or character unless the founder has expressly reserved authority to the trustee to borrow "for" the *wakf* in cases of emergency. In the absence of any such provision, he can only do so with the sanction of the Judge.

Istadânat or the power of borrowing

The law is thus laid down in the *Fatâwai Kâzi Khân*. "When a demand is made on the *Kyyum* for land-revenue (*Kharâj*) or any other tax (*jabâya*) and he has at the time nothing from the income of the *wakf* (*ghallat-ul-wakf*), the Jurist Abu'l Kâsim says that if the *wâkif* had authori ed him to borrow, it would be lawful for him to do so; but if the *wâkif* had given no such directions and he borrows, he will have to pay it out of his own property and cannot have recourse [for repayment] to the income of the *wakf*."

"And the Jurist Abû Lais (may the peace, etc.), has declared that, in case any contingency arises which compels him to borrow, he must do so with the order of the *hâkim* (the Judge); he can then have recourse to the income, for the Kâzi [alone] has the power of borrowing (*istadânat*) for a *wakf*."

"And Nâtiki has stated that when the *mutwalli* intends to borrow to buy with the money [borrowed] seed for cultivation, if he does it with the order of the Kâzi, it is lawful according to all, for the Kâzi has the power to borrow for a *wakf*, and if he were to authorise the *mutwalli* to borrow, his order would be valid—but the *mutwalli* has no power to contract debts [of his own authority]."(2) * * * * should the *Kyyum* desire to pledge [or mortgage] the [property of the] *wakf* for any debt it would not be valid, for that would be tantamount to an avoidance of the *wakf*.(3) And

(1) *Hed.* Vol. II p. 888.
(2) *Fatâwai Kâzi Khân*, Vol. IV, pp. 217-8.
(3) *T'aatil-ul-wakf* may also be rendered "make the *wakf* useless."

as it is unlawful for the *mutwalli*, so it is unlawful for the *ahl-ul-masjid* (the congregation), [in other words the beneficiaries of the trust].(1) And if the *Kyyum* mortgages a house belonging to the *wakf* and the mortgagee resides in it, the jurists have held that he would be liable for the customary rent whether the house is in a condition to yield a rent or not."(2) And again, " if there be not in the hands of the *Kyyum* any of the income of the *wakf*, he must place the matter before the Kâzi so that he may order the *Kyyum* to borrow on [account of] the *wakf* for its benefit.(3) But the *Kyyum* cannot borrow without the order of the Kâzi. And the meaning of borrowing is that there is no income of the *wakf* [in the hands of the trustee] and hence it is necessary to obtain a loan and incur debts."(4)

The same rule is given in the *Durr-ul-Mukhtâr*.(5) " It is not lawful to borrow and create debts (*istadânat*) on a *wakf* except when it becomes necessary for its benefit such as repairs or for buying seeds for cultivation. In those circumstances it is lawful under two conditions, *viz.*, *first*, the sanction of the Kâzi, but if he is far from the Kâzi, he may borrow of his own authority, and *secondly*, if it be not possible to lease the property and spend the rent thereof (for the required purposes)."

Commenting on the passage in the *Durr-ul-Mukhtâr* " it is not lawful to create a debt (*istadânat*) on the *wakf*," the author of the *Radd-ul-Muhtâr* says as follows :—" that is, if it is not under the directions of the *wâkif*." In other words, if the *wâkif* has *expressly* provided that the *mutwalli* shall have power to borrow on the security of the *wakf* property for the purposes of the *wakf*, the matter is not open to discussion. But when there is no such provision and the *mutwalli* has not been specifically empowered to that effect, his position is different from that of an executor.(6)" If the *mutwalli* contracts debts, he is responsible for them, excepting under certain specified conditions.... Abu'l Lais has stated; and his doctrine is accepted, that when the contracting of the debt is un-

The *Mutwalli* cannot borrow on the *wakf* property except with the sanction of the Judge.

(1) This shows that the beneficiaries of all trusts, under the Mussulman Law, stand on the same footing.

(2) *Ibid*, p. 218.

(3) *Islâh* with a *sdd*.

(4) *Fatâwai Kâzi Khân*, Vol. IV, p. 221.

(5) P. 423, Hooghly Ed.

(6) *Radd-ul-Muhtâr*, Vol. III, p. 640.

avoidable (*i.e.*, there is absolute necessity for it), in that case the *mutwalli* may do so with the sanction of the Kâzi, unless he is far away, for the Kâzi is the general supervisor of the affairs of the Mussulmans. Some have said that the *mutwalli* has absolute discretion in the matter of repairs. But the first doctrine is the one recognised by the (Hanafî) school."

Commenting further on the passage "The first condition is, the sanction of the Kâzi"—the author of the *Radd-ul-Muhtâr* goes on to say—"When the (the *mutwalli*) applies for sanction, obviously it should not be entertained without proof (of necessity]" * * * * "'When it is not possible to give a lease of the property,' here the term lease is general and includes leases both for short and long periods, or made up of successive short periods, so that if there is a possibility of giving a lease there should be no borrowing on the *wakf*."

The same rule is laid down in the *Fath-ul-Kadîr*, the *Bahr-ur-Râik* and other works of authority and is the recognised law.

From these statements two principles are deducible in order to justify the borrowing, *firstly*, that there is an actual necessity for the *wakf* which cannot be otherwise met either from its current income or by leasing the property; and, *secondly*, that the Kâzi after an examination of the evidence in support of the necessity, specially sanctions the contraction of the loan by the *mutwalli*.

As a general rule, therefore, private alienation, temporary or absolute, by mortgage, or otherwise of *wakf* lands, even though for the repair or other benefit of the endowment, is illegal according to the Mussulman Law.(1)

In certain cases of *debutters* made by Hindus it has been held that a mere nominal endowment will not prevent alienation,(2) and the same principle has been attempted to be applied to *wakfs* created

---

(1) *Moulvee Abdulla* v. *M. S. Rajesri Dosea* [1840], 7 Sel. Rep., 268; S. D. A., 1846, p. 266; and see *M. S. Qadira* v. *Shah Kubeer-ood-deen Ahmud*, 3 Sel. Rep., 407; *Abdul Hasan* v. *Haji Mohammad Masih Karbalai*, 5 Sel. Rep., 87; *Kulb Ali Hoosein* v. *Syf Ali*, 2 Sel. Rep., 130; *Moulvee Abdoolla* v. *Ramzoo Dye*, S. D. A., 1847, p. 192; *Jewaun Doss Sahoo* v. *Shah Kubeer-ood-deen* [1840], 2 Moo. I. A., 390; s. c., 6 W. R., 3; *Syud Asbeeruddeen alias Kalla Meah* v. *Sreemutty Drobo Moyee* [1876], 25 W. R., 557, supra; *Doyal Chand Mullick* v. *Syud Keramat Ali* [1871], 16 W. R., p. 116; see also *Shoojat Ali* v. *Zumeerooddin* [1866], 5 W. R., 158.

(2) *Puddo Nundan Burral* v. *Kalee Coomar Ghose*, S. D. A., 1852, p. 331; *Gunga Narain Sircar* v. *Brindabon Chunder Kur Chowdhry*, 3 W. R., p. 142.

Nature of a *wakf.*

by Mahommedans. These attempts have, no doubt, been founded on an erroneous comprehension of the Mahommedan Law. As pointed out already, the word "nominal" like the word "pretended" conveys the idea, that though an endowment is purported to be created, in reality the donor never parts with the property.

Under the Mussulman Law, when an endowment is made in terms, with a full knowledge of the meaning and effect of the word *wakf*, there can be no reservation, or *arrière pensée*. The law *detaches* the proprietary right of the donor from the subject of dedication; and, therefore, once the *wakf* is made in express terms it cannot be said to be a *nominal* dedication under the Mussulman Law.

Grants to an individual in his own right for the purpose of supplying means of subsistence have been held not to be *wakf*. It must however, be remarked that the nature of the grant would be modified by the circumstances of the special case. Where the grant is not absolutely to the grantee, and it appears that it is meant to provide means of subsistence to his descendants, the Mussulman Law will regard it as a valid *wakf*. Again, where the grant is made to a person under the name of *wakf* and no mention is made of any further trust, it will nevertheless be effectual in creating a trust for the poor after the decease of the grantee; and his heirs will have no right of property over the subject of the grant.

In one case it was held by the Calcutta High Court that when a heritable estate was burdened with a trust, *viz*., the keeping up of a saint's tomb, it may be alienated subject to the trust.(1) The judgment itself is extremely meagre, and neither the facts nor the nature of the document appears in the report. It is difficult to imagine the principle on which the learned Judges proceeded. In fact the case does not appear to have been argued before the learned Judges who laid down this far-reaching dictum. The first question in such a case was to consider whether the estate was heritable. If there was an actual dedication as *wakf*, it is submitted it would not be heritable. If there was no express constitution of the estate as *wakf*, but the trust had been created expressly for the purpose of maintaining the saint's tomb, the legal effect was absolutely the same. But if the property had

(1) *Fulton Bibee* v. *Bhurrut Lall Bhukut* [1868], 10 W. R., p. 313.

been treated all along as heritable, in that case *only* the principle laid down, in the case referred to, could apply, and the property could be alienated subject to the trust.

Fultoo Bibi v. Bhurrut Lall Bhukut.

The English doctrine against perpetuity is not recognised by the Mussulman Law; and, accordingly, where a property is burdened with a trust which is ostensibly lasting in its character, such property is considered to be tied up for that purpose, and consequently inalienable and non-heritable. In this connection, the remarks of their Lordships of the Privy Council in *Bishen Chand Basawat* v. *Syed Nadir Hossein*(1) are important.

In the case of *Dalrymple* v. *Khoondkar Azeezul Islam*,(2) the Sudder Court held that if an endowment be wholly *wakf*, a *mutwalli* is incapable of granting a lease extending beyond the period of his own life; if, however, the office is hereditary, and the *mutwalli* has a beneficial interest in the endowment, they would look upon the property as an heritable estate burdened with certain trusts, the proprietary right of which is vested in the *mutwalli* and his heirs, and he can exercise the right possessed by other proprietors, of granting leases even in perpetuity. In this case the document of *wakf* was not before the Court, but apparently the office of *mutwalli* was hereditary, and the members of the family had a beneficial interest in the usufruct. At least the learned Judges assumed it to be so and chose to call the "endowment" a heritable estate burdened with certain trusts. By these expressions they did not mean to exclude the "endowment" from the general category of *wakfs*; they simply expressed, perhaps in somewhat inaccurate terms, the reasons which induced them to hold the lease valid. Whether such an estate is called "a heritable estate burdened with certain trusts," or a *wakf*, the usufruct of which is descendible among the *wâkif's* heirs, the result is the same.

Where the property is dedicated in the first instance for *strictly* religious purposes, the mere charge of certain items which must in time cease, does not render the dedication invalid.(3) Nor does the mere stoppage of religious services start limitation against a *wakf*.(4)

(1) [1887], L. R., 15 I. A., p. 1.
(2) S. D. A., 1858, p. 586.
(3) *Muzhoor-ul-Huq* v. *Puhraj Ditarey Mohaputtur*, 13 W. R., 235.
(4) *Doyal Chand Mullick* v. *Syud Karamat Ali*, supra.

Lands occupied by tombs.

Lands belonging to a Mahommedan, which are occupied by tombs, cannot be sold in execution of a decree.(1) Nor can a *makbara* or burial-ground be alienated, for it is *wakf* from its nature.(2) A general dedication of land for the purpose of a cemetery establishes *wakf*, and excepts the same from descent to the heirs.(3) It has been held, however, that the mere existence of tombs on a piece of land, unless it is constituted into a *makbarà*, does not prohibit partition, except as to the actual spot covered by the tombs.(4)

Where land has been used as a graveyard, although the ownership of the soil may be vested in another, members of the family of the dead who are in the habit of performing certain religious services at their tombs, have a right to obtain an injunction restraining such owner from obstructing them. The ground in which human relics are entered are for ever sacred; the permission to bury in the land, granted as it must be subject to the custom of the people whose dead are buried on the spot, carries with it the right to perform all customary rites.(5)

Where certain *inaam* land, granted for the service of a *masjid*, was attached in satisfaction of a decree obtained by a mortgagee of the property against the descendants of the original grantee who had mortgaged it to him, it was held that by the Mussulman Law the mortgage was illegal and void, as land appropriated to religious purposes could not be sold or mortgaged by any of the descendants of the original proprietor; and the Court agreed that the attachment should be raised.

The Mutwalli has no power of mortgaging the *wakf* property without the sanction of the Judge.

The *mutwalli* may, however, under special circumstances, pledge the *wakf* property either wholly or partially, *with the sanction of the Kâzi*, as previously stated, and may even alienate a portion of the property. But any such act done without the permission of the Kâzi is wholly void and inoperative.

Under the Mussulman Law the authorisation or sanction of the Judge is a condition precedent and the earlier cases in the British Indian Courts have almost invariably given effect to this rule.

(1) S. D. A., Beng. Sum. Cases, p. 40, 21st Novr., 1842.
(2) 5th December, 1846, S. D. A., N.-W. P., p. 250.
(3) 5 S. D. A. Rep. (Beng.), p. 136, 30th July, 1831.
(4) Sel. Rep., 204, Bom. S. A., 1839.
(5) *Ram Narayan Bellary* v. *Rustam Khan* [1901], I. L., 26 Bom., 198.

Moulvee Abdoollah v. Rajesri Dossea and another.

In *Moulvee Abdoollah* v. *Rajesri Dossea and another*,(1) which is the leading case on the subject, the plaintiff (who was the appellant in the Sudder Court) sued as the *mutwalli* of a mosque for the rents of certain lands attached thereto. The defendant, Rajesri Dossea, pleaded that one Mahomed Ufzul, the late superintendent, borrowed from her husband 51 rupees for the repairs of the mosque, and mortgaged to him the rents of 8 cottahs and a tank for three years, providing in the deed of mortgage, dated 9th Jeyt 1219 that the debt was to bear interest at 1 per cent. per mensem for those years, and that at the expiration of three years, if the debt was not paid off, the rent of the 8 cottahs 5 sicca rupees per annum should be sold to him for the debt, and the rent for the tank, or 1 rupee per annum, paid to the superintendent for the expenses of the mosque. She contended that as the debt had been incurred by Mahomed Ufzul for the repairs of the mosque, and the mortgage had not been cleared off, the engagement was binding on his successor, the present plaintiff. The first Court decreed the plaintiff's suit on the ground that the mortgage was created for the benefit of the mosque by the late incumbent and was therefore valid, but it was dismissed by the Lower Appellate Court. On appeal by the plaintiff, the Sudder Court held, in accordance with the *Fatwa* of the Law Officers, that the alienation, by mortgage, of land, devoted to religious purposes, and of the produce of such land, was invalid, and that the fact of the land being mortgaged for the repair or other benefit of the mosque did not affect the case.

Necessity no ground for alienation.

In *Nimai Chand Addya* v. *Golum Hossein*,(2) however the Calcutta High Court has expressed a view in conflict with all the previous decisions. In this case the *mutwalli* had created a mortgage without the sanction of the Judge in order to save the property from a threatened sale by the Collector. The mortgage included some personal properties of the *mutwalli* which were also in jeopardy. Upon an action by the mortgagee to enforce the mortgage the Subordinate Judge held that as no sanction had been obtained as provided by the Mussulman Law, it was void as against the *wakf* property. The High Court on appeal considered that as some of the authorities gave a certain discretion to the *mutwalli*

(1) *Supra*. (2) [1909], I. L., 37 Cal., 179, *supra*.

in case the Judge happened to be at a distance, "retrospective approval" was effective in validating a transaction from which a benefit had accrued to the *wakf*. On this point the learned Judges expressed themselves as follows :—"the texts, however, to which we have referred, indicate plainly that the consent of the Cadi is essential whenever he is available, and if so, there is no reason why approval subsequent to the transaction should not be treated as effective in the same manner as approval prior to the transaction. It is but rational to hold that the approval of the Cadi was deemed requisite primarily with a view to make sure that the loan was necessary, and in this view approval, antecedent or subsequent, ought to be equally effectual."

Speaking with respect, the view here expressed misses the principle underlying the rule of Mussulman Law. According to all the authorities the validity of a transaction creating a burden on a *wakf* depends on the *prior* sanction of the Judge, which is essential in every case and not as is said in the judgment merely "whenever he is available." The qualification of the law implied in these words, it is respectfully submitted, is not warranted by the authorities for even the statement that when the *mutwalli* is at a distance from the Judge he may act of his own authority does not vary the law ; it only throws the responsibility on the *mutwalli* himself. *Ex post facto* sanction was never contemplated by the Mussulman jurists. For the permission of the Judge was made an absolute condition to see not only that the loan was necessary, but also whether it was proper, that the terms were not onerous and there was no other mode of meeting the necessity The facts of the case which led the Court to give a number of directions contrary to the terms of the mortgage show that it was not a transaction essentially for the benefit of the *wakf*, or that it was such that a Judge in view of the interests of the trust could have sanctioned without serious consideration. Again, there was nothing to show that the Judge was at such a distance that the matter could not have been submitted for his sanction. Even under English Law the previous sanction of the Court is essential to the validity of a transaction creating a charge on trust-property.

Under the Mussulman Law when a charge has been validly created on a *wakf* property, the income alone is liable for its repayment ; the property itself can under no circumstance be alienated or sold for its discharge. In other words the income only is hypothecated for the debt.(1)

When the sale of *wakf* property is set aside on the ground that it was not alienable, and it has happened that in the interval erections have been made by the purchaser, he would be entitled to remove those erections provided they can be separated from the *wakf* property without injury to it. In the case of erections that can be so removed, as also in the case of trees planted by the purchaser, the Kâzi may, in his discretion, direct a legitimate compensation provided the erections distinctly add to the value of the *wakf* property. If the erections have been made by pulling down the original *wakf* building, or the trees are planted from grafts taken from the *wakf* property, the purchaser is not entitled to receive any compensation for them. He is only entitled to recover back from *his* vendor the value paid by him.

No alteration made in a *wakf* building by the purchaser or anybody else can change the character of the *wakf*. The purchaser will be liable for any loss occasioned to the *wakf* by his alterations or additions to the *wakf* building, and for restoring it to its original condition, but he will not be entitled to any compensation on account of any improvement, unless those improvements are distinctly separable.

The purchaser will not be entitled to remove any erection made by him, if from such erections an advantage accrues to the *wakf*. For example, a man makes a better oven for preparing bread in place of an old one, he cannot remove it, nor is he entitled to any compensation for it. But if he fixes lamps he can remove them, or if they are left, he is entitled to compensation.

The purchaser is entitled to recover from his vendor the value of the building at the time when the sale is set aside and not the price paid by him. For example, if a man purchases a house for ten thousand dirhems and lives in it, and the house has become dilapidated he is not entitled, when the sale is set aside, to the price which he paid for it. If the value has increased, the purchaser would be entitled to receive the enhanced price.

---

(1) *Radd-ul-Muhtâr*, Vol. III, p. 649, Comp. *Narayan* v. *Chintnmon* [1881], I. L., 5 Bom., 393 ; the *Collector of Thana* v. *Hari Sitaram* [1882], I. L., 6 Bom., 546 ; *Pillian* v. *Sannadhi* [1903], I. L., 27 Mad., 465 ; *Narain Chand Addya* v. *Golam Hossain*, supra.

General principles: right to sue.

The applicability of sec. 539 of the old Civil Procedure Code (Act XIV of 1882) to suits for recovery of *wakf* property improperly alienated was discussed in the case of *Kazi Hassan* v. *Sagun Balkrishna*.(1) The plaintiffs sued to recover possession of certain lands, upon the allegation that those lands had been granted in *wakf* to their ancestor and his lineal descendants to defray the expenses for, or connected with, the services of a certain mosque, and that their father (defendant No. 3) and cousins (defendants Nos. 4 and 5), who were *mutwallis* in charge of the said property, had illegally alienated some of the *wakf* property, and had also ceased to render any service to the mosque, whereupon they (the plaintiffs) had been acting as *mutwallis* in their stead. They, therefore, claimed to be entitled as such to the management and enjoyment of the lands in dispute. It was contended by the defendant (*inter alia*) that the plaintiffs could not sue in the lifetime of their father (defendant No. 3), he not having transferred his right to them.

The Court held that the plaintiffs were entitled to sue to have the alienation made by their father and cousins set aside and the *wakf* property restored to the service of the mosque. They were not merely beneficiaries, but members of the family of the *mutwallis*, and were the persons on whom, on the death of the existing *mutwallis*, the office of *mutwalli* would fall by descent, if, indeed, it had not already fallen upon them, as alleged in the plaint, by abandonment and resignation.

When a suit is brought to set aside an alienation made to a stranger, such a suit by the worshipper at a mosque can be maintained and does not fall within section 539 of the Civil Procedure Code (Act XIV of 1882). The section is only applicable where there is an alleged breach of trust created for a public, charitable, or religious purpose, and the direction of the Court is necessary for the administration of the trust. As against strangers, section 539 does not apply.(2)

(1) [1905], I. L., 24 Bom., 170.
(2) *Ibid.*

CHAPTER XVI.

THE SHIAH LAW RELATING TO WAKF.

SECTION I.

GENERAL OBSERVATIONS.

Wakf, according to the Shiah doctrines, is a religious act, the effect of which is to tie up the *corpus* or substance of a thing, and to leave its usufruct free. According to the *Jawâhir ul-Kalâm*, the object of a *wakf* is the continuance in perpetuity of a benefaction in the service of the Deity, and it is an act of *'ibâdat* (worship). The express word by which it may be created is *wakafto*, *i.e.*,—" I have dedicated ;" but, as already pointed out before in relation to the Hanafî Law, a *wakf* may be created by any other expression when the intention is apparent. The *Jawâhir ul-Kalâm* states that there is nothing in law to debar the creation of a *wakf* by the use of any other expression besides *wakafto*. For example, a *wakf* may be created by the expression *haramto* (" I have consecrated"), or *tassadukto* (" I have given in charity.") But as absolute perpetuity is not a necessary incident of these expressions, reference must be made to the intention of the donor. The meaning of this is, when the intention of the grantor is clearly to create a *wakf*, whatever expression he may have used, the dedication will take effect, but where the term *wakf* itself is used, the dedication will take effect as such without any question. If a person make use of an expression which does not, in any degree, convey the idea of *wakf* and yet acknowledge that he intends to make a *wakf* thereby, it will take effect as a *wakf*. If a man were to say, " I have consecrated this house for the poor and given it in perpetuity," it would be a *wakf*. If he were to say, " I have tied up this property and given it in the way of God," or " that I have tied up this property and given the profits in the way of God," it would be a *wakf*.

How *wakf* may be constituted under the Shiah Law.

Phudia Bibi and others v. *Haji Mohammed Kazem Isphahani and others* (unreported).

Where a trust is expressly created, the introduction of words of gift does not change the character of the *wakf*. This question was considered at some length in the case of *Phudia Bibi and others* v. *Haji Mohammed Kazem Isphahani and others*, decided by Pigot, J., on the 31st of March 1884, upon the construction of the will of Nawab Sidi Nazir Ally Khan. By his will the Nawab had devised all his property to an executor, whose heirs the plaintiffs claimed to be, on certain trusts which were purely discretionary. The plaintiffs contended that the devise was an absolute gift to the executor, Meer Mohammed Kazem. The defendants contended that though the term *wakf* was not used in the document, which was in the English language and form, it was a valid *wakf*. The will was as follows :—

"This is the Last Will and Testament of me Nawab Sidi Nazir Ally Khan of Ballygunge in the suburbs of the town of Calcutta, zemindar, whereas I am indebted to various persons in large sums of money such loans being secured to them by mortgages over my real Estate in Calcutta and in the Mofussil, and my Promissory Notes, and whereas being about to leave India I am desirous of making a Testamentary dispositiou of my property in the event of my decease, I give devise and bequeath all my real and personal Estate whatsoever and wheresoever of which I shall be seized and possessed at the time of my death unto Meer Mohammed Kazem Jowahery of Chitpore Road in Calcutta, upon Trust at his discretion and at his absolute authority and as and when he or any other of the Trustee or Trustees for the time being of this my Will shall think fit to sell and dispose of, collect and get in and convert in money all and singular my said real and personal Estate or any or such portion thereof as he the said M. M. Kazem or any other Trustee or Trustees for the time being of this my Will shall, in his or their discretion think fit or advisable and upon further Trust by with and out of the monies to arise from such sales and collection to pay satisfy and discharge all my just debts and Funeral and Testamentary expenses and upon further Trust to lay out and expend such portion of the surplus of the said monies as the said Trustee for the time being of this my will shall think fit in the construction or building of a Mosque, Imambara or Mahommedan religious Institution to be called by my name for the performance and observance of religious ceremonies and festivals and acts of piety and charity inculcated in and enjoined by the Mahommedan religion the nature character and extent of which shall be in the entire and absolute discretion of the Trustee of this my Will for the time being and upon further Trust to lay out and invest the residue of the said monies after payment of the cost of the construction of the said Mosque, Imambara or other Mahommedan religious Institution as aforesaid in or upon Securities of the Government of India or in or upon the purchase or real property in Bengal and I direct that the said Trustee or other the Trustee or Trustees for the time being of this my Will shall hold the interests, rents and profits of the said Securities or real property in which the said monies may from time to time be invested upon trust to apply the same in and towards the repairs, maintenance and preservation of such parts of the said real Estate as shall not have been sold as well as of the real Estate in which the said Trust monies may be invested and the payment of all Rents, Revenues, Taxes and other outgoings and expenses incidental thereto and upon Trust to apply the surplus or balance of such interest rents and profits and also the rents and income arising from such parts of my said Estate as may not be sold as follows, that is to say as to such portion thereof as the said Trustee or other the Trustees for the time being of this my Will shall, in his or their judgment and discretion think fit in and towards the performance and observance of religious ceremonies and festivals and acts of piety and charity inculcated in and enjoined by the Mahommedan religion the nature character and extent of which shall be entirely in the judgment and discretion of my said Trustee or other the Trustee or Trustees for the time being of this my Will and as to the balance or residue thereof to and for the absolute use and benefit of the said Trustee or other the Trustee or Trustees for the time being of this my Will and I give and bequeath the same unto him or them his or their executors administrators or assigns accordingly.

* * * * * * *

Provided also and I further declare that it shall be lawful for the said Trustee or Trustees for the time being of this my Will at any time or from time to time in the discretion of the said Trustee or Trustees to sell or dispose of any stocks, funds, securities or lands wherein any of the Trust monies for the time being shall or may happen to be invested and to invest the money to arise from such sale in any other stocks or funds or other Government Securities or in purchase of real Estates in Bengal and convey or transfer the same as occasion shall require or shall be thought fit. Provided also and I hereby declare that in case the said Meer Mohammed Kazem shall die in my lifetime or shall renounce the execution of the Trusts hereby created or in case the said Meer Mohammed Kazem or any Trustee or Trustees to be appointed under this present provision shall die or shall be absent from Bengal for the space of six consecutive calendar months at one time or shall otherwise become unwilling or unable to act in the aforesaid Trusts then and so often as the same shall happen it shall be lawful for the said Meer Mohammed Kazem or other the Trustee for the time being or if there be no Trustee then for the Executors or administrators of the last deceased Trustee to nominate any fit person or persons to supply the place of the Trustee so dying residing abroad or becoming unwilling or unable to act as aforesaid and that immediately after every such appointment the said Trust Estates monies and effects stocks, funds or securities shall be conveyed or transferred in such manner that the same may vest in such new Trustee and such new Trustee shall have and be capable of exercising all the powers and authorities whatever hereinbefore containing in the same manner to all intents and purposes as if he or they had been appointed a Trustee or Trustees by this my Will.

Dedication for pious purposes.

***Wakf* for one's children.**

* * * * * * *

The learned Judge with reference to the principal contention, held as follows :—

"Now it is contended that by this document Nazir Ally gave his estate to Meer Mohammed Kazem subject to trusts merely colorable and not intended to be carried out. The question is, whether this contention is a valid one. The principal case relied on by Mr. Phillips was *Morrice* v. *The Bishop of Durham.*(1) Now, in

(1) 10 Ves., p. 510.

this case it appears to me the question is not whether a good trust was created, but the plaintiff's case will not succeed, unless it is shown by her that Meer Mohammed Kazem was not intended to take as a trustee. If he was intended to take as a trustee, he would not take any beneficial interest. The deed declares that Meer Mohammed Kazem takes as a trustee. It lies upon the plaintiff to show that he was to take absolutely. There can be no doubt that there was a trust regarding some portion, in the building of the mosque, &c. So far, therefore, he took as a trustee. But as regards the unconsumed income, it has been contended that Meer Mohammed Kazem took absolutely. The Will, however, says that he was to take it as a trustee. If it had said that the office of *mutwalli* was hereditary, a step might be gained in favour of the plaintiff's contention. But it is not so here. It cannot be said that the beneficial interest was given to the heirs of Meer Mohammed Kazem when each trustee has the power of appointing another person as trustee. Then I am to regard the various clauses in the Will regarding the appointment and responsibilities of the trustees. I might, perhaps, if I were not deciding the question judicially, have said that Nazir Ally probably intended that the property should, or expected that it would, descend to his friend's descendants, each of them successively exercising his power of appointment in favour of his heir, or some of his heirs. But I cannot import this conjecture into my judgment for the purpose of construing the plain terms of the Will. Then it was argued that the mere beneficial enjoyment of the unexpended income indicates a strong intention to create a beneficial interest and did in fact create such an interest. Without examining the cases in detail, it is sufficient to say that the cases cited by Mr. Kennedy and Mr. Ameer Ali, notably those of *Doe dem Jaun Beebee* v. *Abdollah Barber* and *Advocate-General* v. *Fatima Bibi*, show that no surmise can be founded upon the fact that the residue or balance of the income was to be enjoyed by the Trustee. That being so, I think the contention of the plaintiff must fail, and the issue raised whether the estate of Nazir Ally formed part of the estate of Meer Mohammed Kazem must be determined in the negative."

The *Sharâya* defines a *wakf* in the following terms :—

"*Wakf* is an act (*'akd*)(1) the (fruit) effect of which is to tie up the original of a thing, and to leave its usufruct free. The only express word by which it can be constituted is '*wakafto*,' 'I have appropriated'; for with regard to '*haramto*,' 'I have consecrated,' and '*sadakto*,' 'I have given in charity' they are not sufficient to constitute *wakf* without accompanying circumstances, as by themselves they are susceptible of another interpretation besides *wakf*. If, however, they are used with the intention of constituting *wakf*, they are obligatory on the conscience of the person employing them without any circumstances to fix their meaning. And if he should actually acknowledge that he used them with that intention judgment should be given against him in terms of his acknowledgment. It has been said, indeed, that if he should say, '*Habasto-wa-Sabalto*,' *wakf* would be constituted even without any circumstances to point this meaning, because, he, on whom be peace, [*viz.*, the Prophet] has said, '*Habis ul asl wa subîl ul sumrat*' (tie up the substance and give away the fruit). Others, however, have maintained that there would be no *wakf* in these cases without corroborative circumstances, as the words by themselves would not commonly be so understood; and this is the more approved opinion."

Definition of the term *wakf*.

The opinion expressed in the *Sharâya* is explained in the *Jawâhir* by the light of the dictum contained in the *Ghunia* and other works of authority. In other words, when a disposition is made by terms which are equivocal in their meaning, reference is to be made to the intention of the donor. If he is alive, he will

(1) The Arabic expression' *akd* is ordinarily translated as meaning a "contract," an act in which two persons are concerned and the obligation arising therefrom depends on the mutual consent of the parties. This is the sense in which Mr. Justice Mahmood, in his elaborate judgment in *Agha Ali Khan* v. *Altaf Hassan Khan* (I. L., 14 All., 429), construed the word, although the *Jâm'aa-ush-Shittât* distinctly states that "the meaning of ' *akd* in this connection (*i.e.*, with the subject of *wakf*) is general and includes (unilateral) declarations," * ایقاع است مراد از عقد درین جا عام از. The learned judge has placed a rather narrow construction on the Shiah Law in the case referred to. This case has been recently overruled by the Privy Council, in the case of *Baker Ali Khan* v. *Anjuman Ara Begum and others*, supra (1902), L. R., 30 I. A., 94, s. c., 7 C. W. N., p. 465. In this case their Lordships of the Judicial Committee lay down the following important principle of interpretation. "It would be extremely dangerous to accept as a general principle that new rules of law are to be introduced because they seem to lawyers of the present day to follow logically from ancient texts, however authoritative when the ancient Doctors themselves have not drawn those conclusions."

explain his meaning; if he is dead, his intention is to be gathered from the nature of the object in favour of which the grant is made or other attendant circumstances. For example, under the Shiah Law, a *hubs* or the creation of a limited estate is lawful; therefore, if a grant is made in favour of an *individual*, by that term, it may either mean a life-grant or a *wakf*. Therefore, reference must be made to the intention of the grantor. If he said '*hubs*' in favour of *A*, and then for the poor, it will be a *wakf*, or if it was a *hubs* in favour of a mosque or any object of public utility (*maslahat*), it will be a *wakf*. A *wakf* may be created for a mosque or any other object of utility (*maslahat*) by any expression; for the nature of the object being permanent and religious, carries with it the meaning of consecration.(1)

As in the case of other obligations, intention is an essential element in the constitution of a *wakf*, and "a dedication by one who is unconscious, غافل, or asleep or drunk is not valid." When the *wakf* is in favour of a specified individual or individuals, who are *sui juris* and are competent to signify their acceptance and in a position to do so, some jurists have held that the beneficiaries should expressly or impliedly accept the benefaction. But by general *consensus* acceptance is not required when the *wakf* is in favour of a minor (*saghîr*), or persons labouring under a disability, or yet unborn or for large bodies of people or for a purpose in which the generality of people are interested (*jihat-ul-'aâmma*).(2) Even in the case of a *wakf* for specific individuals who are *sui juris*, acceptance is not requisite when the *wâkif* himself alters the character of the possession.

Shiah Law: Possession necessary; subject to qualifications.

"And the delivery of possession (*ikbâz*) is a necessary condition for the validity of the *wakf*." But this principle also should

(1) In his judgment in the case of *Agha Ali Khan*, Mr. Justice Mahmood has quoted the following passage from the *Jâm'aa-ush-Shittât*—منعقد نمي شود- بلى صيغهٔ شرط است و بدون آن which he has translated thus :—"yes, the use of formal technical expression is an essential condition and without it *wakf* is not established." (The word "essential" does not appear in the original.) *Sigha* here means merely the formula of *wakf*. The learned Judge omitted to observe that the *approved* doctrine is that the use of the set formula *wakafto*, is necessary only when the dedication is made in favour of an object or objects which are not in their nature permanent or pious or religious. The words necessary to constitute a valid *wakf* under the Shiah Law were considered by the Allahabad High Court in the case of *Salig-un-Nissa* v. *Moti Ahmed* [1903], I. L., 25 All., 418.

(2) This is by no means exhaustive. Mr. Justice Mahmood's rendering of *Jihat-ul-'aâmma* by "public" charities is, with all respect, erroneous.

be taken subject to the conditions pointed out in dealing with the Hanafî Law, that is, actual change of possession is not necessary, constructive transfer being sufficient. For example, it is lawful for the *wâkif* to constitute himself *mutwalli*. In such a case, a formal change of possession is out of the question. *And, therefore, what is intended by the principle is not actual delivery of possession to another, but change in the character of the possession or of the dominion exercised over it.* It is in this sense that the *Mafâtîh* declares that, if the *wâkif* continue to exercise his right over the *wakf* property and make no change in the character of his possession, the *wakf* will not take effect. Where a dedication is for a public purpose, no (express) delivery of possession is necessary, for the user of it by any individual is sufficient to validate the *wakf*.(1)

According to the *Jawâhir*, delivery of possession is not necessary also where the *wakf* is in fact a *sadakah* or a charitable grant. Similarly, in the case of a *masjid* or any *maslahat* or object of general utility, *jihat-ul-'aâmma*. In these cases the mere non-delivery of possession will not avoid the *wakf*. When the *wakf* is in favour of private individuals who are *sui juris*, a trustee should either be appointed and possession delivered to him to hold in trust for the beneficiaries, or if the *wâkif* continues to hold the *wakf*, his possession must be expressly that of a trustee.

When a *wakf* is created for the *wâkif's* minor children, transmutation of possession is not needed. The law presumes the father's possession to be that of a *mutwalli* on behalf of the minors.(2) Similarly in the case of a *wakf* for the poor.(3)

Ikbâz or delivery of possession.

I have dealt with the subject of *ikbâz* in a previous chapter.(4) It is only necessary to explain that under the condition of *ikbâz*,

(1) *Jawâhir-ul-Kalâm*, chapter on *Wakf*.

(2) *Ibid*.

(3) *Ibid ; Ghunia*. The *Sharâya* no doubt says that " if a man were to make a *wakf* and die without giving possession the *wakf* would be void, but if a *wakf* be made in death-bed and *possession be given*, then it will take effect to the extent of a third if the heirs do not consent. Without possession the *wakf* fails whether made in health or illness." And again " it (the *wakf*) does not become binding except by delivery of possession, and when completed (by delivery of possession) it cannot be revoked if made in health, but if made during illness and allowed by heirs (it is operative in full), otherwise it is valid as regards a third." This, in my opinion, does not mean actual delivery of possession, but such a manifestation of intention to transfer the property as is compatible with the physical condition of the person creating the *wakf*.

(4) See *ante*, pp. 112-122.

actual delivery of possession is not requisite. What is required is an indication that the *wâkif* has divested himself of his proprietary interest in the subject of the *wakf*. If the property is immovable, delivery of the title-deeds would satisfy the requirements of the law. If it is a house, the delivery of the key, or if they are Government securities in deposit with any Bank, the delivery of the deposit receipt, or if it is a business, a transfer-entry in the books, as in the case of a gift, would be a sufficient transmutation of possession.

Transmutation of possession.

When all the conditions requisite for the completion of a *wakf* are complied with, it becomes absolute (if made in health) and cannot be revoked. "On this point," says the author of the *Jawâhir ul-Kalâm*, "Abû Hanîfa differs from us, though his disciple Abû Yusuf on arriving at Bagdad dissented therefrom. If the subject of the *wakf* has once changed possession and ceased to be under the *wâkif's* dominion, or has come into the hands or under the control of the beneficiaries or the trustee on their behalf, the *wâkif* cannot revoke it or change the conditions of the *wakf* or withdraw it from the way of God or from the purposes to which it is dedicated."

"If the *wakf* is for minor children, it is irrevocable, though no change of possession has taken place."

All this relates to a *wakf inter vivos*. A testamentary *wakf* (a *wakf bi'l wasiat*) which is to take effect after the decease of the testator, is a revocable disposition.

In the case of *Agha Ali Khan*,(1) it was held by Mr. Justice Mahmood that such a *wakf* was not valid and operative even as regards the disposible one-third, unless possession has been transferred during the lifetime of the *wâkif*.

Effect of a testamentary *wakf*.

His opinion amounts to this that a testamentary *wakf* would be inoperative *in toto*, unless effect was given to it in fact by delivery of possession during the lifetime of the testator, and that the consent of the heirs would not validate it. It is submitted, however, that this view proceeds upon a strained construction of the law and has since been disaffirmed by their Lordships of the Privy Council in the case of *Baker Ali Khan* v. *Anjuman Ara Begum*,(2) where it has been held that a valid *wakf* can be created

(1) Supra, p. 497.

(2) [1902], 7 Cal. W. N., 465, s. c., I. L., 25 All., 236.

under the Shiah Law by will. And in *Muhammad Ahsan* v. *Umardaraz*,(1) the Allahabad High Court has held that a *wakf* created by a Shiah by his will was not invalid on the ground that it was not absolute and unconditional, merely because it contained clauses cancelling the will if any child should be born to the testator in his lifetime and reserving to the testator power to cancel or modify any of the conditions of the will. In this case the testator had directed that the *income* of the property should be devoted to the purposes of the *wakf* only after the death of his widow to whom he gave the life-interest. The High Court held that where it was clear from the other terms of the will that the *corpus* was to be devoted to the purposes of the *wakf*, the mere fact that the property did not at once on the testator's death pass to the trustees of the endowment and their enjoyment wes postponed to the life-interest of the widow for maintenance, did not invalidate the *wakf*.

Wakf made in death-illness valid as to whole if consented to by the heirs.

If a *wakf* be constituted at a time when the *wâkif* is suffering from a *death-illness*, and there is a clear indication of an intention on his part to transfer possession, it will take effect with reference to the entirety of the dedication, provided the heirs consent, *either before or after the death of the wâkif*, otherwise the *wakf* will operate only in respect of one-third of the estate of the testator. "For a *wakf* is like other acts which take effect immediately such as *hiba*, sale and similar obligations." If the *wakf* property is covered by one-third of the estate, then it is valid as regards the entirety of the dedication. If not. each provision will be given effect to with regard to its priority until one-third of the estate is exhausted.

"If a person," says the *Sharâya*, "should, in death-illness make a *wakf*, gift or *muhâbât* (2) sale, or emancipate a slave, and the acts be not allowed by his heirs, then they would be valid if they can be carried into effect out of a third of his estate; otherwise they are to be preferred according to priority of date, and effect is to be given to each in order until the third of the estate is exhausted, after which any that may remain is void."(3)

(1) [1906], I. L., 28 All., 633.
(2) For the meaning of the word *Mubâhât*, see Index of technical terms.
(3) *Sharâya-ul-Islâm*, p. 234.

Agha Ali Khan v. *Altaf Hossain Khan.*

In the case of *Agha Ali Khan*, the learned Judge was of opinion that in the case of a death-bed *wakf*, delivery of possession was equally necessary as in *wakfs* made in health (وقف الصحت). The view is founded upon purely inferential reasoning, for the text cited certainly does not support it. "If a person made a gift or *wakf* or charitable donation in his death-sickness, it is to be satisfied out of one-third, according to the better of the two opinions, excepting in the case of the heirs giving sanction. The same rule applies if he did so in good health and delayed possession till sickness."(1)

This does not show that the latter qualification is applicable to the first part, it only indicates that the effect in both cases is identical. The greatest of Shiah lawyers (Shaikh J'aafar) whilst pointing out the differences between the Sunnis and Shiahs regarding *wakfs* constituted in the last illness does not make a single reference to the delivery of possession being a necessary condition.(2) What is required is a clear indication of the intention of the *wâkif* to create the *wakf* and to transfer possession.

Wasiat bi'l wakf.

A direction to the heirs or to executors to make a *wakf* of a certain property upon the death of the testator is called a *wasiat bi'l wakf*. There is this difference between immediate dispositions of property, *i.e.*, dispositions *inter vivos* and bequests, that in the former case the one-third takes effect in respect of the existing property, whereas in the case of a bequest, consideration has to be paid to the condition of the estate after the decease of the testator. If there happen to be many bequests in a *wakf*, and it is difficult to determine which provision should take priority, *i.e.*, when all the provisions are of the same degree of importance, in that case, according to the Shaikh(3) all the provisions should be given effect to, and the one-third respecting which the *wakf* is operative should be applied to the effectuation of all the objects "When a person," says the *Sharâya*, "has bequeathed pro-

(1) *Sharh Lum'aa* of Shahîd Sâni, p. 108.

(2) In the *Mabsût*. The *Sharâya* says "if one should make an appropriation and die without giving possession it would be part of his inheritance." This again does not mean that there should be delivery of possession in the literal sense; what is required is a change in the character of the possession, indicative of the fact that the *wâkif* has parted with the proprietary right in the property.

(3) *Mafâtîh* after the *Mabsût*; Shaikh Murtaza is meant here. See Introd.

perty for the performance of certain duties, some of which were incumbent on the testator and others only optional, they are all to be carried into effect if a third of his estate be sufficient for the purpose. If the third should not suffice and the heirs refuse their consent, those duties that were incumbent on the testator must first be discharged out of the general mass of his estate, and then the others out of a third of what remains beginning with that first mentioned by the testator, and so on in order. If none of the duties are of the incumbent description, but all optional, they take effect only to the extent of a third of the estate and are to be discharged beginning with that first mentioned by the testator, and so on in order until the third is exhausted."

SECTION II.

CONDITIONS RELATING TO THE SUBJECT OF WAKF.

Under the Shiah Law it is requisite: (i) that the subject of the *wakf* should be *m'aalûm* (specified or ascertained and not indeterminate), (ii) that it should be of such a nature that the benefit accruing therefrom should be permanent, or as the *Sharâya* says "capable of yielding benefit without itself being consumed," and (iii) that it can be transferred from one *mutwalli* to another." This is expressly enunciated in the *Jawâhir ul-Kalâm.* It is also requisite, (iv) that it be the property of the appropriator.

According to the ancients, the *wakf* of anything which did not exist in specie was not valid, *e.g.*, the *wakf* of a debt payable to a person was not regarded as valid,(1) because it was a thing, in their opinion, not existing in specie. The ancient views.

They also held that where a thing could not yield a profit without being consumed in the process, the *wakf* thereof was invalid. Profit *quâ* profit was, upon the same reasoning, considered incapable of being consecrated. But, as will be seen later, the reasons upon which the ancient opinions were founded, have been considerably modified owing to altered circumstances and the development of industry and commerce. The subject of *wakf*.

The observant reader will not fail to notice the close analogy existing between the Hanafî and the Shiah Law on

---

(1) *Sharâya-ul-Islâm*, p. 248. This must, however, be taken subject to qualifications discussed afterwards.

the subject under discussion. The early Hanafî lawyers regarded the *wakf* of movables (excepting a few recognised by tradition) as invalid, because there was no permanency in them, and because they would be consumed in their use. The Shiah lawyers, however, were in advance of the Hanafî jurists in one respect. They held that the *wakf* of anything from the use of which benefit could lawfully be derived, consistently with the preservation of the thing itself, was valid; thus the *wakf* of a trained dog or cat was held to be valid, "from the possibility of benefit being derived from them."(1) They also held on the same principle,(2) the *wakf* not merely of land and houses, but of clothes, ornaments, furniture and lawful instruments to be valid. The *Jawâhir* goes further and adds, "though the *wakf* of food and such like things is not valid, because they are consumed in their use, the *wakf* of violets, or flowers in general, and lamps (*kandîl*), mats, &c., is valid according to custom and times."

Wakf of debts.

As regards the legality of the *wakf* of debts they argued thus: "The *wakf* of a *dayn* which is a thing indeterminate, is not valid by reason of there being no certainty or identity of the same."(3) With reference to the *wakf* of money, they supposed that the element of permanency was wanting. The *Jawâhir-ul-Kalâm* has discussed the subject at some length. "And whether the *wakf* of *dinârs* and *dirhems* is valid or not, the opinion of some is that it is not, and this seems to be in accord with the ancients (*mutakaddamîn*). And in the *Mabsût* it is said that there is general agreement about it, with the exception of those who hold it valid, who are few. The reason is that *dinârs* and *dirhems* are expended and no further use can be derived from them, and this is against the principle that a *wakf* must always be subsisting and its profit should be applied for the relief of the poor and in other good acts; but when the profit of a thing is always subsisting, as in the case of a honeycomb, it is valid." A close examination of the authorities leads to the result that the *wakf* of profits and of moneys, when they can be permanently applied in trade or commerce, so

Modern doctrine.

---

(1) *Sharâya.* This shows how elastic the rule is, and that one must not go by the letter of the law but by its spirit.

(2) *Ibid.*

(3) *Mafâtîh.*

that permanent benefit may be derived from the same, is valid, as will be seen from the remarks which have already been made in respect of the Hanafî Law. This view is in accord with the altered conditions of society. The principle, upon which the more ancient lawyers of the Shiah school have proceeded, in holding that the *wakf* of money and *munâf'aa* (profit) is invalid, is that such subjects either possess no stability or permanence, or that they are expended in their application for the purposes for which they are dedicated. But when money is applied in trade, or where profit is derived from investments, the objection which seemed to them to possess so much force, loses all weight, and it is on this ground that modern Shiah lawyers have upheld the validity of such *wakfs*.(1) Similarly the *wakf* of a debt which is determinate and capable of specification has been recognised to be valid.

The subject of a *wakf* must be specified or be capable of identification.

The subject of a *wakf* must also be particularly specified, so that, if a person were to say "I have appropriated a house or mansion," it would not be valid unless he specifies which house he means. But if the subject of the *wakf* is not distinctly specified, but is capable of being ascertained by enquiry, such *wakf* would be valid.

It is a condition that the property dedicated should belong to the *wâkif*; otherwise the *wakf* is not valid. If the dedication, however, is made of a property belonging to another, the *wakf* would be validated by the ratification of the real owner.

***Wakf* of *mushâ'a* valid.**

The *wakf* of a *mushâ'a* or an undivided share in a thing is valid, and possession of it is to be taken in the same way as in the case of a sale.(2)

SECTION III.

CONDITIONS RELATING TO THE WAKIF.

Conditions relating to the *wâkif*.

It is a condition that the *wâkif* should be *bâligh* (adult); that he should be possessed of complete understanding, and of the capacity to deal with his property, that is, be subject to no "inhibition" on the ground of incapacity. The author of the *Jawâhir* is inclined to think, and rightly, that the latter condition

(1) *Jâm'aa-ush-Shittât.* Even the *Sharâya* which represents the literal and archaic section of the Shiah school says that the "Jurists are inclined to modify the strictness of the rule regarding the *wakf* of *dinârs* and *dirhems*."

(2) *Jawâhir-ul-Kalâm,* Chapter on *wakf*.

depends on the former, and in the *Sharh-i-Lum'aa* the only condition required is sound understanding.

"The creation of a *wakf* is like the performance of devotions, and, therefore, as there is no obligation on a lunatic, and an infant who has not attained puberty, to perform any devotion, their *wakf* too is not valid, for the understanding necessary to the comprehension of its nature and effect is wanting. But there is some difference of opinion regarding the question what would be the effect of a *wakf* when made by a boy who has attained puberty at an early age, say ten years." Presumably his act would not be valid, for the law does not presume discretion until the completion of the 15th year.

Wâkif can retain the superintendence in his own hands.

The *wâkif* can lawfully retain the superintendence of the *wakf* in his own hands or appoint another; but no condition which would enable the *wâkif* to revoke or cancel the trust is valid or lawful. Nor can he reserve to himself the power of resuming the *towliat* whenever he likes after already appointing one to the office.(1) As it is required that the *nâzir* or superintendent should be a man of honesty and should know how to perform his duty if the *wâkif* is incompetent or dishonest, that is, neglects the trust or misdeals with it, he may be removed, or another man may be associated with him.(2) When the *wâkif* has appointed no one for the superintendence of the *wakf*, the power of appointing a trustee devolves on the beneficiaries, when the *wakf* is for specific persons who can appoint a trustee on their own behalf, and on the *Hâkim-ush-Shar'aa* (Judge), when it is for a public purpose, or in the way of God, or for a continuing and variable class of people.

Conditions relating to the _cestuis que trustent_ appointing a trustee.

SECTION IV.

CONDITIONS RELATING TO THE *Mowkoof-Alaih* OR *Cestui qui trust.*

The _mowkoof-alaihim_ or beneficiaries.

Concerning the (first) *moukoof-alaih* there are four requisites:—

(1) He must be existent.(3)

---

(1) This view seems opposed to that taken in the case of *Hedaitunnissa*, 2 N.-W. P. Reports, p. 410.

(2) This subject has been fully dealt with in dealing with the Hanafî Law. There is no difference between the Hanafî and the Shiah lawyers on this point.

(3) The *Mafâtih* states the rule thus: "it is required that the object in whose favour the *wakf* is made be in existence or held to be so or one whose existence is usually possible."

(ii) Must be capable of owning property.

(iii) Must be *m'uayyin* or specified.

(iv) Must be one in whose favour it is not unlawful to make a *wakf*.

As a corollary to the above principles, the *Sharâya* lays down the following doctrine: "Consequently if one should make a *wakf* beginning with a person not in existence—as for instance, one to be born, or a fœtus not yet separated from the womb of its mother—the *wakf* would not be *sahîh* (valid). But if it were in favour of one not in existence, in succession to a person actually in being, it would be *sahîh*." The comment of the *Jawâhir* on this passage is interesting, and brings into prominence the views of the Shaikh (the author of the *Mabsût*) on the subject:—"If one makes a *wakf* for a non-existent person at the commencement, it will not be *sahîh* [according to the *Sharâya*]; for example, a person makes a *wakf* for his child about to be born, or the fœtus which is not separated from the womb, though (in one aspect) it is *mowjood* or existent, and bequests in its favour are lawful and it is entitled to a share upon the partition of the inheritance, yet a *wakf* is not valid in its favour," probably on the ground that it is not capable of holding possession of the property, "but where a *wakf* is in favour of a non-existent object in succession to an existing object which is capable of participating in its benefit, such *wakf* is valid."

Conditions relating to the *mowkoof alaihim* or beneficiaries—(contd.)

When a person makes a *wakf* commencing with a non-existent object and then in favour of an existing object, according to the Shaikh and his followers, it would be valid in favour of the existing object and invalid as regards the non-existing. For example, a *wakf* in favour of an unborn child and after it for the existing children or for the poor will take effect at once in favour of the latter, the invalidity of the *wakf* in respect of the former object which is non-existing, only accelerating its operation in favour of those that are in existence. According to the *Jawâhir-ul-Kalâm* the great jurist Yahya ibn Muwayyid holds the same view, which is apparently conformable to the opinions entertained by a large body of the *'ullâma* (the learned).(1) But a man may make a *wakf* in favour of an existing object, and

Wakf commencing with a non-existent object.

---

(1) *Jawâhir ul-Kalâm; Mabsût; Ghunia.*

lawfully condition that upon certain other person or persons coming into existence, the benefit will go to him or them.

For example, a person, who has no children at the time, may lawfully dedicate his property in favour of *A*, and condition therein that upon his having any children the *wakf* would be for them and for their descendants, in which case the moment a child is born to him, the *wakf* would be diverted from *A*, and the benefit would be applied to such child.(1) What the law requires is, that the commencement in a *wakf* should be made with an existing object, though the remainder may be given to any number of non-existing objects in succession. This, it will be seen, is different from the Hanafî Law, which declares that a *wakf* may commence with a non-existing object, and that until it has come into existence, the *wakf* will be applied for the poor.(2)

Wakf in favour of one's descendants.

It will also be seen from the above that a benefaction in favour of one's children or descendants is absolutely valid.

A *wakf* for *masâlih* valid.

A *wakf* for *masâlih*(3) or works of general utility or for pious or charitable purposes of a *general* character, is valid, "as such a *wakf* is in truth, a settlement on all Mussulmans though some only participate in its benefit." For example, a *wakf* for (constructing or maintaining) bridges and mosques, providing shrouds for the dead, and like purposes is a settlement on all mankind, though a limited number may participate at a time in its advantages; and though no specific individuals may be mentioned as the people for whose benefit such *wakf* is created, it would be valid, because all God's creatures can derive benefit therefrom. Consequently, a *wakf*, the object of which is to confer a general benefit on the public, for example, a *wakf* to a *madrassa* or college, or the *wakf* of books to a library and such like, is valid.

A *wakf* in favour of a *harbi* invalid.

A Moslem cannot make a *wakf* in favour of an *alien enemy*, though he may be a blood-relation, but he can make it in favour of a non-Moslem subject (*zimmi*) of the same sovereign, whether he be a stranger or related to him, for it is the conferring of kindness or charity on a human being, who may be induced to take the right way. The validity of a *wakf* to a *zimmi* is maintained

(1) *Sharâya*, p. 245; *Mafâtih*; *Jawâhir-ul-Kalâm*.

(2) *Sharaya*, pp. 235 and 236; *Mafâtih*.

(3) Pl. of *maslahat*.

on the ground that a *sadakah* or charity may be validly given to him, and also because there is precedent for it, "for Safia, the Prophet's wife, made a *wakf* in favour of her brother," who was a Jew. But it does not follow from this that a Moslem can make a *wakf* in favour of a church, a synagogue or any place of non-Moslem worship, for that would be assisting in the propagation of "infidelity," which is unlawful and forbidden to Moslems. But a *zimmi* can make a *wakf* on a non-Moslem place of worship. A Moslem can make a *wakf* for the benefit of *zimmis* for purposes which are lawful under the Mussulman Law, such as the repair of their houses, erection of hospitals, or places of refuge, &c. So can non-Moslems make a *wakf* in favour of a Moslem place of worship.

A *wakf* for sinful purposes invalid.

"A *wakf* in favour of fornicators, highway robbers or drinkers of wine is not valid, nor for the copying of what are now called *Tourât* and *Injîl* (the Pentateuch and the Christian Gospels) since they are altered and perverted. But if such appropriations were made by an infidel, it would be lawful. No *wakf* which is productive of sin is valid."

A *wakf* for the poor.

If a Moslem were to make a *wakf* in favour of the poor, it would be applied primarily to the benefit of the Mussulman poor, and if there happen to be none, then to other poor; but a *wakf* by a non-Moslem in favour of the poor generally would be applied for the benefit of the poor of his neighbourhood without distinction of creed.

A *wakf* in favour of Moslems generally.

When a *wakf* is made in favour of Moslems generally, all people who are subject to the laws of Islâm, their women and their children, will be included; the use of the expression "Moslem" excludes those who are not subject to Islâm. A *wakf* in favour of *mômins* (those who have the *Imân* or true faith,(1) will be applied only for the benefit of the followers of the twelve Imâms.

A *wakf* in favour of *momins* generally will be applied to such purposes as would be beneficial to them.

---

(1) "Faith has two meanings—(1) general, and (2) special; generally it means to accept from the heart those laws which the blessed Prophet has brought; the special meaning resolves itself into two heads:—(*a*) acting piously, and (*b*) believing in the *Imâmate* of the Imâms."

"If the *wakf* is for *Shiahs*,(1) then, according to our present usage, it will be applied for the benefit of the *Imâmias*. The term *Shiah* includes the *Jârudiahs*, the *Ismailias*, and the *Zaidias*."(2)

Wherever the *mowkoof-alaih* (*i.e.*, the person in whose favour a *wakf* is made) is described by a particular relationship, all those who come within it are held to be included in the benefits of the *wakf*.

"So that if the *wakf* be in favour of the *Imâmias*, it is for all the followers of the Imâms. In like manner, when it is for the *Zaidias*, all those who assert the Imâmship of Zaid, the son of Ali (the second) are included. Likewise, when the connection is relationship to a particular ancestor, all those lineally descended from him by their fathers are included. As, for instance, 'Hâshimis,' comprehend all those descended from Hâshim through Abû Tâlib, Hârith, Abbâs and Abû Lahab; and 'Tâlibis' comprehend all descendants of Abû Tâlib, on whom be peace, both males and females participating if connected with him on the side of their fathers from a regard to custom, though upon this point there is some difference of opinion."

If one should make an appropriation for an indeterminate class of people like the Banî Tamîm, the correct opinion is that it would be valid and should be applied to any of them who can be found.

Wakf in favour of neighbours.

If a person should make an appropriation for (his) neighbours (*jîrân*), a reference should be made to custom for determining who are to be thereby comprehended.

"Some say, however, that any one whose house is within forty cubits is a neighbour, and this opinion is well supported, while others maintain that the meaning of the term extends to all the occupants of forty houses on either side, but this opinion is now abandoned."

A *wakf* in favour of a *maslahat* that has ceased to exist how to be applied.

If one should make a *wakf* for a *maslahat* or object of general utility, when that has ceased to exist, it will, according to the approved doctrine, be applied to any good or pious purpose. It would, however, be better to apply the same with reference to the true intentions of the *wâkif*. So a *wakf* for a mosque will (in case the intended mosque is not in existence) be applied to another

(1) *Jawâhir ul-Kalâm*—"Shiah means a person who propagates the Imâmate of Ali, may the peace of God rest with him."

(2) See the *Spirit of Islâm*, (Ed. 1902), pp. 293-4.

mosque, and that for a madrassa to another like madrassa, and so on, regard being had to the same description of object as was intended by the *wâkif*.(1)

When a *wakf* is made for a good purpose without any specification of the object, it will be applied to any good purpose by which an "approach" is made to Almighty God.(2)

So also in the *Sharh-i-Lum'aa* :—"If one makes an appropriation in 'the way of God,' it will be applied to every purpose by which an 'approach' is made to God, because from 'the way' is meant the path of God, that is, the path of reward [in future life] and the reward and pleasure of God ; this will include, therefore, helping the needy, building mosques and repairing roads, supplying shrouds for the dead, and whatever brings blessings ; some say, it includes holy warfare, others that it includes *Hajj* and *'Umrah* (lesser pilgrimage). But the first view is correct.(3) Similarly, if one makes an appropriation in the way of charity or in the way of *sawâb* (reward), it means the same thing, and the meaning will not be split into two parts. Some [jurists] have said that 'the way of reward' means the poor and indigent, and commencement should be made with his poor relations, and by the 'way of charity' is meant also the poor and indigent, and travellers and debtors who have become indebted in pious acts and the ransoming of slaves, but the intention of the *wâkif* should always be regarded."(4)

Dedication for charity generally.

"If one makes a dedication for charity generally, without any specification of the purposes, it will be applied (or expended) on the poor and all purposes by which an approach (to God) might be made, like conferring benefit on students, building mosques and schools and bridges and *mashâhid* (mausoleums), assisting pilgrims, supplying shrouds for the dead, and it is allowable to spend for the general benefit of Mussulmans."(5)

In the *Jawâhir* this principle is stated thus :—"If a person constitute a *wakf* for a *maslahat* such as a masjid, a bridge or some object of a similar character and all traces of its use and effect have totally vanished (*lit.* have become effaced or annulled),

---

(1) *Mafâtih.*
(2) *Sharh-i-Lum'aa.*
(3) *Mafâtih.*
(4) Comp. the *Jawâhir ul-Kalâm*, Chapter on *Wakf*.
(5) *Riyâz-ul-Ahkâm.*

in such a case the income of the *wakf* property would be expended on good purposes generally. Preference, however, would be given to an object approaching in character as nearly as possible to the object of the original dedication." It will be seen from this that the *cyprès* doctrine is carried much further under the Shiah than even under the Hanafî Law. This will appear more clearly from the following dictum: "If a person were to make a dedication generally for benevolent purposes,(1) then without any difference of opinion, the *wakf* property will be applied for the benefit of the poor and indigent, and for all pious acts and objects which may be the means of approaching the Deity; *birr* or charity is a word which comprehends all good and pious actions (*khair*), such as the relief of the *wâkif's* kindred, the help of the poor, the assistance of the weak, the improvement of the condition of the Mussulmans, the performance of *Hajj*, *Jihâd*, &c."(2)

Ibn-i-Junaid's view.

With the exception of Ibn-i-Junaid, most of the writers are agreed in holding that a dedication, when the object is not mentioned either expressly or impliedly, is void. Ibn-i-Junaid, however, holds otherwise. According to him and his followers where a *wakf* is created but the beneficiaries are not named, the *wakf* will be applied for purposes of *birr* and *ihsân* (charity and good acts). But when a person declares a property a *sadakah* in the way of God (which is another way of saying it is a *wakf*), though he may not mention the people for whom the *sadakah* is constituted, yet it would be applied by *consensus* to the benefit of those whom God has declared to be the recipients of the ordained alms, *i.e.*, the poor and the indigent, the needy and the helpless. Virtually, the views of Ibn-i-Junaid are not opposed to those of the other jurists, for they also hold that in the absence of any express mention of the special object, where the *wakf* is clearly for pious and good purposes, it will be applied to such purposes as are for the good of Mussulmans generally.(3)

A *wakf* for an indeterminate object invalid.

If the *wakf* is created for an indeterminate object it is invalid; *e.g.*, if it is for one of two mosques or for one of two *imâmbâras*, and there is no specification for which mosque or *imâmbâra*, it is void.

---

(1) *Jawâhir ul-Kalâm*, Chapter on *Wakf*.
(2) *Ibid.*
(3) *Ibid.*

A *wakf* in favour of relations generally.

If a person were to make a *wakf* for his children or his brethren or his relations generally, the males and females, the nearer and the more remote, will share equally,(1) unless the order in which they should participate is specified, or it is expressly stated that it is for the males, when the shares will be distributed in accordance with the rule laid down. Where a *wakf* is for paternal and maternal uncles together, they share equally. A *wakf* for those "nearest to the *wâkif*" will be primarily applied to his parents and descendants, then to his brothers and sisters and their descendants, together with the ascendants, and lastly, and on failure of these, to paternal and maternal uncles and their descendants. As in the Hanafî system, so also under the Shiah Law, the directions laid down by the *wâkif*, if not sinful, should be given effect to so far as possible. But if any of the provisions are impracticable, the *Hâkim ush-Shar'aa* (the Judge) can give directions so as to make them conformable to the exigencies of the *wakf*.

SECTION V.

ESSENTIAL REQUISITES TO THE LEGALITY OF A WAKF.

Conditions requisite to the legality of a *wakf*.

There are four essential requisites on which depends the legality of a *wakf*.

(i) That it must be perpetual.

(ii) That it must not be contingent.

(iii) That possession must be given of the thing dedicated, or, more properly, the property should cease to be the property of the donor.

(iv) That the right of the donor should be entirely divested therefrom.(2)

Perpetuity.—With reference to the first condition, the view generally adopted is, that in order that a *wakf* may take effect in *perpetuity* it must be for an object or objects, which, individually or collectively, would presumably last always. A *wakf* for *masâlih* or works of general utility or for pious and benevolent purposes generally, is valid, for any particular *maslahat* which is for the benefit of all mankind is lasting in its character, as it is for

---

(1) *Jâm'aa-ush-Shittât.*

(2) *Haji Kalb Hossein* v. *M. S. Mehrun Bibi*, 4 N.-W. P., 155.

the benefit of humanity at large. A charitable purpose is also perpetual in its nature, for the poor are always in existence. In fact, any continuing object of *birr* and *ihsân* is sufficient for a perpetual *wakf*; for example, a *wakf* to supply water or *sherbet* to the congregation in the mosques or *imâmbâras*, to light the lamps in a place of worship, to keep up the library of a madrassa (college), to wage a sacred war, to support the poor Syeds of Kerbela, to keep in repair the aqueduct there or in any other sacred place and such like.

Wakf in favour of descendants and on their failure for the poor, valid by consensus.

So, also, where a *wakf* is created for specific objects which are liable to failure, if the ultimate reversion is for the poor or for any object of utility or a place of worship such as a mosque or *imâmbâṛa*, the *wakf* is valid. For example, if a *wakf* is created for the descendants of the *wâkif*, and upon their extinction, it is provided that the usufruct should be applied to the poor, or towards a particular mosque, the *wakf* is valid "without difference."

But when the *wakf* is for Zaid, and nothing is said as to how it should be applied after Zaid's death, and there is nothing from which the intention of the donor can be inferred as to the future application of the proceeds of the *wakf*, one body of jurists have held that, in that case, the *wakf* will operate only as an *'umra*(1) during Zaid's lifetime, and on his death will, according to the generally received doctrine, revert to the *wâkif* or his heirs, as the case may be. Similarly, if the *wakf* was for Zaid and his descendants, and no other (continuing or permanent) purpose was mentioned, to which the income should be applied upon the extinction of Zaid's posterity, the *wakf* will take effect as a *hubs*(2) in their favour, giving them a limited estate so long as they are in existence. And on the extinction of Zaid's descendants the property will revert to the heirs of the *wâkif*. According to another school of jurists, the remainder in either case will be for benevolent purposes in general.(3) These jurists are in agreement with Abû Yusuf.

If a property is made *wakf* or *hubs* for two persons, one of whom dies, the survivor will enjoy the benefit of the property

(1) An *'umra* means a life-grant.

(2) *Hubs*, lit. tying-up of property, means a settlement in favour of an individual or individuals for a limited time.

(3) *Jawâhir ul-Kalâm*, Chapter on *Wakf*.

during his lifetime. Another view is, that the moiety of the deceased will revert to the donor. But the former doctrine seems more approved.

A *wakf* for the donor's son for one year or for his lifetime, with the reversion for the poor, is valid (as a perpetual *wakf*) by *general consensus*.

If a person were to constitute a *wakf* for his sons in the following manner, that is to say, for one year for 'Amr, the next year for Zaid and so on, and after them for the poor, in the following manner—for their learned, one year, for their pious in the second year, and for their *mashâikh* in the third year, such a *wakf* is valid and will be given effect to.

A Contingent Wakf.—A *wakf*, the operation of which is made dependent upon a future contingency, is invalid under the Shiah Law. In the *Sharâya*, the principle is stated in these words :—"If a *wakf* is restricted to a particular time or made dependent on some quality of future occurrence it is void." In the *Mafâtih* and the *Irshâd ul-Azhân* the doctrine, thus stated in the *Sharâya*, is more clearly laid down : "Without difference of opinion *wakf* should be made at once ; it cannot be made to depend on the occurrence of an event in the future unless the same be certain and positive." Similarly in the *Sharh-i-Lum'aa*, "besides the above-mentioned matters, *tanjîz* is one of the conditions of *wakf*. Therefore, if the *wâkif* has suspended it upon any contingency or quality [of future occurrence] it is invalid except in cases where the contingency is only in the form of the expression used but none in reality and the *wâkif* is aware of it, such as his saying 'I have made this *wakf* if to-day is Friday,' and such is the rule in regard to other contracts." In the *Mabsût* and *Ghunia* also, the principle is stated in almost similar terms, the effect of which is that if a *wakf* is made dependent for its operation on the happening of an uncertain contingency, it is void.(1)

Meaning of *tanjîz*.

(1) "So if *wakf* is restricted to a particular time, or made dependent on some quality of future occurrence, the *wakf* is void. Such also is the case when it is made in favour of persons who will probably fail. As for instance, if one should make a settlement on Zaid with a restriction to himself or extend it to generations that would probably fail, or if he say generally for his successors without mentioning what is to be done after they fail—in these cases it is maintained by some that the *wakf* should be entirely void, but *others insist that due course should be given to the purposes actually named and this is approved.* Then upon their failure the property would revert to the heirs of the *wâkif*, but some

Syeda Bibi v. Moghul Jan.

The Allahabad High Court, in the case of *Syeda Bibi* v. *Moghul Jan*,(1) has carried the doctrine of *tanjîz* to its furthest limit. A Mahommedan of the Shiah sect had executed a *wakfnâmah*, in which he declared that the deed of *wakf* shall come into force from the date of its registration. The learned Judges held that the condition was repugnant to the doctrine of the Shiah Law, and the *wakf* was therefore invalid.

In the case of *Hamid Ali* v. *Mujawar Husain Khan*,(2) it appeared that a Mahommedan of the Shiah sect had executed a document by which, after dedicating his properties to Hazrat Imâm Husain, and declaring that the ownership of the same as *mutwalli* should belong to him during his lifetime, he proceeded to say :—" I shall reduce into writing in detail and specify the powers which I possess in respect of the management of the *wakf* property in a separate will which should always be acted upon after my death." On the same day he executed the will in which he laid down certain rules of practice.

Seisin under the Shiah Law.

In a suit brought by certain persons for the removal of the defendant No. 1 from the office of *mutwalli* and for a declaration that the property was not saleable in execution of a decree against him, the first Court held that, although the *wakf* was valid, it had never been acted upon. Upon appeal the learned Judges of the High Court came to the same conclusion, though upon somewhat different grounds. The Chief Justice was of opinion that the *wakfnâmah* was an imperfect dedication of the property according to the Shiah Law, " for, although the donor purported to dedicate the property when he executed the *wakfnâmah*, and also purported to assume possession of it as *mutwalli*, no definite objects existed for which he was to hold possession. The *wakfnâmah* was designed not to take effect until the death of Faiyaz Ali, although it assumed in some respects the form of a disposition *inter vivos*."

---

of the doctors maintain that it reverts to the heirs of the *mowkoof-alaih*, or the person in whose favour the *wakf* is made. The first opinion, however, is the most approved." *Tanjiz* means immediate operation.

" If one should say, ' I have dedicated when the beginning of the month should come, or if Zaid will arrive,' the dedication will not be valid."

(1) (1902), I. L., 24 All., 231. It is submitted with respect that the condition in this particular case did not amount to the postponement of the *wakf* until the Registration ; it only gave expression to the *wâkif's* intention that the *wakf* should take effect when the deed can have legal operation under the law.

(2) (1902), I. L., 24 All., 257.

Mr. Justice Burkitt, on the other hand, held that "the appropriation, if valid, was complete under the terms of the first part of the *wakfnâmah*, and that it was not nugatory as being a testamentary *wakf*," but, as it was never acted upon, the *wakf* purported to be created thereunder was invalid.

SECTION VI.

DIVESTMENT OF THE WAKIF'S INTEREST.

Divestment of the *wâkif's* interest.

On this subject, the Shiahs differ from the accepted Hanafî doctrines and approach closely the views expressed by Imâm Mohammed.

"Seisin is a condition for the validity of the *wakf*," says the *Sharâya*, "so that if one should make a *wâkf* and die without giving possession, the subject of it would be his inheritance."(1) The nature of the seisin will depend on the nature of the subject of the *wakf* and of the objects for which it is dedicated. If the dedication is for specific individuals who are *sui juris* and competent to take possession of the *wakf*, seisin is essential. But it does not follow from this that there should be actual delivery of possession. What is required is that there should be a transmutation of proprietary right. If a trustee is appointed, he should take possession of the property. If the *wâkif* himself is the *mutwalli*, he should hold as such.

"If, however, one should make a *wakf* in favour of his minor children, his own possession would be possession on their behalf."(2) The same principle applies to a *wakf* by a grandfather, or any person in whose guardianship the children are.

The possession of the executor of the *wâkif* is effectual seisin in law.

Where the *wakf* is for pious purposes or for the benefit of mankind in general, no seisin is necessary. The *Sharâya* states the principle thus :—"Where a *wakf* is made for the poor or for the learned in law, a superintendent (*kyyum*) must be appointed to take possession of the *wakf* property—while in the case of a *wakf* made for a *maslahat* the creation of the trust is sufficient, the

---

(1) *Sharâya-ul-Islam*, p. 236.
(2) *Ibid.*

condition of acceptance being entirely dispensed with, and as to possession that of the *nâzir* or superintendent is sufficient."

"If a person should dedicate a mosque or place of worship, the dedication is effectual though only one person should pray therein. In like manner, if a person dedicate a cemetery, the same becomes operative by the interment therein even of a single corpse. But though people should pray in a mosque or bury in a cemetery without the formal words of *wakf* being pronounced, neither would pass out of the property of the owner until it is formally dedicated."(1)

Where only appropriate words have been used, but no change in the character of the possession has taken place, the *wakf* would not be operative.

***Wakf* for the *wâkif's* minor children.**

The possession of the *mutwalli* appointed to look after the *wakf* would be sufficient, and the *wâkif* may himself be the *mutwalli*.(2)

As already stated, where the *wakf* is for the *wâkif's* minor children, no express transmutation of proprietary right is necessary, and if the *wâkif* remains in possession, his possession would be on their behalf.(3)

A *wakf* in favour of one's self not valid under the Shiah Law.

Divestment of interest.—With reference to the fourth condition, it will be observed that there is a marked difference between the Shiah and Sunni Law on the subject. According to Abû Yusuf, a *wâkif* is entitled to reserve for himself an interest in the *wakf* property, or as he puts it "to eat thereout." Under the Shiah Law, in order that a *wakf* may be valid, it is necessary that there should be no reservation of interest in favour of the *wâkif*. "If a person were to make a *wakf* for himself," says the *Jawâhir*, "it would not be valid; this is without any difference of opinion. Similarly, a *wakf* commencing with the *wâkif*, *e.g.*, for the *wâkif* and then for another, will be invalid, though some, among them the Shaikh, have held that it would be invalid only as regards himself. The former opinion seems to be generally adopted." "Similarly, if the *wakf* were made in favour of another with a condition for the payment of the *wâkif's* debts and currents expenses, it would not be valid. This is supported by

(1) *Sharâya-ul-Islâm*, p. 237. (2) *Jâm'aa-ush-Shittât.*
(3) According to Mohammed ibn Muslim.

the answer of Abu'l Hassan (the Caliph Ali) (may the blessing of God rest on him) to the letter of Ali bin Sulaimân who wrote to the Imâm thus :—' May I be your sacrifice ; I have no children, and I have some lands which I have received from my father. I intend to dedicate the same for my poor and weak brethren ; if I make a *wakf* in my lifetime, can I eat therefrom whilst I live ? ' To this the reply was, ' I have received thy letter and learnt its purport ; if thou shouldst make a *wakf* of thy lands and make a condition to eat therefrom, it will not be valid. If thou hast heirs, sell the land and give a portion (of the proceeds) to the poor, or reserve a portion which may be sufficient for thy support during thy lifetime and dedicate the remainder.''

The following from the *Jâm'aa-ush-Shittât* throws considerable light on this subject—

'' *Q.* When a person makes a *wakf* of some property in this way, *viz.*, ' I have constituted this a *wakf* in perpetuity, and its *towliat* I have reserved for myself during my lifetime, and after my death for the eldest and fittest of my children in succession, generation after generation (*batnan-b'aad-batn*), and I have appointed that the rents and profits of the *wakf* property after paying all royal taxes and costs of collection, I shall apply for my expenses ; and after my death, one-tenth of the said rents and profits, after deducting the taxes and costs shall be given to the *mutwalli* for his remuneration, and the remainder divided among my children equally, but the share of my daughters shall not go to their children ;' and some time after the *wâkif* died leaving three sons and the sons of predeceased sons, will his grandsons take interest in the *wakf*, &c.?''

Divestment of the *wâkif's* interest.

'' *A.* This *wakf* is void *ab initio*, for the *wâkif* reserved to himself during his lifetime the profits of the property. It is one of the conditions for the legality of a *wakf* that the *wâkif* should take out the subject of the *wakf* from himself. Therefore, when a *wakf* is made on his own *nafs* (self) it is *bâtil* (void), though there are others mentioned after himself as the beneficiaries thereof. With reference to the voidableness of the *wakf* as to himself there is consensus ; as regards the voidableness of the remainder, the general opinion is that it is so, for the arguments in support of the validity of the *wakf* in favour of the others are weak. Similarly, if he were to make a *wakf* and stipulate to defray his every-day expenses or to pay his debts thereout, it would be invalid. *But a condition that his people and children and family should eat out of the wakf is valid*, as is apparent from what was done by the Prophet and his daughter (may the blessings of God rest on them both), and in this respect there is no difference between those who are entitled to maintenance and those who are not. In the same way, it is lawful to fix the allowances of *mutwallis* and *nâzirs*, or to give them permission to eat out of the *wakf* and supply others with food. And in the *Masâlik* it is clearly laid down that when the *wâkif* is himself the *mutwalli*, it is lawful for him to eat out of the *wakf* [as a *mutwalli*] and this 'eating' does not fall within the category of a provision for the *wâkif's* own benefit. The author of the *Kijâyah*, however, doubts whether the *wâkif* can 'eat' out of the *wakf* in this way. It must be admitted that considerable difficulties surround this point, and on this account many people question the lawfulness of the *wâkif* taking any share even as *mutwalli*. For example, a person makes a *wakf* of some property on his children, and conditions that the *towliat* should remain in his hands during his lifetime, and after his death it should go to the fittest among them, and the *wâkif* also conditions that nine-tenths of the profits of the *wakf* should belong to him by right of *towliat*, and the remaining tenth should be given to the children, and that after his death one-twentieth should be given to the fittest of the children by right of *towliat*, and the balance of the income be divided among them equally,—in such a case as this, my view is that the *wakf* would not be valid. Admittedly, it is lawful for the *wâkif* to retain the *towliat* in his own hands during his lifetime, and also to condition that the *mutwalli* should feed himself and others from out of the *wakf*. From these two theses some of our jurists have drawn the conclusion that where the *wâkif* has made a condition for the *mutwalli* for the time being to feed himself and others out of the *wakf* and the *wâkif* happens to be the *mutwalli*, it is lawful for him to eat thereout, though a few have doubted the lawfulness of his doing so. The result is, that the legality of the *mutwalli* eating out of the *wakf* depends on his quality as *mutwalli*, and not upon the fact of the *wâkif* being the *mutwalli*. And the jurists are agreed that where anything has been fixed for the *mutwallis* generally, it is lawful for the *wâkif*, when he happens to be the *mutwalli*, to take so much as is fixed for the other *mutwallis* ;

but I have nowhere seen that it has been held that a *wâkif*, whilst he is the *mutwalli*, can lawfully take for himself anything he likes out of the *wakf* simply because he himself is the *mutwalli*. The meaning of this is, that the retention of such a general power which would authorise his taking the largest share for himself, leaving almost nothing for the beneficiaries, is contradictory to the condition which requires a complete divestment of all proprietary right on the part of the *wâkif*. This, of course, does not apply to a person who has made a *wakf* for the indigent and has himself become poor, or where he has made a *wakf* for the learned and has himself become learned. In such cases, the *wâkif* would be entitled to participate in the benefits of the *wakf*, and it makes no difference whether at the time of the *wakf* he is a *fakîr* or learned, or whether he becomes so afterwards. But if he makes a condition that he, as a *fakîr*, should participate in it, it would not be valid. The result is that where a *wakf* is made for a general purpose (*jihât-i-'aâmma*), a *wâkif* may lawfully participate in it."

But the *wâkif* when *mutwalli* can lawfully take the allowance reserved for the trustees generally.

From the above passage, it is clear that the *wâkif* can lawfully take the allowance fixed for the *mutwallis* generally, when he himself holds the office.

There is another case given in the *Jâm'aa-ush-Shittât* which deserves equal attention with the above as explaining the question how far a *wâkif* may reserve to himself any interest in the *wakf* property.

"*Q.* One Zaid makes a *wakf* of six dams of a certain property and six dams of a certain mill and executes a *wakfnâmah* which is attested by one of the *mujtahids* of the time, who is dead. The purport of the *wakfnâmah* is as follows:—out of the *wakf* four dams should be for the benefit of the *wâkif's* male children, generation after generation; should there be no male children then for the female children in perpetuity; two dams to be devoted to the following purposes, *viz.*, for the expenses of the sacred months of Rajab, Shâbân and Ramazân, in such a way that the good resulting from such disbursements may be for the soul of the *wâkif*, and during the first two months fifteen Koran-readers should be entertained, each of whom should read four parts of the Koran, and, after the death of the *wâkif*, they should offer prayers and fastings for the soul of the *wâkif*, and that during his lifetime the *wâkif* should be *mutwalli* thereof, and after his death his eldest son should be the *mutwalli*, and so on; that during his lifetime he should take $\frac{19}{20}$ths of the proceeds by virtue of the office of *towliat*, and $\frac{1}{20}$th should be given to the children, that after his death $\frac{1}{20}$th should be given to the *mutwalli*, and the rest distributed among his children. Is such a *wakf* valid?"

"*A.* This question cannot be answered without its being discussed in three aspects—

"If the document, the purport of which has been given above forms the only evidence of the conditions of this *wakf*, then it must be pronounced to be wanting in legality on several grounds; (*a*) with reference to the dedication of the two *dâms*, it would appear that it does not come into operation until after the death of the *wâkif*, for the directions given as to the mode of application of the proceeds thereof take effect only as a testamentary provision upon his death, since the *wâkif* declares that the income thereof should be applied in entertaining Koran-readers, feeding the poor, performing prayers, &c., upon his death for the benefit of his soul. But it is a condition for the legality of a *wakf inter vivos* that it should have operation immediately. In the present case, the *wakf* of the two *dâms* is dependent upon the death of the testator; in fact, there is no one entitled to the benefit of that portion unless it be presumed that it is the *wâkif* himself, which would be invalid. And if it were said that the proceeds of the two *dâms* should be applied to charity in general until the death of the *wâkif*, and after his death should be applied to the Koran-reading, &c., mentioned by him, this is clearly opposed to the purport of the *wakfnâmah* itself. The *wakf*, therefore, is clearly invalid, as it is a *wakf* virtually in one's own favour."

Wakf in one's own favour.

Similarly, if one were to make a *wakf* and condition therein that out of the income thereof his debts should be paid, such a *wakf* would be invalid. But if a person were to convey his property in trust to sell the same and out of the proceeds to pay his debts and to invest the remainder for religious or pious purposes, or in erecting a religious building and maintaining religious observances therein, it would be a valid dedication.(1)

A wakf in favour of

If a person were to make a settlement on himself and the poor, only half the property would be validly dedicated, and with refer-

(1) Comp. *Haji Mohammed Kazem* v. *Phudia Bibi*, supra.

ence to the remaining half the *wakf* would not take effect. In the case of *Haji Kalb Hossein* v. *Musst. Mehrun Bibi*,(1) the Allahabad High Court enforced this principle. The decision in this case is so important that it may be usefully set out here *in extenso*.

one's self and the poor.

***Haji Kalb Hossein* v. *Musst. Mehrun Bibi*.**

In the year 1851 one Mussamat Sahibzadee executed a deed by which she appropriated certain moneys and estates, of which she was possessed, to certain religious and other purposes in the following manner, *viz.*, she appropriated two-thirds of the income to herself during her lifetime for her necessary expenses, and the remaining one-third of the income she declared divisible into fifty-five shares, of which some were to be distributed to certain persons therein mentioned, charged with religious duties, and the residue was to be expended on religious ceremonies, which were specified. She appointed herself trustee, and declared that the fifty-five shares as detailed would remain appropriated during her trusteeship, and that neither she nor her assignee, nor representative should have power to transfer the property so appropriated; and she declared further that after her trusteeship, the trustee who might succeed to her should, after discharging the Government revenue and other outgoings and charges of management, divide the balance of the income into 165 shares, and retain 55 shares on account of his trusteeship, and apply the remaining shares as therein directed to the payment of pensions to persons therein mentioned, for the performance of religious duties, and to certain specified religious purposes. By this deed one share out of the 55 shares in the income of the property was to be paid to the plaintiff, who was the respondent in the High Court, during the lifetime of the settlor, and 10 shares out of the 165 shares into which the income was to be divided on the expiry of the settlor's trusteeship, were to be paid to her, and after her death, to her heirs, "generation after generation," subject to the condition that they performed certain religious duties therein particularised.

The settlor died in 1872, and the respondent, having failed in obtaining payment of the shares appropriated to her by the deed of 1851, instituted a suit to recover her allowance thereunder. The Lower Courts decreed the plaintiff's claim. In special appeal it was contended *inter alia* that the respondent ought, prior to the

(1) 4 N.-W. P. H. C. Reports, 155.

Haji Kalb Hossein v. *Musst. Mehrun Bibi*—(contd.)

institution of the suit, to have obtained sanction of the Court under section 18, Act XX of 1863. With reference to this objection the High Court held as follows :—" That section only prescribes the necessity for obtaining sanction when suits are instituted under that Act. This suit is not instituted under that Act : the respondent has instituted this suit to recover a direct pecuniary interest created in her favour by the deed of 1851. The Act, while it empowered persons to sue, whose right to sue independently of the Act may be doubtful, did not deprive persons in the position of the respondent of the right to sue, which they have independently of the Act, nor did it impose on them the necessity of obtaining sanction of the Court for the institution of this suit. Moreover, the Act refers to foundations to which, at the time the Act was passed, the provisions of Regulation XIX of 1810 were applicable ; and it appears to us that to the trust created by the deed of 1851 the provisions of that Regulation were not applicable. The management of the trust-estate had never been assumed by the Government officer, nor was the nomination of the trustee, at the time the Act was passed, vested in the Government or a public officer, nor was the nomination of the trustee subject to the confirmation of Government or any public officer. The nomination of a trustee may hereafter in certain events become vested in a public officer, but these events have not yet happened. We, therefore, overrule this objection."

The learned Judges then proceeded to deal with the principal objection in the following terms :—" It is contended that the deed of 1851 was not a valid deed of *wakf* according to the tenets of the Imamea sect, *first*, because Sahibzadee Begum remained in possession of the property as proprietor up to the date of the gift in 1867, and, *secondly*, because she reserved to herself a benefit out of the *wakf* property, in that she reserved two-thirds of the income for the necessary expenses during her lifetime. To constitute a valid *wakf* according to the doctrine of the Shiahs, it must be absolute and unconditional, and possession must be given of the *mowkoof* or thing appropriated, and it must be taken entirely out of the *wâkif* or proprietor himself. Firstly, then we have to consider whether possession was given of the appropriated property. The law allows the appropriator to appoint himself *mutwalli*, consequently inasmuch as the settlor appointed herself *mutwalli*, and

Haji Kalb Hossein v. Musst. Mehrun Bibi (concld).

by her conduct subsequent to the execution of the deed of 1851 indicated that she held the appropriated property on the trust declared in that deed, we hold there was sufficient proof of possession to satisfy the requirements of the law; but we also hold that as to two-thirds of the property, the deed of 1851 did not create a valid *wakf*. The settlor reserved to herself the benefit of the income of two-thirds of the appropriated property, so much of the property she settled on herself for her lifetime, and consequently this case is not distinguishable from the cases mentioned in the *Sharâya*. It remains to be determined whether the invalidity of the deed of 1851, as a *wakfnâmah*, in respect of the two-thirds, renders it altogether invalid, or invalid only to the extent of the two-thirds. The *Sharâya* declares that where a settlement is made on another with a condition for the payment of the *wâkif's* debts, or necessary expenses, such a settlement is invalid. In that case the reservation is of an indefinite benefit; in the present case one-third of the income, a definite share was, as it appears to us, absolutely and permanently appropriated to purposes other than the temporal benefit of the settlor, and entirely taken out of the settlor, and inasmuch as the *wakf* of a *mushâa*, or undivided share in a thing is valid, we feel ourselves at liberty to hold that the deed of 1851 was valid to the extent of one-third of the income of the property; and that that share of the property is available for the satisfaction of the trust declared by the settlor to take effect after her trusteeship. Consequently the claim of the respondent must be reduced by two-thirds."

Qualification to the rule.—Though it is not lawful for a *wâkif* to create a *wakf* in his favour, "yet if the *wakf* is in the way of God or for a pious or religious purpose, for example, a mosque, it would be lawful for the *wâkif* to derive benefit therefrom, *viz.*, to participate in the prayers held there and to offer his prayers in the place. Similarly, in the case of any other *wakf* of a public character, such as a bridge or hostel (*musâfirkhâneh*)." In other words the *wâkif* can avail himself of the benefit of the institution in the same way as any other member of the public.

In considering the validity of a *wakf* which is not of a public nature, and in the benefit of which the *wâkif* participates to a certain extent by implication, the important question to determine

Participation by the *wâkif* in the benefit of a *wakf*.

is whether the *wâkif* intentionally made a reservation in his favour of that interest. Apparently, the participation of the *wâkif* to a certain extent, which does not show that the *wakf* was a mere device for tying-up the property for the *wâkif's* own benefit, would not be invalid. This view is submitted as the result of the difficult and somewhat casuistical arguments discussed in the *Jawâhir-ul-Kalâm*.

If a person were to create a *wakf* and make a condition that the property should return to him in case of necessity, the condition would be valid and the *wakf* would be void, the transaction taking effect as a mere *hubs* or settlement; when the need arises the property would revert to the owner. The need must be such as is considered valid under custom and usage, but not anything technically called a need. When the property once reverts to the donor the right of alienation will attach to it,(1) and on the death of the owner the property will go to his heirs.

Valid conditions in a *wakf*.

A condition to the effect that the *wâkif* should have the power of excluding any one he liked from the benefit of the *wakf* is invalid. But a condition to introduce fresh beneficiaries is valid except in the case of a *wakf* in favour of children.

When a *wakf* is for one's children generally, children born after the *wakf* will be included, though there may not be any express condition to that effect. But when a *wakf* is made for children and the property is made over to them, after-born children will not be included unless it has been so expressly provided.

When a *wakf* is made for the benefit of one's infant children, the donor will not have the power of so varying the terms of the *wakf* as to include outsiders in its benefit unless he has expressly reserved power to that effect.

Possession.

Seisin.—The seisin which is required is on behalf of the first beneficiary or *mowkoof-alaih* and all regard to possession ceases in the subsequent steps. As already stated, it is not necessary, however, that there should be any actual transfer of possession; what is required is a change in the character of the possession. For a *wâkif* may make a *wakf* and remain in possession as

(1) *Sharâya-ul-Islam*, p. 237. In other words the *wakf* in such a case takes effect as a settlement.

trustee for the beneficiaries of the trust; such retention of possession will not affect the legal character of the *wakf*.

As the provision requiring seisin on the part of the first *cestui que trust* relates to a change in the character of the possession, constructive delivery of possession is sufficient. As under the Hanafî Law, when the possession is already in the hands of the *cestui que trust* or of the trustee, no formal delivery of seisin is necessary. The former possession is sufficient to validate the *wakf*. For example, if *A* were to dedicate a property which is in his possession through an agent *B*, and were to appoint *B* as the *mutwalli* or trustee thereof, no further delivery of possession is necessary, the relation of *B* as agent ceases with the creation of the *wakf* and the property remains in his hands as a trustee.

The passage in the *Sharâya*, therefore, that "the seisin which is required is of the first *mowkoof-alaih*" must be read with due regard to the other circumstances. Nor is the seisin of the beneficiary or beneficiaries themselves necessary. Any one who is actually or constructively their agent may take possession of it. Where a *wakf* is made for a charitable or pious purpose of a public character, as in the case of an appropriation for the poor, for lawyers, for students and such like, it is out of the question for the entire body of beneficiaries to obtain seisin of the property; the possession of the superintendent appointed by the *wâkif* or in his absence of the Judge or of a curator appointed by him for that purpose, will be sufficient.

Wakf in favour of an object of public utility.

The *wâkif* can validly appoint himself as the *mutwalli* of the *wakf*. In the case of a *wakf* in favour of an object of public utility (*maslahat*) such as a bridge, a mosque and such like, acceptance is not a condition nor seisin of any specific person deriving benefit from such object is necessary. The seisin of a *mutwalli* or *nâzir* appointed for the purpose of managing or looking after the maintenance of the *wakf* is sufficient. When the *wâkif* has constituted a *mutwalli* or superintendent no reference is necessary to the Judge. In case of any question as to the validity of his appointment, the Judge, as the guardian of the interests of the Mussulman public, will appoint a *nâzir* or curator.

Dedication of a *masjid* or cemetery.

When a place or building is dedicated for prayers, it will become operative if prayers have been offered there even by one person. Similarly, a cemetery will become dedicated by the burial of one corpse. It must, however, be borne in mind that the intention of the appropriator must be apparent. For example, the permission of the owner of a house to another person to pray therein, or even the continuous offering of prayers in a private house, will not convert the residence into a *masjid* or a place of worship. But if a person declares that he dedicates his house as a mosque and after that allows another person to pray therein, that would be sufficient to create a valid *wakf.*(1) Again, if a person were to erect a building of the customary type of a mosque, and allow another to offer his prayers therein, it would be sufficient, though there may be no express declaration constituting it a *wakf*. Mere interment of a corpse on a land or offering of prayers in a building without express or implied declaration of intention on the part of the grantor, will not be sufficient to constitute the land or building a valid *wakf*.

If a father or grandfather were to make a *wakf* of a certain property belonging to him, for his child or grandchild, and retain possession of it on behalf of such child notwithstanding that a *mutwalli* has been appointed, such possession is lawful, and will be regarded in law as the possession of the *cestui que trust*.

The beneficial interest in such properties as are dedicated for general charitable or pious purposes appertains to God, for there is no *mâl* (property) without a *mâlik* (owner), and inasmuch as there is no specific beneficial owner of such public trust, the property impliedly belongs to the Deity.

Where a *wakf* is made for one's children's children (*awlâd-ul-awlâd*), the children of daughters will participate with those of the son.

Where a *wakf* is made for one's children and *their* children, the descendants of the third generation will not be included, unless it can be gathered that the donor intended all his descendants to share in the benefit of the *wakf.*(2)

When a *wakf* is made for one's *awlâd* and *awlâd* of *awlâd* and their *awlâd*, all the surviving descendants share equally *per capita*,

(1) *Jawâhir-ul-Kalâm.*
(2) *Ibid.*

unless it is laid down that they should take *batn* (generation) after *batn*, when the *batns* will take in succession.

When a *wakf* is made for the *wâkif's* children generally, it will endure to the benefit of all the descendants of the *wâkif*; and upon their extinction *alone* the benefit of the *wakf* will go to the poor. *Wakf* on children.

When a *wakf* is made for a mosque which becomes ruined, and the village or *mahallah* (quarter) in which it is situated becomes deserted, yet the *wakf* will not cease, and the property will not revert to the *wâkif* notwithstanding that, barring the traces of the building, nothing else remains of the mosque. This doctrine says the *Sharâya* is accepted "among us" without a difference.(1)

When a building becomes ruined, so that there are no traces left of it, the land on which it was situated will not go out (of the category) of *wakf*, and cannot be sold. The ruin of the building will not destroy the *wakf*, the characteristic of which is perpetuity.

The *wâkif* is authorised to make a proviso to the effect that the *mutwalli* shall have the power to sell the property and invest the proceeds to better advantage. In the absence of any such provision if it appears that its sale would be to the advantage of the *wakf* or of the beneficiaries by investing the proceeds in some other more profitable property, the *mutwalli* may validly sell it with the sanction of the Judge. Sale of *wakf* property.

When disputes have arisen among the beneficiaries, and it has become apparent that by keeping the property in its original form considerable injury will accrue to the *wakf*, sale also is allowed. Power to alter investment.

When a *wakf* is made for the poor, it will be applied to the poor of the place where it is situated, and such of those as are forthcoming to avail themselves of its benefit. The *mutwalli* has not to search for them and distribute the proceeds among them. Imâm Abû Jaafar II declared in answer to an enquiry by Abû Ali ibn Sulaiman that when land has been dedicated for the poor descendants of so-and-so, it should be applied to the benefit of such of them as are living in the city where the *wakf* is situated, or such as come forward to claim it, and the *mutwalli* is not bound to go in search of them.

---

(1) *Jawahir-ul-Kalam* chap. on *Wakf*.

Neither a *sadakah* nor a *wakf* can be revoked.

A *sadakah* cannot be revoked after possession has once been given, for it is equivalent to a *hiba-bi'l-ewaz*. The object of a *wakf*, as well as of a *sadakah*, is to obtain the favour of God and when it is made the favour is obtained, so it cannot be revoked.

CHAPTER XVII.

THE MALIKI LAW RELATING TO WAKFS.

SECTION I.

THE CONSTITUTION OF A WAKF.

THE Mâliki rules relating to *wakfs* are in the main identical with the Hanafî Law, except in certain features which require special consideration. The Mâlikis also trace the law of *wakf* to the same tradition as the Hanafîs.(1)

The *wâkif's* capacity.

The capacity for making a *wakf* is the same as in respect of other dispositions of property, such as a gift.

The *wâkif* consequently must be :—

(*a*) Free and not a slave.

(*b*) Sane.

(*c*) In good health, or, to be more exact, he must not be suffering from a death-illness. A *wakf* by a "sick" person is similar to a legacy. It is null when made in favour of an heir, and reducible to a third if made in favour of a person who has not the right of inheritance.

"A *wakf* made in favour of heirs," says Khalîl ibn Ishâk, "by a person during the illness of which he dies, is null and void ; but a *wakf* made in favour of descendants of the direct line [who are not heirs] by such a person is valid if it does not exceed the third of the inheritance."

(*d*) Possessor of the property made *wakf*, that is to say, he must have dominion over it.

The Courts of Justice have consequently annulled the *wakf*— (*i*) when the donor died heavily involved in debt, and the property endowed had to be sold to discharge his debts ; (*ii*) when the debts of the settlor exceeded his assets ; (*iii*) when the grantor was not in proprietary possession of the property when he made the *wakf*.

---

(1) 2 Sautayra, p. 374.

(*e*) *Sui juris*, having the full exercise of his or her rights. A (Mâliki) married woman, therefore, cannot make a *wakf* of more than one-third of her property without the consent of her husband.

A non-Moslem who fulfils the conditions above-mentioned can make a *wakf* of the whole or part of his property. The law imposes but one limitation over the liberality of those who do not follow the Islâmic faith; it forbids their constituting a mosque as beneficiary of their *wakf*. "It is unlawful for a non-Moslem," says the text, "to make a *wakf* in favour of a mosque."

The beneficiary.

A *wakf* can be constituted in favour of every person who can possess property; it can also be made in favour of unborn children and non-existing objects. Accordingly, the *wâkif* can designate as beneficiaries:—

(*a*) A Mussulman, or a non-Moslem fellow-subject (*Zimmi*). But "a *wakf* in favour of a non-Moslem living in a hostile country is invalid."

(*b*) Men and women.

(*c*) Majors and minors.

(*d*) Heirs or non-heirs.

(*e*) Strangers.

(*f*) Works of beneficence and charity, for example, a cemetery, a caravanserai, the tomb of a saint, the sacred cities of Mecca and Medina.(1)

(*g*) The poor, the sick, the maimed, etc.

The *wakif's* powers.

The *wâkif* has, therefore, the right to point out the beneficiaries, to take them either from his family or from without. But is the right absolute? Does it go so far as to enable the *wâkif* to exclude his daughters? The words of Khalîl ibn Ishâk on this point are precise—"a *wakf* in favour of sons to the exclusion of daughters is illegal," and this rule has constantly been enforced by the Courts of Justice in Algeria. "Whereas," says a decree made on the 30th December 1864 by the Court of Algiers, "the Koran is the foundation of the religious dogmas and of the civil law of the Mussulmans; and whereas its precepts determine specially the order and manner of succession in families

A *wakf* excluding any child from its benefit not valid.

(1) Comp. the provisions of the Hanafî Law, *ante*.

(Sura IX); and whereas the distribution of property such as it has ordained gives to the children of the female sex a quotient of the inheritance of which the female line cannot be deprived in favour of the male descendants without the wish of the Legislator being ignored, consequently a *wakf* so constituted would be tainted by radical illegality as made in disregard of the commandments of the Prophet, the *wakf* in question must therefore be annulled."

"Considering," says another decree of the 3rd November 1868, "that the *wakf* was made according to the Mâliki school; that according to this school female children cannot be excluded from the benefits of a *wakf*, the deed is null and void."(1) "As for sons," according to Sîdi Khalîl, "the grantor may validly exclude them from the *wakf*." "The reverse" (the exclusion of sons), says Perron, "is legal, but the Courts do not feel justified in acting upon the authorities upon whose opinion this view is based, and have extended the principle laid down by Sîdi Khalîl so as to place the sons on the same footing as daughters, and have declared that neither should be excluded from receiving the benefits of the *wakf*." One of the decrees of the Algerian Court of the 20th March 1865, says:—"That in virtue of a verse in Chap. IV of the Koran, the son has the right to a determinate share in the paternal heritage and cannot be excluded therefrom directly or indirectly, that a *wakf* made by the father in favour of his daughter excluding the son should be regarded as being in reality but a disguised donation having for its object the contradiction of the Mussulman Law, that for these reasons such *wakf* must be set aside."(2)

Descendants of the second degree may be excluded.

In any case, exclusion is only forbidden as regards children of the first degree. Sîdi Khalîl pronounces only those *wakfs* illegal that are made in favour of sons to the exclusion of daughters. Consequently the Courts have sanctioned the exclusion of—

(*a*) A grandson.

(*b*) The female issue of daughters.

(*c*) All the issue of daughters.

(*d*) The daughters of sons.

---

(1) According to the Hanafi Law, it is sinful but not illegal.

(2) These decisions are founded exclusively on the Mâliki doctrines and have no application to the Hanafis. It will be noticed, however, that the validity of a *wakf* in favour of the descendants is not questioned.

The *wâkif* may designate not only the first beneficiaries of the *wakf* but also the successive ones in the order in which each should come. He, therefore, has the power of laying down special rules of devolution different from that appointed in the *Shar'aa* (the Law).

Rules relating to the devolution of a family *wakf*.

The *wâkif* may declare 1*stly*, that the right of representation should be admitted; 2*ndly*, that devolution should take place *per capita*; 3*rdly*, that the division should be made among the beneficiaries according to sex. But if the deed constituting the *wakf* contains no clause on these different points the following rules will be observed :—

In the absence of an express provision regarding the right of representation the ordinary rule of Mussulman Law would apply. In this respect the Mâliki rules are identical with those recognised by the Hanafîs.

Regarding the second point, devolution in the first degree, that is, among children of the *wâkif*, must necessarily go *per capita*. On the other hand, in the second degree and lower down ordinarily it takes place *per stirpes*, according to the rule laid down by the jurist Ibn Rushd and carried out by al-Lakhim, al-Hattab and others. The son inherits from his father and is not excluded by his uncles, because every child succeeds and continues the branch of his father. The *wâkif*, however, can prescribe that the devolution throughout successive devolutions should be *per capita*.

The Algerian Courts have repeatedly given effect to the ordinary rule. One of the decrees, that of the 20th April 1874, was pronounced under the following circumstances :—a *wakf* had, by a series of successive devolutions, come to two brothers Mohammed and al-Hadj Ali. Mohammed died in 1869, leaving seven children, and the Kâzi of Algiers decided, upon the difficulties that arose about the possession of the *wakf* property, by a judgment of the 20th October 1873 (confirmed on the 20th April following), that the children of Mohammed should divide among themselves as representing one branch the half of their father's share, and that al-Hadj Ali as the head of another branch should hold the other half of the *wakf*.

The third point relating to distribution among the beneficiaries is expounded in clear terms by Khalîl ibn Ishâk, " if the *wâkif* has not fixed the proportions, men and women should have equal shares.''

The *wâkif* can provide further that the preferential right of a double line should be maintained, but in default of an express clause the consanguine should share equally with the relations of the full-blood. ''The full brother and consanguine brother,'' says the Shaikh al-Hattab, ''have equal rights, as their relation in respect to the father is equal in degree and in legal force.'' ''If the *wâkif*,'' says Sîdi Khalîl, ''has conditioned that the portion devolving upon such an one should fall to his nearest relative, and if this person has full brothers as well as consanguine and uterine brothers, which of these would have the right to the benefit of the *wakf*; would the full brothers be preferred to the other brothers? No; because they are all equally distant; there are the same number of degrees between them all.'' The commentator Abdul Bâki lays down the same doctrine. ''By the words 'the nearest relative,' it is understood that the full brother and the consanguine brother have equal rights, as their relationship to their father is equal.'' Rules of devolution.

The lower line in the same branch, which is a degree further off, participates with the upper line, which is nearer, where it is provided by the terms of the *wakf*; if not, it is excluded by the upper line.

In order better to understand this rule we subjoin the following genealogical table—

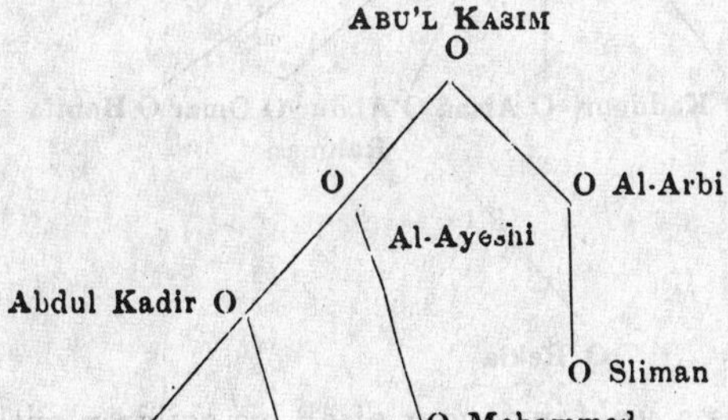

Abu'l Kâsim, the founder of the *wakf*, had two sons al-Arbi and al-Ayeshi who became entitled in equal moieties to the produce thereof. Upon al-Arbi's death, the profits of the *wakf* were divided into two shares, *viz.*, al-Ayeshi retained his half, and

Sliman succeeded to the half of his father's share. Al-Ayeshi had two sons, Abdul Kadir and Mohammed. Abdul Kadir died in the lifetime of his father, leaving him surviving Ahmed and Aissa.

Q. Who should take the half of the *wakf* which had devolved upon al-Ayeshi ?

Rules of devolution —contd.

A. If the *wakfnâmah* does not contain any special condition, Mohammed would take exclusively, because Ahmed and Ben Aissa his nephews, are a degree more distant than he, and because they do not represent their pre-deceased father. Had the *wâkif* made a provision to the effect that all the degree should take equally, the inferior together with the superior, Ahmed, Ben Aissa and Mohammed would have become jointly entitled to the share of al-Ayeshi and would have each taken one-sixth share of the produce of the *wakf*. This is in accordance with a decision of the Court of Algiers passed on the 25th May 1874.

Take another case :

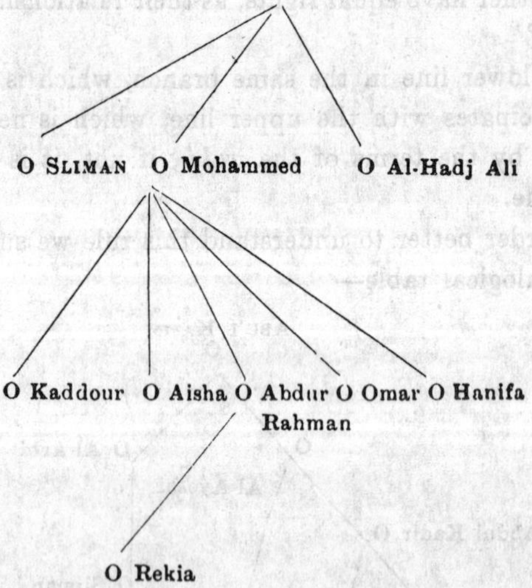

Sliman makes a *wakf* in favour of all his children without distinction of sex ; in default of descendants, in favour of his brothers, Mohammed and al-Hadj Ali, and their issue, similarly, without distinction of sex. Sliman died without issue, and the *wakf* consequently devolved on his two brothers. Mohammed died leaving five children ; they divided equally among themselves the half of that which their father had held. Abdur Rahman then died, leaving his only daughter Rekia, who takes the whole of her father's share contrary to that which happens upon ordinary succession. Then al-Hadj Ali dies without issue.

Q. Upon whom would devolve *his* half of the *wakf* produce ?

A. Kaddour, Aisha, Omar and Hanifa each take one-quarter. As for Rekia, she is not entitled to a share in Ali's portion, as she is a degree more remote from him than her uncles and aunts, and representation not being provided for, she cannot claim the rights of her father predeceased. This is the solution given by the Court of Algiers on the 20th April 1874.

Where one of the beneficiaries dies without issue, his share devolves, as in the last example, upon his nearest relatives. Sometimes the *wâkif* declares this formally. "The one of the two who dies first shall transmit his share to the other."

But more often the deed is silent on this point, and the Courts interpret this silence as though the clause above quoted were inserted. Thus a man named Ahmed bin Abdul-Kâdir made a *wakf* in favour of his children ; one of these dying without issue, his portion was allotted to his four brothers and sisters, each taking a fourth share in accordance with the decision of the *Majlis* of Médéa of the 3rd September 1858. Thus, again, a *wakf* was held by several beneficiaries ; one of these dying, a contest arose among the survivors, and the Court of Algiers, by a decree of the 12th September 1867, decided that his share should be divided into equal portions among those who were of the same degree of relationship with him. This decision has since been confirmed by a judgment of the Kâzi of the 15th Circle on the 10th September and by a decree of the Court of the 25th July 1871. Such a solution admits of no difficulty when the beneficiaries are all descended in a direct or a collateral line from the founder of the *wakf*, because they are all united by ties of relationship, and are all heirs of one another ; but what should be the principle for decision in those cases where the beneficiaries nominated by the *wâkif* do not belong to the same family and one of them dies without issue ? Would his share fall to his co-beneficiaries ? If the deed contains a clause like the one we have quoted in the *wakfnâmah* of 1874 or any other stipulation from which one might surmise that it was the *wâkif's* wish to leave the *wakf* to the survivor, the question would be answered in the affirmative ;

this is clearly deducible from the principle laid down by Khalîl ibn Ishâk :—" A *wakf* granted to ten people for enjoyment during their lives reverts, after all are deceased, to the *wâkif* or in his default to his heirs."

In the absence, however, of any condition to that effect in the *wakfnâmah*, the co-beneficiary has no claim, and the deceased's share would go to the succeeding beneficiary, or would revert to the donor if the succession is not indicated, as exemplified in the following passage in the text :—" When a *wakf* is made in favour of two particular persons, and after them in favour of the poor, these would be placed after the decease of one of the two in possession of his share."

Section II.

What may be constituted Wakf.

The subject of *wakf*.

Khalîl ibn Ishâk has laid down, that all property over which dominion can be lawfully exercised may legitimately be constituted *wakf*. And the jurists have gone so far as to declare that benefit accruing from draught-cattle or horses, and the services of slaves to nurse the sick, may lawfully be dedicated. Whether simple aliment can be made *wakf* depends on the answer to the general question whether movable property can be lawfully dedicated. And it must be admitted that there is considerable divergence among the jurists on this point. But it seems generally agreed that movable property can be made *wakf* as well as immovable property, and Perron has declared that this is in accordance with the spirit of the Mâliki school. A decree of the Court of Algiers has confirmed the above principle. Khalîl ibn Ishâk has declared that the *wakf* of a book for a library or a war-horse or a suit of armour is lawful. But in consideration of the primary object of a *wakf* and of the fact that when an appropriation is made, the intention of the *wâkif* is to reserve property for pious acts, the usufruct being only given to the beneficiaries, the lawyers have held that those things which are liable to be destroyed by use or likely to perish in the course of time, could not be constituted *wakf*.

Wakf of movable property valid.

But a *wakf* may be made of every kind of movable object, when they are to be sold and the price realised therefrom is to be invested in the acquisition of immovable property or other property from which permanent benefit is accruable.(1) Agricultural implements, oxen and other animals for agricultural purposes may be made *wakf* without any question.

Wakf of *mushâ'a* valid.

A fractional share of a particular property may lawfully be dedicated. And when a house has been made *wakf*, and a portion of it has been sold to pay the *wâkif's* debts, the remaining portion will continue subject to the dedication. It is not necessary that the *wâkif* should be in actual possession of the property at the time of making the *wakf*. The law authorises the dedication of future property. This principle has been confirmed by a decree of the Kâzi of Algiers made in 1873 and again in 1874. The latter is worded thus: "A dedication in the name of the Almighty constituting as *wakf* the whole of which a man is possessed, and that which may accrue to him in the future, is lawful, but it will take effect with reference to such properties of which the beneficiary obtained full possession before the death of the *wâkif*."

Formalities relative to the creating of a *wakf*.

"A *wakf* is made," says Sîdi Khalîl, "by the use of the following expressions: 'I make a *wakf*,' or 'I give in alms;' but these formulæ must be emphasised by indicating the object of the dedication."

In spite of its importance the constitution of a *wakf* is not subject to any solemnity or publicity. It is validly made by a declaration before witnesses. But the validity of a *wakf* is subject to some essential conditions, namely, (*a*) that it should bear the character of a pious act; (*b*) that there should be a transfer of the subject-matter of the *wakf*, and (*c*) that the proprietary rights of the *wâkif* should be divested therefrom. The first of these conditions is the result of the constitution of a *wakf* generally. Consequently, when a *wakf* is made in favour of private individuals, the ultimate dedication is always reserved for such objects as the Holy Cities, a mosque, a caravanserai, a cemetery, a sanctuary, the poor, etc. This is done by adding a clause generally worded thus: —"And after the total extinction of the appointed beneficiaries the *wakf* should go to so-and-so." We may add that a pious act may be independent of the idea of *charity*. Sîdi Khalîl expressly mentions this and Perron explains that the *wakf* would be valid

The validity of a *wakf* not dependent upon a charitable purpose.

(1) Comp. the Hanafî Law.

and the act pious, even though the beneficiaries were in the most affluent circumstances.

Delivery of possession necessary.

On the necessity of delivery of possession to a trustee on behalf of the beneficiaries or a change of seisin, the Mâlikis differ from Abû Yusuf but agree with Imâm Mohammed and the Shiahs. "The taking of possession," says Mohammed Assem, "is the soul of a *wakf*, and if the *wâkif* continues to overlook and administer the *wakf* property *and to exercise rights of ownership over it*, this in itself renders the *wakf* null; the law cannot legalise it." What is required, however, is not actual delivery of possession but transmutation of possession, or a change in the character of the dominion exercised over the property dedicated. The *wâkif* may lawfully constitute himself the trustee.

When a *wakf* is in favour of an individual, possession of the beneficiary should be either by himself, if adult, or by his father or guardian, if an infant; when it is in favour of a body of individuals, transfer of possession must be made to a trustee.

In the case of a *wakf* for a pious or religious purpose, possession should be taken by its administrator. Transfer of possession is dispensed with only in case of a *wakf* made by a father in favour of his minor son, provided the circumstances sufficiently show that there was a *bonâ fide* intention to make a *wakf*, *e.g.*, (*a*) that the produce of the *wakf* had been applied to the benefit of the *cestui que trust*; (*b*) that the father did not himself continue to derive absolute benefit therefrom.

When possession should be taken.

The taking of possession is therefore a necessary formality, but at what period should it take place? "The law does not dictate that this formality should immediately follow the deed of constitution; it only requires it to be accomplished while the constituent still retains the necessary qualifications for establishing a *wakf*; that is, possesses the disposing capacity and is able to exercise the right of property over it." "The *wakf* is null," says Khalîl Ibn Ishâk, "when it has not been taken possession of before the death of the grantor, or before the illness to which he succumbed."

The *wâkif* has the power of subjecting the *wakf* to certain conditions, and these conditions must be strictly observed. He may determine the school of law according to which it should be managed, appoint the person or persons to undertake the administration, settle the order of successive devolutions, declare that the beneficiary in case of poverty should have the right to alienate the *wakf*, prescribe that in certain cases the *wakf* should revert to his heirs, and so forth; and, in general, order all measures relating to the execution of the *wakf*; but *there* his power ends, and any conditions contrary to the principle of *wakf* or reserving a power to alter its provisions or to annul the *wakf* or to sell the property, in fact, any condition which would have the effect of destroying the *wakf*, is null and void.

Temporary *wakf* lawful.

According to Khalîl Ibn Ishâk, perpetuity is not an essential condition of *wakf*; and his two commentators, al-Karkhi and Abdul Bâki, explain further that temporary *wakfs*, those made for even a single year or for the lifetime of any given person, are lawful and valid, and that the produce of the *wakf* thus constituted where no beneficiary is indicated, after the expiration of the period for which the trust is created, will go to the poor.

Can the *wâkif* annul the *wakf* of his own motion solely? Can he modify the prescribed clauses before possession of the beneficiary? The jurists, among them Ibn-ul-Hâjib and Abdus-Salâm, have answered these questions in the negative. The constitution, once made, must remain intact and be carried into effect without any modification. And if the clauses of the *wakfnâmah* are obscure, incomplete, or susceptible of diverse interpretation, the difficulty should be taken before the Kâzi, who must pronounce according to the custom and usage of the place or according to the mode in which it has hitherto been carried into effect, if it has existed for some time.

SECTION III.

THE LEGAL EFFECT OF A WAKF.

The legal effect of *wakf*.

The constitution of a property into *wakf* produces three different effects: It renders the property constituted as *wakf* inalienable, imprescriptible and non-heritable. A *wakf* property is inalienable, *because it belongs virtually to Almighty God, being intended for the benefit of mankind, the successive beneficiaries being entitled only to the usufruct thereof and not having the power to alienate it.*

There are, however, several exceptions to this principle. If the *wakf* be of land or of movable property that can no longer be useful, it should be sold and others bought with the price thereof.

If a mosque has to be enlarged, and if the sale of a piece of land attached thereto is the only mode by which funds can be forthcoming therefor, such sale would be permitted. If a beneficiary be poor and the produce of the *wakf* insufficient to procure for him the means of subsistence, alienation might take place with the leave of the Kâzi, whether the *wâkif* provided for this in the deed or not.

If the *wâkif* was so heavily indebted at the time of creating the *wakf* that his debts exceeded his assets, the creditors would be entitled to realise the debt from the property, and after their debts have been satisfied, the balance of the sale-proceeds, if any, should be invested for the benefit of the *cestui que trust*. A *wakf* may be the object of an exchange, but such exchange would only be valid upon approval of the Kâzi, after he has assured himself that the value of the two properties is equal. The exchanged property would then become *wakf* and would be subject to the same rule as the original *wakf*, and if the *wakf* had been for a specific purpose which fails, it would be applied to some other pious object, if possible similar in character to the original purpose; for example, a *wâkif* dedicates some property for the purpose of constructing a bridge or a school, and if those buildings have been constructed by the State, the produce of the property would be applied to some similar object, in default of which the *wakf* would be applied to help the poor kindred of the *wâkif*, preferentially his *asabâh* (agnates).

The beneficiaries have no right to alienate the *wakf* property; they can only enjoy its produce. For that purpose they are entitled to hold possession of it either personally or by a manager or administrator.

Neither the *cestui que trust* nor the administrator can grant a lease of the *wakf* property for a long period. According to Sîdi Khalîl, two years, according to others three years, is the longest term for which a lease may be given unless it is given to the next beneficiary, when it may be for ten years. The lease may, however, be extended if the property needs repairs. It is a principle that property held as *wakf* must be kept in good repair, and that future beneficiaries can, in order to preserve their rights, oblige the usufructor to lease the house that is falling into ruin and to apply the rent wholly to its reconstruction or repair.

(*b*) The second effect of the constitution of *wakf* is to render the property imprescriptible, that is, it cannot be subject to the rights of the sovereign as private property.

The directions of the *wâkif* must be carried out.

(*c*) The third effect resulting from the constitution of *wakf* is, that it renders the property so dedicated non-heritable, and subjects the course of descent, in respect of the beneficial interest, to the succession pointed out by the *wâkif*. On this point all writers agree. "The rules of succession to *wakf* property laid down by the *wâkif* must be strictly observed," says Sîdi Khalîl, and Ibrâhim Halabi(1) adds, that " the *wâkif* has absolute power to make any disposition he wishes regarding the usufruct of this property."

(1) The author of the *Multeka.*

CHAPTER XVIII.

THE LAW OF WAKF ACCORDING TO THE SHÂFEÏ SCHOOL.(1)

It is essential that the *wâkif* should be capable of declaring his will, and that he should have the faculty of disposition over his property, while the subject of the *wakf* must be such as can be made use of perpetually. Therefore, the subject of the dedication may not consist of aliments or odoriferous plants; but with that exception, the *wakf* of movable property is as valid as that of immovable property. But it is not valid to make a *wakf* of a trained dog. The *wakf* of *mushâ'a* or property held in joint tenancy is valid. The validity of a *wakf* of buildings or plantations upon another person's land held by the owner of the buildings or plantations under a lease is acknowledged.

The object in whose favour a *wakf* is created must be capable of taking possession constructively or actually of the *wakf* property. A *wakf*, therefore, in favour of an infant *en ventre sa mère* or a slave is not valid.

A *wakf* may be made in favour of a *Zimmi* (a non-Moslem fellow-subject), but not in favour of an apostate, nor of a non-Moslem not subject to a Mussulman ruler nor *in favour of one's self*.(2) A *wakf* for an unlawful purpose, as for example, the construction of Christian churches or of synagogues is void; but a *wakf* in favour of an hospital for Christians or Jews, made as it is with a pious motive, is lawful. A *wakf* is valid equally in favour of the poor as of the rich, of the learned, of mosques or of schools.

The intention of making a *wakf* must be formulated in explicit terms, "I make a *wakf* of such a thing," or "my field shall be a *wakf* in favour of such a person." The expressions "I consecrate," or "I offer it to such charity," are also explicit.

---

(1) The following is from the *Minhâj-ut-Tâlibîn.*

(2) Comp. the Hanafî and Shiah Law.

The same is the case with the expression, "I make a sacred gift of such a thing," or "endow it," or "it shall not be sold or given to another person." On the other hand, the expression "I give" without any further qualification cannot be considered explicit, even if the intention was to make a *wakf;* and it is only in the case of a *wakf*, not in favour of one or more individuals, but in favour of a class of people or of the public, that this expression accompanied by the intention is regarded as explicit. The expressions, "I consecrate such an object," or "I wish that it should remain eternally in that state," are not explicit; but the words "I destine such a property for the purpose of a mosque" suffice to make the spot consecrated to worship.

Expressions by which a *wakf* may be constituted.

A *wakf* in favour of a certain and particular person is not complete without his acceptance, which acceptance must in no case take place after a previous refusal. A *wakf* made in these terms, "I constitute this my land *wakf* for the term of a year" is void, but if the words used are, "I make a *wakf* in favour of my children, or in favour of such an one and subsequently upon his issue," without adding anything else, the *wakf* remains intact even after the extinction of the family. *The usufruct of the wakf reverts* to the *nearest relative of the founder when the purpose fails* and the *holders nominated by him have become extinct.*

Failure of the object of a *wakf*.

According to the Shâfeï doctrines in every *wakf* a beginning must be made with an object in actual existence; for example, when a *wakf* is made in the following terms, "I make a *wakf* in favour of the child I may have;" it is invalid, for there is nobody to take possession of the *wakf;* but the failure of any of the *intermediate* beneficiaries does not avoid the *wakf*.(1)

Nor can a *wakf* be made dependent upon a contingency which may never occur; as for example, "I make a *wakf* on condition that Zaid should come."

A contingent *wakf*.

Conditions imposed by the *wâkif* must be observed faithfully; as for example, if he has made a condition that the endowed lands shall not be let out, it can only be done with the sanction of the Kâzi; or that a religious building founded be specially dedicated

(1) The Shâfeïs are in agreement with the Shiahs on this point. Under the Hanafi Law, as already observed, if a *wakf* is created for a non-existent object the *wakf* will not be invalid; its income will be applied for the benefit of the poor until the object specified comes into existence.

to a certain persuasion, such as the Shâfeï. In this latter case, the members of this sect alone shall be entitled to share in the benefit of the *wakf*. And this rule applies equally to the founding of a school or of a hostelry. In the case of an endowment in favour of two persons and subsequently in favour of the poor, at the death of one of them his portion of the usufruct reverts to the other and not to the poor,(1) who only profit thereby after the death of both. This doctrine has been supported by Shâfeï himself.

Wakf in favour of children and descendants.

When a *wakf* is constituted in the following terms, *viz.*, "the *wakf* is for my children and my grandchildren," the usufruct must be equally divided among the children and the grandchildren that exist at the time of the *wakf*, even if the words "who are their descendants" or "generation after generation" is added.

When, on the other hand, the following terms have been used "in favour of my children, then of my grandchildren, then of my great-grandchildren, the one after the other," or "the former first," the successive generations have the enjoyment of the usufruct but the first class takes first. The grandchildren, however, have no right to a *wakf* made only in favour of children. The grandchildren born of the daughter of the founder are included in the expressions "posterity," "descent," "progeny," or "grandchildren" unless it has been declared, "the grandchildren that bear my name."

An apposition preceding several words joined together refers to all, as for example in this sentence, "I make a *wakf* in favour of those who are dear to me, my children, my grandchildren and my brothers," it is the children, grandchildren and brothers that are accounted "dear" by the founder. The same is the case with an apposition that follows and of the reservation added to the principal clauses, provided that these words are united by the conjunction "and." For example, "I make an endowment in favour of my children and of my grandchildren and of my brothers who are dear to me" or "provided there are no persons of notoriously bad conduct among them."

The proprietorship of *wakf* property is transferred to God, that is to say, such property ceases for ever to be subject to the

(1) Comp. the Hanafi Law, *ante*, p. 384.

right of private proprietorship and thenceforth it belongs neither to the *wâkif* nor to him in whose favour the *wakf* is made. Only the usufruct of the *wakf* belongs to the beneficiary and he may have the enjoyment thereof either in person or by the intermediation of another, for example, by lending him the endowed object or letting it to him. The holder of the usufruct has the full right to the rent or to that which the endowed property produces, such as fruit, wool and milk, and the young of the animals. After the death of a *wakf* animal, the skin belongs to the holder of the usufruct.

Wakf property not subject to rights of private proprietorship.

The *wakf* of a tree does not, according to the Shâfeï school, become extinct when the tree dies, as the decay of a tree does not preclude the use of the wood, though, according to others, the tree must then be sold by auction and the price used in the same manner as the indemnity for a murdered bondsman which must be applied in obtaining the services of another. The worn-out mats and the broken beams of a mosque may be sold, and this is only lawful on condition that these articles should serve as fuel. The ground on which a mosque stands may, in no case, be sold even if the edifice has fallen into ruin and its reconstruction be impossible.

When the founder has reserved for himself the administration of the *wakf*, or if he has conferred the office upon a third person, the arrangement must be carried into effect; but if nothing of this kind has been stipulated by the *wâkif*, the administration devolves on the Judge who has the power of appointing a manager. It is essential that the administrator of a *wakf* should be of good character and qualified for the office both by his physical powers and intellectual faculties. The functions of the administrator are the custody and consolidation of the *wakf* property and the collecting and distributing of the rents and profits, but he is forbidden to over-step the limits of his powers, if the administration has only partly been given to him. In every case, the founder has the right of deposing his administrator and of appointing another, unless he be nominated administrator in the deed of endowment itself without reservation of such a right. A lease granted by an administrator continues notwithstanding a rise in price or a more advantageous offer.

The rules relating to *towliat.*

CHAPTER XIX.

RULES OF PROCEDURE.

As regards the right of a beneficiary to obtain a declaration that a certain property is *wakf*, or to establish his title to a share in the proceeds of a certain *wakf*, the Mussulman Law is very distinct. It provides that any beneficiary can at any time proceed before the Kâzi and obtain any redress to which he may be legally entitled. The law imposes no restriction as to the manner in which he should proceed. The Indian Legislature, however, has, with respect to a certain class of cases, provided rules which require consideration, especially as the Calcutta and Allahabad High Courts are not in accord with each other in regard to the procedure.

In Mussulman countries, endowments which are in their nature public, or the benefits of which are for the public generally, are under the direction, control and supervision of a special officer appointed by the Government, who is called the *Nâzir-i-Awkâf*. But the Kâzi, as the representative of the sovereign, is the general curator of all *wakfs*, whether public or private. When the British first assumed under the authority of the Mogul Emperor the government of these Provinces, they found scattered throughout the country numerous endowments, chiefly created by the sovereigns and chieftains. For a time matters were allowed to remain in the condition of disorder in which the collapse of the Mussulman Government had left the endowments. But in 1810 it was found necessary to pass a law for the purpose of protecting and preserving these dedications and grants. With that object Regulation XIX of 1810 was passed. Its object is sufficiently clear from the preamble.(1)

---

(1) "Whereas considerable endowments have been granted in land by the preceding Governments of this country, and by individuals for the support of mosques, Hindoo temples, colleges and for other pious and beneficial purposes, and whereas there are grounds to suppose that the produce of such lands is in many instances appropriated contrary to the intentions of the donors to the per-

In 1863, however, it was considered desirable on the part of Government to divest itself of all connection with the religious endowments of Hindus and Mahommedans, and to retain the control only of such institutions as were secular in their character. It was supposed that the connection of a Christian Government with the religious establishments of Hindus and Mahommedans was anomalous and inexpedient. To give effect to this mistaken, but intelligible, policy, Act XX of 1863 was passed.(1)

The preamble and the earlier sections of this Act indicate conclusively its scope, and there can hardly be any doubt that its operation was confined to such trusts or endowments as were transferred to trustees under sections 4 to 7 of the Act. And so

---

sonal use of the individuals in immediate charge and possession of such endowments, and whereas it is an important duty of every Government to provide that all such endowments be applied according to the real intent and will of the grantor, and whereas it is moreover essential to provide for the maintenance and repair of bridges, serais, kuttaras and other buildings which have been erected, either at the expense of Government or of individuals for the use and convenience of the public, and also to establish proper rules for the custody and disposal of *nuzool* property or escheats, the following rules have been enacted to be in force from the period of their promulgation throughout the provinces immediately dependant on the Presidency of Fort William.

"The general superintendence of all lands granted for the support of mosques, Hindu temples, colleges and for other pious and beneficial purposes, and of all public buildings, such as bridges, serais, kuttaras and other edifices, is hereby vested in the Board of Revenue and Board of Commissioners in the several districts, subject to the control of those Boards respectively."

(1) "Whereas it is expedient to relieve the Boards of Revenue and the Local Agents in the Presidency of Fort William in Bengal and the Presidency of Fort St. George from the duties imposed on them by Regulation XIX of 1810 of the Bengal Code, so far as those duties embrace the superintendence of lands granted for the support of mosques or Hindu temples and for other religious uses, the appropriation of endowments made for the maintenance of such religious establishments, the repair and preservation of buildings connected therewith, and the appointment of Trustees or Managers thereof, or involve any connexion with the management of such religious establishments, and whereas it is expedient for that purpose to repeal so much of Regulation XIX, 1810, of the Bengal Code, and Regulation VII, 1817, of the Madras Code, as relate to endowments for the support of mosques, Hindu temples or other religious purposes, it is enacted as follows:—

1. "So much of Regulation XIX, 1810, of the Bengal Code, and so much of Regulation VII, 1817, of the Madras Code, as relate to endowments for the support of mosques, Hindu temples or other religious purposes are repealed."

Section IV furnishes the chief index to the object of the Act.

"In the case of every such mosque, temple or other religious establishment which at the time of the passing of this Act shall be, under the management

Delroos Banoo Begum v. Nawab Syed Asghur Ally Khan.

it was expressly decided in the case of *Delroos Banoo Begum* v. *Nawab Syed Asghur Ally Khan*,(1) in which it was further held that where such transfer had taken place, parties interested in such endowments might come in and apply for leave to sue the trustee or manager thereof,(2) and no suit would be maintainable without leave previously obtained under section 18. But where the charge of the endowments had never been transferred to trustees under the provisions of the Act, no preliminary leave was necessary. In fact, the transfer under sections 4 to 7 was regarded as a test whether the endowment was, in its nature, public or not. If it had been taken charge of by the Board of Revenue under Regulation XIX of 1810, and subsequently transferred to trustees under Act XX of 1863, *primâ facie,* it was such as to entitle the public generally to share in its benefit. And in that case preliminary leave to sue would be necessary before a suit could be maintained. The principle laid down in *Delroos Banoo Begum* v. *Nawab Syed Asghur Ally* with reference to the nature and scope of Act XX of 1863 has been virtually overruled by the decision in *Jan Ally* v. *Ram Nauth Mundul.*(3) In this case, it has been held in effect that every mosque, Hindu temple, college or religious institution for the support of which land had been granted by the preceding Governments, or by individuals, come within the purview of the Act, and that consequently no suit can be instituted with reference to any of these institutions without leave having been

Jan Ally v. Ram Nauth Mundul.

Latifunnissa v. Nazirun Bibi.

---

of any Trustee, Manager or Superintendent whose nomination shall not vest in nor be exercised by nor be subject to the confirmation of the Government nor any public officer, the Local Government shall, as soon as possible after the Act, transfer to such Trustee, Manager or Superintendent all the landed or other property which at the time of the passing of this Act shall be under the superintendence or in the possession of the Board of Revenue or any Local Agent and belonging to such mosque, temple or other religious establishment except such property as is hereinafter provided and the powers and responsibilities of the Board of Revenue and the Local Agents in respect to such mosque, temple or other religious establishment and to all land and other property so transferred except as regards acts done and liabilities incurred by the said Board of Revenue or any Local Agent previous to such transfer, shall cease and determine.'' Section V provides the procedure in cases of dispute regarding the right of succession in case of a vacancy in the office of trustee, &c., to whom property has been transferred under Section IV, and Section VI declares the rights, powers and responsibilities of such trustees.

(1) [1883], 15 Beng. L. R., 167.

(2) See *Kaniz Fatima* v. *Bibi Sahebjan*, 8 W. R., 313.

(3) [1882], I. L., 8 Cal., 32.

first obtained under section 18.(1) This ruling apparently was adopted in another case decided by the Calcutta High Court.(2) In this case the plaintiff had sued to recover possession as *mutwalli* of certain parcels of land alleging that they were dedicated as *wakf*, and that the profits were applied to the feeding of wayfarers and travellers, to lighting the mosque and shrine in the evening, and to meet the expenses of repeating prayers on the occasion of *Id* and *Bakreed*, and that the said profits were never spent for personal purposes. The plaintiff also alleged that her deceased husband had been the former *mutwalli*, that upon his death her step-son took possession of the *wakf* properties and had since given a mokurruri pottah of the dedicated lands to the second defendant. She accordingly prayed that the properties in suit may be declared to be *wakf*, and the sale and lease thereof may be set aside.

She succeeded in establishing that the four parcels of the land in suit were *wakf* and obtained a decree in respect thereof in the first Court which was upheld by the Judge. On special appeal to the High Court of Calcutta, it was urged on behalf of the defendants that the plaintiff had no sufficient interest to entitle her to sue. These contentions were accepted by the learned Judges who dismissed the plaintiff's suit on the following grounds :—

"According to the plaint in this case the trust is one partly for charitable and partly for religious purposes. So far as the trust was 'for the feeding of wayfarers,' it was a trust for the benefit of a considerable portion of the public answering a particular description, and was therefore a trust for a public charitable purpose. The object of the plaintiff's suit was to oust the *mutwalli*, get herself appointed in his place and have the properties vested in her. Section 539 of the Code applies to a suit of this nature which is really one for the administration of the trust, and such a suit can only be brought in accordance with the provisions of that section. But even supposing that the endowment in the case was neither a public charity within the meaning of sec-

(1) Section 18 runs thus :—"No suit shall be entertained under this Act without a preliminary application being first made to the Court for leave to institute such suit. The application may be made upon unstamped paper. The Court on the perusal of the application shall determine whether there are sufficient *primâ facie* grounds for the institution of a suit, and if in the judgment of the Court there are such grounds, leave shall be given for its institution, &c."

(2) *Latifunnissa Bibi* v. *Nazirun Bibi* [1885], I. L., 11 Cal., 33.

tion 539 of the Civil Procedure Code, nor a religious endowment to which Act XX of 1863 is applicable, the plaintiff was not entitled to sue alone to be appointed *mutwalli* and to obtain possession of the property. The first Court holds that she was entitled to bring this suit, because she was a wife of Mokram Ali, the late *mutwalli*, but we cannot agree that this is a sufficient reason. Even if we regard her as suing as a person interested in the trust, then, on the face of the plaint, there are other persons interested and she could only sue on behalf of all who were so interested, and in order so to sue she should have obtained the permission of the Court and otherwise complied with the provisions of section 30 of the Civil Procedure Code; not having done so, we think she had no right of action. In whatever light the suit be regarded, therefore, we think it clear that it was not properly framed and will not lie.''

As will be seen later, this view is clearly opposed to the provisions of the Mahommedan Law, and it introduces restrictions not recognised under that law. The Allahabad High Court has dissented from the views expressed by the Calcutta High Court. It has held that every Mahommedan has an inherent right to maintain a suit for the purpose of establishing a *wakf* or his own right to share in its benefits. In the case of *Zafaryab Ali* v. *Bakhtawar Singh*,(1) certain Mahommedans sued for possession of a ''takia'' known by the name of Najuf Ali Shah, ''by cancellation of an hypothecation thereof, dated the 28th May 1877, and of a decree, dated the 18th May 1880, as well as of a judicial sale, dated the 30th May 1881, by the demolition of two walls and by the ejectment of the defendants.'' They alleged in their plaint that the property in suit was ''*wakf*'' or a charitable endowment including a mosque (imâmbara) and a grave-yard in which there were many tombs, * * * * that defendant No. 1, the manager of the property, and the ancestors of defendants Nos. 2, 3 and 4 hypothecated the premises to defendant No. 5 who, having obtained a decree enforcing the hypothecation, caused the property to be brought to sale, and it was purchased by him and defendants Nos. 6 and 7, that defendant No. 5 having obtained possession of the property, erected two walls on

Zafaryab Ali* v. *Bakhtawar Singh.

(1) [1883], I. L., 5 All., 497.

the land thereby interfering with the purposes for which the property was originally intended, and that the plaintiffs became aware of all these proceedings on the 24th January 1882, and in consequence brought the present suit. The defendants set up as a defence to the suit that the plaintiffs were not competent to sue. The Court of First Instance held that the plaintiffs were competent to sue, observing as follows :—

"It is a rule of daily practice that every aggrieved party is entitled to get his grievance remedied. On the same principle a certain set of the interested Mahommedans in this case have come forward to bring this suit against the defendants to get their complaint redressed by the Courts of Justice. The Mahommedan Law sanctions the course of action by the plaintiffs in this case. Every Mahommedan according to the tenets of his religion is entitled to get public charitable property protected from the hands of strangers."

On appeal, however, the Judge reversed the decision of the first Court, holding that the plaintiff had no right to sue. He also made the following observations :—

"Referring to a recent and closely analogous case decided by the Presidency Court in August last, *Jan Ali* v. *Ramnauth Mundul*,(1) I am of opinion that plaintiffs have no right to bring the present suit which is to have the property declared *wukf* and made over to them as such. They do not, however, pretend to be the trustees or to have a special interest in the alleged endowment, nor do they bring forward any deed creating it ; I do not think that this brings the suit under Act XX of 1863, for they do not really mean to sue the manager for misfeasance, although they have included him in the prayer to set aside his conveyance. But even if it did, the suit is out of rule, as there was no application made to this Court or to any other for permission to sue. If it be alleged that there has been a breach of trust regarding a charitable endowment, then the leave of the Collector ought to have been obtained under section 539, which has not been done. The plaintiffs, moreover, have not made any assertion in any part of their plaint as to any special right of suit, as to their being persons attending or having a right to attend the alleged mosque, but simply state their ground of action to have arisen when they heard of the alienation to the defendants. Were this suit brought by the latter, the Courts could deal with it, but a question (such as lies at the root here) of whether a place was one of public worship, &c., would be more appropriately settled by the Municipal Commissioners of the town as it certainly would be more legal to adopt such a course. For this reason I dismiss the suit

In second appeal, the plaintiffs contended (*a*) that being members of the Mahommedan community, they were legally competent to maintain the suit ; (*b*) that they were not bound to observe the preliminary procedure enjoined by section 539 of the Civil Procedure Code, that section having no bearing on the suit ; and (*c*) that the Lower Appellate Court had misapprehended the scope of the suit which did not seek any of the remedies provided by that section.

---

(1) *Supra.*

The High Court of Allahabad reversed the second Court's judgment, holding as follows :—

"The plaintiffs as Mahommedans, entitled to frequent the mosque and to use the other religious building connected with the endowment, can clearly maintain the present suit, and section 539 of the Procedure Code has no application to such a case ; the endowment in question being, in our opinion, a religious institution within the meaning of section 24 of Act VI of 1871, and therefore governed by Mahommedan Law. We therefore remand the case under section 562 of the Code of Procedure for trial on the merits."

Jawahra v. *Akbur Hossein.*

In the later case of *Jawahra* v. *Akbur Hossein*,(1) which was decided by a Full Bench of the same Court, the question as to the right of a Mahommedan to maintain a suit for the establishment of his right to use a mosque for purposes of devotion was discussed at considerable length.

The plaint in this case stated that, in a village belonging to the plaintiff, there was an "old dilapidated mosque intended for Mahommedan worship" which "was protected and looked after" by him and other Mahommedans of the village ; that in consequence of the mosque and its appurtenances being *wakf*, it had been excluded from the partition of the village, and the plaintiff intended to repair the mosque ; that the defendants had enclosed a part of the land and had also erected a mill on a part of it ; that they had by means of certain erections of thatch and mud converted the mosque into a place for storing straw, all of which acts they had wrongfully done ; that the plaintiff had remonstrated with the defendants and asked them to remove the things, but they paid no attention to this request, and prevented the plaintiff from making repairs ; and that these "unlawful acts of the defendants were calculated to affect the character of the said endowed property and were an insult to their religion." Upon these allegations the plaintiff claimed "a declaration of his right to repair the old dilapidated mosque......by removal of the defendants' interference" and the demolition of the compound, by removal of the mill, the thatches and the straw stored in the mosque. The plaint concluded with these words—"Suit brought according to the doctrines of the Mahommedan religion and on written and oral evidence." The defendants did not deny the acts imputed to them by the plaintiff. They defended the suit upon the grounds, amongst others, that the building which was

(1) [1885], I. L., 7 All., 178.

the subject-matter of the suit was not a mosque but an "atta or fortress made for the purpose of shelter from robbers in former days," and that the plaintiff had no right to repair it. The Court of First Instance found that the building was a mosque and not an "atta," and held that "the plaintiff, as a Mahommedan and guardian of religious buildings, was entitled to repair the mosque." It, therefore, gave the plaintiff a decree as claimed. On appeal the defendants contended that "a claim for endowed property cannot be instituted and heard without the permission of the Advocate-General under Act XX of 1863." Upon this point the Court observed as follows :— *Jawahra v. Akbur Hossein—contd.*

"The first ground of appeal must be overruled. In a similar case— *Zafaryab Ali* v. *Bakhtawar Singh*(1)—our own High Court have just ruled that section 539 of the Civil Procedure Code would not apply, and that the plaintiffs, as persons entitled to frequent the mosque, can maintain the suit. This, however, is quite opposed to a ruling of the Calcutta High Court—*Jan Ali* v. *Ram Nauth Mundul.*"(2)

The decree of the Court of First Instance was accordingly affirmed.

On second appeal the defendants contended (*a*) that the suit was not maintainable in its present form, as no special right to sue in the plaintiff was disclosed, and (*b*) that as there were probably other Mahommedan residents in the village, the suit was not maintainable without compliance with the provisions of section 30 of the Civil Procedure Code.

Upon these facts and contentions, Chief Justice Petheram delivered the following judgment :—

"I have no doubt that the plaintiff was competent to maintain this action. The question has arisen in consequence of the peculiar way in which property of this kind is held. According to Mahommedan custom, the property in a mosque and in the land connected with it is vested in no one. It is not the subject of human ownership, but all the members of the Mahommedan community are entitled to use it for purposes of devotion whenever the mosque is open. Now, the Mahommedans are only a part of the population of this country, so that the right is not vested in the general public, and therefore it resembles a right in a private way. Every one who has such a right is entitled to exercise it

(1) [1883], I. L., 5 All., 497.
(2) *Supra.*

Jawahra v. *Akbur Hossein*—contd.

without hindrance, and has a right of action against any one who interferes with its exercise. It is not a joint right, it is a right which belongs to many people. Section 30 was meant to apply to a case in which many persons are jointly interested in obtaining relief; and where under the old law it would have been necessary for all of such persons to be joined, section 30 prevents the record from being unnecessarily encumbered by many names, and allows one or more with the permission of the Court to sue or defend on behalf of all. The rule was introduced in order to prevent rich persons from joining together and putting forward a pauper to conduct the suit and thus escaping all costs. In the present case it is clear that an individual right has been violated, and that an action will therefore lie."

Mr. Justice Mahmud's remarks are also well worthy of consideration:—

"I wish to add a few observations regarding the Mahommedan Law as to endowments generally, and in particular as to mosques. It must in the first place, be shown that the Mahommedan people have a right to maintain a suit like the present. But authorities on such a point need not be cited, for the principle is too well known among Mahommedan lawyers. The rule of the Mahommedan Law on the subject is that, when any one has resolved to devote his property to religious purposes, as soon as his mind is made up and his intention declared by some specific act, such as delivery, &c., an endowment is immediately constituted; his act deprives him of all ownership in the property, and to use the technical language of Mahommedan lawyers, vests it in God in such a manner as subjects it to the rules of divine property whence the appropriator's right in it is extinguished, and it becomes a property of God by the advantage of it resulting to His creatures."

"A mosque is an endowment of this kind, and the Mahommedan community or any member of it has a right to enter the mosque and to pray there. The learned Chief Justice has shown that, under the circumstances, in India, a mosque cannot be regarded as vested in the public at large, but in the Mahommedan part of the public, and it cannot be said that any Mahommedan is bound to maintain a suit on behalf of the public generally. The right of a Mahommedan to use a mosque is, as the learned Chief

Justice has said, like the right to use a private road ; any one who has the right may maintain a suit in respect of it. This settles the question as to section 30 of the Civil Procedure Code. That section applies only to cases where no individual right is interfered with, but here we have the case of a mosque in a small village, and one of the worshippers in that mosque is obstructed in his use of it for purposes of devotion. He had a private right and it was violated. In regard to section 539 of the Civil Procedure Code, I was one of the Bench who made this reference, and I wish to add my reasons for holding that the section does not apply to the present case. There is here no question of trust or trustee or of malversation of trust-funds or other breach of trust. The object of such a suit as this is not such as is contemplated by any of the various clauses of section 539. In conclusion, I have a few words to say regarding the case which has been cited, *Jan Ali* v. *Ram Nauth Mundul*,(1) decided in the Calcutta High Court by Prinsep and Field, JJ. Towards the end of the judgment in that case the following observations occur : ' Now so far as regards these prayers, we think that the plaintiffs were not authorised to institute this suit merely by reason of having that interest which is set out in para. 10 in the plaint, that is, an interest created by their being followers of the Moslem religion living in the vicinity of the mosque and being in the habit of attending the musjid. That interest is common to them with a large number of other persons—common to them with, we will not say all the Mahommedan population of the country, but certainly with all the Mahommedan residents in the vicinity, and we think that this is a case which falls within the provisions of section 30 of the Civil Procedure Code. That section enacts that ' where there are numerous parties having the same interest in one suit, one or more of such parties may, with the permission of the Court, sue or be sued or may defend in such suit on behalf of all parties so interested.' It may be quite possible that if these plaintiffs had applied to the Court under the provisions of section 30, they would have obtained permission to institute this suit, but not having obtained that permission, they certainly were not entitled to institute the suit ; and under the circumstances we think that the ground of objection taken by the defendants in the second paragraph of their written statement, and

(1) This will become clear later.

which forms the subject of the second issue, was a good objection, and that this suit was properly dismissed by the District Judge.' Now, with all due deference to the learned Judges who delivered that judgment, I dissent from the remarks which I have just read. I hold that it is an undoubted principle of Mahommedan Law that the persons who have the most direct interest in a mosque are the worshippers who are entitled and accustomed to use it. It is impossible to imagine whose interest in the mosque can be direct if theirs is not, and I should say that, even if this case fell under the purview of section 539, they would have *locus standi* to maintain the suit. But for the reasons which I have already given I am of opinion that neither section 30 nor section 539 of the Civil Procedure Code applies to the present case, and that the plaintiff was competent to maintain the suit.''

The judgment of the Allahabad High Court in conformity with the Mahommedan Law.

The judgment of the Allahabad High Court is in conformity with the provisions of the Mahommedan Law. Every Mussulman who derives any benefit from a *wakf* or trust is entitled to maintain an action against the *mutwalli*, to establish his right thereto, or against a trespasser to recover any portion of the *wakf* property which has been misappropriated, without joining any other person who may participate with him in the benefit.

This is clear from the rules enunciated in the *Durr-ul-Mukhtâr* and the *Radd-ul-Muhtâr*. "Some of the beneficiaries," says the *Durr-ul-Mukhtâr*, "can sue on behalf of the others, as some of the heirs can represent the rest; and according to the *Ashbâh* there is no third case [in which this may be done]." "But,'' proceeds the author of the *Durr-ul-Mukhtâr*, "I say that similarly the insolvency of a debtor may be established in the presence of one creditor [in other words, one creditor may represent the rest]. Jurists have said that the evidence of insolvency may be taken in the absence of the plaintiff (المدعی). The same rule applies to the objections [to the marriage of a minor] on the part of guardians standing in a position of equality (الاولیا المتساوین) So also with regard to a guarantee of safety (الامان) granted by one Moslem and the right of retaliation and in seeking the removal of public injuries (ضرر العام) from the path of Moslems in general....Be it noted that one heir can represent all the heirs in the demand for a debt but not for the corpus so long as the property is not in his hands......Some of the beneficiaries can sue on behalf of all when the *wakf* is in favour of a body (اذا كان وقف بين جماعة) and the *wâkif* of it is one; in that case one person or his deputy (*wakîl*) can sue on behalf of all, provided the existence of the *wakf* is established but not otherwise."(1)

On this the comment of the *Radd-ul-Muhtâr* is as follows:—"Similarly, that is similar to the right of some of the beneficiaries, مستحقين, to represent all) some of the *nazzâr* (*mutwallis*) of the *wakf* may sue as plaintiffs on behalf of all as is stated in the 11th chapter of the *Tâtâr-Khânièh*.(2)

"A person makes a *wakf* in favour of his kindred and another person claims to be one of them, if the *wâkif* is alive at the time he will become the claimant's opponent (خصمه)(3) otherwise the *Mutwalli*. Even though there may be several *Mutwallis* a suit against one is permissible; it is not a condition that they should all be joined (لا يشترط اجتماعهم). Neither the heir of a deceased person nor one beneficiary can be made a defendant."

"And one heir may represent all the others regarding the realisation of the assets of the deceased......and the insolvency of a debtor established in the presence of one creditor will bind the others... Similarly the consent of one guardian of the same degree will bind the other guardians."

"In the same way the grant of an *âmän* (guarantee of safety) by one Moslem to a *harbi* (alien)(4) will bind all Moslems, as is stated in the *Siyar* [*kabîr*]."

"So the grant of a pardon [or the waiver of the right of retaliation by one *walî* of the murdered person] will destroy the right as if all the *walîs* had granted the pardon. Whether a pardon granted by adult *walîs* will bind minor *walîs* there is a difference. The rule is that as the right of pardon cannot be divided pardon by one is tantamount to pardon by all unless the adult is a stranger (الا اذا كان الكبير اجنبيا) to the minor. For example if the person killed left a minor son and a widow who is not the mother of the son."

---

(1) اذا كان اصل الوقف ثابتا و الافلا, *Durr-ul-Mukhtâr*, p. 420.

(2) A well-known work on law compiled in the 13th century in India in the reign of Feroze Shah, called after its author, Tâtâr Khan.

(3) That is, he should be made the defendant to the actions.

(4) See *ante*, p. 276

"So also one person may sue on behalf of others [*lit.* other Moslems] to remove general injuries from the path of the public [*lit.* Mussulmans] (in other words, sue to abate nuisances). For example, a person makes a new cess-pool or drain, any member of the public affected thereby may represent the others in an action for its abatement."(1)

The mere fact that the defendant to an action by a beneficiary or a *mutwalli* disputes either the *factum* or the validity of the *wakf* will not alter or affect the right of the plaintiff to maintain the action without joining the other beneficiaries or *mutwallis* as the case may be. It is only where the action is brought for the establishment of the *wakf* that the Mussulman Law apparently contemplates a different course, *viz.*, the necessity of representation on the part of the other persons alleged to be interested in the *wakf* and that condition is complied with when the suit is brought with the leave of the Kâzi.(2)

Unless, therefore, an endowment has been dealt with under Reg. XIX of 1810 and Act XX of 1863, and has come into the possession of trustees under this later Act, no leave is necessary as a condition precedent to the maintenance of an action by a person entitled to the benefit of a *wakf*.

Section 92 of Act V of 1908 (the Code of Civil Procedure) which has taken the place of s. 539, Act XIV of 1882, provides as follows :—

"In the case of any alleged breach of any express or constructive trust created for public purposes of a charitable or religious nature, or where the direction of the Court is deemed necessary for the administration of any such trust, the Advocate-General, or two or more persons having an interest in the trust and having obtained the consent in writing of the Advocate-General, may institute a suit, whether contentious or not, in the principal Civil Court of Original Jurisdiction or in any other Court empowered in that behalf by the Local Government within the local limits of whose jurisdiction the whole or any part of the subject-matter of the trust is situate to obtain a decree—

(*a*) removing any trustee ;
(*b*) appointing a new trustee ;

(1) *Radd-ul-Muhtâr*, Vol. III, pp. 627-8. (2) See *post*, p. 562.

(c) vesting any property in trustees;
(d) directing accounts and inquiries;
(e) declaring what proportion of the trust-property or of the interest therein shall be allocated to any particular objects of the trust;
(f) authorizing the whole or any part of the trust-property to be let, sold, mortgaged or exchanged;
(g) settling a scheme; or
(h) granting such further or other relief as the nature of the case may require.

(2) Save as provided by the Religious Endowments Act, 1863, no suit claiming any of the relief specified in sub-section (*1*) shall be instituted in respect of any such trust as is therein referred to except in conformity with the provisions of that sub-section."

It will thus be seen that to make the provisions of section 92 applicable to a *wakf*, it must appear that the trust is for a *public* charitable or religious purpose—in other words, that it is vested in the public, or that the beneficiaries are selected from the general body of the public.

"The section presupposes the existence of a public trust and a suit for the administration, either partially or completely, of that trust. It enables the persons mentioned therein to sue trustees to enforce the better administration of the trust. Where, however, it is said that the section presupposes a trust this does not mean that the defendant must admit the trust before the section can apply, but that the suit must proceed upon the allegation of the existence of a trust which may or may not be admitted by the defendant."

"Private trusts concern only individuals or families for private convenience or support. By public trusts may be understood such as are constituted for the benefit either of the public at large, or of some considerable portion of it answering a particular description. In private trusts the beneficial interest is vested absolutely in one or more individuals, who are, or within a certain time may be, definitely ascertained, and to whom therefore collectively, unless under some legal disability, it is, or within the allowed time will be, competent to control, modify or determine the trust. A public or charitable trust on the other hand, has for its objects the members of an uncertain and fluctuating body, and the trust itself is of a permanent character. The trust may be charitable, such as for the relief of the poor, or the advancement of learning, religion or objects of general public utility, or religions, though all religious uses are charitable uses."(1)

What are public trusts under the Mahommedan Law.

A Mussulman mosque (unless it is a *masjid-i-jâm'aa*), a private Imâmbara, *wakfs* created for the disbursement of private charity (such as appeared to be in the case of *Lutfunnissa Bibi* v. *Nazi-*

(1) Woodroffe and Ameer Ali's Civil Procedure Code, pp. 356-7.

run Bibi,(1) or for the benefit of a more or less restricted body of people, is not regarded by the Mahommedan lawyers to be vested in the public. The Mussulman Law makes a broad distinction between *wakfs* which are public in their nature and those which are private. The *wakfs* in which the public have an interest and which may, perhaps, come within the scope of section 92 are the *mâsalih-i-'aâmma, e.g.*, public or *jâm'aa-masjids*, bridges over which the entire body of the public have a right of way, caravanserais, where anybody and everybody can alight; public hospitals, public cemeteries; public libraries; public Madrassahs and public Imâmbaras, like the Imâmbara of Hâji Mohammed Mohsin at Hooghly.

With reference to such *wakfs* as are private or only *quasi*-public the provisions of section 92 are in no way applicable. And if they were not taken charge of under Reg. XIX of 1810, and were not transferred to trustees under Act XX of 1863, the provisions of this latter Act would not apply.

In respect of such *wakfs*, therefore, it is submitted the right to bring a suit would be regulated by the general provisions of the Mahommedan Law.

Who may sue to recover trust-property.

It has already been remarked that where the nature of the *wakf* is undisputed, or where the fact of the property being trust-property is admitted, and there are several trustees, one or more of them can bring a suit in respect of the trust-estate without joining the others. If there is no trustee or none willing to act, any one of the beneficiaries or some of them can sue on behalf of the others without leave of the Kâzi. If there is any dispute regarding the *wakf*, some of the trustees, and in their absence, some of the beneficiaries can sue on behalf of the others with the permission of the Kâzi. A right to sue for recovery of property alleged to be *wakf* belongs not to the heirs or descendants of the settlor but to the *mutwallis* jointly.(2) But a person who has been convicted of having misappropriated *wakf* property cannot obtain the assistance of the Court to recover the property to enable him to exercise the functions of a *mutwalli*.(3)

(1) Supra.

(2) [1879] *Phate Saheb Bibi* v. *Damodar Premji*, I. L., 3 Bom., 84.

(3) *Aga Mahommed Kumul Tehranee* v. *Aga Abbas Tehranee*, S. D. A., 1859, p. 285.

The beneficiaries of a *wakf* or some of them are entitled to maintain a suit to restrain the *mutwalli* from wasting the trust-estate or misapplying it.(1)

Regarding the procedure to be observed when there are several *mutwallis* and some of them are unwilling to join the others in bringing a suit to recover the alleged trust-property, the ruling in the case of *Bechu Lall* v. *Oliullah*(2) is in point. In that case it was held that where there are several *mutwallis*, all of them, if possible, should be made plaintiffs; but if any of them refused, then they should be made defendants. *Bechu Lall* v. *Oliullah.*

It would seem, however, from the following principles that the ruling in this case falls short of the Mahommedan Law :—

"If the *wâkif* do not appoint a *mutwalli* until death comes on him and then give directions to some person (as to how he is to act after his death), such person will become the *wasî* of his estate and effects, and will be the *mutwalli* of his *wakf* Hillâl has stated that the executor of a person who has made a *wakf* will be associated with the *mutwalli* in the work of the trust [in the same way] as if he also was appointed a *mutwalli* therefor, as is stated in the *Muhît.* And if a person makes one person the *mutwalli* of his *wakf* and then appoints an executor, the latter will become a partner of the *mutwalli* in the governance of the *wakf.*"(3)

"If there are two *mutwallis* of a *wakf* appointed by the Kâzis of two different cities, according to the Shaikh Imâm Zâhidi, each of them will be entitled to administer the properties within the jurisdiction of the Kâzi appointing him."

"If the *wâkif* entrusts the governance of the *wakf* to two persons, or to a *mutwalli* and a *wasî*, neither of them would be entitled singly to sell the proceeds of the *wakf*, though, according to Abû Hanîfa, each might act with the sanction of the other when the person acting would be regarded as the mandatory of the other; so it is stated in the *Hâwi.*"(4)

"If two *wâkifs* join in making one dedication and jointly appoint two *mutwallis*, both these *mutwallis* would be like one. If

---

(1) *Abdur Rahman* v. *Yar Mahommed* [1881], I. L., 3 All., 636.
(2) [1885] I. L., 11 Cal., 338.
(3) Fatâwai Alamgiri, Vol. II, pp. 505, 509.
(4) *Ibid,* Vol. II, p. 506.

they are separately appointed by two different Kâzis of two different places, they may each act as far as the property within their respective jurisdictions is concerned according to Imâm Zâhidi.''(1)

"Some of the beneficiaries can sue on behalf of the others. So also some of the *mutwallis* can stand(2) as litigants on behalf of the entire body; this is like the position of a *wasî-bi'n-nikâh* (a guardian for marriage); all these guardians, if more than one and belonging to the same class, stand on the same footing, and, therefore, if one of them is authorised by the others to consent on behalf f all, no outsider can raise any objection.''

"Where there is a *mutwalli*, a *cestui que trust* cannot lay a claim without leave of the Kâzi for the recovery of any property which has been wasted or usurped [by an outsider], for that right pertains to the *mutwalli*, but a beneficiary can sue the *mutwalli* if *he* is a *ghâsib* (misappropriator), and may establish his title to a share in the profits of the *wakf*.''

Some of the persons interested may sue on behalf of the entire body, when the property is admittedly *wakf*, without leave of the Kâzi.

Right of suit when property is admittedly *wakf*.

"In the *Bâzâzia* it is stated from the *Durrar wa'l Ghurrar* that when a property is dedicated for the poor or for any purpose among the purposes acceptable to the Almighty God, and it has been wrongly taken hold of by an usurper, the *mutwalli* has ordinarily the right to sue for its recovery. And if the *ghâsib* has made any erections or planted any trees, and they can be removed without any damage to the *wakf* premises, he will be allowed to do so, not otherwise. In the latter case, if his possession commenced *bonâ fide*, he would only get ordinary compensation.(3)

When the *mutwalli* is himself the *ghâsib*, or has, in breach of his trust, conveyed the property to another, the beneficiaries are entitled to sue the *mutwalli* or to sue him jointly with his assignee to recover the property.

Right of suit where the character of the *wakf* is in dispute.

But even where the character of the *wakf* is in dispute, a person who alleges to be beneficially interested jointly with others in the

(1) *Fatâwai Kâzi Khân*, Vol. IV, pp. 304-306.

(2) The word used here is (ينصب) which is intransitive and means, can stand or can be constituted.

(3) *Surrat-ul-Fatâwa*, p. 437.

wakf, is entitled to sue for its recovery, if it is misappropriated, with the leave of the Kâzi, without any difference of opinion. If he sues without such leave, and the *wakf* is in favour of a limited number of individuals, there are two opinions regarding the question. But the more correct view is that he cannot sue for the possession of the property, because he is only entitled to an interest with other specific individuals in its income. For example, if the *wakf* is for the sons of *A*, or for Zaid, Bakr, 'Amr and Hafsa, one of them cannot sue singly to recover an usurped property without leave of the Kâzi. The reason on which this rule seems to be founded is obvious. The other beneficiaries not caring to have the property or to launch into a speculative suit, the Kâzi will have to see whether there are *primâ facie* grounds for the institution of the suit. But a person who is the sole beneficiary may sue without such leave. Where, however, the *wakf* is in favour of, or alleged to be in favour of, a body of people, varying in number, *some of them may sue without leave of the Kâzi*, for the right to the benefit of the *wakf* is not vested specifically in each beneficiary, but they are all collectively and separately entitled to its benefit as a whole. For example in the case of a mosque any person who is in the habit of praying there is entitled to its full use; his right to its user is wholly independent of the right of other Moslems; nor is there any limit to the number of people who may offer their prayers therein. *Consequently, any one of the devotees may sue without leave of the Kâzi.*

These distinctions were overlooked in the Calcutta cases.

When there are several people entitled to the benefit of a *wakf* some of them may sue the others for embezzlement.

"The position of a *mutwalli* and an executor is alike. The dealing of one of two *wasîs*, like the acts of one of two *mutwallis*, is void, for the two *mutwallis* and the two executors are alike in certain matters. This is the saying of the *Ashbâh* and *Kinia*. The result is, that if one of two executors, or if one of two *mutwallis* were to give a lease of the *wakf* land, it would not be valid without the assent of the other, though both may have been appointed separately. Some jurists have no doubt held that they can act separately. And Abû Lais has held that this is the approved doctrine, and we ought to adopt it. But the first doctrine is mentioned in the *Mabsût* as the correct one, and it has been accepted in the *Durrar*, and Kahastâni has stated that it is the right view." The author of the *Radd-ul-Muhtâr* then proceeds to say, "my view is, that this is so when the two *mutwallis* or the two executors have been appointed by the same *wâkif* or testator or by one Kâzi. Accordingly, the act of one will be valid when ratified by the other, and no renewal of the obligation will be necessary as is mentioned in the *Manah*. So is the position of an executor associated with a *mutwalli*. And it is mentioned in the *Hâmidia* from the *Ism'ailia*, that if a *wasî*, without the knowledge of the *mutwalli*, deals with the estate and some of it is lost, he would be liable for damages."(1)

Acts of one executor or one *mutwalli* how far valid.

"But the acts of one of two executors or of one of two *mutwallis* are valid in respect of the buying of shrouds for the testator or *wâkif* and his funeral, and in demanding and litigating for the debts due to his estate and for his *rights*. The doctrine of the lawfulness of one *mutwalli* or of one executor demanding by himself the dues to the estate of the deceased or bringing a suit therefor is founded upon reasons of necessity. [For example, the other executor may refuse to act, and owing to his conduct the *wakf* property may be about to be wasted or the other *mutwalli* may be absent.] So it is mentioned in the *Nikâya*, and its commentator Kahastâni implies the same. The right to litigate is supported by the *Zakhîra*. But Abû Yusuf has held that either *mutwalli* can act by himself, unless the *wâkif* has expressly provided that they must act together.(2) If one *mutwalli* refuses to act he must be taken to have renounced the trust. And the other *mutwalli* can act for the protection of the estate until the Kâzi has appointed another or authorised him to act as the sole *mutwalli*."(3)

"The permission for one *mutwalli* alone to bring a suit without joining the others is founded on the reason that they cannot act jointly in preferring their claim, and even should they join, only one can be allowed to plead. This is in the *Durrar*."(4)

"When a person has appointed two executors, and one of them dies appointing the other as his executor, the surviving

---

(1) *Radd-ul-Muhtâr*, Vol. III, p. 689.
(2) *Ibid*, Vol. III, p. 690.
(3) *Fatâwai Kâzi Khân*, Chapter on Wills, p. 434.
(4) *Radd-ul-Muhtâr*, Vol. III, p. 690.

executor can act for the original testator as the sole executor.''(1)

"If one man appoints two executors, according to Abû Hanîfa and Mohammed, neither of them can act singly in dealing with the properties of the testator, and the acts and dealings of one of them are not valid without the permission of the other, except in certain matters, *viz.*, the funeral of the deceased, the payment of his debts and legacies, the emancipation of his slaves, the restoration of deposits and usurped properties. But they cannot act singly in taking possession of properties and debts restored to, or paid to his estate, *though any one of them may sue singly to recover his rights due from other people.*''(2)

"Any one of the trustees may act singly in the following matters, *viz.*, the buying of shrouds, burying the testator, supplying the food and raiment of his infant children, returning the deposits with the testator, paying off his debts and legacies, emancipating his slaves, and *litigating for his rights.*'' If there are co-trustees of lands, any one of them may receive the rents, though all must join in a conveyance.(3)

Where a person creates a *wakf* and appoints two *mutwallis* with powers to nominate their successors "acting conjointly and in unanimity with each other,'' and one of the *matwallis* happens to die, if the *wâkif* is not alive, the proper course for the surviving *mutwalli*, according to all the authorities, would be to apply to the Kâzi (in other words the principal court of civil jurisdiction) to associate another trustee with him for the purpose of nominating a successor to the original *mutwalli*.

(1) *Fatâwai Kâzi Khân*, Vol. IV, p. 441.
(2) *Ibid*, p. 440.
(3) *Fatâwa's Sirajia* ; *Cf.* Jarman on Wills, II, p. 432.

CHAPTER XX.

THE LAW RELATING TO WILLS.

SECTION I.

PRELIMINARY DISCOURSE.

Ancient Arab customs.

THE records that have been handed down to us from antiquity regarding the customs and usages of the pre-Islâmite Arabs seem to establish abundantly that testamentary dispositions were not unknown among the pagan tribes of the peninsula. But it is difficult to say, from the materials in our possession, what were the conditions which regulated the validity or invalidity of wills made by them.

The Rabbinical Law.

The Rabbinical Law which was in force among the Jewish tribes prohibited the testator from depriving his lawful heirs from succession; it also precluded him from constituting a stranger as an heir. But when a disposition was effectuated by the immediate delivery of possession, the Rabbinical Law apparently regarded it as valid. A will could be made either verbally or in writing, but, generally speaking, the first mode was considered as the more preferable of the two.

The rule of the Koran.

The Koran expressly sanctioned the power of making a testamentary disposition, and regulated the formalities and conditions to which it is subjected.(1)

"Wills," says the *Hedâya*, "are lawful on a favourable construction. *Analogy* would suggest that they are unlawful, because a bequest signifies an endowment with a thing in a way which occasions such endowment to be referred to a time when the property has become void in the proprietor (*i.e.*, the testator), and as an endowment with reference to a future period (as if a person were to say to another, 'I constitute you proprietor of this article on the morrow,') is unlawful, supposing even that the donor's property in the article still continues to exist at that time, it follows

---

(1) Koran, Chap. V, verse 75.

that the suspension of the deed to a period when the property is null and void (as at the decease of the party), is *à fortiori* unlawful. The reasons, however, for a more favourable construction in this particular are two-fold:—*First*, there is an indispensable necessity that men should have the power of making bequests, for a man, from the delusion of his hopes, is improvident and deficient in practice, but when sickness invades him, he becomes alarmed and afraid of death. At that period, therefore, he stands in need of compensating for his deficiencies by means of his property—and this in such a manner that if he should die of that illness, his objects (namely, compensation for his deficiencies and merit in a future state) may be obtained—or, on the other hand, if he should recover, that he may apply the said property to his wants—and as these objects are attainable by giving a legal validity to wills, they are, therefore, ordained to be lawful. *Secondly*, wills are declared to be lawful in the Koran and the traditions, and all (our) doctors, moreover, have concurred in this opinion."

The remarks of M. Sautayra on this subject are deserving of special consideration:—

"A will from the Mussulman's point of view is a divine institution, since its exercise is regulated by the Koran. It offers to the testator the means of correcting to a certain extent the law of succession, and of enabling some of those relatives who are excluded from inheritance to obtain a share in his goods, and of recognising the services rendered to him by a stranger, or the devotion to him in his last moments. At the same time the Prophet has declared that the power should not be exercised to the injury of the lawful heirs."

"The tradition reported by Abi Wakkâs supports the above view and forms the foundation for the restriction which the Mahommedan Law imposes on the power of testamentary disposition possessed by a Mussulman. He says:—'In the year of the conquest of Mecca, being taken so extremely ill that my life was despaired of, the Prophet of God came to pay me a visit of consolation; I told him that, by the blessing of God, having a great estate but no heirs except one daughter, I wished to know if I might dispose of it all by will.' He replied: 'No.' And when I severally interrogated him, 'if I might leave two-thirds or one-half,' he also replied in the negative—but when I asked if I might leave

The rule of law prescribed by the Prophet.

a third, he answered, 'Yes, you may leave a third of your property by will, but a third part to be disposed of by will is a great portion, and it is better you should leave your heirs rich than in a state of poverty which might oblige them to beg of others.' "

The result of these directions is, that under the Islâmic Law, a testator cannot by a testamentary disposition deprive his lawful heirs of their share in the inheritance nor dispose of more than one-third of his estate.(1) A bequest to an heir is under no circumstance valid, though a bequest in favour of a non-heir is valid to the extent of a third of the estate of the testator, although the heirs of the testator may not give their assent thereto. These principles, however, will be developed fully in their proper place.

Having so far pointed out the basis on which the Mahommedan Law relating to wills is founded, I shall now proceed to discuss what is the definition of a will under the law of Islâm, and the conditions requisite for making a valid testamentary disposition, or giving a valid testamentary direction; in other words, the testamentary capacity of the person making a will.

SECTION II.

FORM AND CHARACTERISTICS OF A WILL OR WASIAT.

Under the Mahommedan Law a will may be made either verbally or in writing.

A will is defined by Jarman to be "an instrument by which a person makes a disposition of his property to take effect after his decease, and which is, in its own nature, ambulatory and revocable during his life."(2) Under the Mussulman Law, however, a will may be made either verbally or in writing.(3) And consequently a *wasiat* is defined in the *Fatâwai Alamgiri* "to be the *conferment* of a right of property in a specific thing, or in a profit or advantage, in the manner of a gratuity to take effect on the death of the testator."(4)

The *Sharâya* defines a *wasiat* somewhat similarly, namely, as the act of conferring a right in the substance or the usufruct of a thing after death.

---

(1) Tirmizi; Ibn Mâja; *Radd-ul-Muhtâr*, Vol. V, p. 639.

(2) Jarman on Wills, p. 16.

(3) A written will is termed a *wasiatnâmah*, while a noncupative will is called simply a *wasiat*. A will need not, under the Mahommedan Law, be in writing; *Tumeez Begum* v. *Furihut Hussan*, 2 N. W. P. R., 15

(4) Compare also the *Radd-ul-Muhtâr*, Vol. V, p. 640.

How a *wasiat* may be constituted.

Under the Mussulman Law, a testamentary disposition need not be in writing, nor is any particular form even of verbal declaration necessary to constitute a *wasiat* ;(1) so long as it is apparent that the intention of the testator is to make a disposition operative on his death, any expression that sufficiently indicates that intention will be regarded as a *wasiat*. The devise may be either to the legatee beneficially or in trust for some purpose or object, and may be constituted, by saying, "I have bequeathed such a thing to such an one,"(2) or "I have bequeathed towards such an one," or by any other words or expressions that convey the idea of a disposition dependent for its operation upon the death of the testator.

In the case of *Aulia Bibi* v. *Ala-ud-din*(3) it was found that a document purporting to be the will of a Mahommedan lady was in fact drawn up in accordance with instructions given by the testatrix to a vakil at a time when the testatrix was competent to make a will; the High Court of Allahabad held that such a document was a valid will notwithstanding the absence of the signature of the testatrix.

A letter written by the testator containing directions as to the disposition of his property to take effect after his death has been held to constitute a valid will.(4)

A will may be made also by signs, as in the case of a dumb person who does not possess the faculty of speech, but who can express his meaning by signs. So also in the case of a person who is a *marîz*, that is, suffering from a mortal illness and unable from weakness to speak.(5) "A sick man makes a bequest, and being unable to speak from weakness, gives a nod with his head, and it is known *that he comprehends what he is about* ; in these circumstances, if his meaning be understood, the bequest is lawful but not otherwise. And it is implied that he dies without regaining the

---

(1) "According to the Mahommedan Law, a will may be made either verbally or in writing and no special form or solemnity for making or attesting a will is prescribed," Stanley, C. J., and Banerji, J., in *Aulia Bibi* v. *Ala-ud-din*, infra ; Comp. *Mahomed Altaf Ali Khan* v. *Ahmed Baksh* [1876], 25 W. R., 12.

(2) The difference between the two expressions arises from the use of the two prepositions "towards" (*ila*) and "to" (*le*), the first signifying the conveyance of a beneficial interest to the legatee and the second by way of trust.

(3) [1906], I. L., 28 All., 715.

(4) *Mazhar Hussein* v. *Bodha Bibi* [1898], I. L., 21 All., 91.

(5) *Radd-ul-Muhtâr*, Vol. V, p. 636.

power of speech; for then it is evident that there was no hope at the time of the bequest of his being able to speak, and his condition was therefore the same as that of a dumb man.''(1)

In some cases the disposition may, *primâ facie*, appear to convey an immediate interest, and yet the intention may not be to give it operation during the lifetime of the testator; when that is so, the disposition will take effect as a *wasiat*. Mere postponement of the actual enjoyment of a property conveyed to a person does not necessarily make the disposition testamentary, as appeared in the case of *Nawab Amjad Ally Khan* v. *Mohamdi Begum.*(2) The character of the disposition, whether it is a will or a disposition *inter vivos*, whether it operates *in præsenti* or *in futuro* as a *wasiat*, is dependent upon the intention of the testator.

A contingent *wasiat*.

A *wasiat* may be conditional or contingent. In such a case its operation will be dependent upon the happening of the contingency, and if the contingency does not happen, it will not be given effect to.(3) A reference to some impending danger is common to most of these cases. For example, a man may say, "should I die of such a malady," or "should I not return from the pilgrimage to the Holy Shrine I leave, &c.," or "I bequeath so-and-so in case anything happens to me on my voyage to Mecca," the *wasiats* in these cases would not take effect if the contingencies apprehended do not happen, whether the will be in writing or by word of mouth. The jurisconsults, however, draw a distinction between a contingent *wasiat* in writing and one made verbally. They hold that when there is only a verbal *wasiat* dependent for its operation on the happening of a contingency which does not happen, the *wasiat* is revoked *ipso facto*. But if the wish of the testator has been reduced into writing, and that writing has been confided into the hands of a third person, and after the possibility of the contingency ever happening has ceased, if the testator does not withdraw the writing from the hands of such person, it will be presumed that he did not intend to revoke his *wasiat* made before, and effect will be given to it. If the

(1) Baillie, p. 652; *Fatâwai Alamgiri*, Vol. VI, p. 168.

(2) [1867] 11 Moore's I. A., p. 517.

(3) And it will not be admitted to probate, 1 Jarman, p. 16; *Parsons* v. *Lance*, 1 Ves., 190; *Sinclair* v. *Home*, 6 Ves., 607.

will always remained in the hands of the testator no such presumption would arise. But when the *wasiat* is in the following terms "should I die" or "if I die, such a thing," or "so much of my inheritance shall belong to such an one," it will not be a contingent will but a *wasiat*, pure and simple, because it is the essence of a *wasiat* that it should take effect upon the death of the testator.(1)

SECTION III.

THE CAPACITY OF TESTATORS.

There is considerable difference between the several schools regarding the capacity to make a will. Freedom, however, is regarded by all the schools as a necessary condition. A slave, whether in the absolute control of his master, or one who has obtained a qualified freedom upon a covenant for ransom,(2) cannot make a testamentary disposition of his property. But a bequest made by a person labouring under this disability would be valid when its operation is referred to a time subsequent to his attaining his freedom.(3) A prisoner incarcerated for an offence is not subject to this disability, for he is not debarred by his loss of freedom under the direction of the law, from dealing with his property, as his conviction of the offence does not vest the property in anybody else, whereas the slave, whether absolute or qualified, can only hold property subject to the control of his master.

The capacity of testators.

Freedom.

Sanity also is a necessary condition to the validity of a *wasiat*. "A bequest," says the *Fatâwai Alamgiri*, "by any one who is incompetent to perform a gratuitous act is null. Hence, bequest by an insane person or a *mokâtib*(4) or al *mâzoon*(5) is void. And if a person is insane at the time of making a *wasiat*, but afterwards recovers from his insanity and then dies, still the bequest is unlawful for want of competency at the time of making it."

Sanity.

According to the English Law, a will made during a lucid interval is valid. In other words, though the fact of a person being

(1) Sautayra, p. 341.

(2) A *mokâtib*.

(3) Example of this will be given later.

(4) A slave who has entered into an agreement with his master for his ransom or emancipation.

(5) Licensed slave—a slave who has obtained license to work for himself.

found insane is *primâ facie* evidence of habitual insanity, and consequently of the invalidity of the will, yet it does not preclude proof that the execution occurred during a lucid interval. The principle of the Mahommedan Law is apparently different;—for, according to Kâzi Khân, if a person makes a *wasiat* and subsequent thereto becomes a permanent lunatic, in such a case the *wasiat* will become void. But when the madness has not lasted over six months, the bequest will not be voided.

The law requires a perfectly disposing mind, and a person who becomes mad shortly after making a bequest, or who is mad at the time, is presumed not to be capable of exercising the faculty of properly considering the nature of the act. Similarly, if a person were to make a bequest, and then become subject to hallucinations and afterwards lose his mind, and remain in that condition until his death, the *wasiat* would be void.(1) It would follow from the above *dictum* that when a person is a lunatic, and makes a bequest during a state of lucidity, the bequest would be invalid, for the reasons upon which the *waisat* of a person who loses his mind after the bequest, is held to be void. Is perfect sanity, however, an essential condition? The *Sharâya* speaks of "perfect understanding" as necessary to the valid constitution of a will; but it would seem from the cases given in the *Jâm'aa-ush-Shittât* and the general purport of the Hanafî Law, that what is required is a mind that comprehends the nature of the testamentary act, in other words, a disposing mind. So long as the capacity to understand the nature of the act is present, and the person entering into the obligation is possessed of understanding sufficient to comprehend the effect of the disposition, the mere existence of partial delusions will not destroy the capacity to make a will.(2) As a general rule, it may be stated that the principles of the Mussulman Law with regard to the disposing capacity of persons afflicted with any mental delusion on any particular subject, which, however, does not interfere with their powers of comprehension, are analogous in the main to the principles recognised by the English Law.

Hanafi and Shiah Law. Disposing mind necessary to the validity of a *wasiat*.

Absolute insanity may not be the only cause of destroying the disposing capacity. The will of an idiot is of course void. Mental

(1) *Radd-ul-Muhtâr*, Vol. V, p. 651.

(2) See the case of *Banks* v. *Goodfellow*, L. R., 5 Q. B., 549.

imbecility arising from advanced age, illness, or any other cause may destroy the testamentary power. The loss of the disposing capacity may be either temporary or permanent. A temporary loss may be caused by drinking, drugging, illness, &c. Undue influence exercised over a weak mind may also lead to the same effect.

Dispositions by a person suffering from a fatal illness.

Under the Mussulman Law, the acts of disposition by a person suffering from an illness which induces the apprehension of death and which eventually causes death, have only a qualified effect given to them. For example, when a person suffering from such an illness makes a gift or *wakf*, such disposition, though an act of immediate operation, takes effect like a will and is valid only so far as a *wasiat* may be valid.(1)

This is independently of any question regarding the disposing condition of the testator's mind or the spontaneity of his action. The law presumes that a person in such a state is devoid of a complete disposing faculty. In considering, therefore, the operative character of voluntary dispositions to which effect is given immediately, regard is to be had to the state of the disposing party at the time of the disposition. If he was then in health, they are valid as against the whole of his property; and if he was not then in health, they are valid as against a third of it, provided the disposition is not in favour of an heir. By acts of disposal are to be understood such acts as are initiatory or creative of right, and have in them something gratuitous. For the acknowledgment of a debt in sickness operates against the whole of a person's estate, and a marriage contracted in sickness is in like manner operative against the whole to the extent of the proper dower. An act of disposal which is not to take effect till after the death of the disposing party, as when a man says—"Thou art free after my death," or "This is to Zaid after my death," is good only to the extent of a third of his property even though it were made in health. Emancipation, *muhâbât*,(2) *wakf*, gift and *ziman* or suretyship by a sick man have all the same effect as bequests, and operate only

(1) The will of a person suffering from a *marz-ul-mout* is valid only as to a third; *Radd-ul-Muhtâr*.

(2) *Muhâbât* is an act by which the donor makes a gratuity to the donee either by reducing the price or increasing the value of the property sold. *Muhâbât* is derived from *hubwat*.

against a third of his property.(1) The diseases which naturally give rise to an apprehension of death and which are technically called *marz-ul-mout* or *death-illness* have been explained in a previous chapter.(2) Some further explanations may usefully be added here.(3)

Marz-ul-mout (Hanafî doctrines).

"The approved doctrine as stated by Kahastâni is that *marz-ul-mout* is an illness from which death results though the sufferer be not confined to his bed. A long-standing illness is not regarded as a death-illness so as to restrict a person's capacity to make a disposition of his entire estate, on the ground that when it has existed for a long period, it has become a part of his nature as in the case of the blind, the lame, &c., and he no longer apprehends the imminence of death. A death-illness is, accordingly, a disease from which death is imminent, and this happens when it goes on increasing until it ends in death ; but where it remains stationary for a long time, or the progress is so imperceptible as to cause no fear to the sufferer, or when he becomes habituated to it, it is not."

"When a death occurs after the lapse of a full twelvemonth from the commencement of the disease, the disposition is valid with reference to the entire estate. But when a death has occurred before that period from a disease which usually ends fatally, and the deceased was disabled by it from leaving his house to attend to his ordinary avocations, or, if a woman, from performing domestic duties in the house, such a disease is regarded as death-illness and the disposition will take effect with reference to one-third."(4) "A gratuitous disposition by a woman about to be confined is valid with reference to one-third ; so also if two bodies of men come into collision with each other which ends in bloodshed and the death of some, the rule of *Marz-ul-mout* would apply (*i.e.*, the disposition made after the people had started for the fight would only take effect with reference to a third, but not if there was no collision). So also the disposition of a person overtaken by storm at sea and of the prisoner ordered to be executed."(5)

---

(1) *Fatâwai Alamgiri*, Vol. VI, p. 168 ; Baillie's Dig., p. 651.

(2) *Ante*, p. 57.

(3) From the Chapter on Wills, *Radd-ul-Muhtâr*, Vol. V, p. 639.

(4) This is according to Zailye and others.

(5) *Radd-ul-Muhtâr*, Vol. V, p. 650 ; according to the *M'irâj*.

The provisions of the Shiah Law on this branch of the subject are analogous, and yet there are some features of difference which deserve especial attention. According to the *Jawâhir-ul-Kalâm*, "dispositions of property by a person suffering from a mortal illness are of two kinds :—such as are deferred and not intended to have operation until after the death of the testator; and such as take effect immediately. The first are to be treated in every respect as legacies according to the unanimous opinion of 'our' doctors and like the acts of a person in health, which are done with reference to his death so as not to take effect till after it. The second description of acts are such as are of immediate operation like *muhâbât* or connivance at loss in contracts of exchange, and gift, *wakf* and emancipation. These are good according to some of 'our' doctors as against the whole of the settlor's property, and according to others only as against a third. Both opinions, however, agree in this that if he should recover from his sickness they are valid against himself and against his heirs, and the difference of opinion is only when he dies of the same disease."

Shiah Doctrines.

Shiah doctrines as to *Marz-ul-mout.*

"Here it is necessary to note the diseases which restrain a man from disposing of more than a third of his property. Upon this point we may say that every disease which is usually accompanied with apprehension of death is said to be dangerous,(1) such as hectic fever, consumption, hemorrhage, &c. Diseases, again, from which there is usually recovery have no other effect on a man's disposal of his property than if he were in a state of health, such as temporary fever, headache, whether with continued augmentation or not, ophthalmia, and a tubercle on the tongue Diseases, again, which admit of being classed as either, that is, as *dangerous* and *undangerous* are putrid fever, diarrhœa, and a phlegmatic swelling. It were, however, better to ascribe the effect under consideration to all diseases which are, in fact, accompanied with, or terminate in death, whether they are customarily dangerous or not. *But occasions of actual conflict in war, or of a child-birth with women, or of storms at sea have not the effect alluded to, namely, that of impairing a person's power to dispose of his property, because, in point of fact, the term disease is quite inapplicable* to them."(2)

(1) Comp. Query, *Droit Musulman*, I, p. 635.
(2) On this point the Hanafis differ.

The effect of testamentary dispositions by a person labouring under an illness of which he eventually dies, is thus explained in the *Sharâya* :—

"(*a*) When a person in sickness has made a gift and also entered into a *muhâbât* transaction, and the third of his property suffices for both purposes, there is no question that effect is to be given to both. But if it should fall short, the first act of the deceased is entitled to preference, and effect would be given to the other acts in succession until the third is exhausted when the deficiency would fall solely upon the last.

(*b*) When a gift of immediate operation and one whose effect is postponed or suspended are made at the same time, preference is to be given to the former, but effect will also be given to the latter if the third of the estate is sufficient for both purposes, but if not, the latter is valid so far as the third will bear and void as to the remainder.

(*c*) When a sick person having no more than a *kurr* (measure) of grain of some kind of the value of six dinars sells it for a *kurr* of inferior grain of the value of two dinars the loss by the *muhâbât* is a half of his whole estate, whereas all that he can lawfully dispose of is no more than a third and the purchaser should accordingly restore a sixth to the heirs, but that would be usurious, and in order to make a valid transaction it is necessary that he should give back to the heirs one-third of their good *kurr*, and that they should give back to him one-third of his inferior *kurr* ; there will thus remain with the heirs two-thirds of the *kurr*, or two dinars in value, and with the purchaser two-thirds of a *kurr*, or four dinars in value, which will only be an excess of two dinars or one-third of six (the whole estate) which is just the amount which the seller could lawfully dispose of in his last illness.

(*d*) If a sick person should sell some article of the value of two hundred for one hundred and afterwards recover of his disease, the contract is necessarily binding. But if he should die, and the heirs refuse to ratify the sale, it would be valid so far as a half of the article is opposed to what he actually paid, and that is three parts out of six and the *muhâbât* is good as to two-sixths or one-third of the six, and these together, amount to five-sixths of the article to which extent then the sale is valid, and void only as to the remaining one-sixth which, therefore, must be returned to the heirs. The purchaser, however, has an option and may cancel the sale on account of the partial invalidity of the bargain or abide by it, but should he adopt the latter alternative and offer the heirs a compensation for a sixth of the article, they also have an option either to reject or accept, their right being involved in the substance of the article.''

The result of these provisions is, that a testamentary disposition by a person suffering from a death-illness is valid as to a third of his estate, if at the time of the *wasiat*, the testator was sufficiently in his senses, and the act was a spontaneous expression of his own wish or intention.

There is considerable difference, however, between a gratuitous disposition made on a death-bed or in contemplation of death, and the acknowledgment of a liability. Acknowledgment of a liability on death-bed.

"It is to be observed as a general rule,'' says the *Hedâya* "that where a person performs with his property any gratuitous, deed of immediate operation (that is, not restricted to his death), if he be in health at the time, such deed is valid to the extent of all his property—or, if he be sick, it takes effect to the extent of one-third of his property, and where a person performs such deed with his property restricted to the circumstance of his decease, it takes effect to the extent of a third of his property, whether at the time he be sick or in health. If, on the contrary, a person make an acknowledgment of debt, such acknowledgment is of effect to the whole extent of his property, notwithstanding it be made during sickness as this is not a *gratuitous* deed. Still, however, a declaration of this nature made in health precedes a declaration of the same nature made in sickness. It is also to be remarked that a sickness, of which a person afterwards recovers, is considered in law as health.''

"If a sick person make an acknowledgment of debt in favour of a strange woman, or make a bequest in her favour, or bestow a gift upon her and afterwards marry her and then die, the acknowledgment is valid, but the bequest or gift is void; for the nullity of an acknowledgment in favour of an heir depends on the person having been an heir at the time of making it; whereas the nullity of a bequest in favour of an heir depends on the legatee being so at the time of the testator's death as has been already explained, and as the woman was not an heir at the time of the acknowledgment but had become so (by marriage) at the time of the testator's death, the acknowledgment is therefore valid, but the bequest is void, and so likewise the gift, it being subject to the same rule as the bequest."

"If a sick person make an acknowledgment of a debt due by him to his son, or make a bequest in his favour, or bestow a gift upon him at a time when the son was a Christian, and he (the son) afterwards previous to his father's death became a Mussulman, all those acts of acknowledgment, gift or bequest are void, the bequest and the gift, because of the son being an heir at the death of his father as above explained, and the acknowledgment, because, although the son on account of the bar (namely, difference of religion) was not an heir at the time of making it, still the cause of inheritance (namely, consanguinity) did then exist, which throws an imputation on the father, as it engenders a suspicion that he may have made a false declaration in order to secure the descent of part of his fortune to his son. It is different in the case of marriage as above stated, for there the cause of inheritance (namely, marriage), occurred posterior to the acknowledgment and had no existence previous thereto, for supposing the marriage to have existed at the period of making the acknowledgment, and that the wife being then a Christian, should afterwards, before the husband's death, become a Moslemah, in that case it (the acknowledgment) would not be valid."

"If a sick person make an acknowledgment of a debt due by him to his son who is an absolute slave or a *mokâtib*, or bestow a gift upon him, or make a bequest in his favour, and the son should afterwards, before the death of his father, obtain his liberty, in that case none of these acts is valid, because of the reasons explained in the preceding example."

Similarly, Kâzi Khân declares, "When a sick man has acknowledged a debt to a woman who is a stranger to him, or bequeathed a legacy to her, or made her a gift and has subsequently married her and then died, the acknowledgment is lawful according to 'us,' but the legacy and the gift are void. And when a sick man has made a bequest to his son who is an infidel, or a slave, or has made a gift to him with delivery, or acknowledged a debt to him, and the son is then converted to the faith, or is emancipated before his death, the whole of his act is void."

But when the acknowledgment is not for a specific amount, or for a specific thing, it will be given effect to from the one-third of the estate. For example, if a person were to say to his heirs on his death-bed, "I am indebted to Zaid, and you must credit what he says," in that case the claim of Zaid to any amount not exceeding a third of the estate must be admitted, although the heirs should claim it. "This proceeds upon the basis of a favourable construction."(1)

Similarly, if the testator were to say to his heirs, "if Zaid come and claim anything from you on my behalf, pay him the same to whatever amount," which declaration would be recognised and complied with to the amount of one-third of the estate, and the acknowledgment being thus equivalent to a bequest, the declaration of Zaid must be credited to the amount of one-third of the acknowledgor's estate and no more. If, therefore, besides the acknowledgment in question, the testator had made various bequests, in favour of others, one-third of his estate must be set apart for the legatees and two-thirds for the heirs. And the heirs and legatees will be called upon to declare if the testator said anything to Zaid, and if they admit any liability, it will be discharged out of the estate and effects of the acknowledgor in proportion to the respective shares of the heirs, and the legatees must be required to verify the declaration to Zaid to such extent as they may think proper." "Now, if both parties acknowledge that there is something owing to Zaid, it is evident that there rests a debt upon the estate affecting the shares of each respectively and consequently this being so, it follows that if Zaid should claim more than what is admitted by the heirs and legatees [and has no other proof, excepting the unspecific acknowledgment of the testator], the affirmation on oath of the heirs and legatees, 'to the best of their knowledge,' or, in other words, to the effect that they do not know of any more being due to Zaid will be believed; for they cannot be required to swear positively, as their oath regards a matter between the claimant and the acknowledgor merely, and in which they are not principals."

If a person bequeath any article jointly to one of his heirs and a stranger, in this case the bequest in favour of the heir is not

(1) *Hedâya* (Hamilton), Vol. IV, p. 494.

admitted, and a moiety only of the legacy is given to the stranger, because as an heir does not possess the capacity of being a legatee, he therefore obstructs the stranger in the title which he would otherwise have to the complete legacy. It is not so when a legacy is left jointly to one person living and another dead, for here the whole goes to the living legatee, since a dead person cannot take a bequest.

The capacity of an infant. Shiah Law. Shâfeï and Mâliki doctrines.

Regarding the capacity of an infant to make a testamentary disposition, the divergence between the schools is very great. The Shiah Law declares that perfect intellect and freedom are indispensably requisite to the validity of a bequest, and the will of a *majnûn*(1) and of a *sabî* (youth or child) under ten years of age is not valid; when he has attained to that age all bequest by him for proper purposes in favour of his relatives and others are lawful according to the most common and approved doctrine, provided *he is capable of discernment.*

The Shâfeïs and Mâlikis agree generally with the Shiahs. According to the Shâfeï doctrines, an infant may validly constitute a *wasiat* if he is morally in a condition to understand the nature of his act.(2) In other words, there is no hard-and-fast rule as to the limit of age when capacity would be presumed. The Mâlikis, also, do not regard infancy in itself a disability, but the jurists of this school do not seem to be agreed as to the characteristics of a *wasiat* made by an infant. Whilst some of them hold that only such dispositions by a minor should be regarded as valid as are in favour of pious objects, others are of opinion that the right of a minor to make a *wasiat* should not be restricted to these objects alone, but should be extended to all dispositions when it appears that they are not contradictory and the minor possesses the comprehension to understand the nature of his act.

The Mâliki views.

Hanafi doctrines; incapacity of an infant to devise by will.

The Hanafîs, on the other hand, consider an infant who has not attained puberty as wanting in reason or comprehension and refuse him the power of making a *wasiat*. The *Multeka* expressly declares "that the validity of a *wasiat* requires several conditions one of them being that the testator should be adult." So also the *Fatâwai Alamgiri*; "a bequest by a youth under puberty whether

---

(1) A lunatic. (2) Sautayra, p. 319.

he be a *murâhik*(1) (adolescent) or not is unlawful according to us. And it makes no difference whether the youth be permitted to trade or be under inhibition, or whether he die before or after puberty. So also, though he should say, 'if I arrive at majority, a third of my property is to such an one,' the *wasiat* is not valid for want of competency at the time of making it."

According to the *Radd ul-Muhtâr*, "the *wasiat* of a minor, though possessed of discernment, is not valid, except with respect to the provision for his funeral expenses (on the authority of Omar, may God be pleased with him, in the matter of the *wasiat* of an adolescent)."

The *Hedâya* points out the difference between the Hanafî and Shâfeï Law in some detail. "Bequest by an infant is not valid. Shâfeï maintains that it is valid, provided it be made to a discreet and advisable purpose, because Omar confirmed the will of a *sabî* (a youth who has nearly attained maturity), and also because in the execution of it a degree of advantage results to the infant inasmuch as he acquires the merit of the deed—whereas in the annulment of it he is deprived of all advantage. The argument of 'our' doctors in support of their opinion upon this point are two-fold. *First*, a will is a voluntary act concerning which an infant has not a capacity of forming a proper judgment. *Secondly*, the declaration of an infant is not of a binding nature, but if the validity of a bequest by such were admitted, that effect would follow of course. With regard to the tradition of Omar, the term *sabî* there used must be understood to mean a person just arrived at the age of maturity, or 'the will of the *sabi*' relates merely to the celebration of the obsequies which is lawful in the opinion of 'our' doctors. Besides the annulment of the will is advantageous to the infant, since in allowing his property to pass to the heirs, the rights of natural affection are maintained, as before mentioned. With respect to the assertion of Shâfeï that, in the execution of the will an advantage results to the infant, it may be replied that the point to be attended to in cases of advantage or loss is the immediate tendency of any act or deed, and not what may eventually result from it; in other words, if the deed itself, in its immediate tendency, produce advantage, the execution of it on account of the

Hanafî doctrine.

(1) One approaching puberty.

infant is preferable, but in the case here considered the deed (that is, the bequest) in its immediate tendency leads to a loss of property, although eventually the infant have an advantage, the bequest having been made with a view to obtain merit in the eye of God, and since the bequest of the infant, in its immediate tendency, occasions a loss, it is not valid, in the same manner as in the case of a divorce, in other words, if an infant divorce his wife or his guardian do so on his behalf, it is not binding notwithstanding a divorce may on many occasions be attended with advantage, as where an infant having a wife who is poor wishes to divorce her and marry her sister who is rich and handsome. In short, bequest by an infant is invalid according to 'our' doctors, and in the same manner if an infant should make a will and die after he had attained majority, the will is not valid as having been made at a time when he was unqualified for such an act, and so likewise if an infant should say, 'It is my will whenever I reach the age of maturity that a third of my estate be considered as a legacy in favour of a particular person,' the will is not valid, because an infant being unqualified, is not competent to make a will that shall be deemed valid immediately, or that can be rendered so by being suspended to a future period, in the same manner as he is incapable of divorcing or emancipating.(1) It is otherwise with respect to a bondsman or a *mokâtib*, for they possess a complete competency obstructed merely by the right of their master, and therefore all their acts (such as divorce, bequest and so forth) are perfectly valid if referred to a period when that bar no longer exists, as where a bondsman (for instance) says, 'I declare my wife to be divorced whenever I am free.''

Bequest by an infant invalid.

Ratification after the attainment of majority.

The provisions of the Hanafî Law amount to this, that an infant *under the age of puberty* does not possess the capacity of making a disposition of his property by will. What would be the limit of age under the Indian Majority Act (Act IX of 1875) is a question which has been considered at some length at a previous stage of this work.(2) But a *wasiat* made by a minor becomes effective *ab initio* upon his confirming or ratifying the same after attaining majority.

(1) Comp. the *Radd ul-Muhtâr*, Vol. V, p. 645.

(2) See Vol. II in *loco*.

As regards the capacity of a person who is condemned to death for an offence, there is no provision in the law to deprive him of the power of making a will. A soldier engaged in an expedition, a person travelling and away from his property, in fact, every sane and free person, whether man or woman, can validly make a bequest.

Difference of creed is no objection to the power of devising by will. The *Multeka* lays this down expressly; "the difference of religion between the testator and the legatee is no ground for impugning the lawfulness of a *wasiat*. Accordingly, a Mussulman can make a disposition in favour of a non-Moslem (unless he is an alien) as a non-Moslem can make one in favour of a Mussulman."(1) With regard to the validity of a will made by a Moslem who afterwards apostatises there seems to be some divergence between the schools. According to the Mâlikis the *wasiat* is annulled by the fact of apostacy. According to the Hanafîs, the will would have effect given to it if it is valid according to the sect to which he has apostatised.

The will of an apostate from Islâm; Hanafî doctrine.

"If a Moslem should apostatise to Christianity, Judaism or Magianism, and then make some of the bequests referred to, such of them as would be valid, if made by a Moslem, remain in suspense until he returns to the faith or is put to death, or dies naturally, or takes refuge in a foreign country, and such of them as are not valid, if made by a Moslem, are void according to Abû Hanîfa; but, according to the two Disciples, the acts of an apostate are operative for the present, so that whatever is valid according to the sect to which he apostatises is valid in him, and if the bequest be an act of piety with them, but sin with 'us,' it is valid though to a sect of persons who are not particularised. With regard to a female apostate, her bequests are valid so far as the bequests of the sect to which she has apostatised would be valid, because she is not liable to be put to death for her apostacy."(2)

Under the Mahommedan Law the will of a suicide is held to be invalid.(3) But where certain dispositions of a testamentary

(1) The Shâfeis differ.

(2) *Fatâwai Alamgiri*, Vol. VI, p. 141; Baillie's Dig., p. 675; *Radd ul-Muhtâr*, Vol. V, p. 643; *Hedâya*, Vol. IV, p. 537.

(3) *Muzhar Hussain* v. *Bodha Bibi* (1898), I. L., 21 All., 91; s. c., L. R., 25 I. A., 210.

character were made in a letter written shortly before the testator's death in which he stated that he had taken poison, the statement was construed by the Judicial Committee of the Privy Council as a representation of the state of things as they would present themselves when the letter arrived ; and it was held that the onus was on the party impugning the will to show that the letter was written after he had taken the poison.(1)

Another essential requisite to the validity of a testamentary disposition is, that the testator should be proprietor of the subject of the will or should be entitled to it when it happens to be a right.(2)

Bequests of an insolvent testator.

But when the subject of the bequest is the property of a testator who is so burdened with debt that his liabilities exceed his assests, the disposition will not have effect given to it unless the creditors discharge the estate from the payment of their debts.(3)

The Shiah doctrines on this point are explained thus in the *Sharâya* :(4)—" When a person who is in debt directs by will the emancipation of his bondsman,(5) and the value of the bondsman is twice the amount of the debt, the bondsman is emancipated, but must labour for five-sixths of his value, but if his value is less than the debt the legacy is valid. The reason is that debts

(1) *Muzhar Hussain* v. *Bodha Bibi.* supra.

(2) Sautayra, p. 421.

(3) In Baillie's Digest this principle is stated as follows :—" When a man makes a bequest, being in debt to the full amount of all his property, the bequest is not lawful, unless the creditors agree to release the property *pro tanto.*" It will be observed that the way in which the principle is stated here is in its effect somewhat different from the principle as given in the text. And the English version of the *Hedâya* accentuates the difference in the following passage " if a person," it says, " deeply involved, bequeaths any legacies such bequest is unlawful and of no effect, because debts have a preference to bequests, and the discharge of debts is an absolute duty, whereas bequests are gratuitous and voluntary and that which is most indispensable must be first considered. If, however, the creditors of the deceased relinquish their claims, the bequest is then valid, the obstacle to it being removed, and the legatee being supposed to stand in need of his legacy." But an analysis of the expressions used in all the texts shows clearly that the dicta refer to the invalidity of testamentary dispositions by persons whose debts leave no margin for the payment of legacies, and who, to use Arabian phraseology, are " drowned in debt."

(4) *Jawâhir ul-Kâlâm ; Sharâya.*

(5) The illustration is somewhat characteristic of the modes of thought prevailing at this time, but it seems to explain fully the meaning.

taking precedence of legacies must be first discharged, and it is only out of a third of what remains of the estate that the emancipation can take effect. It is otherwise in the case of a gratuitous emancipation by a master on his death-bed when the law is, as before mentioned, on the ground of an express decision recorded by Abdur Rahman as coming from the Imâm Jaâfar as-Sâdik on whom be peace."

A *wasiat* is lawful for any purpose which is considered proper under the law, and which may be carried into effect at the time of the testator's decease. This principle, however, is subject to certain limitations, the consideration of which is necessary before we come to the discussion of the person for whom a *wasiat* may validly be constituted.

A bequest to a person who causes the death of the testator; Hanafî doctrines.

(1) A *wasiat* in favour of a person who intentionally causes the death of the testator is unlawful according to all the schools. According to the Hanafîs, a bequest is not lawful to a person who causes the death of the testator even unintentionally, by accident or misadventure, unless the person causing the death is an infant or an insane person.(1) And the bequest is unlawful whether it was made before or after the injury resulting in death. But if the heirs assent to the bequest it will be valid according to Abû Hanîfa and Mohammed, though not according to Abû Yusuf. When the death is caused by an infant or a lunatic legatee, the assent of the heirs is not necessary to the validity of the bequest. "The Prophet has declared," says the *Radd ul-Muhtâr*, "'there is no legacy for the person slaying,' for he has hastened an event which God might have delayed, and therefore a bequest to the murderer is unlawful whether it was made before the mortal wound was given or subsequently, for the tradition is general and this is the view of Zailye. By hastening the event is meant that the act of the murderer is the immediate cause of the death of the deceased, for otherwise, as held by the followers of the true doctrine, the death was an event which was inevitable." "If a person simply wounds another, but the actual slaying is done by a third person, the legacy to the person wounding is not invalid, for he is not the murderer, this is the view of Ula'l-walji. The person causing the death of

(1) "This exception in favour of an infant and a lunatic is made," says the *Radd ul-Muhtâr*, "because they are not liable to punishment."

another forfeits the legacy whether his act was intentional, or the result of accident or misadventure, for example, if a man digs a well and the person who has left him a legacy falls into it, the legatee forfeits the legacy."

"A bequest to a slayer will be valid according to Abû Hanîfa and Mohammed if the heirs of the testator should consent. Abû Yusuf, however, disagrees on this point, and holds that it is absolutely void though the heirs should consent. According to Sharnibilâlièh, a bequest made before the murder is void according to all of them though the heirs should consent."(1)

Mâliki doctrines.

According to the Mâlikis the testator has the power of condoning the offence committed on his person, and if after receiving the mortal wound he makes a *wasiat* in favour of the person causing the wound, it will be presumed that he pardoned the offence and the bequest would be valid.

Shiah principle.

According to the Shiahs, the homicide must be intentional to avoid the legacy to the person causing the death. According to the Hanafî Law if the person causing the death is the only heir of the testator, the bequest to him would be lawful according to Abû Hanîfa and Mohammed, though not according to Abû Yusuf.

---

(1) "A bequest," says the *Alamgiri*, "to a person who slays the testator either intentionally or by accident is not lawful whether the bequest were made before the death-wound or after it. But if the heirs assent to the bequest, it is lawful according to Abû Hanifa and Mohammed. And if the slayer be a youth under puberty or insane, the bequest to him is lawful without the consent of the heirs, or if the slayer be himself the sole heir, a bequest to him is lawful according to Abû Hanîfa and Mohammed. A bequest to the conditionally enfranchised bondsman or *umm-ul-walad* (the bondswoman who has borne children to her master) of the slayer is also unlawful without the consent of the heirs."

The *Hedâya* states as follows :—"If a person makes a bequest in favour of another from whom he has received a mortal wound, it is not valid whether the murderer be one of his heirs or a stranger, or whether he may have wounded him wilfully or by misadventure provided he be the actual perpetrator of the deed, because it is recorded in the traditions that there is no legacy for a murderer, and also as the person who gave the wound has hastened the death of the testator, he is by way of punishment excluded from the benefit of the will in the same manner as a person under similar circumstance is excluded from inheritance. So likewise where a man having made a bequest in favour of a particular person is afterwards killed by that person, such bequest in invalid. If, however, in these cases the heirs should give their consent, the bequest then becomes valid according to Abû Hanifa and Mohammed. Abû Yusuf is of a contrary opinion because the offence of the murderer which is the cause of the invalidity of the will still exists." The former view is the one generally accepted by the sect.

But though a legacy to one's murderer or homicide is unlawful, a bequest in favour of his parents, children or any other ascendant or descendant would be lawful.

(2) According to all the schools a bequest to any one of the heirs is invalid without the consent of the others.(1) Whether the person in whose favour the devise is made is an heir or not must be determined not at the time of the will but at the testator's death. A grandson whose father has died in the lifetime of the testator is a non-heir when he co-exists with a son; and a bequest to him not exceeding a third is valid. Bequest to an heir. Hanafî doctrine.

"A bequest," says the *Radd ul-Muhtâr*, "to a stranger (or non-heir) is valid to the extent of one-third of the testator's estate, but it may be validated respecting a larger proportion with the assent of the heirs after the death of the testator; *consent given during the lifetime of the testator is of no effect*; the consent in order to be effectual must be not only after the death of the testator, but the parties must be adult and *sui juris*. The consent of heirs before the death of the testator is ineffectual because the right to the inheritance does not vest in them until his death. When consent is given according to 'us' the legatee would derive his title from the testator: according to Shâfeï, the right will be derived from the consenting heir. When some of the heirs consent and others do not, the legacy will be valid in proportion to the shares of the assenting heirs. It is requisite that the consenting heirs should be adult and possessed of understanding. Consequently the consent of the infant and the *non compos mentis* is not valid. The consent of the person who is sick is subject to the same rules as his legacy. Whether a person is an heir or not must be considered with reference to his right of inheritance at the time of the testator's death. Therefore, when a person leaves a legacy to his brother at a time when he has no children, and afterwards children are born to him and he dies, the legacy to the brother is valid, for in the presence of the children he has no right of inheritance. Similarly, if a person were to make a bequest to his wife and afterwards were to divorce her, the legacy would be valid for she is not an heir at the time of the testator's death; Consent of the heirs to a bequest.

---

(1) See *Bafatun* v. *Belaiti Khanum* [1903], I. L., 30 Cal., 683; *Khajooroonissa* v. *Roushan Jehan* [1876], L. R., 3 I. A., 291; s. c., I. L., 2 Cal., 184.

the marriage relation having been dissolved, the right of inheritance also falls to the ground.''(1)

Consent of the heir—how far valid.

If the heir is sane and adult and, therefore, possessed of the capacity of disposition but happens to give his consent at a time when he is suffering from illness, if he recovers from that illness, his consent is valid. But if he were to die of the illness, his assent would have the same effect as if it was a bequest, so that if the original legatee was an heir of the assenting heir, the assent is not lawful unless concurred in by the other heirs of the sick person, but if the original legatee was not the heir of the assenting heir who has died, the assent would validate the legacy to the extent of one-third of his share in the inheritance of the original testator.(2)

Such consent may be given either expressly or may be indicated by unequivocal conduct such as signing the will with a full understanding of its meaning, without outside pressure or undue influence, or allowing the devisee to enter into possession without objection.(3)

Acknowledgment of a debt.

But though a bequest in favour of an heir is invalid, an *ikrâr* or acknowledgment of a debt, as stated before, is valid.(4)

If a man were to make a bequest in favour of a part of his heirs, it is not valid because of a traditional saying of the Prophet, ''God has allotted to every heir his particular right,'' and also because a will in favour of a part of the heirs is an injury to the rest, and therefore, if it were deemed legal, it would induce a breach of the ties of kindred. Besides it is said in the traditions ''a bequest to particular heirs is unjust.'' It is to be observed that in judging whether the legatee be an heir or otherwise, regard is paid to the time of the testator's death and not, as pointed out already, to the period of making the will. If some of the heirs should give their consent and part withhold it, the bequest then becomes valid in proportion to the amount of the shares of those who consent, and invalid in proportion to the amount of the shares of the others.

---

(1) *Raddul-Muhtâr*, Vol. V, p. 644.

(2) *Ibid.* Comp. Baillie's Dig., p. 626; *Fatâwai Alamgiri*, Vol. V, p. 148.

(3) *Doulatram* v. *Abdul Kayum* [1902], I. L., 26 Bom., 497; *Sharifa Bibi* v. *Gulam Mahomed Dastgir Khan* [1892], I. L., 16 Mad., 43.

(4) See *ante*, p. 579, *Radd-ul-Muhtâr*, Vol. VI, p. 644; *Hedâya*, Vol. IV, p. 472.

To recapitulate :—The persons who cannot be excluded from succession by a testamentary disposition are those who are entitled upon the decease of the testator to a share in his inheritance whatever may be the category of their heirship. This principle is founded upon the direction contained in Chap. IV, verse 7, of the Koran: "To every one have we appointed kinsfolk as heirs from their parents and relatives, and those with whom we have joined their right hands; so give them their portions, for verily God is over all a witness." The rights of the heirs, say the jurists, are thus irrevocably fixed by the Koran, and the harmony which has been established by the divine law among the different degrees of relations who would be entitled to succession to the estate of a deceased person should not be broken by his leaving a larger share to one heir. The author of the *Multeka* has declared in consequence that a testamentary disposition is null from the time when the succession opens, when the legatee is an heir, and the Mâliki lawyer, Khalîl ibn-Ishâk, has held that all legacies to the heirs are void.

In consequence of these directions, the Mussulmans scarcely ever make bequests in favour of an heir. When they intend making any variation in the shares of their heirs, they either make a *hiba* or an acknowledgment of a debt in favour of the heir whom they desire to prefer. Occasionally, the devise is made nominally in favour of one who is not an heir but really in favour of an heir.

But a bequest in favour of a relation who is not entitled to a share in the inheritance of the testator or who, though an heir at the time of making the devise, is excluded by any circumstance from succession at the time when the inheritance opens, is valid in law; for example, when a person has two sons and one grandson, —the son of a predeceased son,—to whom he makes a bequest not exceeding one-third of his property, such bequest is valid. Similarly, if a man has a son and a daughter's son or a daughter's daughter, the daughter's son, not being an heir, a bequest to him is valid. When a person has only a brother, and no children, the bequest to him would be invalid, but if a child be born to the testator after the bequest, it would be valid, provided, of course, it does not exceed the disposible third. If a man were to make a *wasiat* in favour of his wife, it would be invalid, but if she is divorced before his death, it would be valid.

A case given by Sautayra will exemplify one branch of these principles. A man of the name of Bou-Medina acknowledged himself to be a debtor of his wife to the extent of 250 dirhems, and subject to the payment of that debt, left all his estate and effects in equal shares to his said wife and two strangers; held under the Mahommedan Law that the debt should be first paid out of the estate, and that the estate should be thereafter divided in the following manner among the legatees and heirs,—

To the widow	..	3/12	being 1/4 the share of the widow.
To each of the legatees	..	4/12	being 1/3 of the quantity disposable.
To the heirs	..	5/12	
Total	..	12/12	

Bequest to an heir valid with consent of the other heirs.

All the Sunni schools agree in holding that a bequest in favour of an heir is invalid. A legacy, says the author of the *Multeka*, in favour of one heir is valid if the other heirs consent thereto. And the Shâfeï lawyer, Abû Khoja, has laid down the principle in similar terms, and the Mâliki jurist, Khalîl ibn-Ishâk, has declared that where a disposition is made in favour of an heir and ratified by the other heirs, the legacy will take effect as an act of liberality on their part.

Shiah doctrines consent may be given either *before* or *after* the death of the testator.

According to the Shiah law, however, as we shall see presently, a testator can leave a legacy to an heir so long as it does not exceed one-third of his estate. Such a legacy is valid without the consent of the other heirs, but where it exceeds one-third it is not valid without the consent of all the heirs. Such consent may be given either *before* or *after* the death of the testator. Under the Sunni law ratification must always be *after* the death, an assent before death being of no effect.

Under the Sunni law, the assent must be a free and voluntary act on the part of the heirs, and accordingly where the testator has held out any threat in his will, the effect of which may be to bias the mind improperly, the bequest will not take effect. "A legacy to an heir," says Khalîl ibn-Ishâk, "would be annulled when the testator has used the following expression, namely, 'if my heirs do not ratify these my dispositions my property shall go to the poor.' But a legacy expressed in the following terms: 'I bequeath such a legacy to the poor unless my heirs consent to give it to my son ' is valid, because the heirs are free either to give or refuse their consent."

Of the heir's consent during the last illness of the testator.

The voluntary assent given by the heirs during the last illness of the testator is irrevocable because the heir is supposed to have then acquired a right.

When a person has no heir he can leave his entire property to any one whom he likes.

Shiah doctrines.

The author of the *Sharâya* has laid down that when a testator has excluded one of his children from succession and left the property wholly to the others his direction is entirely invalid, and the inheritance will be apportioned among the heirs according to their legal shares.

But supposing a father makes an unequal division of property among his children or other heirs to take effect after his death (a *taksîm-bi'l-wasiat*), if it is assented to by the heirs it is lawful without question, but if no such assent is given what would be the effect? An example of such a case is given in the *Jâmaa ush-Shittât*. A person who was going on a pilgrimage made a partition of his estate among his children in the following manner :—(*a*) To some he gave properties in excess of their legal shares on account of the dower due to their mother ; (*b*) to others he gave certain sums of money in excess of their shares to defray the expenses of their marriages. A question was raised by the heirs, who received smaller shares, as to the validity of the *taksîmnâmah-bi'l-wasiat*. The dictum of the Mujtahid was to the following effect :—

" The dower is a debt which is bound to be discharged before the payment of the legacies. The properties given in lieu thereof have been lawfully devised. The sums of money left to some of the children in excess of their legal shares are in the nature of legacies and must come out of one-third of the testator's estate. The remainder of the property must be divided among the children according to their legal shares."(1)

As under the Hanafî law, a bequest in excess of the one-third is valid with the assent of the heirs. When there are several heirs, and one or more of them allow the excess it is valid to the extent of his or their share in it. The assent of an heir is effective when given after the testator's death. Whether it is equally valid

(1) *Jâmaa ush-Shittât ;* comp. Baillie's *Imâmia Law*, p. 233.

before his death is a question on which there are two opinions, *the more common and approved of which is in favour of its being binding on the heir.* When the consent is given after the testator's death it is a ratification of his act and not a gift *de novo* from the heir, consequently it does not require possession by the legatee to complete its validity.

(3) A *wasiat* by a Moslem in favour of an alien infidel is unlawful according to all the schools.(1)

(4) Bequest for the following purposes were discountenanced by the old Hanafî Law.(2)

"If a person should direct by his will that his body after his death should be carried to a certain place and there interred, and that a *rubât* is to be erected at the place, Abu'l Kâsim has held that the bequest is lawful as to the *rubât,* but is void as to the removal of the body, and that if the executor should incur any expense in removing it without the sanction of the heirs he will be responsible for the amount expended, though if he has their authority for the removal he does not incur any responsibility. A direction by will to ornament the testator's tomb is void. But with regard to a direction to provide food for mourners after the testator's death and for those who may be present at his funeral, the lawyer Abû J'aafar has said that it is lawful as regards a third of the estate, and that all may lawfully partake of the provision who prolong their stay at the funeral, or who come from a distance, rich and poor alike, but that if there is any lavish expenditure in the preparations the executor is liable for the excess. According to Shaikh Imâm Abû Bakr of Balkh, a direction by will to provide food for three days after the testator's death is void. * * * In the *Wakiât-i-Nâtiki* it is stated that if a person should direct that a thousand dinârs or ten thousand dirhems be expended on his shroud, no more than a medium expense is to be incurred on that account and only the cloth which the testator used, for going to the mosque on Fridays should be used. And if a woman should direct her husband to pay for her shroud out of the dower due to her by him, it has been said that whatever she may direct or forbid on that subject, is alike void. When a person directs that he shall

(1) *Radd ul-Muhtâr*, Vol. V, p. 643. *Fatâwai Alamgiri*, Vol. VI, p. 141. *Sharâya*; *Jawâhir ul-Kalâm.*

(2) See Baillie's Dig., p. 633.

be buried in his mansion, the bequest is void unless he direct the mansion is to be converted into a general cemetery for Moslems. A direction that the testator's grave be plastered and a vault or arch placed over is unlawful except in places where such precautions are required against the ravages of wild beasts. So also a direction that so much of one's property be given to persons for reading the Koran over the testator's grave is void even though special readers be appointed for the purpose.''

This passage embodies a number of sumptuary regulations which, according to present usage, have fallen into complete desuetude.(1)

Shiah doctrines.

Under the Shiah Law bequests are lawful for the following purposes :—

(*a*) for offering prayers for the testator in perpetuity or for a limited period ;

(*b*) for carrying the body of the deceased to Kerbela or any other holy place ;

(*c*) for some one to perform a pilgrimage on behalf of the testator ;

(*d*). for burning lights and putting flowers on his grave or in the shrines of the Imâms ;

(*e*) for relieving the poor Syeds of Kerbela and Najaf ,

(*f*) for feeding the poor on particular holy festivals ;

(*g*) for reading *mursias* (elegies) in the Imâmbaras ,

(*h*) for offering *sherbet* or supplying water in the time of the *Moharram* and such like objects ;

---

(1) See the *Radd ul-Muhtâr*, Vol. V, p. 677. The illegality of hiring a person for reading the Koran over the grave of the testator is founded on the unlawfulness of hiring people for performing one's devotions ; " it is only in cases of necessity," says the *Radd*, " that persons may be hired to perform devotional functions, such as the teaching of the Koran or law or performing the *azân*. The jurists are agreed that a person cannot be hired for performing fasts, prayers, *hajj*, etc." As regards the reading of the Koran over the grave, the modern doctrine, founded on Imam Mohammed's opinion, is that it is legal ; see *ante*, p. 431.

(*i*) A *wasiat* may be made by one person to another for the performance of religious ceremonies on the testator's behalf; for example, *A* on the point of death may ask *B* to perform the prayers which he has left unperformed during his lifetime, and *B* accepts the *wasiat*, it is valid and he will be bound to perform the same.(1)

---

(1) *Jâmaa ush-Shittât.*

CHAPTER XXI.

THE CONSTITUTION OF A WASIAT.

SECTION I.

WHO MAY BE LEGATEES OR DEVISEES.

The Musi-lahu.

IN principle, a *wasiat* is lawful for any person or object actually or constructively in existence at the time of the disposition.(1) "It is an indispensable condition," says the *Shâraya*, "that the legatee be in existence at the time of the bequest, and if he should not be alive, the legacy is not valid, in the same way as a legacy to a person deceased, or to one supposed to be alive, but who is afterwards proved to have been dead at the time of the bequest." So also it is stated in the *Alamgiri*, that "there is no bequest for the *non-existing* or the dead."

Shiah rule

Hanafî doctrine.

We will now consider the objects or persons in whose favour a *wasiat* may validly be made :—(*a*) With the exception of the Shâfeïs, who regard a bequest by a Moslem to a non-Moslem to be unqualifiedly unlawful, all the other schools admit the validity of a *wasiat* in favour of a non-Moslem who does not belong to the *Dâr ul-Harb* and, consequently, is not an alien.(2) The *Radd ul-Muhtâr* and the *Fatâwai Alamgiri* lay down this principle with the utmost distinctness. "A Moslem," says the *Alamgiri*, "may lawfully make a bequest to a *Zimmi* or *vice versâ*, but a bequest to an alien who is not a *Mustâmin* (3) is not lawful. If a Moslem make a bequest to an alien living in a *dâr ul-harb* or hostile country, the bequest is not lawful, even though the heirs should give their

A bequest to a *Harbi* invalid.

(1) *Radd ul-Muhtâr*, Vol. V, p. 661.

(2) For the reasons which compelled the Moslems to withhold the privilege from the *Harbis*, see "*The Spirit of Islam.*" The Mahommedan Law is decidedly more generous than the English Law was until a few years ago. The incapacity of aliens in England was removed only in 1870.

(3) A non-Moslem subject of a non-Moslem State who had taken up his residence in a Moslem country.

consent. And if the alien should come into Moslem territories under an *âmân* or protection, intending to take his legacy, he cannot do so even with the consent of the heirs. This is when the testator and the alien legatee were both in the *dâr ul-Islâm* at the time. If the testator were also in the *dâr ul-harb* 'our' doctors differ as to the legality of the bequest. When the alien is a *Mustâmin* residing in Moslem territory, it seems, on the authority of the *Zăhir ur-Rawâyèt*, that a bequest to him would be lawful to the extent of a third of the testator's property without the consent of the heirs and beyond that amount with their consent."(1)

Shiah doctrines.

A similar rule obtains among the Shiahs on the subject. The *Sharâya* declares—"With regard again to legacies in favour of *harbis* or hostile infidels there is some doubt, but according to the most authentic traditions they are forbidden and null."(2) And in the *Radd ul-Muhtâr* a *harbi* or hostile non-Moslem is regarded as civilly dead.

But whilst a devise by will is invalid in favour of an alien, presents and gratuities may lawfully be made to him. "In the *Sharh ul-Kabîr* of Sarakhsi it is stated," says the *Radd ul-Muhtâr*, "that there is no objection to a Moslem making presents or giving rewards to infidels whether they be relatives or not, and whether they be aliens or *Zimmis*, and the legality of this is founded on the tradition that the Prophet (may the blessings of God rest on him) sent various presents to Abû Sufiân ibn Harb and Sufiân ibn Ommeyya for distribution among the poor of Mecca.(3) And the reason of this is that presents to one's relations is commendable to every man and acceptable in every religion, and to strangers because it is an act of kindness and generosity. Accordingly, presents may lawfully be made to aliens, excepting of arms and armour."(4) But a bequest to an apostate is not lawful under any of the schools.(5)

---

(1) For the rules relating to the Wills of the non-Moslem subjects of Mussulman sovereigns, see *post*.

(2) *Sharâya*; Baillie's *Imâmia Law*, p. 244.

(3) Who were infidels at the time.

(4) *Radd ul-Muhtâr*, Vol. V, p. 643.

(5) *Ibid*, p. 664; see also *Fatâwai Alamgiri*, Vol. VI, p. 140; *Sharâya*; Sautayra, II, p. 342. Act XXI of 1850 makes no difference in the provisions of the Mahommedan Law on this subject.

A bequest to an unborn child.

(*b*) A disposition in favour of an infant *en ventre sa mère* is valid according to all the sects, but, according to the Hanafî Law, the child should be born within six months from the date of the *wasiat*, in which case it is presumed to have been in existence at the time of the bequest.(1) In the case of infants (including an infant *en ventre sa mère*), acceptance will be presumed unless it would cause injury to the devisee or legatee. The right of the infant *en ventre sa mère* to the bequest is established upon birth, and until then no person can exercise any right on its behalf, for example, commute the bequest or compromise the claim of the unborn legatee. The *Radd ul-Muhtâr* expressly lays down that for the "child in the womb there is no *walî*,(2) for the word (*mowla*) requires a *walî* in order to secure tender care and the infant in the womb does not stand in that need; as a matter of fact it is a part of the mother, and as the father has no right of guardianship in respect of the mother, consequently the father cannot be the *walî* of the child in the womb, nor can the mother be the *walî* of the child in her womb, and accordingly she cannot exercise any right in respect of any legacy left to such child, for though it is a part of her body, yet really it is a soul entrusted to her charge, *and the soul being in existence a bequest to it is lawful.*"(3) "A *wasiat*, from one point of view, is *tamlîk* and from another point of view appointing a successor to the rights of the testator (in a portion or the whole of his estate), and therefore though no *walî* can be appointed for an infant *en ventre sa mère*, according to all the authorities, such as Allâmah Ibn-Shibli, Halwâni and other *Mashâikh*, an appointment of a *wasî* or executor for such an infant is lawful, as is lawful the appointment of a *wasî* in the case of a *wakf* for unborn children. Such appointment takes effect upon the birth of the child when its right vests in the bequest."(4)

Bequest to an infant *en ventre sa mere.*

---

(1) A bequest to a child in the womb if born within six months from the date of the bequest is valid; *Fatâwai Alamgiri*, Vol. VI, p. 140; *Radd ul-Muhtâr*, Vol. V, p. 661. Baillie's Dig., p. 627. In the *Nihâya* it is stated that the six months should be computed from the date of the death of the testator; *Radd ul-Muhtâr*, Vol. V, p. 662.

(2) "A fœtus can neither be constituted a *walî* (guardian) nor can a *walî* be constituted for it."

(3) *Radd ul-Muhtâr*, Vol. V, p. 642.

(4) *Ibid.*

When the father of the child is alive, the birth of the child should be within six months from the date of the bequest in order that the right to the legacy may vest in it, but when the father is dead or the mother is divorced, the birth should be within six months from date of bequest and within the longest period of gestation (recognised by law) computed from the date of the father's death or the *talâk* of the mother. For, should the birth take place after this period, the child cannot be presumed to have been conceived at the time of the bequest.

A testamentary *wakf* to an unborn child.

But though a direct *wasiat* or a legacy, in other words, a *testamentary gift* to an unborn child is valid only when it is *en ventre sa mere* and is born within six months from the date of the bequest, yet the law recognises the validity of a *wakf bi'l wasiat, viz.*, a testamentary *wakf* in favour of unborn children to come into existence at any time, *when a commencement is made with a person in existence.* For example, a *wasiat* in favour of *A* (a living person) and his unborn children and descendants in perpetuity *is valid according to all the schools.* Such a *wakf* will have effect given to it by the appointment of *wasîs* who would carry out the trusts of the *wakf*.(1)

Shiah Law

Under the Shiah Law there is no restriction as to the time when the child should be born to take the benefit of the bequest. It will be sufficient if the child is born within the longest period of gestation recognised by the Shiah Law from the date of the bequest.(2) "A bequest to a fœtus in the womb actually existent is valid, but it requires that the child be produced alive, and if it is still-born, the *wasiat* is void; while if it is born alive, though it should die immediately after, the legacy descends to its heirs."(3)

Hanafî Law.

Under the Hanafî Law a child must also be born alive to be entitled to the legacy. "When a person makes a bequest to what is in the womb of a woman and she is delivered of a dead child, after his death, and a month after the bequest, the legacy is not for such child, but if the child be born alive, and then die, the bequest is lawful to the extent of a third of the testator's property, and is divisible among the child's heirs. If the woman should

(1) *Raddul-Muhtâr, in loco.* (2) See Mahommedan Law, Vol. II, *in loco.*
(3) *Sharâya-ul-Islâm*, p. 253.

bring forth two children, one dead and the other alive, the living child takes the whole legacy, but if both be born alive and one of them die, the legacy is divided into moieties, one for the living child, and the other for the heirs of the dead one by way of inheritance. When a person makes a bequest in these terms : 'If there be in the womb of such a person a girl, she is to have a legacy of a thousand dirhems, and if there be a boy, I bequeath to him two thousand dirhems,' and the woman is delivered of a girl within a day of the six months after the bequest, and of a boy two or three days later, the legacies to both are valid to the extent of a third of the estate.''(1)

(3) A *wasiat* is also lawful in favour of the following objects :—

(*a*) To the poor generally or a particular body of them ;

(*b*) To the Holy Shrine of the K'aaba or any mosque ;

(*c*) To Almighty God or to spend in the way of God (*sabîl illâh*) ;

(*d*) For *wujûh-ul-khair* or *wujûh-ul-birr* (good or meritorious purposes) generally ;

(*e*) "To fight in the way of God," *i.e.*, in the propagation of the Faith ;

For the performance of religious ceremonies over the tombs of deceased person (*urs*), celebration of the *moharram*, &c.; (2)

(*f*) For the children of one's heir, the kindred, neighbours. *kowm* (community or nation), *&c.* ;

(*g*) For the emancipation of slaves ;

(*h*) For the payment of one's debts ;

(*i*) A bequest for feeding cattle is also lawful.(3)

Wasiat for poor Christians Hanafî doctrine.

(*a*) A bequest for the poor is lawful. It may be for the poor generally or for a particular body of them. According to the Hanafî Law. "it is lawful for a Moslem to make a *wasiat* in favour of poor Christians, for that is no sin, contrary to building a church for them which is sinful, and he who assists in building churches for them is a sinner.(4) And this principle applies to the

(1) *Fatâwai Alamgiri*, Vol. VI, p. 142.

(2) See the will in the case of *Bishen Chand Basawat* v. *Syed Nadir Hossain*, L., R., 15 I. A., 1.

(3) *Radd ul-Muhtâr*, Vol. V, p. 652.

(4) *Fatâwai Alamgiri*, Vol. VI, p. 148.

poor of all creeds. Therefore, when a *wasiat* is generally for the poor, it will be applied to the poor of all creeds.

A *wakf* for the poor —Shiah Law.

Under the Shiah Law, it is different. "When a Moslem," says the *Sharâya*, "has made a bequest to beggars [in general terms], it is payable only to those of his own religion, and in like manner if the testator be an infidel such a bequest is only to those of his own persuasion."

Abû Yusuf's views.

A bequest for providing shrouds for the *Moslems generally*, or for digging their graves, or constructing aqueducts for them is bad according to Abû Yusuf as mentioned in the *Nawâdir*. But a bequest for the same or like purposes for *poor* Moslems is lawful. But this view does not seem to be followed and when a bequest is made for such purposes for Moslems *generally*, it is applied to *poor* Moslems only.

Bequests in favour of a mosque.

(*b*) Regarding a *wasiat* in favour of the Holy Shrine or a mosque, the *Fatâwai Alamgiri* provides as follows :—"If a person should bequeath a third of his estate to the Holy Shrine, the *wasiat* is lawful, and the third should be expended upon its buildings, lamps and the like ; so also the bequest of a third of one's estate to be laid out on a *masjid* is lawful, and the third should be expended on its buildings and lamps." A man may, according to all the jurists, devise his land for the construction of a mosque. Similarly, it is stated in the *Radd ul-Muhtâr* that "where a bequest is made of a third in favour of the *Bait-ul-Mukaddas*(1) it is lawful, and it will be applied in [maintaining] the building and lighting it and for like purposes. The same rule applies to a bequest in favour of a *masjid*, and the legacy will be applied in its maintenance and preservation, and according to Kâzi Khân, in lighting it in the Ramazân [and other seasons]. In the *Mujtaba*, it is laid down, however, that when a bequest of a third is made in favour of the K'aaba, it should be expended for the benefit of the poor of the K'aaba (*i.e.*, who derive alms from there) ; and similarly in the case of *wasiats* to a *masjid* and the *Bait-ul-Mukaddas*." Then the author proceeds to add—"respecting a bequest in favour of a *masjid* there are two opinions, *one* that it is not valid, and *the other* that it is valid. There is some difference among those who uphold the validity of

(1) The Holy Shrine [at Jerusalem].

such a *wasiat* regarding the mode of its application; some say, that it should be applied in maintaining the mosque, that is, in keeping the building in repair and in lighting it; whilst others hold that it should be spent in charity for the poor attached to that mosque. Mohammed upholds the former view; whilst the latter is adopted by the author of the *Mujtaba*. As regards the question of invalidity, two jurists alone hold that opinion, but when the bequest is made in specific terms that it should be spent for the mosque, it is valid by *consensus*......It is advisable, however, to give the *Fatwa* to the effect, that when it is made in favour of a *masjid*, it should be expended in charity to the poor of that mosque. And Saijâni has explained this in detail and reference ought to be made to the *Sharh-i-Wahbânieh* also. In the *Khulâsa* it is stated that it is preferable to spend on them, but is lawful to give to the other poor also. This is the opinion of Abû Yusuf and *Fatwas* are given according to it."(1)

A man may lawfully devise by will his land in favour of a *masjid*, though according to Abû Hanîfa, he may not bequeath the same to make a burying-ground for the indigent, or for the purpose of erecting an inn for the passers-by.(2) It is somewhat difficult to understand the reason of this distinction. The Disciples, however, differ from the master and uphold bequests in favour of the latter objects also.

(*c*) When a person makes a *wasiat* in the following terms, "I bequeath a third of my property to Almighty God," the devise is valid according to Mohammed,(3) and it would be applied or expended on good objects, *i.e.*, meritorious or pious purposes generally. A *wasiat fi-sabîl-illâh* (*i.e.*, in the way of God) will be applied in striving to spread the religion and can be applied lawfully to the help of a poor Hâji who has lost his means. In the *Nawâzil* it is

---

(1) *Radd ul-Muhtâr*, Vol. V, pp. 652, 653.

(2) *Fatâwai Alamgiri*, Vol. VI, p. 149.

The following passage, which occurs in the *Fatâwai Alamgiri*, must be read with the light of the comment in the *Radd ul-Muhtâr* : "When a person has said I have bequeathed a hundred dirhems to such a masjid, or such a bridge, the bequest is valid according to Mohammed, and should be laid out in preparing and improving it, but according to Ibn Zyâd when no mention has been made of repairs and improvements, the bequest is void, and the *Fatwa* is in accordance with his opinion."

(3) "And decisions are given according to his word."—*Radd ul-Muhtâr*. Abû Hanîfa holds such a bequest void.

stated, the bequest may be applied in lighting lamps and promoting religion generally. According to the Shiah Law "if the testator should direct a bequest to be expended in the way of God, it must be applied in some way for which reward is promised in a future state, but according to some exclusively in the propagation of the Faith. The first opinion, however, appears to be *better founded.*"(1)

Shiah doctrines.

Bequests for good purposes.

(*d*) When the bequest is made for good purposes (*wujûh-ul-khair* or *wujûh-ul-birr*, *objects of charity or liberality*), it includes all meritorious and pious objects and may be applied in erecting bridges or *masjids*, colleges or hospitals, or supporting the students of learning, or the poor, &c.(2)

"When a bequest is made 'to fight in the way of God' on the part of the testator, maintenance is to be given to a *ghâzi* or religious warrior for his sustenance in going and returning and remaining with an expedition; but no part of it is to be expended on his family, and if there is any surplus it must be restored to the heirs. Though the warrior be rich that is no objection, and the executor himself or the son of the testator may fight on his account."(3)

Bequests to the children of one's heirs.

(*e*) A bequest is valid for the children of one's heirs without difference, since they are in the position of strangers. In fact, a legacy may validly be left to any relation who does not take a share in the inheritance.

Bequest in favour of the kindred. (Shiah doctrines.)

The *Sharâya* declares that a bequest in favour of one's kindred is highly proper whether they be his heirs or not. When a person bequeathes a legacy to his *akriba* or nearest of kin it is to be regulated by the rules of inheritance, and nothing is to be given to a remote heir while there is a nearer in existence.

Under the Shiah Law, "If a person should make a bequest to his kindred (*zû karâbat*) it is to be understood as intended for all known to be of his *nasab* or the same paternal descent. Some writers have said that it includes all those who are related to him through his most remote progenitors, both father and mother, who professed the faith of Islâm; but this opinion is destitute of any testimony in its support. If, again, the bequest be to his *kowm* or race it includes all those who speak the same language, and if

(1) *Mafâtîh ; Jawâhir ul-Kalâm.*

(2) "It cannot, however, be applied in erecting prisons, for that duty belongs to the Sultan."—*Radd ul-Muhtâr*, Vol. V, p. 653.

(3) *Fatâwai Alamgiri*, Vol. VI, p. 148.

to the people of his house (*ahl-ul-bait*) it includes his children, father and paternal grandfather. Further, if he were to say to his family, the nearest only of his *nasab* are to be understood as included in the bequest."(1)

" If a person make a bequest to his neighbours (*jirân*), it includes, according to some doctors all those whose houses are within forty cubits (*zir'aas*) of his, in every direction. But there is another opinion, which is far-fetched and unreasonable, that extends it to the occupants of forty houses on either side of his."

(*f*) The emancipation of bondsmen is highly commendable under the Mahommedan Law and religion, and consequently we find the regulations relating to the testamentary emancipation of slaves laid down in some detail by the jurists of all the schools. The subject is, however, of no practical importance, and therefore it is unnecessary to dwell upon it.

(*g*) The testator can by will direct his executor to sell his property, and after paying his debts, invest the remainder, either as *wakf* for charitable purposes, or distribute it among his heirs.

Section II.

Rules of Interpretation.

Rules of interpretation. (Hanafî Law.)

The following rules have been adopted by the Hanafî lawyers, for the purpose of supplying a safe guide to the interpretation of devises and bequests, which may be involved in doubt and obscurity :—

(1) When the testator uses the expression, " I bequeath to the relations of my wife," the bequest would be for the benefit of her relations, both paternal as well maternal.

(2) When a legacy is left to " the nearest of kin," it would go to the maternal kindred only in default of paternal kindred.

(3) When a disposition is made in favour of the relatives of a stranger, it would be for the benefit of all his relatives, be they his blood-relations or not.

(4) When the testator bequeathes his goods to the orphans, the blind, or " the people " of such a race, or of such a locality, the legacy would be divided among all those who answer the description, without distinction of age, or sex, or fortune.

(1) *Sharâya in loco.*

(5) When the testator makes a disposition in favour of the *heir* of *A*, and *A* dies leaving several heirs, the legacy would be divided among them, in the proportion of their legal shares.

(6) When the bequest is in these terms, " I bequeath to such a family " (mentioning it by name), according to Abû Hanîfa, the bequest will be in favour of the head of that family. According to Abû Yusuf and Mohammed, the legacy will be divided, as in the preceding case, among all the members of his family.

(7) When the legacy is left to the neighbours, it will go to such of them as are nearest, or whose residence is contiguous to the testator's. Abû Yusuf and Mohammed hold that if several people reside in that house, the legacy will go to all of them in equal shares including women and children.

(8) When a legacy is in favour of soldiers and " the afflicted," it does not impose on the heir, or the executor, or the Kâzi, the obligation of finding out all those people who satisfy the condition. It is allowable to the administrator or executor to distribute it among those who are forthcoming, unless they are specifically mentioned or indicated.

Bequest to a neighbour.

If a person make a bequest in the following terms :—" I bequeath one thousand *dirhems* to my *neighbour*," according to Abû Hanîfa it would go to the person whose house is contiguous to that of the testator. Abû Yusuf and Mohammed maintain that it should go to all the inhabitants of the vicinity, who belong to the same mosque. The *Fatwa*, however, is with Abû Hanîfa if only one neighbour is meant ; but if the testator meant more than one, the matter should be left to the discretion of the Judge.(1)

The passage in the *Fatâwai Alamgiri* on this subject is to the following effect :—" When a person bequeathes a third of his property to his neighbours, some say, that if they can be numbered, the third is to be divided among them all, rich and poor. And it is to be divided in like manner if he should say ' to the people of this *masjid.*' The definition or meaning of ' cannot be numbered,' according to Abû Yusuf is, that the persons cannot be computed without the aid of a written account but according to Mohammed it refers to a number exceeding a hundred. Others, however, have said that the matter should be left to the discretion of

(1) *Fatâwai Alamgiri*, Vol. VI, p. 142.

the Judge and the *Fatwa* is to that effect, though Mohammed's rule is easier. If the neighbours cannot be numbered, the legacy is void; and so also when the legacy is to the people of the *masjid*, or of the *sijn* (or prison), and they cannot be numbered. Mohammed has said that when a bequest is made to the orphans of the *bani* (posterity) of a particular person and they can be numbered, the legacy is to be expended on all, in the same way as if it were on 'the orphans of *this* street' or 'of *this* mansion,' rich and poor participating alike: but if they cannot be numbered, the legacy is to be expended on the poor among them."

"With regard to who among the neighbours are entitled to share in the bequest, the *Mashâikh* are of opinion that every person may be included under the description of neighbour, whether the proprietor of a house or not, or whether a man or a woman, a Mussulman or a *Zimmi*; the term neighbour being equally applicable to all of them. Abû Hanîfa also holds that an absolute slave possessed of a house in the neighbourhood is entitled to the benefit of the will."

Bequest in favour of the *ashâr*.

If a person were to make a bequest in favour of his *ashâr*,(1) all the relations of his wife within the prohibited degrees (such as her father, brother and so forth), are included in the description, and likewise all the relations of his father's wife [his step-mother] and of his son's wife [his daughter-in-law], within the prohibited degrees, as these all stand in the relation of *ashâr* to the testator. It is to be observed that all the kindred of the wife within the prohibited degrees are included in the bequest notwithstanding that she was at the time of the death of the testator observing the *iddat* from a reversible divorce. But if the divorce was irreversible, her relations are not to be included, as the existence of the relationship entitled *ashâr* depends on the actual existence of the marriage at the time of the testator's death, and by an irreversible divorce marriage is utterly annulled.

If a person were to make a will in favour of his *relations* (*akriba*), it is construed to be in favour of the nearest of kin within the prohibited degrees, and in their default to be in favour of the next in proximity, and so on in regular succession. According to Abû Hanîfa, the bequest in question is restricted in its operation to the

(1) With a *sád*, *i.e.*, people connected to him by affinity.

prohibited relations of the testator, whereas according to the two disciples it extends to all the descendants of the most distant progenitor, professing the faith of Islâm; whilst Shâfeï maintains that it is confined solely to the testator's father [and his offspring.]

Bequest in favour of relations.

If a person, having two paternal and two maternal uncles, were to make a will "in favour of his relations" [*akriba*], according to Abû Hanîfa, it will be in favour of the paternal uncles only. According to the disciples, all the four uncles will be included. If, on the other hand, the testator were to leave only one paternal and two maternal uncles, the half of the legacy in that case goes to the paternal uncle, and the other half to the two maternal uncles. If the bequest had been for the next of kin the whole legacy would go to the paternal uncle, and nothing to the two maternal uncles. When there is only one paternal uncle, he is entitled only to a moiety.(1) If, however, the testator died leaving him surviving a paternal uncle and aunt and a maternal uncle and aunt, the legacy would be divided in equal shares between the paternal uncle and aunt both being related to him within an equal degree of affinity, and the tie of blood between them and the testator being regarded as stronger than that existing between him and the maternal uncle or aunt. A paternal aunt, moreover, although she is not entitled to inherit, is nevertheless capable of taking a legacy, "in the same manner," adds the *Radd ul-Muhtâr*, "as a relation who is a slave or an infidel. In all these cases, if the testator leaves no relation within the prohibited degrees, the bequest is null, because it is confined in its operation to those relations only".

Bequest in favour of orphans, etc.

"When a bequest is made in favour of the orphans, the blind, the lame, or the widows of the race of a particular individual, and they are determinate in their number, the bequest would be in favour of all of them indiscriminately, whether rich or poor, male or female; for the execution of the bequest is practicable in this instance because of the ascertainment of the legatees. According to Abû Yusuf this phrase, 'if they can be enumerated' comprehends as many as can be counted, without the aid of written calculations; whereas Mohammed holds that it extends no further than to one hundred, any greater number being considered as beyond enumeration.

---

(1) For the reasons of these principles, see the *Hedâya* and the *Radd in loco*.

Some, on the other hand, allege that the determination of this point rests entirely with the Kâzi, *and decrees pass accordingly.* But, if the individuals of the race named be incapable of being enumerated the poor only are included in the bequest, not the rich, for it [the bequest] is of a pious nature, and the object of it (namely, the approval of God) is best attainable by removing the wants of the poor. Besides, as the very description used indicates a degree of want and distress on the part of the legatees, it is proper to admit this to have been the testator's meaning. It is otherwise where a person makes a bequest 'to the youths or the maids of a particular race,' who are innumerable in such case the bequest is void, because, as the description used does not indicate want, the words of the testator cannot be construed to apply to the poor ; neither can the bequest possibly hold valid in favour of all the individuals of the class named, since as they cannot be enumerated it is impracticable to define them, and a bequest to unknown legatees, is void. For a bequest is an act by which the testator invests another with the right of property, and it is impossble to confer that right on persons unknown. It is to be observed that in the case of bequests to the poor or distressed, the legacy must be paid at least to two paupers, two being the smallest number of plurality in *wasiat.*"

Where a bequest is made to the children (*awlâd*) of the race of a particular person—the males and females have an equal right in such bequest, as the term *awlâd* comprehends all the descendants. A bequest to the heirs of a particular individual will be divided among the heirs of the person named, according to the rules of intestate succession, a male getting double the share of a female because there is reason to imagine, that the object of the testator in using the word " heirs " was, that the same distinction might be observed in the partition of the legacy, as in the case of inheritance.

Bequest to the *awlâd* of a particular person.

If a person were to bequeath to a certain person a portion of his property exceeding the disposible third, his disposition would be reduced to the third.

" And when a man," says the *Fatâwai Alamgiri,* " has bequeathed a third of his property to one person and a third of it to another, and both bequests are allowed by the heirs, the legatees have two-thirds and the heirs one-third, and if the bequests are not allowed by them, the legatees have the third between them in halves. Where the testator has bequeathed a third of his

Hanafi Law.

property to one person and one-sixth to another, the reduction must be proportionate, for example, the first legatee instead of getting one-third will get two-ninths, and the second legatee one-ninth, together constituting one-third."

So also in the *Radd ul-Muhtâr* :—" If a person were to bequeath a third of his estate and effects to Zaid, and a third to another and the heirs do not assent to the bequest, a third will be divided equally between the two legatees. If he were to give a third to one and one-sixth to another, the third would be divided among the two in the proportion of two to one. If he were to bequeath the whole of his property to one and one-third to another, the third will be divided among them equally."

There is considerable dispute, however, as to the division of the bequest, should the heirs consent, though in the result it appears that the entire estate and effects will be divided into four *sahams* or shares, one of which will be given to the latter legatee, and three to the former.

Shiah Law. Under the Shiah Law the second legacy would fall to the ground, the first legatee getting the entire disposible third. The *Sharâya* has stated the principle in the following terms :—

" If a person should bequeath a third of his estate to one legatee, a fourth to another, and a sixth to another, and the heirs should refuse to confirm his bequests, a third of the estate is to be given to the first legatee and the other legacies are void. But if he should bequeath a third of his estate to one person, and then a third or the same portion to another, this would be a revocation of the legacy to the first in favour of the second, and should a doubt arise as to the person first mentioned it must be determined by drawing lots. If a person bequeathes one article to two persons, and the value of the article exceeds a third of his estate while the heirs refuse their assent to the excess, so much of the article as is covered by a third of the estate is the joint property of the legatees. If, on the other hand, he were to bequeath a thing to each of the two, a beginning must be made in favour of the person to whom the bequest was made first and the deficiency must fall solely on the second."(1)

The operation of this principle extends equally to indeterminate as well as specific legacies; for example, if a person were to bequeath to one person a sum of money, or a share in his inheritance, and to another that which would be sufficient for his maintenance for a limited period of time, this last legacy would be appraised or valued, and then the two legacies will be dealt with according to the principles already stated.

When a bequest is made to two persons respectively of a half and one-fourth of the testator's estate and effects, the legatees will receive the shares given to them, provided the heirs consent, the residue going to the heirs. But if the heirs do no assent to the bequest, according to Abû Hanîfa the legacies will have effect given to them out of the disposible one-third, which is to be divided into seven parts, four being given to the legatee of the half, and three to the legatee of the one-fourth. But, according to Abû Yusuf and Mohammed, whose opinion seems to be recognised for the *fatwa*, the third is to be divided into three shares, two of which will be given to the legatee of the half, and one to the legatee of the fourth.(1)

Hanafî Law.

Where a bequest is made of specific sums of money,(2) say of a thousand dirhems to one person, and two thousand dirhems to another, and the disposible third only amounts to one thousand dirhems, according to Abû Hanîfa, each legatee takes in proportion to the full amount of his legacy, and the thousand is divided between them accordingly. In all these cases, the legatee takes in proportion to the full amount of his legacy, because *primâ facie* it is valid since the testator may have left so much other property that this amount may come within a third of it. And all the jurists are agreed that when each one of several legacies does not exceed a third of the property, as for instance, when a third is bequeathed to one, and a fourth to another, and the heirs do not allow both, each legatee is entitled to a share in proportion to the full amount of his legacy whatever it may be, and the third is to be divided among them accordingly.

When a bequest is made in an indefinite form, for example, if a testator were to say, " I give a portion of my property to so-and-so," he can at any time whilst alive explain his intention. After

(1) *Fatâwai Alamgiri*, Vol. VI, p. 150. (2) Technically called *mursalla*.

his death the explanation of the devise rests with the heirs. If the bequest is of a *saham* or *juzz*, some hold that the heirs are entitled to give what they please, but in the *Mabsût* it is stated that the legatee of a *saham* should have the equivalent of the smallest share of the heirs, provided it does not exceed a third; this is according to the disciples. When the testator bequeathes a *saham* of his property to a particular person and leaves no heirs, the legatee takes a half and the remaining half goes to the *bait-ul-mâl* or the public treasury,(1) "and the case is as if he had left two sons, when the estate would be equally divided between them."

Principles of construction.

If a person should bequeath *his son's or his daughter's share*, and he has a son or a daughter, the bequest is not valid because he is in fact giving away what belongs to another. But if he has neither son nor daughter the bequest is lawful. And if the bequest is of the *like of his son's or daughter's share*, the bequest is lawful, though he should have a son or a daughter, *for the like of a thing is not the thing itself but something different*. The son's *share* is then to be ascertained, and an equal amount given to the legatee · but if that should exceed a third of the estate, the bequest requires the consent of the heirs, while if it be only equal to or less than a third it is lawful without their consent. Consequently, if a person were to make to another the bequest of a son's share, and he has only one son, the legatee will take half of his property if the heir consents, otherwise only one-third. Similarly, if he has two sons the legatee will take one-third, according to Zailye. When the testator dies leaving him surviving an only daughter, and the legacy is "of a daughter's share" the legatee will get half provided the daughter consents, otherwise one-third. If there are two daughters, the legatee will get one-third according to the *Manah*, and if there are three daughters he will get only one-fourth. And this view is supported by the reference from the *Mujtaba* "which is the work of Imâm Zâhidi." If a testator leave him surviving a son and a daughter, and the bequest is "of a daughter's share," the legatee will get one-fourth. And if a testatrix leaves a husband, and three sisters of three kinds (*e.g.*, full, consanguine and uterine), and the bequest is of the share of a consanguine sister the legatee will take one-tenth. This is the doctrine laid down in the *Mujtaba*. And

---

(1) See *post*, p. 617, footnote.

the *Hindièh* (*i.e.*, the *Fatâwai Alamgiri*) explains this rule thus :—the husband takes his specified share, and the residue is divided among the legatees and the sisters in the proportions fixed for them by the law. If a testator dies leaving a mother and son, and the bequest is of "a daughter's share," the property will be divided into seventeen shares, five of which will be given to the legatee, ten to the son, and two to the mother.

Principles of construction. —contd.

To explain this case it is necessary first to take as if there were no legacy, and then the estate would be divisible into six shares, whereof the mother would have one, and the son the remaining five. The bequest of a daughter's portion, if there had been one, requires an addition to be made to such a share, which being half that of a son, the addition must be two shares and a half, which would make the whole eight and a half, or doubling them to get rid of the fraction, seventeen shares, whereof the legatee takes first five shares, for the legacy here is less than a third of the estate and takes precedence of the heritage of the heirs ; and of the remaining twelve shares one-sixth or two shares are given to the mother and the other ten to the son.

If there be a daughter and sister, and the legacy is of a daughter's share, the legatee will take one-third whether the daughter and sister consent or not. This is laid down in the *Fatâwai Nomânia* by Saijâni.

And if a person should leave a wife and a son, and make a bequest of the share of another son, if there had been one, "the estate must be arranged into fifteen shares," *supposing the heirs to assent to the legacy*. Of these, the legatee would take seven shares, the wife one share, and the son seven shares. Here, as in the last case but one, let us first suppose that there was no legacy, and on that supposition the estate would be divided into eight parts, whereof the wife would take one and the son seven. But now taking the legacy as the share of another son, if there had been one, we must add seven more to the number of shares, thus making them up to the fifteen. In this case, however, as the legacy is more than a third of the whole estate, the assent of the heirs is made a condition without which the legacy would not be lawful.

When a person has died leaving a daughter and a brother, and has bequeathed to another person the share of a son, there being no son, the legatee has two-thirds of the estate, and the other third is divided between the daughter and brother in halves, that is, when the heirs consent to the legacy ; but if they do not consent, the legatee has only one-third, and the other two-thirds are to be divided equally between the daughter and brother. When again the bequest is of *a like to the share of a son if there were one*, and the other circumstances are the same, the legatee has two-fifths of the property if assented to by the heirs. When again a person has died leaving a brother and sister, and has bequeathed to another person *the share of a son if there were one*, and the bequest is allowed by the heirs, the legatee takes the whole property, leaving nothing to the brother and sister ; while if he had bequeathed *the like of the share of a son if there were one*, and the heirs had allowed the legacy, the legatee would only have a half, and the other half would be divided between the brother and sister in thirds, (that is, two portions to the male and one to the female). In both cases, if the legacy were disallowed by the heirs, the legatee would only have a third, while the other two-thirds would be divided in the same way between the brother and sister.

All this refers to cases where the testator leaves heirs behind. In default of heirs, should a testator leave a legacy, describing it as the share of a particular heir, the legatee will get one moiety and the remainder will go to the *Bait-ul-mâl*. This is according to the approved doctrine and the *Jouhara*. The heir is the *sâhib-ul-hakk* and cannot be deprived absolutely of a share in the inheritance.(1)

Shiah Law.

Under the Shiah Law, when a legacy is bequeathed to several persons or to a class of persons, it is divisible among them all equally. For example if a person were to make a bequest in favour of his children, some of whom are males and some females, the legacy will be divided among them all equally without distinction of sex. Similarly, when the legacy is in favour of uncles and aunts, whether paternal or maternal, or both together. But where the testator has made a distinct apportionment, giving more to some than to others, his directions must be given effect to.

Death of the legatee. Hanafî and Shiah doctrines.

Under the Hanafî Law, the death of the legatee in the lifetime of the testator causes the legacy to lapse ; under the Shiah Law, it is different. If the legacy is not adeemed by the testator, the death of the legatee does not cause a lapse. It descends to the

(1) *Radd ul-Muhtâr*, Vol. V, p. 659.

legatee's heirs; should he leave nobody, it would revert to those of the testator.

If a bequest is made of a third of the testator's estate to 'Amr and Zaid, but 'Amr is dead at the time of the bequest, the entire third will go to Zaid, and the rule is, that there is no right in the non-existing or dead. Abû Yusuf holds that if the testator was unaware of the death of 'Amr at the time of the bequest, a moiety only will be given to Zaid. This is according to Zailye. For a bequest to 'Amr and Zaid, when 'Amr is dead, is like a bequest to Zaid and an inanimate object. But when a legacy is left *between* 'Amr and Zaid, and 'Amr is dead at the time, half alone will be given to the surviving legatee, for the word "between" implies that it was to be given in moieties."(1) Hanafî Law.

If a person were to make a bequest in the following terms, "my executor shall give one-third of my property to *A* and to the son of 'Abdullah, if the latter is in want at the time of my death;" and at the decease of the testator, the son of 'Abdullah is found to be rich, only half of the third will be given to *A*.(2)

---

(1) *Radd ul-Muhtâr*, Vol. V, p. 659.

(2) "If a man should bequeath a third of his property to Zaid and Bakr, Bakr being dead at the time, whether with or without the knowledge of the testator, or to Zaid and Bakr if he be alive, he being in fact dead, or to him and to the person in a house, no one being in that house, or to him and to his posterity (*'akab*); or to him and to a child of Bakr, and his child dies before the testator, or to him and to the poor of his children, or to him who may become poor of his children, and the condition fails at the time of his death, the whole legacy is to Zaid, in all of these cases, for the non-existing or the dead can have no right, and there being no one to contend with Zaid, the legacy is the same as if it were to him alone With regard to the case of Zaid and his posterity as they are to follow him after his death, they are to be considered as non-existing at present. In all these cases the competitor with Zaid is out of the contest from the beginning, but if he were at first competent to contend with him, and should subsequently become disqualified by failure of a condition, Zaid would have only a half. Thus, if a person should say,—'A third of my property to Zaid and Bakr if I die, he being alive or poor,' and the testator dies when Bakr is dead, or rich, or if he should say 'to him and to Bakr if he be in the house' and he is not in it, or 'to him and the children of such an one if they become poor,' and they do not become poor till the testator dies or 'to him and to his heir;' in all these cases the legatee has only half of the third. The principle in these cases is, that when the person conjoined with another has entered into a bequest, and then comes out of it by the failure of a condition, he does not occasion any accession to the right of the other, and that when he has not entered into the bequest for want of personality or competence (*ahliat*) the other takes the whole. And if one should say—'A third of my property between Zaid and Bakr,' Bakr being dead at the time, Zaid would have only a half of the third, because the word 'between' implies a division in half, insomuch that if he were to say between Zaid and then stop,

Death of the legatee—its effect.

The same result would follow, if one of the legatees should die during the lifetime of the testator. The principle is this, that when the legacy is in favour of existing objects or persons, and one of them should cease to exist after the *wasiat*, the other legatees would receive their original shares, and the share of the deceased legatee would lapse into the residue of the estate; but if one of the legatees was non-existing at the time, or not possessing the quality required by the testator to take the bequest, then the whole would go to the existing legatees. This is according to Zailye.(1) For example, if a bequest were made in favour of *A* and of persons residing in a particular house, the whole bequest would go to Zaid, for there is no bequest in favour of the *m'aadûm* or non-existing persons.(2) The same would happen if a person were to say "this is for *A* and

---

Zaid would have a half also, yet if one should say, 'A third of my property between the sons of Zaid and the sons of Bakr,' and one of them has no sons, the whole third belongs to the sons of the other. If one should bequeath a third of his property to Zaid and to 'Amr, or should say between Zaid and 'Amr, and should then die, and one of the legatees should die after him half of the third would belong to the survivor, and the other half of it to the heirs of the deceased legatee. So also if one of them should die after the testator, but before acceptance of the legacy and the survivor should then accept, both legatees would be entitled to the bequest. But if one of them should die before the testator, the share of the legatee so dying would revert to the testator."

"When a person says: 'A third of my property to such an one (*falán*, a particular individual) and to whomsoever may become poor of the children of 'Abdullah' and then dies, all the children of 'Abdullah being rich at the time, such an one gets the whole third. But if some of them should become poor before the death of the testator, the third would be divided between such an one and the poor children of 'Abdullah according to the number of heads (*per capita*). If, again, the children of 'Abdullah had never ceased to be poor from the time of their birth to the death of the testator, it would seem that none of them would be entitled to any part of the third, but that the whole of it would devolve on the other legatee. If the children of 'Abdullah in existence at the time of the bequest should die, and other children be born to him who at first being rich should become poor before the death of the testator, 'the third would be divided between them and the other legatee' according to the number of heads. So also if the terms of the bequest were, 'A third of my property to such an one and to the child of 'Abdullah,' and the child of 'Abdullah dies but another is born to him before the death of the testator, the legacy is between that person and that child of 'Abdullah. And if one should say, 'A third of my property to such an one and to the offspring of 'Abdullah if they become poor,' and they do not become poor till the death of the testator, the other legatee is entitled to a share of the third, regard being had to the number of heads;" *Fatâwai Alamgiri*, Vol. VI, pp. 161-162: Baillie's Dig., p. 642.

(1) *Radd ul-Muhtâr*, Vol. V, p. 661.

(2) *Ibid.*

his *'akab*," for *'akab* are the people whom a person leaves surviving, and they cannot be determined at the time of the bequest. This is in the *Durrar*. Similarly, if he were to say " this legacy shall be for Zaid and for the son of 'Abdullah, if he lives in my house ;" and the son of 'Abdullah were not to live in that house, the entire legacy would go to Zaid. But when a legacy is in favour of 'Amr and Zaid, and 'Amr dies after the testator's death, 'Amr's share will go to his heirs.(1)

Under the ancient doctrine, if a woman died leaving a husband, and bequeathing half of her property to a stranger, the husband would take a third, the legatee a half, whilst, the remaining sixth would go to the *bait-ul-mâl*. The old lawyers reasoned thus : the legacy to a stranger has precedence to the extent of a third over the rights of the heirs, and there remain two-thirds of the property to be divided as inheritance. Of this one half, *i.e.*, a third of the whole, belongs to the husband, leaving a third to which no other heir is entitled. The remainder of the legacy therefore becomes operative against it, and the legatee thus gets the half bequeathed to him ; and there being no heir entitled to the remaining sixth, it goes to the *bait-ul-mâl*.(2) Under the modern rule, the remaining sixth reverts to the heir.

If a man died leaving a wife, and bequeathing *all his* property to a stranger, and the widow did not assent to the bequest, she would be entitled to a sixth of the property and the legatee to the remaining five-sixths. For he is entitled to a third by virtue of the bequest, and of the remaining two-thirds the widow takes a fourth, which is equivalent to a sixth of the whole, and the legatee takes the remainder.

When a man bequeathes a third of his property to the sons of a particular person, and the person has no son at the date of the bequest, but sons are subsequently born to him before the testator's death, these sons are entitled to the third. And even though the person had sons at the date of the bequest, yet if they were not mentioned by their names as Ahmed, Zaid and Bakr, or otherwise

---

(1) *Radd ul-Muhtâr*, Vol. V, p. 661.

(2) Public treasury *for the benefit of all Mussulmans ;* see *Mahommedan Law*, Vol. II, *in loco*. Any property coming by way of escheat to the *Bait-ul-mâl* was for the benefit of the general body of Moslems.

specifically indicated, the bequest would be for all the sons existing at t e time of the testator's death. So that if those in existence at the date of the bequest should die, and others are subsequently born who are living at the time of the testator's death, these are entitled to the third of the property. If, however, the existing sons are mentioned by name, or are otherwise distinctly indicated, the bequest is only for them, and becomes void in the event of their death. Thus, when legatees are named or otherwise distinctly indicated, the bequest to them is said to be special, and regard must be had to the time at which it was made.

When a man bequeathes a third of his property to his *umm-ul-walad*(1) being three in number, *and to fakîrs* and *miskîns* (beggars and indigent persons), the property will be divided into five shares, out of which three will be given to the *umm-ul-walad*, one to the *fakîrs* and the remaining one to the *miskîns*. This is according to Abû Hanîfa and Abû Yusuf. Mohammed would divide the property into seven shares, and give three to the *umm-ul-walad*, and two each to the beggars and indigent. The former opinion is the one approved. Similarly, if a man should bequeath a third of his property to Zaid and the *miskîns*, Zaid takes half, and the latter take half according to Abû Hanîfa and Abû Yusuf.(2) When a person bequeathes one-third of his property to Zaid, the beggars and the indigent, according to Abû Hanîfa the property will be divided into three shares, according to Abû Yusuf into two moieties, and according to Mohammed into five shares, and this is the approved doctrine. When a person bequeathes a third to the poor, it may be expended, according to Abû Hanîfa and Abû Yusuf, on one poor person, but Mohammed holds that there must be at least two poor persons. But when a body of *miskîns* is indicated, the bequest cannot be expended on one only; there is general consensus on this point.

If a person were to make a bequest for the poor of Balkh, it may lawfully be expended on other poor also, according to Abû Yusuf. And the *Fatwa* is on this.

---

(1) Bondswomen who have borne him children and have consequently become emancipated.

(2) *Radd ul-Muhtâr*, Vol. V, pp. 662, 663; Mohammed would divide the property into three shares.

When a person bequeathes a third of his property to one man, and then says to another, "I have made you a partner and joined you with him," the third belongs to them both. And if, after bequeathing to one man a hundred, and to another a hundred, he should say to a third, "I have made you a partner with them," the person addressed would be entitled to a third of each hundred.

When a man makes a bequest to *A* and *A's* heir, *A* takes half of the bequest, and the remainder is void, and in like manner if the bequest be to *A* and the testator's murderer.

If a person possessed of three garments of different qualities, one good, the other middling, and the third bad, bequeathes them to three different legatees, and one of the garments is then lost or destroyed, but which of them is not known, and the heirs refuse to make delivery of the remaining garments to any of the legatees saying to each of them, 'the garment in which you had a right has been destroyed,' under these circumstances since the right of the parties is not defined, and the ignorance of this fact prevents any valid judgment being pronounced in the matter, and no effect can be given to the testator's wishes the bequest must be pronounced as void, "unless the heirs will deliver up the remaining garments." "If they should do so, the objection is removed, and the legatee of the best is entitled to two-thirds of the better of the remaining garments, the legatee of the middling garment is entitled to the remaining third of the better and a third of the worse, while the legatee of the worst is entitled to the remaining two-thirds of the worst garment."

Increments to bequests.

Any increment, such as the young of cattle or the produce of grain, arising out of the subject of a bequest before the death of the testator is the testator's property, and subject to the same liabilities as the rest of his estate. An increase that occurs after his death and after the partition or distribution of his estate belongs to the legatee. An increase that occurs between these events or after the testator's death, but before partition, may occur either before or after the acceptance of the legacy by the legatee. In the former case, it is a legacy because it is an accessory to the original subject of bequest and must come out of the third of the estate, that is, is valid only if it falls within the third. But is it so in the latter case also, that is, when it occurs after acceptance and before partition? On this point Mohammed has

Hanafî doctrines.

not left any express *dictum*, but Kudûri has related that in this case the increase is not a legacy and comes out of the whole of the property. The general opinion, however, seems to be that it is a legacy and must come out of the third.

When a separable accession to the subject of a bequest takes place after the death of the testator, if the original subject and the accession both come out of the third, they belong to the legatee. If they exceed the third, effect is to be given to the legacy, in the first place as against the original subject, and then as against the accession according to Abû Hanîfa, but against both *equally* according to the two Disciples. "For example if the testator has left six hundred dirhems and a mare, of the value of three hundred dirhems, which, after the testator's death but before the partition of his estate, foals and the young animal is also valued at three hundred dirhems. Under such circumstances (the principal and accessory bequests amounting together to six hundred dirhems), the legatee is entitled, according to Abû Hanîfa, to the mare and one-third of the foal (making together four hundred dirhems or a third of the whole) while according to the two Disciples, he is entitled to two-thirds of each. This is on the assumption that the mare foals before the acceptance by the legatee of the original bequest, as well as before partition. If the mare foals after the legatee has accepted the bequest and after partition, it belongs to him; but if after acceptance but before partition, Kudûri holds that it is not a bequest, while 'our' Shaikhs have held that it is a bequest, and is to be regarded as coming out of the third in the same way as if the mare had foaled before acceptance. If it takes place before the death of the testator, the foal never comes within the bequest, but is subject to the same rules as the rest of the deceased's property."

Shiah doctrines.

According to the Shiah Law, "if a person should make a bequest of half of his property, and the heirs at first should assent, but afterwards declare that they thought the amount to be trifling, decree is to be given against them for the amount which they insist that they thought the legacy to be, and they are to be put upon their oaths as to the excess, but this is subject to some doubt. And if the bequest were of a slave or a mansion, and the heirs after first assenting to it should then allege that they thought it was no more than a third of the deceased's estate, or if more, only so in a trifling degree, such claim or allegation on their part cannot be attended to, because their consent in this case involves a known object of the value of which they cannot pretend ignorance at the time of assenting to the bequest. If a person should bequeath a third of his property by way of *mushâ'a*, the legatee is entitled to a third of everything of which he died possessed. If, again, he bequeathes a specific article which is of the value of a third of his estate, the legatee becomes by his death the sole proprietor of the article bequeathed, nor have the heirs any ground of objection thereto. And if the deceased should have left both present and absent effects (such as ready-money and debts,) so much of the specific thing must be surrendered to the legatee as a third of the property presently available will admit of, while he will have to wait for the remainder of it until it is recovered by the heirs, since what is not forthcoming is liable to loss or destruction and may never be realised.

Shiah doctrines—contd.

Specific legacies.

" When a person has made a bequest, and then another which is repugnant to it, effect must be given to the latter."

Two bequests, one repugnant to the other.

" When a person has said, 'if there be a male in the womb of this woman, he is to have two dirhems, and if there be a female she is to have one dirhem' and the mother is delivered of both a male and a female they are to have three dirhems; but should he have said, 'if what is in her womb be a male he is to have so-and-so, and if a female so-and-so' and the woman is delivered of both a male and a female they are not to have anything."

" If a person should bequeath the service of his bondsman the fruit of his garden, the residence of his house or anything else of a usufructuary nature for ever, or for a fixed time, the advantage or profit to arise therefrom must be valued and should it not exceed a third of a testator's estate, the bequest is valid, while if more than a third the legatee is to have as much as the third will cover, and the legacy is void as to the excess."

Usufructuary wills.

Where the subject of a bequest is a mere right of residence for a fixed period, the obligation of maintaining the house in proper repair rests on the testator and not on the legatee, as this is a duty which is dependent on the ownership of the house and the legatee is entitled to no more than to a right of residence while all the other rights of ownership appertain to the heirs, as sale, mortgage and the like, none of which, however, has the effect of invalidating the rights of the legatee.

"In all cases where a testator may have employed a term which is common or equally applicable to several things, the heirs have an option to fix on whichever of the things they please and give it to the legatee. If, again, the testator should say 'give him my bow' and only one is found in his possession, that one must be given to the legatee of whatsoever description it may be."

Bequest of a portion of an heir.

"When a person has bequeathed to a stranger the like of his son's portion having only one child, this is in fact a partition of his estate between them, and the legatee is entitled to a half of it unless the heir refuses his consent to the full bequest, in which case the legatee's interest is reduced to a third. If, again, the testator has two sons, the legacy is a third of the estate, and if three, it is a fourth. The general rule is that the legatee should be added to the other heirs and treated as one of them, if they are all entitled to share equally in the inheritance; while if their shares differ, the shares of some being more and of others less, he ranks with the weakest of them or the one whose share is the least, unless the testator has expressly said that his share is to be equal to that of the highest, in which case effect must be given to the terms of the bequest. Further, if the testator should have said like the share of my daughter, the legatee according to 'us' is entitled to a half when there is no other heir besides the daughter, but his share is reduced to a third if she refuses her consent to the full legacy, because according to our doctrine daughters inherit the whole estate to the exclusion of the *asabâh* [agnates] and the legatee thus becomes like a third daughter."

"If a person having three half-sisters by the mother and three half-brothers by the father, should bequeath to a stranger the like of the portion of one of his heirs, the legatee is to be treated as one of the sisters, and so to receive one share out of ten parts into which the estate must be divided, while the half-sisters take three and the half-brothers the remaining six conformably to the rules of intestate succession. If, again, the testator having a wife and daughter bequeathes the like of the share of the daughter and the heirs assent, the legatee is entitled to seven parts of the estate, the daughter to as many, and the wife to two, the whole being divisible in such a case into sixteen portions. Nevertheless it would be more proper to say in this case that the wife is entitled to no more than one part out of fifteen, that being the number of shares into which the estate should be divided. If, again, a person having four wives and a daughter should say, 'like the share of one of them,' the division of the estate would be into thirty-two portions, whereof an eighth or four shares would be equally divided among the wives, the legatee would take one share like one of them and the remaining twenty-seven would pass to the daughter."

"If a person should bequeath to a stranger 'the portion of his child,' the bequest according to some is void, because it is a bequest of what belongs to another, but it is more agreeable in principle to say that the bequest is valid and should be construed in the same way as if it were the like to his share.(1) If, again, the testator having a son who, afterwards becomes his murderer, should bequeath the like of his share, here though some say that the bequest is valid, yet it is more in conformity with the principles of law to say that it is invalid."

"When a person has bequeathed the double of his child's portion, the legatee has two equivalents of the portion and if he were to say *zuafân* (in the dual) or two doubles of it, the legatee would have an equivalent to four portions, but only to three according to some whose opinion is preferred as being more certain; and the same is the law when the testator has used the expression *zuaf-i-zuaf* or double of the double of his portion."

"When a person whose property is scattered about in different places has bequeathed a third of it to the poor, it is lawful to apply whatever is found in the city to the poor of the place, and even the whole of it may be lawfully expended on the poor of the testator's city and on those of them who are on the spot, without following or searching for any who are absent. According to the best authority the number of those who are to share in the gift must, however, be three or more by reason of the testator's expression being in the plural. In like manner, if he should say,— emancipate slaves (in the plural), it is incumbent on the executor

---

(1) The *bequest* of a child's share to another is invalid under the Hanafi Law as being the testamentary gift of the right of another, *i.e.*, of the child who can under no circumstance be excluded from inheritance.

to emancipate at least three, unless a third of the testator s estate should fall short of the object.''

"When a person has bequeathed a mansion which falls down and is levelled to the ground before the testator's death, the legacy is void because the name of mansion (*dâr*) is no longer applicable to it. But this is liable to doubt.''

"When a testator has said, 'Give Zaid and the poor a certain sum,' Zaid, according to some doctors, is entitled to a half, but according to others only to a fourth. But the first doctrine is the best supported.''(1)

The acknowledgment of a debt. (Hanafî Law.)

In order to avoid the operation of the rule by which legacies over a third are reduced to the disposable quantity, recourse is usually had to the acknowledgment of a debt; but when the acknowledgment is made on a death-bed or is not founded upon a prior actual consideration, the law treats such acknowledgment also as a simple legacy subject to reduction. "If a person,'' says the *Ḥedâya*, "on his death-bed say to his heirs, 'I am indebted to Zaid and you must credit what he says,' in that case the claim of Zaid to any amount not exceeding a third of the estate must be admitted although the heirs should falsify it.''

(1) These principles of the Shiah Law have been given from the *Sharâya* illustrated from the *Jawâhir*. It will be noticed that throughout these doctrines, there are two divergent views running side by side. The Mohakkik, the author of the *Sharâya*, invariably states both the views, but gives the preference to those of his own school. The contrary views are those entertained by Shaikh Murtaza, Ibn Junaid, Mohammed ibn Idris al-Hilli and Ibn Zuhra Halabi (author of the *Ghunia*), who in most matters, are in advance of the patristic school of the author of the *Sharâya*. I have given these extracts from the *Sharâya*, in preference to clothing the old views in my own words. I have followed in the main Mr. Baillie's rendering, though I prefer, for general accuracy, M. Querry's French version.

CHAPTER XXII.

RULES RELATING TO WILLS BY NON-MOSLEMS.

THE rules with reference to the wills of the non-Moslem subjects of Mussulman sovereigns are thus stated in the *Fatâwai Alamgiri* :—

" The will of a *Zimmi* for secular purposes is valid, according to all opinions. Other than secular purposes are of four different kinds. *First,* there are purposes which are a means of approach (*kurbat*) to Almighty God, both with them and with us, and bequests for such purposes are valid whether they be to a set of particular persons or not ; *second,* there are purposes which are sinful both with them and with us, and bequests for these purposes are valid if they are to a specified body of individuals and the bequest is a *gift without regard to the purposes,* but if the persons are not specified, the bequest is void ; *third,* there are purposes which are pious according to us but sinful with them, and a bequest for these purposes is valid if in favour of a body of specified persons and is a gift without regard to the purposes, while if the persons are not specified, the bequest is void ; *fourth,* there are purposes which are sinful according to us, but pious according to them and bequests for these are valid, according to Abû Hanîfa, whether the persons be specified or not, but void according to the Disciples when the persons are not specified. Thus when a *Zimmi* has directed by his will that slaves be purchased and emancipated on his account, whether with or without a specification of the individuals, or that a third of his property be bestowed in charity on beggars and the indigent, or expended in lighting the Holy Shrine, or in making war against the Turks [the infidel Tartars], the bequest is valid. And if a *Zimmi* bequeathes a third of his property to mourners and singers the bequest is valid if they are specified and it is a gift to them, but if they are not specified, it is void. And if the third is to be expended in sending a set of Mussulmans on pilgrimage, or building a *masjid* for Moslems, and the persons are specified the bequest is valid, and a gift, so that they may perform the pilgrimage and erect the buildings or not as they please, but if the persons are not specified, the bequest is void. If he were to bequeath a third of his property for the erection of a church or a synagogue, or direct that his house should be converted into a church or a synagogue, the bequest according to the Disciples is void, unless it is for a specified body, when it is a gift to them; but according to Abû Hanîfa it is valid under all circumstances." The opinion of Abû Hanîfa is the law in force, although the later Hanafî jurists have endeavoured to confine its operation to villages.

Bequest of a *Mustâmin.*

"When an alien, who is a *Mustâmin*, makes a bequest to a Moslem or a *Zimmi*, it is valid for the whole of his property, unless his heir had come into the *Dâr-ul-Islâm* or Moslem territory with him, and in that case the bequest as to the excess over a third is dependent on the assent of the heir. But if he has no heir, it is valid as to the whole of his property in the same way as the will of a Moslem or *Zimmi* is valid in the like case. So, also, though he has an heir in the foreign country. If he has bequeathed only a part of his property, the remainder is to be given to his foreign heir. If a *Zimmi* bequeathes more than a third of his property or makes a bequest to one of his heirs, it is not valid as in the case of a similar bequest by a Moslem. But if he bequeath to a person of a different religion, it is valid as in the case of inheritance. If, however, the bequest is to an alien who is not a *Mustâmin* it is not valid."

So also in the *Hedâya*:—If a Jew or a Christian, not suffering from a mortal disease were to build a church or a synagogue and then die, such building would descend to his heirs because Abû Hanîfa holds an erection of this nature to be equivalent to a *wakf* or pious appropriation, which (agreeably to his tenets) is not absolute, whilst Abû Yusuf and Mohammed hold all such erections to be sinful in their nature and, therefore, not valid as lawful *wakf*. But if a *Zimmi* were to declare that, after his death, his house shall be converted into a church or synagogue as the case may be for a specified sect of people, the bequest would be valid according to all the doctors, and would take effect to the extent of a third of the testator's property "because a bequest has two different characters—the appointment of a successor and an actual endowment, and the testator is competent to do either of these."

"If a Jew or Christian will that 'his house be converted into a church or synagogue for a sect of people,' without specifying the particular sect, the bequest is valid according to Abû Hanîfa. According to the two Disciples, on the contrary, it is not valid, for a deed of that nature is in reality sinful, although it may appear pious to the testator; and a will for a sinful purpose is null because the execution of it would be a confirmation of sin. The argument of Abû Hanîfa is that the founding of churches or synagogues is held by these persons to be an act of piety, and as we are enjoined to leave them to the exercise of whatever may be agreeable to their faith, the bequest is therefore lawful in conformity with their belief."

"*Objection.*—What is the difference between the building a church or synagogue at the time of health and the bequeathing it by will that Abû Hanîfa should hold it inheritable in the former instance and not in the latter?"

"*Reply.*—The difference is this: that it is not the mere erecting (of the church, &c.), which extinguishes the builder's property, but the exclusive dedication of the building to the service of God, as in the case of mosques erected by Molsems; and as an infidel place of worship is not dedicated to God indisputably, it, therefore, still remains the property of the founder, and is consequently inheritable (in common with his other effects)—whereas a bequest, on the contrary, is used for the very purpose of destroying a right of property." The opinion of Abû Hanîfa is recognised as law.

"The bequests of *Zimmis*." says the *Hedâya*, "are of four kinds:—(1) Those made for purposes held pious in their belief but not in the belief of Mussulmans, such as the building a church or a synagogue (as already mentioned), or the slaughter of hogs to feed the poor of their sect, in which cases Abû Hanifa holds the bequest to be valid in conformity with the faith of the testator, whereas the two Disciples deem it invalid as being sinful. (2) Those made for purposes held pious with Moslems but not with *Zimmis*, such as the erection of a mosque, a pilgrimage to Mecca, or burning a lamp in a mosque, in all of which instances the bequest is invalid in conformity with the belief of the testator according to all our doctors, unless, however, it be made in favour of some particular persons, in which case it is valid—as under such circumstances it is an investiture, the mention of building a mosque or so forth being considered merely in the light of a counsel—(in other words, as if the testator had bequeathed his property to particular persons counselling them to erect a mosque therewith). (3) Those made for a purpose held pious both by Mussulmans and *Zimmis*, such as burning a lamp in the holy temple (of Jerusalem), or waging war against infidel Tartars which are valid whether made in favour of specific persons or not. (4) Those made for purposes not held pious either by *Zimmis* or Mussulmans, such as the support of singers, and dissolute women—which are invalid as being of a sinful tendency—unless, however, they be made in favour of particular persons and then they are valid."

"If a *Mustâmin* were to bequeath the whole of his property to a Mussulman or a *Zimmi*, it would be valid, for a bequest of the whole of an estate is deemed illegal only as it affects the right of the testator's heirs (whence it is that if they assent, such bequest is valid); but the heirs of the *Mustâmin* [if resident in an alien land] are possessed of no cognisable rights they being as it were dead, so far as they relate to the Mussulman government, because of their being in a hostile country. Besides, the property of a *Mustâmin* is in security only in virtue of the protection he receives from the State, which protection he enjoys in his own right, not in right of his heirs."

"If a *Mustâmin* bequeath a part of his property the bequest is executed accordingly, and the remainder is transmitted to his heirs, notwithstanding they be residents in a hostile country such being the law with respect to *Mustâmins*."

"If a *Mustâmin*," says the *Hedâya*, "immediately before his death, were to emancipate his slave or make him a *mudabbar* (*i.e.*, give him conditional enfranchisement) in the territories of Islâm, it would be valid and the slave would be free, notwithstanding his value were to exceed a third of his master's estate, for a bequest beyond a third of the property is deemed illegal only as it affects the right of the testator's heirs, but a *Mustâmin's* heirs (residing in a hostile country) possess no cognisable right as already mentioned."

"If a Mussulman or *Zimmi* were to make a will in favour of a *Mustâmin* it would be valid, for a *Mustâmin* so long as he resides in a Moslem country is considered in the light of a *Zimmi* and as the exercise of generosity and benevolence in favour of such is, therefore, allowed to Mussulmans during life, it is also permitted them to extend such acts to a period after their death. (It is said that Abû Hanîfa and Abû Yusuf held wills in favour of *Mustâmins* to be illegal because of their intention to return to their own country, and also because the Mussulmans not only allow this, but even do not suffer them to reside in their dominions, more than a year, unless they submit to the payment of the capitation tax.—The former is, however, the better opinion.)"

"If a *Zimmi* were to bequeath more than a third of his estate to a stranger or to an heir, it would not be valid as being contrary to the laws of the Mussulmans to which they have agreed to conform with respect to all temporal concerns."

"If a *Zimmi* were to make a will in favour of a non-Moslem of a different persuasion it would be valid, because of the analogy of legacies to succession by inheritance, all the different descriptions of those persons who disbelieve in the true faith being considered as of one class."

"If a *Zimmi* residing in a Moslem country were to make a will in favour of a non-Moslem subject of a State at war with that country, it would not be valid, for as inheritance does not obtain between them because of the difference of country, it follows that a bequest from the one to the other is of no effect, bequest being similar to inheritance."(1)

NOTE I.

ACKNOWLEDGMENTS BY A PERSON SUFFERING FROM DEATH-ILLNESS.

"If a person suffering from a mortal disease were to make an acknowledgment of debt in favour of a woman not related to him or were to make a bequest or gift in her favour and afterwards were to marry her and were then to die, the acknowledgment would be valid, but the bequest or gift would be void, for the nullity of an acknowledgment in favour of an heir depends on the person having been an heir at the time of making it, whereas the nullity of a bequest in favour of an heir depends on the legatee being so at the time of the testator's death as has already been explained, and as the woman was not an heir at the time of the acknowledgment, but had become so by [marriage] at the time of the testator's death the acknowledgment is therefore valid, but the bequest is void and so likewise the gift, it being subject to the same rule as the bequest."

---

(1) See also the *Radd ul-Muhtâr*, Vol. V, p. 683.

"If such a sick person were to make an acknowledgment of a debt due by him to his son or were to make a bequest or gift in his favour at a time when the son was a Christian, and he [the son] afterwards, previous to his father's death became a Mussulman, all those deeds of acknowledgment, gift or bequest are void, the bequest and the gift, because of the son being an heir, at the death of his father as above explained; and the acknowledgment, because, although the son on account of the bar (namely, difference of religion) was not an heir at the time of making it, still the cause of inheritance (namely, consanguinity) did then exist, which throws an imputation on the father as it engenders a suspicion that he may have made a false declaration in order to secure the descent of part of his fortune to his son. It is different in the case of marriage as above stated, for there the cause of inheritance (namely, marriage) occurred after to the acknowledgment and had no existence previous thereto, for supposing the marriage to have existed at the period of making the acknowledgment, and that the wife, being then a Christian, should afterwards, before the husband's death, become a Mussulman in that case [the acknowledgment] would not be valid."

CHAPTER XXIII.

WHAT MAY BE DEVISED

ANYTHING movable or immovable, over which the right of property may be exercised or which may form the subject of exchange or barter, or a fractional share thereof, or the usufruct of a thing, may be lawfully disposed by will.

The *Sharâya* says :—" A bequest may be either of the substance or the usufruct of a thing, but with regard to both, it is indispensable that they are such as can lawfully be possessed or enjoyed." The bequest of anything which is unlawful for a Moslem to possess or from which no benefit can be derived is invalid. " But the bequest of trained dogs used for hunting or catching of game or for domestic purposes, such as guarding houses and watching in corn-fields, is lawful."

A bequest remains valid and operative, though the subject-matter should undergo a change or improvement after the constitution of the will, unless the alteration is so substantial as to give rise to the presumption that the testator, in making such change or improvement, intended revocation.

In the same way, the legatee bears any loss or deterioration to which the property may have been subjected during the interval. Should any encumbrance have been created by the testator upon the property, the legatee will receive it subject to the same. Where a piece of land has been left to a person by *wasiat*, and subsequent thereto a building is erected upon it by the testator, the rule is that the land should, upon the decease of the testator, go to the legatee, and the house to the heir ; both being co-proprietors with regard to their respective rights.

If the testator, instead of building on the land bequeathed by him, pulls down the existing structures, houses, sheds, &c., the legatee will receive the land devoid of any erection. But where a building is bequeathed, and it is pulled down subsequently by the testator, the legacy is adeemed, and the *wasiat* becomes annulled *ipso facto*.

The legacy of even a lawful object is void, if it is made on condition that the legatee should commit an unlawful act, for example, that he should set fire to any building or kill somebody, or prevent a person from going on a pilgrimage. When any property forms the subject of a *hiba,* to which operation has been given, it cannot be bequeathed.

Extent of the power of disposition.

A testator, as pointed out already, has the power to dispose by will not more than a third of the property belonging to him at the time of his death. This is an invariable rule fixed by the Law, and there is a general consensus of opinion on the point among the jurists of the various schools. The authors of the *Multeka,* the *Hedâya* and the *Minhâj-ut-Tâlibîn* have laid down the principle in distinct terms, and the author of the *Sharâya* enunciates the rule thus:—" Further legacies, whether of substance or of usufruct, are restricted to one-third of the testator's estate, and if the whole of his bequests should exceed that amount they are void as to the excess, unless allowed by the heirs. The third of a testator's property, and consequently the extent to which he may lawfully bequeath out of it, is determined by its state at the time of his death, and not by its state at the time of making the will. So that if a person, who was in good circumstances at the time of making his will, should be indigent at the time of his death, no regard is to be paid to his previous wealth in determining the amount of his valid bequests. In like manner, if he were poor at the time of making his will, and has become opulent at the time of his death, it is his latter condition, and not the former, that must determine the legal amount of his legacies."(1)

And these principles have been repeatedly affirmed by the Courts of Justice in India. One difference, however, between the various schools is worthy of note. Under the Hanafî Law, when a man, having no heir, bequeathes his whole estate, the bequest is valid, and there is no need of assent on the part of the *bait-ul-mâl* or public treasury, though it is the *ultimus hœres.* Under the Shiah Law the rule is the same.(2)

(1) See also the *Radd ul-Muhtâr,* Vol. V, p. 248.

(2) According to the Shiah doctrines, in no case is there an escheat to the *bait-ul-mâl.* The *Jâm'aa ush-Shitât* declares that "the idea of a *bait-ul-mâl* is abhorrent to us." (See *Mahommedan Law,* Vol. II, where I have discussed this subject very fully.)

But according to the Mâliki and the Shâfeï doctrines there is no power of constituting a universal legatee.(1)

When the bequest is of a specific sum of money and the testator leaves actual property and outstanding debts due to him the legacy is to be paid immediately, if it do not exceed a third of his assets ; but if it exceed a third, one-third is to be delivered to him, and as the debts come in he is entitled to take a third out of every payment until his legacy is paid in full.(2)

According to Abû Yusuf *dirhems* and *dinârs* (*i.e.*, money in general) are ' *ain* [objects in specie].

When the testator leaves a specific legacy of a thousand *dirhems*, and his property consists of cash and effects besides debts, the legatee is to get his thousand *dirhems* from the third of the assets ; but if the third does not satisfy the legacy, a third of the debts as they are realised will be paid to the legatee, until the legacy is satisfied. According to Abû Yusuf, whose opinion is recognised as law, the *assets* refer to the cash left by the deceased and not to the household effects, apparel, or ornaments left by him. So that the thousand *dirhems* will be paid out of the third of such cash left by him, and if that is not sufficient, out of the third of the debts owing to him as they are realised.(3)

When two legacies left to same person.

Supposing the testator leaves two legacies to the same person would both of them take effect ? Khalîl ibn Ishâk (the Mâliki jurist) says both legacies will take effect if they are composed of different things, provided they do not together exceed a third of the estate, but if they are not different either in quantity or number, the last legacy will take effect. So also the *Fatâwaî Alamgiri* :—" When a person has said, ' a sixth of my property to such an one,' and then says on the same or a different occasion ' a third of my property to him,' and the heirs consent, he is

(1) According to the earlier Hanafî jurists, when a person died leaving a particular heir who took only a specific share, and was not entitled to the residue by right of return, such residue went to the *bait-ul-mâl*. If there was a general legatee he took the residue. But the modern jurists have held and the Courts of Justice in India have given effect to the rule laid down by them that whenever there is an heir, there is no right in the *bait-ul-mâl*. Consequently, if a person died leaving a widow and bequeathing half his estate to *S.*, the one-sixth which remained over after allotting the widow's share and the legacy would be given to the widow.

(2) *Radd ul-Muhtâr*, Vol. V, p. 560.

(3) *Ibid*, p. 660.

entitled to a third of the property, that is, to no more than a third, though they consent, because the sixth is comprehended in the third, whether it precedes or follows. And if a person should say, ' sixth of my property to such an one,' and then say on the same or another occasion, ' a sixth of my property to such an one,'' he would have only one-sixth unless there is evidence that another sixth was intended."(1)

If a person were to bequeath a particular or determinate share of his estate and effects, reference would be made to what he leaves at his death, and not to his possession at the time of the bequest. But where a specific property or a determinate share thereof is bequeathed, *e.g.*, a third of the testator's flock, and the flock is destroyed before his death, the legacy falls to the ground. For, where the *wasiat* was respecting a particular share in a particular flock, the non-existence of that flock destroys the legacy, even though he may have acquired other flocks afterwards. But if he was not possessed of any flock at the time of the bequest, and subsequently acquired one, according to the approved doctrines, the legacy would take effect for the legacy being demonstrative, effect should be given to it when the objects, from which the legacy should be paid, come into existence after the bequest.(2) If the testator were, however, to say, " my executors shall give to so-and-so a sheep out of my property," and there are no sheep belonging to the testator at the time of his death, the value of a sheep would be given to the legatee. But if he had said, " my executors shall give Zaid a sheep out of my flock," and he died without leaving any flock, the legacy would be void. This rule applies to all kinds of property.(3)

---

(1) Comp. the *Radd*, p. 660.

(2) *Ibid.*

(3) When a man who bequeathes a third of his property has no property at the time of the bequest, the legatee is entitled to a third of whatever he may be possessed of at the time of his death. But if the bequest be specific or of some particular kind of property, as a third of his flocks and they all perish before his death, the legacy is void in so much that if he should afterwards become possessed of other flocks, or another specific thing of the same kind the right of the legatee would not attach to the subsequent acquisition, yet if he had no flocks at the date of the bequest, but afterwards acquires them and then dies, the bequest is valid. And if he should say ' a sheep from my property' and have none, the value of a sheep must be given. If the bequest were only of a sheep without the addition of words referring it to his property, the bequest, according to some, would be valid, while according to others it would be invalid. But if the expression were ' a sheep from my flocks' and the testator had no flocks, there is no doubt that the bequest

It often happens, that the testator, instead of leaving a legacy to a grandchild, simply provides by will that he should take a son's share in his inheritance. Supposing then the testator leaves a son as his only heir, and the son consents, the inheritance will be divided between him and the grandson equally; otherwise the legatee would take one-third and the son two-thirds. But if there be two sons, the assent of the sons is not necessary, and the property is divided in equal shares among the sons and the grandson. Similarly, if there be four sons and a grandson, and the testator leave a son's share to the grandson, he takes a fifth. If a testator leave a widow, two sons and a daughter, and a grandson by a predeceased son, and will that the grandson should take a son's share in his inheritance, the division would be made in the following way:—

Widow $=\frac{1}{8}$	Each son $=\frac{1}{4}$
Daughter $=\frac{1}{8}$	Grandson $=\frac{1}{4}$

If there had been only one son, the widow would have taken $=\frac{1}{8}$

Son $=\frac{21}{60}$

Daughter $=\frac{7}{40}$

Grandson $=\frac{21}{60}$

Total $=\frac{120}{120}=1$.

---

would be void. And in like manner with regard to other kinds of property such as cows, camels and the like. When a person says, 'I have bequeathed to thee a sheep, from my property,' the bequest is confined to the sheep that he may have at his death, but applies to the sheep that may be among his property at his death, and since this is the case, if the testator should afterwards die leaving property comprehending sheep with other things, the heirs are at liberty to give one of the sheep or its value. There is nothing in the books as to the sheep being of the best, worst or medium quality, but according to a report of Hassan bin-Ziád, the Companions [of the Prophet] were of opinion that the heirs might in such a case either give a sheep of medium quality or its value. When a person says, 'My roan Turkish horse is a bequest to such an one,' these words are held to refer to a horse then in his possession, not to one which he may afterwards acquire. So also, if the expressions were 'my blind slave or my Sindian or Abyssinian slave' while if the terms of the bequest were only 'my slave to such an one' or 'my Turkish horse to such an one' without further addition or qualification it would include his property at the time, and his subsequent acquisitions."

"When a person says, 'This cow for such an one,' according to Abû Nasr the heirs would have no right to give its value, but if it were bequeathed to the poor it would be lawful for them to bestow its value in charity."

Sunni Law. We have seen already that when there are several legacies, all of the same degree of importance, which, together exceed a third, according to the Sunni Law, all of them suffer a proportionate abatement. This is a general rule, subject, however, to the exception that when the bequests are for the accomplishment of religious duties or pious purposes, they must be given effect to in their entirety in the following order :—

(1) for purification ;

(2) for prayers ;

(3) for alms ;

(4) for fasting ; and

(5) for pilgrimage.

This exception applies equally to duties of a religious and pious character, though not of the same degree of importance as the fundamental religious practices. These duties have to be carried into effect before the payment of legacies to individuals, and they are classified as follows :—

(1) Ransoming of prisoners.

(2) Emancipation of slaves to whom freedom has been promised by the testator.

(3) The payment of the dower due to the woman whom the testator marries in his last illness and consummates the marriage.

(4) The payment of the *zakât.*

(5) The payment of the *zakât-ul-fitr* and *uzzha* (Id and Bairam festivals).

(6) The expiation for *zihâr.*

(7) The expiation due for a vow.

(8) Expiation due for the non-observance of the obligatory fast.

(9) Emancipation of slaves.

(10) Performance of the non-obligatory pilgrimage.

The *Radd ul-Muhtâr* has the following on this subject :—It should be remembered that bequests are necessarily of two kinds, either entirely in favour of Almighty God, or for His servants, or for both jointly, and it is laid down that bequests in favour of Almighty God should have precedence over all others, for the legatee is One, but when the legatees are several, there is no precedence for one over the other. Therefore, when a bequest is for human beings, no legatee can be preferred over another. For example, if a person make a bequest of one-third to one person and then to another, both bequests would take effect, unless it is distinctly specified that either of them has preference over the other, or where it is a *muhâbât* or emancipation. But when a bequest is in favour of Almighly God, if all the directions are (i) for the performance of that which is *farz* (absolutely obligatory duties) as *zakât* or *hajj* ; (ii) or for the performance of duties which are simply obligatory, such as the payment of expiations, fulfilment of vows, the *Fitr* alms ; (iii) or for the performance of *nafliat*, such as non-obligatory pilgrimage and alms to the poor,—then commencement should be made with that which the testator directed should be performed first ; but if they are all mixed together, then commencement should be made with those which are absolutely obligatory, whether the testator mentioned them first or not ; then with the *wâjibât*, the simply obligatory, and the third will be applied proportionately in fulfilment of the testator's last wishes......Consequently, if a man were to say that a third of his property should be applied to defray the expenses of *hajj*, *zakât*, expiations and of Zaid, the third will be divided into four shares, Zaid will get one share and the remaining three shares will be applied to the three purposes respectively. But if the person for whom the legacy is intended is not specified such as the poor, there will not be a division into four shares for all belongs to God, and the most obligatory duties will be discharged first.(1)

---

(1) See the *Fatâwai Alamgiri*, Vol. VI, pp. 177-178, where also the question is fully discussed. "When the legacies have been added up," says the *Fatâwai Alamgiri*, "and the third of the estate is sufficient to meet them all, they are all to be paid out of it, whether they be bequests to Almighty God or to mankind. By bequests to Almighty God are to be understood 'bequests of approach,' or which are the means of drawing nigh to Him, such as the obligatory *hajj* or pilgrimage to Mecca, the *zakât*, fasting, prayers, expiations, vows, *sadakat-ul-fitr* and *uzzha*, non-obligatory *hajj* and fasts, the erection of masjid and the like. And by bequest to mankind are to be understood such as bequests to Zaid, Bakr and Khâlid. All the legacies are to be paid in like manner, when, though the third of the estate is sufficient to meet them, they are allowed by the heirs. If the third of the estate be insufficient to meet all the legacies and they are not allowed by the heirs, then it is to be considered whether they all be to Almighty God, or all to mankind or some be of one class and some of the other. If they are all to Almighty God, then it is further to be considered either whether they are all *farâiz* [that is obligatory duties], or *wâjibât* [that is, things which though not actually obligatory are yet incumbent], or *nawâfil* [which are voluntarily assumed obligations], or whether they are partly of one kind and partly of another. When they are all equally prescribed and appointed duties, beginning

Shiah Law. According to the Shiah Law "when a person has bequeathed property for the performance of certain duties some of which were incumbent on the testator and others only discretionary, they are all to be carried into effect if a third of his estate be sufficient for the purpose." If the third be not sufficient and the heirs should refuse their consent, those duties that were incumbent on the testator must first be discharged out of the general mass of his estate and then the others out of a third of what remains, beginning with the first mentioned by the testator, and so on in order. If none of the duties are of an incumbent nature but merely optional, they can take effect only to the extent of a third of the estate, and are to be discharged beginning with the first mentioned by the testator, and so on in order until the third is exhausted.

---

is to be made with that which the testator began with; when the bequest is for *hajj* and *zakât*, a commencement is to be made with the former though it were verbally last. It has been said with regard to *hajj* and *zakât* that they both take precedence of expiations, and expiations take precedence of the *sadakat-ul-fitr* (or alms of the *fitr*) and these of sacrifices, though sacrifices are also *wâjib* [or necessary] according to us. With regard to the alms in question all are agreed that they are *wâjibât*, but whether sacrifices be so is a point that is still within the province of *ijtihâd* or juridical discussion and what all are agreed about is still stronger. Thus, also the alms of the *fitr* are preferred to expiation of the *fitr* in the month of Ramazan. And it has been said that the former have also precedence of vows, and vows of sacrifices, and these of *nâwâfil* or voluntary obligations. In all this that has been said it is assumed that there are no legacies of emancipation to take effect at once during death-sickness and no emancipation dependent on death, which is *tudbîr*. If there be any such they have preference, for those emancipations do not admit of being revoked, and are, therefore, stronger and entitled to preference. A bequest of emancipation, if it be *wâjib* or necessary as an expiation, is like other expiations of which we have spoken already, but if they are *not wâjib*, their effect is like that of spontaneous bequests to the poor, the building of musjids, voluntary pilgrimage and the like."

"When the legacies are partly to Almighty God and partly to mankind, as for instance, to a class of persons, the portion of the latter is to be taken out of the third and to be divided among them without preference of any one over the others, and with regard to the portion of Almighty God it is to be applied first to *farâiz*, next to *wâjibât* and then to *nawâfil*. And if, with the legacies to Almighty God there is a legacy to one person in particular, each of the kinds of approach is to be treated as single. Thus, if one were to say, 'A third of my property in *hâjj*, *zakât*, expiations and to Zaid,' the third would be divided into four portions —one for Zaid, one for *hâjj*, one for *zakât*, and one for expiations."

"When all the legacies are to mankind, preference is to be given to the strongest, so that if there be among them an emancipation to take effect immediately, it is to have the precedence; but if all are equal in strength, each is to rank for its amount agai[nst] the third of the property without any regard to the order in which they may have been mentioned by the deceased;" Baillie's Dig.

CHAPTER XXIV.

GENERAL PRINCIPLES.

SECTION I.

THE LEGAL EFFECT OF A WASIAT.

Wasiat is defined as "the conferment of a right of property (*tamlîk*) in a specific thing or in a profit or advantage, to take effect after the death of the testator." "It is proper for a man to make a will when there is no right against him on the part of Almighty God, but it is a duty to do so when there is such a right, as for instance, when he has omitted to pay his *zakât* or to fast, or to perform the *hajj* or pilgrimage to Mecca, or to say the prescribed prayers."

Hanafî doctrines.

Any expression which signifies the intention of the testator is sufficient for the purpose of constituting a bequest. Examples of this are given in detail in the *Fatâwai Alamgiri*.(1)

"When a person has said, 'this my slave to such an one, and this my mansion to such an one,' without using the word bequest, and there is no mention of bequests nor of the words 'after my death,' the expressions constitute a gift both by analogy and on a favourable construction, and if possession be taken during the life of the donor the gift is valid, but if possession is not taken of it till after his death the gift is void. If a person should say, 'I have willed that a third of my mansion be given to such an one after my death,' this is a bequest, and possession during the lifetime of the testator is unnecessary. So also when one, whether in sickness or in health, has said, 'if any event should happen to me, then such thing to such person' this is a legacy, death being understood by 'us,' as the event alluded to. So also if he should say, 'to such an one a thousand *dirhems* from my third,' this would be a bequest though no allusion is made to

(1) *Fatâwai Alamgiri*, Vol. VI, p. 145.

death. But if the words were 'to such an one from my property, or 'from the half' cr 'the fourth of my property,' they would be of no effect unless uttered in connection with bequests, in which case they would constitute a legacy. When a person has said, 'if I die on this my journey, to such an one there is against me a debt of a thousand *dirhems*,' it is a bequest out of his third."

Shiah doctrines.

Under the Shiah Law there are certain rules relative to ambiguous legacies, which are deserving of notice, though in their application they will need some modification in view of the different conditions of society prevailing in our times:—

"When a person has bequeathed a *juzz*, or part of his property there are two traditions as to the proper interpretation of his words. Of these, the most authentic assigns a tenth of the testator's estate to the legatee; but according to the other, he should receive only a seventh of the third. If, again, he should bequeath a '*saham*,' or share, the proper interpretation is an eighth; while if it were a *shai*, or a thing, it should be interpreted as meaning a sixth."

"If a person should make a bequest for several purposes, of which the executor has forgotton one or more, he should dispose of it in some good or proper way, although some of our lawyers have expressed an opinion that it should fall back into the deceased's inheritance."

"If a person should bequeath a particular sword which is in a scabbard, the scabbard and mounting or ornaments are included in the bequest. In like manner, if a person should bequeath a box containing clothes, or a boat or vessel which has merchandise on board, or a bag containing linen, in all these cases, the things actually bequeathed, and the other things contained in them, are included in the legacy. Some jurists, however, hold another view, though it does not deserve much consideration."

"If a person should make a will excluding some of his children from their share in his succession, the exclusion is not valid. But whether his words are to be treated as entirely inoperative is a question on which there are two opinions. According to one of these, they are quite futile and of no efficacy whatever; but, according to the other, the same effect should be given to them as in the case of the bequest of the whole of a person's estate to a stranger, excluding his heirs, when the bequest is valid as far as a third of his property, and the heirs have their legal portion in the remaining two-thirds. The first opinion, however, appears to be better founded in law, though the other is supported by a tradition which is now rejected.

"If a person should make a bequest in terms so ambiguous that the law affords no interpretation of them, it must be left to the heir to explain them as he may think proper.

"It is preferable that legacies should be kept below a third of the testator's property, and consequently the bequest of a fourth is better than that of a third and of a fifth better than of a fourth.

"In cases of ambiguous legacies, like the preceding, if the legatee should demand any particular thing as being conveyed in the testator's meaning, the statement of the heir would be preferred. If the legatee should still insist upon it, the heir would be required to confirm his statement by his oath not otherwise."

When property is devised in absolute terms, conditions in restraint of the power of alienation on the part of the devisees have been held to be ineffective.(1)

Section II.

The Revocation of Wills.

A will is essentially revocable in its nature. It may be revoked at any time, even during the last illness of the testator.

Revocation of wills.

Revocation may be either express or implied, made either directly or indirectly. It is express when the testator revokes the *wasîat* in express terms. It is implied or indirect when the testator indicates by his conduct or his subsequent acts that he does not intend to maintain the legacy.(2) "Every act the effect of which is to extinguish the proprietary right in any property, when committed by a testator in respect of the subject of a bequest, causes revocation; and in like manner every act of the testator which occasions an addition to the subject of a bequest, when it cannot be delivered without the addition, has the effect of revoking it; similarly, any disposition subsequently made to which operation is given has also that effect."(3)

(1) *Abdul Karim Khan* v. *Abdul Qayum Khan* [1906], I. L., 28 All., 342.
(2) *Fatâwai Alamgiri*, Vol. VI, p. 144.
(3) *Radd-ul-Muhtâr*, Vol. V, pp. 657, 658.

The different modes in which revocation may be effected.

As regards the mode and capability of revocation, bequests are usually divided into four categories; the first can be revoked either in express terms or by implication, *i.e.*, by conduct. The second kind may be revoked only by express words. The third by conduct only; and the fourth cannot be revoked at all. The first kind of bequests consists of specific legacies which can be revoked by an express declaration of the testator to that effect, or by his selling or transferring the subject of the bequest in such a manner as to place it beyond his power to cancel or reverse the transfer. The second kind of bequest is where the testator bequeaths a third or fourth share of his property to any person. In such a case, the legatee is entitled to that particular share in any property which might be left by the testator at the time of his death, and consequently unless a revocation of the bequest is made in express terms, the legacy will take effect. The third kind of bequest is qualified emancipation which can be withdrawn only by express conduct. The fourth kind of *wasiat*, which cannot be cancelled either expressly or impliedly, is absolute emancipation.

Abû Hanîfa's opinion.

According to Abû Hanîfa, on whose opinion in this matter the *Fatwa* seems to be, a mere change in the shape of an article effected at the instance of the testator does not amount to a revocation. For example, if a person were to bequeath to another a piece of silver which he subsequently made into a ring, this is not a revocation of the bequest according to Abû Hanîfa, though according to Abû Yusuf and apparently Mohammed, it would be so. If a person should sell a specific thing which he had bequeathed and then re-purchase it, or make a present of it and then revoke the gift, the bequest would continue valid. "The slaughter of a bequeathed sheep is the revocation of a bequest of it, but the washing of a bequeathed garment is not so." The mere denial of a bequest does not, according to Abû Yusuf, amount to a revocation, but Mohammed holds a different view. If the testator were to say the legacy left by him to *A* or *B* was void, it would have the effect of revoking the will though it would not be so, if he merely said it was unlawful (*harâm*) or usurious.

If a testator were to devise a specific thing to *A*, and afterwards to *B*, the subsequent devise does not necessarily avoid the first. If it appears from the phraseology used or otherwise, that the intention of the testator was to give the subject of the bequest to both legatees jointly, effect will be given to such intention.(1) But if it appears that the intention was to give the legacy to the second legatee by cancelling the first bequest, it would amount to revocation. The general rule, however, is that the last legacy takes effect.(2)

Hanafî doctrines—contd.

If the second legatee were dead at the time when the subsequent bequest was purported to be made, the first bequest would remain valid by reason of the second being void, while if the second person were living at the time when the bequest was made and should subsequently die before the testator, both legacies would be void, and the subject of the bequest would revert to the heirs of the testator.

Under the Hanafî Law the pledging of a property will not avoid the bequest,(3) for it does not extinguish the right of the proprietor in the subject of the pledge; the right of the testator to redeem would devolve on his death to the legatee; in other words, the legatee takes the devised property *cum onere*,(4) unless the testator whilst creating the mortgage, use terms expressly from which a distinct revocation of the previous devise may be clear.

If one should bequeath a mansion and then whitewash it or pull it down, that would not amount to a revocation, but if he were to plaster it over with earth, that would be a revocation, if done "largely." If he should bequeath land and sow it with vegetables that would not be a revocation, while if he makes a vineyard of it or plants trees on it, the bequest would be revoked according to Kâzi Khân.

(1) According to the *Fatawai Alamgiri*, the pledge of a slave already bequeathed amounts to a revocation; but this effect is restricted to the special kinds of property analogous to the property referred to.

(2) This is different from the English Law, where the legatee, unless a contrary intention appears, is entitled to have the estate disencumbered out of the personal estate of the testator not specifically bequeathed.

(3) Sometimes the attempt to convey may have the effect of revoking a devise, though owing to some want of formality the conveyance itself may not take effect. But where the conveyance is initially invalid, for example, when it has been executed by a person who was under an incapacity it will not act as a revocation.

(4) *Fatâwai Alamgiri*, Vol. VI, p. 143; Baillie, p. 628; *Radd-ul-Muhtâr*, Vol. V, p. 647.

Shâfeï doctrines.

Similarly, under the Mâliki and the Shâfeï Law, among the various acts by which a *wasîat* is indirectly revoked are the sale and gift of the subject of the bequest.

The *Sharâya* gives the Shiah principle in these terms :—

Shiah doctrines.

"A *wasîat* is an *'akd jâiz* on the part of the testator whether it be [the bequest] of property or the nomination of a *walî ;* and it may be revoked during his lifetime either by express language or by any act which ignores or contradicts the *wasîat*. Thus, if the testator should sell the subject of the bequest, or by another will direct it to be sold, or should bestow it in gift putting the donee in possession of it, or should pledge it, every such act would amount to a revocation. In like manner, if he should make such a use of it that it could no longer be called by the same name ; as for instance, if he had made a bequest of grain and afterwards ground it into flour or meal, or a bequest of flour or meal and then converted it into leaven or bread, this would be a revocation of the bequest. Further, if a person should bequeath a quantity of oil and afterwards mix it with some of a better quality, or of grain and then mix it with some of another species so as to remove the possibility of distinguishing and separating one from the other, that likewise would be equivalent to a retractation of the bequest. Whereas if he should make a bequest of bread and subsequently break it into crumbs there would be no revocation of the legacy."(1)

It will be observed that both under the Sunni and Shiah laws although various examples are given in the law-books as to what would amount to revocation and what would not, the general rule is that revocation depends on intention which may be evidenced by a variety of acts or circumstances.

Acceptance of the legatee.

The validity of a *wasîat* is submitted to another formality, namely, the implied or express acceptance of the *wasîat* by the legatee. "The acceptance of a bequest," says the Mâliki lawyer, "is a necessary condition ;" and the Hanafî jurist lays down that "in default of acceptance a *wasîat* is null." Similarly, under the Shiah Law the acceptance of the legatee is required to vest the legacy in him. But there is considerable divergence between the Shiah school on one side and the Hanafî on the other regarding the period when the acceptance should be made.

---

(1) *Sharâya-ul-Islam*, p. 247.

According to the Shiah doctrines, an acceptance *before* the death of the testator is lawful, though it is discretionary with the legatee. An acceptance *after* the testator's death is conclusive, even though it should be delayed for some time after the occurrence of that event, provided there was no rejection on the part of the legatee after the testator's decease and before acceptance. But when the rejection was during the lifetime of the testator, the legacy may still be accepted after his death, as such a rejection has no effect in law. But if rejected after his death without having been accepted, the legacy is cancelled. A *wasîat* would similarly be cancelled if rejected by the legatee even though possession had been actually taken, provided there was no acceptance. Where there has been no possession, but the legacy is rejected after the testator's death as well as the legatee's prior acceptance, it is cancelled, according to some of the jurists, while others maintain that it is not, and this opinion is more approved. If, however, there has been both acceptance and possession, and the legacy is subsequently rejected, there is no doubt that the rejection is ineffectual and the legacy is not cancelled because the right of property has then become already established in the legatee. **Shiah doctrines—acceptance before testator's death valid.**

If a legatee should reject part of a bequest and accept the remainder, such partial acceptance would be valid and his right established to that extent. If a legatee should die before acceptance his heirs take his place and may accept the bequest.(1)

According to the Hanafî Law, *an acceptance before the death of the testator is of no effect*. The bequest may be accepted either expressly or by implication. If the legatee died before expressing either rejection or acceptance of the bequest, his death becomes, and would be presumed to amount to, an acceptance and his heirs would inherit the legacy. There is this difference between testate and intestate succession,—an heir enters upon the possession of inherited property without acceptance, but a legatee does not enter upon the possession of bequeathed property without acceptance. The acceptance of a bequest must be made *after* the death of the testator insomuch that if it be accepted or rejected during his life, either act is void and the rejector is still at liberty to accept after the testator's death. **Hanafî doctrines.**

(1) *Jawâhir-ul-Kalâm.*

Legal effect of a bequest. The legal effect of a bequest is to confer on the legatee a right of property in the same way as in the case of a gift, (1) and the bequest becomes vested in him on acceptance, "so that if he were to accept after the death of the testator his ownership in the thing bequeathed would be established, whether he takes possession of it or not; but if he were to reject the bequest it would be cancelled." But when a bequest is made to a body of people such as the poor, or is in favour of a *general* religious or pious purpose, the acceptance of the legatee is presumed.

SECTION III.

THE WASIAT OF USUFRUCT OF LANDS, GARDENS, HOUSES, SECURITIES, STOCKS, &c.(2)

As pointed out already, the Mahommedan Law distinctly recognises perpetuities. So long as commencement is made, in the case of a settlement or devise, with a life in being, it is not necessary that the persons who take the remainder should be in existence.

Accordingly, one may lawfully bequeath to another, for a limited period or in perpetuity, the produce (*ghallat*)(3) of lands and gardens, the rent or occupancy of a house, the use of animals or trees, income accruing from securities, stocks, going concerns, &c.

If the term for which the bequest is made is indefinite, it would be regarded as made in perpetuity.(4)

The effect of such a bequest is to *detain* the subject thereof in the ownership of the testator's heirs and to give to the legatee only the right to take its profits, "in the same way as a person in whose favour a *wakf* has been made."

---

(1) Comp. *Abdul Karim Khan* v. *Abdul Kayum Khan*, supra.

(2) The title of this Chapter, in the *Fatâwai Alamgiri* (Vol. VI, p. 188), furnishes a sufficient indication of the scope of the provisions in the Arabian Law regarding the bequest of usufruct:

فی وصیة بالسکنی و الخدمة و الثمرة و غلة العبید و غلة البستان و
غلة لارض و ظهر الدابة و غیرها

See also the *Radd-ul-Muhtâr*, Vol. V, p. 678.

(3) *Radd-ul-Muhtâr*, Vol. V, p. 677. See also 4 H ed., Chap. V, Bk. II, p. 527; the term *ghallat* is a generic expression and includes produce, rent, income, profits of all kinds, the service of slaves, &c.; *Jâm'aa-ul-Lughât*.

(4) *Radd-ul-Muhtâr*, Vol. V, p. 679.

The bequest may be for a particular year, *e.g.*, the year of the Hegira 460. If the year is past at the time of the testator's death, the bequest is void. If a portion only of the year has expired, it would take effect with respect to the unexpired portion.

If the subject of the bequest falls within the third of the testator's estate, its usufruct would be given to the legatee, in accordance with the use thereof provided in the *wasîat*. For example, if the bequest is of the right of occupancy of a house, and the house falls within the disposable one-third, it would be made over to the legatee for use and occupation.(1) If the rents and profits of the house alone are bequeathed, the legatee would get the same, but he would not be entitled to occupy it. If the subject of the bequest exceeds the third, the legatee will get the benefit of that portion which is covered by the third. Where the bequest is of the use of some property which is in its nature impartible, the legatee will have the right to its service or use for one period and the heirs for double that period. The example given in the *Fatâwai Alamgiri* of a slave explains this principle thoroughly :—

"If the slave does not come within a third of the property he is to serve the legatee for one day and the heirs for two days alternately, until the completion of the year, and when it has been completed he is finally to be delivered up to the heirs. If one year in particular be specified, and the slave falls within a third of the property, or the legacy is allowed by the heirs, he is to be delivered up to the legatee to serve him for a whole year and then to be restored to the heirs. If he does not come within a third of the property, and the legacy is not allowed by the heirs, the slave is to serve the legatee for one day and the heirs for two days alternately for three years, and when the three years have passed the bequest is fulfilled by the service. If the legatee should die, the slave reverts to the heirs of the testator, and if he die in the testator's lifetime the bequest is void."

Death of the legatee.

If the legatee should die before the expiration of the term limited for the bequest, the subject of the legacy would immediately revert to the heirs of the testator. If the legatee dies during the lifetime of the testator the bequest at once falls to the ground. The testator may bequeath the usufruct of a thing to one person

(1) Similarly, if the *wasîat* be of the service of a bondsman, and he were to fall within the third, he would be made over to the legatee for the period fixed.

and the *corpus* to another; and if the subject of the bequest falls within the disposable third, each legatee is entitled to his particular bequest. And if the bequest of the usufruct is absolute, the legatee is entitled to hold possession of the subject till his death, after which it is to be transferred to the legatee of the *corpus* if he be alive; if not, it is to be transferred to the heirs of the testator.(1)

In the case of a bequest of usufruct—mode of enjoyment.

When the bequest is of the rents and profits of a house, and the legatee wishes to occupy it himself he cannot lawfully do so.(2) "If the bequest be of the occupancy of a mansion and there is no property besides, the legatee may occupy a third of the mansion and the heirs have no right to sell the two-thirds of the mansion in their possession.(3) Neither is the legatee of the occupancy of a house entitled to let it,(4) nor to remove the slave whose services are bequeathed from the testator's place of residence to another, unless the legatee and his family (*ahl*) are in the latter place, when the slave may be taken there for the purpose of serving them."(5) The reason of this decision is, that the bequest must take effect and be executed in conformity with the intent of the testator, and in a case where the family of the legatee reside in the same place with the testator, his intention is that the legatee should avail himself of the services in that place, but where the legatee resides in a different city, the testator's intention must be presumed to be that the legatee should have the slave's services there.

When the occupancy of a house is bequeathed to a person without any limit of time, he is entitled to it as long as he lives. And when the income is bequeathed, if the house falls within a third, though the income may exceed the same, still it would be valid. Similarly, with regard to the income of an estate or earn-

(1) *Radd-ul-Muhtâr*, Vol. V, p. 679.

(2) *Ibid.* According to Allâmah Sharnibilâlièh there seems to be some difference of opinion on this point, but he himself upholds its validity.

(3) According to the *Zâhir-ur-Rawâyét*, the heirs are not entitled to sell the two-thirds share allotted to them, as that would be prejudicing the interests of the usufructuary legatee. Abû Yusuf seems to think such sale lawful. The doctrine in the *Zâhir-ur-Rawâyét* is more approved. "Besides," says the *Hedayâ*, "the legatee has a controlling power over the heirs with respect to their portions, so far as to restrain them from executing any deed which may injure his share."

(4) According to the Shâfeïs he is entitled to do so.

(5) *Radd-ul-Muhtâr*, Vol. V, p. 680.

ings from a business, or the produce of a garden, etc. "When a bequest is of a slave to serve the legatee until he can do without those services,—if the legatee is a child, the service is to continue till he is of age ; if he is adult and poor the service is to continue until he is able to buy a slave to serve him ; but if he is adult and rich the legacy is void."(1)

If a person were to leave one year's earnings of his business or the income of his house to another, and he has no other property except such business or such house the legatee in that case receives one-third of a year's earnings or income, because such income, as being property, is capable of division. But the legatee cannot require the heirs to make a partition of the house in order that he may himself collect the rent of his own share (*viz.*, the third).

Bequest of the produce.

When the bequest is of the *produce* of the testator's garden, the legatee is entitled to the existing and the future produce. But when the bequest is of the fruit of his garden in *perpetuity*, the legatee is entitled to the fruit thereof until his death. But if the word "*abad*" (*for ever*) is not used, and there is fruit in the garden on the day of the testator's death, the legatee is entitled to it to the extent or value of the disposable third, but he is not entitled to the future fruit, it being supposed that the intention of the testator was to give one set of fruit. But where there is no fruit in the garden on the day of the testator's death, the bequest takes effect on the fruit which comes into existence subsequent to the death of the testator but prior to that of the legatee.(2) When a bequest is of something which is an accretion to something else, the specific accretion in existence at the time of the testator's death will be given to the legatee, though the words "for ever" may have been used. This is different from the legacy of the rents and profits.(3)

If the legacy be of the third of the *income* of a house, according to Abû Yusuf, the heirs may partition the house, giving the legatee

(1) This is according to the *Fatâwai Alamgiri*.

(2) *Fatâwai Alamgiri*, Vol. VI, p. 148 ; *Radd-ul-Muhtâr*, Vol. V, p. 681 ; *Hedâya*, Vol. VI, p. 527.

(3) The reason of this is explained in the *Radd-ul-Muhtâr*. In the *Alamgiri* the rule is stated thus :—"When a man has bequeathed to another the wool of his flock or their progeny or milk for ever and has then died, the legatee is entitled only to the wool that may be on their backs or the young that may be in their bellies, or the milk that may be in their udders—whether he say 'for ever or not.'"

Bequest of the produce —contd.

a third. If the third yields any income, the legatee gets it, while if it is not productive he has nothing. The heirs may also sell him their two-thirds, whether before or after the partition.

When the bequest is of the *produce* of a piece of land and there are no trees upon it and no other property besides, the land is to be let and a third of the rent given to the legatee. If there be palm or other trees on the land, a third of the produce is to be given to him and the land is not to be given out in *muzâribât*.(1)

When the bequest is of the produce of a garden, the legatee may purchase the garden from the heirs of the testator, but that would cancel the legacy. In like manner, if they satisfy him with something else, he may surrender his third of the produce and release them from it. "So also the occupancy of a house or the service of a slave may be lawfully compounded for, though a sale to an outsider of these rights is not lawful."(2)

A bequest of the income of a house or of the income arising from securities, stock, etc., or of the earnings of a business to the poor generally is lawful, but a bequest of the *occupancy* of a house to the poor is not lawful unless the persons are particularised.

When a bequest is made of the principal and the accessory to two persons respectively in one and the same will, each legatee takes the legacy specifically given to him. For example, if the testator were to say, "I give this ring to so-and-so and the stone to so-and-so."

But when one of the declarations is separated from the other though the effect is the same according to Abû Yusuf, according to Mohammed the legatee of the principal is exclusively entitled to the principal and the two legatees are partners in the accessory.

The following is important as showing how effect is to be given to two legacies respecting the same article, one arising out of the other: "If a person should bequeath 'this slave to one and his service to another,' or this mansion to one and its occupancy to another,' 'or this sheep to one and its wool to another' both persons being specified, each legatee takes what is bequeathed to him and there is no difference of opinion on this point, whether the bequests are made separately or together.. But if a beginning is made

---

(1) *Muzâribat* here means an arrangement by which the cultivator and the landlord divide the produce according to certain shares.

(2) *Radd-ul-Muhtâr*, Vol. V, p. 681.

Subsidiary bequests.

in these cases with the accessory, and the principal is then bequeathed, as, for instance, if the service of the slave is first bequeathed to one person and then the slave to another, or the occupancy of a mansion to one person and the mansion itself to another, or the fruit to one and the tree to another, it is only when the bequests are made connectedly that each legatee is entitled to what has been named for him specially, for if they are mentioned separately, the legatee of the principal is exclusively entitled to the principal, and the accessory belongs to them both in halves. And if a mansion is bequeathed to one person and a particular apartment in it to another, the apartment is to both in equal shares. So, also, if a thousand dirhems are bequeathed to one person and a hundred out of them to another, the legatee of the thousand is entitled to nine hundred exclusively, and the hundred is to be equally divided between them and in this there is no difference of opinion."

When the bequest is of the use of the young of an animal which is unfit for service, the person in whom the right to the substance of the thing is vested is bound to maintain it. So, also, when the produce of palm-trees has been bequeathed to one person for ever, and the trees themselves, being yet immature, to another, the latter is liable for the expense of watering and tending them until they arrive at maturity and are in bearing, after which the liability is on the former, and when they have begun generally to bear, though they should subsequently fall off and produce nothing, the legatee of the produce would still be liable for the expense, in the same way as a legatee of service is liable for the maintenance, "both during night and day, though the slave sleeps and does no work during the night."

If twenty dirhems a year are bequeathed to a person from the produce of a garden, which is sometimes more productive and sometimes less, the legatee is entitled to have a third of the produce appropriated or set aside every year, and twenty dirhems out of it applied to his maintenance so long as he lives. Similarly, if a person were to declare that *A* should get a monthly sum for his support out of the testator's property, however small the allowance may be, a full third of the property must be appropriated or put aside that the legatee may obtain his monthly maintenance as directed by the testator.(1)

(1) *Fatâwai Alamgiri*, Vol. VI, p. 150; *Radd-ul-Muhtâr*, Vol. V, p. 680.

Rules relating to annuities.

If a testator should bequeath a third of his property to one person, five dirhems a month for maintenance to another so long as he lives, and five dirhems a month for the maintenance of a third person so long as he lives, and the heirs allow all the legacies,—the estate is to be divided, according to Abû Hanîfa, into nine parts, one of which is to be given to the legatee of the third, and the remaining eight to be appropriated for the other legatees, four parts each; but according to Abû Yusuf and Mohammed, the property is to be divided into seven parts, whereof one is to be given to the legatee of the third, and the remaining six is to be appropriated for the other legatees, three for each. This principle applies to those cases where the heirs allow all the legacies. But suppose that they do not assent, in such a case the division is to be into seven parts as before according to Abû Yusuf and Mohammed; but according to Abû Hanîfa, the case is to be treated as if all the legatees were equally entitled to the third, which is consequently to be divided into three parts among them. Under these circumstances, if both the annuitants should die before the fund is exhausted, the surplus is to revert to the legatee of the third; and if one of them should die, the surplus is to be divided and one share given to the legatee of the third and the other reserved for the survivor, according to Abû Hanîfa; while according to the Disciples only a fourth is to be given to the legatee of the third and three-fourths is to be reserved for the survivor. The views of the Disciples are adopted for the *Fatwa*.

If the testator should bequeath five dirhems a month for the maintenance of *A* so long as he shall live and ten dirhems a month for the maintenance of *B* and *C* so long as they shall live (whether jointly or separately), and the heirs allow the legacies, the property is to be divided into two equal shares, one-half to be reserved for *A* and the other half for *B* and *C*, for *A* is to be considered as a legatee of the whole, and *B* and *C* are to be considered together as one legatee of the whole, so that the property is to be divided between them in halves according to all opinions; and if *A* should die, what remains is to be reserved for *B* and *C* and ten dirhems a month applied to their maintenance, and if one of them should die before *A*, the share set apart for them together would be applied for his

Bequest of annuities—contd.

surviving co-legatee, and five dirhems would be given for the latter's maintenance every month. If the heirs do not allow the legacies, a third of the property is to be divided, by general consensus, into halves, one-half of the third being set apart for *A* and the other half for *B* and *C*. But if a person were to bequeath out of the third of his property a maintenance of four dirhems a month to *A* so long as he shall live, and a maintenance of ten dirhems a month to *B* and *C* so long as they shall live, and the heirs allow both legacies, one-third of the property is to be appropriated for *A* and another third for *B* and *C* jointly and on the death of *A*, the third set apart for him, or so much thereof as is not exhausted reverts to the heirs of the testator; and if either *B* or *C* should die, what remains of his share is to be reserved for his co-legatee, and when the other dies if anything should remain, it is to revert to the heirs. If the heirs do not allow the legacies, the third is to be divided into halves and one-half of it is to be reserved for *A* and the other half for *B* and *C*.

According to Mohammed, when a bequest is in the following terms, "I bequeath my third to be set apart for Zaid, that he may have four dirhems out of it for his maintenance every month so long as he lives, and I bequeath my two-thirds to Bakr and 'Amr that they may have ten dirhems laid out for maintenance every month as long as they live," and the heirs allow the legacies, a full third of the property is to be delivered up to the first legatee in his absolute right, and the other two-thirds to be delivered to the two legatees between them in the same way, and when any of them dies, his portion goes to his heirs. But if the heirs do not allow the legacies, the first legatee is to have a half of the third, and the other two legatees to have the other half. Similarly, if the bequest were as follows, "I bequeath my third to Zaid that he may have four dirhems a month out of it for his maintenance, and I make a bequest to Bakr and 'Amr that they may have five dirhems a month out of it for their maintenance," and the heirs allow the legacies, the first legatee is to take a third of the whole property and the other two legatees to take another third between them in halves in absolute right; while if the heirs disallow the legacies, Zaid is to have half of the third, and Bakr and 'Amir to have the other half of it between them, and the share of whoever of them may die, goes to his *own* heirs.

Shiah doctrines.

According to the Shiah Law, if a person should bequeath the fruit of his garden, the residence of his house, the earnings of his business or anything else of a usufructuary nature for ever or for a fixed time, the advantage or profit arising therefrom must be valued, and should it not exceed a third of the testator's estate the bequest is valid, while if more than a third, the legatee is to have as much as the third will cover and the legacy is void as to the excess.

When a person has bequeathed a right of residence in a house for a fixed period, its upkeep must be defrayed by his heirs, as this is a duty which follows or is dependent on the ownership of the house, and the legatee is entitled to no more than a right of occupation while all the other rights of ownership appertain to the heirs of the deceased, as sale, mortgage and the like, none of which, however, has the effect of invalidating the rights of the legatee.

Nuncupative wills valid.

A verbal will is valid according to all the schools.(1)

The *Sharâya* declares that "wills or bequests are established in law by the testimony of two witnesses who are Moslems and just persons, or, in case of necessity, when two just Moslems, witnesses are not to be had, by that of two *Zimmis* or non-Moslems subjects. And in cases where property only is concerned, the testimony of one witness on oath may be received, or of one male witness and two females, and the testimony of even a single female witness may be received as establishing the right of a legatee to a fourth part of what she testifies to; of two women as supporting his claim to a half, of three as to three-fourths and of four as to the whole. But an appointment of executors or guardians by will can be established only by the testimony of two male witnesses, and in this case the testimony of women cannot be received, nor further, according to the most obvious analogy, can that of one male witness on his oath be received." These views, however, relate to procedure and cannot be treated as substantive law.

"The testimony of an executor cannot be received in matters connected with his own executorship, nor as to anything from which he may derive advantage to himself or to his office. And if

(1) *Aminooddowlah* v. *Roshun Ali Khan*, 5 M. I. A., 199.

appointed executor for the expenditure of a specific part of his testator's property, his testimony cannot be received in favour of the deceased to prove that his property does not exceed a third of his estate.''

In Mahommedan countries, when a will is made in the presence of witnesses the usual rule is for these witnesses to embody their depositions on the will; subjoined is a copy of one of such depositions made in Algeria :—" We bear witness to God we were present when Sâlih-ibn-Rafah said to us, 'I take you as witness against my person that I bequeath to Zaid the third of my goods that I may have, the rest will be for my heirs.' ''

As stated before, a bequest may be made by any form of expression or even by signs, which may serve to indicate the idea and intention of the testator. In India, however, *wasîats* are generally embodied in writing and attested bv witnesses when they are called *wasiat-nâmahs.*

CHAPTER XXV.

Executors.

Section I.

Who may be appointed as Executors.

The testator has the power of confiding the execution of his last wishes to whomsoever he likes; and subject to certain restrictions to which I shall presently call attention, the executorship may be entrusted to either a man or a woman, a stranger or a relative. And though a testamentary disposition may be invalid, the appointment of the executor, so far as the guardianship of the minor children and their education are concerned, would be valid. The executor(1) is bound to carry out the wishes of the testator that are valid in law with the utmost fidelity,(2) to watch the interests of his children, and to administer to his estate and effects.

The appointment may be either limited to a special purpose or may be general.

"If a person were to appoint as executor a minor (*sabî*) or the bondsman of another (*'aabdi ghairihi*) or a non-Moslem or a *fâsik* (*lit.* reprobate) he should be replaced and the Kâzi should appoint another in his stead for the completion of the work; and the word *badal* (substitution) implies the validity of the *wasîat*, and that any act committed by them before removal is valid, so in the *Sirâjia*."(3) "And if [before the removal] the infant attains majority or the slave is enfranchised, or the non-Moslem or apostate adopts or reverts to Islâm, or the *fâsik* abandons his evil ways (*lit.* repents), according to the *Mujtaba*, the Kâzi must not remove him (as in the case of the appointment of a minor as trustee of a *wakf* which is valid by *istehsân*,) for the reason for his

---

(1) The executor is called a *wasi* or *musa-ilehi*.

(2) *Jâm'aa ush-Shittât; Radd-ul-Muhtâr* and *Fatawai Kâzi Khân in loco*.

(3) *Durr ul-Mukhtâr*, p. 835.

removal has ceased; excepting when the *wasî* commits breach of trust.''(1)

The *Fatâwai Alamgiri* states the principle thus :—" When a person appoints as executor an infant or an insane person, whether permanently so or with lucid intervals, it is not valid.....But if he entrusts the executorship to a woman, or a blind person, and similarly to one who has undergone the specific punishment (*hadd*) for slander,'' it is valid. When a minor has been appointed an executor, the Kâzi should remove him and appoint another in his stead, says Khassâf. And jurists have differed as to whether any act committed by the minor before his removal by the Kâzi takes effect like the act of a *Zimmi* (non-Moslem subject) or a bondsman; some have said it takes effect whilst others have said it does not, and this is *correct* (وهو الصحيح.) (2)

A minor executor.

It will be seen, therefore, that there is a pronounced difference of opinion between the *Durr ul-Mukhtâr* and the *Fatâwai Alamgiri* on the question of the validity of the acts of a minor executor before he attains majority. The latter authority has evidently adopted the view expressed in the *Sharh-i-Wahbâniêh* where it is stated that " when a person has appointed as executor a minor or a bondsman [of another] the Kâzi should remove him, for a minor does not possess the capacity of entering into legal transactions. And jurists have differed as to whether any act done by him (the minor) is operative or not; some have said it is, whilst others have said, not—and this is correct.''

The opinion of the author of the *Radd-ul-Muhtâr* seems to incline in the same direction.(3)

As regards the question whether a person laboring under the disability of status (like a *Zimmi* or bondsman) or under the disability of non-age continues as executor and his disability ceases *before* removal, he would remain lawfully in office, the *Fatâwai Alamgiri* answers it in the affirmative. In other words the *Zimmi* on becoming a Moslem or the bondsman on being emancipated remain in their offices. With regard to the minor it states there is a difference between Abû Hanîfa and his disciples—the

(1) *Durr ul-Mukhtâr*, p. 835. (2) *Fatâwai Alamgiri*, Vol. VI, p. 214.
(3) *Radd-ul-Muhtâr*, Vol. V, p. 689.

former holding that the minor ceases to be the executor, whilst Abû Yusuf says he does not, and Mohammed agrees with him. And the jurist Abu'l Kâsim has held similarly.(1)

A minor, though he cannot validly be appointed an executor by himself, can be associated with an adult in the office, but he cannot interfere in the administration of the estate until he has attained puberty.

Joint executors, one of whom is a minor.

When two persons are appointed executors, one of whom is a minor and the other adult, the adult executor may act alone until the minor has arrived at puberty, but when that happens the adult executor can no longer act singly. If, however, the minor should die, or, on attaining puberty, should prove to be of unsound judgment, the other may continue to act singly, and the Judge cannot in this case force an associate on him because there is still an executor to the deceased appointed by himself. Further, whatever may have been done by the adult executor during the minority of the other cannot be undone by the latter on his attaining puberty, unless contrary to the nature and object of the trust.

An alien infidel cannot be appointed executor.

The appointment of an executor being for the education of the testator's children, for the protection of their interests and the due execution of the testator's last wishes, the law jealously provides against the appointment of an alien (non-Moslem) as executor.(2) According to all the schools, a Moslem cannot appoint a *harbi*, a non-Moslem subject of a hostile power, to be his executor whether such non-Moslem be a *Mustâmin*(3) or not. In case of such an appointment it is incumbent on the Kâzi to cancel it. The appointment of a *Zimmi*, a non-Moslem fellow-subject, stands on a different footing; for the Kâzi *may* set it aside. It follows, therefore, that whilst the appointment of a non-Moslem alien is void *ab initio*, the appointment of a *Zimmi* is valid unless set aside by the Judge. And this was the view enunciated by the Law Officers in two cases decided by the Sudder Court in 1825.

---

(1) *Fatâwai Alamgiri*, Vol. VI, p. 214; s. 8 of the Probate and Administration Act (V of 1881) declares that probate cannot be granted to a minor.

(2) "Because he is an enemy;" *Radd-ul-Muhtâr*. "An infidel cannot be lawfully appointed executor to a Moslem even though he be his relation by blood, but an infidel may be the executor to one like himself:" *Alamgiri*, Vol. VI, p. 214.

(3) A *Mustâmin* is a non-Moslem subject of a non-Moslem sovereign who has entered the country of Islâm under a guarantee of protection.

In *Moohummud Ameen-oodeen and another* v. *Moohummud Kubeer-oodeen* (the first of these cases), a Mussulman female had bequeathed the whole of her property to a stranger and had appointed a Hindu as the executor to her will. Upon a reference by the Judges of the Sudder Court to the *Kâzi-ul-Kuzzât* and the Law Officers of the Court, they pronounced, (*a*) if the testatrix left no heirs she was at liberty to bequeath the whole of her property; (*b*) if she had heirs, the bequest of more than one-third would depend on the consent of such heirs; and (*c*) though the appointment of other than a Moslem as executor to the will of a Moslem is lawful, yet it is incumbent on the Kâzi to eject him from being executor. "The reason why the appointment," added the Law Officers "though not perfectly correct is said to be legal is because his official acts are valid until he be ejected by the Kâzi. The appointment does not affect the validity of the will so far as relates to the right of the legatee."(1)

Moohummud Ameenooddeen and another v. *Moohummud Kubeerooddeen.*

The other case, *Henry Jarlach and another* v. *Mussumaut Zuhurunnissa Khanum*,(2) reiterates the same principle. The Kâzi is vested with this discretion, from an apprehension that a non-Moslem executor may interfere with the religion of his testator's children. That reason does not, however, seem to hold good under the present conditions of society. And, therefore, when a testator has expressly appointed a non-Moslem as his executor, the Judge would hardly be justified in removing him and placing in his stead a Moslem, unless, of course, the executor endeavours to tamper with the religion of his wards or educates them improperly, or against the directions of the testator, when the Judge would be bound to remove him, or to revoke the probate of the will. Until such removal, whether owing to such conduct, or because it is expedient he should be removed, his appointment remains valid and his administration is effectual.

Henry Jarlach and another v. *Mussumaut Zuhurunnissa Khanum.*

A Moslem husband married to a *Kitâbi* wife (*i.e.*, following one of the revealed religions), may lawfully appoint her his executrix and the guardian of her children.

---

(1) [1825], Sel. Rep. IV, pp. 49, 55.
(2) [1828], Sel. Rep. IV, p. 301; See also *Jehan Khan* v. *Mandy* [1868], 1 B. L. R. S. N., 16; s.c., 19 W. R., 185.

But though the appointment of a non-Moslem executor is valid unless set aside by the Judge, and until then he is the lawful guardian of the children of the testator, the Kâzi or Judge *cannot* appoint a non-Moslem as guardian to the children of a Moslem.

As already stated, if an executor labouring under the incapacity of difference of creed or minority or slavery attains, by conversion to Islâm, or emancipation, or by coming of age, the capacity required by law he would continue to be executor unless he has been removed already. But there is this difference between the acts of a minor-executor and those of a non-Moslem and a slave-executor that whilst the latter are valid, the former are absolutely invalid.(1)

The appointment by the will of a Mahommedan of a non-Moslem executor does not invalidate the will. All the acts of such an executor and his dealings with the property under the will, until he is removed and superseded by the Civil Court, are good and valid.(2)

When it appears to the Kâzi that the executor appointed by the testator is really unable to perform the work, or is weak and inefficient, he should appoint another administrator to act with or assist the executor; or, if the inability appears to be permanent, he may appoint another person in the place of the *wasî*, which would be tantamount to removing him from the office.(3)

If the executor should represent himself unable to perform the work imposed on him, the Judge should not admit his representation without an inquiry to ascertain the fact; but should it appear that he is really incompetent, the Judge should appoint another in his stead. Some jurists have held, that if the Kâzi were to remove an executor appointed by the testator who was fit for his duties, such removal would take effect, though the Kâzi may have, in doing so, acted unjustly and be guilty of committing a sin. In the *Ashbâh*, however, it is stated that there is a conflict of opinion on this point among the jurisconsults. Many of them, says

---

(1) *Radd-ul-Muhtâr*, Vol. V, p. 687.
(2) *Jehan Khan* v. *Mandy*, 1 B. L. R. S. N., 16; 10 W. R., 185.
(3) *Durr ul-Mukhtâr*, p. 838; *Radd-ul-Muhtâr*, Vol. V, p. 687

the *Sharh-Wahbânieh,* regard such an order of the Kâzi operative, but in the *Fusûlain* it is laid down that it is incumbent to hold such removal not to be valid, "though it is imperative [on the Judge] to remove the misfeasor and untrustworthy." The author then adds, "in the 27th section of the *Jâm'aa-ul-Fusûlain* it is stated, hat when the executor appointed by the deceased is a just man, it is not proper that he should be removed by the Kâzi; and if he does so, many jurisconsults have held that the removal will not take effect. In my opinion this is correct, for the testator is more bounteous to himself than the Judge, and the *Fatwa* should be in accordance with this view, for the Kâzis of the day are the cause of disputes." "All this relates to an executor appointed by the testator, for the Kâzi is entitled to remove an administrator appointed by him at any time, whenever he considers it expedient.(1)

"When an executor is an *amîn* (a person worthy of trust) able to dispose of property, the Judge is not to remove him from office. So also when the heirs complain of an executor to the Judge, he ought not to remove him without malversation, but when that is established he should remove him."

The Shiah Law.

The provisions of the Shiah Law regarding the qualifications requisite in an executor are analogous. It is requisite that an executor should be a person of understanding and a Moslem. Some jurists also require that he should be an *'aâdil* or just person, because a *fâsik* (dishonest person) is unworthy of trust. Whilst others consider this qualification as unnecessary, because all Moslems are trustworthy and because the executor is appointed by the testator. But the Judge is bound to remove one who, though trustworthy at the time of his appointment, proved to be otherwise after the death of the testator; for his appointment must be considered as nullified because the trust reposed in him by the testator was founded on a belief of his probity and would have been withdrawn on the confidence being found to be misplaced.(2)

It is not lawful to appoint another person's slave as an executor without the consent of the master. A person can lawfully

---

(1) *Fatâwai Alamgiri,* Vol. VI, p. 212.

(2) *Sharâya,* p. 253; Comp. the rules in the *Jâm'aa ush-Shittât.*

appoint his own slave an executor, if his children are minors, but not if they are adults.(1) Where an executor becomes permanently insane the Kâzi should appoint another in his place. If no such appointment is made and the executor recovers his reason, he remains as such.

Section II.

Appointment of Executors, how made.

The executor is termed *wasî* and is defined to be an *amîn* or trustee appointed by the testator to superintend, protect and take care of his property and children after his death. He is also his *Kâim-mukâm* or personal representative.(2)

There are three kinds of executors :(3)—The first is a trustee who is capable of performing the duty which has been committed to him by the testator and such an executor is fixed (*mukarrar*) and *cannot be removed by the Judge* without proved breach of trust.(4) The second is a trustworthy person but who is unable to do the work or who is weak and inefficient, with whom the Judge should associate another for assisting him. The third is a *fâsik*,(5) a non-Moslem or a bondsman [of another], whom it is proper that the Judge should remove and appoint another in his stead as is stated in the *Khazânat ul-Muftin*.(6) The word 'substitution' implies that the appointment is valid in the first instance, for otherwise there could be no removal.(7)

---

(1) *Radd-ul-Muhtâr*, Vol. V, p. 687.

(2) "It is not advisable to accept the office of an executor, for it is a perilous matter on account of what Abû Yusuf is reported to have said—'To enter upon an executorship for the first time is a mistake, for the second a fraud, and for the third, a theft;'" *Fatâwai Alamgiri*, Vol. VI, p. 211; *Radd-ul-Muhtâr*, Vol. V, p. 685. This extreme view is not adopted in practice.

(3) There is considerable difference in the position of the *wasî* under the Mahommedan Law and that of an executor under the English Law. The *wasî* is the *locum tenens* of the testator for the management and preservation of the deceased's property, but the legal estate does not vest in him. Comp. the provisions of the Probate Act (V of 1881).

(4) See *ante*, p. 553.

(5) A corrupt or untrustworthy person.

(6) *Fatâwai Alamgiri*, Vol. VI, p. 211.

(7) *Radd-ul-Muhtâr*, Vol. V, p. 687; *Durr ul-Mukhtâr*, p. 835.

Acceptance

As stated before, the testator may appoint any person (subject to the exceptions already mentioned) as his *wasî*, and the appointment will take effect upon the acceptance of the person so appointed. Such acceptance may be either by word or deed, *i.e.*, may be either express or implied, and may take place either in the testator's lifetime or after his death. Any dealing with the testator's property after his death amounts to acceptance.(1)

The person appointed is entitled to renounce the executorship or to refuse to accept it, and if he does so, the appointment does not take effect. When the appointment and the refusal take place in the presence of the parties, there is no difficulty. But when an executor is appointed in his absence, and on being informed of the appointment after the testator's death, says, 'I do not accept,' but subsequently says, 'I accept,' the acceptance is lawful, "unless the Judge had removed him from office before he expressed his acceptance."(2) But if he had expressed his refusal during the testator's lifetime and should, after his death, desire to accept the office, the acceptance would not be valid. Though, if he were merely silent in the presence of the testator instead of saying, 'I do not accept,' and should subsequently, either in the lifetime or after the death of the testator, express acceptance it would be lawful, whether made in the presence of the Judge or not, unless the Judge had previously to his saying so removed him from office, when his subsequent acceptance would not be valid.(3)

After the appointment has once been accepted or property dealt with, the executorship cannot be renounced without the sanction of the Judge.(4) In other words the executor can only obtain his discharge from the Judge. Mohammed has laid down in the *Jâm'aa-us-Saghîr* that when a person has been appointed an executor and has accepted the office in the testator's lifetime, the executorship is binding on the acceptor, so that if he should wish to withdraw from the office after the death of the testator, he is not at

(1) *Durr ul-Mukhtâr*, p. 834.

(2) *Ibid*, p. 835; *Fatâwai Alamgiri*, Vol. VI, p. 211.

(3) *Fatâwai Alamgiri*, Vol. VI, p. 211.

(4) *Radd-ul-Muhtâr*, Vol. V, p. 686; *Fatâwai Alamgiri*, Vol. VI, p. 212. It would seem, however, from what is stated in the *Ashbâh* that he may do so, if there is a provision to that effect in the will.

liberty to do so. But if he renounces in the lifetime of the testator and "before his face," the renunciation is valid, but if it is not made "before his face" it is not valid. What is meant by saying, "before his face," is with *his* knowledge, and "not before his face" is without his knowledge. This is according to the *Muhît.*(1) If an executor should accept in the presence of his testator, and the testator should say when he is absent, 'take witness that I have discharged him from the executorship,' the discharge is valid.(2) But if an executor should reject his appointment in the testator's absence (after he has once accepted), the rejection according to the Hanafîs is void.(3)

If he should say in the absence of the testator, 'I do not accept,' and should communicate his refusal to him either by letter or messenger, and after this should say 'I accept,' the acceptance would not be valid.

Shiah Law. The provisions of the Shiah Law are analogous. It is declared that an executor may lawfully reject his office while the testator is alive, provided that he is duly informed of the rejection; but if the testator should die before the rejection or after it, without the information having reached him, no effect can be given to the rejection, and it is incumbent on the executor to take upon himself the duties of the office.

If an executor is incapable of discharging the duties of his office, the Judge may appoint an assistant to him, but if he is guilty of fraud he must be displaced and another appointed in his stead.(4)

General doctrine. An appointment of an executor may be made in any terms which indicate the intention on the part of the testator to make him his *locum tenens* or *Kâim-mukâm* after his death. If a person were to say to another, "thou art my *wakîl* after my death," that would amount to the appointment of an executor.

Appointment of an executor. In the *Fatâwai Kâzi Khân*, the *Khulâsa* and other works, it is stated that if a person, were to say to another "I consign to you my children after my death," or "take care of my children after my death," or use any similar expression by which authority is given to another to do certain acts on behalf of the testator after

(1) *Fatâwai Alamgiri*, Vol. VI, p. 212.

(2) *Ibid*; *Radd-ul-Muhtâr*, Vol. V, p. 686.

(3) "It would be fraud on the testator to keep silent in his lifetime and then refuse;" *Radd-ul-Muhtâr*.

(4) *Sharâya-ul-Islâm*, p. 252.

his death, it would create an executorship. Ulal-w'aljih states that if a person were to say to some people, "do this for me after my death," that would constitute all of them as his executors. And if they all remain silent until after the death of the testator, when some of them only accept, these alone would be *wasis*. But if only one accepted, he will not be entitled to act as executor, until the Kâzi has associated another person with him in the administration of the testator's estate, for it was clearly the intention of the testator to confide the executorship to more than one person.(1)

An executor can be removed without his assent, and without his knowledge. This is different from the removal of an agent, who must be informed by his principal that he has been removed.

Generally speaking the powers and duties of executors in British India are now regulated by the provisions of the Probate and Administration Act (V of 1881), but as a Mahommeden executor is not bound to take out probate of the will, in order to entitle him to act, and as nuncupative wills are valid under the Mussulman Law, it is important to know its main principles on the subject.

The powers of several executors.

Under the recognised Hanafî rule when there are two executors one cannot act singly in the disposition of property. S. 92 of the Act, however, declares that "when there are several executors or administrators, the powers of all may, in the absence of any direction to the contrary in the will or grant of letters of administration, be exercised by any of them, who has proved the will or taken out administration." But as apparently the procedure laid down in the Act is applicable only to a will in writing, the Hanafî rule remains intact in such cases where probate is not taken out or the will cannot be proved under the provisions of the Act.

When a man has appointed two executors, "the act of any one of them acting singly," says the *Durr-ul-Mukhtâr*,(2) "is void like the act of two joint-*Mutwallis* acting singly, for two *Mutwallis* are like two executors [in their legal position] as is stated in the

---

(1) "A man addressing a number of persons says to them 'Do so after my death.' If they accept they all become executors, and if they remain silent till the testator's death and two or more of them accept, these become executors and may lawfully carry the will into execution. But if only one of them accepts though he is the executor he cannot lawfully carry the will into execution without bringing the matter before the Judge who may either appoint another [to act] with him or authorise him to act by himself;" *Fatâwai Alamgiri*, Vol. VI, pp. 218-219.

(2) P. 835.

The powers of one of two executors acting singly.

Ashbâh and in the *Kinia.*" The acts of one of two executors acting singly is void, although they may have been appointed separately by the testator; some jurists have said that each may act singly and Abû Lais has held this to be correct and that we adopt it." "But" goes on the *Durr-ul-Mukhtâr*, "in the *Mabsût* the first is stated to be the *correct* doctrine and it is relied upon in the *Durrar-*[*ul-Ahkâm*] and [in the work of] Kahastâni as most worthy of acceptance." "I say that the principle declaring the act of an executor or *Mutwalli* acting singly to be invalid is applicable to cases where the executors or the *Mutwallis* have been appointed by one testator or under one *Wakf* or by one Kâzi. Where, however, two executors or two *Mutwallis* have been appointed by two Kâzis of two different cities each will be competent to deal with the property lying within the jurisdiction of the Kâzi appointing him.............. "The act of one *wasî* acting singly is valid in the purchase of shrouds for the deceased for his funeral, the litigation of his rights, buying necessaries for his infant children, accepting donations for his infant children, emancipating specially designated bonds-people, return of deposits with the deceased, and the handing over to the legatees their specific legacies. And the *Sharh-i-Wahbâniéh* has added ten more matters, among these being, the return of things usurped by the deceased,(1) cancelling invalid sales, demanding debts to the testator and such like. So also in the sale of things likely to be lost, and to collect things that were being wasted.(2) Abû Yusuf states that an executor can act singly unless the testator has laid down that the two must act jointly; this is according to the *Sharh-i-Wahbâniéh:* should one executor die appointing his colleague or any other person his own *wasî*, the administration of such appointee will be valid and there will be no necessity on the part of the Kâzi to appoint another. But if the deceased executor has died without appointing any one, the Kâzi is bound to associate another with the surviving executor; this is according to the *Durrar-*[*ul-Ahkâm*]."(3)

---

(1) Evidently with the object of avoiding a judicial process.

(2) In the *Hedâya*, it is stated that one of the executors may act singly in the realisation of the testator's property but not in its disposal; *Hed.*, Vol. IV, p. 1043), though he may purchase shrouds and hire bearers, for carrying the body to the cemetery.

(3) Because as Zailye says, it was the intention of the testator that the administration of his estate should be in the hands of two persons. It is only when one executor dies appointing the other as his executor that the necessity of a second *wasî* is dispensed with; Tahtawi.

SECTION III.

POWERS AND DUTIES OF EXECUTORS.

Similarly it is stated in the *Fatâwai Alamgiri* that "when a man has entrusted the executorship to two persons, according to Abû Hanîfa and Mohammed, neither of them can act singly, and acts done by either of them singly are not operative without the sanction of his associate, except in the following matters such as the washing and shrouding of the deceased's body and its removal to the grave, the payment of debts out of assets of the same kind (*jins*) as the debts, the delivery of specific bequests, the restoration of deposits, or of things usurped by the deceased or acquired under invalid sales, the manumission of a specific slave. But they cannot act singly in taking possession of deposits belonging to him, nor in receiving payment of debts due to him, though they may in suing for his rights against people; in accepting a gift for a minor, sanctioning his acts, making partition of things weighable or measurable, and selling what is liable to spoil.(1) When the deceased has directed certain specified portions of his property to be bestowed in charities on beggars and indigent persons without particularising them, one executor cannot act separately from the other according to Abû Hanîfa and Mohammed, though he may do so according to Abû Yusuf, but if the objects of the charity are specified he may act alone according to them all. In what has been said it is supposed that the two executors have been appointed together at one and the same time, *lit.* in one sentence (*kalâm*). When one was appointed at one time and the other at another time, Shams-ul-Ulama Halwâni(1) has stated there is a difference of opinion among jurists, some holding that each of the executors may act separately, while others have declared that, according to Abû Hanîfa and Mohammed, they cannot act separately in any case in disposing of property, and this has been adopted by Shams-ul-Ulama as-Sarakhsi, according to the *Fatâwai Kâzi Khân*. If, however, the two executors are appointed with the express provision that either of them may act singly, or if the testator has declared that each of them is a complete executor (*wasî tâmm*) each one of them may act singly, according to the *Khazânat-ul-muftiin*.(1)

How far two executors jointly appointed can act separately.

---

(1) *Fatâwai Alamgiri*, Vol. VI, p. 214.

It will thus be seen that when there are two executors, the acts of any of them are void unless ratified by the other like the acts of one of two *mutwallis*. The result is, that if one of them gives a lease of *wakf* lands, it would not be valid until consented to by the other, even though the executors may have been appointed separately. This is the case when the two executors or administrators are appointed by the deceased or by one and the same Judge; but as the author of the *Durr ul-Mukhtâr* points out if the administrators have been appointed by two separate Kâzis, they can act separately, for as the Kâzis can act validly in their separate jurisdictions, the administrators, as their *naibs* or delegates, can also validly do so.

The ratification of the co-executor does not amount to a renewal of the contract, it only imparts the necessary validity which was originally wanting. If one *wasî* acts without the knowledge or the consent of the other, and any property is lost, the trustee or executor so acting will be liable to recoup the loss. One executor can appoint his co-executor his *wakîl* or delegate, in which case the acts of the co-executor by himself will be valid.

Abû Yusuf's opinion.

As already pointed out, Abû Yusuf thinks that when there are several *mutwallis* each can act singly. So according to him one of several executors can act validly in all matters. But according to Abû Hanîfa and Mohammed none of them can act by himself whether they have been appointed jointly or separately. The latter doctrine is recognised as the binding rule. Where, however, the testator has declared by his will that the executors may act jointly or severally, each may act singly according to all jurists.

Commenting on the passage already quoted from the *Durr ul-Mukhtâr*,(1) the author of the *Radd-ul-Muhtâr* makes the same statement. "But the acts of one executor singly, like the acts of any one *mutwalli*, will not be *bâtil* respecting the purchase of shrouds for the testator, his funeral,(2) in the litigation of his rights,(3) in the

(1) *Ante*, p. 665.

(2) "This exception is founded on the reason of necessity, for delay in these matters would lead to the corpse decomposing. And for this reason neighbours are authorised to take charge of the funeral of a deceased; and fellow-travellers of a person dying on the road."—*Radd-ul-Muhtâr*.

(3) "Because several do not join in litigation and when they join, only one pleads."—*Durrar* of Mulla Khusru.

purchase of necessaries for his children,(1) in the acceptance of gifts made to the testator, in the emancipation of specified slaves, in returning deposits (with the testator) and payment of specified legacies. In the *Sharh-i-Wahbânièh,* the following matters are included as being within the scope of an executor acting singly, *viz.*, he may lawfully return things acquired by the deceased by 'embezzlement,' or under an invalid sale; partition things which can be measured or weighed (perishable commodities); he may demand from the debtors of the deceased specified debts due to the testator, and pay the same."

The acts of a single-executor.

When there are two executors, and one of them is absent, the other executor can validly act by himself, if the absentee is at such a distance that no *kâfila* or caravan can reach him. Such an absence is technically called *ghîbat-i-munkat'aa.* The rule is founded on the necessity of two executors acting in consultation. When one is so far away or residing in such a place that no letter or news can either reach him or be received from him, the law regards him as non-existing for the time, and does away with the necessity of two executors acting together. And a single executor may validly sell any thing which it is feared may be lost.

Shiah Law—joint executors.

The Shiah Law is slightly different; it says that when two persons have been appointed in general terms or with an express condition that they are to act jointly, one of them cannot act singly without the other, and if either of them should do so, his

(1) "This also is founded on the reason of necessity, for otherwise the infants would suffer."

"Things deposited with the deceased must be returned by one executor, but the deposits of the deceased can be received by the two; this is the view of Saijani given in the *Hindiyèh* (*Alamgiri*)."

"This is the view of Ibn Shahna; but where something is to be sold in order to pay the legacy, it cannot be done without the consent of the co-executor."

Kâzi Khân adds that "one executor can lawfully take possession of any inheritance which might have devolved on the testator before his death, provided there is no debt attached to it; and of properties and deposits in the residence of the testator, to preserve them from loss or damage. He can also redeem pledges."

He can also, it would seem, make a partition of such things with the partner of the testator.

Though one executor may not grant a receipt or discharge for a debt due to the deceased, yet he may validly make a demand for it and prefer a suit for the same.

In the *Hedâya* these principles are set forth with considerable distinctness and may be studied with advantage.

acts would not be lawful, except such as are positively incumbent or necessary, as for instance, the providing of clothes and food for the infant children of the testator. And it is held to be incumbent on the Judge to compel them to act jointly, and when that is impracticable he may appoint others in stead of both. So when there are two executors, they cannot apportion the property between themselves for the purpose of separate management. If one of them should fall ill or become incapable of performing the duties of the office, the Judge must appoint an associate to the other who is competent, but this power cannot be exercised when one of them dies or becomes *disqualified*, for the remaining executor is empowered to act singly, and the Judge has no authority while there is an executor of the deceased surviving and competent to act.(1) If the testator has made it a condition that the executors are to act jointly and separately, in that case the acts of each singly are lawful. They may, also, lawfully divide the property between them and each take upon him the management of a part, in the same way as they might have acted separately before the partition.(2)

Hanafî Law; executors for a special purpose.

According to the Hanafî rule when two executors are appointed for two different purposes, *e.g.*, one for the payment of the testator's debts and the other for the administration of his estate, according to Abû Hanîfa and Abû Yusuf, both are general executors, competent to act in all matters; though Mohammed differs and holds that the authority of each is restricted to the purpose for which he is appointed. But where it is made an express condition that one executor shall not act in the matter to which the other is appointed, Mohammed ibn ul-Fazl states that, according to all opinions, the powers of each executor will be restricted within the limits laid down by the testator, and it is only where he has not made such a condition that there exists the difference of opinion above-mentioned, "the *Fatwa* being with Abû Hanîfa and Abû Yusuf."(3)

"If a person should appoint another as executor and direct him to act in conformity with the instructions of a third person, *e.g.*, "with the knowledge of so-and-so," the executor may act

---

(1) The author of the *Sharâya*, however, thinks this view is open to doubt.
(2) *Ibid.*
(3) *Fatâwai Alamgiri*, Vol. VI, p. 215.

without that third person's knowledge. But if he (the testator) had said "do not act without his knowledge," it would not be lawful for the executor to act without his knowledge, and the *Fatwa* is to that effect. Or if he were to say, "Act in accordance with the opinion of so-and-so," or "Do not act except with the opinion of so-and-so," in the first case the person addressed would be the executor, in the second they will be both executors according to the approved doctrine(1) (*'ala'l mukhtâr*) according to the *Khazânat-ul-Muftiin*. Abû Nasr has declared that if [the testator] says to another "Act in the matter with the orders of so-and-so," he [the person addressed] would be a special executor; while if he had said, "Do not act without his orders," both would be executors, and this seems most in accord with the doctrine of "our" masters according to the *Muhît*....When a man appoints one person his executor and another *mushrif* or supervisor over him, the first is the executor for dealing with the property, not the *mushrif*, the effect of whose appointment is that the executor cannot act without his knowledge according to the *Khazânat-ul-Muftiin*."(2)

Derivative executors.

When one of two executors dies, appointing his co-executor as his own executor, in that case the surviving executor can act singly in respect of the original testator. If the deceased executor appoints another person as his executor, such person will become associated with the surviving executor of the original testator, who will not be entitled to act alone. Where the deceased executor has appointed no executor for himself, the Kâzi should associate another person with the surviving executor, for it was the intention of the testator that the execution of his will should be entrusted to two persons. "This is stated in the *Durrar-ul-Ahkâm*."(3)

If one of two executors becomes insane or otherwise incapable, the Kâzi shall appoint a substitute for him, but he cannot assign the executorship to the co-executor. But if one of them turns out to be dishonest, the Kâzi may either associate another person or authorise that other to act by himself.

The executor of an executor, however removed, can act as the executor of the first testator. Shâfeï differs on this point.

---

(1) *Fatâwai Alamgiri*, Vol. VI, p. 218.
(2) *Ibid.*
(3) *Durr ul-Mukhtâr*, p. 836; *Fatâwai Alamgiri*, Vol. VI, p. 216.

With reference to the powers of a derivative executor, the doctrine is put by the *Radd-ul-Muhtâr* in four aspects. (*a*) Either the deceased executor, whilst appointing an executor, leaves his powers regarding the estate of the original testator, undefined, *e.g.*, he may only say, "I make so-and-so my *wasî*;" (*b*) defines his powers, *e.g.*, says, "I make so-and-so the *wasî* of my estate;" (*c*) or declares expressly "I make so-and-so the *wasî* of the estate of my *musi* (testator);" (*d*) or says "of both estates."

When the powers are left undefined or it is expressly declared that he is to be the executor of both estates, the executor of the deceased executor will, according to the majority of jurisconsults, become the executor of the original testator. On this point Shâfeï and Zuffar differ.(1)

Where it is simply declared that he is to be the executor of the estate of the deceased executor, Abû Hanîfa holds according to the most approved report that he would be the executor of both estates; whereas the Disciples, according to the most authentic account, have declared that his powers will be restricted to the estate of his own testator. And this seems to be the doctrine recognised as law. If the deceased executor said, "I constitute this person executor of the original testator," it would be so. "This is according to all the jurists as it is stated in the *Tâtâr-Khâniëh*, *Sharh-i-Tahtâwi* and other works of authority."

How far two executors jointly appointed can act separately.

In the *Fatawai Alamgiri*(2) the above principles are stated thus:—"When a man has appointed two executors and one of them dies, the survivor cannot, according to Abû Hanîfa and Mohammed, dispose of the property, but should lay the matter before the Judge, who, if he sees proper, may make him sole executor and transfer to him the power of disposal, or associate another with him in the place of the deceased. According to Abû Yusuf, however, the survivor can act alone, as he would have been while the other was alive. And this is one of three rules. The second is if a man appoints two executors and one of them accepts after the death of the testator and the other should not accept, the single executor is incompetent to act by himself according to Abû Hanîfa and Mohammed, while according to Abû Yusuf he is competent. The third is if one of two executors is *fâsik* (corrupt)

(1) *Durr ul-Mukhtâr*, p. 836, *Sharh-ul-Wikâya.*
(2) Pp. 215—216.

the Judge may authorise the other to act singly or may join another with him instead of the *fâsik*, in which case the just one could not act without the other according to Abû Hanîfa and Mohammed, while according to Abû Yusuf he could. . . . . . A person appoints two executors, one of whom dies, having first appointed his co-executor to be his executor. this is lawful, and the co-executor may dispose of the property of the first deceased, for as he could have done so with the sanction of his co-executor in his lifetime, so he can in like manner do so after his death. There is another report, however, against the legality of the disposal, but the first is correct.''

Shiah doctrines.

According to the Shiah doctrines, an executor cannot entrust the management of his testator's property to his own executor, *without the power having been reserved to him.* When an executor has his testator's authority for bequeathing the management of the estate at his own death, he may lawfully do so by consensus. When the testator has left no express direction, the executor has no power according to the approved doctrine to entrust the administration of the estate to another person. Thus when there is no provision in the original testator's will, the superintendence of his estate, upon the death of the executor, devolves upon the Judge. In like manner, if a person should die without appointing an executor, the superintendence and care of his estate belongs to the Judge. "And if there is no Judge present on the spot, any true believer in whom confidence can be placed may lawfully assume the care and management of the estate, though there is doubt and difference of opinion on this point.''

Hanafî doctrine.

When there is an executor appointed by the testator, the Kâzi cannot appoint an administrator unless the executor is absent, such absence amounting to a *ghibat-i-munkat'aa ;* this is stated in the commentaries of Mufti Abû S'aûd.

Claims against the estate.

If a person were to prefer a claim against the estate of the deceased and the executor be absent, the Kâzi would appoint a person as defendant to represent the testator. If the executor is present and consents to the debt, the Kâzi may, at his discretion, appoint another person to represent the testator, so that the plaintiff may properly prove his claim against him. For the acknowledgment of the *wasî* is not valid against the testator, and the plaintiff cannot recover a decree against the estate of the deceased by the mere consent of the executor. This, however, does not mean that, in every instance, the executor must insist on the claim being established in a Court of Justice. What is meant is that the mere acknowledgment of the executor is not sufficient to establish a claim against an estate; and he cannot make any payment unless satisfied upon proof that the claim is just and well founded.

Where the property of an infant child is managed by the father, who wastes it, the Kâzi can take it away from his hands and place it in the hands of a curator to act as a *wasî*.

NOTE.

"If a man appoint two executors, neither of them is entitled, according to Abû Hanîfa and Mohammed, to act without the other, except in particular cases, of which an explanation shall be hereafter given. Abû Yusuf is of opinion that in all cases either of them may act without the other, because an executor is endowed with his power of action in virtue of the will of the testator; and as power of action is a thing sanctioned by the law, and incapable of division, he enjoys his power complete and perfect in the same manner as a complete authority to contract their infant sister in marriage appertains to each of her brothers respectively. (The ground of this is that executorship is a succession, which succession cannot be established in the executor, unless the authority of the testator devolves to him in the same degree in which it had appertained to the testator, that is, completely and perfectly). The testator's choice, moreover, of the two to be his executors is an argument of the particular attachment of each to his interest, which attachment is equivalent to the consanguinity of two brothers in the point of contracting their infant sister in marriage. The argument of Abû Hanîfa in support of his opinion are twofold. First, the power of an executor being derived from the testator is of consequence to be exercised in the manner prescribed by him: and in the case in question the testator has entrusted this power to both the executors on the condition of their being united in the trust, for he does not expressly assent to their acting otherwise than jointly, and the above condition is moreover attended with advantage, as the deliberations of two persons are better than of one. It is otherwise with two brothers, in the circumstance of contracting their infant sister in marriage [as adduced by Abû Yusuf], since the cause of such authority being vested in them is relationship a cause which exists equally in each. The contracting in marriage, moreover, is a right of the infant, resting upon her guardian [insomuch that if the infant require her guardian to contract her to any person being her equal for whom she has a liking, he must comply], whereas, in the case here considered, the acting (with the estate) is the right of the executor himself, not of another resting upon him. In the case of contracting the infant in marriage, therefore, if one of the two brothers so contract her, he merely discharges a duty incumbent on the other brother and his act is therefore valid, whereas in the case of executorship if one of the two act alone, he exercises a right appertaining to the other and his so doing is therefore invalid—in the same manner as where two persons owe a sum of money to one, in which case it would be perfectly lawful for either of them to discharge the whole debt, whereas supposing one man to owe a sum of money to two others, it would not be lawful for him to pay the whole to either of them."

"The cases excepted by Abû Hanîfa and Mohammed in which they hold the acts of either executor, singly, to be valid, are such as require immediate execution. Thus, it is lawful for either executor singly to disburse the funeral charges, as a delay in this might occasion the body to become offensive, whence it is that a similar power is vested in the neighbours. In the same manner either of the executors singly may purchase victuals or clothes for the infant children of the testator, this being a matter of urgency and which admits of no delay."—*Hedâya*, Chapter on Wills.

"So, likewise, it is lawful for either of the executors to restore an usurped article, or deposit or a thing purchased by the testator under an invalid contract. In preserving the estate of the testator also, and in discharging his debts, the act of either executor is lawful independent of the other. For none of these are considered as an exercise of power but merely the performance of a duty, insomuch that the depositor has himself a right to seize and carry away his deposit, if he find it among the effects of the deceased, and the creditor has a similar right with regard to his debt, and it is moreover the duty of every one into whose hands property may fall to attend to the preservation of it, whence this comes under the description of aid and assistance not of an exercise of power—neither do any of these acts require thought or consideration. Either of the executors has also a right singly to discharge a legacy or emancipate a slave, if directed by the testator, because such deeds require no thought or consideration."

"In the same manner, either of them may institute a suit in claim of the rights of the testator, because a conjunction of both in so doing would be impracticable, since, if they were to do it at one and the same time in the assembly of the Kâzi, they must occasion noise and confusion (whence it is that only one of two agents for litigation is allowed to plead at a time). The acceptance of a gift for an infant is likewise an act which either may perform singly, for in case of delay there is a possibility of the gift being rendered null by the death of the donor previous to delivery of possession. These acts, moreover, being permitted to a mother and nurse is a proof that they are not exertions of power. It is likewise permitted to any of the executors singly to sell goods where there is an apprehension of their spoiling as in the case of fruit and the like, and also to collect together and preserve the scattered property of the testator as a delay might occasion the destruction of it, and such permission is, moreover, given to every person into whose hands property may fall whence it may be inferred that this is not an exertion of power. [It is recorded in the *Jâm'aa-us-Saghîr* that none of the executors, where there are more than one, has singly the power of selling goods or receiving payment of debts because these are exercises of power which they must perform jointly in conformity with the will and intention of the testator."]

"If a person appoint two executors in a separate manner, as if he should first say to the one, 'I have appointed you my executor,' and again at a different period to the other, 'I have appointed you my executor,' some allege that in this case each of them has individually a power of exercising the functions of the appointment without consulting the other, in the same manner as two agents where they are appointed by different commissions—the reason of which is, that the testator, in appointing the two separately, indicates his assent to each acting from his own judgment without the other's assistance or advice. Others again say, that concerning this case a disagreement subsists between Abû Hanîfa and Mohammed on one side and Abû Yusuf on the other, because a will is not established until the death of the testator, and at that time both are executors together, notwithstanding they had been appointed separately. It is otherwise with two agents appointed under different commissions, for the appointment of each of those still continues distinct and separate as settled by the constituent."

"If one of two executors die, it is incumbent on the Kâzi to appoint another in his room. This is the opinion of Abû Hanîfa and Mohammed, because according to their doctrine the remaining executor has not of himself power to act on every occasion and the interest of the deceased, therefore requires the appointment of another to operate with him, and it is also the opinion of Abû Yusuf, because, although the remaining executor be (according to him) empowered to act of himself, still it behoves the Kâzi to appoint another his companion, for the design of the testator evidently was to leave two successors for the management of his concerns, and as this may be fulfilled by the appointment of a substitute for him who dies, one must be appointed accordingly."—*Hedâya*, IV, Bk. LII, Ch. VII, pp. 543-546.

SECTION IV.

THE POWERS AND DUTIES OF THE EXECUTORS, (Contd.)

The powers of an executor in the Mahommedan system are governed by rules closely analogous to those under the English Law. But there are points of difference which require careful attention.

When an executor may sell.

When the heirs of the testator are minors, the powers of the executor are, within certain limits, absolute. In case of necessity, he has the power of selling the property and investing the proceeds, after discharging any debts of the testator or those incurred in the maintenance of his infant children, in other and more profitable kinds of property. The sale, however, must be for an adequate consideration, "such as is reasonable among people of business."(1) The executor cannot sell the property to himself or to any relative of his, whose evidence, under the Mahommedan Law, would be inadmissible against him.(2) He can enter into a partition with the co-sharers of the deceased or the legatee, in respect of the minor's shares in all kinds of property, both movable and immovable, "even with a *slight* inadequacy in the terms (*ghubn-i-yasîr*)." A partition, however, where the inadequacy "is manifest or glaring, (*fâhish*)" *i.e.*, great, is ineffective.

Dealing with the powers of an executor, the *Durr-ul-Mukhtâr* says "It is lawful for the executor to sell other than immovable property against an absent adult heir, to pay the debts (of the testator); even the sale of immovable is valid if there is imminent

---

(1) *Durr-ul-Mukhtâr*, p. 837.
(2) *Ibid*; *Fatâwai Alamgiri*, Vol. VI, p. 220.

danger of its being lost; so has stated 'Uzmi-Zâdêh, referring to the *Khanièh* (the *Fatâwai Kâzi Khan*). I say, as is stated by Zailye and Kahastâni, that the more correct doctrine is, that the sale of immovable property is not valid as its becoming lost is extremely improbable (*lit.* rare)." But says Tahtâwi in his commentary on the *Durr-ul-Mukhtâr* "If the deceased dies heavily involved in debt, then by *consensus* a sale of immovable property is valid." And the *Durr-ul-Mukhtâr* proceeds to add—"When the testator's heirs are minors, a sale of his immovable property by the executor is valid to some person other than himself at double its value or for the maintenance of the infants or for the discharge of the debts of the deceased, or for the payment of specific legacies which cannot be given effect to in any other way or where the income does not exceed the cost of its up-keep (*maunat*) or where this risk of its becoming waste or destroyed or where it is in the hands of a *muta-ghallab* (powerful misappropriator). This is the substance of what is stated in the *Durrar* and the *Ashbah*." "I," proceeds the author of the *Durr-ul-Mukhtâr*, "say that the power of sale given to the executor in these cases does not belong to the executor appointed by a mother or brother, for such an executor has no power at all (مطلقا) to dispose of the immovable property of a minor. And he cannot purchase anything for the minor excepting food and clothes (*i.e.*, necessaries)." According to Ibn-i-Kamâl,(1) the father has the power, in such cases to sell the immovable property of the minor provided he is a man who bears a good character among people or nothing is known against him."

The powers of a *wasî* appointed by the mother.

It will be noticed from the above statement that the powers of an executor or guardian appointed by a mother or any other relation, such as the brother or uncle, are very limited. He has no authority to deal with the immovable property of his ward under any circumstance, nor with any property inherited by the minors from any person other than their mother. If he is the mother's executor he can only deal with movable property inherited by them from her, or enter on their behalf into a partition in respect thereof,

---

(1) The author of the *Fath-ul-Kadir*.

provided the father be not alive, and there be no executor appointed by him.(1)

The same rule is enunciated in the *Fatâwai Alamgiri*, the authority quoted being the *Fatâwai Kâzi Khan*. After stating that the executor of the father is in the position of the father, and the executor of the father's father (*jadd*) is in the position of the father's executor, it goes on to say "but the executor of the mother or of the brother [do not come within that category]; and if the mother dies leaving infant children or a brother dies leaving infant brothers or sisters, it is lawful for her or his executor to sell anything of the inheritance of the deceased except immovable property, but he has no power to sell the *'akâr;* nor *such* executor can buy anything for the infants save food and raiments and necessaries.

When an executor may partition.

When *all* the heirs are minors, the allotment by the executor of the legatee's share, and the retention by him of the residue for the heirs, is valid and effective. And in case any portion of their share is lost in the hands of the executor, the minors have no right to be recouped either by the legatee, or by the executor, unless it is occasioned by his wilful neglect or default. But when some of the heirs are adult and *absent*, the executor can lawfully enter into a partition on their behalf with the legatee in everything except *'akâr or what is immovable*, and to hold the shares of the minors for them. If all the heirs are adult or some of them are *adult* and *present*, any partition made by him is void against those heirs who are adult, both with respect to movable and immovable property. But if the heirs, though *sui juris*, are *absent*, the partition affected by the executor is inoperative so far as the immovable property is concerned, in other words, if the heirs are adult but not present, a partition of movable property alone made by the executor with the legatee is valid.

Specific bequests.

When the testator has left specific bequests to individuals, a division of the property by the executor among the heirs, in the absence of the legatees, is not effective; and in case the share or shares allotted to the legatees should perish, they would be entitled

(1) The limitations on the powers of executors appointed by any person other than the father are set out at considerable length in the *Fatâwai Alamgiri*, Vol. VI, p. 223.

to claim a share to the extent of a third of the estate from the shares given to the heirs.(1)

But when the partition is effected by the Judge, and the portion allotted by him to the legatee is held in his custody, the division is valid, and if the legatee's portion should perish in the hands of the Judge or the curator appointed by him, the legatee would have no right of recourse against the heirs, neither would the Judge be responsible.(2) "This rule applies, however, only to those things which can be *weighed or measured*—a partition of which is, in fact, a division. But with respect to things that are not so, a partition would in effect amount to a mutual exchange, like a sale, and, consequently, would be unlawful, for it is not lawful to sell another person's property."(3) "And when the Judge has appointed a guardian (*wasî*) for an orphan *in all things*,(4) and he has made a partition on his behalf, whether of movable or immovable things, the partition is lawful, but if the appointment is only for a special purpose, as for the maintenance of the orphan or the conservation of his property, the partition is not lawful."

Partition by an executor.

When an executor makes a partition *among* the heirs, who are all minors,(5) the partition is unlawful. If they are all adults, but some of them are absent,(6) and a partition is made with those who are present and their shares separated from the mass, the partition is lawful with respect to *chattels* (*matâ'a*) but not as regards immovable property.(7) If there are both minor and adult heirs, but the adults are absent, the partition is unlawful. If the adults are present and their share is given up to them and the shares of the minors separated from the shares of the adult heirs, and kept *in a mass without partition among the individual minors*, the division is lawful. When the share of each minor or adult is separated from the rest, the whole partition is invalid. But if the portion of

(1) "The legatees can claim also against the executor, according to Zailye. All this when a partition is made without leave of the Kâzi."—*Radd.*

(2) *Radd-ul-Muhtâr*, Vol. V, p. 692; *Fatâwai Alamgiri*, Vol. VI, p. 220.

(3) *Fatâwai Alamgiri*, Vol. VI, p. 220.

(4) *i.e.*, with general powers.

(5) "An executor cannot make a partition of the shares of the minors among themselves."—*Radd.* See also the *Fatâwai Alamgiri*, Vol. VI, p. 221.

(6) "If the heirs are absent at three days' journey or more; this is according to Kahastâni." The distance must in every case be such that it is difficult to communicate without delay.

(7) *Fatâwai Alamgiri*, Vol. VI, p. 222.

the adults is surrendered to them, and the portion of the minors retained, and subsequently on their attaining majority, divided among them, the partition, as between the adults and the minors is valid.

When the testator has left a direction in the will empowering the executor to sell his property and invest the proceeds in any other kind of property, the executor can lawfully do so.

Debts contracted by the executor.

When the executor contracts a debt on behalf of the minor without any necessity therefor, it will not be operative against the minor, and if any loss accrues to the orphan therefrom the executor will be liable.

Power of sale by an executor.

"When an executor appointed by the father sells anything belonging to his estate the legality of his act presents itself in two aspects :—

Ancient views.

"The *first* is, when the deceased has left neither debts nor legacies ; the *second* is, when he has died either leaving debts or legacies. With regard to the *first* it is stated in the 'Book' [the *Mukhtasar-ul-Kudûri*] that when the heirs are all minors, he can sell anything belonging to the estate out of chattels (*matâ'a*), furniture and *'akâr*, but the sale of anything other than *'akâr* is dependent upon its protection and the preservation of its price. Similarly as to the sale of *'akâr*. Shams-ul-aïmma Halwâni, however, has said that, what is stated in 'the Book,' was the opinion of the ancients ; this is according to the *Fatâwai Kâzi Khan ;* but that, according to the moderns, sale of the *'akâr* of a minor is lawful only when there are debts left by the deceased which cannot be discharged otherwise than by the price of the *'akâr* or when, *if the minor has need for the price thereof*, or a purchaser is eager to obtain it by giving double its value, and on this is the *fatwa*, according to the *Kâfi*. Or when there is a specific legacy which cannot be given effect to without the price of the *'akar*, or when its sale is to the benefit of the orphan as when its tax (*kharâj*) has to be paid, or when the expenses for its upkeep exceeds its income, or when being a shop or a house it is becoming dilapidated. When a necessity arises for the minor to pay the *kharâj*, and there is belonging to the estate other property (*'arûz*)(1) besides *'akâr*, that pro-

(1) *Arûz* also means "property not being lands, houses or money."

perty is first to be applied towards its payment, and if that is not sufficient the *'akâr may then be sold* for its proper value, or a price not much less than its value, but it is not lawful for the executor to sell it at a greater depreciation than is common among people in such cases. And, in like manner, an executor cannot lawfully purchase for a minor anything at a price much above its value.''

Modern doctrines. Rule now prevailing.

In the *Radd-ul-Muhtâr* the principle is stated more explicitly, the substance of which is as follows :—The ancients held that an executor could sell the immovable property of the minors according to his discretion, but modern jurists have imposed restrictions on the power of sale possessed by the executor, in the case of immovable property belonging to his minor wards. These restrictions are specified in the *Fatâwai Kâzi Khan*, and Zailye states that Sadr-ush-Shâhîd has declared the *Fatwa* is according to the modern view. (1) These restrictions are as follow :—(*a*) if the testator has died leaving debts, and it is necessary to sell a portion of the property to discharge such debts, *i.e.*, the debts cannot be paid off without selling some portion of the immovable property, he may lawfully do so for adequate value ; (*b*) if the testator has directed the payment of legacies in money and he has left no cash out of which such legacies can be paid, the executor can sell a portion of the immovable property sufficient to pay off such legacy ; (*c*) if there is a reasonable apprehension of the property being lost by decay or dilapidation, like a house falling into ruin, etc.; (*d*) when the property is in the possession of an usurper, and there is no prospect of its being recovered ; (*e*) when the expenses connected with the management or preservation of the property exceed the income ; (*f*) when it is necessary to pay the royal taxes, and there are no funds wherewith to pay them ; (*g*) when the price offered for the property is double its real value, *i.e.*, considerably higher.

The executor can lawfully sell to any person other than himself any movable property belonging to his minor wards or purchase for them any property from such persons, *but it must be for the consideration usually current in transactions of that kind.* If the sale or purchase is for an inadequate consideration, it is not valid and can be set aside, and the executor would be liable.

---

(1) *Radd-ul-Muhtâr*, Vol. V, p. 696.

An administrator or guardian (*wasî*) appointed by the Kâzi cannot purchase anything belonging to his minor wards, nor can he sell to them anything belonging to himself; but where an executor appointed by the father of the minors enters into such a transaction, it is valid, according to Abû Hanîfa, if it is to the *manifest* advantage of the minor. The Disciples hold the transaction to be invalid and decrees are passed according to their opinion.

"When an executor," says the *Fatâwai Alamgiri*, "sells the orphan's property to himself, or his own to the orphan, the sale is lawful according to Abû Hanîfa, and according to Abû Yusuf also by one report, when the sale is to the manifest benefit of the orphan though unlawful when it is not to his manifest benefit. According to Mohammed and Abû Yusuf by another and more probable report such a sale is unlawful under any circumstances."(1)

According to some jurists, the father may sell his infant children's property, provided he is an *amîn* or a person worthy of trust, and the sale is to their *manifest* advantage. "But where the father is an untrustworthy person, the minor, on attaining majority, can set aside the sale, unless it was for double the real value of the property, and the *Fatwa* is according to this doctrine. And Hamâwi has stated in his commentaries on the *Ashbâh*, that a father has no greater power than an executor, and his powers are subjected to the same restrictions. Hanouti has also passed *Fatwas* according to this view. All this applies to the sale of immovable property. With respect to movable property, the father [if *de facto* guardian] can sell an infant's goods for the current price, if it is to the advantage of the minor and even with a slight inadequacy, but such inadequacy must not in any case be great, otherwise the sale would be invalid."(2)

The powers of the executor. "An executor," says the *Fatâwai Alamgiri*, "may give out the property of a minor in *muzâribat*,(3) and may enter into a

(1) *Fatâwai Alamgiri*, Vol. VI, p. 222; see also p. 230.

(2) *Radd-ul-Muhtâr*, Vol. V, p. 696 et *seq.*

(3) It means a contract of partnership in which one person supplies the capital, whilst the other is the working partner, with a share in the profits. Where land is let out for cultivation, on the condition that the person cultivating should give a share of the crops to the owner, it is also *Muzâribat*.

partnership with another in respect of it according to the *Muhît*(1).... If the executor gives a long lease (*ijârat-ut-tawîla*) of part of the estate for the payment of the deceased's debts it would not be lawful.... He has no power to lend to another the property of the orphan, according to all authorities (consensus of opinions or reports) says the *Muhît*, and if he should do so he would be responsible. *Neither has the Judge the power to do so.*" With regard to the power of the father there is a difference of opinion among the jurists. The correct doctrine is that the father is in the position of the executor and not of the Kâzi.(2) "If an executor or a father were to pledge the property of an orphan for his own debt, the pledge ought not by analogy to be lawful, but it is so on *istehsân* (a liberal construction of the law). But it is not lawful for the executor to pay his own debt with the property of the orphan. If [however] a father should do so it would be lawful..... And if an executor were to sell the orphan's property in exchange for his own debt to his creditor it would be lawful(3) according to Abû Hanîfa and Mohammed and the price becomes a set-off against his debt, but he is responsible to the minor according to the *Muhît*."

Doctrine of Abû Yusuf —the recognised law.

This opens up such a serious question regarding the powers of a father, or an executor, to give in pledge the property of a minor, that I think it advisable to give here a translation from the *Fatâwai Kâzi Khân*, on the authority of which the passage in question purports to be founded, as it will show that the rule in force is in accordance with the opinions of Abû Yusuf, who held such dealings to be unlawful. "The *wasî* (executor) is not entitled to lend out the property of the orphan; and if he does so, he will be liable. The Kâzi, however, has the authority to lend. With regard to the father, there is difference among the jurists..... *The correct doctrine is that the father is like the executor and not like the Kâzi.* If the executor borrows himself the property of the minor, it is not lawful and it will be a *dain* (debt) upon him. It is reported from Mohammed that, according to Abû Hanîfa, the *wasî* has no authority to borrow from the property of the minor; but Mohammed expresses a hope that if the *wasî* does so

(1) *Fatâwai Alamgiri*, Vol. VI, p. 227.
(2) *Ibid*, p. 228.
(3) So far as the buyer is concerned.

when he is able to repay, his act may not be reprehensible. If the *wasî* or father pledge the property of the minor for his (the *wasî's* or father's) own debt, according to *kyâs* (analogy), it would not be valid; but according to *istehsân* (a liberal construction) it would be valid. *And it is stated from Abû Yusuf that he has adopted the (doctrine of) kyâs* (analogy) [in other words that he holds it to be illegal]. If the *wasî* discharges his own personal debt from the property of the minor, it will not be valid; if the father does so, it will be valid, for the *wasî* has no power to buy the property of the minor for himself according to current price, but the father can lawfully make such a purchase. And a pledge is like the payment of a debt; and [accordingly] the father may discharge his personal debt from the property of the minor, but it will not be lawful for the *wasî* to do so. And the same is the case with a pledge. And in the *Jâm'aa-us-Saghîr* it is stated, that when the father pledges the property of his minor child for his own debt, and the value of the property pledged is greater than the debt, and the property is lost or destroyed in the hands of the pledgee, the father will be liable for the amount of debt [which he has paid off] and not for the price of the article. But Shams-ul-Aïmma Sarakhsi has held, that the father and *wasî* will be equally liable for the value of the property pledged. *According to Abû Yusuf, as neither the father nor the wasî are entitled to pay their debts with the property of the minor, so they are not entitled to pledge his property for their debts. And Bashr ibn-i-Walîd has stated that the father has no power to pledge the property of his child for his own personal debt.* It is generally accepted that according to [the letter of] the law the father or *wasî* can pledge; but according to *kyâs* (analogical reasoning) they cannot, and when the property pledged is lost or destroyed, they are both liable for its value."

Abû Yusuf's rule the accepted doctrine.

"If the *wasî* (executor) sells the estate for the payment of the deceased's debts, which do not cover the entire estate, according to Abû Hanîfa, the sale is lawful, but it is not so according to the Disciples. If there is no debt due from the inheritance, and the heirs are minors, and the Kâzi sells the entire estate, according to Abû Hanîfa, the sale will take effect. Abû Hanîfa has drawn a distinction between the [powers of the] *wasî* of the deceased and of his father. The *wasî* has the power of selling the inheritance for paying the deceased's debts, and to give operation to his legacies.

But the father of the deceased, that is, the grandfather of the minors can sell the inheritance *for* his own son but he is not empowered to sell the estate for the payment of the debts due from the minor children on behalf of his son [*i.e.*, their father].''(1)

Shams-ul-Aïmma al-Halwâni states this as the doctrine laid down by Khassâf. But Mohammed has placed the grandfather in the position of the father. In ''the Book'' (*i.e.*, the *Mukhtasar-ul-Kudûri*), it is stated that when a person dies leaving a father and an executor, the executor is preferred to the father. If there is no executor, the father is preferred [for the administration of the deceased's estate] and so on in order, until the grandfather's executor, after whom comes the *wasî* or administrator appointed by the Kâzi. Shams-ul-Aïmma al-Halwâni has stated that ''the *Fatwa* is according to the doctrine laid down by Khassâf.''(2)

''If the father of a minor, who has inherited property, is a spendthrift and likely to commit waste, so as to be liable to inhibition, he is not entitled to the guardianship of his child's property.''

Administrator appointed by the Kâzi.

''Shams-ul-Aïmma al-Halwâni has stated in his *Sharh* (gloss) on the *Adâb-ul-Kâzi* [of Abû Yusuf] that when a Kâzi appoints a *wasî* (guardian or administrator) for an orphan, the *wasî* so appointed will be like the *wasî* appointed by the father, if the Kâzi appointed him in a general manner in all matters. But if he has been appointed in any special matter, he will be a *wasî* for that matter alone. This is not the case with the *wasî* appointed by the father......When the *wasî* appointed by the deceased is a just and qualified person (عدلا كافی) it is not advisable for the Kâzi (لا ينبغی) to remove him, but if he is not 'just,' he should remove him and appoint another. And if he is just but is not thoroughly efficient (لوكان عدل غيركافی), the Kâzi cannot remove him, but should join with him a competent administrator. If the Kâzi, however, were to remove him, he will be removed, and, similarly, if the Kâzi were to remove one who is both just and competent, it has the effect of removing him. So it has been stated by the Shaikh-ul-Imâm, known as Khâher-Zâdeh. But several jurists aver that the order of the Kâzi removing a just and competent *wasî* has no effect, for

(1) *Fatâwai Alamgiri* Vol. VI, p. 228. (2) *Fatâwai Kâzi Khân*, Vol. IV, p. 426.

he derives his authority from the deceased, and, therefore, he is to be preferred to the *wasî* of the Kâzi. And Kudûri has stated that the Kâzi has no power to remove the *wasî* appointed by the deceased or join another with him, unless he has committed a breach trust of or is a *fâsik* so as to be known as a bad man, (لو كان فاسقا معروفا بالشر). In such a case the Kâzi can remove him and appoint another in his stead, or if he is a virtuous man but inefficient [in his work], the Kâzi can associate another person with him. So it is stated also in the *Asl* and its *Sharh* by Tahâwi. But it is not mentioned whether, if the Kâzi does remove a just and competent *wasî*, it will take effect or not.(1) Shaikh Imâm Abû Bakr Mohammed ibn-ul-Fazl says that when the *wasî* is unable to carry out the disposition of the testator, he ought to be removed.''......

''The *wasî* is empowered to do all acts from which benefit may accrue to the orphan, so is the father.''

Powers of the executor.

The executor cannot trade with the goods of the infant on his own account, but, according to the *Durrar*, he can do so for the orphan, if it is to the latter's advantage. If the executor should engage in trade with the property of his minor ward, the profits derived therefrom should, according to some jurists, be given in *sadakah* or charity, and the money so employed recouped to the estate of the minor. According to Abû Yusuf, the profits made in such trade would belong to the minor, and Kâzi Khân declares the *Fatwa* is according to this view. But the Kâzi can authorise the executor to trade for the infant with his goods or enter into partnership with another.

Executor cannot mortgage without leave of the Judge.

The executor can, if it is to the advantage of the infant and there is a need for it, let out the infant's property on hire, but he cannot create a mortgage *without the leave of the Kâzi*. He is authorised, however, to pledge or sell chattels, if it is necessary for the maintenance of the infant children of the testator.

If the executor sells the goods on credit, the period for which credit is given must be the customary period. But where it is to the disadvantage of the infant or the period for which credit is given is either too long or not customary, according to Ramli the transaction will not be valid.

---

(1) The *Radd-ul-Muhtâr* is explicit on this point, that it does not take effect.

Where there are two infants under the guardianship of two separate executors, the sale of the goods of one infant by his guardian to the other is stated by Kâzi Khân not to be lawful. And this view is accepted in the *Fatâwai Alamgiri.*(1) The correctness of this principle has been questioned in the *Radd-ul-Muhtâr*, where it is laid down that there is no reason to render such a sale invalid, "for," the author adds, "the dealing by the executor is not for himself, and the sale of a particular property on behalf of one infant may be as much advantageous to him as its purchase by the other."

The executor is liable for any serious inadequacy in the consideration of any property sold or purchased on behalf of the infant.

The executor must not spend at the funeral of the testator more than is customary.

When an infant has not attained discretion, and the executor has made over the property to him and it is lost, the executor is liable. Discretion (*rushd*) means the capacity to take care of one's property. Abû Hanîfa holds that an executor should not make over the property until the ward has attained his 25th year. But the Disciples are of opinion that discretion should be presumed when the infant attains majority, but the presumption may be rebutted by proof of the fact that he is weak in intellect or unqualified to take proper care of his property.

When the testator devises one-third of his estate to be disposed of according to the *joint* discretion of his executors,(2)—and if one of them dies before the exercise of that discretion, "the third will be returned to the heirs."

When the heirs are all *sui juris* and present, the executor can not sell any portion of the estate except under their authority. In case they are absent, he can only sell the chattels belonging to the estate, but not the *'akâr* or immovable property. He may, however, should there be any necessity for it, lease the immovable estate. The reason of this restriction is founded on the principle

(1) "And when an executor of two orphans sells the property of one of them to the other, the sale is unlawful. So, also, when he authorises them to enter into such a transaction with each other and one accordingly sells his property to the other, the sale is unlawful."—*Alamgiri*, Vol. VI, p. 228.

(2) *Lit.*, to do whatever they together like with it.

that an executor has the power of preservation over the property of an absent person, and as it may be necessary to dispose of the movables which may be likely to be wasted, the executor has the power to do so and realise for the absentee the price of such goods. But *'akâr* or immovable property is secure in itself, and the executor has no authority to part with it, *except in the case of its falling into decay*, and in that case it may also be sold. When all the heirs are adult and one of them is *absent*, while the others are present, the executor may, by general consensus, sell the share of the absentee in all that is not *'akâr* and hold the proceeds for the absent heir. According to Abû Hanîfa, the *wasî* may also sell the shares of those who are present; but, according to the Disciples, he has no such power and a sale by him of their shares is illegal and this is the accepted doctrine.

Powers of the executor—contd.

All this refers to cases where the testator has left no debts nor legacies. But if there are debts and they cover the whole of the estate, the executor may sell the whole by consensus; and when the debts do not cover the whole estate, he may sell as much of it as may be necessary for the payment of such debts. When, however, an executor has actually sold *'akâr* or immovable property in good faith for the payment of debts while he has other property in his hands sufficient for that purpose, the sale is lawful.(1) Similarly there are general legacies, the executor may sell as much of property as may be necessary for their liquidation (not exceeding of course a third of the whole after payment of the debts).

If a person dies leaving several heirs, one of whom is a minor and the rest are adult, and his estate is not burdened either with debts or legacies, and consists entirely of chattels, the executor may sell the share of the minor and invest the proceeds in some more profitable property.(2)

The *wasî* cannot borrow from the funds in his own hands belonging to the infant.

---

(1) I take it that the heirs would be entitled to question the validity of his dealings and to show that the sale was not made in good faith.

(2) This is *bi'l-ijmâ'a* or by general agreement; Abû Hanîfa is of opinion that he may sell the shares of the others also, but in this view, Abû Yusuf and Mohammed differ.

The executor can take his fixed allowance from the estate and nothing more, but the father, if in want, can support himself "to the extent of necessity" from the property of his infant child. This, however, does not apply to the executor.

But unless any remuneration is fixed by the testator the executor cannot take anything for himself from the estate; but the Kâzi has the power to fix an allowance for an administrator or *wasî* appointed by him.(1)

In the *Fatâwai Kâzi Khân*, however, it is stated that, where no allowance is fixed for the executor, he can take a limited and reasonable sum for his remuneration "to the extent of his necessity; and, if there is any need for it, he can make use of the infant's conveyances in going to and fro on the work of the infant, though several jurists hold that this would not be valid." The recognised doctrine, however, is that where no allowance is fixed by the testator, and the executor wants a remuneration, it must be fixed by the Judge.

Among the Hanafîs, the executor of the father is entitled to the curatorship of the testator's infant children in preference to the grandfather.

The *wasî* cannot make a binding acknowledgment of a debt against the estate of the testator, and the acknowledgee (مقرله) would not be entitled to receive his demand until he establishes his claim by proof.(2)

Nor can the *wasî* acknowledge that somebody else is entitled to a share in the inheritance, unless he himself is an heir, when the acknowledgment will have operation against his own share.

When a person has died intestate without appointing an executor and no reference is made to the Kâzi,(3) one of the neighbours (*ahl-ul-mahalla*) may legally administer "according to necessity." And the *Fatwa* is on this.

---

(1) *Durr-ul-Mukhtâr*, p. 838.

(2) "And if the *wasî* pays to the claimant what he demands, the *wasî* will be liable. If the claimant has no proof, but the executor knows that the demand is just, recourse must be had to the procedure mentioned by Kâzi Khân."

(3) "If injury be apprehended from reference to the Kâzi."

Father's executor.

The right of guardianship in respect of the property of infant children belongs preferentially to the father; in his absence to his executor; when the father has died without appointing an executor, the guardianship appertains to the grandfather, and in his absence to *his* executor, and to his executor's executor. If there are none of these, the guardianship belongs to the Kâzi and his appointee.(1)

In the *Fatâwai Alamgiri* the above principle is stated in the following terms:—"The executor of a father is in the place of the father. So, also, the executor of the grandfather is in the place of the father's executor, and the executor of a grandfather's executor is in the place of the grandfather's executor. And the executor of the Judge's executor is in the place of the Judge's executor *when his appointment was general.*"

If the father dies after appointing an executor and leaving him surviving several children, some of whom are adult and some minor; and, subsequent to the testator's death, some of these children were to die leaving them surviving infant children, the executor of the father would be the *wasî* of these children also, and would be entitled to manage their properties both movable and immovable, or to sell them [under the restrictions mentioned before].

An executor appointed by the mother—his powers.

But a *wasî* appointed by the mother, brother, uncle or any other relation has no such powers. They cannot sell the immovable property of the minor; and are only authorised to take care of the infant and his property; they cannot trade for him; and they can only buy things which are necessary for the infant, such as food and raiment; and they can only sell chattels inherited by the infant from the person who has appointed the executor, "for the preservation of the price of chattels is easier than of the things themselves."(2)

The *Fatâwai Alamgiri* dealing with the power of an executor appointed by the mother states as follows:—"The executor of a mother has no power to sell anything that a minor has inherited from his father whether movable or immovable, and whether the

(1) According to Mohammed, the grandfather comes after the father; the view in the text is that of Khassâf, according to whom is the *Fatwa.*

(2) *Radd ul-Muktâr,* Vol. V, p. 697.

property be involved in debt or free from it. But of what the minor has inherited from the mother when it is free from debts and legacies, the executor may sell what is movable, but he cannot sell the *'akâr*. If the estate be involved in debt or legacies, and the debt is such as to absorb the whole, he may sell the whole, the sale of *'akâr* coming within his power; but if the debt does not absorb the whole he may sell as much of it as is necessary to defray the debts. Regarding his power to sell the surplus there is a difference of opinion among our Jurists (Shaikhs)."

"If all the heirs are adult and present, the estate being free from debt, the mother's executor can sell no part of her estate; and if the estate is in debt, the answer to be given as to the power of the mother's executor is like that in the case of the father's executor, both in respect of matters in which opinions agree and in which they differ."

"If there are both adult and minor heirs, and the adult are absent, the estate being free from debt, the mother's executor may sell what is movable, of her estate, whether it belongs to the share of the minor or the adult, but cannot sell the *'akâr* of her estate, the shares of the minors and the adult being in this case the same. If the adults are present and the estate free from debt, the executor may sell the minor's share of her movable estate; but whether he can sell the share of the adults opinions differ; while he certainly cannot sell the *'akâr*."

"Whatever has been said as to the executor of the mother is true of the executor of the brother, and the paternal uncle, the principle being that the power of the executor is measured by the power of the testator."

To summarise—a *wasî* appointed by the mother has no power to intermeddle with any property which her children may have inherited from their father or any other relation, whether it be involved in debt or not; nor can he sell any portion of the immovable property inherited from her, unless it is involved in debt or burdened with the payment of legacies. If the estate is involved in debt or burdened with legacies, he can sell any portion of the property, whether movable or immovable, sufficient to pay off the debt. If all the heirs are adult and present, and the estate is free from debt, he can sell no portion of it, but if the estate is involved in debt, his powers are subject to the same rules which apply to an executor appointed by the father. If some of the heirs are adult and some minors, and the adult are absent, and the estate is free from debt, he can sell what is movable, whether it belongs to the share of the minor or the adult, but cannot sell the *'akâr* of either the minors or adults. If the estate be involved in debt, his powers are exactly similar to those of the father's *wasî*. If the adult are present and the estate free from debt, the executor may sell the minor's share of the movable estate, but as to whether he can sell the share of the adults opinions differ, but he certainly cannot sell the *'akâr*. The mother's *wasî* cannot lawfully purchase anything for her minor children, except food and clothing which are necessary for their preservation. * * * Whatever has been said as to the executor of the mother is true of the executor of the brother and the paternal uncle, the principle being that the power of the executor is measured by the power of his testator."(1)

Executor appointed by the mother.

The executor is entitled to repay himself any expenditure incurred by him on behalf of the infants, *but he must keep proof thereof*. In the *Fatâwai Kâzi Khân*, there is a passage to the effect that he may recoup himself, though he may have no witnesses of the fact that he has incurred the particular expenditure. The recognised doctrine, however, is as stated above. Although this rule does not apply to a father or mother, when either of them happens to be the guardian, it is regarded as *preferable* that they should also keep evidence.

Executor bound to keep proof of his dealings.

The executor is also entitled to recover from the estate in his hands any expenses incurred by him out of his own pocket, for the funeral of the testator or of any of his heirs; or in the discharge of the debts of the testator or his heirs.

Where an executor pays any claim made against the estate of the deceased *without due proof* thereof, he will not be entitled

(1) *Fatâwai Alamgiri*, Vol. VI, p. 235.

to any credit for such payment in the administration of the testator's assets, when the payment is questioned by the heirs or creditors of the deceased. But no responsibility attaches to him if the payment is made upon satisfactory evidence. "Whether he can pay when two just persons testify to a debt in his presence but do not testify to it before the Judge, and the debt is denied by the heirs, is a point upon which 'our' shaikhs have differed, some saying that he may pay the debt and others that he may not."(1)

Executor's liability.

Where the executor has satisfied one creditor without an order of the Judge, he is responsible to the other creditors; but it is otherwise if he made the payment under the direction of the Judge. Similarly, when a debt has been made obligatory on the estate of the deceased by the decree of a Judge, and the executor has satisfied it, after which another person prefers a claim against the estate, the executor is not liable if the payment was made under the Judge's order. But the second creditor may have recourse against the first for a share of what he received proportionate to the debt, if what he received be still subsisting; and if it has perished in his hands, he is responsible to the second in the same proportion, but the executor is in nowise liable. If, on the other hand, the executor had paid without the order of the Judge, the second creditor may claim either from the executor, or the first creditor, a due proportion of what was received by the latter.(2)

When an executor has expended the whole of the estate upon the infant children of the testator and nothing remains, after which a claim is made against the estate and is established by proof before the Judge who decrees it, can this creditor make the executor liable? Some of the lawyers have held that if the expenditure was made by order of the Judge, the executor is not responsible, whereas if it were made without the Judge's order, he is liable. The meaning of this seems to be

(1) *Ibid.* This, however, is a matter of procedure.

(2) "When an executor wishes to pay a debt to a creditor and is apprehensive of other creditors appearing against the deceased, he may sell something belonging to the estate to the creditor in exchange for the debt, and will not then be responsible, should another creditor appear as apprehended."—*Alamgiri*, Vol. VI, p. 235. This device is hardly likely to be countenanced by the Indian Courts.

that if the estate of the deceased has been applied in the maintenance, education or advancement of the testator's children with the sanction of the Court, the executor is absolved from all liability in respect of the deceased's creditors. It would apparently be otherwise, if the executor applied the whole estate for these purposes without such sanction.

Shiah Law—Liability of the executor.

According to the Shiah Law, an executor is not responsible for any loss or destruction of the deceased's property, unless occasioned by his departure from the conditions or rules of his office, or by some personal neglect. If he be a creditor of the deceased, he can lawfully pay himself out of the property in his hands without the order of a Judge *when he has proof of the debt*, though some lawyers think he may do so in all cases without a Judge's order. According to the *Sarâir*, the executor cannot purchase for himself on his own account any portion of the deceased's property, but the author of the *Sharâya* thinks "he may lawfully do so at a just valuation." The doctrine of the *Sarâir*, however, seems to be the recognised law.

The Shiahs differ from the Hanafîs in holding, that the appointment of any other person, as *wasî*, is not valid whilst the father of the deceased is alive, for the right of guardianship over the minor children belongs to the grandfather to the exclusion of the father's executor. Ibn Junaid, however, thinks that the nomination by the father is valid "to the extent of a third of his property and for the discharge of all rights or claims upon his estate."

Competency of an executor—Hanafi Law.

According to the Hanafîs, the competency of an executor has reference to the time of the testator's death. For example, if a minor is appointed as a *wasî* and he attains his majority before the testator's decease, the appointment is effective. Some of the Shiah jurists hold the same view, pre-eminently Ibn Junaid. According to the *Sharâya*, however, the generally received doctrine is, that the qualifications required in an executor have reference to the time of his appointment, and, consequently, the appointment of a minor, or a slave, or any person otherwise incompetent, is initially invalid, though the disability may cease prior to the testator's death.

The testator can appoint a *wasî* or guardian for every person, over whom he can exercise the *patria potestas* of the Mussulman

Law, as for example, a child how low soever in descent, provided that the child is of tender age or a minor. But if a person should appoint an executor for his children who are *sui juris*, the appointment is of no effect in law. And even though the appointment should be for the superintendence of property which the testator himself has left to the parties, the executor has no right to deal with it even to the extent of a third. He can, however, lawfully separate from it enough for the discharge of the testator's debts and bequests.

When a person appoints one executor for a particular purpose, *e.g.*, for the payment of his debts, and another for the administration of his property generally, or if he uses the following expression, "I have appointed so-and-so my executor to pay my debts and do not appoint him for anything else, and I have appointed so-and-so my executor for all my property," both are executors in all matters, according to Abû Hanîfa and Abû Yusuf, as if he had appointed them both *generally*, but according to Mohammed each is restricted to the particular purpose for which he has been appointed. Where it is made an express condition that one shall not be executor in the matter to which the other is appointed, it has been said by Mohammed Ibn-ul-Fazl that their powers will be limited according to the directions of the testator, and it is only where he has not made any such condition that there is the difference of opinion mentioned above, the doctrine enunciated by Abû Yusuf being the law in force.

Limited executorship. Hanafî Law.

With reference to the transmissibility of the office of executor, there is considerable difference, as pointed out already, between the Hanafîs and the Shiahs. The provisions of the Hanafî Law are, in some respects, analogous to the principles of the English Law. For example, although under the English Law, the executor cannot assign the executorship, yet the interest vested in him by the will of the deceased may, generally speaking, be continued and kept alive by the will of the executor; so that if there be a sole executor of *A*, the executor of the executor is, to all intents and purposes, the executor and representative of the first testator. Similarly, under the Hanafî Law, an executor may, on the approach of death, appoint a successor though the power may not have been expressly reserved to him by the

Derivative executors. Hanafî Law.

testator.(1) It is not necessary that the executor should expressly constitute *his* executor to be the *wasî* of his testator's estate; the mere appointment as *wasî* to the executor carries with it the power to administer both estates. And if *A* appoints *B* as his executor and *C* appoints *A* as his executor, upon the death of *A* and *C*, the executorship of both *A* and *C* devolves on *B*.

Shiah doctrines.

According to the generally approved doctrine among the Shiahs, the executor can transmit the office, or appoint a successor, only when the testator has authorised him to entrust to another the management of the estate at his own death. When a person dies without appointing an executor, or when an executor dies to whom the authority to appoint a successor was not given, the superintendence of the original testator's estate devolves upon the Judge. If there is no Judge present on the spot, any true believer in whom confidence can be placed may lawfully assume the care and management of the estate. "But, on this point," says the author of the *Sharâya*, "there is room for doubt and difference of opinion."(2)

Hanafî doctrines.

"A person dies leaving two minor children. These on attaining majority demand their inheritance from the *wasî*, who says that the entire inheritance left by their father was 1,000 dirhems which had been spent on them. One of the sons affirms the statement of the executor, but the other does not. The latter will be entitled to recover, according to Zuffar, 250 dirhems from the first but not from the executor. And this also is the view of Abû Hanîfa. Ibn Abî Malik, however, reports from Abû Yusuf that he can. So it is said in the *Muhit-i-Sarakhsi*."(3)

"If a person die leaving minor children and a father, but without appointing an executor, the father is in the position of an executor for the protection of the inheritance (فی حفظ الترکة) and can administer the property in whatever way it may be necessary. And if the deceased has left heavy debts (دین کثیر) the father,

---

(1) In the case of *Shaikh Hafiz-ur-Rahman* v. *Khadim Hossain*, 4 N. W. P. Reps., p. 106, it was held that under the Mahommedan Law, an executor is entitled to nominate a successor to carry out the purposes of the will under which he was made executor. This, of course, is under the Hanafî Law.

(2) In the *Jâm'aa ush-Shittât* the approved doctrine is stated to be that where reference to a Judge is impossible, it is incumbent (*wâjib*) upon the just "Momins" (faithful Moslems) to assume the management.

(3) *Fatâwai Alamgiri*, Vol. VI, p. 221.

that is, the grandfather of the minors, has no authority to sell the inheritance for the payment of the debts. Similarly, if a person authorises his adolescent son (صغير المراهق) possessed of understanding to buy and sell, and he enters into any transaction and becomes indebted, after which he (the son) dies leaving his father, the father will have no power to deal with the son's property to pay his debts.''(1)

"A person, who is in debt, makes certain bequests, all of which after the payment of the debt, can be discharged out of the third. He dies leaving a house ; and the *wasî* cannot pay his debts or discharge the legacies, without the price of the house ; but the heirs are not agreeable to the sale of the house, when the debts do not cover the whole house or the major portion of the house,—in such case, the *wasî* is empowered to sell the house, and he should sell it if he is aware that the debts will remain unpaid for a long time if he does not sell it.''(2)

When the estate of a deceased person is subject to debts, but the debts do not overwhelm the estate, in other words, do not exceed the assets, and it is divided among the heirs ; and subsequent to the partition, a creditor of the estate appears, he will be entitled to recover the debt due to him proportionately from the different heirs. He can do this, however, only by taking all of them before the Kâzi. But if he proceeds(3) against any one of them, he can recover his debt to the extent of the share in such person's hands whatever that be.(4)

Rights of creditors.

(1) *Fatáwai Alamgiri*, Vol. VI, p. 225.
(2) *Ibid*, p. 227.
(3) *Lit*,, "if he can get hold of any one of them."
(4) For the case-law on the subject see Appendix.

CHAPTER XXVI.

MISCELLANEOUS PRINCIPLES.

THERE are numerous decisions under the Mussulman law regarding the rights of creditors against the estate of a deceased Mahommedan. By way of illustration I give here a few references It has been held that under the Mahommedan law, a decree against one heir of a deceased debtor cannot bind the other heirs.(1) It has been further laid down that under the Mahommedan law, the estate of an intestate descends in its entirety, together with all the debts due from and owing to the deceased. The creditor of an intestate Mahommedan must, therefore, enforce his claim against the estate in a suit properly framed for the purpose. Such a suit is properly framed if all the persons in possession of that particular portion of the estate, which it is intended to charge, are made parties to it. The right of a Mahommedan heir claiming the property of his deceased ancestor, who died indebted, is a right of representation only, and except as representative he has no right to the property whatsoever.(2)

The creditor of a deceased Mahommedan cannot follow his estate into the hands of a *bonâ fide* purchaser for value, to whom it has been alienated by the heir-at-law, whether the alienation has been by absolute sale or by mortgage. But where the alienation is made during the pendency of a suit in which the creditor obtains a decree for the payment of his debt out of the assets of the estate which have come into the hands of the heir-at-law, the alienee will be held to take with notice, and be affected by the doctrine of *lis pendens*.(3) The debts of a deceased Mahommedan are not a charge

---

(1) *Sita Nath Dass* v. *Roy Luchhmiput Singh*, 11 C. L. R., 268; *Assamathemnissa Bibi* v. *Roy Lutchmeeput Singh* [1878], I. L., 4 Cal., 142; s. c., 2 C. L. R., 223.

(2) *Ibid.*

(3) *Bazayet Hossein* v. *Dooli Chund* [1878], I. L., 4 Cal., 402; s. c., L. R., 5 I. A., p. 211; *Land Mortgage Bank* v. *Roy Luchmiput Singh*, 8 C. L. R., 447.

upon the estate which gives the creditor a priority over all persons who after his death purchase or take a mortgage of his estate.(1)

The Calcutta High Court has held that when a creditor of a deceased Mahommedan sues the heir in possession, and obtains a decree against the assets of the deceased, such a suit is to be looked upon as an administration-suit, and those heirs of the deceased who have not been made parties cannot, in the absence of fraud, claim anything but what remains after the debts of the testator have been paid.(2) This view, however, has been dissented from by the Allahabad High Court, which has held that upon the death of a Mahommedan intestate the ownership of his estate devolves immediately on his heirs, and such devolution is not contingent upon and suspended till the payment of his debts.(3) A decree relative to his debts, passed in a contentious or non-contentious suit against only such heirs of a deceased Mahommedan debtor as are in possession of the whole or part of his estate, does not bind the other heirs who, by reason of absence or other cause, are not in possession, so as to convey to the auction-purchaser, in execution of such a decree, the rights and interest of those heirs who were not parties to the decree.(4)

According to Mahommedan law, a gift made in contemplation of death, though not operative as a gift, operates as a legacy. Ordinarily it conveys to the legatee property not exceeding one-third of the deceased's whole property, the remaining two-thirds going to the heirs. In the absence of heirs, a will carries the whole property.(5)

It has been held that the consent given by heirs to a testator's will before his death is no assent at all; to be valid, it must

---

(1) See *Bazayet Hossein* v. *Dooli Chand* [1878], L. R., 5 I. A., 211; s. c., I. L., 4 Cal., 402; *Land Mortgage Bank* v. *Bidyadhari Dasi*, 7 C. L. R., 460.

(2) *See* also *Muttyjan* v. *Ahmed Ally*, I. L., 8 Cal., 370, and *Amir Dulhin* v. *Baij Nath Singh* [1894], I. L., 21 Cal., 311.

(3) *Pirthi Pal Singh* v. *Hussaini Jan* [1882], I. L., 4 All., 361; *Jafri Begum* v. *Amir Muhammad Khan* [1885], I. L., 7 All., 822.

(4) *Ibid.*

(5) *Ekin Bebee* v. *Ashruf Ali*, 1 W. R., 152. With regard to the invalidity of Wills divesting heirs of their right of inheritance or made without their consent, see the following:—*Jumesnooddeen Ahmed* v. *Hossain Ali*, 2 W. R. Mis., 49; *Qadir Ali Khan* v. *Nowsha Begum*, 2 Agra, 154: *Mahomed Mudun* v. *Khoderunnessa* alias *Khookee Bibee*, 2 W. R., 181; *Muhammad* v. *Imamuddin*, 2 Bom., 53, 2nd Ed., 50; *Abedoonnissa Khatoon* v. *Ameeroonnissa Khatoon*, 9 W. R., 257.

be given after the testator's death.(1) This must be confined, however, to persons subject to the Hanafi Law.

A Mahommedan testator, who died in 1861, by his will left his property in equal four shares to his second and third sons, V and E, to the lawful son (if any) of his eldest son M and to his (the testator's) brother A. His eldest son M he disinherited. He directed that the property was not to be divided until V and E had attained the age of twenty, and as to the share of the lawful son of M it was to be held in trust until such son should reach the age of twenty. At the time of the testator's death no son of M was living. Shortly after his death, a son was born to M, but he lived only a few months. The testator's brother A was appointed executor of the will. In 1878, V and E sued the executor A and his son S for an account and division of the property, and by a consent decree passed in 1881 three-fifths of the property were given to V and E, and the remaining two-fifths to A and S. The estate was duly divided in accordance with the decree, and the parties got possession of their respective shares. In February 1884, another son was born to M, and in May 1884 the infant brought this suit by his father and next friend, claiming to be entitled, on his attaining the age of twenty, to one-third of the property received by V and E, under the consent-decree. It was held that the plaintiff could not recover, not having been in existence at the date of the testator's death.(2) It is submitted that the principle is laid down here much too broadly, for under the Mahommedan Law if the devise is first to a person in existence and then to a person *not* in existence it is valid.

A Mahommedan testator directed by his will that his immovable estate should not be divided or alienated by any of his heirs, and that his executor should appropriate the net income, according to a schedule annexed to his will, among certain specific persons divided into two classes, *viz.*, those who took and those who did not take by inheritance. It was held that the intention of the testator was to endeavour to prevent any partition of the estate

(1) *Nusrut Ali* v. *Zeinunnissa*, 15 W. R., 146; *Cherachom Vittal Ayisha Kutti Umah* v. *Valia Pudiakel Biathu Umah*, 2 Mad., 350.

(2) *Abdul Cadur Haji Mahomed* v. *Turner* (*Official Assignee*) [1884], I. L., 9 Bom., 158.

and not to convert his heirs-at-law into mere annuitants taking grants from him. The executor held the estate in trust to pay the profits in certain defined shares to the heirs, and his representatives could not plead adverse possession against them so as to bar their claims by lapse of time.(1)

---

(1) *Khajoorunnissa* v. *Rohemunnissa*, 17 W. R., 190.

CHAPTER XXVII.

THE LAW OF WILLS (SHAFEI DOCTRINES).

SECTION

GENERAL OBSERVATIONS.

The power of devising by will.

THE power to will is vested in everybody, Moslem or non-Moslem, without distinction of sex, who is *sui juris*, possessing reason, who is free, and, "according to the Shâfei doctrines," not labouring under the inhibition of imbecility.

The power is not given to an alien, to a person in an unconscious state, or to a minor, though a jurist has maintained that this prohibition should not extend to a minor, who has attained the age of discretion. According to some jurists, the will of a bondsman is not valid unless he had been liberated after he had made his will, and had died without having revoked the same.

Testamentary dispositions in favour of the public must have a lawful object; thus a will cannot be made for the support of a Christian church or a synagogue. A legacy in favour of one or more individuals is lawful if the person or persons designated are capable of exercising the right of proprietorship. Thus, a legacy in favour of a child *en ventre sa mère* only takes effect on the two-fold condition, that such child should be born alive, and that the conception should have taken place before the disposition, that is to say, that the birth should take place before six months should have elapsed from the date of the will. If the birth takes place beyond the period of six months, the child is supposed not to have been conceived previous to the testamentary disposition, at least if the parents have not ceased to cohabit with each other. In the opposite case, conception is admissible for a maximum term of four years.(1) A will in favour of a

(1) This doctrine is, however, not in force now ; see Mahommedan Law, Vol. II, p. 193.

bondsman reverts to the master, unless he has been enfranchised before the testator's decease. As for subsequent liberation, followed by an acceptance on the part of the slave, the result depends upon the question, whether the possession of the legacy has been acquired or not before the death of the testator. Testamentary dispositions in favour of animals are absolutely void, whether the intention was expressed to constitute the animal as proprietor, or whether nothing to that effect had been mentioned; but if a declaration has been made that the animals should never want for necessary food, traditional doctrine admits the validity.

A legacy for the support of a mosque is legal, and even a will "in favour of a mosque," without adding anything else. However, in this case, the disposition is supposed to have been made, not only for the support, but also for the embellishment of the edifice. Moreover, a will may be made in favour of a non-Moslem, either subject to a Mahommedan sovereign or not, of an apostate, and of one's own murderer. A legacy in favour of an heir can only take effect with the unanimous consent of the co-heirs, pronounced after the succession has passed. This consent is necessary even if the co-heirs renounce the succession, *and it cannot be given before the death of the testator*, as the disposition is only rendered invalid by the existence of co-heirs at the time of the decease, and this cannot be declared previously. A testamentary disposition, the effect of which is to leave each heir his legitimate inheritance, is null and void; but there is no impediment against giving any one heir, by testament, any particular thing being the value of the portion due to him by law. Only the act must be approved of by the co-heirs.

Wills in favour of *Zimmis*.

A person may lawfully devise the following objects:—

1. The usufruct of things that do not suffer in the course of time.

2. The future fruit of a tree, the future young of an animal, &c.

3. One of two objects, the legatee to take his choice.

4. An impure thing, provided its use is not prohibited by law, for example a trained dog, the juice of grapes not meant for fermentation, &c.

A legacy worded as "one of my dogs," must be carried out by the heir giving any dog belonging to the defunct, and the disposition is null and void if the testator possessed none. A person, who possesses many dogs among his property, may give away all or some of them by will, even if the dogs constitute the major portion of the heritage. If a person possess two drums, the one a musical instrument for amusement, the other an instrument to be used legitimately—for example, a war-drum, or a drum used by pilgrims, the bequest of "a drum" without further particulars would refer to the latter. Furthermore, a special legacy of a drum for amusement is null and void, unless it can, at the same time, be used for warlike purposes and pilgrimages.

Section II.

Rules as to the Third.

Testamentary dispositions should not exceed the third of the property of the testator; and such as have been made contrary to the precepts of the law will be reduced to the allotted portion, upon demand of the heir or heirs. When, on the other hand, the heir declares his approval of the disposition, it takes effect, whatever the amount may be; but, according to one jurist, it is then considered as a pure donation by the heir.

The reduction is determined by collecting all the property existing on the day of the decease, or, according to others, on the day the disposition is made. By the dispositions to which effect should be given out of the third are understood to be the following:—

(1) Gratuitous emancipation which is to be effected upon the death of the testator.

(2) Voluntary dispositions, such as *wakfs* and *hibas*, constituted during the last illness.

(3) Payment of lawful debts.

In case all these should exceed the disposable third, the following rules must be observed in the reduction:—

1st. When the testamentary disposition consists simply of a direction to enfranchise slaves, lots must be drawn in order to decide which of them should be deprived of his liberty in consequence of the reduction.

2nd. When the testamentary dispositions consist of bounties of different kinds, all are subject to a proportionate reduction.

3rd. When the dispositions include the liberation of bondsman as well as other bounties, the portions available must first be divided in proportion to the two categories of the legacy, and then the same rule as we have mentioned in the 1st and 2nd clauses must have effect.

Marz-ul-mout.

A person, who is suffering from an illness from which there is an apprehension of death, cannot make a valid disposition of more than one-third of his available assets; but if he recovers against all hope, his dispositions cannot be impugned. If a person be suffering from a slight illness involving no danger to his life, he can dispose of his property unrestrictedly; and even if he dies unexpectedly during this illness his dispositions take their full legitimate effect. This would not be the case if the death was the natural result of the illness from which he was suffering, though it be not considered of a dangerous nature, for under such circumstances it proves itself to have been mortal. In case of uncertainty about the character of the disease, it must be referred to two doctors, free and irreproachable. The following are considered by the law to be dangerous diseases:—colic, pleurisy, incessant bleeding from the nose, chronic diarrhœa, hectic fever, the commencement of (even partial) paralysis, the vomiting of food without its having undergone any change in the stomach, and even vomiting in general if it is very bad and accompanied by pains and effusion of blood, continual or intermittent fever, but not ague. "The following circumstances are assimilated by 'our' doctrines to mortal diseases:—having been made prisoner of war by infidels who give no quarter; being in a routed army corps, assailed by the conqueror; having been condemned to death in retaliation, or to be stoned to death; being in a vessel during a storm, or in a rough sea; a woman undergoing great labour-pains, be it before or after confinement, as long as the fœtus has not severed the membrane."

Testamentary dispositions are formulated thus:—"I leave to him such or such thing," "Remit it to him," "Give it to him after my death," "I make it his," "It shall be his after my death," but in saying only, "It is his," not a legacy but an avowal is pronounced. On the contrary, if it be said—"It is his in my succession," it is a valid testamentary disposition. "Testamentary dispositions can be formulated in another manner, which, though not so explicit, equally indicates the last will, for example, a written statement containing the will given to the witnesses."

Legacy in favour of a class.

A legacy in favour of a class of people, as for example, "the poor" need not be accepted expressly, but the decease of the testator renders it irrevocable; while, on the contrary, a legacy in favour of one or two specific people must be formally accepted by them. This acceptance, like the repudiation of a legacy, cannot take place during the testator's lifetime, and it is, even, not customary that the legatee should declare his wish immediately upon the testator's decease. A legacy becomes null by the pre-decease of the legatee; if he dies after the testator but before having accepted the legacy, the right of acceptance devolves upon his heirs. As regards the question,—when does the property become the legatee's, some jurists consider he becomes entitled to possession immediately upon the death of the testator, provided he accepts the legacy; others maintain that he only becomes the proprietor upon accepting it; others, again, hold that previous to the acceptance the legacy is suspended, but that the legatee is the actual possessor from the time of the testator's death if he accepts, otherwise the heirs are presumed not to have lost possession thereof. The three different doctrines we have enunciated on the subject of legacy between decease and acceptance, also exist with regard to fruit and to earnings realised by a bequeathed bondsman as well as with regard to other expenses, such as the support of a bondsman and the money to be paid to him for observing a fast. According to the authors, who admit that a legacy remains suspended until the legatee has accepted or rejected the same, he must, nevertheless, provide for the temporary support of the bondsman or of the animal bequeathed.

Section III.

The Legatees.

If a person were to bequeath "a sheep from my flock," the disposition will be void if the testator possessed no flock of sheep; but if he had said "a sheep from my inheritance," in case the testator should leave no sheep one must be bought and given to the legatee.

A legacy in favour of "the child of which a certain woman is *enceinte*," devolves upon the two children if she gives birth to twins; and upon the child born alive, if she gives birth to twins of which one is still-born. If, on the contrary, the testator added, "if it be a boy," or "if it be a girl," the birth of twins, if one be a boy and the other a girl, renders the disposition null and void. The legacy can only be claimed by the boy exclusive of the girl, should the testator have added, "if she bears a boy." Finally, a legacy worded thus is also valid, "in case the woman in question should give birth to two twin boys;" and the heir can, under these circumstances, give the bequeathed object to one of the children according to his own choice. Constitution of a legacy.

A legacy in favour of a person's "neighbours" extends to forty houses in four different quarters; a legacy in favour of "learned men" includes all those who study law, that is, the Koran, the traditions of the Prophet and jurisprudence. But it does not extend to simple readers of the Koran, to men of letters, interpreters of dreams and doctors, nor, according to most jurists, to theologians, properly speaking. This archaic rule, however, has been considerably modified in recent times.

A legacy in favour of the poor also implies the indigent and *vice versâ*; in both cases, the legacy must be divided into two equal portions—one for each class, provided it consists of at least three persons. The testator may, also, bequeath to one of the persons of the category in question, more than to the others who have the right; while, according to "our" doctrines, a legacy "to such a person and to the poor," results in the person designated not receiving more than one separate portion, however little that portion may be, so long as there is some value. Only the person mentioned must not be entirely excluded. Legacy in favour of the poor.

One may also bequeath not only to a certain category of people without indicating the number of individuals of which it is composed, for example "to the Alides" (the descendants of the Caliph Ali), but also to a fixed number, for example, "to three persons" of a certain category, and "to the relations" of a certain person. Regarding this latter form of legacy, it must be remarked that it implies all the relations even the most distant, excepting relations in the direct line, be it ascendant or descendant. However, the relatives on the mother's side are not understood in the testamentary dispositions made by the Arabs in favour of "relations" unless specially mentioned. In order to find out the "relatives" of the person favoured by the testator—you must take the nearest ascendant, and this person's descendants remaining in the tribe, are those the testator must be considered to have had in view. If, on the other hand, the testator used the expression, "the nearest relatives" the distinction applies also to the direct line, always providing that the son takes precedence over the father, and the brother over the paternal grandfather, but beyond these exceptions the law gives no preference under these circumstances to either sex. The father and mother, sister and brother are all equal participators in the legacy, and even the son of the daughter takes precedence over the agnatic great-grandson. A legacy in favour of a person's own relatives (*akriba*), does not include the rightful heirs.

What may be bequeathed.

One can bequeath the usufruct of a house, as well as the lease of a shop. The sale of a thing, the usufruct of which to the extent of one-third has been bequeathed for a limited period of time, has the same consequences as the sale of any other object; but a perpetual usufruct may not be sold unless to the legatee.

A person may legitimately direct his heir to make, or to cause to be made, a voluntary pilgrimage which he himself intended to undertake. In this case, the heir must pay the journey to Mecca, from the station fixed by the law, unless the deceased mentioned any special town whence the pilgrimage should start. As regards the obligatory pilgrimage neglected by the deceased, this act of devotion falls to the charge of the bulk of the property; though, if the testator has enjoined the heir to bear the costs either from the bulk or from the disposable third, his last will must be regarded. If the deceased expressed no wish on this point, the charge imposed upon the heir to accomplish the neglected compulsory pilgrimage, falls upon the bulk; although some hold that it must come out only of the disposable third; but in every case this charge relates to the journey commencing from the station fixed by the law. Any person, though he be not one of the family, can make the necessary pilgrimage on behalf of the deceased, without any express mandate from him

The heir must also take upon himself the discharge of pecuniary liabilities for expiations fixed by the deceased, the fulfilment of which had been neglected. With regard to other expiations, the heir may, according to his own choice, give food or clothing to the poor, if necessary, and even enfranchise a bondsman. In any case, and whatever be the nature of the expiations, the heir can fulfil it at his own cost if the inheritance be not adequate, and it counts equally as an act of the deceased. If the expiation is made by a person other than a member of the family, the conditions are the same as regards the distribution of food and clothing, but not if the expiation consists in enfranchising a bondsman. The soul of the deceased is benefited by alms and pious invocations made on his behalf, whether they be offered by his heirs or any other persons.

Revocation.

A testamentary disposition is wholly or partially revocable. It may be revoked :—

1. Verbally, for example, by pronouncing the words "I cancel the will," "I annul it," "I revoke it," "I renounce it," or "the thing which I have bequeathed, shall nevertheless be my heirs."

2. By the fact of having disposed of the bequeathed object, by sale, enfranchisement, marriage, gift, or by pledging it, even if, in the two latter cases, the seisin by the donee or the creditor has not taken place.

3. By a charge imposed in a later will upon the heir to dispose of the object bequeathed in any manner mentioned in para. 2.

4. By the order to sell the thing bequeathed, by putting it up for sale, even if unsuccessfully, or by the fact of mixing other objects with the thing which has been bequeathed. If a particular kind of wheat is bequeathed and it is mixed with some other wheat, that very fact is sufficient to constitute an ademption even though the wheat added to the heap is of a superior quality. But if it be of equal, or inferior quality, the fact of having mixed it with the first wheat, does not constitute a revocation of the bequest. Revocation also results from the following facts :—from having ground the bequeathed wheat, having sown one's field with it, having made the bequeathed flour into bread, having spun the cotton bequeathed, having woven the threads bequeathed,

having made a bequeathed piece of stuff into a shirt, having built or planted upon bequeathed ground.

Executor.

The Prophet has introduced the custom of appointing testamentary executors, to take charge of the payment of the testator's debts, of the execution of his last will, and the guardianship of his infant children. An executor must be a Moslem, *sui juris*, possessed of full reason, free, irreproachable and capable of the charge entrusted to him. A non-Moslem subject of a Mussulman prince may be appointed executor by a co-religionist; nor is blindness any cause for incapacity.

Mother can be appointed guardian of her children.

The law does not exact that the executor should be of the male sex; the mother of the infant children ought to be considered more capable of bringing them up than any other person.

An executor must be deposed for notorious bad conduct; this principle applies also to a Judge, but not to the Head of the State.

This right of appointing an executor to undertake the payment of debts and the execution of the last will of the testator is accorded to all Mussulmans of age, possessed of understanding and free; but the right of vesting the executor with the guardianship of young children, belongs exclusively to the person who is their legitimate guardian. An executor cannot in his turn appoint by will a person to replace him after his own death, unless such power had been given him by the primary testator. Nothing prevents the nomination of two executors to succeed one another: this can be done by the words, "I make you my testamentary executor until the majority of my son," or "until the arrival of Zaid and then my son," "or Zaid will take charge of this will." On the other hand, a testamentary executor cannot be appointed to the guardianship of the children, during the lifetime of their paternal grandfather, their natural guardian, if he is capable of undertaking the guardianship.

Derivative executorship.

It is prohibited to give the executor the power of making a contract of marriage for the son of the deceased during minority or to represent the daughter of the deceased in a similar contract.

The words by which an executor may be appointed are:—"I nominate you my testamentary executor," "I entrust my affairs to you," etc.; but there is no impediment against adding a suspensive condition Besides this, the duty with which the executor is being charged must be clearly defined, for if nothing more is said than, "I nominate you my executor," the disposition is void. The nomination of an executor has no effect before the duty has been accepted, and this acceptance must take place during the testator's lifetime.

If the testator has appointed two executors, neither of them can act without the assistance of the other, unless the power has been formally given to him. The testator can revoke the nomination at any time, and the executor can renounce it even after acceptance if he think fit. Upon an infant attaining majority, an executor charged with the guardianship must give an account of his administration, and in case of difference the law presumes in favour of the executor's words, if the question concern the minor's maintenance. On the other hand, the law presumes in favour of the latter if the dispute relates to any sum which the executor maintains he gave to his ward after he attained majority.

CHAPTER XXVIII.

THE LAW OF PRE-EMPTION (*SHUFA'A.*)

SECTION I.

GENERAL OBSERVATIONS.

Meaning of the word *Shufâ'a*.

The right of pre-emption or *Shufâ'a* means the right possessed by one person to acquire a property sold to another in preference to that other by paying a price equal to that settled, or paid by the latter; and in the Mahommedan system owes its origin to motives of expediency and a desire to prevent the introduction of a stranger among co-sharers and neighbours likely to cause inconvenience or vexation.

The Sunni Hanafî Law of Pre-emption was introduced in India with the Mahommedan Government, and in certain places it has become a part of the *lex loci*; for example in Behar, (1) parts of the Punjab and the United Provinces, both Hindus and Mahommedans are entitled to claim the right of pre-emption. And so well-established is that right, that it is almost invariably recorded in greater or less detail in the village-administration-papers called the *Wajib-ul-Arz*.

In other places the right depends on custom. Generally speaking in Lower Bengal the right is confined to Mahommedans, but in some places Hindus and Christians have exercised the right of pre-emption.

Hanafî Law.

It applies only to immovable property, whether held jointly or separately, and whether capable of partition or not, and comes into operation when the property in respect of which the right is claimed is transferred for a *consideration*.

To entitle a person to claim the right of pre-emption, the *milkiat* or proprietary interest in the property on which he bases his right must be in him, but it is not necessary that he should

---

(1) See *Fakir Rawot* v. *Emam Bukhsh*, B. L. R. Supp. Vol., p. 35.

be in actual possession of it.(1) Thus a tenant(2) or a mortgagee or a mere *benamidar* is not entitled to pre-emption on any of the grounds recognised by law.

A Hindu widow, however, holding a life-estate and not in possession of land merely in lieu of maintenance, represents the full estate, and her possession carries with it the right to pre-empt.(3)

It is not a right of "re-purchase" either from the vendor or from the vendee involving any new contract of sale; but it is simply a right of *substitution* entitling the pre-emptor by reason of a legal incident to which the sale itself was subject to stand in the shoes of the vendee in respect of all the rights and obligations arising from the sale under which he has derived his title.(4)

Property in respect of which it is enforceable.

It does not, therefore, take effect with regard to property which has devolved by right of inheritance, or which has been received in gift without any consideration or as a legacy.(5) Nor does it arise in respect of property bailed to another or given in lieu of services rendered or to be rendered, or by way of a reward, or as a compensation for *khulâ*, or as a dower to a wife. In other words, when a woman conveys a property to her husband in consideration of his granting a divorce, or which a man conveys to a wife in consideration of marriage, no right of pre-emption arises thereto. Similarly, if a man were to marry without settling on the wife any dower and after the marriage were to settle on or convey to her a property in lieu of dower, there would be no right of pre-emption. When a property is conveyed to a wife in discharge of the dower-debt, there is also no right of pre-emption. But when a house is sold to a third person in order to enable the husband to satisfy with the proceeds thereof the dower of his wife, the right of pre-emption comes into operation.(6) The reason of these rules is self-evident. The wife conveying to the husband

---

(1) *Sakina Bibi* v. *Amiran* [1888], I. L., 10 All., 472; Comp. *Bani Shankar Bhelhat* v. *Mahpal Bahadur Singh* [1887], I. L., 9 All., 480.

(2) *Gooman Singh* v. *Tripolo Singh* [1867], 8 W. R., 437.

(3) *Muhammad Yusuf Ali Khan* v. *Dal Kuar* [1897], I. L., 20 All., 148.

(4) *Gobind Dayal* v. *Inayatullah* [1885], I. L., 7 All., 775, *per* Mahmood, J.

(5) Comp. *Amir Ally* v. *Pearun*, W. R., 1864, 239; *Har Narain Pande* v. *Ram Prasad Misr* [1891], I. L., 14 All., 333.

(6) The decision in *Fida Ali* v. *Mozuffer Ali* [1882], I. L., 5 All., 65, appears to proceed on a wrong interpretation of the law.

and *vice versâ* do not thereby introduce a stranger among co-sharers or neighbours.

Nor does the right of pre-emption apply to leases in perpetuity, however small the rent reserved may be.(1) Nor where there has been no real and *bonâ fide* sale according to Mahommedan Law.(2)

Circumstances under which the right of pre-emption arises.

The right of pre-emption takes effect with regard to property conveyed to another by virtue of a compromise of a claim. For example, if a defendant were to compromise a suit by resigning or making over a house to the plaintiff after having denied his claim, or were to acknowledge it after having refused to accede to it, the right of pre-emption would take effect in respect thereof.

It takes effect also in respect of property conveyed by a *hiba-ba-shart-ul-ewaz*, when the settled consideration has been paid by the transferee, for a *hiba-ba-shart-ul-ewaz* is a sale in its effect. But so long as the *ewaz* has not passed there is no right of pre-emption.

When the right of pre-emption arises.

The right of pre-emption arises only when the contract transferring the right of property from the vendor to the vendee has become complete.(3)

A mere executory contract does not give rise to a right of pre-emption. "Accordingly when a property is sold with a condition of option no right of pre-emption arises, for the power reserved by the seller forms an impediment to the extinction of the seller's right of property and the right of *shufâ'a* is founded and rests upon the extinction of the seller's right of property as has been already explained."(4)

Nor does the right take effect in respect of a transfer made under an invalid sale, for the transferor under such a sale maintains all his rights intact and, so long as he has not delivered the property to the purchaser, can himself exercise his right of pre-emption over the transfer of an adjacent property.

---

(1) *Ram Golam Sing* v. *Nursing Sahoy* [1875], 25 W. R., 43; *Dewanutulla* v. *Kazem Molla* [1887], I. L., 15 Cal., 184.

(2) *Mohno Bibee v. Juggurnath Chowdhry*, 2 W. R., 78.

(3) *Soonder Koer* v. *Lalla Rughoobur Dyal*, 10 W. R., 246; *Bukhsha Ali* v. *Tofas Ali*, 20 W. R., 218.

(4) When the buyer or seller repudiates the sale, the Calcutta High Court has held that there can be no right of pre-emption; *Ojheoonnissa* v. *Rastam Ali*, W. R., 1864, 219.

Accordingly, the right of pre-emption does not arise in respect of a property transferred under an invalid sale either before or after the vendee has obtained possession thereof, "because before possession the house belongs to the vendor and his right of property is not extinguished, and after possession there is still a probability that the bargain may be dissolved since the law admits the dissolution of a sale in case of invalidity."

But when once the vendor's right in the property transferred under an invalid sale has been extinguished and the title has vested in the vendee, he is entitled to exercise the right of pre-emption.

The right of pre-emption again accrues only when a complete transfer of the right title and interest of the transferor has taken place and not where there is a mere agreement to sell or transfer, or where the transfer is only fictitious or, as already stated, the sale is invalid. The question whether the transaction amounts to a complete transfer will be determined on the basis of the Mahommedan Law and not of the Transfer of Property Act.(1)

As a corollary to the above principle it follows that no right of pre-emption arises in respect of property leased in perpetuity(2) or mortgaged even though by a conditional sale until foreclosure of the equity of redemption.(3)

When the right of pre-emption accrues.

Where one co-sharer mortgages his share in a certain property none of the other sharers have any right of pre-emption until the equity of redemption is foreclosed.(4)

And where the transferor has delivered possession of the property and paid the consideration, although no sale-deed has been executed, it has been held that in a suit for pre-emption the Mahommedan Law would apply.(5)

The right of pre-emption is lost by the acquiescence of the claimant in the sale. For example, when he has agreed to pur-

---

(1) *Najm-un-Nissa* v. *Ajaib Ali Khan* [1900], I. L., 22 All., 343; *Begam* v. *Muhammad Yakub* [1894], I. L., 16 All., 344.

(2) *Baboo Ram Golam Singh* v. *Nursing Sahai* [1875], 25 W. R., 43; *Dewanatullah* v. *Kajemmolla* [1887], I. L., 15 Cal., 184.

(3) *Begam* v. *Muhammad Yakub*, supra; *Gurdial Munder* v. *Teknarayen Singh* [1865], B. L. R., Supp. Vol., 166; s.c., 2 W. R., 215.

(4) *Begam* v. *Mohammed Yakub*, supra.

(5) *Gurdial Munder* v. *Teknarain Singh*, B. L. R., Supp. Vol. 166, s. c., 2 W. R., 215; see also 11 W. R., 282, and 6 B. L. R., App., 114.

chase(1) or to a take a lease of the property from the vendee it amounts to abandonment. In other words the person claiming a right of pre-emption can expressly or impliedly relinquish or waive his right, and once relinquished it cannot be asserted again.(2)

Acquiescence with a knowledge of the sale would amount to waiver. And, accordingly, where it was found that the plaintiff in a suit to enforce the right of pre-emption, whilst alleging that the true consideration for the sale was less than the amount stated in the sale-deed, made no communication to the vendor after he became aware that a sale was being negotiated, nor made it known to him that, while he stood upon his pre-emptive right, he declined to pay the price stated in the deed, because it was not the consideration agreed on between the vendor and the vendee, it was held that he had waived his right. The plaintiff was bound, instead of remaining silent, to communicate to the vendor that he was prepared to purchase at the sale-price within a reasonable time, that not having done so he must be taken to have countenanced the completion of the bargain with the vendee.(3) What constitutes acquiescence is a question of fact. Mere offer to take the property from the vendor paying him the sale-price with a view to avoid litigation has been held not to amount to acquiescence or waiver. So, also, if a pre-emptor enters into a compromise with the vendee, or allows himself to take any benefit from him in respect of the property which is the subject of pre-emption, he by so doing is taken to have acquiesced in the sale and to have relinquished his right of pre-emption.(4)

But when once the right has vested in consequence of a completed contract, the dissolution of the contract by the vendor and the vendee by agreement or in exercise of the right of rejection on discovering any defect would not destroy the right of the pre-emptor to take the property for the price paid by

---

(1) See *Toral Komhar* v. *Achhee* [1872], 9 B. L. R., 253, s. c., 18 W. R., 401; also 24 W. R., 198; *Abadi Begam* v. *Inam Begam* [1877], I. L., 1 All., 521, where it was held not to have been abandoned.

(2) *Bhairon Singh* v. *Lanman* [1883], I. L., 7 All., 23.

(3) *Habib-un-Nissa* v. *Barkat Ali* [1886], I. L., 8 All., 275.

(4) *Muhammed Nasir-ud-din* v. *Abdul Hassan* [1894], I. L., 16 All., 300; *Muhammad Yunus Khan* v. *Muhammad Yusuf* [1897], I. L., 19 All., 334.

the vendee.(1) For the pre-emptor is no party to the dissolution by mutual agreement between the seller and purchaser, nor can he be affected by the rejection of the vendee as he has no control over the latter's action, and accordingly, when once the right of pre-emption has come into existence, it cannot be destroyed by the action of others,(2) but may be destroyed by his own acts.

In order to debar a party entitled to pre-empt a sale from exercising his right an opportunity to purchase must be given when a definite agreement to purchase at a fixed price has been entered into with a stranger.(3) The ordinary law of pre-emption is not applicable to compulsory sales in execution of decrees,(4) but where a sale is effected by the Collector under the orders of the Civil Court by private contract, the pre-emptive rights of persons entitled thereto were not ousted.(5)

SECTION II.

PERSONS ENTITLED TO PRE-EMPT.

The Sunni Hanafî Law relating to the right of pre-emption is the law in force in this country either territorially or by custom. According to the Hanafî Law three classes of persons are entitled to claim the right of pre-emption, not simultaneously, but in succession to each other. And the right may be claimed by one or more persons equally entitled to it.(6) It appertains:—

Persons entitled to pre-empt.

(1) to the co-sharer in the property, called a *shafî-i-sharîk* "pre-emptor by right of co-parcenary;"

(2) to a sharer in the rights and appurtenances, called a *shafî'i-khalît*,—"a pre-emptor by virtue of a right of easement over the property sold." In other words, persons who have a right of easement in respect of the property which forms the

---

(1) "Neither manhood, puberty, justice, or respectability of character are conditions of pre-emption under the Mahommedan Law," 1 Agra, p. 236.

(2) *Bhadir Mahomed* v. *Radha Churn Bolia*, 4 B. L. R., A. C., 219.

(3) *Kanhai Lall* v. *Kalka Prasad* [1905], I. L., 27 All., 670.

(4) *Baijnath* v. *Sital Singh* [1890], I. L., 13 All., 224.

(5) *Kanhai Lall* v. *Kalka Prasad*, supra.

(6) *Gureeboolla Khan* v. *Kebul Lall Mitter*, 12 W. R., 124.

subject of sale,—to use the language of the Arabian lawyers are " sharers in the appendages," are next entitled to claim the right of pre-emption;

(3) to a person whose property is contiguous to the subject of the sale technically called a *shafi'i-jâr*, " pre-emptor by right of vicinage."

The *shafi'i-sharîk* has a stronger right than the *shafî-i-khalît* and so the latter has a preferential claim to the *shafî-i-jâr*. In other words, one who has actually a share in the property has a stronger claim than a person who has a mere easement over the property. Similarly, a person claiming by right of vicinage or proximity stands in an inferior position to one who possesses a right of easement over the property sold.

Shafi-i-khalit.

In the case of *Gurreebullah Khan* v. *Kubul Lall Mitter*(1) the Calcutta High Court with reference to the word *sharîk* said as follows :—" The term *sharîk* cannot be restricted to cases in which the parties enjoy the properties jointly. In the contemplation of Mahommedan Law those who occupy other houses in the same mansion are regarded as partners together with the person, the sale of whose share in a house gives rise to the question of pre-emption."

A co-sharer has a right of pre-emption in large estates but a neighbour's right is much more restricted.(2)

In the case of *Chand Khan* v. *Niamat Khan*,(3) the owner of a piece of land, through which the land in respect of which the right of pre-emption was claimed received irrigation, was held entitled, and correctly on principle, to a preferential right to purchase against a mere neighbour. In other words, the owner of a dominant tenement is entitled to a right of pre-emption in respect of the servient tenement and *vice versâ*, in preference to a person claiming on the ground of vicinage. In the case of *Ranchondas* v. *Jugaldas*(4) the Bombay High Court has held that the right of support is not an appendage to property; it is merely included in the incident of

---

(1) 13 W. R. 124.

(2) See *post*, p. 722.

(3) [1869], 3 B. L. R., A. C., 296; S. C., 12 W. R., 162.

(4) [1899], I. L., 24 Bom., 414; *Karim* v. *Priyo Lall Bose* [1905], I. L., 28 All., 127.

neighbourhood. And, accordingly, where *A's* house joined the house in dispute towards the east; and *B's* house joined the house in dispute towards the south and was separated from it only by a wall, *B's* house was subject to the easement of support in favour of the house in dispute and *A's* house was subject to the easement of receiving and carrying off the rainwater falling from the roof of the disputed house. *A*, as owner of the servient tenement, was a "participator in the appendages" of the house in dispute, and, as such, had a preferential right to purchase the house in dispute over *B*, who was a mere neighbour.

A joint owner of a part of the property (such as a partner in a particular room or in a cistern or a reservoir in a field) has a superior right to one whose property is merely adjacent to that room or cistern or reservoir. And his right is superior even to that of one who is merely a neighbour to the entire property.

When a building situated in a private lane contains several houses and one of these houses is owned by two persons, one of whom sells his share to an outsider, the right of pre-emption appertains first to the vendor's co-sharer in the house, then to the partners in the building thereof, and next to the people in the street who are all alike. "If all these give up their right it belongs to the *mulâsik* or contiguous neighbour by whom is meant the neighbour behind the mansion sold who has a door opening into another street."

Right of pre-emption based on vicinage.

A house belonging to two persons is situate in a street which has no thoroughfare and one of the partners sells his share to a stranger, the right of pre-emption belongs first to the partner in the house, then to a partner in a party-wall, then to all the people in the street equally, and then to the person whose house is behind that which is sold.

A person having a right of way over the property sold has a preferential claim to one who has only a right of water without any interest in the site of the water.

So where a piece of land is sold over which one person has a right of way and another a right to discharge the water of his house, the former's claim is stronger.

Between neighbours, proximity to the subject-matter of the claim gives the preference, for example, one who is nearest is preferred to one who is further off.

If a house situated in a blind lane shut up at one end, communicating through another blind lane but of greater extent, happens to be sold, the residents of the short lane only are entitled to the right of pre-emption ; whereas if a house situated in the long lane were sold, the inhabitants of both lanes would be so entitled. The *Hedâya* gives the reason of this thus : "that the right of egress and ingress in the short lane is participated only by its own inhabitants ; whereas the right in the long lane appertains equally to the inhabitants of both, and therefore the residents of both lanes are entitled to claim the house by the right of pre-emption."

Abandonment by one pre-emptor.

If the person who has a preferential right waives or relinquishes his right or claim, the person next in order would be entitled to enforce his own right. For example, if a *shafî-i-sharîk* abandon his right of pre-emption, it would devolve on one who is the holder of a dominant tenement, and if he also give up his right it would devolve on the *shafî'i-jâr* or neighbour.

The *jâr-i-mulâsik* or a person whose house is situated at the back of that which is sold, has a better claim than other neighbours, the reason being that his house is close to the living apartments of the house sold.

But when the house sold is large consisting of several residences, the right of pre-emption belongs to the person residing adjacent to the house without any distinction as to the side on which he lives. Similarly, if any portion of the premises is sold. The reason of this is that when the house is large, consisting of several residences, to insist on the proximity of the living apartments would be useless.

Right of pre-emption on the part of neighbours.

When a house situate in a street without a thoroughfare belongs to two persons, one of whom sells his share, the right of pre-emption belongs, in the first place, to the other partner in the house. If he abandon his right, it would belong to the inhabitants of the street equally, without any distinction between those who are contiguous and those who are not, for they are all *khalîts* in the way. If they all surrender that right, it belongs to a *mulâsik* or contiguous neighbour. If there be a lane leading from this street and without any egress through it, and a house in it is sold, the right of pre-emption belongs to the inhabitants of this inner lane because they are more "specially intermixed" with it than the people of the other street ; but if a house in the outer street were sold the right of pre-emption would belong to the people of the inner lane as well as to those of the outer street, for the right of way possessed by the residents in both happens to be equal. But were the lane open with a passage through and a mansion in it were sold, there would be no right of pre-emption except for the adjoining neighbour. Similarly, where there is a thoroughfare, which is not private property, between two mansions (that is, when they are situate on opposite sides of the way) and one of them is sold, there is no pre-emption except for the adjoining neighbour. If the road be private property, it is the same as if there were no thoroughfare. But when the people residing in a particular street have no right to close it at any time, in other words when it is a public thoroughfare, persons residing on one side have no right of pre-emption in respect of any property on the other side. The Allahabad High Court has held in accordance with this principle that in order that two persons may become *Shafi 'i-khalîts* or persons having a right of pre-emption in virtue of the common enjoyment of, *e.g.*, a road, it is necessary that such road should be a private road and not a thoroughfare.(1) Among persons who are *Shafi 'i-khalîts* by reason of being sharers in a right of way all those who are sharers in such right of way have equal rights of pre-emption, although one of them be a contiguous neighbour.

When there are a number of persons entitled to claim a property by right of pre-emption(2) and some of them are absent, the Kâzi will adjudge the property to those who are present; but if the absentees appear subsequently and assert their claim, they would be entitled to their proportionate shares.(3) In none of these cases it is necessary that the site should also be sold.(4)

The right of pre-emption extends to agricultural estates.

It has been held that the right of pre-emption extends to agricultural estates, and is not confined merely to urban properties or small plots of lands.(5) And though the right founded on the basis of vicinage has been limited by the Courts in India to parcels of

(1) *Karim Bukhsh* v. *Khoda Bukhsh*, [1894], I. L., 16 All., 247.
(2) See *Moharaj Singh* v. *Lalla Beechuk Lall*, 3 W. R., 71.
(3) Comp. *Saligram* v. *Kalishankar* [1905], I. L., 27 All., 465.
(4) *Zahar Ali* v. *Nur Ali*, [1878], I. L. 2 All., 90.
(5) *Karim Bukhsh* v. *Kumuruddin Ahmed*, 6 N. W., 377.

land and houses,(1) such a right founded upon actual co-parcenary has been held to apply to villages or large estates.(2)

In *Mahommed Hossein* v. *Mohsin Ali*(3) the Calcutta High Court distinctly laid down that though a neighbour could not, under the Mahommedan Law, claim a right of pre-emption in respect of a share in villages or large estates, a co-sharer undoubtedly could, and that a neighbour's right extends only to houses, gardens and small plots of land.

The Calcutta High Court has also held that, when a Mahommedan co-owner of a property sells his share to a Hindu, his co-sharers have no right of pre-emption.(4) The reasoning of this decision is far-fetched and somewhat difficult to follow; and it has been expressly dissented from by the Allahabad High Court in *Brij Mohun Lall* v. *Abul Hassan Khan*,(5) in which it was held that in a case where the pre-emptor and the vendor are Mahommedans, and the vendee a non-Mahommedan, the Mahommedan Law is to be applied to the matter in advertence to the terms of s. 24 of Act VI of 1871 (The Bengal Civil Courts Act). The learned Judges added further, and it is submitted, correctly, that though the Courts are not bound to administer the Mahommedan Law in claims for pre-emption, yet on grounds of equity that law had always been administered in respect of such claims as between Mahommedans, and it would not be equitable that persons who were not Mahommedans, but who had dealt with Mahommedans in respect of property knowing the conditions and obligations under which the property was held, should, merely by reason that they were not themselves subject to the Mahommedan Law, be permitted to evade those conditions and obligations.

Applicable to a non-Moslem vendee.

---

(1) *Abdul Azim* v. *Khundkar Hamid Ali*, 8 B. L. R., A. C., 63; *Ejnash Koer* v. *Amjad Ali*, 2 W. R., 261; *Chowdhury Joogul Kishore Singh* v. *Poocha Singh*, 8 W. R., 413.

(2) See also *Govind Doyal* v. *Inayatullah*, I. L. [1885], 7 All., 775; *Mahommed Hossein* v. *Mohsin Ali* [1870], 6 B. L. R., 41; S. C., 14 W. R., F. B., 1; see also *Ukhoy Ram Shahaji* v. *Ram Kant Row*, 15 W. R., 225.

(3) Supra, see also *Jehangir Bukhsh* v. *Lalla Bhikari Lall* (in review), 7 B. L. R., 24; *Shaikh Karim Bukhsh* v. *Karim-ud-din Ahmed* [1874], 6 N. W. P. Rep., 377; *Abdul Rahim Khan* v. *Kharaty Singh* [1892], I. L., 15 All., 104.

(4) *Kudrutullah* v. *Mohini Mohun Shaha* [1869], 4 B. L. R., F. B., 134.

(5) [1885], I. L., 7 All., 775.

Where a pre-emptor by reason of the claim of other persons entitled equally with himself to claim pre-emption is only entitled to a certain portion of the property in respect of which he claims pre-emption and not to the whole of it, he is not bound to frame his suit for the whole of the property sold, but only for so much as he would be entitled to, having regard to the claims of the other pre-emptors.(1)

A pre-emptor not bound to frame his suit for whole property if only entitled to a share.

Where a pre-emptor sued for possession, by right of pre-emption of certain property sold by one and the same sale-deed, claiming as to one portion of the property sold under the Mahommedan Law and as to another under the *wajib-ul-arz*, and it was found that he had by his own acts or omissions disentitled himself from claiming that portion of the property to which the Mahommedan Law applied, it was held that he was not entitled to pre-emption in respect of any portion of the property covered by the deed of sale.(2)

SECTION III.

CONDITIONS ON WHICH THE RIGHT OF PRE-EMPTION DEPENDS.

There are two essential formalities the performance of both of which is a condition precedent to enable a person to claim the right of pre-emption.(3)

A person who intends to advance a claim based on the right of pre-emption in respect of property which has been sold to another, must immediately on receiving information of the sale, express in explicit terms his intention to claim the property. *The intention must be formulated in the shape of a demand.* No express formula is necessary so long as the assertion of the right, or what is called a demand is expressed in unequivocal language; this is called *talab-i-mowâsibat* or *immediate demand.*(4)

In making this demand there must be no delay on the part of the pre-emptor. It must follow immediately upon the receipt of

(1) *Abdullah* v. *Amanatullah* [1899], I. L., 21 All., 292.
(2) *Mujibullah* v. *Umed Bibi and another* [1898], I. L., 21 All., 119.
(3) *Jadu Sing* v. *Rajkumar* [1870], 4 B. L. R., A. C., 171.
(4) *Ibid.* See also *Prokas Sing* v. *Jogeswar* [1868], 2 B. L. R., A. C., 12; and *Jugdeo Singh* v. *Kazi Sayed Mahomed Afzal*, supra.

the information. It has been held that any delay in making this demand on hearing of the sale defeats the right of pre-emption.(1) It is not necessary, however, that it should be made in the presence of witnesses.(2)

As already stated no particular formula is necessary, so long as the claim is unequivocably asserted. Nor is it material in what words the claim is preferred ; so long as they imply a *claim* they are sufficient. "Thus," says the *Hedâya*, "if a person were to say 'I have claimed my *shufâ*' or 'I shall claim my *shufâ*' or 'I do claim my *shufâ*,' all these are good, for it is the meaning and not the style or mode of expression which is here considered."

"Similarly, if he said 'I have demanded,' or 'I take the mansion by pre-emption,' or 'do demand pre-emption' it would be lawful."

But if he were to say to the purchaser 'I am thy *shafî*' or 'pre-emptor,' it would be void. The reason of this distinction is evident, as a mere statement of a fact does not evince any desire on his part to avail himself of his right.

As the presence of witnesses is not necessary at the formulation of this demand, the evidence regarding the performance of this preliminary formality generally rests on the evidence of the pre-emptor.

But the demand must be made after the sale has been completed. If made whilst negotiations are going on between the vendor and the vendee it is of no avail.

(2) The second condition is that the pre-emptor should, with as little delay as is possible under the circumstances, repeat before witnesses his demand, (*a*) *either on the premises in dispute, or* (*b*) *in the presence of the vendor or* (*c*) *of the vendee, calling on the the witnesses to bear testimony to the fact.*(3) *This formality is called talab-i-ishtish-hâd* or *demand by invocation of witnesses.*

As the right to pre-emption is *strictissimi juris*, failure to perform the "demands" in accordance with the requirements of the law would defeat the claim.

---

(1) *Ali Muhammed* v. *Taj Muhammed* [1876]. I. L., 1 All., 283 ; *Jarfan Khan* v. *Jabbar Meah* [1884], I. L., 10 Cal., 383 ; see *post* p. 739.

(2) *Jadu Sing* v. *Raj Kumar*, supra.

(3) *Mubarek Husain* v. *Kaniz Banu* [1904], I. L., 27 All., 161 ; *Ganga Prasad* v. *Ajudhia Prasad* (1905), I. L., 28 All., 24.

This formality is insisted upon with the object of getting evidence of the fact that the pre-emptor has really asserted his right. It must be performed within a reasonable time and without any unnecessary delay after the first demand. An unnecessary delay in the assertion of the second demand would defeat the claim. The question of time or delay is one of fact, and would depend on the circumstances of the particular case.(1)

Talab-i-ishtish-hâd.

In order to entitle the claimant to perform the second demand in the presence of the vendee it is not necessary that he should be in possession of the property in respect of which the right is claimed.(2) For the performance of the ceremony of *Talab-i-ishtish-hâd* the pre-emptor must take some witnesses with him to the vendor, if the property sold be still in his possession, or to the vendee or to the property which is the subject-matter of the claim. And there, in the presence of the witnesses, he must say to the following effect: "such a person bought such a property (sufficiently indicating the same) of which I am the *shafî*; I have already claimed my right of *shufâ* and now again claim it, be therefore witness thereof."

The Courts in India have held that at the time of making this second demand the pre-emptor should distinctly state that he has already made the *talab-i-mowasibat*.(3) They have also held that where certain persons claimed pre-emption in respect of a share in an undivided village and proved that they made an immediate assertion of their intention to pre-empt in the presence of witnesses within the area of the zemindari to which the share sold belonged, in the absence of any indication that the demand was not made *bonâ fide*, the demand of pre-emption was a good demand made "on the premises" within the meaning of the Mahommedan Law.(4)

---

(1) *Ali Muhammad Khan* v. *Muhammad Said Hussain* [1896], I. L., 18 All., 309; *Jaridan* v. *Latif Hossain*, 8 B. L. R., 160.

(2) *Rajjub Ali Chopdar* v. *Chandi Churn Bhaddra* [1890], I. L., 17 Cal., 543; *Abbasi Begum* v. *Afzal Husain* [1898], I. L., 20 All., 457; *Ali Muhammad Khan* v. *Muhammad Said Hussain* [1896], I. L., 18 All., 309.

(3) *Rajjub Ali Chopdar* v. *Chandi Churn Bhaddra*, supra; *Mubarak Hossein* v. *Kamiz Banu* [1904], I. L., 27 All., 160; *Abbasi Begum* v. *Afzal Husain*, supra; *Zamir Husain* v. *Dantal Ram* [1883], I. L. 5 All., p. 110.

(4) *Kulsum Bibi* v. *Faqir Muhammad Khan*, [1896] I. L., 18 All., 298.

Talab-i-ishtish-hâd (contd.).

These formalities may be observed by the claimant personally or by proxy.(1) It has also been held that the personal performance of the *talab-i-ishtish-hâd* depends on the claimant's ability to perform it. He may do it by means of a letter or a messenger or may depute an agent, if he is at a distance and cannot attend personally.(2) The law requires that the performance of the ceremonies must be strictly established. But the course of decisions in India has not been uniform in the application of the principle.

The pre-emptor must offer to pay the price that has been paid by the vendee, or, if he considers the consideration alleged as not real, must express his willingness to take the property for the actual price paid for it.(3) But he is not required to tender the price at the performance of either ceremony.

The right of pre-emption, even where resting on custom is, generally speaking, co-extensive with the rules of the Mussulman Law.(4) And unless it is proved that it is not customary to perform both the *talabs*, the party claiming the right of pre-emption is bound to comply with the requirements of the Mussulman Law. But where it is customary not to perform either of the two demands, even a Mahommedan pre-emptor is not bound to go through all the formalities.(5)

It has been sometimes held(6) that the demand must be in the form given in the *Hedâya*, but that does not seem to be a correct view of the law; what the law requires is that the demand must be to that effect and no more.

---

(1) *Syed Wajid Ali Khan* v. *Lalla Hanuman Prasad* [1869], 4 B. L. R., A. C., 139; s.c., 12 W. R., 484; *Imamuddin* v. *Shahjan Bibi* [1870], 6 B. L. R., 167, note; *Ali Muhammad Khan* v. *Muhammad Said Khan*, supra. Where the property is in the charge of the Court of Wards, the manager is entitled to perform the ceremonies; *Jadu Lall Sahu* v. *Maharani Janki Koar*, P. C. 20th March 1912.

(2) *Lagu Prasad* v. *Debi Prasad* [1880], I. L., 3 All., 236; *Karim Bakhsh* v. *Khuda Bakhsh* [1894], I. L., 16 All., 247.

(3) *Mujib-ullah* v. *Umed Bibi* [1898], I. L., 21 All., 119; Comp. *Abdulmajid* v. *Amolak* [1907], I. L., 29 All., 618.

(4) *Prokas Singh* v. *Jageswar Singh* [1868], 2 B. L. R., A. C., 12; *Jadu Singh* v. *Rajkumar* [1870], 4 B. L. R., A. C., 171; *Ali Mohammed* v. *Taj Mohammed* [1896], I. L., 1 All., 285; see also *Harihar Deb* v. *Sheo Proshad* [1884], I. L., 7 All., 41.

(5) *Ramdular Misser* v. *Jhumak Lall Misser*, 8 B. L. R., p. 455; s. c., 17 W. R., 265; *Gordhun Das Girdhurbhai* v. *Darankar*, 6 Bom. A. C., p. 263.

(6) *Fakir Rawat* v. *Emam Bukhsh*, B. L. R., Supp. Vol., p. 35; s. c., W. R., F. B., 143.

But the *talab-i-ishtish-hâd* may be combined with the *talab-i-mowâsibat, e.g.*, if at the time of the *talab-i-mowâsibat*, the pre-emptor had an opportunity of invoking witnesses in the presence of the seller or the purchaser or on the premises to attest the immediate demand, it would suffice for both demands, and there would be no necessity for the second.(1)

If the property was sold for a price payable at a distant period, the claimant may either wait until then to pay the price and take the property, or he may pay it immediately and take the property at once, but unless the vendor had given any time to the purchaser for the payment of the price, the pre-emptor cannot claim any respite therefor.

The claimant by virtue of the right of pre-emption is bound to pay for any improvement effected by the purchaser unless the improvements are detachable. In case of deterioration in the hands of the purchaser, the pre-emptor is entitled to a deduction, unless the deterioration has taken place without the instrumentality of the purchaser, in which case the pre-emptor must pay the full value.

If a house has been sold in exchange for goods or effects, the pre-emptor is entitled to take it for the value of such effects "for effects are amongst the things denominated *zât-ul-kâyim* or things which being estimable are compensable by an equivalent in money. If, on the other hand, a man sells a house for compensation in wheat, silver or any other article estimable by measure or weight, the *shafî* may take it for an equal quantity of the same article, because these are of the class of *zât-ul-imsâl* or things compensable by an equal quantity of the same species."

If a piece of land is exchanged for another piece, the pre-emptor of each piece would be entitled to take it for the value of the other land "being of the class of *zât-ul-kâyim* or things compensable by an equivalent in money."

If the property has changed hands and is in the possession of the vendee, the pre-emptor must take it on the price stated by the purchaser to have been paid by him.

---

(1) [1869], 4 B. L. R., A. C., 171; but see 8 B. L. R., 455. Comp. (1870), 4 B. L. R., A. C., p. 139; 6 C. L. R., p. 166; *Nundo Pershad Thakur* v. *Gopal Thakur* [1884], I. L., 10 Cal., 1008.

It is otherwise if the property is still in the hands of the vendor, in such a case the consideration mentioned by him should be paid by the pre-emptor.

Abatement of price by the vendor.

Any abatement in the price made by the vendor in favour of the purchaser would accrue to the benefit of the pre-emptor. But should the vendor, after the conclusion of the sale, remit the whole of the price to the vendee, the pre-emptor would not be allowed to avail himself of the remission.

The reason of the distinction is that an abatement in the price is connected with the original bargain or sale and the pre-emptor is therefore entitled to claim its benefit, whilst an entire remission is unconnected with the transaction, and is more in the nature of a subsequent gift.

Should the vendee, after the bargain is concluded, agree to an augmentation of the price in favour of the seller, the pre-emptor would not be liable for such increase, for his right is founded on the original contract.

Similarly, if a house be sold for one price and afterwards another contract be made in respect of the same house with the same purchaser settling a larger price, the pre-emptor is not prejudiced by such augmentation, but is entitled to his right of pre-emption for the price first agreed upon.

Period of limitation.

Under the Mussulman Law there is no fixed period within which a pre-emptor, whose claim is not acceded to, should prefer his claim called *talab-i-khusûmat* or *talab-i-tamlîk* in Court. Under Schedule II of the Indian Limitation Act (XV of 1877) Art. 10, however, the period of limitation for a suit to enforce a right of pre-emption is one year.

If a suit is not brought within that period, the claim would be barred.

SECTION IV.

THE PROCEEDINGS IN COURT.

Where the claim to pre-emption is based either on custom or special agreement, the British Indian Courts have held that in order to assert the right, the vendor and claimant must both be subject to Mahommedan Law.(1)

The Calcutta High Court has introduced a further qualification. It has held that the vendee should also be a Mahommedan,(2) which destroys the whole policy of the Mahommedan Law. The Allahabad High Court, on the contrary, has laid down, it is submitted rightly, that in order to maintain the right, *it is not necessary that the vendee should be a Mahommedan.*(3) It holds as already stated that it would not be equitable that persons who were not Mahommedans, but who had dealt with Mahommedans in respect of property knowing the conditions and obligations under which the property was held, should, merely by reason that they were not themselves subject to the Mahommedan Law, be permitted to evade those conditions and obligations.

When a plurality of persons belonging to the same category are entitled to the privilege of pre-emption their rights are equal without reference to the extent of their shares,(4) *e.g.*, if *A*, *B* and *C* are co-sharers in a property, *A's* share being one-third, *B's* being half, and *C's* being one-sixth, and *A* sells his share to *D*, *B* and *C* will become entitled to *A's* share in equal moieties.

A Full Bench of the Calcutta High Court has held that when one co-sharer conveys his share to another co-sharer no other co-sharer if any, can have a right of pre-emption, the right of all being equal, and the reason on which the right is founded being therefore absent.(5)

The Allahabad High Court has taken a different view and held that when there are more than two co-sharers and one sells his

---

(1) *Dwarka Das* v. *Hossain Bakhsh* [1878], I. L., 1 All., 564; *Poorno Singh* v. *Hurry Churn Surmah* [1872], 10 B. L. R., A. C., 117.

(2) *Sheik Kadratullah* v. *Mahini Mohan Shaha* [1869], 4 B. L. R., A. C., 134

(3) *Brijmohan* v. *Abdul Hasan Khan* [1885], I. L., 7 All., 775.

(4) *Moharaj Singh* v. *Lalla Bheechuk Lall* [1865], 3 W. R., 71. In the case of *Abbas Ali* v. *Maza Ram* [1888], I. L., 12 All., 229, a Division Bench of the Allahabad High Court held that under the Shiah Law, no right of pre-emption exists in the case of property owned by more than two co-sharers. This view is opposed to two other decisions of the same Court, and its correctness is open to question; *firstly*, on the ground that the Sunni Hanafi Law furnishes the guiding rule in this country in cases of pre-emption; and, *secondly*, that the Shiah Law is by no means as explicit as has been assumed in this case.

(5) *Lalla Nowbut Lall* v. *Lalla Juvan Lall* [1897], I. L., 4 Cal., 831.

share to another, the remaining co-sharers are entitled to take the share sold in equal parts with the vendee co-sharer.

For example, if there are four co-sharers *A*, *B*, *C* and *D*, and *A* sells his share to *B*, *C* and *D* would be entitled respectively to one-third of that share.

This view is undoubtedly in conformity with the enunciations of the Mahommedan jurists. The principle is based on the following ground.(1) As all the pre-emptors have equal rights against a stranger, their rights are the same *inter se*, and it would be unfair to give preference to one sharer over the others. And any one pre-emptor may pre-empt in respect of his specific share.(2)

But both Courts are agreed that where a co-sharer associates a stranger with him in the purchase of a share, another co-sharer is entitled to pre-empt the whole of the property sold, but it is not obligatory upon him to impeach the sale so far as the co-sharer vendee is concerned.(3)

Nor is the owner of a piece of land entitled to pre-emption in respect of a house standing thereon, when his right in the land is wholly separate and distinct from the right in the house which belongs to another person with whom he has nothing in common.(4)

The pre-emptor is not bound to produce or tender the price during the pendency of his suit. It is necessary, however, that he should tender the price to the buyer or deposit it in Court when once the decree has been made in his favour. But a delay in the payment of the price does not defeat the right which under the decree has become vested in the pre-emptor. It is usual, however, for the Courts of Justice in India to fix a period of time within which the price should be paid. If not so paid the right drops.

The buyer is entitled to retain the property in spite of any decree in favour of the pre-emptor until he has received the price.

Effect of a decree declaring the right.

When two or more persons are entitled to the right of pre-emption in a particular property, each one of them can claim the

(1) *Amir Hasan* v. *Rahim Bukhsh* [1897], I. L., 19 All., 466, 831.

(2) *Abdulla* v. *Amanatullah* [1899], I. L., 21 All., 292.

(3) *Manna Singh* v. *Ram Dhin Singh* [1881], I. L.. 4 All., 252; *Harjas* v. *Kanhya* [1884], I. L., 7 All., 118; *Saligram Sing* v. *Raghubar Dyal* [1887], I. L., 15 Cal., 224.

(4) *Pershadi Lall* v. *Irshad Ali*, 2 N. W. R., 100.

property in its entirety. But when a decree has been made in favour of two and one of them gives up his share, or even if without a decree, one of the two pre-emptors surrenders his right after taking possession of the property, the other does not become entitled to the share so given up or surrendered. In other words, before the right has become effectuated by actual delivery of the property by the buyer to the pre-emptor, or by the decree of the Judge, each of several pre-emptors has a right to the whole, and a waiver by one gives to the other a right to the whole. But after the right has effectuated as above, each one has a separate interest and can surrender it to the buyer if he pleases, without giving any right to his co-pre-emptors.

When a decree is made in favour of one who is entitled to the right of pre-emption in the second or third degree and subsequent thereto a person with a superior claim asserts his right, the latter would be entitled to a decree for the whole by cancellation of the first.

Option of inspection.

The pre-emptor has the option of inspection even after decree by Judge. "If the Kâzi," says the *Hedâya*, "were to make a decree in favour of the pre-emptor before he has seen the property in dispute, the pre-emptor has an option of inspection and if any defect be afterwards discovered in it he has an option from defect, and may, if he please, reject it notwithstanding the purchaser should have expected such defect from the bargain, or in other words, should have exempted the seller from responsibility for such defect." "Because, as the transfer of property by right of *shufâ'a* is the same as a transfer of property by sale, the pre-emptor has, therefore, under both the above circumstances the power of rejection in the same manner as any other stranger, and this power in the pre-emptor is not destroyed by the purchaser having seen the property or having so exempted the seller, for he (the purchaser) was not deputed by the pre-emptor, and his act of course does not affect the pre-emptor's right." The validity of the objection taken by the pre-emptor must, it seems, depend upon how far it is *bonâ fide*, or made merely for harassing the other parties.

Improvements made by the buyer.

If the buyer has made any improvements in the property the pre-emptor must either pay their value or cause them to be removed. But if he has grown a crop on the land, the pre-emptor must wait for its ripening, after which he will take the land at the full price.

Should the buyer erect buildings or plant trees upon the land and a decree is made for the land, the pre-emptor has the option of taking the land together with the building or trees, paying the value of both or compelling the purchaser to remove them.

Deterioration.

When the property, which forms the subject-matter of dispute, deteriorates in the hands of the purchaser, the claimant is entitled to a proportionate reduction in the price, unless the deterioration has not been caused by the purchaser, in which case the pre-emptor must either pay the whole price or resign his claim.

If the purchaser wilfully breaks down any buildings or structure, the pre-emptor may either resign his claim or may take the area of land for a proportionate part of the original price, but he is not entitled to the materials because they form now a separate property, and are no longer appendages of the land, and the right of pre-emption extends only to the land and to things so attached to it as to be appendages.

When any portion of a house or garden is destroyed by accident or natural causes, the pre-emptor has the option of either resigning the whole or taking it, paying the full price. It is otherwise with land, and if a portion thereof is diluviated the pre-emptor may take the remainder, paying a proportionate price therefor. The reason of this distinction is said to be that a house or garden is a mere appendage to land, whereas land is the real subject to which a right of pre-emption appertains.

When a person after his purchase pulls down the buildings, the price is to be divided according to the value of the buildings as they were while standing and the value of the cleared space, and the pre-emptor is to take the land at so much of the price as corresponds to the latter.

If the buildings are burnt down or swept away by an inundation so as to leave nothing in the hands of the purchaser, the pre-emptor must take the site at the full price. In other words, the purchaser is not damnified by loss occasioned by what in English law would be called "an act of God."

Any intermediate dealing by the buyer with the property is voidable at the instance of the pre-emptor, for example, if the purchaser disposes of the subject of the claim, such sale is void so far as the pre-emptor is concerned. If the pre-emptor has, after obtaining possession of the property, made any improvements in it by erecting buildings, planting trees and so forth, and if it be proved that the land belonged to some person other than the vendor or vendee, in such a case the pre-emptor is entitled to recover back the price paid by him from whomsoever he had taken the property, and is at liberty to remove what was done by him upon the property or land in question, but he cannot recover from either party the value of the improvements made by him.

Relinquishment of the right.

The right of pre-emption may be relinquished either expressly or impliedly.

The pre-emptor may expressly forego the right of pre-emption, with or without any compensation.

Implied relinquishment depends upon inferences deducible from his conduct. If he omits without any sufficient cause to perform the demands after learning of the sale, the inference is that he has abandoned his right; and the law, therefore, holds that such omission avoids the right. Acquiescence in the sale either by offering to purchase from the buyer the property sold, or by asking him if he would give it up to him, or by taking it from him on lease, amounts in law to a relinquishment.(1) But these acts have that result only when they are done with the knowledge of the sale.

According to the Hanafî Law the right of pre-emption is a personal right and does not survive to the pre-emptor's heirs. Of course, if they are themselves entitled to claim the right, they stand on a different footing.

Hanafî doctrine.

Thus the right of pre-emption is rendered void by operation of law when the pre-emptor dies after making the necessary demands, but before he has taken over the property which forms the subject-matter of dispute, or before he has obtained a decree therefor from the Court.(2) But it is not rendered void by the death of the purchaser, and the pre-emptor can, therefore, assert his right and take the property from his heirs.

---

(1) See *Habib-un-nissa* v. *Barkat Ali* [1886], I. L., 7 All., 275.

(2) *Muhammed Husain* v. *Niamatunnissa* [1897], I. L., 20 All., 88.

Shiah and Shâfeï doctrine.

According to the Shâfeïs and the Shiahs the right of pre-emption is a heritable right and devolves upon the heirs of the pre-emptor.

When a man purchases from one by a single bargain several houses in a street in which there is no thoroughfare and the pre-emptor desires to take one of them, if his right of pre-emption is based on partnership in the right of way, he cannot take a part of the purchased property, for this would be to divide the bargain without any necessity ;(1) but if the right be based on neighbourhood and he is neighbour only to the house which he wishes to take, he may lawfully take that alone.(2)

According to the *Hedâya* when the purchased property consists of several parts, each separate and distinct from the other, as for instance when two houses are purchased by one bargain, the pre-emptor cannot take one of them without the other if he is pre-emptor of the two together. He must either take both or leave both, whether the houses are adjacent to or separated from each other, and whether they are situate in the same or different cities.

In accordance with this doctrine it has been held that when the deed of sale covers two properties in respect of one of which only the claimant has a right of pre-emption he is entitled to sue for that alone. But if his right extends to the entire subject-matter of the particular transaction he cannot split it up so as to take one part of the property and reject the other part. He must abide by the bargain as a whole.(3) He must, therefore, take or leave the whole whether the purchase be by one person from one or by one from two or more.

But where a property is purchased by several persons in specified shares the pre-emptor may take the whole or the portion of any of them.

When the person claiming the right of pre-emption sells previous to the decree of the Kâzi the property upon which his right is founded, that right becomes extinguished.

---

(1) Comp. *Kazee Ali* v. *Mussutullah,* 2 W. R., 28 ; *Surdharee Lal* v. *Lopoo Moodee,* 25 W. R., 500 ; and *Durga Persad* v. *Munsi* [1884], I. L., 6 All., 423, and the other cases referred to there.

(2) *Roushan Koer* v. *Ram Dial Roy,* 13 Cal. L. R., 45.

(3) *Durga Prasad* v. *Munsi,* supra ; *Amir Hassan* v. *Rahim Bakhsh* [1897], I. L., 19 All., 466.

When the pre-emptor has different rights of pre-emption, the extinction of one does not affect the other, and therefore when he is both a partner and a neighbour, and he sells his share on which his right in the former capacity is founded, he may still assert his claim on the ground of neighbourhood.(1)

Right relinquished upon mis-information.

Where the right had been relinquished upon mis-information of the amount, or the kind of price, or of the purchaser, or of the property sold, the pre-emptor can assert the right on being informed of the true facts. For example, if he relinquished his right on being informed that the price was 1,000 dirhems, whereas in reality the price was less, he may, on coming to know of the truth, still assert his right.(2)

Relinquishment of the right.

Nor does relinquishment in favour of one operate in favour of another. For example, if the pre-emptor on learning that *A* is the purchaser, waive his right, he can, on subsequently learning that the purchaser is in reality *B*, assert his title.

If the pre-emptor act as an agent of the vendor in the transaction he has no right of pre-emption ; it is otherwise if he acts as an agent for the purchaser.

Where a minor is entitled to a right of pre-emption, his guardian may abandon the right if he consider it necessary.

Where the pre-emptor brings an action to assert his rignt, and it is found that he had, before suit, transferred to another the property on which his right was founded, his action must fall to the ground.(3) In order to obtain relief his right must be subsisting at the time of the decree.(4) But to destroy the right the alienation must be absolute and not partial.(5)

The pre-emptor cannot transfer his *right of pre-emption* before decree,(6) although he may convey the property sued for after decree.

---

(1) In two cases the Calcutta High Court has held that where a plaintiff sought to enforce a right of pre-emption upon the ground of partnership, he could not obtain a decree on the ground of vicinage ; *Kunja Behari Lal* v. *Girdhari Lal* [1868], 1 B. L. R., S. N., 12 ; s.c., 10, W. R., 182 ; *Shiu Sahai Mullick* v. *Hari Sahai Sing* [1869], 3 B. L. R., All., 142. But this is different from the superior right becoming extinguished by operation of Law.

(2) Comp. *Abadi Begum* v. *Imami Begum*, supra ; and *Bhairon Sing* v. *Lalmon* [1884], I. L., 7 All., 23.

(3) *Janki Parshad* v. *Ishar Das* [1899], I. L., 21 All., 374.

(4) *Ram Gopal* v. *Piari Lall* [1897], I. L., 21 All., 441.

(5) *Rajo* v. *Lalman* [1882], I. L., 5 All., 180.

(6) *Ram Sahai* v. *Gaya* [1884], I. L., 7 All., 107.

A right of pre-emption, based on the village settlement record or *wajib-ul-arz* in the North-Western Provinces, is not in all respects analogous to the pre-emptional right under the Mahommedan Law. It has been held by the Allahabad High Court that when there are several co-sharers in a village and one of them sells his share or part of his share to another co-sharer and a stranger, under one and the same deed of sale, if the interest conveyed to the stranger can be separated from that conveyed to the co-sharer, the remaining co-sharers would be entitled to claim the stranger's interest, otherwise they would be entitled to succeed against both vendees.(1)

Where a right of pre-emption arises on the foreclosure of a mortgage under the Transfer of Property Act (IV of 1882) the right to sue for pre-emption accrues, not from the date fixed in the decree under section 86, as the date upon which payment is to be made by the mortgagor, but from the date on which the mortgagee obtains an order absolute under section 87 of the said Act.(2)

The law allows certain devices for the evasion of the right of pre-emption, *e.g.*, where a man sells the whole of his house excepting only the breadth of one yard extending alongside the house of the pre-emptor, the latter is not in this case entitled to claim the right of pre-emption, because he is no more a neighbour. Similarly if the vendor were to grant the intervening part of his house as a free gift to the purchaser and put him in possession.

---

(1) *Ram Nath* v. *Badri Narain* [1896], I. L., 19 All., 148; *Sheobharos Rai* v. *Jiach Rai* [1886], I. L., 8 All., 462.

(2) *Batul Begum* v. *Mansur Ali Khan* [1898], I. L., 20 All., 315; *Anwar-ul-Haq* v. *Jwala Prasad*, ibid., 358; *Raham Ilahi Khan* v. *Ghasita*, ibid., 375.

CHAPTER XXIX.

THE SHIAH LAW OF PRE-EMPTION.

THERE is great divergence between the Shiahs and the Hanafîs with regard to the persons who may claim the right of pre-emption.

Under the Shiah Law, co-sharers in the property, that is *shafî'i-shârîk* alone are entitled to the right of pre-emption ; but as the Sunni Hanafî Law of pre-emption is the law in force in this country either territorially or by custom, a Sunni would be entitled to pre-emption on the basis of a right of easement or vicinage when the vendor is a Shiah.(1) The same rule would apply if the vendor happen to be a Sunni. The Allahabad High Court, however, has held that when both the vendor and the vendee are Sunnis, a pre-emptor belonging to the Shiah sect claiming on the ground of vicinage has no right of pre-emption.(2)

Although according to the Shiah Law only a partner in the property sold can claim the property by right of pre-emption, there is no right of pre-emption when there are several sharers, and one of them only sells his share.(3) Some legists, however, are of opinion that even where there are more than two partners and one sells his share, a right of pre-emption arises in favour of the other co-sharers.

It is not necessary, however, that the person claiming the right of pre-emption should be a partner in the substance of the thing. So long as he has an existing interest of a substantial nature which is likely to be interfered with or disturbed by the introduction of a stranger, the law will recognise the right. For example, if two persons hold two tenements separately, but have a pathway or road or watercourse in joint enjoyment by virtue of their holdings either of them will have a right in respect of the other's tenement.

(1) *Jugdeo Singh* v. *Kâzi Sayed Mohamed Afzal* [1905], 9 Cal. W. N., 26.
(2) *Kurban Hosain* v. *Chote* [1899], I. L., 22 All., 102.
(3) See *Domi* v. *Ashasha Bibee*, 2 N. W., 360.

A man, who has only an easement over another's property, or a mere neighbour has no right to claim the property in question in preference to a third person. If the easement is one of right or has vested by operation of law, it will not be interfered with by the purchaser, and no inconvenience can accrue to the holder of the dominant tenement; so also in the case of a neighbour, no question of inconvenience can arise.

Who may exercise the right.

When a person entitled to claim a property by right of pre-emption is not *sui juris*, being either under age or *non compos mentis*, his guardian should exercise the right on his behalf, provided the same be for the advantage of the ward.

Failure on the part of the guardian to make the demand does not extinguish the right of the person entitled; and should the guardian abandon the claim, the minor on attaining puberty, and the insane person on recovering his reason, may still assert it.

A person, who was absent at the time of sale, is entitled to prefer his claim, however prolonged his absence might be, in case he was during his absence unable to prosecute it in person or through an agent.

A sick person, or one who is undergoing imprisonment and therefore unable to prefer his claim, stands in the same position as one who is absent.

Right comes into operation on the conclusion of the contract.

According to the Shiah Law, the right of pre-emption comes into operation immediately on the conclusion of the contract, and not merely on the completion of the transfer.

As in the Hanafî Law, the pre-emptor must take the whole of the property or abandon the whole, he cannot split up the contract in his favour.

He must take at the contract price, whether the real value of the share be more or less, without being liable for incidental expenses.

If the purchaser add something to the price after (completion of) the contract and expiration of the period of option, such addition is not an augmentation of the price but a gift, and the preemptor will not be liable for it.

If, however, the augmentation is made during the period of option, the Shaikh has declared that it constitutes a part of the original price and stands on the same footing as if it had been stipulated in the contract; but "this opinion," says the author of the *Shâraya*, "is attended with some difficulty as being inconsistent with what has already been said of the transfer being completed by the contract."

In like manner, if the seller should make any abatement from the price, such abatement is unconnected with the contract, and the purchaser is by no means bound to surrender the share until he has received the full price settled at the making of the contract.

If a person were to purchase a property in exchange for a jewel or such like article, the pre-emptor may take the property at its value at the time of the contract, which must be properly appraised.

Unavoidable delay in preferring claim does not occasion loss of right.

The pre-emptor should prefer his claim as soon as he is informed of the contract. Unavoidable delay caused by absence, illness or incarceration preventing his preferring the claim through an agent, does not lead to the extinction of the right.

Similarly, if the delay is owing to his having been wrongly informed of the amount or kind of price, his right does not drop.

Due diligence necessary.

He must use due diligence in prosecuting his claim. For example, when travelling with that intent, he is not obliged to use greater expedition in his journey than is habitual to himself. Further, should he be engaged in the performance of any religious duty, whether indispensable or discretionary, he is not obliged to break it off, but may lawfully wait till it is completed. In like manner, if the time of prayer is at hand, he may wait till he has purified himself, and perform his devotion without hurry or restraint.

Neglect on the part of a person, who receives intelligence of a sale whilst on a journey and unable to prefer his claim by personally appearing or appointing an agent to call upon witnesses to attest his intention to demand it, does not extinguish his right. But when he is in a position to assert his claim either in person or by appointing an agent and neglects to do so, his right is entirely lost. Should the vendor and vendee agree to rescind the contract that would not destroy the right of the pre-emptor, and he may, despite such rescission, claim to have the property conveyed to him.

Acquiescence.

As under the Hanafî Law, acquiescence in the sale, either express or implied, will extinguish the right.

No dealing by the vendee would affect the right of the pre-emptor, and if he sells the subject of the claim to a third person, the pre-emptor would be entitled to take it from him.

The pre-emptor's right is against the vendee, and he takes the property from him and not from the vendor, but if the property continues in the hands of the latter, he may take it from him, though the responsibility rests upon the vendee.

If the subject of sale should perish or become damaged without any act on the part of the purchaser, or by his act but before it was demanded by the *shafi'i*, in that case it is optional with the latter to take the property at the full price, or abandon it entirely, and in the event of his taking it, he is entitled to all the ruins or fragments that remain, whether they are still on the spot or have been removed from it.

If, on the other hand, the property has become injured or has deteriorated owing to some act of the purchaser after demand made by the pre-emptor, the purchaser is responsible.

Erections made by the purchaser.

If the vendee should, before any demand has been made, plant trees or erect buildings upon the land, he is entitled at his option to take up the trees or remove his buildings without levelling the ground, while it is optional with the pre-emptor to take it at the full price, or to relinquish his right absolutely.

If again, the vendee should decline to remove the trees or buildings, the pre-emptor has three courses open to him, *viz.*, he may either remove them himself, paying the purchaser compensation for any loss he may sustain thereby, or he may take possession of the whole, paying in addition to the price the value of the trees or buildings which thus become his property with the consent of the purchaser, or he may abandon his claim altogether.

Accretions to the property.

If the subject of the claim should increase in such a manner that the increase is connected with and forms part of it, the accretion would belong to the pre-emptor, but if the accretion is separable from the *corpus*, it would belong to the vendee.

If a person should sell his share in two houses, and the pre-emptor is a partner in both, he may lawfully take or abandon both or he may take one and forego his claim in respect to the other. But in the case of a single mansion he cannot forego his claim to a part.

If the sale is in the nature of an exchange, the price being a specific article, and it turns out to be the property of some person other than the vendee, as the sale is null, there is no right of pre-emption. But if the price was fixed in some commodity estimable by weight or measure as wheat or grain or corn, the right would be fully established, even though the articles in question should turn out to be the property of another person. Similarly, if the consideration is in coin or money, which is found to belong to somebody other than the vendee, the right of pre-emption, having once come into existence, will not fall to the ground.

If the subject of the sale should appear to be defective, and the vendee in consequence thereof should receive a compensation for the defect, the pre-emptor is entitled to a deduction in the price. But should the vendee keep the subject of the sale without seeking any compensation for the defect, the pre-emptor must either take it at the full price, or abandon his claim altogether. Should the pre-emptor abandon his claim upon being informed that there are two vendees, and it then appear that there was only one, or if he was informed that there was only one vendee, and it turns out that there were two, or if he was told that the purchaser bought for himself, and it afterwards appear that he bought for another, in all these cases the right is not lost.

Right of pre-emption heritable.

The Shiahs agree with the Shâfeis in holding that the right of pre-emption devolves by inheritance upon the heirs of the pre-emptor, so that if he should die leaving a widow and a child, an eighth of it goes to the widow and the remainder to the child.

And if one heir were to relinquish his share of the right, it would not drop or be extinguished, but the other might take the whole.

Attaches only to immovable property.

The right of pre-emption attaches only to immovable property. With respect to trees and buildings, the right of pre-emption is established if they are sold as appendages of the ground on which they stand.

The right of pre-emption is established with respect to rivulets, roads, baths, &c., provided the division thereof would not occasion a loss or damage such as to render the property useless.

By damage the Shiahs understand such injury as would render the property useless after division, in which case the person who would be injured cannot be compelled to make a partition.

Where, again, the bath or road or rivulet is of such a character that its utility would not be destroyed by division, the co-owner may be compelled to admit of a partition, and (if he should sell his share) the right of pre-emption would take effect in favour of his partner.

If a person should sell a piece of land which is his exclusive prop and with it his share in another joint tenement by one bargain, the right of pre-emption attaches to the share exclusively at the due proportion of the price.

When the right of pre-emption comes into existence.

It is an indispensable condition for the operation of the right of pre-emption that the share of the property should have been transferred by sale. If the share has been assigned as a dower or given in charity or bestowed by way of gift or in composition for a claim, it is not subject to the claim of pre-emption.

If a mansion should be partly *wakf* and partly free, and the portion which is free be sold, the beneficiaries of the *wakf* have no right of pre-emption. The author of the *Jawâhir* says, however, that "a right would be established."

When the pre-emptor takes possession of the property and then discovers a defect which existed prior to the sale, if both he and the purchaser were equally aware of the defect neither of them has any option (in the matter); but if they were both ignorant of the defect, and the *shafi'i* returns the property to the purchaser, the latter has an option either to reject the sale altogether, or to demand a compensation for the defect from the seller.

If, however, the *shafi'i* should elect to retain the property, the purchaser has in that case no right to cancel the sale because the share has passed out of his hands.

So also if the pre-emptor was acquainted with the defect and not the purchaser. But if the purchaser was apprized of it and not the pre-emptor, the latter only would have the right of rejection.

There are devices not recognised under the Hanafî Law, for defeating the right of pre-emption, two of which are the following:—

The property may be sold for a price above its value, and then something of trifling value may be received in exchange for it, which would compel the pre-emptor to pay the full price if he choses to avail himself of his privilege.

In like manner, if the property is sold at an excessive price, and the seller receives part of it giving a release for the remainder, this also obliges the pre-emptor either to submit to a considerable loss, or to abandon his claim.

CHAPTER XXX.

BAILMENT.

SECTION I.

THE DIVISIONS OF BAILMENT.

BAILMENT under the Mahommedan Law is a contract by which one person entrusts to another a certain thing for a determinate or indeterminate period, or for a specific purpose without consideration. If consideration is agreed upon, it may be made payable either at stated periods or on the completion of the work or on the return to the bailor of the thing bailed. It may even be payable in advance.

There is no special word in the Mahommedan Law to convey the general meaning of the term bailment, but it is treated under several heads according to the purpose for which the thing is bailed, *e.g.* (1) *'Aâriat* or commodate loan ; (2) *Ijâra* or hire, which includes all kinds of specific bailment ; (3) *Wadi'at* or deposits ; (4) *Rahn* or pledges, and so on.

I shall deal briefly with the subject of specific bailment in this chapter, touching on the subject of *'Aâriat* only slightly to indicate the analogy existing between the Mussulman Law and the English Common Law.

SECTION II

IJÂRA.

Specific bailment.

When a person has been let into the occupation of a house or land, he is bound to pay the stipulated rent, even although he should not reside in or make use of it, because as it is impossible to make delivery of the usufruct, the delivery of the subject from which the usufruct is derived is a substitute for it, "since in delivering the article ability to enjoy the usufruct is established."

But when no hire is agreed upon, and the bailment is not gratuitous, the tenant is liable for the customary rent.

But if after obtaining possession of the subject of hire, he was to lose possession by some wrongful act of a third person, the tenant is no longer responsible for the rent.

If it be not otherwise specified in the contract, rent may be demanded from day to day and upon the hire of an animal (upon a journey) from stage to stage.

But a workman who is entrusted with a job is not entitled to his recompense until his work is finished.

Where an article has been bailed to another for some specific purpose upon a stipulated consideration, the bailee has a lien for the price upon the article bailed ; "for example, a baker hired to bake bread may detain the bread until his hire has been paid. So also a tailor may detain the clothes prepared by him."

The bailee is not responsible in case of accident during such detention.

But where the work is of such a nature that it does not produce any visible effect in the article, it cannot be detained.

Where the bailment is special, the bailee cannot entrust the article to any other. For example, if a book be given to *A* to be copied by him specially he cannot give it to another for that purpose.

Where the contract is unqualified or absolute, the bailee is at liberty to give the use of the article to any person. The hire of an animal is lawful, either for carriage or for riding. If, therefore, the riding be absolutely expressed, the hirer is at liberty to permit any person he pleases to ride on the animal. In the same manner, also, if a person hire a dress for the purpose of wearing it unrestrictedly and in an absolute manner, he is at liberty either to wear it himself or to give it to any other person to wear.

But in a restricted contract, any deviation with respect to the use renders the bailee responsible for the article bailed, unless it be of a nature not liable to injury from such deviation. "Land, however, and every other article not liable to be differently affected by a different occupant (such as a tent or pavilion) is not restricted in point of use by the mention of a particular person, and consequently the hirer is at liberty to put any one to reside in it that he pleases, since the exclusive restriction is of use only because of its preventing a difference of effect."

Specific bailment.

Where the nature of the use to be made of the thing bailed is specified in the contract, the bailee cannot deviate therefrom. "If a person were to hire an animal to carry a burden and the person who lets it were to specify the nature and quantity of the article with which the hirer is to load the animal, such as five bags of wheat, the hirer in this case is at liberty to load the animal with an equal quantity of any article not more troublesome or prejudicial in the carriage than wheat, such as barley or rape-seed, as all articles of that description are included in the permission contained in the contract. The hirer, however, is not at liberty to load the animal with any article of a more prejudicial nature in the carriage than wheat, such as salt, &c., as this would be in violation of the contract between the bailor and the bailee."

Nor would a person who has hired an animal to carry a certain quantity of cotton be at liberty to load the animal with a similar quantity of iron, since it is highly probable that the carriage of the iron may be more prejudicial to the animal than the carriage of the cotton.

Where the bailee uses the article beyond that specified, he incurs a proportionate liability in case of accident, *e.g.*, a rider taking up an additional rider, incurs responsibility for half the value of the animal. And where a hired animal perishes from ill-usage, the hirer is liable for its value.

Where an animal is hired or borrowed for a specific journey, any deviation therefrom induces responsibility.

The change of a saddle for another of the same sort does not give rise to a liability, unless the weight be different, when responsibility attaches in proportion to the excess. But if the nature of the saddle be different, responsibility attaches *in toto*.

A person employed to carry a burden does not incur any liability by any immaterial deviation from the prescribed road.

Land hired for cultivation.

Where land is hired for cultivation any injurious mode of dealing with it gives rise to a proportionate responsibility.

A tailor is responsible for deviating from his orders.

An invalid condition attached to a contract of bailment avoids it altogether.

Specific bailment.

An indefinite thing may be bailed lawfully, *e.g.*, a person may let his share or portion in a house.

Responsibility does not attach from the customary use of an article under an indefinite contract.

Bailees are generally divided into two classes, common or particular.

A common bailee is one to whom an article is bailed in the ordinary course of his work.

A particular bailee is one to whom an article is entrusted not by virtue of his calling, but upon a special contract.

The article committed to a common bailee is a deposit in his hands. If the article should perish whilst in his possession he is responsible for its loss, unless it is lost or destroyed by any irremediable and irresistible accident, such as a fire burning down his house, or robbers, who could not be repelled, taking it away forcibly. But when the article is lost from any cause which might have been avoided, such as usurpation or theft, it would amount to negligence, and the bailee would be responsible, in the same manner as a trustee who lets on hire the deposit in his hands.

A surgeon or farrier, acting agreeably to customary practice, is not responsible in case of accident.

The liabilities of a particular bailee are governed by the contract.

A gratuitous bailee incurs no responsibility beyond taking ordinary care of the article entrusted to his charge.

Section III

'Aâriat or Commodatum.

"In the language of law," says the *Fatâwaî Alamgiri*, "'*aâriat* means the constituting a person, the owner of the usufruct of a property without consideration. This is according to Abû Bakr Râzi and the universality of our masters, and it is correct as stated in the *Sirâj-ul-Wahâj*."

"Its essential is the consent of the giver of the loan, the consent of the bailee not being necessary. This is the opinion of our three masters" [*viz.*, Abû Hanîfa, Abû Yusuf and Mohammed].

"The consent of the bailor may be given in these words, 'I have given this to thee by way of '*aâriat*,' or 'I have given this cloth or house for thee,' or 'this slave for thy service,' or 'this beast for carrying thy burden,' or 'this land is for thy sustenance';

if there is no intention of making a *hiba*, all these will constitute an *'aâriat*."

"Similarly if he were to say 'this house is a *sukna* (abode) for thee or '*umra sukna* (abode for life)'; so it is stated in the *Badâya*."

"In reality it ['*aâriat*] is the giving to another the usufruct of a thing which is not liable to destruction in the use of it for a period of time, either determinate or indeterminate."

"Understanding is a condition but not puberty, and accordingly a boy who has been authorised by the Kâzi to engage in trade may lawfully give a thing in '*aâriat*."

"It is also a condition that the thing is capable of being used without being destroyed; but if liable to be consumed, its '*aâriat* is not lawful. So it is stated in the *Badâya*."

"In the *Kitâb-ul-Kâfi* it is stated from Hâkim Shahîd that the '*aâriat* of *dirhems* and *dinârs* is a loan; and so of all articles that are capable of being weighed or measured......But when *dirhems* and *dinârs* are borrowed for being used as weights or ornaments, then they form the subject of an '*aâriat*. And it is not valid to derive any benefit from the subject of an '*aâriat* than is bargained for. So it is stated in the *Ghâit-ul-Bayân*."

"There are several kinds of '*aâriat*, (1) where the period as well as the mode in which profit may be derived from it is left indeterminate, in which case the bailee may use it as he likes, and whenever he likes; (2) where both the period and the mode of user are expressly fixed, the bailee cannot contravene the conditions, unless for the safety of the thing bailed; (3) where the period is fixed and not the mode of user; and (4) where the mode of user is fixed, but not the period."

"Its legal effect is that the bailee is entitled to the use or usufruct of the thing bailed without having to pay any compensation therefor."

"The subject of '*aâriat* is a trust. If it is lost or destroyed without the neglect or default of the bailee, he is not liable. There is a difference among 'our' jurists as to the validity of a condition by which the bailee has bound himself for any loss to which he has not contributed by his neglect or default. Some jurists have held such a condition to be valid; others not."

"But when he has contributed to its loss, he is liable by *consensus*. For example, if he has knowingly used a beast of burden by day or night in work for which it is unfitted, he would be liable for its loss."

The rules relating to the liability of a person who has taken a thing on *'aâriat*, and other matters connected therewith, are minutely laid down in the *Fatâwai Alamgiri*, but it is unnecessary to go into them here, as the Indian Contract Act is applicable to all those questions.

APPENDIX.

CHAPTER I.

TRANSLATION OF EXTRACTS RELATING TO WAKF.

THE SHIAH LAW.

Ghunia.

" For the validity of a *wakf* several conditions are necessary. Some of them are the following :—That the *wâkîf* is the owner of the property, and that he possesses the capacity of disposition. If the *wâkif* is under inhibition from insolvency the *wakf* is not valid."

" It is also necessary that the *wakf* should be express in terms ; and that an approach to Almighty God should be intended therefrom."

" The express terms [for the constitution of a *wakf*] are *wakafto*, *habasto* or *sabalto*, ' I have consecrated,' ' I have tied up,' or ' I have given in the way [of the Lord].' If he says *tassadukto*, it is capable of two interpretations. Such is the case with *haramto* and *abadato*."

" It is also necessary that the subject of the *wakf* should be *m'aalum* (known), capable of being delivered, and of yielding profit, retaining its existence [for ever]. By consensus both movable as well as immovable property, *mushâ'a* as well as separated property are equal [that is, a *wakf* of these is equally valid]."......

" And as to [the validity of] *wakf* of *mushâ'a*, [the proof is] that the Prophet [may the blessings, &c.] told Omar (may God be pleased with him) with respect to his share of the lands of Khaibar ' tie up the substance (*asl*) and give its usufruct in the way of the Lord,' although the shares of Khaibar were *mushâ'a*, and had not been partitioned by the Prophet (may the blessings, &c.,) but were [only] specified."

"And the majority hold that a *wakf* of *dirhems* and *dinârs* [to be retained in specie] is not lawful, for profit cannot be derived from them whilst retaining their substance in existence." [But according to the later jurists when profit can be derived by investment of money in trade or commerce, the *wakf* thereof is lawful.]

"Another condition is that the *moukoof-alaih* be different from the *wâkif*; accordingly if a *wakf* is made upon one's self it is not valid." [Here lies the principal point of difference between the Shiahs and the Hanafîs.]

"But there is a difference of opinion" [on this point].

"When a *wakf* is made in favour of a generality of Mussulmans, in such a case without any difference of opinion, the *wâkif* may participate in its benefits."......

"Another condition is that the object of the *wakf* be known and capable of identification, and that a *wakf* thereof would obtain the approval of the Deity."......

The object of the *wakf* must be known.

"And without difference of opinion a [commencement in] *wakf* cannot be made on a child *en ventre sa mère* or a slave."

"But a *wakf* on children who are in existence and descendants to be born afterwards is valid by *consensus*."(1)......

[In other words, a beginning must be made with an object in existence.]

"A *wakf* on masjids, bridges, &c., is valid, for from those objects good accrues to all Moslems."

"Another condition is that the *wakf* should be perpetual. So that if a person were to say I have made this *wakf* for a year, it will not be valid."

"It is also necessary that the property should be transferred to the beneficiaries or to some person on their behalf."......

"When all these conditions are found in a *wakf*, the right of the *wâkif* becomes extinguished for ever; and he cannot revoke it nor alter in any way the purpose or purposes for which he has made the consecration."

"Among 'us' the beneficiaries may lawfully sell the subject of the *wakf* [only] where no profit is derived from it, and there is risk of its being ruined or destroyed."

(1) That is, if commencement is made with children in existence, the *wâkif* may lawfully include his after-born children, as well as the progeny of his children who are not in existence yet.

"The directions laid down by the *wâkif* for the application of the usufruct must be carried out."

"When a *wakf* is made in favour of *awlâd* (children), and the *awlâd* of the *awlâd*, in such a case by consensus, the children of daughters will be included, for, etymologically as well as legally, the term *walad* is applicable to a daughter."

"When a man makes a *wakf* on his *nasl* (posterity) or *'akab* or *zurriat*, in such a case *nasab* will be recognised through the mother," [that isall persons tracing their descent to the *wâkif* on their mother's side will be included in the benefit of the *wakf*].

"If the *wakf* is in favour of one's *'itrat*, it is equivalent to saying that it is for his descendants."......

"If the *wakf* is in favour of one's neighbour, and they are not named, then all persons residing on all sides within the space of forty yards in the neighbourhood of the *wâkif's* house will be included in that *wakf*. This is by consensus."

"If the *wakf* is for a beneficial purpose, but the term 'beneficial' is *bâtil* regarding it [that is, if the purpose is *not* beneficial], or when the beneficiaries of the *wakf* have become extinct in such cases, the *wakf* will be applied to purposes of benevolence (*wujûh-ul-khair*). Some have said that the *wakf* will revert to the heir's [of the *wâkif*], but the former [opinion] is the most approved."

Extract from the Kitâb-ul Intisâr.

"The *Imâmias* are alone in holding that when the [subject of a] *wakf* has become ruined and it is not possible to derive any profit from it, in such a case the beneficiaries may sell it and derive benefit from its price."

Extract from the Nihâya.(1)

"Whatever property a man possesses, a *wakf* thereof is lawful, wheher it be held jointly or separated."

"It is necessary that a *wakf* should be perpetual. To make it for a period is not lawful."

[If it is made for a period it would take effect as an *'umra* or *hubs*. Under the Hanafî Law limited estates not being recognised, a *wakf* for a period takes effect as a perpetual *wakf*.]

---

(1) A work of great authority in India, see Morley's Dig., Introd., p. cclxxxvi.

" A *wakf* is not valid on an object that is not in existence." [And this again is different from the Hanafî Law.] But if, commencement is made with an existing object the *wakf* may be continued for objects not in existence.

" But when a man has made a *wakf* for his children, although they are infants, he may lawfully include the progeny that may be vouchsafed to them."(1)

" He may also include his own subsequently born children."

" When a man has made a *wakf* in favour of his *awlâd*, and they are both males and females, in such case if he has given preference to one over the other, his condition should be regarded. But if he has not mentioned anything about it, in that case the male and female among his children and children's children will share equally, for the term *walad* includes all. But if he says they will take according to the Book of God, the male will take double the share of a female."

" A *wakf* for the *K'aaba*, mosques and *mashâhid* [mausoleums of the Imâms] or for the general good of the residents of a particular locality is an approach to the Deity and lawful."

" The subject of the *wakf* can never be sold or given in *hiba* or in charity. But when the *wakf* is in imminent danger of being destroyed, or if the beneficiaries are in such emergent need that the sale of the *wakf* is absolutely beneficial for them, or if serious disputes have arisen among the beneficiaries, the property may be sold and the proceeds applied in the same way as directed by the *wâkif*. [This will presumably be done under the directions of the Judge.] But in no other circumstance, the sale of a *wakf* is lawful."

(1) That is, if commencement is made with children in existence, the *wâkif* may lawfully include his after-born children, as well as the progeny of his children who are not in existence yet.

CHAPTER II.

TRANSLATION OF EXTRACTS RELATING TO WAKF.

THE HANAFI LAW.

Kinia't-ul-Munia.(1)

"When a *wakf* is made upon children and children's children, males and females are equally entitled therein;" p. 198.

"In the *wakf* of Hillâl [it is stated], *wakf* may be of three kinds, one kind being *wakf* for the poor exclusively; another kind being for the affluent, and *after* them for the poor; and the third being for the rich and poor alike, such as *rubâts*, *khâns*, cemeteries, mosques, aqueducts, bridges, &c., for both rich and poor have their needs attached to such objects;" p. 201.

"When the *wâkif* appoints a *mutwalli*, the latter cannot discharge himself by saying, 'I have discharged myself,' *i.e.*, cannot discharge himself *suo motu*, but he must ask the *wâkif* or the Kâzi to discharge him, who will thereupon remove him; p. 209.

Wakf created by the Prophet.

Allâmah at-Tahtâwi's *Commentary on the Durr-ul-Mukhtâr.*(2)

"Imâm Shâfei (may God be pleased with him) says: it is established that the Prophet (may the blessings of God be with him) dedicated several houses in Medîna. .... which are still in existence; and the *Râshidin* Caliphs (the first four Caliphs) and others of the Companions [of the Prophet] made *wakfs*. So also it is laid down in the *As'aâf*;" Vol. II, p. 528.

"In the *Bahr-ur-Râik*, it is laid down, as will appear more clearly afterwards, that the universality of [*Hanafi*] Jurists give *Fatwa* according to Abû Yusuf;(3) only some few have followed Mohammed, but no one has followed the *Imâm* [*viz.*, Abû Hanîfa];" *Ibid.*

---

(1) By Mukhtâr bin Mahmûd bin Mohammed az-Zâhidi, *al-Imâm-ul-ullâma* (the Imâm of the learned), styled *Najm-ud-din*; d. 658 A. H., (A. C. 1259) a commentary on the *Nafis ul-Kudûri.*

(2) A work of great authority, see Morley's Dig., Introd., p. cclxxviii.

(3) That is, with regard to the absoluteness of the dedication merely by the declaration.

" Abû Yusuf holds the mere use of the word *wakf* or *mowkoofa* sufficient. And Shahîd [*viz.*, Sadr-ush Shâhid] has stated that in accordance with universal practice, *we* decide according to it. And it is stated that the jurists of Balkh decide according to the opinion of Abû Yusuf, and hold the *wakf* to be valid when it is merely declared to be *wakf* but no object is mentioned, nor it is said that the *wakf* is in perpetuity."

" In a *wakf* on the affluent there is *kurbat* [approval of the Almighty]."

Inhibition and imbecility.

" Among the conditions of *wakf* are that the *wâkif* should not be under the inhibition of the Kâzi for want of intellect or insolvency as Khassâf and Kamâl have stated. And Kamâl has said that if an imbecile (*safîh*, *i.e.*, a person deficient in understanding) makes a *wakf* on himself and after that on an object which is not liable to failure, such a *wakf* according to Abû Yusuf is valid, and the learned (*Mohakkakîn*) *hold this to be correct.* And according to all, when the Hâkim [Judge] has made an order [in respect thereof it will be valid]. The *Bahr-ur-Râik*, however, has combated this view and has said that a *wakf* is a *tabarr'u* (an act of bounty or charity), and a person of weak intellect is not capable of making any disposition. This objection may be answered thus: a person of weak intellect cannot do an act of generosity in favour of another, but there is no prohibition to his making a *tabarr'u* in his own favour; and [when he makes a *wakf* on himself] it is an act of benevolence for himself, but when after his death others are to get the benefit of the *wakf*, in that case sanction [of the Kâzi] must be obtained."

How far the act of an imbecile may be regarded as valid.

" And the jurists have held that when a person who is indebted to such an extent that his debts surround his property, whilst labouring under a death-illness makes a *wakf*, his dedication should be set aside, and the property should be sold for [the liquidation of his] debts. But when the *wakf* is made in health, it will be *binding* even though the debts should surround his assets, if the *wakf* was made before the inhibition [of the Kâzi]. Such a *wakf* by *consensus* cannot be cancelled. So also it is stated in the *Fath-ul-Kadîr*."

Wakf by an insolvent or one immersed in debt made in death-illness; made in health—binding.

" According to the Imâm (Abû Hanîfa) and Mohammed, it is one of the conditions of *wakf* that it should be ultimately destined for an object which will not fail in perpetuity, and if he [the *wâkif*]

Mention of perpetuity not necessary according to Abû Yusuf.

does not mention such a purpose, according to the Imâm and Mohammed, it will not be valid. And Abû Yusuf (may God's blessings, &c.) says that the mention of such a purpose is *not* necessary, but the *wakf* will be valid even if he has only mentioned an object likely to fail, and after that [*viz.*, its extinction] the *wakf* will be for the poor, though he may not have mentioned them, for the intention of the *wâkif* is [from the use of the word] that it, the *wakf*, should be for the poor, though not named. Thus, this condition will be imported by necessary presumption of law. So also it is in the *Hindièh* [*Fatâwai Alamgiri*]."

Wakf of movables.

"Another condition is that the subject is suitable for dedication. According to the correct doctrine both immovable and movable property may be made *wakf*. [With respect to the latter] anything which by usage and practice it is customary [to dedicate] like the Koran, &c., may lawfully be made *wakf*. From this it follows that though in the neighbourhood of Egypt, it not being customary a *wakf* of current coins may not be valid, in the countries of *Rûm* [the Turkish Empire] the *wakf* of *dirhems* and *dinârs*, being customary, is lawful. When such a *wakf* [*viz.*, the *wakf* of *dinârs* and *dirhems*] is made, it will be invested in *muzâribat* (business or commercial transactions), and the income will be devoted [to the purposes of the *wakf*]."

Wakf of a house without the land valid.

"And the *Fatwa* is on this rule that without the land, houses and trees may lawfully be made *wakf*. So it is stated by the Kâri ul-Hedâya."

"The *wakf* must be immediately operative and not remain in suspense" [*i.e.*, be dependent for its operation upon the happening of some contingent event which may or may not happen].

Wakf of an apostate from Islâm.

"The *wakf* of an apostate from Islâm will be invalidated whether he suffers the extreme punishment of the law or does not...... But if he returns to Islâm and confirms it, it will take effect. So Khassâf has explained it at the end of his book."

"Abû Yusuf used to agree with the Imâm [*viz.*, Abû Hanîfa] in the opinion, that a *wakf* did not become binding until after the decree of the Kâzi or unless made by way of a testamentary disposition. But when he went to Medîna on a *hajj* with [the Caliph] Hârûn ar-Rashid and saw there and in its neighbourhood all the numerous *wakfs* created by the Companions of the Prophet, he abandoned Abû Hanîfa's opinion, and made decrees declaring the obligatoriness of a *wâkf*. In fact all the jurists have followed the rule of the two Disciples; and have held that the *Fatwa* is thereon. ......So it is stated in the *Bahr-ur-Raik*."

"The ultimate destination of a *wakf* should be for an object of piety not likely to fail, but existing in perpetuity. Some say that perpetuity is a condition by *consensus*, but according to Abû Yusuf the mention of perpetuity or of an unfailing object is not necessary, for the words *sadakah* and *wakf*......distinctly imply that. I have already stated that *wakf*, like emancipation, is the extinguishment of the right of property without its transfer to anybody else, and, therefore, it is stated in the 'Book' [*Mukhtasar-ul-Kudûri*] that after the failure of the objects mentioned it will be for the poor, and *this is correct*."

Ultimate destination to an object not likely to fail.

Mention of perpetuity not necessary when intention express or implied.

"In the *Sharh-ul-Multeka* it is stated that when a *wakf* is *mussajjil* [*i.e.*, when the document creating it has been sealed or endorsed by the Kâzi], though all [other] evidence regarding it is lost, and the descendants of the *wâkif* want to set it aside, Mufti Abû S'aûd, in his *M'aarûzat*, has laid down that the Kâzis should be prohibited from listening to such claims. So this should be borne in mind."

"In the *Hindièh* it is laid down that when a man erects a mosque, his right to the property does not become extinguished until he has separated it [from his other property], and given permission [to people] to pray therein "......" And if he constitutes one person as *muezzin* and *imâm* and he gives the *azân*, calls out the *takbîr* and offers the prayers, though by himself, it will become a *masjid* by *consensus*. And if he consigns the building to the *mutwalli* appointed for the purpose, it will be obligatory and lawful, though no prayer has been offered therein, *and this is correct*. So also if he consigns it to the Kâzi or his deputy." [This is in the absence of a formal dedication.]

Dedication of a mosque.

"In the *Multeka* and its commentary, it is stated that it is laid down by Abû Yusuf that by the mere declaration [of the *wâkif* that he has constituted a property *wakf*], his right therein becomes extinguished absolutely. And the *Tanwîr* [*ul-Absâr*], the *Durrar-ul-Ahkâm*], and the *Vikâyah*, &c., have preferred the rule of Abû Yusuf, and you know that it is preferred in *wakf* and in judicial decisions;" p. 536.

Declaration sufficient.

"And according to Abû Yusuf it is lawful for the *wâkif* to reserve the usufruct of the *wakf* or its governance for himself, and on this is the *Fatwa*;" p. 544.

"The conditions as to alteration or exchange [*i.e.*, alteration of investment] is lawful by *ijmâ'a* though some have ascribed this rule to Abû Yusuf. The *Fatwa* is thereon. And in the *Bahr* [*ur-Râik*] it is stated that it is universally agreed that when the *wâkif* has made a condition for himself of altering the *corpus* of the *wakf* [in other words, of altering the investment], both the *wakf* as well as the condition will be valid, and he will have the power to do so."

"In the *Bahr-ur-Râik* it is laid down that if he has conditioned that he may alter it into land, then it will not be lawful to turn it into a house, for he has no power to alter the condition."

"In the *Sharh-ul-Multeka* it is stated from the *Ashbâh* [*-un-Nazâir*] and other [authorities] that the *Fatwa* is on the *kowl* [rules] of Abû Yusuf regarding the constitution of a *wakf* [without the necessity of consignment to a *matwalli*];" p. 545.

"The opinion of Mohammed is adopted for *Fatwa* in holding that the reading of the Koran near a grave is not abominable."

Accretions to dedicated property.

"Trees planted in a mosque become the property of the mosque, as they are on the same footing as a building erected within the mosque [premises]. But trees planted by the side of a public road, a public canal or a village reservoir, remain the property of the owner, and he can transplant them [when he likes]."

Dedication of mortgaged property.

"When the dedicated property is mortgaged to another, and the mortgagor dies before redeeming it, but leaves property along with the debt, it will be satisfied out of such property, and the *wakf* will take effect. But if he leaves no [other] property, the matter will be taken before the Kâzi, and the *wakf* will be cancelled, and the property will be sold to satisfy the debt."

"So long as any one of the kindred of the *wâkif* is fit for the *towliat* a stranger should not be appointed......when a stranger has been appointed and a person qualified among the kindred is forthcoming, the *towliat* should be given to him."

Wakf property cannot be burdened with debt.

"It is not lawful to burden a *wakf* with any debt. It is stated by Ulalw'alji that if revenue or arrears thereof is demanded from the *mutwalli* of a *wakf*, when he has nothing in his hands from the property of the *wakf*, if the *wâkif* has authorised him to raise money by loan to pay the revenue, it will be lawful for him to do so; in such a case what Abû Lais has said is to be adopted. If without borrowing there is no help, the matter should be taken before the Kâzi who will authorise the *mutwalli* to raise the loan to be paid afterwards from the produce. This is because the Kâzi has this power. But if he is at a great distance from the Kâzi and to appear before him is impossible, in that case the *mutwalli* may borrow himself, and this is when there is no income that year. But when there has been produce and he has distributed it among the beneficiaries, without reserving anything for the *Kharâj*, he will be responsible to the amount of the *Kharâj*. This is the abstract of what Hamâwi says, and so it is in the *An'faa-ul-Wasâil*."

Wakf in favour of the *wâkif's* descendants.

" If a man makes a *wakf* of his land on his children and children's children for ever so long as his posterity lasts, the produce will be divided equally among his descendants, and no preference will be given to males over females, *for the wâkif established an equal right for all of them*; in the *Zâhir-ur-Rawâyèt*, (approved traditions)(1) it is stated that in such a *wakf* the descendants *through* females [*lit.* daughters] will not be included; on this is the *Fatwa*;" p. 562.

Practice as to application of proceeds.

" In the *Anf'aa-ul-Wasâil* it is written from the *Zakhîra* that the Shaikh-ul-Islâm was questioned regarding a well-known *wakf* as to how it should be applied, and what should be spent on the beneficiaries, it being involved in doubt; he answered regard should be paid to what was customary in former times, and to the practice of former *mutwallis*;" p. 564.

" In the *Bahr* [*ur-Râik*] it is stated regarding the allowance of a *mutwalli*, that if he be the *mutwalli* of the *wâkif* [in other words, if he be appointed by the *wâkif*] he will get what is provided [in the *wakf*], though it may be more than the customary salary; but if he be appointed by the Kâzi, he will get what is usual;" p. 566.

" The *Fatwa* is on the legality of taking wages for the reading of the Koran on any specified spot, and also on the saying of [Imâm] Mohammed that it is not sinful to have the Koran read near a grave; so in the *Bahr*."

Fitness a test for appointment to the curatorship.

" If the *wâkif* has fixed the *towliat* for the fittest and *then the fittest*, in such case the *mutwalliship* will be for the fittest of his children; if the fittest happen to be *fâsik* [addicted to vice], then

(1) A collection of approved traditions commonly known by that name.

the one nearest to him in fitness will get the *towliat*. If afterwards the former abandons viciousness and becomes just and is superior in fitness to the latter, the *wilâyèt* should be given back to him. If the fittest rejects the *wilâyèt*, then the *towliat* should be given to the one nearest to him in fitness. If they are all equal in fitness, then the one older in age should be appointed, whether that person be a man or a woman. And if there is none among them fit, in that case the Kâzi may appoint a stranger; but when any fit person is forthcoming among them afterwards the *wilâyèt* is to be given back to him;" p. 567.

If all equal in fitness.

"The Kâzi-ul-Kuzzât [or the Chief Kâzi] alone has the power of appointing *mutwallis* and executors and by Kâzi is not meant every Kâzi. So also it is stated in the 27th section of the *Jâm'aa-ul-Fusâlain*;" p. 567.

"In the *Hindièh*, it is stated that when a *wakf* is made on one's *nasl* and *zurriat*, in that are included one's descendants through males as well as through females, whether near or remote;" p. 568.

"When a person says this land of mine is *wakf* on my *walad* [child in the singular], in that case, the produce will be for the child [or children] of his loins, whether male or female. And if he said, this is a *wakf* for my male *walad*, then the produce will be only for the male child [or children] of his loins. And when the children of his loins cease to exist, then the produce will be expended on the poor, it will not go to the *walad-ul-walad* [he having used the singular expression (*walad*), the presumption is that he meant to restrict the *wakf* to his own children]. But if at the time of the *wakf* [created with the word *walad*], there was no child of his loins in existence, but a child [or children] of his son whether male or female, then the produce will be spent only on such grandchild [or grandchildren] and none of a lower generation will share in it. And in the *Zâhir-ur-Rawâyèt* it is stated that the child of a daughter will not be included therein, and the *Fatwa* is on the *Zâhir-ur-Rawâyèt*."

"And if the *wâkif* had said that this is a *wakf* for my *walad* and the *walad* of my *walad*, and he did not restrict it for males, in such a case the children of his loins and the children of his sons and the children of his daughters will be included, and this is correct. All these will share equally in the produce, and the *wâkif's* own children will not be preferred to the children of his sons, nor the children of his sons to the children of his daughters, unless he has restricted it to males, then the male children of his sons and daughters will be included. And this is correct."

"And if he added the third generation and said thus, 'on my child and the child of my child, and the child of my child's child,' in this *wakf* his *nasl* [posterity] will be included, and so long as his prosterity lasts, the produce will be expended on his descendants; and *if there is a single one of his descendants existing, however remote, nothing will be given to the poor.* If the *wâkif* [*in such a wakf*] has used any expression which denotes that his descendants will take in such an order, *e.g.*, if he has said thus, 'the nearest will be nearest,' or thus, 'on my child and then on my child's child,' or thus '*batnan-b'aad-batn*,' in all such cases, a commencement will be made [*in the distribution of the produce*] as condition by the *wâkif;* [thus it is stated in the] *Durrur* [*ul-Ahkâm*]."

"If the *wâkif* at the outset used the plural expression, on my *awlâd* [children], in that case the *wakf* will be for his descendants so long as they exist, and the near and the remote will be equal unless the *wâkif* indicated the order in which they should take."

Khazânat-ul-Muftiïn.(1)

EXTRACTS FROM THE CHAPTER ON WAKF.

"Etymologically the meaning of *wakf* is detention. In.... law, according to Abû Hanîfa (may the mercy, &c.), the detention of the substance of a thing in the proprietorship of the owner and the consecration of its usufruct on the poor or on any object among objects of benevolence. Thus, this will be in the same way as an '*aâriat* and therefore will not be binding, and it will be lawful for the *wâkif* to revoke it and sell the property."

"And according to the Disciples, it is the detention of property in the ownership of Almighty God, and the right of the *wâkif* becoming extinguished in it [*viz.*, the property dedicated], it is transferred to Almighty God for the purpose, that its profits may be expended on His creatures. And therefore it [a *wakf*] is binding and [the subject of] it can never be made a gift of, nor can it be inherited nor sold, and it is on the footing of a mosque."

(1) "The Treasure-house of the Muftis," frequently quoted by the Law Officers and referred to in the *Fatâwai Alamgiri* and in the cases given in Macnaghten's Principles and Precedents of Mahommedan Law, see p. 332 and p. 342. See also Morley's Dig. Introd., p. cclxxxvii.

"According to Imâm Mohammed there are four conditions for the validity of a *wakf*, to consign it to a *mutwalli*, to separate it [from the other property of the *wâkif*], not to reserve for one's self any interest in the produce of the *wakf*, and to make it perpetual in this way that its ultimate application should be for the poor... And Abû Yusuf has laid down that no such condition is necessary and the *Mashâikh* of Khorasân have adopted the opinion of Abû Yusuf; the jurists of Bokhara that of Mohammed." "If a man make a *wakf* of his land on a specified body of people attached to a mosque, though he may not have destined its end for the poor according to the universality of jurists, the *wakf* would be valid. And this is recognised as authoritative. If he has constituted his house as a mosque and appointed a person as *muezzin*, and this person gives the *azân* and makes the *ikâmat* and offers the prayers [though] by himself, this will amount to consignment and this is recognised. ....."When a mosque is ruined and people have no need for it, the jurists hold that it is a mosque for ever, and this is most correct."

"The burying of one corpse in a cemetery, the alighting of one person in a *khân*, the passing of one person along a road, the drinking of one person at a well......is equivalent to consignment and is sufficient [even without formal dedication], according to the authoritative opinion."

Mushâ'a. "*Shuyu'u* is in truth a bar to complete seisin, but those who do not consider consignment as a condition of *wakf*, also uphold the validity of the *wakf* of *mushâ'a*. According to the *Mashâikh* of Khorâsân the *wakf* of *mushâ'a* is valid; according to Mohammed it is not, and this was adopted by the jurists of Bokhara. [But] all moderns have decreed according to the rule of Abû Yusuf that it [the *wakf* of *mushâ'a*] is lawful, and this is authoritative."

"It should be known that when a 'confused' [joint undivided] property is not capable of partition, it can be lawfully dedicated without difference of opinion."

Wakf of money and movable property in general. "If a man makes a *wakf* of *dirhems* or food or whatever is weighed or measured according to Imâm Zuffar it is lawful. When asked how such things can be made *wakf*, he answered the money should be invested in *muzâribat* and whatever profit is derived therefrom will be devoted to the purposes of the *wakf*; and what is weighed or measured will be sold and its price like *dirhems* will be invested in trade or business. And the jurists have held, and analogy is so, that if the *wâkif* provide thus 'this measure of wheat will be loaned to the poor, for purposes of cultivation for themselves : and that after they have reaped the crops, the same measure will be taken back from them, and similarly for ever it should be loaned to other poor [people]'; this will be lawful. And like this there are numerous *wakfs* in Damawand and the hilly tracts of Tabaristan."

"When a man has made a *wakf* and has [expressly] conditioned the *wilâyèt* [governance] for himself or anybody else, in that case the governance will be for him or that person. And the *wâkif* is superior to anybody else. And whoever has constructed a mosque has a superior right to appoint its *muezzin* and to spread its carpets [that is, to manage its affairs]."

"If the *wâkif* is not trustworthy, the Kâzi out of regard for the interest of the beneficiaries will take away the *wakf* from his hands and will appoint another *mutwalli* in his place, whether the *wâkif* reserved the *wilâyèt* for him or not. Even though he reserved the *wilâyèt* for himself and conditioned that the Kâzi shall not have the power of removing him, that condition being contrary to the *Shar'aa* is *bâtil*. But the Kâzi will have the power to remove him and appoint another when it has been proved that he is not trustworthy. This power is similar to the power of the Kâzi to remove an executor appointed by a deceased for his minor child who proves himself untrustworthy."

The Mutwalli

"And all that has been stated in relation to the question of the government of a *wakf* is founded on the rules laid down by Abû Yusuf with whom is the *Fatwa*......In the *wilâyèt* of a *wakf* the *wâkif* is superior, and then his heirs and his kindred, unless they are *fâsik* [addicted to vice] or have become *fâsik* in which [latter] case it will be taken away from them and a stranger may be appointed. If they become fit again, it [the office] will be returned to them."

"......If the *wâkif* appoints a stranger as his *mutwalli*, and then wishes to remove him and take up the *towliat* himself, he will have that power."

"The *mutwalli* may lawfully make a *wasiat* [in respect of the trusteeship] to another for after his death."

"If the *wâkif* has said to another 'you are my *wasi* in this *wakf*,' this is *tawkîl* [i.e., the appointment of an agent], and so long as the *wâkif* is alive, the *wilâyèt* will be for him [the person so appointed], and after the *wâkif's* death, the *wilâyèt* will cease unless the *wâkif* had said that the *wilâyèt* will be [also] for that person after his death."

"If there is no *mutwalli* for the *wakf* until death has approached the *wâkif* and then he made a *wasiat* to another in this way that he wrll be the *wâkif's wasî* in all his *amwâl* [property] and the *mutwalli* of his *wakf*—it will be so. And if the *wâkif* afterwards appoints another *wasî*, this latter will not be the *mutwalli*.

"If no *mutwalli* was appointed until the Kâzi appointed one, the *wâkif* will not have the power of removing him in order to have himself the *towliat*.

"If the *wâkif* has appointed two persons as the *mutwallis*, and one of them dies appointing the other as his *wasî*, the surviving *mutwalli* will have the power over all the affairs of the *wakf*."

"The beneficiaries have no right to partition the *wakf* property among themselves......nor can the *mutwalli* hypothecate it for any debt he may have incurred for the *wakf*, and if he has done so, and the mortgagee has been in possession for any time, he shall be liable for the usual rent (*ujr-ul-misl*)."

The powers of the *Mutwalli*.

"If the *wâkif* has consigned by will the *wakf*, and upon that has made a condition that the executor will not have the power to leave the trust to another, this condition will be lawful."

......"And if the condition be that the *wilâyèt* will be for so-and-so and after him for so-and-so this will be lawful, for this is like a *wasiat*."

"If he has made a *wasiat* [in respect of the trusteeship of the *wakf*] to two persons, and one of them should accept and the other decline, the Kâzi in that case should appoint another in the latter's place, so that the intention of the *wâkif* that the affairs of the *wakf* should be conducted by the joint judgment of two persons may be carried into effect."......"And the Kâzi may lawfully entrust the entire *wilâyet* to him who has accepted."

"If the *wâkif* says that the most excellent (*afzal*) of his children will be the *mutwalli*, in that case the *wilâyèt* will be for the *afzal* among them. If he proves to be wicked, then the next to him should be appointed, and if he abandons his wickedness and adopts the ornaments of piety and dignity, and is better qualified than the second, the *wilâyèt* will be restored to him. And when both are equal in honesty, uprightness, judgment, and excellence, then the one best acquainted with the affairs of the *wakf* will have a superior claim, and if one of them is superior in piety and virtue and the other in the knowledge of the affairs of the *wakf* and is not likely to deceive, the latter should be preferred.''

'' And if he has consigned the trust to 'Abdullah until Zaid's arrival, it will be done as he said.''

'' And if the *wâkif* has consigned the trust to another and that person dies during the lifetime of the *wâkif*, the *wâkif* will have the power of appointing another *mutwalli*, though the last one might have been nominated by the Kâzi.''

'' When the descendants of the *wâkif* and members of his family are in existence, a *mutwalli* should not be appointed from among strangers. But when there is no one fit among them, a stranger may be appointed, and if a stranger has been appointed, and then some one fit among the members of the *wâkif's* family is forthcoming, the *towliat* should be given to him.''

'' A *mutwalli* may lawfully consign the trust to another by way of a *wasiat* to take effect upon his death. But if he wish to appoint another for himself during his lifetime and whilst in health, it will not be lawful, unless the trust to him is in a general manner [*'aala sabîl-ut-t'aamîm*.] ''

The powers of the *Mutwalli* (contd.).

'' According to Abû Yusuf, consignment is not necessary for the validity of a *wakf*, and therefore in cases of a khân, cemetery, reservoir, etc., neither the delivery of seisin nor the alighting of one traveller, nor the burial of one corpse, nor the drinking of one individual which [according to Mohammed] amount to delivery of seisin—is necessary. Simple testimony [as to the formal declaration of the *wakf*] is sufficient.''

'' If a man say ' this land is a *mowkoofa* or *sadahah-mowkoofa* on myself,' this is as lawful as if he had made a condition that during his lifetime he should himself eat out of it and feed others therewith. Therefore it is approved as authority that this *wakf* is valid.''

'' A man makes a *wakf* on the poor and makes a condition that he should eat out of it, saying that ' it will be lawful for me to eat of it' ; this is lawful.''

'' And if he says ' this land of mine is a *sadakah-mowkoofa* or *mowkoofa* in perpetuity for Almighty God, that so long as I am alive its produce should be [*lit.*, remain current] for me,' and adds no more, it will be lawful. And when he dies, the *wakf* will be for the poor."

"And if he says, 'whilst I am alive its produce will be for me, and after me for my child and child's child and their *nasl* so long as their *nasl* exist' it will be for them, and when they cease to exist it will be for the poor; this is lawful."

"And when the *wâkif*, besides his maintenance, has made this condition that his debts should be paid out [of the produce], this condition will be lawful."

The Ashbâh-wan-Nazâir(1) *with Hamâwi's Commentary.*

"To decide contrary to the conditions of the *wâkif* is tantamount to deciding contrary to the prescriptions of the Lawgiver, and therefore such decision will not take effect, for the jurists have held unanimously that the conditions laid down by the *wâkif* are like the prescriptions imposed by the Lawgiver [*viz.*, the Prophet]." P. 146. [This is well worthy the consideration of our Indian Law Courts so apt to run away with their own conceptions of law and equity.]

"In the *Zakhîra* and the work of Ulalwa'lji, &c., it is stated thus, that unless the *wâkif* has so provided, the Kâzi cannot lawfully appoint a *farrâsh* for a mosque."

"From this it is clear that it is not lawful to introduce in *wakfs* new allowances [not provided for by the *wâkif*."]......

"If the *wâkif* has authorised the *mutwalli* to appoint servitors in a mosque [or any such institution], he may lawfully appoint new servants, not otherwise; nor can the Kâzi authorise him to do so;" *Hamâwi*, p. 162.

"If a man make a *wakf* on his *zurriat* [posterity] without giving the order of the generations, then all high and low will take equally;" *Ashbâh*, p. 179.

"But if he has made a *wakf* on generations with this condition that the prior will take first and thereafter and thereafter,

(1) Calcutta Edition, 1260, A. H. The *Ashbâh-wan-Nazâir* is a celebrated work [see Morley's Dig., Introd., p. cclxxi] by Moulâna Zain-ul-'aâbidin Ibrahim (commonly known as Ibn-Nujaim) al-Misri al-Hanafi [*i.e.*, of Egypt, belonging to the Hanafi sect]. The commentary is by Moulâna Syed Ahmed bin Mohammed al Hanafi al-Hamâwi [of Hamah], who died in Cairo on the 8th of Rajjab, 970.

[that is in succession to each other] and does not say anything more, in that case so long as there is any one of the first generation, no one of the second will take anything. When a man has made a *wakf* in favour of his children and *their* children and *their nasl*, in such a case the child, whose father has died before the *wakf*, will not be included in it, for the *wâkif* has restricted [the *wakf*] to the children of the beneficiaries, so his child who has died before could not come under the *wakf*." [This is only a question of construction and depends on the language used to indicate the intention of the *wâkif*. If the *wâkif* had said *my* children and children's children and children's children's children there could be no question as to the inclusion of the child of a predeceased child.]

"If a person make a *wakf* upon his *awlâd* and the *awlâd* of his *awlâd* and his *zurriat* [posterity] on this condition, that it should commence with the first *batn* [generation] and *thereafter* and *thereafter*, in such a case, I say there is nothing for the second generation whilst there is one of the first. If one of the second generation dies, whilst the first generation are in existence, leaving a child, that child will not participate with the second generation, when they get the benefit, as he belongs to the third generation, but he will get his share when the third generation get the benefit."

"If a person make a *wakf* on his *awlâd* and the *awlâd* of his *awlâd* and his *zurriat* and *nasl*, and give no order [in which they should take], but condition that whenever one of them dies leaving a child, the share of the deceased will go to such child,—in such a case, the distribution between a child and child's child will be equal, and accordingly what the deceased was to get will be for his child, and such child will [then] get two shares, one in his own right as participating in the *wakf* and the other the share of his parent which devolves on him."

"If a person make a *wakf* on the children of his loins, male and female, and on the male children of his children, and on their *awlâd's awlâd* and *nasl*—in such a case his male and female children and the male children of his sons and daughters will share equally and in it will be included the children of the daughters as well of the sons. If he said that the first *nasl* will be first and *thereafter* and *thereafter*, in such case the children of his loins, male and female, will take first; after them it will be for the children of his sons and not for the children of his daughters; and then for the children of his son's children in perpetuity;" p. 180.

"If he were to make a *wakf* on his daughters and on their *awlâd* and on their *awlâd's awlâd* in such a case, the rule is that the produce will be for his daughters and for their *nasl.*"

"It is not lawful to create a debt over a *wakf*, but if there arises a necessity for borrowing for the benefit of the *wakf*, such as for its repairs or for buying seed, in that case borrowing is lawful under two conditions; *first*, that it must be with the sanction of the Kâzi, and *secondly*, that it is not possible to meet the necessity by its rent, if let for a limited period. So has Ibn-Wahbân written. To have to spend on the beneficiaries is not such a necessity [as would justify borrowing], so it is stated in the *Kinia.*"

"It is not necessary for the validity of a *wakf*, that the object for which the *wakf* is being created should be in existence at the time of *wakf*; therefore, if a *wakf* be made on the children of Zaid, though Zaid has no children [then], the *wakf* will [nevertheless] be valid; and until Zaid has children, such *wakf* will be expended on the poor."

"It is incumbent to observe the conditions imposed by the *wâkif*, for the jurists have declared that they are like the *Nass* [prescriptions] of the Lawgiver......But [they may be departed from] in the following particulars:

"(1) If he has conditioned that the *Nâzir* shall never be removed, the Kâzi has still the power of removing a *Nâzir* who is unfit.

"(2) If he has conditioned that the *wakf* property should not be leased beyond a year, but there is nobody willing to take a lease for a year, or if there is greater benefit to the beneficiaries from a longer lease, the Kâzi has the power of contravening the condition laid down by the *wâkif* but not the *Nâzir*.

"(3) If the *wâkif* has conditioned that the Koran should be read over his grave, such fixing should be excluded."

According to Hamâwi, however, "most of the learned have held it to be clear that the view [expressed in the third head] is founded on the opinion of Imâm Abû Hanîfa who considered the reading of the Koran near a grave to be abominable; so according to him the *wâkif* saying that it should be read over his grave would be void. But [on this point, *viz.*, on the lawfulness or otherwise of having the Koran read over the grave], the *Fatwa* is on the opinion of Imâm Mohammed, according to whom the reading of the Koran by the side of or over the grave is not illegal. So it is in the *Khulâsa*. Therefore the *wâkif's* condition is binding. The author's statement that it is void is weak."

"(4) If the *wâkif* has conditioned that the balance of the *wakf* income should be given to whoever begs at a particular *masjid* every day, no regard should be paid to this condition." Hamâwi says, "this is according to the *Kinia*, but he [the author] has said afterwards that it is preferable to pay a regard to this condition."

"(5) If the *wâkif* has conditioned that the beneficiaries should get fixed rations of bread and meat every day, the *kyyum* [*mutwalli*] may make them cash payments, and in another place it is stated that the beneficiaries may demand and take payments in cash."

"(6) If the allowance fixed for the imâm is not sufficient, and he is learned and pious, in that case it is lawful for the Kâzi to increase his allowance." (Hamâwi says, "he has no such power unless the imâm is learned and pious and the pay fixed by the *wâkif* is insufficient.")

"(7) If the *wâkif* has conditioned that the investment shall never be altered, if the alteration is beneficial to the *wakf*, the Kâzi may authorise its being changed. And he (the Kâzi) cannot dismiss a *mutwalli* if appointed by the *wâkif* without misfeasance. Nor can he remove a *mutwalli* upon the mere complaint of the beneficiaries (*mustahakîn*) unless they establish misfeasance against him. And so in the case of an executor."

"If the *wâkif* dismisses a *mutwalli*, if he made a condition [reserving the power of discharging and nominating], such dismissal will be valid by *consensus*. But if [he did] not [so reserve this power], it will not be valid according to Abû Yusuf. And the jurists of Balkh have adopted Abû Yusuf's rule;" P. 309.

Hamâwi says that the rule of Abû Yusuf has been held to be valid by a large body of people; and in the *Fath-ul-Kadîr* it is stated that it is most *approved* among the learned.

"The founder [of a mosque] is primarily entitled to appoint the *imâm* and *muezzin*; and his child and his people [*ashirat*, tribe, class] are better entitled than strangers."

"When two persons are appointed by the *wâkif* to do a work, they cannot act singly; but when the *wâkif* has conditioned that he and another shall have the power of altering the investment, he will have the power of doing so himself, so it is [stated] in the *Fatâwai Kâzi Khân.*"

"Hisâmi has stated in his *Wâk'iât* that the Kâzi has the power of appointing a *mutwalli* without any provision [to that effect in the *wakf*], but he cannot appoint [new] servants in a mosque without such a condition."

"It is abominable to give to the *fakîr* of a *wakf* two hundred *dirhems*......but when the *wakf* is in favour of [the *wâkif's*] indigent kindred so much may be given; so it is stated in the *Ikhtiâr.*"

"When a man makes a *wakf* of a house on his two sons and on their children for ever so long as their posterity exists, and they intend residing in it, none of them has a right to do so......for it is evident that when the *wâkif* applied the term *wakf* to the house, he devoted the rent of the house to the beneficiaries; therefore it will not be used for their residence."

Sharh-ul-Wikâya.(1)

Text [of the *Wikâya.*]—"The meaning of *wakf* [according to Abû Hanîfa] is to tie up a property, like an *'aâriat*, in the proprietorship of the *wâkif* and to devote its usufruct [upon mankind] and according to the Disciples [the meaning of *wakf* is] the tying up of the substance of a thing in the ownership of the Almighty. And according to the Disciples a *wakf* [once made] is obligatory and on this is the *Fatwa*;" P. 223.

Comment.—"There is difference of opinion with regard to the condition relating to the constitution of a house into a mosque. According to Abû Yusuf (may God's mercy, &c.), the mere declaration [of the *wâkif*] that 'I constitute this into a mosque,' is sufficient, for according to Abû Yusuf consignment is not necessary for the validity of a *wakf*. According to Mohammed, it is necessary prayers should be offered in *Jamâ'at* [assembly]. According to Abû Hanîfa the prayers of one man would be sufficient."

Text.—"And according to Abû Yusuf mere saying 'I have made this *wakf*' will extinguish the right of property."

(1) Frequently quoted by the Law Officers of the Sudder Court.

Comment.—"In other words, the mere declaration of the *wâkif* extinguishes the right of property in him and transfers it to the Almighty. Accordingly, consignment to a *mutwalli* is not necessary."

Text.—"To fix the produce of the *wakf* for one's self, and to make a condition that he may change the land of the *wakf* for another land when he likes, are valid according to Abû Yusuf."...

"According to Abû Yusuf a *wakf* is valid even though it is not expressly destined to an unfailing purpose, and when the purpose [named] has become extinct, then it will be spent on the poor."

Tahtâwi Vol. II.

Pages 569—70 .(Text).

Chapter on matters connected with a wakf in favour of children.

" From the *Durrar*, etc., and from the *Mawâhib*(1) on *wakf* in favour of one's self, his child, his generation, and his descendants :— If a person fixes the usufruct for himself during his lifetime and thereafter, and thereafter, it will be lawful according to the second (Imâm Abû Yusuf) ; and on this is the *Fatwa*, &c."

COMMENTARY.

Page 570.

Chapter on matters connected with a wakf in favour of children.

And females are included because the word *walad* (one born) is derived from *wilâdat* (birth) which is found in them.—Halabi from the *Durrar*, " If there be no child born of his loins," means when the child born of his loins in whose favour the *wakf* was made dies leaving a child, the latter shall not be entitled to anything of the *wakf* property. In like manner; if, at the time of his making the *wakf*, there be a child born of his loins, as well as the child of his child, and the child born of his loins dies, the *wakf* will go to the poor and not to the child of his child. " To the poor," because the person in whose favour the *wakf* was made was no more.—*Durrar*, " It will go exclusively to the child of his son," because the child of his son shall, in the absence of the child born of his loins, be considered as the child born of his loins.—*Durrar*, " It is correct." This is the *Zâhir-ur-Rawâyèt*, and it has been adopted by Hillâl, because the children of daughters belong to the same lines as their fathers, and not to those of their mothers ; the case with a son's child being just the opposite.—Halabi from the *Durrar*— " And if the words ' and the child of my child ' be added...........,"

---

(1) By Moulâna Burhân-ud-din Trabulasi (of Tripoli), Sâhib-i-As'âf (the author of the *As'âf*), placed on the same footing with the author of the *Hedâya* by d'Ohsson.

according to Allâmah Nûh (may he be immersed in the mercy of God), it purports that if the word *walad* (child), which is related to, or possessed by *ya* ('my'), the possessive pronoun of the first person, be not qualified by the word male, it would mean child born of his loins, the male and the female equally, and if it be so qualified it would mean exclusively the male child born of his loins. If a man were to say, 'I have made a *wakf* of this land of mine in favour of my child,' the produce would go to the child, male or female, born of his loins; and if he were to say, 'I have made the *wakf* in favour of my male child,' the produce would go exclusively to the male child born of his loins; and in the absence of the child born of his loins, the produce would go to the poor, and not to the child's child. This would be the case, if there be a child born of his loins at the time of his making the *wakf*. If, at the time of his making the *wakf*, there be no child born of his loins, but there be a male or female child of his son, the produce would go to him or her exclusively; and none of his posterity, save that person shall partake of the produce; and a daughter's child is not included therein; this is the *Zâhir Rawâyèt*; and according to this *Fatwa* is given. If he says 'in favour of my child, and the child of my child,' and does not qualify it by the word male, it would include the child born of his loins, and the children of his sons and daughters.—According to the correct *Rawâyèt*. They would partake of the produce, neither the child born of his loins having preference to the son's children, nor the children of the son to those of the daughter; and if he so qualifies it, it would include the male children of sons and daughters, according to the correct *Rawâyèt*.—Finis. "It is restricted to the said two," that is to say, to the child and the child's child. [But] "if he adds the third generation (and says 'in favour of my child, the child of my child, and the child of the child of my child,' it would include all his descendants"— (*Durrar*). The produce would then go to his children (descendants) so long as his posterity continues, and not to the poor, till any of his children (descendants) be alive, be he of a degree howsoever low. Because when he made mention of three generations it indicated distance, that is to say, numerousness of degrees. Hence the restriction is removed, and what remains to be taken into consideration is lineage, in the sense of the word, which includes all; because it is found in one who is the next as well as in one who is the remotest in descent. The case with the second generation is otherwise, because it is removed by one degree only. "But in the event of his using terms denoting order——," *e.g.*, If he says in this way "nearest, then nearest," or says in favour of my child, and then in favour of the child of my child," or says, "generation after generation," it would begin from one mentioned first by the person making the *wakf*.—*Durrar*. "As, for instance, he says first of all, 'in favour of my children, using the plural form ——,' it would make the next in descent as well as the one far removed equal, but not in case of his using terms denoting order'; and this will apply to what follows."

ZAILYE.

Takhrîj-ul-Hedâya.

Book on Wakf.

Imâm Zailye in his work called the *Takhrîj-ul-Hedâya* gives in detail the prescriptions of the Lawgiver of Islâm which form the foundation of the law relating to *wakf*. "The first tradition," he says, is as follows:—Said the Prophet, peace be on him, to Omar when he (Omar) wanted to give in charity his land, called Samâgh, "consecrate just as it is, so that it may neither be sold, nor conveyed by gift, nor inherited." I say this tradition has been cited by six Imâms. Bokhârî has cited it at the end of the *Chapter on Evidence*, Muslim and Abû Dâûd in the Book on *Wills*, Tirmizî and Ibn-i-Mâja in the Book of *Ahkâm* and Nisâî in the Book on *Wakf*; and all of them have taken it from Nâfi, who got it from the son of Omar, who said "Omar got a piece of land in Khaibar, whereupon he came to the Prophet, may peace and safety be unto him, and said, 'I have got a piece of land, a better thing than which I never got, what is your order to me about it.' The Prophet said, 'if you like you make a *wakf* of it, as it is, and bestow it in benefaction.'" Omar thereupon bestowed it in charity on his relatives, and the poor, and slaves, and in the path of God, and travellers, in a way that the land itself might not be sold, nor conveyed by gift, nor inherited, and that there would be no harm if the *mutwalli* applied the produce of the land to meritorious purposes, and fed with it his friends who were not well-to-do.—*Finis.* In a place in Bokhâri it is stated that the Prophet, peace and safety be unto him, said in this way, "consecrate it as it is, so that it may neither be sold nor conveyed by gift, but (people) may be fed with it," and that Omar Ibn-ul-Khattâb thereupon dedicated it as directed. He (Bokhâri) has also stated that it was a date-orchard. Abû Dâûd has added that Yahya, son of S'aîd, said "Abdul Hamîd, son of 'Abdullah, son of Omar Ibn-ul-Khattâb sent to him a copy of the deed of *wakf* executed [by Omar]:—'In the name of God, the most merciful. This is what is written by the slave of God, Omar, in respect of Samâgh.'

"He then stated (therein) what had passed between him (and the Prophet) in the way it has been recited by Nâfi, and said :—

'If the *mutwalli* like, he may purchase a slave with the price of its produce, to look after it.'

"It was in the hand-writing of Mutaqab, and was witnessed by Abdullah, son of Arkam."

"'In the name of God the most merciful, this is what has been willed by the slave of God, Omar, the Commander of the Faithful. If anything happen to me, the *mutwalli* of Samâgh and of that which surrounds it, *viz.*, the mounds, and of the slaves in it, and of the one hundred parts in Khaibar, the slaves there, and of the one hundred parts in Wâdi made *wakf* by Mohammed, peace and safety be on him, shall be Hafsa's, during her lifetime, and after her such member of her family as may be intelligent. They shall neither be sold nor purchased. The *mutwalli* shall feed therewith his relatives, and beggars, and those who have received no inheritance, whomsoever he may choose ; and there will be no harm if the *mutwalli* should eat out of their produce, or feed others with it or redeem with it slaves.' "—*Finis.*

The word *Akala* with the long sound of the letter *a* means *fed.*

* * * * * *

Hâkim recites in his book called *Mustadrak* in the Chapter on *Fazâil* from Wâkidi, who said :—

"Omar, son of Hind, recited to me this tradition from 'Abdullah, son of Osmân, and he from Arkam, son of Abi'l Arkam Makhzumî, who said his father recited it to him from Yahya, son of Osmân, and he from Arkam(1) and he says it was handed down to him by Osmân, son of Abi'l Arkam, who said, 'I am the son of a *Sab'aa-us-salâm*, (*viz.*, of a man who embraced Islâm in the seventh year from the time Mohammed declared himself a Prophet). He had a house close to Safa. This was the house dwelt in by the Prophet, peace and safety be unto him, at the time of the promulgation of Islâm, and it was in this house that he asked people to embrace Islâm. A large number of people embraced Islâm in this house, of whom Omar Ibn-ul-Khattâb was one, and the house was therefore called 'the house of Islâm.' Arkam dedicated the said house on his child [meaning children], and the deed of *wakf* was read out.

(1) The usual process by which the authentic traditions are traced. See Morley's Dig., Introd., p. ccxxviii

" 'In the name of God the most merciful. This relates to how Arkam disposed of the usufruct of his property, which lies close to Safa, that is to say, he has bestowed it in charity(1) upon his child [children], together with the place where it lies, *viz.*, its environs, so that it may neither be sold nor inherited.' "

" This was witnessed by Hishâm, son of 'Aâs, and by the slave of Hishâm, the son of 'Aâs. This house all along continued to be a permanent *sadakah* [*wakf*], his descendants living in it, letting it out on rent, and they alone appropriating its proceeds. And none raised any question."

* * * * * *

" Ibrâhim of Hari says in his book *Gharîb-ul-Hadîs* that he learnt from Abû Bakr, son of Abû Sh'aibah, he from Hafîs, son of Ghyâs, he from Hishâm, son of 'Urwa, and he from his father, that Zubair, son of 'Awwâm, made a *wakf* of his house in favour of one of his daughters who was *mardudah.* He says *mardudah* means a woman who has been divorced, and *fâkid* a woman whose husband is dead."

* * * * * *

" It is stated in the *Khilâfiât* of Baihaki, that Abû Bakr 'Abdullah, son of Zubair Humaidi, said :—

' Abû Bakr bestowed in charity [meaning *wakf*] on his child [meaning children] his house at Mecca, which (charity) does up to this day continue ; and Omar bestowed in charity on his children the usufruct of his property, which lies close to Marwa and Saniya ; and this (*wakf*) does up to this day continue ; and Ali bestowed in charity on his children, his land in Egypt, and his property in Medîna, which does up to this day continue ; and S'aad, son of Abî Wakkâs bestowed in charity on his children his houses in Medîna and in Egypt, which does up to this day continue ; and Osmân bestowed Rûma in charity, which does up to this day continue ; and 'Amr, son of 'Aâs, bestowed on his children in charity *Wahat* in Tâif, as well as his houses in Mecca and Medîna, which *wakf* does up to this day continue.

* * * * * *

The fourth tradition.—....................The Prophet, peace and safety be unto him, used to appropriate (the proceeds of) the things bestowed by him in charity. Muzayyif says it (*charity*)

(1) May also be translated "dedicated it."

means *wakf*..................Ibn Ali Shaiba writes in his book *Musannaf*, in the chapter in which he has cited the traditions on the strength of which he opposes Abû Hanîfa, that Ibn 'Utaibah (Atbah) recited to him a tradition from Ibn Tâûs, and he, from his father, who said—

" I have been informed by Hajar of Mar [a Companion of the Prophet] with regard to the property bestowed in charity by the Prophet of God, may peace and safety be on him, that this (the Prophet's) family used to appropriate the proceeds thereof lawfully and not unlawfully."—*Finis.*

The fifth tradition.—The Prophet, peace be to him, said—

" The thing with which a man maintains himself is a charity."

The author adds Miqdâm, son of M'aadi Karab, and Khuzri, and Jâbir, and Abi Imâma have also quoted this tradition. As regards the tradition narrated by Miqdâm, Ibn Mâja has recited it, in the *Chapter on wakf*, from Ismâîl, son of 'Ayâshi, he from Buhair, son of S'aad, he from Khâlid, son of Miqdâm, he from Miqdâm, son of M'aadi Karab, and he from the Prophet, peace and safety be unto him, who said :—

" Of the things earned by a man nothing is better than what he earns by the labour of his hands. What a man spends for himself or for his family, children and servants is charity on his part."—*Finis.*

Nisâi recites this in his book *Ashrat-un-nissa* from Bakia and he from Buhair with these words—

" That with which you feed yourself is a charity on your part, that with which you feed your wife is a charity on your part, that with which you feed your children is a charity on your part, and that with which you feed your servants is a charity on your part."—*Finis.*

As regards the tradition narrated by Khuzri, Ibn Habbân has recited it in the first Chapter of the first part of his book " *Sâhih*," from the *Dirâj* of Abi Samah, that Abû'l Haisam recited to him the tradition from Abi S'aid Khuzri, and he from the Prophet, may peace and safety be on him, who said :—" If a man earns something lawfully, and therewith feeds and clothes himself, and others of the creatures of God ; this is a *zakât* (charity) on his part."—*Finis.* Hâkim has also recited this in his book *Mutadrak* in the Chapter on *Atunah.*

* * * * * *

Muslim recites in his *Sâhîh* in the Chapter on *Zakât* from Abi Zubair, and he from Jâbir who said that the Prophet said to a man "Begin with yourself. Give charity to yourself, and if there be anything left, give it to your wife, then to your relatives, and then so on and so on."—*Finis.* The *Ashâb Sunan* [the authors of the works on the Prophet's ordinances] recite from Mughaira and he from Abû Huraira, that the Messenger of God said "Give charity." A man thereupon said, "I have got one dinâr." The Prophet said "Give it in charity (*sadakah*) to yourself." He said, "I have got another dinâr." The Prophet said, Give it in charity (*sadakah*) to your wife." He said, "I have got another dinâr." The Prophet said, "Give it in charity (*sadakah*) to your children." He said, "I have got another dinâr." The Prophet said, "Give that in charity to your servants." He said, "I have got another dinâr." The Prophet said, "You know better how to dispose of it."—*Finis.* Ibn Hâbân has recited this in his *Sâhîh*, and Hâkim in his *Mustadrak*, and they have declared the authorities on which it is based to be correct.

Zakhîrat-ul-Fatâwa.

Page 449.

It is laid down in the *Ajnâs* of Nâtiki that if a man makes a *wakf*, and lays down in it with respect to himself that he would, during his lifetime, eat out of it, and feed those whom he likes, that after him, it would go to his child, his child's child, and to his posterity, for ever, so long as it may continue, and that upon its becoming extinct, it would go to the poor; this is valid according to Abû Yusuf, may the mercy of God be on him, and this is not a *wasiat* (disposition by way of a will) in favour of his child, the child eating out of a property belonging to God, the Most High. Do you not see that when a man makes a *wakf* in favour of his children, and their children so long as their posterity may continue, and gives it afterwards to the poor, it is valid? Now, this case is just like it.

SADAKAH OR CHARITY.

Mishkât-ul-Masâbîh.(1)

"The Apostle of God said, 'Every good act, is charity; and verily it is of the number of good acts, to meet your brother with an open countenance, and to pour water from your own bag into his vessel.'"

From Abu Dhar—"The Apostle of God said, your smiling in your brothers' face is charity, and your exhorting mankind to virtuous deeds is alms; and your prohibiting the forbidden, is alms; and your shewing a man the road, in the land in which they lose it, is charity for you; and your assisting the blind, is charity for you; and your removing stones, thorns and bones, which are inconvenient to man, is alms for you.'"

From Abû Huraira and Hâshim-bin-Hizâm—"The Prophet said, 'The best of alms is a thing from which is left sufficient for a man's sustenance and his family; and begin by bestowing on those you have affection for.'"

From Ibn-Mas'ûd—"The Apostle of God said, 'when a Mussulman bestows on his family and kindred, for the intention of rewards, it becomes alms, although he has not given to the poor, but to his family and children."

Abû Huraira—"The Apostle of God said, 'There is one dinâr which you have bestowed in the road of God, and another in freeing a slave, and another in alms to the poor, and another given to your family and children; that is, the greatest dinâr in point of reward, which you gave to your family."

Thawbân—"The Apostle of God said, 'The most excellent dinâr which a man bestows, is that which he bestows, upon his own family; and a dinâr spent upon quadrupeds, in the road of God,

---

(1) *Mishkât-ul-Masâbîh.* Capt. Mathew's Translation, Vol. I, p. 447 & pp. 453-456.

For the authority of the work see Morley's Dig., Introd., p. cclviii. and the Translator's Preface.

Khazánat ul-Muftiin.

If one says, "I make a *wakf* of this land of mine in favour of my child and afterwards in favour of the poor," the income thereof will go to his child and his child's child till they be dead, and none of them be alive, and even if the third generation be forthcoming, the income will go to the poor, and not to the third generation. If he says, "In favour of my child, my child's child, and the child of my child's child," making mention of three generations, the income will be spent on his descendants for ever, so long as his posterity continues, and not on the poor till any of his descendants be alive, be he of a degree howsoever low. The result of this is that when the person making the *wakf* makes mention of three generations, the *wakf* will be in their favour, as well as in favour of those lower than them, the next and the remotest being equal, excepting when he, at the time of making the *wakf*, says "the next shall be the next," or says "in favour of my child, and after them in favour of my child's child," or says, "generation after generation," in which case, it shall begin with him with whom the person making the *wakf* has commenced.

which is combating for the faith, and a dinâr which a man bestows upon his friends, in the road of God.' "

Umm-Salmah—" I said to the Prophet, is there any good tidings for me of rewards, for my bestowing on the sons of Abû-Salmah ? His sons are no other than mine. The Prophet said ' then give to them ; and for you are the rewards of what you bestow upon them.' "

Zainab, wife of ' Abdullah bin-Mas'ûd says—" The Apostle of God said, ' Give alms, O, assemblage of woman ! although it be your ornaments.' " She said, " then I returned from His Highness' presence, when I heard this, to ' Abdullah, my husband ; and I said, ' verily thou art a poor man ; and verily the Prophet has ordered me to give alms, therefore go to His Highness and ask him, if it is sufficient for me to give to thee and thy children ; and if it should be so, I will perform it, and lay out upon you ; and if it is not sufficient, I shall expend on others." Then ' Abdullah said, " Do you go and ask ; do not trouble me." " Then I went to the Prophet ; and behold ! I saw a woman of the Assistants,(1) at the Prophet's door, whose necessity was like mine ; that is, that woman had also come to ask about this matter : and verily there was so much awe and fear in approaching His Highness that no person could go to him without his permission. Then Bilâl came out to us from the Prophet ; and we said to him, ' Go to His Highness and inform him that there are two women at the door, and they ask thee, is it not sufficient for them to bestow on their husbands, and on orphans (2) who are under their protection, but do not inform him who we are ; that is, do not tell him our names.' Then Bilâl went in to the Prophet and asked him about this matter. He said, ' who are they?' Billâl said, ' one of them is of the Assistants, and the other Zainab. Then the Prophet said, ' which of the Zainabs is it ? ' Bilâl said ' Zainab, wife of ' Abdullah bin-Mas'ûd.' Then the Prophet said, ' it is sufficient for them to give to their husbands and the orphans ; and for them are two rewards ; one for their kindred, and another for alms.' "

Sulaiman bin-'Aâmir—" The Apostle of God said, ' Giving alms to the poor has the reward of one alms ; but that given to

---

(1) Ansâr, the people of Medina who assisted the Prophet.

(2) Meaning the motherless children of their husbands.

kindred has two rewards; one, the reward of alms; the other the reward of relationship.' "

Abû Huraira said, a man came to His Highness, and said, 'I have got one dinâr.' He said, 'expend it upon yourself.' The man said, 'I have got another dinâr.' The Prophet said, 'expend that upon your children.' The man said, 'I have got another dinâr.' He said, 'expend it upon your relation, your wife, father and mother.' He said, 'I have got one other dinâr.' The Prophet said, 'extend that upon your servants.' The man said, 'I have got another dinâr.' He said, 'you know best the condition of the person most worthy of it; and who ever you know to be so, give it?"

HANAFÎ LAW RELATING TO WAKF.

Bahr-ur-Râik.(1)

" In law, according to Abû Hanîfa, the meaning of *wakf* is the tying-up of the substance of a thing in the ownership of the *wâkif* and the devotion of its usufruct. According to the Disciples it means the tying-up of property in the ownership of Almighty God and the devotion of its usufruct to purposes of benefit to His creatures. In the *Fath* [*ul-Kadîr*] further explanation is added *viz.*, that the *wâkif* may give the usufruct to whomsoever he likes."

" And in the *Zakhîra* it is laid down that a consecration in favour of the affluent is *kurbat*, [an act of approach to god]."

" The motive of *wakf* is to obtain the affection of the living in this world, and to approach the Lord of Lords (may his name be glorified) in the next."

" Its conditions are the same as in acts of mere bounty, *viz.*, that is, the *wâkif* must be sane, *bâligh* (adult) it must be operative at once and not suspensive."

" There are twenty-six express words by which it may be constituted :—

(1) This land is a permanent *sadakah-mowkoofa* on the poor or on anybody, and on this there is no difference.

(2) This is *sadakah-mowkoofa* ; Abû Yusuf, Hillâl, and all others are agreed thereon.

(3) This is *hubs* and *sadakah*.

(4) This is *sadakah-muharrama*. Both these are like the second.

(5) This is *mowkoofa*. According to Abû Hanîfa and Abû Yusuf this word by itself constitutes a *wakf* and implies its final destination for the poor.......... And Sadr-ush-Shâhîd has laid down that the *Fatwa* is thereon and the *Mushâikh* of Balkh have given *Fatwa* according to Abû Yusuf's rule, and it is customary with us all to decide according to the rule of Abû Yusuf.

---

(1) A work of great authority ; see Morley's Dig., Introd., p cclxx, frequently quoted in the Sudder Dewanny Adawlut cases ; see specially 1 Sel. R., p. 17.

(6) This is *mowkoofa* on a *fakîr.*

(7) This is *mahboosa.*

(8) This is *hubs.*

If both these expressions in the language of the place imply permanent appropriation, then it is obligatory as if he had said *mowkoofa* or *wakf.*

(9) If he says 'this is for a *sabîl* (path),' if the customary meaning of the word is permanent dedication, it will be so, otherwise he will be asked as to his meaning. If he says he meant *wakf*, in that case it will be *wakf.* If he says he meant a *sadakah*, then it will be a mere votive offering.

(10) 'I have made this for the indigent.'

If the customary sense of these words is *wakf*, it will be *wakf.* If not, he will be asked as to his intention, if he says he meant *wakf*, in that case it will be *wakf*, if he says he meant a *sadakah*, then it will be a votive offering.

(11) *Muharrama.*

(12) His mere saying *wakf.* And this is correct. And among the people of Hijâz(1) it is universal. It is equivalent to saying *hubsun mowkoofun.*

(13) And it is like saying shortly, *mowkoofatun.*

(14) His saying 'I have made the fruit of my vine trees *wakf.*' This will be *wakf* [of the trees] whether there are grapes on the trees or not.

(15) His saying 'I have constituted the usufruct [of this property] in this way.'

(16) His saying 'this is *mowkoofa* for Almighty God,' it is equivalent to saying *sadakah-mowkoofa.* All this is stated fully in the *Fath-ul-Kadîr.* And in the *Bazâzia*, it is laid down that a *wakf* created by the mere word *wakf* or *mowkoofa* is valid.

(17) If he says 'this is *mowkoofa* on *wajjah-ul-khair*, good purpose, or *wajjah-ul-ihsân*, benevolent purpose,' it will be a *wakf* for the poor.

(18) If he says 'this is *sadakah-mowkoofa* for my *hajj* or for my' *umra*,' it will be a lawful *wakf.*

(19) If he says 'this is *sadakah*, it will not be sold,' it will be a votive offering, but if he add 'it will not be given in gift, and

(1) The part of Arabia where Mecca and Medina are situated.

inheritance will not apply to it,' in that case it will be a *wakf* for the poor.

(20) If he says 'you buy out of the produce of this house every month ten *dirhems* worth of bread and give it to the needy,' the house will be *wakf*."

[The rest are unimportant.]

"There is no difference as to the validity of a *wakf*. The only difference is as to when it becomes obligatory and binding. Abû Hanîfa says it becomes binding on the decree of the Judge [and that], until then it is revocable. The Disciples hold it becomes binding at once, and cannot be sold or given or inherited......... All the jurists have adopted the rule of the Disciples and the *Fatwa* is thereon. And in the *Fath*-[*ul-Kadîr*] it is laid down that it is correct, and on that is the *consensus* of the universality of the Companions of the Prophet............ According to Abû Yusuf, a *wakf* is like the emancipation [of a slave] and becomes operative and binding by the mere declaration of the *wâkif*. Mohammed says it becomes binding after delivery of *seisin* to the *mutwalli* and separation and mention of perpetuity."

"If the person making a *wakf* reserves the income thereof for himself, or appoints himself the *mutwalli*, it will be valid, that is to say, if he lays down this condition at the time of making the *wakf*, the condition will be good: The first, however, is valid according to Abû Yusuf, and invalid according to the analogy of what Mohammed says, because he [Mohammed] makes the delivery [of the *wakf* property] to the *mutwalli*, a condition. It is also said that they differ as to the delivery of possession and division being necessary conditions for *wakf*. It is also said that this difference is a new point altogether. The difference being in the case where the person making a *wakf* makes the condition that a portion shall be enjoyed by himself during his lifetime, and after him, by the poor; and in the case where he makes the condition that the whole shall be enjoyed by himself during his lifetime, and after him, by the poor."(1)

"The reason for what Mohammed says is, that a *wakf* is valid when any one is made owner of a property in the manner herein before described by me. Hence the condition under which the whole or a part is enjoyed by one [making the *wakf*] makes it

(1) That is, there is a difference in both cases.

[the *wakf*] invalid, for it cannot be realised how one can make himself the owner. It would be just like a conditional charity, and the reservation of a portion of the site of a mosque for one's self."

"Abû Yusuf relies on what has been related regarding the Prophet, peace and safety be on him, *viz.*, that he used to eat out of his *sadakah*, which is understood as *sadakah-mowkoofa*, but it is not lawful to eat out of it, unless there be a condition to that effect; hence the above shows the validity of the condition. Besides, *wakf* is the depriving of one's self of a property, and dedicating it to God, the Most High, in the manner stated above with the object of (*kurbat*) drawing near to God. Hence, if a man reserves a part or the whole for himself, he takes for himself a thing belonging to God, and not a thing belonging to himself; and this is lawful. It is just as a man builds a house for the reception of travellers and strangers, or constructs reservoirs to keep therein water for the use of the travellers, or converts a piece of land into a burial-ground, and makes the condition that he also should put up, or drink, or be interred there. Besides, the object of [the person making a *wakf*] is to do a pious act, and making provision for himself is such. Said the Prophet, peace be on him, 'Provision made by a man for himself is a charity.' It is stated in the *Fath-ul-Kadîr*, 'Preference is given to what Abû Yusuf says.' Sadr-us-Shâhîd says, *Fatwa* is given according to what Abû Yusuf says. We also give *Fatwa* in accordance with what Abû Yusuf says, in order to encourage people to make *wakf*. The *Mashâikh* (jurists) of Balkh have also adopted the same view; and this is what appears from the *Hedâya*, because it gives the arguments in its support and does not refute them. In a case of reservation for one's self, if a man says that the debts due by him should be paid from the income of it [the *wakf* property]; and in like manner, if he says that in the event of his dying in debt, his obligation should be paid off first with the income of this *wakf* property and that the remainder should be spent in the way of God; in each of these cases the *wakf* shall be valid. In the Book of *Wakf* by Khassâf, it is stated, 'if one makes this condition that he would apply the usufruct of the said *wakf* property for the maintenance of himself and his children, servants, and family, and if the produce thereof comes [into his hands] and he sells it, and takes it into his custody the price of the same, and then dies before spending it, to whom shall it go, whether to his heirs, or to those in whose favour the *wakf* was made ? It is said, 'It shall go to his heirs, because the usufruct (as conditioned by him) belonged to him, and he had obtained it. But this does not specify the part they each should get, whether one half, or a fourth, [*viz.*, the whole of the usufruct which came into his hands would be for them jointly].' And such also will be the case if any one says, 'If so-and-so, meaning the person making the *wakf*, dies, one part, say out of ten parts, shall every year be taken out of the usufruct of this *wakf* property, and be spent in the performance of the *hajj* for his benefit, in doing penance for the oaths broken by him, and in such and such acts, naming several things,' or if he says, 'So many *dirhems* shall every year be taken out of this property given in charity, for being spent for such and such purposes, and the remainder in such and such acts as he (the *mutwalli*] considers proper.'—*Finis.* It is stated in the *Hâwi*, 'This rule of Abû Yusuf has been adopted for the *Fatwa*, in order to encourage people to make *wakf* and increase benefaction.' From this difference of opinion it may also be inferred that if any one were to make a *wakf* in favour of his male and female slaves, it would be invalid according to Mohammed and valid according to Abû Yusuf, in the same way as the condition for one's own benefit. Some have drawn the same inference also from the above as to the enjoyment of the usufruct by *mudabbars* and *umm-ul-walads*.(1) This, however, is weak; *and what is correct is this, that it* (the enjoyment of usufruct by *mudabbars*, etc.,) is lawful, both the authorities agreeing in it. Mohammed argues that inasmuch as they (the *mudabbars* and *umm-ul-walads*) shall become free upon the death of the man, a *wakf* in their favour shall be just like a *wakf* in favour of strangers; and it (freedom) is found in them during his lifetime in anticipation of what would be the case after his death. What is said in the *Hedâya* and *Mujtaba* as to their really differing on the said point, is weak."

"All our *Mashâikh* have adopted the rule of Abû Yusuf...... So that what is written in the *Khâniéh* (*Fatâwai Kâzi Khân*) that 'if a person were to make a *wakf* on himself, and on so-and-so, half of it would be valid, *viz.*, the share of the other,—and the share of himself would be void, or if he were to say that it is a *wakf* for himself and

---

(1) *Mudabbar* is a conditionally enfranchised bondsman; *amin-ul-walad* is a bondswoman who has borne a child to her master and has thus obtained her freedom.

then for so-and-so, or if he were to say, that it is a *wakf* for so-and-so, and then on himself, half would be valid, and the other half would be invalid,' is a matter for surprise. How did the author come to say this? It must be an interpolation. You must know that whatever conditions a *wâkif* has laid down must be given effect to." . . . .

Wakf on descendants **valid without difference.**

"*There is absolutely no difference* [*as to the validity*] *when a man makes the condition that the usufruct shall be for his children, so that when he makes a wakf in favour of his children, it includes both the male and female, but if he restricts to the male, it would exclude the female children.* * * * * * *And when he mentions the third generation, nothing of the usufruct will be spent on the poor, so long as any of his descendants, however remote, is in existence.*"............

"In the *Tâtâr-Khâniéh* it is stated that when a *wakf* is in favour of a specified and known class or people whose number is capable of limitation [or ascertainment], if they appoint a *mutwalli* without taking the opinion of the Kâzi it will be valid if they are people of judgment. The ancients say that it is preferable to place the matter before the Kâzi, but all modern jurists say it is preferable not to do so.......our masters and modern *Mashâikhs* are agreed that it is better such people should appoint their own *mutwalli*.

Tahtâwi.

Page 528.

Text of the *Durr-ul-Mukhtâr.*—" According to both [Mohammed and Abû Yusuf,] it [*wakf*] means the detention of a thing in the ownership of Almighty God, and the application of the usufruct thereof for whomsoever he [the person making the *wakf*] likes, though that person may be rich. Consequently the *wakf* would be binding, he [the person making the *wakf*] not being competent to annul it, and it, [the *wakf*] not being heritable. And on this is the *Fatwa ;* Ibn Kamâl and Ibn Shahnah. Its object is to make one's self beloved in this world, and to obtain in the next the reward [of God], that is to say, if it is made by a person possessing the capacity to form an intention [*niat*], because it (making a *wakf*) is *mubâh* [lawful], inasmuch as it is valid even if made by an infidel, and sometimes it is *wâjib* [obligatory] on account of a vow." *Comment* of Tahtâwi :—" The author has added the words '*lau fil jumlati*' (if in any sense or at any time) admitting [or accepting] what is said in the *Fath-ul-Kadîr*. Ibn Kamâl has adopted the same opinion. The *Fath-ul-Kadîr* says ' or spending the usufruct thereof for whomsoever he likes,' for the reason that a *wakf* is valid even if made in favour of the rich, without any intention of *kurbat* [an approach to God]. Such *wakf*, although its ulti ate purpose must be for *kurbat* ana permanency, will be a *wakf* even before the rich are cut off and even if there be no mention of giving alms to the poor, just in the same way as a *wakf* for the poor and for defraying the expenses of a mosque. This addition makes the definition comprehensive. The inference to be drawn from the [above] statement is that the object of making a *wakf* is doing a benefaction in any sense or at any time. This also appears from what is said in the *Muhît*, where it is stated that if a *wakf* be made *exclusively* restricted to the rich it will not be valid, as there is no *kurbat*, the case being quite different when it is last of all destined for the poor, for there is *kurbat* on the whole."

Page 529.

Text.—"Abû Yusuf considers the word [*Mowkoofa,*] only as sufficient. Shahìd says 'I also give *Fatwa* in accordance with the same having regard to customary practice.'" *Comment* :—"The author says 'the word [*Mowkoofa*] &c.' He [Abû Yusuf] says when a *wakf* is constituted by this word [alone], it is for the poor, and when it conveys a particular mode of application, *viz.*, a dedication for the poor, it necessarily becomes permanent, because the poor can never be extinct, *Bahr-ul-Râik.* He says [further]:—"Sadr-us-Shahîd says, 'and I also give *Fatwa* in accordance with the same.'" And the *Mashâikhs* [Jurists] of Balkh have also given *Fatwa* in accordance with it. *Fatwa* is given according to Abû Yusuf, who says a *wakf* shall be valid by the use of this word alone, though no mention be made of permanency or of the object in whose favour it is made."

The ancient lawyers generally discountenanced as a superstition the reading of the Koran over the grave of a deceased person. The practice, however, has now become universal and has received the sanction of modern jurists, who base their approval, as has already been pointed out, on a *dictum* of Imâm Mohammed; see p. 634.

The non-Moslem subjects of a Mahommedan State are called *zimmis* or *ahl-ul-zimma*; from the fact that they, on their side, have sworn allegiance to the head of the State and have received from him, as the chief representative of the Moslem nation, the pledge of protection and security for their person and property, and for the free enjoyment of their civil rights.

A non-Moslem subject of a non-Moslem State entering a Moslem country under a *guarantee of protection or âmân* was called a *mustâmin.*

That guarantee might be special, extended to him personally or might be *general*, under a treaty with his sovereign extending to all the subjects of that particular State. A special *âmân* can be given by any Moslem whatever his position to an alien arriving on Moslem soil, but such protection would be restricted in its duration; a *special âmân* granted by the State would extend to the entire period of the *mustâmin's* stay in the country.

Wakfnamah in *Doe dem. Jaun Beebee* v. *Abdollah Barber* (Fulton's Reports, p. 345).

"Praise unto God, the bestower of grace and support, and blessings on Mohammed, the chief of the prophets, his descendants and companions, who are perfect and united, after which I, the declarant, Masummat Goonda Bibee, wife of the late Sheikh Culloo Khansamah, inhabitant of Mawza Colinga in Dehu Berjee, one of the Mahullas of the town of Calcutta, being sound in body and mind, competent to perform all legal acts, of my own free will, without aversion or compulsion, make the following binding and lawful declaration :—

"Whereas different spots of ryotty land, and land in my own occupation purchased by me without the participation of others as appears by the vouchers granted by the vendors that sold the same unto me, and property formerly belonging to my husband, received by me as my marriage portion, all which landed property is duly defined by pottahs and bills of sale, and well-known limits, are held by me in my own exclusive possession, under my proprietary right thereto, free from the participation of others, and old rights included therein, or otherwise appertaining thereto, both great and small, I hereby grant and dispose of the same, as a pious donation to please God, who is above all, on the following conditions :

"1st.—Whereas the aforesaid lands, subject to rent, are situated in the town of Calcutta, I will appropriate as much of the produce thereof as is required by my own use unto the said purpose, after defraying the revenue and taxes thereof, and the remainder to hereditable and charitable purpose, and my several relatives, that is, my grandson and grand-daughter and daughter-in-law, and daughter's son and daughter's daughter, who are now receiving maintenance living together, united in meals shall continue to receive the same in like manner, and the power of increasing or decreasing the number of incumbents according to the increase or decrease in the produce will remain with me, and the repairs of the mosque, and salary of the Mowuzzin, Khatib, and other expenses connected therewith, in the seasons of Ramazaun Mobarek, and the Eed, shall be defrayed from the produce; and the person who is hereafter appointed *mutwalli*, will enjoy the same powers as I myself possess.

"2nd.—I will continue *mutwalli* as long as I live, and on my decease my daughter's son Abdollah, son of Sheikh Joomun, inhabitant of Calcutta, will become *mutwalli*, after the said Abdollah, one from among my relations who is the most fit and possesses integrity, temperance, intelligence, and respectability and appears most deserving.

"3rd.—After my decease, neither my heirs nor the *mutwalli* will have the smallest right to sell or give away or transfer the above-mentioned lands in any manner whatsoever. Part thereof which is expended in hereditable, charitable and benevolent purposes, shall be disbursed under my own control and direction.

"These few words are, therefore, written by way of a voucher of a pious donation, to serve as a binding and decisive document when occasion requires. [A specification of the lands comprised in the above pious donation then followed.]

"Written on Thursday, the last of the month of March of the year 1832 of the Christian era, corresponding with the 19th of the month of Phalgoon, of the year 1283, Bengal style, corresponding with the 27th of the month of Ramazaun Mobarek, of the year 1247, of the Hegira."

GENERAL INDEX.

E

N

O

Z